WILDLIFE MANAGEMENT TECHNIQUES

THIRD EDITION: REVISED

Edited by: ROBERT H. GILES, JR., PhD
Associate Professor
Virginia Polytechnic Institute

Illustrated by: LARRY TOSCHIK
Phoenix, Arizona

Prepared by the Wildlife
Techniques Manual Committee

THE WILDLIFE SOCIETY
WASHINGTON, D. C.

1969

This book is the third in a series on wildlife techniques published by The Wildlife Society

Editor, Henry S. Mosby
    Manual of Game Investigational Techniques
        (1) First Edition—May 1960
            Second Printing—February 1961
    Wildlife Investigational Techniques
        (2) Second Edition—May 1963
            Second Printing (Revised)—March 1965
            Third through Sixth Printing—March 1966 to September 1968

Editor, Robert H. Giles, Jr.
    Wildlife Management Techniques
        (3) June 1969
            Library of Congress Catalog Card Number: 68-17250

THE WILDLIFE SOCIETY

The Wildlife Society has for its major objectives the establishment of high professional standards, the encouragement of management of wildlife along sound biological lines, and the dissemination of information to accomplish these ends. The members of The Wildlife Society believe that wildlife and other natural resources have a permanent place in our culture. The Society supports programs to enhance the esthetic, recreational, and economic values of wildlife and seeks to insure the wise use of this natural resource as part of our living standard.

These objectives, rising from unselfish motives, are directed toward the well-being of all occupants of our planet. They are carried out in a large number and variety of ways, primary among these being the publications of the Society, all edited by volunteers. *The Journal of Wildlife Management,* our 33-year old scientific quarterly, has grown to more than 1000 pages per annual volume. Scientific papers too lengthy for inclusion in *The Journal of Wildlife Management* are published in the Society's *Wildlife Monograph* series. Through 1968, 16 *Monographs* have been published on a wide variety of subjects such as: waterfowl, bighorn sheep, prairie dogs, brook trout, stream ecology, and the wildebeest in Africa. This techniques manual is another attempt to attain our goals.

The Society's wide and diverse professional interests and responsibilities are reflected in its stylized hieroglyphic emblem adopted in 1937, the Society's first year of existence. The horizontal lines of figures, from top to bottom, may be translated as: beasts, birds, fishes, and flowering plants.

It is the hope of The Wildlife Society that this techniques manual will be of immense value to students and practitioners alike, and that the volunteer committee efforts represented herein will also be of use and interest to those in related disciplines.

Your own comments on The Wildlife Society's efforts will be most helpful.

Fred G. Evenden
Executive Director

June, 1969

CONTENTS

PREFACE

Wildlife Management Techniques is an evolutionary step on a continuum that started with Howard M. Wight's *Field and Laboratory Techniques in Wildlife Management* in 1938. An edition of *Manual of Game Investigational Techniques* was the second step taken by a committee of The Wildlife Society and author-editor Henry S. Mosby. The third and fourth steps were an edition and revision of *Wildlife Investigational Techniques*. The evolutionary force was generated by Dr. Mosby in whose footsteps this editor follows proudly both as student and as editor, dwarfed by the magnitude and strength of the previous editions. The strength of the previous editions is explained in their lengthy Preface and Acknowledgments which attest to the great support of Society members. Their support, bolstered by dozens more unnamed reviewers and assistants, lives on in this book.

Wildlife Management Techniques is a textbook and manual for well-educated people working with game mammals and birds. The content is purposefully sketchy in all areas, since the objectives are to describe major approaches to problem solving, suggest ways of implementing these solutions, describe and direct readers to some of the better techniques and tools now known, and indicate gaps in our knowledge. The overriding goal is to improve the management of the wildlife resource through more rapid development and improved use of techniques.

No recommendations are made for standard techniques; best methods are not suggested. The state-of-knowledge as of mid 1966-67 has been presented with the expectation of need for re-vision soon. Catalogs or exhaustive bibliographies to species, problems, or techniques are given in only a few chapters. Literature was selected for demonstrating an approach or describing techniques in detail. Questions of "how" have been of primary concern in the book; questions of "why" are of first order but herein treated as of secondary importance.

Readers will find one major topic omitted under the large scope of the title. The omission is man management or social engineering. Though to some readers there will be negative connotations to the terms, to others, the manipulation of habitat, wildlife populations, and man and their interactions to achieve stated goals is wildlife management. Gilbert's (1964) treatment of the topic must suffice until wildlife managers see more clearly the man-land-game conflicts and attempt to solve the management problem by studying the techniques of education, sociology, psychology, legislation and politics as diligently as they study plants and animals. The human aspect of the wildlife management problem can be solved; it cannot be left to non-wildlifers. One day these necessary chapters will be written—when there is more support and wisdom.

There has been evolution in past editions; hopefully the present edition is "fit"; expectantly, future editions or sub-editions will survive and reflect the creative improvements of time and human involvement in a worthwhile task.

Robert H. Giles, Jr., *Editor and Chairman, Wildlife Techniques Manual Committee*

CHAPTER ONE

THE APPROACH

ROBERT H. GILES, JR., PhD

Associate Professor, Wildlife Management
Virginia Polytechnic Institute
Blacksburg, Virginia

THE WILDLIFE MANAGER
THE PRACTICE OF MANAGEMENT
THE SCIENTIFIC METHOD
DEFINING TECHNIQUES
EVALUATING TECHNIQUES
THE EXAMPLE OF THIS BOOK

Wildlife management is the science and art of changing the characteristics and interactions of habitats, wild animal populations, and men in order to achieve specific human goals by means of the wildlife resource. These goals may frequently be sport recreation, but may also include or be restricted to esthetic, economic, and ecological goals. Those working in the area of wildlife management (wildlifers) are ultimately involved in the manipulation of the complex man-land-animal triad. Their success depends upon them giving assistance in clearly articulating the goals of those whom they serve; their scholarly application of scientific information and methods to impediments to achieving these goals; their ecological perspective; and their execution of programs to maintain past successes, to prevent repetition of past failures, and to prepare for future needs.

THE WILDLIFE MANAGER

Wildlifers are a heterogeneous group, for, like the very ecology which is the basis of their practice, they are an interacting group of specialists and generalists with widely varying interests, experience, and academic training. They are united in the resource with which they work, the goals which they seek, and the common agree-ment of the need for a sound, basic developing understanding of the relations of animals (including man) to each other and to their total environment. Their united action is research, education, planning, administrative aid, and development of techniques, all of which culminate in the management act. The management act, in the final analysis, is a display of the total achievement of all that is called wildlife management and of a particular manager's understanding and artistry.

THE PRACTICE OF MANAGEMENT

Wildlife management is no more a science than is medicine; it is both science and art. While the argument is scholarly old-hat, it is important that it not yet be closed, for in the act of making the argument, the significance of talent, personal committment, enthusiasm, skill, special sensitivity, clear interpretation, and synthetic uniqueness, might be seen again . . . and again.

Since admonition does not make artists, this book does not attempt to deal directly with the artistry of wildlife management. It does, however, present the techniques of wildlife management chapter by chapter in an order appropriate to the fulfillment of the scientific method. The book itself becomes the demonstration of an acceptable approach to wildlife management. The chapters and their authors have been selected so that the reader, when he has experienced the book as a whole, will not only have an understanding of the scientific process but also might have caught a glimpse of the meaning of wildlife management as an art, and can begin becoming an artist, as well as a scientist.

THE SCIENTIFIC METHOD

The scientific method is a widely accepted and appropriate approach to wildlife management. The method is not exclusively for research, but there its utility is obvious. It is also generally appropriate as a model of managerial rationality.

The six basic components of the scientific method are:

Observation—The scientist is first and foremost an observer, one who sees things clearly and exactly as they are.

Hypothesis—Based on observation, the scientist, the wildlife manager, formulates a tentative, working explanation for his observation. The hypothesis is a statement of a problem whose essence is a general principle or relation of cause and effect. It is important to comprehend fully at this point the importance of the hypothesis. It has been said with woodsy wisdom that if you ask the wrong question you invariably get the wrong answer. The ancient philosophers used the scientific method but, because they started with false premises or improperly formulated or untestable hypotheses, they frequently got the wrong answers. The scientist may intellectually construct many hypotheses but only the best or most real must be selected for testing.

Tests of the Hypothesis—There are three major types of tests: (a) Further observation—More critical general observations are made to reevaluate the hypothesis; (b) Logical deduction—Based on the hypothesis, deductions are made to verify the hypothesis; (c) Experiment—Controlled or constant phenomena are compared to treated phenomena. An effort is made to isolate or to observe only particular phenomena under certain specific conditions.

Within the test there must be:

(a) Collection of data bearing directly on the problem. Data must be collected according to plan, copiously, aided whenever possible by instruments of precision, and for a purpose. They must be recorded in definite terms, measurements, and specific statements.

(b) Organization of data for efficiency, economy, ease of detection of relationships (positive or negative), and future use, not only by the original investigator but by those who must continue the study—either due to illness, death of the investigator, or due to personnel changes during a continuing study.

(c) Analysis to detect similarities, variations, activities, processes, causes, and results. Study, using of statistics, data organization, careful thought, and time to allow insight bring the investigator to the use of his tests, i.e. evaluation or interpretation.

Interpretation of Results—The test results are carefully studied in order to formulate general principles or theories. Reasoning is from known principles, imagination, and insight, to produce solutions or explanations for the problem. This is the intellectual phase between test and conclusion. Beveridge (1957) sheds much light on this and other aspects of the approach for the wildlifer.

Conclusion—The intellectual conclusion to a study is the statement of a theory. The theory is the result of deductive reasoning and has a degree of proof behind it.

Reporting of Results—Publication is the indispensable outcome of research. The mechanical conclusion to a problem is not reached when an intellectual conclusion has been reached. Science is for people, and knowledge gained by the arduous and rigorous scientific method must not be wasted. To prevent waste, results must be presented to intelligent people for their best uses.

There is no scientific law or principle that can ever be regarded as absolutely proved. All laws are subject to modification with the accumulation of more data and the increase of knowledge. Some are more acceptable than others, for they fit more situations and have similarities in other areas of study.

DEFINING TECHNIQUES

Throughout this book "tool," "instrument," "technique," and "method" are used loosely. There seems little purpose in bandying around these words other than to provide the context for significant differences which will be seen within the book as well as in the years immediately ahead. Ackoff (1962:5-6) makes the distinctions. "Tool" and "instrument" are synonymous and are physical or conceptual like hammers, microscopes, and mathematical symbols. "Techniques" are courses of action or *ways* of using tools. "Methods" are decision-rules or ways of selecting techniques, actions, or conclusions. The scientific method establishes a set of rules for the employment of many tools and techniques. Ackoff (1962:6) said, "Methods are rules of choice; techniques are the choices themselves." Example 1; a desk calculator is a *tool* for calculating means; the calculation of a "t" value is a *technique* for determining a relationship between two means; a "t-test" is a *method*, based on certain decisions on confidence, for testing for the probability of real differences between the calculated means or other values. Example 2; a centimeter rule is a *tool* for measuring bird wing feathers; measurement of lengths of feathers is an observational *technique* for birds; comparison of feather lengths to certain criteria is a *method* for sexing some birds.

The zone between "technique" and "method" will become increasingly gray as techniques become integrated into systems of techniques and as techniques become the actual functioning of a system or a decision to modify. Of greater importance, however, is the rapid technological shift from physical to conceptual techniques and methods. This change is from tool to intellectual technology with the "systems concept" coming into full bloom. It will involve precise, logical, analytical, and often computer-based approaches to problem solution and decision making. These approaches will see new intrusions of yet other groups of specialists into the wildlife manager's social ecology—those dealing with operations research, model building, and simulations. Their work will materialize in predictions, elaboration of alternatives, and aids to selection of best alternatives—to decision making for the management act.

EVALUATING TECHNIQUES

Techniques are so diverse that to generalize on their desirable characteristics is difficult. However, the frequency with which techniques fail, are used inappropriately, and deserted only to be resurrected years later, suggests that there is a continuing need to compare tools and their use against certain criteria. Desirable techniques (1) can achieve the objectives intended, (2) are employable in a priority of usefulness and need, (3) are compatible with the assumptions made about them, (4) are economically feasible in that the pieces of information obtained or the units of game or habitat produced are "worth the costs," (5) are within budgetary constraints, (6) can be used with a reasonable amount of training or experience, (7) can be operated with the number and training of personnel available, (8) will accomplish objectives within the time available, (9) will require minimum supervision and inspection, (10) can be readily evaluated, (11) have broad application and flexibility for use under various changes, and (12) are humane and have relatively high social acceptability.

THE EXAMPLE OF THIS BOOK

This book is organized to show the top priority of planning and the need to articulate goals and objectives. It shows the essential nature of an information foundation. It shows the need for a holistic approach to the scientific process with the need for communication of the results of work as a necessary part, correlative to all other steps, in the process.

Recording observations and employing ways of improving on the human capability for making them are treated in the next three chapters. Techniques relating to the investigation, analysis, and manipulation of habitat and populations follow.

A viable approach to the study and development of wildlife techniques is largely one which is basic to problem-solution, to goal achievement—whether managerial, research, administrative, or educational. The approach of this book is therefore largely that of "a problem in search of a solution." Rising in the face of warnings against "gadgeteering" and "losing sight of the primary job" is a newcomer to the research scene: "A solution in search of a problem." No longer amused or threatened, scientists and managers who see great accomplishments being made by various technology developments have started to seek and experiment with applications of these developments to problems of the wildlife manager. They have taken new tools and techniques and sought application to whatever problems they found that would yield. Radiation measurement, computers, and infra-red photography are examples. Such an approach represents to some an exciting philosophical shift and suggests that tomorrow another might occur.

There is argument that conceptual but not technological break-throughs will produce significant quantum jumps in wildlife managerial effectiveness. There is no meaningful "either/or" argument between technology and conceptualization, or between research and management, or between science and art. The perceptive ecologist sees clearly the imperative of an attitude of "both/and." Thus liberated, he can advance to achieve sought-after human goals through the wildlife resource.

CHAPTER TWO

PLANNING WILDLIFE MANAGEMENT INVESTIGATIONS AND PROJECTS

THOMAS H. RIPLEY, PhD

Assistant to the Deputy Chief for Research
USDA, Forest Service
Washington, D. C.

PROGRAM DEVELOPMENT
PROBLEM STATEMENT
STATE OF KNOWLEDGE
THE PLANNING PROCESS
  THE PROSPECTUS
  THE INVESTIGATIONAL PLAN
  THE MANAGEMENT OR DEVELOPMENT PLAN
SUMMARY

Those who study and manage wildlife populations and habitats are involved in the processes of solving problems to develop knowledge or to achieve some managerial objectives. Whether deciding the seeding mixture for renewal of a food patch or testing an hypothesis about density-stress, the root process is intellectual; i.e., planning.

This chapter, and indeed much of this volume, is concerned with planning the investigation or management project.[1] The chapter outlines how the study is selected and described, how alternatives for approaches are identified, and how the prospectus and the investigational plan are prepared. The interrelationships of the prospectus and plan are discussed since these are the commonly used documents in research program development. A parallel discussion for management plans emphasizes the management problem solution. Other chapters in this book treat the tools and techniques available for conducting investigations and achieving management objectives. Knowledge of them is essential for effective planning. Such knowledge allows choice between alternatives, establishes realistic constraints, allows plans to be more "practical," and speeds the development of efficient research methodology.

PROGRAM DEVELOPMENT

A conservation objective, or set of objectives, is achieved only through a program that identifies and removes obstacles in an orderly and efficient manner. This attainment requires the development of a logical sequence for programming work. Thus, effective program development and planning are inseparable.

The common root of all investigations is a deficiency of knowledge: (a) There is a problem to solve or (b) someone is curious. Few wildlife workers are privileged to pursue a research effort out of sheer curiosity. Usually, there are one or more problems to solve in order to

---

[1]In this chapter, a *project* will be considered as a work unit (organizationally) which exists to solve some problem or accomplish some managerial goal. The term *investigational* will be synonymous with *study* and construed to mean any unit of inquiry, however small or large, developed to assemble or acquire knowledge or develop methods, techniques, and procedures.

6

accomplish some conservation or resource-management objective. The solution may involve a major project effort with numerous investigations or studies, or it may be a brief, direct question for which a single investigation will fully satisfy the deficiency.

The probability of solving wildlife research and management problems increases with good planning. The problems vary widely in magnitude, clarity, importance to total programs, relation to similar problems, and ease of solution. *Ease of solution* is controlled by time, labor, equipment, finance requirements, accessibility, and technological advancement. Because of these differences, wildlifers must be keenly aware of the need for assigning priorities to work and investigation.

One of the most fundamental needs in assigning priorities is acceptance of the concept of working sequentially through problems toward major goals. This concept is contrasted to the "brush-fire" and "stop-gap" types of research and management action, but should provide for innovative diversions and creative new paths of study.

It is a difficult and intriguing problem to determine how much relative effort to put into basic and applied research. Some insight into this problem is given by Sherwin and Isenson (1967), who found that a very high percentage of technological advance in weapons, at least for a short run, came from "directed" science. On a longer time scale, however, the need for "undirected" or basic study is undeniable. The problem is real for those who must secure as much benefit as possible from the research dollar. The researcher often can and should make some effort to conduct a cost-and-benefit ratio study for applied studies. Such studies are very unlikely for basic research. Therefore, the administrator-researcher must recognize the need to provide funds, either directly or indirectly, to basic study. At the present state of wildlife management, it is difficult to specify a desirable ratio between basic and applied study.

If the benefits of research or management can be measured in comparable terms such as dollars, it may be desirable to determine priorities by some optimizing procedure. The dangers of using common terms to compare benefits accruing differently have been noted by many. The question of optimizing returns from expenditures has received considerable attention in recent years. It is not within the scope of this chapter to deal with the question of optimizing knowledge output or achieving degrees of problem solutions.

It is important, however, to recognize that such optimization is becoming a well-known and widely considered step in research program planning and will soon find its way into wildlife research. The investigator who may wish to review the subject as it relates to a natural resources research question should study Bethune (1967). An excellent treatment of the general subject is given by Ackoff (1962).

Collectively, the important considerations in setting priorities are: (1) Probability of solution, (2) ease of solution, (3) budgetary constraints, (4) prediction of future research needs, (5) predictions of future goals and objectives, (6) predictions of availability of funds, and (7) predictions of administrative support for (a) long-term vs. short-term research management programs, (b) similar or diverse research, and (c) supportive personnel and facilities.

PROBLEM STATEMENT

The development of a clear problem statement is one of the most important steps of planning. Reduction of problems to the lowest common denominator, to the most precise question, or to the simplest hypothesis is not easy. However, no time spent on this effort will be wasted. If the problem can be stated, it can be solved—or the reasons given for why it cannot.

Problem statements vary according to research or management program needs, but all specify one or more obstacles which must be overcome. If the problem is large, or a problem-complex, it should be broken into meaningful interrelated segments so that results from segments can be synthesized toward solution. The following example constitutes a general problem statement for wildlife habitat research; it is one of several problems identified for analysis and study by the U. S. Forest Service, Wildlife Habitat Research Project at Blacksburg, Virginia.[2]

Problem—Determination of the Need and Opportunity to Supplement Forest Wildlife Habitat in the Mountains of the Southeast

Attempts by game managers to correct habitat deficiencies through supplemental

[2]Unpublished Problem Selection Document (1966). USDA, Forest Service, Southeastern Forest Experiment Station. Project SE-1801. *Improved Management of Wildlife Habitat in the Southeast.*

measures are legion, and most of this work involves the use of untested measures—such as clearings planted to improved forage species. Questions can appropriately be raised whether these measures are necessary since there is little evidence in support of their widespread use. On the other hand, there is little evidence to suggest that they are not of benefit, and many techniques are very popular with the public in general.

This problem probably has a most direct bearing on poor site Ridge and Valley lands, but it will involve considerations for supplementation on all forests in the Southeastern mountains. There appears to be a consensus that forage supplementation may be useful on lands with limited disturbance from timber operations. On better site commercial hardwood lands, it appears that wildlife production objectives may be met by skillful coordination of timber management activities to maximize and stabilize production of important habitat elements. Thus, the question of supplementation and its role as a wildlife habitat management might be best investigated initially on poor site, mixed oak-pine mountain lands.

Actually, we have given considerable attention to this problem, and the long-term cooperative compartment studies which have been undertaken with the Virginia Unit in Broad Run may shed some light on the contribution of supplemental habitat measures and this work should be reviewed closely. Current studies that bear on this problem will be continued, but the problem is of lower priority generally, and new research will not be programmed until work on other and more vital problems has been fully implemented. Note: A thorough analysis of this problem has been made (Larson 1966), and studies have been programmed for its solution in keeping with the priority consideration indicated above.

STATE OF KNOWLEDGE

The first and most absolute requirement of investigative action or any planning effort is to examine objectively the "state of knowledge" to determine the real nature of the problem. After priorities have been established, and a top priority problem decided upon, the question of why it yet exists should be answered. Two possibilities are: it exists because information has not yet been compiled (or published); or, because exist-

ing information or solutions have not yet been studied or discovered. Failure to recognize this distinction has probably wasted more energy, money, and time in redundant or duplicate effort than has been spent advancing knowledge. Some workers wonder at lack of interest in their efforts even though they are working on "old hat" projects only slightly different from past or current work. Not much is gained by working on problems that, in one sense, no longer exist; they have been solved. Very early in the consideration of a problem the literature must be searched. By determining the state of man's knowledge of the problem, a major step will have been made toward its solution, perhaps the final step.

THE PLANNING PROCESS

Usually, the researcher works between the *synthesis* of the known into a solution and the *probe* beyond the fringes of knowledge. Investigations, therefore, normally require both critical literature review and a program of observation and experimentation. It is necessary to develop at this point, either formally or informally, an analytical process and plan of study. Whether such a plan will be formalized and a research prospectus developed, or only a few mental notes made, will be determined by the scope and complexity of the selected problem.

The manager is equally concerned with the planning process. Planning is a continuous process, of alternative seeking, which leads to a decision on actions. He must specify how he will overcome a managerial obstacle (solve his problem). If the problem is complex, long term, or of major consequence, it may require a formal set of plans and specifications; if not, it may be only a mental noting of how some job will be done.

Once several approaches to the solution of the selected problem have been imagined, the need arises to determine which approach, within the constraints of funds, manpower, etc., offers the highest yield of benefits.

In research, selection of the approach will indicate the general literature review requirements and the amount and type of field and laboratory work required. The planner must refocus on the purpose of the work to seek an approach to the problem that will avoid "over-solving" or, perhaps more importantly, avoid an inadequate or unrealistic attack on the problem.

The same general considerations go into the selection of the approach as in the selection of a problem. It is unlikely that sophisticated cost-benefit analyses will be practical since alternatives are usually sharp and their relative merits rather obvious. When working with a large problem of a number of parts, stepwise or simultaneous solutions should be considered, and if necessary, a phasing schedule should be set.

One of the most effective tools available to the research and management planner is the use of simulation. At its lowest level, it is like playing a game of "what if?" The planner who regularly uses this technique will simulate or mentally create possible problems or chains of events. By solving these hypothetical problems, he can develop alternative approaches, evaluate his techniques, and study the practicality of his research design, and the possibility of solving the problems.

Early in research planning, hypotheses should be developed concerning results, conditions, or outcomes. Both null and alternate hypotheses should be stated if classical methods of experimentation are to be used. Even though not stated specifically, hypotheses should be implied within or intrinsic to statements of research objectives. The hypothesis of each research or management objective should be accorded three general possibilities of treatment after study: acceptance, rejection, or inconclusive.

The Prospectus

The results of the prestudy or preplanning activities just discussed should be documented for all major research and management efforts in some type of prospectus. A prospectus outlines early thinking on a problem, describes problem analysis, establishes tentative objectives, states what will not be studied, suggests approaches and techniques of solution, and estimates needs. Prospectuses vary widely in form, depending on the situation, author, and audience. For example, they may be lengthy letters, several pages of narrative, or brief outlines. Their purpose is to record past thought, to solicit advice and assistance, and to communicate current interests, awareness, and ideas. They may, in the case of a complex problem, detail a group of studies with separate objectives and establish priority and schedules. Responses to prospectuses prevent researchers from duplicating past work, from missing significant ideas, from pursuing unprofitable or impossible objectives, or from establishing faulty study priorities.

The prospectus may later become a preamble to a report in documentation of the reasoning and selection mechanics for both problem and approaches.

The Investigational Plan

The following discussions are obviously relevant to the scientific method (Chapter 1) and the outline for reports (Chapter 5). The investigational plan is a complete "blueprint" for a research effort to meet and answer one, or often more specific questions. There are no alternative courses open at this level of planning. The plan describes *the* selected course of action which tells what, when, where, how, and by whom the work is to be done. The investigational plan is not only a desirable document; it is absolutely essential. Investigational plans may be scant or detailed, simple or complex, depending upon the problem and research requirements. As much time as possible should be spent in careful preparation of the plan.

An expanded outline (checklist) of the components of an investigational plan follows. This is a typical case and would have to be altered for specific study needs:

I. *Title*—A meaningful group of approximately 10 key words that clearly indicates the essential consideration of the study. This title is usually more inclusive than the final report title or titles for publications.
II. *Problem Definition and Selection*
 A. Scope—A brief statement of the problem and the context in which it exists. Specify related areas or approaches that will not be explored. A total project "abstract" often is useful in this position of the paper.
 B. Objective—A precise statement of goals and purposes of the study.
 C. Hypotheses—Major hypotheses compatible with the objectives should be stated.
 D. Source—The origin, cause, or stimulus of the idea.
 E. Justification—the needs, suitability, implications, potential benefits, and values of the work. List the inferences which may be expected and some alternatives, consequences, and applications of these hypothetical results. Often "future outlook" is included in this category.
III. *Study Approach and Situation*
 A. Past Work—A literature review and summary of work in progress, past experiences, and present knowledge of the problem and possible solutions.
 B. Descriptions

1. Study area or laboratory descriptions and general suitability for achieving objectives.
2. Population (habitat or animal) descriptions and characteristics pertinent to sampling and observations to be made. Statistical variances and expected difference of means of populations to be observed should be denoted here as reported or estimated.

IV. *Solution Procedures*
   A. Study resources—briefly state the kinds of people, facilities, and materials, to be applied to the study.
   B. Assumptions—List the major assumptions necessary for meaningful sampling, observation, and analyses or results.
   C. Analyses
      1. Define the elements, components, and subtopics to be studied.
      2. State the research procedures, designs, and sampling plans to be used on each element of the problem.
      3. Specify the kind and amount of data needed and to be sought.
      4. Describe in detail how all data are to be obtained including details of instrumentation, equipment, and development needs.
      5. Describe how the data are to be treated, including specifying what statistics are to be calculated, what models will be used, what tests of data will be used, what mathematical procedures and consultants will be employed, what electronic data processing or computer facilities will be employed, what existing machine programs will be used, and what programs must be developed.
      6. List checks and balances, especially those to prevent observations of "things that are not there" including replications, backup instruments, and accuracy checks of personnel and equipment. Consider here the effect of the research procedure on the objects and systems under study.

V. *Timing*
   A. Proposed date of initiation.
   B. Duration.
   C. Other time considerations like report deadlines, environmental or land-use changes, and time-related budgetary constraints.

VI. *Costs*

(Prepare detailed budgets in categories such as)
   A. Capital outlay—equipment and construction of facilities (laboratories, pens, etc.).
   B. Salaries—permanent and part-time employees and consultants.
   C. Expendable supplies.
   D. Rented equipment and depreciation costs.
   E. Travel—local and scientific conferences.
   F. Publication costs.
   G. Overhead, insurance, compensations, and administrative costs.
   H. Contingency—5 to 10% of total.

The entire plan should be evaluated to be sure all sections are consistent and directed toward the accomplishment of the stated objectives. The plan must be prepared so that any other scientist in a related field can understand and criticize the entire plan. Such plans, no matter how difficult to prepare, are essential to efficient, successful studies. Many past failures in wildlife management research can be directly attributed to inadequate or faulty planning, lack of documents to maintain continuity when personnel move, and lack of documented planning to allow past errors to be avoided.

The Management or Development Plan

Very similar to the investigational plan, the wildlife management plan is a description of the objectives and goals which will be met by the manipulation of habitat populations, and people, and the ways these objectives will be reached. Helpful publications for this planning are Davis (1966), Anon. (1955), and the vast literature of forest and agricultural management.

Desirable management plans like research plans are objective oriented. They specify units of desired output for various goals like man-hours of hunting, or numbers of harvestable animals. Such plans also emphasize land development for "target game species," although usually they will attempt to optimize the total production of desired benefits from several major species on an area.

Plans dealing with relatively small programs in small areas or concerning a single species or management technique are informal and require only limited documentation. Examples would be a series of forest clearings, trails, and waterholes for the Wardensville Wildlife Management Area, Hardy County, West Virginia; a dike building and repair operation on an Ohio public waterfowl hunting area; the use of systemic insecticides in a grove of high mast-producing trees in an eastern forest; a program to use chemosterilant bait for coyote control in several counties of a western state.

Such plans normally include:

1. A letter of transmittal (e.g., to farmer, supervisor, granting agency).

2. A cover page stating title, location, date, author, and affiliation of author.

3. An abstract.

4. Location of area or facilities and general descriptions.

5. Statement of objectives.

6. Justification, including past experiences, expected benefits and values, wildlife use, estimated human accessibility, and expected use over time.

7. Description of procedures, operations, construction, repairs, and management activity; including maps, sketches, and flow-diagrams.

8. Cost estimates and summary.

9. Sources of funds (where appropriate).

10. Provisions for evaluation.

11. Literature cited.

Another type of plan is the one for large land areas. One published work, suggestive of the level of sophistication and type of study and planning needed is *Focus on the Hudson* (USDI 1966).

Major land-use plans integrating wildlife management objectives or special-use plans are needed as land values and demands for, and pressures on, wildlife increase. The following outline provides the essential considerations for a wildlife management plan for a farm, refuge, ranger district, or park. It is far more detailed than needed for most situations, but it can serve as checklist and be fitted to the situation. The cost of such a plan in man-hours of study and preparation are great, but it is essential for coordinated best use of land and wildlife populations. Such plans steer the activities and establish duties, provide for personnel changes, protect past management investments, and on public lands establish policy necessary for continued wise management under changing economic, political, and social conditions.

I. *Letter of Transmittal*—The purpose of this letter is to introduce the report to the landowner or reader. It should include: (1) A reference to the original order or request for the plan, (2) a brief statement of the purpose of the report and any fundamental premises which have been assumed, (3) the scope or what main considerations have been included and excluded, and (4) brief acknowledgments to technical personnel engaged in the planning and reviewing of the plan. It also serves the purpose of dating the plan and indicating the present employment status of the author.

II. *Title, Author, and Date*

III. *Table of Contents*

IV. *Acknowledgments*—Courteous acknowledgment with specific services rendered by personnel or agencies involved in the plan.

V. *Purpose of Plan*—A general statement potentially the same for all such plans. Specifics should also be included such as, "This plan also attempts to meet the recreational needs and hunting pressure being exerted by the rapidly expanding (1961) suburban community of Ridgevale."

VI. *General Management Objectives and Goals*

VII. *Description of Area*

A. General—Include a map of the area showing boundaries and working units, and a location map showing the area in relation to well-known landmarks.

B. Past conditions—an ecological history

C. Topography

D. Geology

E. Nature of soils

F. Water and climate

G. Land-use types

H. Vegetative cover

I. Flood, fire, and other calamity history

VIII. *Wildlife Population Status*—Using every index available, from conversations with older residents, statewide records, and detailed research, make some estimate or expression of wildlife occurrence and abundance as a basis for species management and as a datum for management effects.

A. Fish

B. Big game

C. Small game

D. Furbearers

E. Game birds

F. Songbirds and other animals

IX. *Needs of the Human Population Using the Area*

A. Employment and social strata of adjoining areas and communities

B. Economic status of adjoining human populations

C. Percentages of resident and nonresident hunters using the area for hunting, fishing, or wildlife recreation

D. Pertinent interests, customs, and prejudices of the groups using the area.

E. Directives for management deduced from appraisal of user-needs and desires functioning in a democracy

X. *Coordinating Measures and Broad Management Objectives*—Write measures that must be used to provide multiple-use of resources, adjustments needed to insure the fulfillment of the definition of conservation, and special considerations for "tying in" wildlife management with other land uses including:

A. Range and cropland management

B. Timber management

C. Watershed management

D. Recreation

XI. *Area Wildlife Management Practices*—Make a general statement about priorities of practices and needs for integrating practices.

A. Habitat improvements

  1. Fish

    a. Construction of ponds, riffles, use of gabions, etc., including diagrams.

    b. Stocking and feeding—including schedule.

    c. Shoreline improvement—including materials, species, labor, and costs.

    d. Others, including, for example, fencing to exclude livestock or fences to allow wildlife passage.

  2. Game and furbearers

    a. List each practice. State the primary or "target" species of the practice and list with total costs all seed, planting stock, materials, equipment, labor, time, and annual maintenance time required. Include acreages and sketch on a map or map overlay the recommended locations and types of all suggested improvements. Indicate existing desirable food and cover that should be maintained or slightly modified for increased benefit. Show improvements in relation to other wildlife needs such as water and distance from dwelling. Make waterfowl recommendations for resting, feeding, or nesting sites.

    b. Include provisions for protection of practices from fire, grazing, insects, and disease.

    c. Include a reasonable schedule for establishment of recommended practices. A 10-year general plan is recommended with a specific 2-year plan of action an essential.

B. Regulation of the harvest

  1. General principles and bases for legislative recommendations.

  2. Suggestions for landowner and his staff on how to influence state and national game regulations affecting his lands.

  3. Recommendations for posting and limiting hunting areas.

  4. Maximum harvest limits for game species to insure continued resource use.

  5. Sharing of costs by users of the area, including licensing; fees; sharing portions of the kill; contributions of time, equipment, or materials for habitat improvement; hunting lodge construction with guaranteed use only within seasons; leasing of quality game habitat; etc.

  6. Permit systems and regulation of numbers of hunters on all or portions of the area where kill is to be encouraged or discouraged.

  7. Law enforcement

    a. Purposes.

    b. State and federal coordination.

    c. Additional needs, including provisions for transportation or outside help such as specialists or laboratory work.

C. Access

  1. Principle of providing access for hunting, fishing, or research.

  2. Road construction needs, including map and estimated costs of construction and maintenance.

  3. Foot trail construction needs, including maps and estimated costs of construction, marking, and maintenance.

  4. Boat or bridge access needs, including landing costs, boat and operation costs, bridge costs, and maintenance.

  5. Guides to road, trail, or bridge, gating or closure.

6. Road, trail, and bridge standards and sketches of needed work.
D. Refuges and closed areas
   1. Principles and needs of refuges.
   2. Recommendations for establishment, including costs of posting, fencing, advertising, and enforcement.
   3. Equate benefits with costs.
E. Predator control
   1. Principles of use.
   2. Recommendations, including costs of chemosterilants, traps, poison, gas, fencing, repellent, labor, and effective periods of use.
   3. Equate benefits with costs.
   4. Specify disposition of predators; e.g., pelts and carcasses.
   5. Special considerations for free-running dogs and other feral animals.
F. Other practices; e.g., salting, feeding, and stocking.
XII. *Surveys and Inventories*
   A. Disease and parasite surveys that should be made with recommendations for preservation of specimens and their transfer to competent authorities.
   B. Field records of observations with system described and plans for its use stating by whom, when, and why certain observations will be summarized and used.
   C. Provisions for records on all habitat improvement practices including description of practice, initial costs, maintenance, fertilizer, etc. Also include provisions for future use of such records for improvement of management practices.
   D. Inventory
      1. General observations with record system.
      2. Specific studies; e.g., pellet counts, live-trapping, seining.
      3. Bag and creel checks.
      4. Required reporting of game or fish taken off area.
XIII. *Measures for Testing the Effectiveness of the Plan in Action*
XIV. *Provisions for Compliance Checks. Periodic Review of Plan and Revisions*
XV. *Special Equipment Needed*
XVI. *Budget*
   A. Estimated annual and total costs.
   B. Estimated benefits and profits.
   C. Financial source or aid.
XVII. *Amendments*

SUMMARY

An effective program of research or management results from critical planning and documentation to solve a definable problem or to overcome knowledge or environmental obstacles. The documentation must include complete display of the approaches and methods that will be used in assembling and utilizing information. Planning documents must be prepared so that any competent professional can understand and criticize any or all of the essential steps. A big order? Not at all! Well-prepared plans provide for direct and effective development of new knowledge and effective wildlife management.

CHAPTER THREE

USING THE LITERATURE
ON WILDLIFE MANAGEMENT

ROBERT W. BURNS, JR.

Librarian for Research and Development
Colorado State University
Fort Collins, Colorado

AUDIENCE, PURPOSE, AND SCOPE
OF THIS GUIDE

This chapter is addressed to both the consumers and producers of the professional literature in wildlife management with the hope that they may more effectively use their literature and thereby become better producers of that literature. The purpose of this chapter is to introduce the reader to some of the standard library source materials in the field of wildlife management, show how and under what circumstances they are best used, and finally, to point out some of the more important library tools for disciplines closely related to wildlife management. The chapter has been designed with the needs of both the mature investigator and the wildlife major at the upper division or graduate level in mind. Following the practice adopted in previous editions of this manual, greatest emphasis has been placed on the literature covering the Mammalia and Aves, especially those hunted for recreation or commercially. Every effort has been made to include only publications which are easily available. This approach has ruled out many important publications with a limited circulation such as processed material, in-house reports, open-file reports, agency publications listed as "Not for Publication," and papers presented orally at meetings.

A library, like any other investigational tool, will produce good or poor results depending upon how it is used. The library user faces complex and far-reaching problems which can delay or even destroy the credence of his research. Indeed, in the eyes of many, bibliographic research must be taken as seriously as research in the laboratory or field. Proper use of library tools is made only when the investigator clearly understands why he is using the literature, the range of tools available to him, and the proper function of each bibliographic tool.

Mosby (1963) in an earlier edition of this book noted that one of the most common errors made by the North American wildlife worker engaged in a bibliographic problem was his failure to make use of the foreign literature. For this reason many sources published outside the U. S. have been included in the following pages in a deliberate attempt to bring more of these publications to the attention of the wildlife researcher.

This chapter is not a list of the best books written in the field, although many of them will be included here. Nor is it intended to serve as a list of recommended items for a working library, although most of these sources should be available in any library supporting the work of wildlife biologists. This guide is a representative collection of library tools important to the wildlife biologist arranged by subject, form, or particular function. The reader will discover that many items have been omitted. No guide can include everything and probably should not try, since to do so would only overwhelm the reader with more material than he could assimilate successfully.

In the sense in which it is used in this chapter the word "literature" refers to the total body of printed as well as nonprinted materials which the scholar uses in his work—the recorded word, as opposed to the spoken word—whose sole purpose is to preserve for the use of present and future generations the achievements of mankind. The literature of a subject field will include books, journals, serials, reports, memorandums, newsletters, newspapers, patents, theses, tables, translations, in-house or open file reports, pamphlets, films, all forms of microtext, tapes, and drawings, as well as all types of ephemeral or fugitive materials, both published and unpublished.

Since this chapter is limited to the literature of interest to the wildlife biologist, it is important that the characteristics of this particular body of literature be listed. They are as follows:

1) Unlike many other scientific disciplines, the literature of wildlife management is not well behaved or compact. Just as there are no neat, well-defined boundaries to the field of wildlife management, so there are no well-defined boundaries to the literature of this field. The wildlife biologist might use zoology and biology journals one day and mathematics books the next. Wildlife management is a composite discipline, and any discussion of its literature must take into account this basic characteristic.

2) No one knows how large this body of literature is, how much is being produced, or even what percentage is worth keeping.

3) The literature of wildlife management is international and will appear in many of the world's languages. This means that some of the literature will appear in languages not understood by the scientist who must use it.

4) Each scientific discipline contains terms which have meaning only for the individual trained in that particular discipline. This jargon creates difficulties for the wildlife biologist who must be able to move easily through the literature of many disciplines. Further complicating this problem is the fact that the meaning of a given term will change from discipline to discipline.

5) Important papers will be published in obscure journals. This means that no library will be able to supply everything required by a wildlife researcher in his work.

6) The necessity for currency in this discipline, as in any other scientific discipline, means that a very large share of the literature of science is going to be serial in nature. The journal is of primary importance to the work of the wildlife biologist.

7) A large part of the literature of wildlife biology is regional in coverage and therefore of limited use to the biologist in another location. There are many local museums, conservation societies, academies of science, and naturalist groups publishing this type of material.

8) Much of the wildlife literature is free or inexpensive and can be obtained simply by having one's name placed on a mailing list.

These characteristics should not be taken to imply that the problems facing the wildlife manager are unique to his field. Most of these are the same problems faced by other scientists who must make effective use of the literature in their respective disciplines. The volume, diversity of publication mediums, numerous languages of publication, together with the inability of any single library to contain everything needed by the biologist, all contribute to a situation which is becoming more and more difficult to manage properly.

THE LITERATURE OF SCIENCE WITH SPECIAL EMPHASIS ON WILDLIFE MANAGEMENT

Serial Literature

Serials are defined as publications issued in successive parts and intended to continue indefinitely (Brown 1956). Cagle (1960) has estimated the number of biological serials at between 15,000 and 25,000, while Porter (1964) places the number of journals in pure biology at approximately 7,000. Keeping these figures in mind it is interesting to note that *Biological Abstracts* in a recent tabulation (Dec. 15, 1967) indexed 7405 serial publications including journals, annual reports, review annuals, U. S. Government reports, conference reports, congresses, and symposia published in 94 different countries while *Wildlife Review* screens slightly more than 258 serials. Table 3.1 is a list of important serials in the field of wildlife management. It is not intended to be complete but to point out a few of the more prominent titles and to indicate their relative coverage by the index/abstract (I/A) services. No attempt was made to determine whether indexing was on a comprehensive or selective basis for the individual titles.

No one knows the extent of the serial literature necessary to the wildlife worker. Indeed, individual needs will probably vary from worker to worker. Nevertheless, some idea of how many titles exist, to what extent they are used, in what languages they appear, from what countries they come, and the extent of their coverage are appropriate topics for research by wildlife biologists. The article by Hein (1967) is an example of the type of study proposed. Similar investigations have been conducted for other disciplines. Numata (1958) has prepared an interesting list of Japanese publications in the fields of plant and animal ecology, while P. K. Anderson (1966) has investigated the periodical literature of ecology using the technique of citation counting. More analytical work of this type is necessary if intelligent decisions are to be made regarding what materials best meet our need to communicate with one another, and what types of material are to be placed in libraries.

Lists of serials, especially union lists, are helpful in determining the locations of journals, their recommended abbreviations, price, publisher, language, country of origin, etc. The *Union List of Serials in Libraries of the United States and Canada*, 3rd ed. is the fundamental reference work for determining the location of a journal in the U. S. and Canada. In addition to listing libraries which own part or complete holdings of a particular serial, the *Union List* will indicate the bibliographic history of a journal showing former titles, deaths, mergers, supplements, etc. It is kept up-to-date in a very limited way by a monthly publication from the Library of Congress called *New Serial Titles*, a list of serials which began publication after 1949. *Ulrich's International Periodicals Directory*, now in its twelfth edition, has for many years been a valuable aid in locating the price, publisher, and pertinent bibliographic information about the more prevalent journals in all disciplines. The *World List of Scientific Periodicals, 1900-1960* (Brown and Stratton 1963), published by Butterworths is a much more inclusive list of scientific journals. The fourth edition of this monumental work is kept up-to-date by an annual publication from the same publisher. The Department of Zoology in the British Museum (Natural History) and the Library of the Zoological Society of London have each prepared lists of their serial holdings. In the United States the Center for Research Libraries (formerly called the Midwest Inter-Library Center) has published a list of its serial holdings covering many of the more obscure journals indexed in *Biological Abstracts*. These are made available by the Center to other libraries in the United States on interlibrary loan.

Monographic Literature

Keeping aware of new books and the new editions of old titles as they are published, as well as determining what books are in print within one's field, are not difficult problems for books in the English language. Many indexing/abstracting services such as *Biological Abstracts* have sections listing new books. Most of the professional journals will include critical book reviews, and examples of indices will be given later in this section which guide the reader to these reviews.

It is possible to determine the most recent domestic books published in one's field by following the monthly issues of the *American Book Publishing Record*, a publication of the Bowker Corporation. The scientific, medical and technical sections of ABPR are cumulated annually into a hardcovered series called *American Scientific Books*, also published by Bowker. In January 1967 Bowker initiated a similar publication covering books announced but not yet published called

Table 3.1. Serials of interest to the wildlife biologist and where they are indexed.

	Wild-life Rev.	Biol. Abstr.	Zool. Rec-ord	Bibl. of Agric.	For-estry Abstr.	Chem. Abstr.
American Midland Naturalist	X	X	X	X	X	X
American Naturalist	X	X	X	X	X	X
Animal Behavior	X	X		X		
Animal Kingdom	X	X	X			
Audubon Field Notes	X	X				
Audubon Magazine	X	X	X			
Auk	X	X	X	X		
Avian Diseases	X	X		X	X	X
Bird-Banding	X	X				
British Birds	X	X	X			
CSIRO Wildlife Research	X	X	X	X	X	X
California Dept. of Fish and Game. Game Bulletin	X	X		X		
California Fish and Game	X	X	X	X		X
Canadian Audubon	X	X	X			
Canadian Field Naturalist	X	X	X	X		
Canadian Wildlife Service. Occas. Papers	X	X	X			
Condor	X	X	X			
Conservationist (New York)	X	X		X		
Danish Review of Game Biology	X	X				
East African Wildlife Journal	X	X	X		X	
Ecological Monographs	X	X	X	X	X	X
Ecology	X	X	X	X	X	X
IUCN Bulletin		X				
Ibis	X	X				
Idaho Wildlife Review	X					
Illinois Nat. Hist. Sur. Biol. Notes, Bull., and Circulars	3X	3X	3X	3X	3X	3X
International Assoc. of Game, Fish & Conserv. Comm. Proc.		X		X		
Journal of Animal Ecology	X	X	X	X	X	
Journal of Applied Ecology	X	X		X	X	
Journal of Ecology	X	X	X	X	X	
Journal of Mammalogy	X	X	X	X	X	X
Journal of Range Management	X	X		X	X	X

Table 3.1. Continued.

	Wild-life Rev.	Biol. Abstr.	Zool. Record	Bibl. of Agric.	For-estry Abstr.	Chem. Abstr.
Journal of the Bombay Natural History Society		X	X	X	X	X
Jour. of the East Africa Nat. Hist. Soc. and Coryndon Museum	X	X		X		
Journal of Wildlife Management	X	X	X	X	X	X
Koedoe	X		X			
Meddelelser Fra Statens Viltundersokelser (Paper of Norwegian State Game Research Institute)		X				
Michigan Conservation	X			X		
Missouri Conservationist	X	X		X		
Natural History	X	X	X	X		
Nevada Wildlife	X	X				
New York Fish and Game Journal	X	X		X		
New Zealand Ecological Soc. Proc.		X	X	X		
North American Wildlife and Nat. Res. Conf. Trans.	X	X	X		X	
Northeast Section of Wildlife Society (U. S.) Proc.	X	X				
Oryx	X	X	X		X	
Pennsylvania Game News	X	X				
Puku	X	X	X			
Riistatieteellisia Julkaisuja (Finnish Game Research)	X	X	X	X		
Southeast Assoc. of Game & Fish. Comm. Proc. of Annual Conf.	X	X			X	
Southwestern Naturalist	X	X	X	X		
Suomen Riista	X	X				
Terre et la Vie	X	X	X	X		
Texas Game and Fish	X	X				
U. S. Fish & Wildlife Service. Circular	X	X		X		X
U. S. Fish & Wildlife Service. Spec. Sci. Rept.—Wildlife	X	X	X	X		X
U. S. Nat. Museum Bulletin	X	X	X	X		X
U. S. Nat. Museum Proceedings		X	X	X		
Univ. of Kansas Museum Nat. Hist. Misc. Publ.	X	X	X	X		
Viltrevy	X	X	X			
Virginia Wildlife	X	X				
Wildlife Disease Assoc. Bulletin	X	X				
Wildlife Diseases		X		X		

Table 3.1. Continued.

	Wild-life Rev.	Biol. Abstr.	Zool. Rec-ord	Bibl. of Agric.	For-estry Abstr.	Chem. Abstr.
Wildlife in North Carolina	X	X		X		
Wildlife Monographs	X		X	X		
Wilson Bulletin	X	X	X			
Zeit. für Jagdwissenschaft	X	X			X	
Zeit. für Saugetierkunde	X		X			

Subject Guide to Forthcoming Books: a Bi-monthly Subject Forecast of Books to Come. Bowker also publishes a monthly guide to *Paperbound Books in Print;* the *Publishers Trade List Annual,* which is arranged by the name of the publisher giving all the currently available titles of each; *Books in Print: An Author-Title-Series Index to the Publishers' Trade List Annual;* and a *Subject Guide to Books In Print.* The *Cumulative Book Index,* a monthly publication of the H. W. Wilson Company, is a world index to current books in the English language as they are published. The *National Union Catalog* and its sister publication the *Library of Congress Catalog Books: Subjects* act as guides to a large share of the world's current book and serial production. Many state and foreign publications which would otherwise have been difficult to locate can be found by using these tools. In addition to being indices, they also act as union lists by including a limited number of locations where books may be seen and used in the United States, Canada and Puerto Rico.

The out-of-print market for books and journals has become increasingly important because of the large number of new libraries being created. One result of this increasing demand has been the appearance of a large reprint market. This has meant that quite often a title which was out-of-print and has not been available for many years will again become available. University Microfilms in Ann Arbor, Michigan is producing on demand copies of out-of-print books in microfilm or xerox form. The *Reprint Expediting Service Bulletin* announces new books or periodicals which have been reprinted from several sources and in many disciplines. The *Guide to Reprints* published by Microcard editions is an annual list of reprints of books, journals, etc. reprinted in the United States. University Microfilms has pre-

pared a similar catalog of OP books and journals for sale.

Another result of this increasing demand for OP books has been a brisk trade among the dealers. There are many dealers in the U. S. and Europe who make a specialty of natural history books. The *American Book Trade Directory* lists publishers, booksellers, wholesalers, etc., in the U. S. and abroad with dealers specialties noted.

BOOK REVIEWING MEDIA

A few years ago George Sarton (1960) wrote a short article in which he stated that the purpose of book reviewing is to communicate to the public the results of one's analysis. Any reader looking for the ingredients of a good book review can do no better than to read this short but very cogent essay on the book review and its preparation. Sarton's essay should be of interest to all who read as well as write, for it includes many pertinent remarks on these twin arts. He reiterates what many of us knew, but had forgotten, of the purpose and function of the book review, and he reminds us of the important parts played by the table of contents, preface, and bibliography.

The reader can expect to find detailed, critical reviews of the world literature in the *Journal of Ecology, Journal of Wildlife Management, Nature, Scientific American, Science, American Scientist, Endeavor,* and *Journal of Mammalogy.* Shorter reviews and critical notes concerning new books may be found in the *Quarterly Review of Biology, Biologisches Zentralblatt, Audubon Magazine, Oryx,* and *BioScience.*

Nature, Science, and *Natural History* prepare annual surveys of science books which are helpful to anyone wishing to survey the year's book production. The *Natural History* cumulation appears in December and covers only the science books written for young people. The book review supplement for *Nature* appears in December.

Book reviews can be located by scanning the journals or by examining the indexing services which index book reviews such as: *Biological and Agricultural Index, Book Review Digest* (BRD), *Book Review Index* and *Technical Book Review Index* (TBRI). BRD and TBRI consist of short paragraphs taken from the original review as it appeared in a journal. In TBRI heavy emphasis is placed upon books in the physical sciences, engineering, and mathematics.

Critical annotations, which are usually shorter than the conventional book review, appear in *Choice* and *Science Books*. *Choice* is a monthly publication sponsored by the Association of College and Research Libraries and notes books for the college and university audience. *Science Books* is a new quarterly sponsored by the AAAS covering trade books, textbooks, and reference works in the pure and applied sciences for students in the elementary or secondary grades, the first 2 years of college, as well as selected advanced and professional books useful for reference.

SOME EXAMPLES OF BOOKS IMPORTANT TO THE WILDLIFE BIOLOGIST

All scientific disciplines rely heavily on the monograph whether it be a textbook, reference book, manual, or handbook. Indeed, many disciplines have standard manuals or handbooks which are essential to its workers. Many of these will be of help to the game biologist although they relate only indirectly to his work. Quite often these manuals are known only by the name of the original author, which makes them difficult to locate. Most are landmarks in their respective fields and considered essential to anyone working in that area. Some examples of these basic guides are Hitchcock (1951) on grasses; Ward and Whipple (Edmondson 1959) on fresh-water biology; Bergey (Breed, Murray, and Smith 1957) on the bacteria; Gray's (Fernald 1950) manual on flowering plants and ferns of the Central and Northeastern United States and adjacent Canada; the Merck veterinary (Siegmund 1961) and pharmaceutical (Anon. 1952) manuals; the Society of American Foresters handbook (Forbes 1955); three biological handbooks from the Federation of American Societies for Experimental Biology covering general biological data (Altman and Dittmer 1964), growth (Altman and Dittmer 1962), and blood and other body fluids (Altman and Dittmer 1961); the Chemical Rubber Co. mathematical

tables (Selby 1964); and the Fisher (1963) statistical tables for biological, agricultural, and medical research. The game manager should have at least a speaking acquaintance with these general reference books. In addition, there are a number of texts more closely related to his work. Although it is not possible to list here all of the books which will be of interest, some mention should be made of a few of the more important titles. The reader will find many others throughout this and other chapters. Any wildlife manager will no doubt have several favorites of his own not included here. This list is incomplete. It is intended to serve only as a partial reference list and for suggestions. It is not a list of books to own, for many of them are out-of-print and now quite expensive.

The fiction and non-fiction of Ernest Thompson Seton will always rank near the top on any list of books covering wildlife. Although now somewhat dated, his *Lives of Game Animals* is a wildlife classic. Other titles of importance are Beebe (1926), Allen (1956), McAtee (1945), and Delacour (1951) on the pheasant; Elliott (1897), on the North American game birds; Errington (1963) on the muskrat; Einarsen (1948) on the pronghorn antelope; O. Murie (1951) on the elk in North America; Peterson (1955) on the North American moose; Lydekker (1898) on deer; Taylor (1956) on the North American deer; Darling (1937), Whitehead (1964), and Millais (1897) on the "deer" of the British Isles; Schorger (1966) and Hewitt (1967) on the wild turkey; Young on the coyote (Young and Jackson 1951), the puma (Young and Goldman 1946), the wolves of North America (Young and Goldman 1944), and the bobcat (1958); A. Murie (1944) on the wolf; Roe (1951) on the North American buffalo; Gabrielson (1941) on wildlife conservation; and three important studies on zoogeography, one by Darlington (1957), one by Bartholomew, Clarke and Grimshaw (1911), and the AAAS Symposium (Hubbs 1958); Leopold (1933), Trippensee (1948-1953) and Allen (1962) on game management; Martin (1951) on wildlife food habits; the record book of the Boone and Crocket Club (1964) with its counterpart for game records of Africa (Best 1962), and Fitz (1963) on how to measure and score trophies; Special Publications nos. 11, 12 and 13 of the American Committee for International Wild Life Protection on the extinct and vanishing birds and mammals; the list of *Rare and Endangered Fish and Wildlife of the United States* issued as Resource Publication no. 34 by the U. S. Bureau of Sport Fisheries and Wildlife; two Survival Service Commission *Red Data Books* of the International Union For

Conservation of Nature and Natural Resources, one on the birds and one on the mammals; and a monograph on the Anatidae in Great Britain (Atkinson-Willes 1963) sponsored by the Wildfowl Trust.

Bibliographic Tools for the Control
of Scientific Literature

INDEXING AND ABSTRACTING SERVICES

Basic to any literature search or review is a thorough knowledge of the indexing and abstracting services (I/A) available for that particular field. Of these two, the abstracting service is more satisfactory when locating and identifying references because it tells something of the nature of the material, whereas the indexing services include only titles and bibliographic information. Both types can and often do serve as alerting or current awareness services. However, special tools for this particular function will be discussed later with several examples.

The wildlife biologist is faced with a number of alternatives when selecting an index or abstract serial for his literature searching. Which one he chooses will depend upon the characteristics of each service and upon his understanding of the purpose and function of that service. His choice will also depend in part upon the type of literature search he wishes to conduct—current-awareness searching, retrospective searching, or searching merely for specific information relative to some topic. The characteristic which distinguishes an index to be used as a retrospective-searching tool from one to be used for current-awareness purposes is the presence of a cumulated internal index enabling the user to move through the index without having to consult each individual issue.

There are only a dozen or so I/A services which the wildlife biologist must know well. Apart from this group lie the I/A services designed to meet special needs by covering a limited subject in more detail or by covering a chronological period which has no other I/A coverage. Of these latter the wildlife manager needs only a speaking acquaintance and the knowledge that such tools exist. The easiest way to discover them is to consult a guide to the literature (see the section in this chapter on Guides to the Literature). A better understanding of the potential value of each of these I/A services can be obtained by studying Table 3.1.

Included in the core of essential I/A services

for the English speaking wildlife manager are *Biological Abstracts* and its supplementary partner *Bioresearch Index, Wildlife Review* and its cumulations *Wildlife Abstracts,* the *Zoological Record, Bibliography of Agriculture, Biological and Agricultural Index* and its predecessor the *Agricultural Index, Forestry Abstracts,* and *Chemical Abstracts.* The wildlife biologist will not necessarily use each of these services every time he performs a literature search, nor are these the only I/A's he needs to consider when undertaking a literature search. However, this group is capable of meeting all but his most specialized needs in literature searching.

Best use of this basic group will be made when the searcher has a thorough knowledge of the characteristics of each. Table 3.2 will give the reader a better understanding of how I/A services support one another. This knowledge will be of assistance in helping the searcher make the most efficient use of his time and the material before him. Outside this core of basic I/A services is a large group of specialized subject-oriented services sponsored by societies, governmental agencies, bureaus, private publishing houses, associations, foundations, information groups, etc. The National Federation of Science Abstracting and Indexing Services (1963) has compiled a bibliography which will help guide the wildlife manager to these specialized services.

Biological Abstracts

Biological Abstracts (BA) published by the BioSciences Information Service, BIOSIS (Parkins 1966), is an outstanding index to the world's published and unpublished biological research literature, both monographic and serial. Since 1926, when its coverage began, BA has published more than 1,600,000 abstracts (Anon. 1966). It was created by the merger of *Botanical Abstracts* with *Abstracts of Bacteriology.* Today it indexes 7405 serial-type publications many of which are from state, provincial, or national fish and game offices, or wildlife societies. A list of these serials has accompanied the November 1 issue since 1965 (In 1967 this list accompanies the 15 Dec. issue). Coverage in the early days of this service was spotty, and often the time interval between publication of an article and its subsequent indexing was longer than the user might expect. However, no recent examples of these difficulties have come to this author's attention. Today (i.e. 1967) BIOSIS estimates that BA will cover 125,000 reports of research although BA

Table 3.2. Index/Abstract services which include selected material from other I/A services.

I/A Services	Other I/A Services Covered						
	Dissertation Abstracts	Bibliography of Agriculture	Biological Abstracts	Chemical Abstracts	Forestry Abstracts	Wildlife Review	Zoological Record
Biological Abstracts	X	X	X	X		X	X
Chemical Abstracts	X	X	X	X	X		
Forestry Abstracts	X	X	X	X	X		
Wildlife Review	X	X	X	X		X	
Zoological Record	X		X				X
Bibliography of Agriculture	X	X			X		

has not covered papers delivered at scientific meetings (Anon. 1964) since 1964.

There are three internal indices published in each issue of BA. These are author (both personal and corporate), biosystematic, and a topical index called CROSS (Computer Rearrangement of Subject Specialties). At one time, geographic and geologic indices were prepared, but this practice has been discontinued. A fourth internal index to BA is the subject index which is issued separately under the title BASIC (Biological Abstracts Subjects in Context). BASIC is a computer-generated index consisting of keywords from the author's title with additional terms added by BA's editorial staff. Each of the keywords in this string of words serves as an indexing term and is placed so as to stand in the center of the column thereby putting the string in its proper place in the alphabetic sequence. The string is then repeated as many times as there are keywords. Each of the four internal indices are cumulated annually.

As is the case with many indices, BA includes other I/A serials in its coverage. In addition to those shown in Table 2, BA includes citations taken from *Index Medicus, International Abstracts of Biological Sciences* and from seven sections of the *Referativnyi Zhurnal*, the Russian National I/A service. Since 1961 BA has included doctoral theses by indexing *Dissertation Abstracts*, and to a very limited extent, the translated literature through its coverage of *Technical Translations*.

Such a system of interlocking references can be very helpful, but it is also deceiving since the searcher is never quite certain what ground he has already covered. As a result, the literature searcher must often search in several I/A services anyway to insure complete coverage.

In addition to the services described above, it is possible to obtain from BIOSIS each subject section of BA on microcards on a semi-monthly basis, individual abstracts on 3 x 5-inch cards according to abstract numbers or subject specified by the searcher, or the entire issue on microfilm on an annual subscription basis (Parkins 1966). This latter service is extended only to subscribers who have already ordered the printed edition. Should the searcher wish to see the complete text of a reference, he may write to John Crerar Library, 86 East Randolph Street, Chicago, Illinois for a photostat or microfilm negative of the original.

Bioresearch Index

Bioresearch Index (prior to January 1967 called *BioResearch Titles*) is an international title listing service which extends the coverage of *Biological Abstracts*. It was first published in September 1965. Material reported in *Bioresearch Index* (BRI) is not reported in BA. Coverage by BA is limited to the most important, longest established, and best known journals. BRI covers papers delivered at scientific meetings, symposia, and the newer, lesser-known journals (Robert R. Gulick, BioScience Information Service, 1966, pers. communication).

Zoological Record

The *Zoological Record* (ZR) has been a bulwark of zoological bibliography for many years and is one of the oldest index services in continuous operation in the zoological sciences. It indexes both monographs and serials. Coverage began in 1864, and it has been issued annually since 1865. ZR is one of the most important if not the most important index to the international literature for all branches of zoology. Neave (1950) describes it as a unique example of scientific bibliography. It is particularly important for the systematist seeking to locate the original citations for new genera and species. Its coverage of local and regional natural history societies in the British Isles is especially important. ZR is composed of 20 separate sections with one section titled a "List of New Genera and Subgenera," another "Comprehensive Zoology," and 18 additional sections each devoted to a zoological group, such as Protozoa, Aves, Mammalia, etc., arranged in phylogenetic order. These sections may be purchased separately. Each of the sections covering a zoological group is arranged in three parts: 1) an author index, 2) a subject index, and 3) a systematic index. The chief difficulty encountered in using the ZR is that publication is often 2 to 4 years behind coverage. Because of its importance and the demand for early issues, Johnson Reprint Corporation is reprinting the early volumes of ZR. Volumes 43-51, for the years 1906-1914 were also issued as vol. 6-14 of the *International Catalogue of Scientific Literature*, Section N, Zoology.

Wildlife Review

Wildlife Review (WR) began in 1935 as an irregular publication of the USDA's Bureau of Biological Survey. Today it is a quarterly publication, issued by the Bureau of Sport Fisheries and Wildlife, monitoring slightly more than 258 serial titles and a few monographs from the world's wildlife literature. Despite its many drawbacks it serves a useful function by alerting the wildlife manager to publications which might be of interest to him. Both WR and its cumulations, *Wildlife Abstracts*, will be available in U. S. Government Depository Libraries. WR is best used as a current-awareness service since there are no cumulations after 1960. Three cumulations were issued between 1935 and 1960 under the misleading title *Wildlife Abstracts* without abstracts.

WR has been exchanging citations with *Biological Abstracts* since 1957 (Anon. 1957). The first citations from WR appeared in the October 1, 1957 issue of BA. In addition to *Biological Abstracts*, *Wildlife Review* receives citations from a number of other I/A services, including the *Veterinary Bulletin, Technical Translations, Nuclear Science Abstracts, Helminthological Abstracts, Dissertation Abstracts*, the Centralized Title Service Cards of the Commonwealth Forestry Bureau, and indirectly from the *Referativnyi Zhurnal: Biologia* through *Biological Abstracts*. WR also covers Soil Survey Maps of the U.S.D.A. A discussion of WR's coverage appears in no. 75, 1954.

Bibliography of Agriculture

The *Bibliography of Agriculture* (BOA) is an index to all important monographs and serials received by the National Agricultural Library (NAL) in Washington, covering agriculture and its related disciplines. In 1965 BOA indexed 110,172 items (B. L. Oliveri, Assistant Director of Program Coordination Services, National Agricultural Library, 1966, pers. communication) from over the world. This service started in 1942 and is issued once a month. The term "agriculture" is used in a very broad sense by BOA to cover publications relating to plant science, soils, forestry, entomology, animal industry, etc. Because of this, it covers much material that is of interest to the wildlife manager. One very important class of publications indexed by BOA are those coming from the various agricultural experiment stations. A list of the serials indexed in BOA has been published by the National Agricultural Library (1965). The reader will find a short discussion of BOA's coverage including time and language limitations given on the first page of each issue.

Monthly issues of BOA are arranged by very general subject categories and are accompanied by author, subject (beginning in July 1967), and organizational indices. A cumulated subject index appears in December. Copies of publications indexed by BOA may be purchased in either microfilm or photoprint from the National Agricultural Library in Washington, D.C. Each issue has separate sections listing new serials, new translations, U.S.D.A. publications, publications from the Food and Agriculture Organization of the United Nations, and state agricultural experiment station publications newly received by NAL.

BOA includes in its coverage a very limited number of other I/A services. In addition to those listed in Table 2, it indexes material from *Helminthological Abstracts, Animal Breeding Abstracts, Veterinary Bulletin, Soils and Fertilizers*, and *Nutrition Abstracts and Reviews*.

National Agricultural Library Catalog

The *National Agricultural Library Catalog* (NALC) is a list of all titles added to the NAL collection during the previous month, not including articles in journals. The National Agricultural Library contains approximately 1,248,000 volumes, with publications in 50 languages from over 155 states, countries, organizations, etc. (NAL, 1966, Pers. Communication, Dec. 21). NALC started publication in 1966 and its coverage is intended to compliment that of the *Bibliography of Agriculture*. However, NALC differs from BOA in that it includes publications regardless of their date, language, or subject. The monthly issues of NALC will keep the new *Dictionary Catalog of the National Agricultural Library, 1862-1965,* current.

Biological and Agricultural Index

The *Biological and Agricultural Index,* formerly called the *Agricultural Index,* started in 1919 and goes back to 1916 in its coverage. This monthly publication is presently a subject index to a very limited group of English-language periodicals, including both trade and professional journals, all of which are indexed by other I/A services. Prior to September 1964 it covered publications from state (U.S.) agricultural experiment stations, the U. S. Department of Agriculture, some publications from the state (U.S.) agricultural extension departments, current book titles, book reviews, and some miscellaneous literature relating to agriculture. Today these publications have been dropped (except book reviews) and more emphasis placed on biology. The advantages gained by using this index are the ease with which it is handled and the high quality of the periodicals covered. Cumulations are prepared quarterly, semiannually, annually and biannually.

Forestry Abstracts

Forestry Abstracts (FA) is a quarterly publication of the Commonwealth Forestry Bureau. It started in 1939, with coverage beginning in 1937-38, as an index to the world's forestry literature appearing in monographic or serial form. Its primary emphasis is on forestry, but it also includes some material on entomology, soils, and wildlife. Individual issues often begin with a review article on some aspect of forestry. Normally, these include detailed subject bibliographies. Individual issues have only an author

index. Cumulated author, subject, species, and geographical indices are published annually. FA also appears four times a month on cards or flimsy slips offering the reader a ready-made card file.

Chemical Abstracts

Chemical Abstracts (CA) is one of the largest, if not the largest, I/A service in the U. S. It started in 1907, appears weekly, and indexes more than 13,000 different serial type publications. It is important to the wildlife manager for several reasons, the most important of these being that it indexes on a selective basis such important periodicals as the *Journal of Wildlife Management, CSIRO Wildlife Research, Arctic, Quarterly Review of Biology, Biological Bulletin,* etc. In addition, it covers many subjects becoming more and more important to wildlife research. These include pesticides, drugs and their physiological effects, water, mammalian biochemistry, biochemical methods, etc.

Chemical Abstracts has five internal indices—author (personal and corporate), subject, patent, formula and ring. Another valuable feature for the literature searcher are the 5 and 10 year cumulations, which enable the searcher to survey large blocks of the literature with a minimum of effort. CA includes several other I/A services in its coverage including 46 sections from *Referativnyi Zhurnal,* two of which are *Biologiya* and *Veterinariya.* For a list of other services covered by CA see Table 2.

Some I/A Services for Related Disciplines

Outside the nucleus of essential I/A services discussed in the preceding paragraphs is a multitude of special purpose indexing services. Their use is determined partly by their availability, partly by the needs of the searcher for specialized coverage, and partly by the knowledge of the searcher regarding their existance.

Two national I/A services are worth mentioning here. One is published in France and the other in Russia. The French publication is called *Bulletin Signaletique* and appears in 18 *Sections Mensuelles.* The Russian publication is called *Referativnyi Zhurnal* (RZ) and appears in approximately 50 subject sections. Both of these are indices to the world's scientific literature. RZ publishes 800,000 abstracts yearly from the periodicals of 104 countries in some 72 different languages (Anon. 1966). Many sections from RZ are indirectly available to the western scientist because they have been included in western I/A serials.

The following I/A serials are also worthy of the wildlife manager's attention. However, their use is limited and care should be exercised in their selection, always keeping in mind the special areas they cover:

● Arctic Bibliography

Arctic Bibliography was first published in 1953 as a continuing index to the literature covering all phases of scientific endeavor involving the arctic or near-arctic regions. Volumes 1-12 of this set were issued as U. S. Government depository items.

● Antarctic Bibliography

Antarctic Bibliography started in 1965 as a continuing project of the Library of Congress and the National Science Foundation to bring the literature concerned with this region under bibliographic control. The index is arranged by broad headings: biological sciences, oceanography, expeditions, etc., with the citations arranged by subtopics under each main heading. It should not be confused with a single-volume bibliography bearing this same title published in 1951.

● Nutrition Abstracts and Reviews

Nutrition Abstracts and Reviews started in 1931 and is a publication from the Commonwealth Bureaux of Animal Nutrition. NAR covers publications on the chemical composition of foodstuffs, physiology of nutrition, feeding of animals, etc.

● Soils and Fertilizers

Soils and Fertilizers is an index to the world's literature in the fields of pedology, soil physics, classification, biology, grassland, etc. It started in 1932 and is published by the Commonwealth Agricultural Bureaux. SAF has been collected into four-year cumulations under the title *Bibliography of Soil Science* without the abstracts.

● Index Veterinarius

Index Veterinarius started in 1933 and is a publication of the Commonwealth Bureau of Animal Health. Emphasis is on diseases and their incidence or prevention in domestic animals, but it covers much material that will be of interest to the wildlife biologist. *Index Veterinarius* includes everything covered in the *Veterinary Bulletin* plus some additional material. The difference is that the *Bulletin* provides the reader with an abstract of the material. Another indexing service, the *Accumulative Veterinary Index* covers only a selected list of American periodicals. Its advantage lies in the fact that it does not overwhelm the user with references to material in publications he cannot locate, or in languages he cannot read.

● Meteorological and Geoastrophysical Abstracts

Meteorological and Geoastrophysical Abstracts published since 1950 by the American Meteorological Society is a monthly index to the meteorological literature of 100 countries in more than 30 languages. Internal indices are prepared for author, subject, and geographical location. Annotated bibliographies often accompany the individual issues. Some of the subjects for which bibliographies have been compiled include aerobiology, forest micrometeorology, dew, frost, limnology, radiation, bioclimatology, etc.

● Pesticides Documentation Bulletin

Pesticides Documentation Bulletin is a biweekly prepared by the Pesticides Information Center in the National Agricultural Library. It started in 1965 and is designed to serve as an index to the world's literature on diseases, insects, nematodes, parasites, etc., affecting plants, animals, man, or our natural resources.

● Index-Catalogue of Medical and Veterinary Zoology

Index-Catalogue of Medical and Veterinary Zoology is a publication of the U.S.D.A., Bureau of Animal Industry, dating back to 1902. It is a depository item covering the world's literature on trematodes, cestodes, roundworms, and similar parasites.

● Helminthological Abstracts

Helminthological Abstracts is a quarterly publication of the Commonwealth Agricultural Bureaux indexing the world's literature on helminths and their vectors. Individual issues are accompanied by review articles, as well as subject and author indices which cumulate annually.

Indices Covering the Nineteenth and Early Twentieth Centuries

Quite often the investigator will need to trace a literature reference or carry his search for material back into the nineteenth century. The I/A's covering this period are limited in number. The *Zoological Record* offers the searcher a subject approach to the literature of the second half of the nineteenth century. The *Catalogue of Scientific Papers* of the Royal Society of London is an author index to the contents of 1,555 periodicals from the learned societies and academies of Europe published during the nineteenth century. As might be expected, comprehensive bibliographies can be of great help in locating material published during the nineteenth century. Meisel (1924-1929), Phillips (1930), and Altsheler (1940) will support this type of literature searching as will many of the more specialized subject bibliographies. The reader should seek additional titles in the section covering bibliographies of this chapter.

There is only one broad-based index covering the first decade of the twentieth century. This is the *International Catalog of Scientific Literature* issued annually in 17 sections from 1901-1914. Sections of special interest to the wildlife biologist are L, covering general biology; M, covering botany; and N, covering zoology.

Current-Awareness Searching

There are a number of different ways for the wildlife biologist to keep himself aware of what is currently being published in his own field and in the fields closely related to his specialty. The reader's attention is invited to that section of this chapter covering "Research In Progress" for additional material on this topic.

In a limited sense the I/A serials mentioned earlier will help satisfy this need. The reader should note the discussion of *Wildlife Review*. Traditionally I/A serials have answered the need for both current-awareness and retrospective searching. However, the sheer bulk of material to be covered is mediating against this with the result that new techniques are being developed to answer the needs of the scientist for keeping abreast of the publications in his field. One new technique for keeping the reader aware of what is currently being published is known as SDI or selective dissemination of information. However, like KWIC (Key Word In Context) indexing, it depends upon selection of the proper keyword by both the searcher and the indexer.

A very common method for keeping oneself aware of the current publications in a particular discipline is to use the "Current Literature," "Schriftenschau," or "Referate" sections in the professional journals. Of direct interest to the wildlife biologist are sections in the *Journal of Mammalogy, Zeitschrift für Jagdwissenschaft, Animal Behavior, Auk*, and *Bird-Banding*. Closely related to the work of the wildlife biologist are the alerting sections found in journals for the following disciplines: botany, the *Bulletin of the Torrey Botanical Club;* herpetology, the journal *Herpetologica;* for ecology, the *Journal of Animal Ecology*, and *La Terre et La Vie;* and for new publications in systematics the journal *Systematic Zoology*.

Another method for keeping alert to what is currently being published is to use *Current Contents*, a weekly information service published by the Institute for Scientific Information. This is a collection of "Tables of Contents" taken from current journals. Quite often these are available before the journal is published, enabling *Current Contents* to print the Table of Contents very close to the time when the issue of the journal appears. CC is published in two editions, one of which covers the chemical, pharmaco-medical, and life sciences.

A third way of keeping alert to the current literature is by scanning a current title-listing service or using one of the KWIC indices such as BASIC or *Chemical Titles*.

New Developments in the I/A Field

No discussion of the I/A services would be complete without some mention of new developments in this field. KWIC indexing has proved to be satisfactory and, today, several I/A services are using this concept in a modified form to include a limited number of supplementary terms. Citation indexing is coming to the fore, but still remains controversial, and has yet to be proven as a multidisciplinary searching tool for the sciences. The *Science Citation Index* has taken the lead in this area. SCI has received both praise (Garfield 1964) and criticism (Steinbach 1964) from its users. It was first published in 1963 by the Institute for Scientific Information. Coverage begins with the 1961 literature. For many libraries it is prohibitively expensive, and the fact that it offers the searcher only one route to the material he seeks is a serious disadvantage. Traditionally, there have been at least three approaches open to the user of an index—author, subject and title. SCI exploits only one of these— the author approach. It differs from traditional indexing in other ways. The searcher who uses it must move forward in time rather than backward as do most other I/A services. The user is expected to begin with the name of an author who wrote a landmark or fundamental paper in his field then move to other papers which have cited this landmark paper.

SUBJECT BIBLIOGRAPHIES

Subject bibliographies can be extremely valuable when used as source materials to survey the literature of a particular field. Indeed, as Page (1965) points out, bibliographies serve a number of useful purposes by keeping an orderly record of the knowledge in a field, helping to prevent needless repetition, keeping arguments about priority reasonably clean, and aiding the library user in his search for material. One need only point to the bibliographies of Strong (1939-1959), Crispens (1960), Karstad (1964), Makepeace (1956), Godin (1964), Yeager (1941) in order to better appreciate their potential for literature research. Despite all this, the bibliography is often ignored or passed over.

In a sense, guides to the literature as well as the I/A services are subject bibliographies. Both are treated in other sections of this chapter. This section has been limited to the nonrecurring bibliography listing references on a particular subject (Godin 1964), region (McKinley 1960), period (Phillips 1930), or individual (Schorger 1966). Continuing subject bibliographies are covered in the section on I/A services.

Bibliographies can be found in a variety of places. They are normally used to document articles and books of a research nature. They are often published independently, in book or journal form, and occasionally as supplements to both. The last volume of Walker et al. (1964) is an excellent classified bibliography on the mammals of the world and will give the literature searcher a starting point for work in mammalogy. However, it should be supplemented by the second volume of Hall and Kelson (1959) and the various specialized bibliographies. UNESCO (1963) published a review, including bibliographies, on the soils, flora, and fauna of Africa. Both the Utah Cooperative Wildlife Research Unit and the Colorado Department of Game, Fish, and Parks have published literature reviews. From the latter, examples are reviews on the sage grouse (Gill 1966) and pronghorn behavior (Prenzlow 1965). Other places to look are in the terminal bibliographies which normally accompany review articles appearing in serials with the titles *Annual Review of . . . , Fortschritte der . . . , Advances In . . . , Progress In . . . , International Review of . . .*, etc.

Because they are scattered through the literature, the searcher must expect to look in several places to determine if a bibliography exists. The logical place to begin such a search is at the library card catalog. Here he can expect to find bibliographies noted as parts of books by a statement on the individual cards, as well as under the heading "Bibliography" or under the subject. It should be pointed out, however, that individual practices will vary from library to library. From the card catalog a search can be carried to the *Bibliographic Index*, the volumes of Besterman (1955), and into the indexing services such as the *Monthly Catalog of United States Government Publications, Biological Abstracts, Zoological Record* or *Wildlife Abstracts* where one can find bibliographies listed under the heading "Bibliography" and/or under the subject. One I/A service, *Meteorological & Geoastrophysical Abstracts*, issues annotated subject bibliographies which often accompany the individual issues of this index. Several examples of these bibliographies have been noted in the I/A section of this chapter.

It is a fairly common practice to include extensive bibliographies in the general textbooks and field guides on natural history. These terminal bibliographies can be of tremendous value to the reader by enabling him to work deeper into the literature, or to pursue an interesting topic outside his immediate interest. Examples of such bibliographies occur in Bourliere (1964), Smith (1966), Ingles (1965), Peterson (1966), Dasmann (1964), Southern (1964), Cockrum (1962), Taylor (1956), Benton and Werner (1966), and at the end of this book.

Another approach which can be used in the search for material on a particular subject is to use the lists of publications which accompany many of the biographies of outstanding scientists. Illustrations of this occur in the lists of publications by Elliott Coues (Allen 1909) and C. H. Merriam (Osgood 1947) which accompany their biographical sketches. Equally useful are the bibliographies given in the *Biographical Memoirs of Fellows of the Royal Society*. One should also keep in mind the bibliographies which often accompany obituaries. Excellent bibliographies of J. F. Dymond (Scott 1965), William Rowan (Salt 1958), Rudolph M. Anderson (Soper 1962) and Paul L. Errington (Schorger 1966) have appeared in this way.

Still another location for bibliographies are the journals themselves where one can occasionally find extensive bibliographies on topics such as wildlife diseases (Halloran 1955). The journals *Wildlife Diseases* and *BioScience* have each issued a number of such bibliographies. *BioScience* has published bibliographies on amphibians (Highton 1965), biotelemetry (Adams 1965), mammalogy (Musser and Hooper 1966), insects (Downey 1966), embryology (Coulombre 1966) and animal ecology (Seidenberg 1966) to mention only a few.

Under special circumstances the National Library of Medicine (NLM) and the National Agricultural Library (NAL) will prepare bibliographies for research workers. Bibliographies prepared at NAL usually appear in one of two USDA publication series: "Library Lists" or as "Miscellaneous Publications." A list of all currently available bibliographies can be obtained from the National Agricultural Library as Library List no. 25, *Available Bibliographies and Lists* with revisions. The Wildlife Disease Association has a number of committees preparing bibliographies on the diseases of wildlife. The Pesticides Information Center in the National Agricultural Library expects to be able to produce on demand bibliographies by June of 1967.

Another important group of subject bibliographies is that of the large multivolume sets devoted to a single broad subject area. Recently, there has been an influx of such publications chiefly from the press of G. K. Hall. These are, for the most part, duplications of library, museum, or herbaria card catalogs. They represent a substantial addition to the literature of a subject and are especially useful for retrospective searching since they enable the searcher to survey a great deal of material in a minimum amount of time. Examples of these book catalogs have been produced for the Yale Forestry Library (1962), the Plant Science Catalog of the U. S. Department of Agriculture Library (1958), the Bernice P. Bishop Museum (1964), U. S. Geological Survey Library (U. S. Dept. of the Interior 1964), Blacker-Wood Library of Zoology and Ornithology at McGill University (1966), the National Agricultural Library (1966), and the Natural History Library of the British Museum (1903-1940). The *Catalogue of the Museum of Comparative Zoology Library* at Harvard University and the *Dictionary Catalog of the Department Library* from the U.S. Department of the Interior have been announced for publication in 1967.

Some Examples of Library Publications—How They are Located and Used

GOVERNMENTAL PUBLICATIONS

Government publications are of major importance to the wildlife biologist. Federal, state, provincial, dominion, etc., governments have many agencies whose publications relate directly to the work of the game biologist. In 1958 the National Science Foundation began a series called *Scientific Information Activities of Federal Agencies* which outlines their policies and procedures relative to the various aspects of scientific information. Numbers have been issued covering the U. S. Department of Agriculture, no. 1; National Science Foundation, no. 6; Department of the Interior, no. 12; Smithsonian Institution, no. 13; and the National Agricultural Library, no. 30. Especially noteworthy is the discussion of U. S. Fish and Wildlife Service publications given in no. 12.

Of special importance to the wildlife manager in the field is a system of depository libraries for U. S. Government documents. Under this program many, but not all, federal publications are automatically sent by the Superintendent of Documents to selected libraries over the United States. These publications are designated by a large round dot next to their entry in the *Monthly Catalog of the United States Government Publications* (hereafter referred to as the *Monthly Catalog*). Many libraries choose to keep their documents separate from the library's main collection and do not list them in their central card catalog. Depository collections are to be found in some public libraries, all land-grant colleges, most university libraries, all state or territorial libraries, and a few specially designated institutions. A list of depository libraries is given in Schmeckebier and Eastin (1961), and in the September issue of the *Monthly Catalog*.

It is possible to locate government documents by using private I/A services. However, it is dangerous to generalize about their coverage and the searcher would do well to search carefully through the I/A's devoted exclusively to governmental publications before considering his search complete. The best place to begin looking for a recent federal (U. S.) document is in the *Monthly Catalog*. This index is sent free to all depository libraries. The *Checklist of United States Public Documents, 1789-1909*, published in 1911 is the best source for locating Federal publications from this early period. However, the *Checklist* is arranged by corporate author (issuing agency) and, for this reason, will seldom be used in the initial steps of a subject search. The coverage of the *Checklist* is carried through 1940 by the *Catalog of the Public Documents of the 53d to 76th Congress and All Departments of the Government of the United States for the Period March 4, 1893, to December 31, 1940*, an author-subject-title index in 25 volumes, more commonly known as the "Document Catalog." After 1940 one must use the *Monthly Catalog*.

It is possible to locate Federal documents in

other ways. The U. S. Government Printing Office (GPO) regularly issues price lists of its publications in special subjects. Often individual Departments will issue lists of their publications. The Smithsonian has compiled an index to its annual reports (Stemple 1963) and the U. S. National Museum prepared *A List and Index to the Publications of the United States National Museum (1875-1946)* in 1947 as Bulletin 193. A supplement to Bulletin 193 was issued in 1958 covering the period 1947-June 1958.

One series from the National Museum of special interest to the game biologist is by Arthur Cleveland Bent and is titled *Bent's Life Histories of North American Birds*. This series first appeared in 1919 as Bulletin 107. *Bent's Life Histories* continue an earlier series begun by Major Charles E. Bendire, whose studies were published in 1892 and 1895 as Smithsonian Institution Special Bulletins nos. 1 and 3. Bent's publications are in great demand and because of their scarcity have been reprinted by the Dover Publishing Co. Bulletins of special interest to the game biologist in Bent's series are North American Diving Birds (No. 107), North American Wild Fowl (No. 126, 130), North American Marsh Birds (No. 135), Gallinaceous Birds (No. 162), and Birds of Prey (No. 167, 170). Although Bent died in 1954 his project has been continued by the Nuttall Ornithological Club.

Another series of special interest to the game biologist started in 1933 and is called *Fauna of the National Parks of the United States*. This is a monographic series dealing exclusively with the vertebrate fauna of our National parks. To this series belong such classics as the work by Murie on *The Wolves of Mount McKinley,* the work by Ralph and Florence Welles on *The Bighorn of Death Valley* and the monograph by Mech on *The Wolves of Isle Royale*. This series should not be confused with the older and much broader series called *North American Fauna* which includes systematic synopses and regional studies covering birds as well as land and ocean mammals.

State (U. S.) publications follow a pattern similar to that of Federal documents in their indexing but lack the comprehensiveness and facility available at the Federal level. A list of state fish and game, conservation and wildlife serial publications with their publisher and address appears in the *Conservation Yearbook* published in Baltimore, Md. The *Monthly Checklist of State Publications* published by the Library of Congress is a list of the publications emanating from state agencies. However, it includes only those state documents received by the Library of Congress

and should be thought of as a checklist rather than as an index to state publications. The early state literature (prior to World War II) is best covered by searching in *Wildlife Abstracts*, or Corbin (1965) and, for the first part of the nineteenth century, Meisel (1924-1929).

THESES AND DISSERTATIONS

The location of a science thesis can be one of the most challenging bibliographic problems faced by a literature searcher. Coverage by the I/A services is uneven at best and has often lacked sufficient depth in its subject approach. Only recently have the subject-oriented I/A services included theses in their coverage and then only for masters or doctoral theses produced in the United States. Theses produced outside the United States still remain difficult to discover and to obtain once they have been discovered.

Up until a few years ago library agencies in the U. S. made little attempt to acquire foreign theses systematically. Fortunately, the Center For Research Libraries, 5721 Cottage Grove Ave., Chicago, Ill. 60637, is now attempting to remedy this situation. In 1961 (Anon. 1961) the Center had close to 400,000 foreign doctoral dissertations. Currently, the Center receives all doctoral dissertations from France, together with a limited number from German, Russian, Dutch and Scandinavian universities. These are made available by the Center to other libraries in the United States through interlibrary loan. The Library of Congress also has large holdings of foreign theses (Bishop 1959) which are listed in the *Library of Congress Catalog-Book: Subjects*. Bishop (1959) has suggested a number of tools which the searcher can use to help locate a thesis prepared in the United Kingdom, France, Germany, or the United States, as well as where to write in order to obtain a copy.

Doctoral theses produced in the United States have been indexed since 1912 (U. S. Library of Congress 1913-1940). From 1898-1915 *Science* carried an annual title listing of doctoral theses prepared in the United States, but no attempt was made to index these early theses. The current index to doctoral dissertations prepared in the U. S. is called *Dissertation Abstracts*. It appears in two parts with part B covering "the Sciences and Engineering." At one time theses were indexed in the standard I/A services only after they had been published in a book or journal. This is no longer true. *Dissertation Abstracts* is itself indexed in *Biological Abstracts* (since 1961), in *Wildlife Review* and in *Chemical Abstracts*. This allows for subject indexing in greater depth making theses easier to locate than was possible earlier. The *Bulletin Signaletique* carries abstracts of theses produced in France. The *Monthly Index of Russian Accessions* lists dissertations from Russia which are available in the United States. Until recently there has been no attempt to index systematically masters' theses prepared in the United States. In 1962 University Microfilms began publication of *Masters Abstracts— Abstracts of Selected Masters Theses on Microfilm,* a quarterly publication covering a very limited group of masters' theses. Earlier, Barton Bledsoe (1954) prepared a single volume list of masters' theses.

Another and often more satisfactory approach which can be taken in the search for a thesis is by way of the subject bibliographies, which are issued separately or as bibliographies in journals. Black (1965) has prepared a guide to these special sources arranged by subject and by school. *Wildlife Review* (nos. 59 and 63) has compiled two bibliographies of doctoral and masters' theses covering the ecology and management of wildlife. They cover theses written during 1934-50. Doctoral dissertations are currently included in *Wildlife Review* as a result of WR's coverage of *Dissertation Abstracts.* Master's theses have been listed in WR after 1950 only as they came to the attention of the editors. In 1960 WR (no. 98) issued a third bibliography of theses. However, only masters' theses for the period 1956-58 are included here, and these were taken from the forestry bibliography by Osborn, Yoder, and West (1959), supplementing an earlier publication by Hughes (Hughes, Yoder, and West 1953). Once a year *Forest Science* compiles a list of forestry theses accepted by colleges and universities. Another useful bibliography of theses (doctoral and masters) covers the field of range management and appears in the *Journal of Range Management* (Box 1966). In 1962 the *Forestry Chronicle* (Smith 1962) published a bibliography of Canadian theses. In 1954 the *Auk* (Wolfson et al. 1954) carried a list of unpublished theses in ornithology from the U. S. and Canada.

Many schools publish lists of the theses accepted as part of their degree requirements. These lists can also serve as aids to help locate theses of interest to the wildlife researcher. Black (1965) will be of great assistance in this connection since she has arranged part of her bibliography by the name of the school. Of particular interest to the wildlife biologist are the bibliographies from Louisiana State University (Crow 1965) and Stanford (Storey 1957).

Most schools will loan their master's theses through interlibrary loan. The usual procedure is to request that your local library borrow the thesis. Doctoral theses are treated in a different fashion, and the fact that they are usually not loaned often surprises the requester. Most doctoral dissertations prepared in the United States must be purchased from University Microfilms either as microfilm or xerox copy. The former is much cheaper (usually a third to a fourth) but takes special equipment to read. This problem has been partially overcome by the new reader-printers which prepare hard copy from the film. The reader will find more material on this medium in the section of this chapter covering "Micromaterials."

TRANSLATIONS

A very large block of material concerning wildlife management has been written in languages other than English. Wood (1966) found that 25% of the papers in *Biological Abstracts* and slightly less than half of the papers in *Index Medicus* were not in English. Wood's study goes on to verify what many scientists had already felt intuitively, that the most important foreign languages for the scientist are Russian, German and French. One observer (Abelson 1965) has even gone so far as to call Russian the second language of science. Unfortunately, too few scientists are able to read Russian. For these reasons, this section is concerned principally with the identification and location of scientific material translated from the Russian.

Martin (1960), Kaiser (1965), and Parker (1959) have prepared good introductions to the problem of locating foreign scientific literature in translation. Martin covers only the Russian literature and includes a list of indexes, a list of commercial translators, and a summary of U. S. activities in the translation field. Although dated, his treatment of the literature in translation will help the researcher put the entire translation problem into a better perspective. More up-to-date and in many ways the most useful of the three guides is that of Kaiser. Her publication is a directory of translators, and translation pools.

The problem of locating translations has become particularly important in recent years. Much foreign work is of high quality and should not be neglected. Undoubtedly, this same trend will occur in other disciplines, making that part of the scientific literature available in translation even more important to the scientific community.

The logical place to begin a search for a translation is in one of the indices covering the literature available in translation. *Technical Translations* (vol. 1, 1959 to date. Twice monthly), *Index Translationum* (New Series. vol. 1, 1948 to date. Annual), a new index, the *Translations Register-Index* (vol. 1, 1967 to date. Semimonthly) and the *Monthly Index of Russian Accessions* (vol. 1, 1948 to date. Monthly) are perhaps the best known and the most easily accessible to the investigator in the United States. *Index Translationum* is an annual publication indexing only books. It is not restricted to the sciences or to publications in English. *Technical Translations* and the *Monthly Index* are automatically sent to depository libraries and so should be easily obtainable. There is another index to translated literature, the *Bibliography of Medical Translations* which is also sent to depository libraries, but this duplicates entries already given in *Technical Translations* and so will not be discussed here. The *Bibliography of Agriculture, National Agricultural Library Catalog,* and *Forestry Abstracts* list new translations but they should not be used as indices.

Technical Translations (TT) is very satisfactorily used as a current-awareness tool. It can be used for retrospective searching, but when approached in this fashion it is an awkward tool at best. The only satisfactory approach to TT when making this kind of search is by way of the semi-annual cumulated author indexes. A much quicker way to use TT when doing retrospective searching is to work through *Biological Abstracts,* which has indexed TT since 1960. However, this should be done with care since BA is not always as complete as one would like.

TT indexes books, reports and journals (both single articles and cover-to-cover). Prior to 1966 it covered only the scientific and technical literature. At present slightly more than 190 serials are listed in TT as being translated on a partial or cover-to-cover basis. A current list is normally published with one of the January issues. The actual preparation of the translations themselves is done by a number of agencies in all parts of the world.

Kaiser (1965) contains a list of agencies and individuals which prepare translations and the American Translators Association (P. O. Box 489, Madison Square Station, New York) can also supply a list of individuals who prepare translations. In Great Britain a similar function is performed by the Institute of Linguists.

Translations Register-Index is a very recent publication issued semimonthly by the Special Libraries Association. It announces and indexes all translations currently received in the SLA Translations Center as well as all translations covered in TT.

Although it does not relate directly to the problem of locating translations, the *Monthly Index of Russian Accessions* (MIRA), published by the Library of Congress, is sometimes useful in determining if a Russian publication is in the United States. MIRA covers Russian-language publications, both monographic and serial, issued in and outside the Soviet Union, which are available in the United States, principally those coming to the Library of Congress. MIRA is divided into three parts as follows: Part A lists monographic liter-

ature, Part B lists Russian periodicals showing their tables of contents in English, and Part C acts as a subject index to Parts A and B. This index is coded to show which libraries have a particular item and, therefore, serves as a union list. MIRA lists Soviet journals being translated on a cover-to-cover basis, including the date when translation began, and it includes a very general subject index to these journals. It is a major U. S. bibliographical guide to Soviet publications in all fields, both translated and not translated. Like TT it is also indexed in *Biological Abstracts.* The *East European Accessions Index,* which ceased in 1961, performed much the same function for publications coming from countries in eastern Europe.

Another approach which can be used by the investigator with a limited knowledge of foreign languages consists of using the abstracting services. Most of those which originate in countries using English as the mother tongue include abstracts in English for foreign language material. Using such services is a relatively painless approach to the more exotic languages and often the only way an investigator can obtain any understanding of the ideas in a paper or book. In fact, *Biological Abstracts* is now translating into English abstracts taken from seven sections of its Russian counterpart, *Referativnyi Zhurnal.* This gives the investigator indirect access to many publications not otherwise available to him in the United States.

It is possible to locate a translation by using one of the translations pools. These are libraries or society-sponsored groups which have large holdings of translations. The Special Libraries Association Translation Center (SLATC) located in John Crerar Library, 35 West 33rd Street, Chicago, Illinois, 60616, and the Clearinghouse For Federal Scientific and Technical Information (CFSTI) in Springfield, Virginia are the two most important translation pools in the United States. SLATC is responsible for collecting translations from nongovernment sources, both domestic and foreign, while CFSTI collects translations from foreign and U. S. Government sources. Both are prepared to answer questions concerning the location or availability of completed and in process translations. Although their collecting responsibilities are different, their collections are the same because of an exchange agreement between the two collection Centers. Other translation pools in the United States are maintained by the American Geological Institute, the National Agricultural Library, the Library of the U.S. Department of the Interior, the Institute of Paper Chemistry and the Federation of American Societies for Experimental Biology.

The Special Foreign Currency Science Information Program, a government program administered by the National Science Foundation, has resulted in a number of translations being produced in Israel, Poland and Yugoslavia. This program is financed by the sale of surplus agricultural commodities abroad and has resulted in the translation of seven volumes from the series *Mammals of the USSR and Adjacent Countries* by S. I. Ognev (1962-1966) covering Insectivora, Chiroptera, Rodentia, and Carnivora; the translation of several parts from the Fauna SSSR (Novikov 1962; Flerov 1960); the translation of Bulletin nos. 2 and 4 titled *Conservation of Natural Resources and The Establishment of Reserves in the USSR* (Academy of Sciences of the USSR, 1962; Dubinin 1960); and in the translation of numerous books and articles covering methods of censusing terrestrial vertebrate resources (Isakov 1961), studies of mammals in government preserves (Yurgenson 1961), etc.

In addition to the various governmental agencies (National Institutes of Health, Atomic Energy Commission, NASA, etc.) which sponsor or issue translations, there are many private firms publishing translations. The Consultants Bureau publishes a number of Russian journals in translation. Academic Press, American Elsevier, Faraday, Interscience, Gordon and Breach, Pergamon and Macmillan all publish translations. The quickest way to locate a translation from one of these firms is to examine its catalog. The American Institute of Biological Sciences, the Academy of Natural Sciences of Philadelphia and the Federation of American Societies for Experimental Biology (FASEB) prepare and issue translations. Those from FASEB appear in the translation supplements to *Federation Proceedings,* a practice which began with volume 22, 1963. AIBS with Academic Press and the American Psychological Association have sponsored the translation of a series of Russian monographs as well as journals into English. The Canadian government has also been active in the translation field. One series from Canada of special interest to the wildlife biologist is the *Translations of Russian Game Reports* (Department of Northern Affairs and National Resources, 1957-59). Unfortunately, this series has now been discontinued.

The U. S. Forest Service, Division of Forest Management Research, issued a series of translations of forestry-related subjects from 1934-1940. *Wildlife Review* (nos. 76, 81, 84 and 99)

has sections listing translations made from the Russian literature.

THE CRITICAL REVIEW

The review is that portion of the scientific literature intended to survey, evaluate, summarize and synthesize for the scientist recent work in a particular field or segment of that field. A review is not a report of original work. The review literature was mentioned earlier as a fertile source for the location of subject bibliographies. Critical reviews may appear in the professional journals as introductory articles in the I/A serials, or in serials published solely for the purpose of issuing critical reviews. The latter have seen a tremendous growth in recent years with one publisher, Academic Press, responsible for almost 75 titles. Another publisher in this field, Annual Reviews of Palo Alto, California, is a non-profit corporation publishing only reviews. The corporation currently issues 13 annual review serials. This is not to imply that these two are the only publishers in this field. Pergamon, Wiley/Interscience, Plenum, Butterworths, and the American Institute of Biological Sciences all publish review serials. It is quite common for review serials to begin with such words as *Annual Review of . . . , Advances in . . . , Progress in . . . , Reviews of . . . , Fortschritt . . . , Ergebnis . . . , Jahresbericht . . . ,* etc. However, publishers will occasionally issue proceedings, transactions, or symposia of international meetings with the titles "Advances" or "Reviews." These should not be confused with the critical reviews. Critical reviews of special interest to the wildlife biologist are contained in the following serials: *Quarterly Review of Biology, Advances in Ecological Research, Advances in Botanical Research, Advances in Parasitology, Advances in the Study of Behavior, Biological Reviews, International Review of General and Experimental Zoology, Fortschritte der Zoologie, Survey of Biological Progress, Advances in Marine Biology, Advances in Veterinary Science,* and *International Review of Forestry Research.*

MICROMATERIALS

This is a storage technique in which the printed page is reduced in size and stored on sheets or rolls of film or on opaque cards. Collectively, these are known as micromaterials, a term which covers all of the various forms in which they appear — microfilm, microfiche, microprint, microcard, etc. For the most part these are reprints of publications which initially appeared in a more conventional form such as newspapers, theses, journals, or books.

Some years ago the Wildlife Disease Association showed remarkable foresight in the production of a primary research journal entirely in microform with its microfiche journal *Wildlife Disease*. This journal was first published in 1959 on microcard. After a period of experimentation during which the Association strove to develop the most effective medium for the exchange and storage of ideas, the present 4 X 6 inch sheet of negative film was adopted. Each sheet can hold up to 60 normal size pages reduced in size by a ratio of 1:18. This experiment has proved successful, and the journal shows every sign of continuing in its present form.

Some idea of the tremendous amount and variety of material available in microform can be gained by looking through the current catalog from Microcard Editions of Washington, D. C. called a *Guide to Microforms In Print*. This is a comprehensive annual list covering publications available in microform. It covers publications of all types (with the exception of theses) currently available from publishers in the United States. A list of these publishers with their addresses is in the front of each issue. The reader should also consult the union list by Tilton (1964) when looking for a publication in microform.

In the past the selection and purchase of proper equipment has presented serious problems to the would-be user of micromaterials. However, a number of excellent readers are now on the market. It is even possible to combine a reader with a printer which will prepare take-home copy for the user. A guide to readers and the related equipment necessary to make effective use of these materials is available (Ballou 1962). This catalog includes cameras, readers, hand viewers, contact printers, accessories and equipment such as cameras with special capabilities, autotutors, etc.

PUBLICATIONS OF SOCIETIES, NATIONAL AND STATE ACADEMIES OF SCIENCE, MUSEUMS, ZOOS, AND GEOLOGICAL SURVEYS

These agencies are prolific publishers of annual reports, bulletins, journals, proceedings, occasional papers, monographs, etc. They have published guides to regional faunas, descriptions of collections, floras, keys, descriptions of specimens and expeditions, technique manuals, lists of type specimens, etc. Directories for determining the addresses, names of staff or officers, and the professional activities of these organizations have been listed under the section on directories in this chapter. Only the publications of these agencies will be discussed here.

Clapp (1962) has prepared a detailed bibliography of the publications issued by museums, zoological gardens, and aquariums. It is arranged by subject and covers both the monographic and serial publications issued by these agencies. Meisel (1924-1929) has prepared a similar publication for the eighteenth and nineteenth centuries which lists the natural-history publications of nearly 90 scientific societies, 25 journals, 15 natural-history museums and botanic gardens, 36 state geological and natural-history surveys, and over 70 Federal exploring expeditions spanning the period 1769 to 1865. Walker et al. (1964) has a short list of museum publications on page 737, a list of publications from or about zoos on page 766, and a list of annual reports from zoological societies on page 678. Skallerup (1957) discusses American state academy of science publications with a list of their science publications arranged by series—proceedings, news letters, transactions, bulletins, special papers, etc.—without giving the titles of numbers within each series. Regular publications issued by societies are listed in Gray and Langord (1961) and Murra (1962) for both U. S. and foreign societies, while a directory sponsored by the National Academy of Science—National Research Council (1961) lists publications of societies in the U. S. and Canada. Corbin (1965) has compiled a bibliography of State Geological Survey publications, not including Alaska and Hawaii, arranged by author, subject, series title and series number. This bibliography is especially important because of the many publications from State Geological and Natural History Surveys (often combined) of interest to the wildlife biologist. Connecticut, Michigan and Wisconsin have outstanding examples of such publications.

Special Purpose Bibliographic Tools
Listed by Their Function

ABBREVIATIONS, ACRONYMS, SIGNS, SYMBOLS AND CODEN

It is hard for many people to fully appreciate how easily abbreviations and acronyms can be misunderstood. This applies especially to abbreviations used for the names of scientific journals when Z. can stand for Zeitschrift, Zentralblatt, or Zhurnal. The American Standards Association has helped to standardize abbreviations with their list of recommendations. Their suggested standards for periodical abbreviations are worthy of note (American Standards Association 1964). In addition, the reader will find the ASTM (Kuentzel 1963) Coden with its specific title recommendations a valuable supplement to the ASA list. It should also be pointed out that many of the I/A services publish lists of abbreviations for the serials they index. These are useful when consulting the individual indices but are of little value when using other I/A services. The reader should note the list of abbreviations in the 1 Nov. 1966 issue of *Biological Abstracts*. Another source for abbreviations of serial titles worth noting is the *World List* (Brown and Stratton 1963). Although used predominently by British I/A serials it is still of value in locating abbreviations encountered over the remainder of the English-speaking world.

Many of the handbooks, almanacs, style guides (Conference of Biological Editors 1960), encyclopedias and dictionaries (Kenneth 1963) include lists of commonly used abbreviations, signs and symbols. These will answer most of the questions about abbreviations encountered in general reading. It is also possible to find the meaning of an unknown combination of letters by looking in the card catalogue of a library and in the *National Union Catalogue* at the beginning of each letter of the alphabet. Schwartz (1955) has included a list of proofreaders' marks, as well as the Russian, Hebrew, German, and Greek alphabets. Zimmerman and Lavine (1948), although dated, are helpful in locating scientific abbreviations, signs or symbols. Gale (Anon. 1960) has published an acronyms dictionary and Buttress (1966) has prepared a general list of abbreviations.

DICTIONARIES, GLOSSARIES AND SINGLE-VOLUME ENCYCLOPEDIAS

This section includes those source materials to which one goes for a paragraph or page-length discussion of a topic, or for a one or two line definition of a term, or to locate a corresponding term in another language. The single-volume dictionary is the best example of this class of source material, although one occasionally encounters glossaries in the scientific journals. Walker et al. (1964: 3:692) gives a short list of dictionaries.

Van Nostrand's Scientific Encyclopedia, now in its 3rd edition, is a single-volume compilation of scientific terms and is considered one of the best examples of an all-purpose scientific encyclopedia. Articles range from a paragraph to a page or two and include numerous illustrations. Similar treatment has been given the biological sciences by Gray (1961), ornithology by Sir A. Landsborough Thomson (1964), microscopy by Clark (1961), and a general hunter's and outdoorsman's encyclopedia (Trefethen and Miracle 1966). Each of the above, with the exception of Van Nostrand, and the hunter's encyclopedia, is characterized by long signed articles written by a specialist in that field and accompanied by a list of references.

A single-volume dictionary of great importance to the biologist is Henderson and Henderson (Kenneth 1963). In addition to its one- or two-line definitions, this dictionary includes the pronunciation and derivation of terms. In this respect it resembles two books by Jaeger, one a sourcebook (1955) which includes definitions, the other a pronunciation handbook (1960) without definitions.

There are several dictionaries which have been compiled for the more specialized needs of the biologist. Many of these will also answer the needs of the game manager. A list of these follows: wildlife terms (Krumholz 1957); range management (Huss 1964); botanical terms used in range research (Dayton 1950); zoology (Pennak 1964; Leftwich 1963); biology (Abercrombie, Hickman and Johnson 1962); economic plants (Uphof 1959); forest terminology (Society of American Foresters, Committee on Terminology, 1958); ornithology (Newton 1893-1896); ecology (Hanson 1962; Carpenter 1938); water terminology (Veatch and Humphrys 1966); weather (Thiessen 1946); specialized mammalian terminology for a group, adult, male or female, and juvenile (Manville 1962); the terminology of soil and water conservation prepared by the Glossary Committee of the Soil Conservation Society of American (1952); and a botanical dictionary (Usher 1966) which includes definitions of terms used in soil-science, statistics, and biochemistry as well as definitions of phyla, classes, orders and families but not genera or species.

The De Vries dictionaries rank at the top of the list for those supplying English equivalents of general scientific terms in German (1959) or French (1962). Carpovich (1960) has prepared a Russian-English dictionary with emphasis on the medical sciences and more recently Dumbleton (1964) has published a Russian-English dictionary for the biological sciences. MacLennan (1958) has prepared a useful Russian-English glossary for the ornithologists covering 712 of the bird species found in the Soviet Union. However, the last three are difficult to use because all Russian terms are in Cyrillic alphabet.

DIRECTORIES

The reader will find international organizations, agencies, associations, etc., listed in Murra (1962), in a directory from UNESCO (1965), in Gray and Langord (1961), *Index Generalis*, the *World of Learning*, and in the *Yearbook of International Organizations*. The *Yearbook* offers very brief descriptions of all types of international organizations. Murra is an index to the information services and publications of 449 international scientific organizations arranged in alphabetical order by the English name of the organization. The UNESCO publication is a guide to the science information and documentation services of 144 institutions arranged alphabetically by the name of the country. Specialized directories at the International level have been prepared for collections of zoological specimens in tropical institutions (UNESCO 1962), institutions engaged in arid-zone research (UNESCO 1953), biological field stations (Jack 1945), agricultural research institutions in Europe (Devred 1963), conservation organizations (Anon. 1961-66), natural history collections (Sherborn 1940), as well as African National parks and organizations concerned with wildlife conservation in Africa (United Nations Educational, Scientific and Cultural Organization, 1963).

In the United States, the National Referral Center for Science and Technology acts as a clearinghouse for the information resources of the scientific community by directing the inquirer to the organization, institution, or individual capable of answering his request whether it be for material or information. To accomplish this the Referral Center keeps on file a list of agencies and individuals with their various specialties. In addition to its *Directory of Information Resources In the United States: Physical Sciences, Biological Sciences, Engineering* (1965), the National Referral Center For Science and Technology has prepared similar directories for information resources in the Federal Government (1967), and Water (1966). Additional directories are available for the following agencies and institutions: scientific and technical societies (National Academy of Sciences—National Research Council 1961); university research bureaus (Anon. 1960); museums (American Assoc. of

Museums 1965); research centers (Palmer and Kruzas 1965); associations (Ruffner 1964); zoos and aquariums (Hoff 1966); mammal collections (Anderson, Doutt and Findley 1963); organizations, agencies, and officials concerned with the use and management of our natural resources (National Wildlife Federation 1966); information resources in the United States including libraries, information centers, Government agencies and other resources for scientific and technical information (National Science Foundation 1961); inland biological field stations (Arvey and Riemer 1966); marine, freshwater, mountain, desert, and special laboratories (Vernberg 1963); wildlife refuges in the United States (U. S. Dept. of the Interior 1965); and a directory of facts, figures and people connected with American conservation (Kauffman 1962).

Directories are available for the following agencies and institutions in Europe, Russia, and China: scientific societies in Great Britain (Anon. 1958) and Germany (Domay 1964), natural history societies in Great Britain (Lysaght 1959), and institutions engaged in arctic research in the USSR (Stanka 1958).

It is possible to locate the names of manufacturers of specialized scientific instruments by using the annual "Guide to Scientific Instruments" issued by *Science* or by using the annual buyers guide to the journal *Instruments and Control Systems* which includes a directory of laboratory supply-houses and manufacturers. Both of these annuals are arranged by the name of the instrument or its function and include the names and addresses of dealers supplying such equipment. The journal *Chemical Week* also publishes an annual buyer's-guide issue which lists chemicals and services for sale as well as giving trade names. *Modern Veterinary Practice* publishes in the fall (October) a veterinarians desk reference book which consists of an equipment and supply directory, a therapeutic index and a catalog of drugs and biologicals with their prices. Another source for locating the names of dealers handling the more common chemicals, raw materials, equipment, etc., is *Thomas' Register of American Manufacturers*. This directory is published annually in several volumes and includes the names of dealers handling such items as animal trap and telemetering equipment. The U. S. Fish and Wildlife Service has issued in its *Wildlife Leaflet* series directories showing manufacturers of animal traps (no. 263, 1962), rodenticides (no. 465, 1964), chemical animal repellents (no. 464, 1964), and bird control devices (no. 409, 1964).

SOURCES FOR BIOGRAPHICAL INFORMATION

The traditional sources of biographical information include directories, who's who type publications, membership lists, newspaper reports, etc. Typical of the information available in these sources are titles, addresses, positions held, degrees, occasionally lists of publications, together with general information about an individual's career, personal information regarding family, membership in social or professional groups, etc. For many years the H. W. Wilson Co. has published a continuing index to this type of information called the *Biography Index*. Ireland (1962) has prepared a single-volume index to biographical information for scientists living or deceased. The who's who type publications, of which there are many, will supply limited information of a current nature for individuals still living. One of the best known directories for biographical information about scientists is the *American Men of Science,* whose title is somewhat misleading since it includes both American and Canadian men and women. This important publication now in its 11th edition is kept up-to-date by a semiannual supplement. Similar directory-type publications have been prepared for British (Anon. 1963) and Soviet (Telberg 1964) scientists. Specialized directories are available covering Soviet zoologists (Strelkov and Yur'yev 1962), Polish zoologists (Polska Akademia Nauk, Komitet Zoologiczny 1962), specialists in plant taxonomy (De Roon 1958), zoological taxonomists (Blackwelder, R. E. and Ruth M. 1961), professional workers in state agricultural experiment stations (Cooperative State Research Service, U.S.D.A. 1965), research workers in agriculture, animal health, and forestry in the British Commonwealth (Anon. 1959), the annual address list of refuge managers prepared by the U. S. Fish and Wildlife Service (See USFWS *Wildl. Leafl.* 397, 408ff), a *Naturalists' Directory* with its 40th edition in 1966, and the *Index des Zoologistes* published in Paris by the Union Internationale des Sciences Biologiques in 1953.

GUIDES TO THE LITERATURE AND CHECKLISTS OF RECOMMENDED BOOKS

Guides or literature manuals have as their purpose the double function of guiding the research worker through the literature of his discipline and introducing the novice to some of the tools for his trade. These are much more than subject bibliographies, for they usually include more bibliographic detail, contents notes, and a list of the important tools with a discussion on how to make the best use of them. In general, they give the reader a better concept of the extent of the literature for his field. It is unfortunate that there are no literature guides available for the wildlife manager comparable to the manuals which have been prepared for the chemist, mathematician, physicist, or geologist. In fact, only a handful have been published covering even the related disciplines. The wildlife biologist should note the new edition of R. C. Smith's (Smith and Painter 1967) guide to the literature of zoology and the excellent guide by Bottle and Wyatt (1967) to the literature of biology.

A literature guide can be very short, such as the one by Ficken and Ficken (1966) to the literature of avian field ethology, or it can be book length like the early study made by Wood (1931) of the zoological literature. This study by Wood covers vertebrate zoology and is important because of its historical treatment of the literature. Adomaitis et al. (1967) have reported on the chemical and related technical literature in wildlife conservation. Stone (1933) has prepared an historical summary of the American ornithological literature published from 1883-1933. Two introductions to the Russian ornithological literature have been prepared by Vaurie (1964 and 1966) which up-date the earlier work of Johansen (1952).

Several authors, notably Southern (1964), (Hickey 1943), Mosby (1963), as well as Benton and Werner (1966) have included chapters discussing the literature in their respective areas. The appendix in Benton and Werner lists books and journals of interest to the field biologist covering the following topics: lower plants, wildflowers, trees and shrubs, invertebrates, vertebrates, amphibians and reptiles, birds, and mammals. Olson (1958) has discussed the Russian literature for the natural sciences in his review of its history, scope, patterns, style, and use with a discussion of the problems encountered in its procurement and evaluation.

The Society of American Foresters has published a checklist (Eakin 1958) for a forestry library which included a section on the wildlife literature. The Society of Systematic Zoology (Blackwelder 1963) prepared a list of books for zoologists, teachers, and anyone interested in the natural history of animals. This list along with the Society's annual book exhibit is intended to bring to the attention of the zoologist the commercial books (text as well as trade) in his field.

THE SYSTEMATIC LITERATURE

The systematic literature of biology is voluminous and complex. Only a few of the basic publications will be discussed here. The reader who needs additional help should review the chapter in R. C. Smith (1962) on taxonomic indices and the section in this chapter on "Field Guides." The manuals of George G. Simpson (1945) and Ernst Mayr (1953) are basic and will enable the wildlife biologist to acquire an understanding of the fundamentals of taxonomy. Simpson's publication on the classification of mammals is essential to any taxonomic work in this class. A more recent book by Simpson (1961) will help the reader with a general introduction to the science of classification. For general reference work on the mammals, Burton (1962) has written a systematic dictionary covering the more common species with their general characteristics including such things as food, breeding, habitat, range, longevity, temperature, and pulse. Blair et al. (1957) have prepared keys to the vertebrates of the United States including fishes, amphibians, reptiles, birds, and mammals to the species level. A very limited collection of taxonomic keys to the more common animals (not including birds) of the North Central States has been prepared by Eddy and Hodson (1961). Ingles (1965) has a number of keys scattered through his book including a general key to the orders and an artificial generic skull key for mammals.

The International Commission on Zoological Nomenclature is responsible for making recommendations for ammendments or additions to the International Code of Zoological Nomenclature (1964); rendering opinions on questions of zoological nomenclature; and compiling official lists of family, generic, and specific names in zoology. The *Bulletin of Zoological Nomenclature* is the official organ of the Commission. In addition to its other work, the Commission publishes official lists of invalid and rejected names at the generic and species levels. The *Zoological Record* publishes annually a "List of New Generic and Subgeneric Names . . ." recorded for that year.

In tracing the origin of a particular zoological name, the wildlife biologist will find the work of Neave (1939-1940) supplemented by the *Zoological Record, Biological Abstracts,* and the numerous regional faunas, checklists, and catalogues of great assistance. Neave's *Nomenclator Zoologicus* is a list of the names of genera and subgenera used in the literature from 1758 to the end of 1935 with the bibliographic information for the original citation. A fifth and sixth volume bring coverage up to 1955.

Catalogs listing type specimens of recent mammals available in their collections have been prepared by the American Museum of Natural History (Goodwin 1953), the Chicago Natural History Museum (Sanborn 1947), and the United States National Museum for mammals (Poole and Schantz 1942) and birds (Deignan 1961).

Of direct interest to the North American wildlife biologist seeking to determine correct nomenclature, phylogenetic relationships, or to locate the original description of an animal are two books, one by Miller and Kellogg (1955), and the other by Hall and Kelson (1959). Both of these bring an earlier work by Anderson (1946) on Canadian recent mammals up-to-date. Miller and Kellogg summarized the results of taxonomic studies of North American mammals and indicated the specimens represented in the collections of the United States National Museum up to 1 January 1953. The work by Hall and Kelson, which Simpson (1959) considers indispensable to the professional mammalogist, brings this up to 1959 and in many ways replaces the earlier work of Anderson, Miller, and Kellogg. For similar problems relating to the Aves the reader is directed to the checklist for birds of the world by Peters (1931 to date), the checklist of the American Ornithologists' Union (1957), a parallel publication from the British Ornithologists' Union (1952), the descriptive catalog for birds of North and South America by (Ridgway and Friedman 1901-   ), Wetmore's (1960) systematic classification for birds of the world, and to a classified arrangement of recent birds (Mayr and Amadon 1951).

*FIELD GUIDES, REGIONAL FAUNAS
AND CHECKLISTS*

The game biologist will find field guides, manuals, handbooks, and regional faunas of great assistance in his work. Field guides are especially useful and range in subject matter from algae and astronomy to seashore life, bird watching (Hickey 1943), wildflowers, mushrooms (Smith 1963), mammals and birds. They can be used to identify specimens, tracks, scat, or habitat. One of the best known writers and editors of field guides is Roger Tory Peterson, who has been turning out field guides since 1934. His books on birds are indispensable to the field observer.

Houghton Mifflin has issued a series of field guides edited by R. T. Peterson known as the Peterson Field Guide Series. This publisher's series includes books on birds, shells, mammals, animal tracks, trees, reptiles, amphibians, butterflies, rocks, etc. Putnam, Doubleday, Golden Press, Comstock, McGraw-Hill, Dutton, the University of California Press, the American Museum of Natural History, and The Canadian National Museum have also issued field guides. In Great Britain, Warne publishes the Wayside and Woodland Series, while Collins publishes a series known as the New Naturalist Series. The Mammal Society of the British Isles is publishing a series called Field Guide to British Mammals with the first book in this series covering the British deer (Page 1959). Although there are many field guides, each will include special features of interest to the reader such as bird songs (Robbins, Bruun, and Zim 1966), animals in winter (Morgan 1939), pictures of skulls (Palmer, E. L. 1957; Burt and Grossenheider 1964), flight silhouettes (Peterson 1961; Peterson, Ferguson-Lees, and Wallace 1966; Robbins, Bruun, and Zim 1966; Collins 1959), dental formulae (Burt and Grossenheider 1964; Ingles 1965), distribution maps (Anthony 1928; Peterson, Ferguson-Lees, and Wallace 1966; Burt and Grossenheider 1964; Robbins, Bruun, and Zim 1966; Ingles 1965; Perkins 1954; Booth 1950; Collins 1959), illustrations in color (Peterson 1961; Peterson, Ferguson-Lees, and Wallace 1966; Collins 1959; Anthony 1928; Burt and Grossenheider 1964; Robbins, Bruun and Zim 1966), an index of common names (Peterson 1961; Peterson, Ferguson-Lees, and Wallace 1966; Pettingill Jr. 1951; Anthony 1928; Robbins, Bruun and Zim 1966; Collins 1959), drawings of tracks (Palmer, E. L. 1957; Ingles 1965; Burt and Grossenheider 1964; O. Murie 1954; Page 1959; Perkins 1954; Collins 1959; Seton 1958), or scat (Palmer, E. L. 1957; Ingles 1965; Seton 1958; O. Murie 1954), picture keys (Booth 1950), color keys (Chapman 1912), and coverage of both domestic as well as wild animals (Palmer, E. L. 1957). There are wide variations in the coverage and quality of these manuals and the reader should exercise great care in their selection.

Although there may be wide differences in coverage and subject matter, most of these field guides will include bibliographies, which though often short, can lead the reader into more specialized publications. Peterson (1961) and Peterson, Ferguson-Lees and Wallace (1966), E. L. Palmer (1957) and Pettingill (1951, 1946) include short bibliographies. Anthony (1928), Pettingill (1946), as well as Burt and Grossenheider (1964) have arranged their bibiliographies to show publications for various localities. In addition, An-

thony has prepared a short bibliography to serve as a point of departure for a literature search involving the Insectivora, Rodentia, Carnivora, Artiodactyla, and life zones.

Supplementing these general field guides are the numerous state, provincial, or regional guides to birds and mammals. These are published by local clubs, museums, academies of science, societies, governmental agencies, natural history surveys, universities or university-affiliated groups and private publishing houses. One way to locate these regional faunas is to examine the bibliographies found in the field guides. The reader should also note the section in this chapter on the systematic literature and on the subject bibliography, especially Walker et al. (1964).

There is no comprehensive bibliography of faunas comparable to a guide prepared for the world's floras by Blake and Atwood (1942 and 1961), or to Terres' (1961) bibliography of regional checklists for birds of the United States, Canada, and the West Indies. Chapman's (1912) early "Faunal Bibliography" on birds is still useful although dated. Morris (1965) has compiled a short list of regional faunas followed by a critical discussion of the principal regional authorities. A comprehensive, well-indexed, up-to-date bibliography covering regional descriptions of recent mammals and birds would make a worthwhile project. Malcles (1958), Walker et al. (1964), the *Zoological Record* and *Wildlife Review* have sections listing regional faunas. The *North American Fauna* series contains a number of systematic synopses for recent mammals. One other bibliography of faunas is worthy of mention. This is a work prepared by Smart and Taylor (1953) on the British fauna and flora. The following are a few examples of regional guides available for: Colorado mammals (Warren 1942) and birds (Bailey and Niedrach 1965), mammals of Michigan (Burt 1948), Minnesota (Gunderson and Beer 1953), Missouri (Schwartz, C. W. and Elizabeth R. 1959), Nevada (Hall 1946), Wisconsin (Jackson 1961), Kansas (Cockrum 1952), and a semipopular handbook by Hall (1955) much of which was based on Cockrum, Lake Tahoe (Orr 1949), the Great Lakes region (Burt 1957), the Sierra Nevada (Sumner 1953), the Pacific States (Ingles 1965), the mammals (Cockrum 1960) and vertebrates (Lowe 1964) of Arizona, mammals of the eastern United States (Hamilton 1963), mammals of eastern Canada (Peterson 1966), Canadian recent mammals (Anderson 1946), mammals of Great Britain (Southern 1964), terrestrial mammals of western Europe (Corbet 1966), Mexico (Leopold 1959), Ellerman and Morrison-Scott

(1951) on palaearctic and Indian mammals, a popular guide to the mammals of South Africa (Roberts 1951), and the older checklist of Allen (1939); and birds of East and Central Africa (Williams 1963), Eastern and North Eastern Africa (Mackworth-Praed and Grant 1957), South Africa (Roberts 1940), the books on Canadian birds by Taverner (1953) and Godfrey (1966), birds of Oregon (Gabrielson and Jewett 1940), Wisconsin (Gromme 1963), Idaho (Larrison, Tucker and Jollie 1967), Alaska (Gabrielson and Lincoln 1959), New Mexico (Ligon 1961), Massachusetts (Forbush 1925-29), California (Dawson 1923), Georgia (Burleigh 1958), and a handbook of British birds (Witherby et al. 1943-1944).

TECHNIQUES USED BY THE WILDLIFE BIOLOGIST IN THE FIELD OR LABORATORY AND THEIR LOCATION IN THE LITERATURE

The location and selection of the best technique for the solution of a problem, be it a field, laboratory, or statistical problem, is a difficult undertaking. The reader can expect to find field and laboratory techniques scattered through the literature with discussions ranging in complexity from the simple cook-book type description to detailed discussions of complex instruments and statistical techniques. For additional bibliographic material the reader should study the other chapters of this book.

The *Journal of Wildlife Management, Nature, Laboratory Practice, Science, Biometrics, Biometrika, Stain Technology, Journal of Mammalogy, Quarterly Journal of Microscopical Science, Curator,* as well as the house organs from several of the scientific supply houses, are a few of the sources for articles describing techniques useful to the wildlifer. This would suggest that one or more of the indexing services might be an appropriate place to begin a literature search for a technique. Specialized techniques are indexed in *Biological Abstracts* under the name of the technique, the name of its originator, or the name of the instrument. *Wildlife Review* has a section listing techniques under each of the main headings: wildlife, mammals, and birds. The *Journal of Wildlife Management* has its own index with a heading for techniques, and the *Zoological Record* has a subsection on techniques in the Mammalia section.

There are a number of bibliographies which list publications covering techniques. Mosby (1963) has included a 33-page bibliography arranged by author, volume 3 of Walker et al. (1964) has a two page bibliography on techniques

and methods, R. M. Anderson (1965) and Southwood (1966) have a number of useful bibliographies scattered through their texts, Knudsen (1966) provides a short bibliography on the collecting techniques for each of the major groups of plants and animals, Morris (1967) has compiled a bibliography of statistical methods for grassland research, and Humason (1962) has a 26-page bibliography on animal tissue techniques.

As far as the texts themselves are concerned Mosby (1963) and R. M. Anderson (1965) probably come closest to answering the immediate needs of the wildlife biologist. Their work can be supplemented by the Atlantic Waterfowl Council (1963) manual on waterfowl techniques, the earlier work of Wight (1938) on field techniques, the interim suggestions of Ansell (1965) on the standardization of field data taken from mammals, including such things as measurements, apparatus, and standards of accuracy, Mahoney (1966), and Cowdry (1952) on laboratory techniques supplemented by Atkins (1960) and Oster (1955-1962) for specialized techniques of biological research, Moyer (1953) on taxidermy, the short chapters in Ingles (1965) and Hall and Kelson (1959) on the collection and preparation of specimens for study, and the suggestions of Van Tyne (1952) on collecting bird specimens for taxonomic work. Southwood's (1966) manual on ecological methods, although principally concerned with insects and large populations, will be of assistance in the selection of statistical techniques involving measurement and sampling. These in turn can be augmented by the more detailed publications describing an instrument, a research technique, or methods for collecting, skinning, preserving, and mounting the specimen. Such manuals have been prepared for invertebrates (Wagstaffe and Fidler 1955), birds (Chapin 1946), mammals (Dice 1932, Anthony 1950), and agricultural specimens (Fessenden 1949), etc. In addition, the reader will find the reference manual by Hale (1965) of immense value in the laboratory and field. This pocket size manual contains a wealth of information on such things as pH buffers, staining, standard deviation, decalcifying fluids, twistdrill gauges, etc.

Many museums publish descriptive manuals on the preservation, preparation, and collection of natural history specimens. The Smithsonian Institution and the U. S. National Museum have issued collectors manuals covering birds, rough skeletons, bird's eggs, and study specimens of small mammals in Bulletin no. 39, and in Smithsonian Institution Pub. 3766, a general "Field Collector's Manual in Natural History." The British Museum

(Natural History) publishes a series called "Instructions for Collectors." Handbooks of interest to the wildlife biologist in this series have been published for mammals, birds, and bird eggs; reptiles, amphibians, and fishes; insects; invertebrata, animals other than insects; plants; alcohol and alcoholmeters; and worms. The University of Kansas Museum of Natural History has issued a pamphlet on collecting and preparing study specimens of vertebrates (Hall 1962). The Chicago Museum of Natural History has a numbered series of pamphlets illustrating various museum techniques called "Fieldiana: Techniques." The American Museum of Natural History (Anthony 1950, Lucas 1950, Chapin 1946), the National Museum of Canada (Anderson, R. M. 1965), and the Cleveland Museum of Natural History (Bole 1939) have published material on the preparation of biological specimens which will be of interest to the wildlife biologist. The magazine *Curator* will occasionally include articles on the preparation of biological specimens. Many examples from this journal are noted in the Borhegyi and Dodson (1961) bibliography. The General Biological Supply House, 8200 S. Hoyne Ave., Chicago 20, Illinois, issues the *Turtox Service Leaflets*, many of which discuss the preparation and preservation of specimens for the simpler organisms used in the biological laboratory.

Some examples of the more specialized publications are those covering staining (Gurr 1962, Conn 1961), microtechnique (Lee 1950, Gray 1964), limnological methods (Welch 1948), the analysis of rodent populations (Davis 1956), cutting of thin sections (Steedman 1960), field techniques for sexing and aging game animals (Thompson 1958), techniques for measuring understory vegetation (U. S. Forest Service 1959), the study and preparation of animal tissue (Humason 1962), use of telemetry (Slater 1963), nature photography (Kinne 1962), and a handbook of biological illustration (Zweifel 1961).

In addition to the single-volume handbooks there are a number of series covering techniques which begin with the words *Methods in* . . . These exist for cell physiology, virology, soil analysis, serological research, vitamin assay, cancer, and immunology. They serve a useful function by bringing to the reader's attention the latest research techniques in these special areas.

The reader should also be aware of the various ancillary manuals for range research. The Joint Committee of the American Society of Range Management and the Agricultural Board (1962) prepared a standard textbook for advanced students on the problems and techniques of range research. Other methods manuals have been prepared by the U. S. Forest Service (1963); the Grassland Research Institute (1961); and the Joint Committee of the American Society of Agronomy, American Dairy Science Association, American Society of Animal Production, and the American Society of Range Management (1962). In the latter, emphasis is on pasture and range research involving domestic animals.

ENCYCLOPEDIAS, HANDBOOKS AND TRAITÉ SETS

It often happens that a game biologist finds himself in need of a lengthy, detailed discussion of a scientific topic or of a particular animal or group of animals. This may necessitate referring to a broad-based scientific encyclopedia such as the *McGraw-Hill Encyclopedia of Science and Technology* or to one of the more detailed encyclopedic, multivolume sets similar to the German Handbucher or French Traité series may be necessary. These are usually cooperative works prepared by many contributors each of whom is considered an expert in his own segment of the broad field. Such contributions offer the reader an introduction to his topic and are often the best summaries of what is known about a particular subject or organism. It is characteristic of this type of publication that volumes or parts may appear out of sequence. Many of the titles mentioned here are still being published and have no planned date of completion. Examples of these multivolume sets which should be familiar to the game biologist are Dr. H. G. Bronn's *Klassen und Ordnungen Des Tierreichs* founded in 1859 and still being published (the early volumes of this set, many of which have been out-of-print for several years, are being reprinted by Johnson); *Handbuch der Zoologie* by Kükenthal; Pierre-P Grassé, *Traité de Zoologie; Das Tierreich* by Franz Schulze, and two older works *Treatise on Zoology* by Sir Ray Lankester and the *Cambridge Natural History* by S. F. Harmer and A. E. Shipley. R. S. Palmer's *Handbook of North American Birds* is an example of this type of publication prepared for the ornithologist. Another example of the knowledge in a special field being systematically organized and presented is the American Physiological Society's *Handbook of Physiology*, which covers both vertebrates and invertebrates.

Miscellaneous Reference Sources

LAWS, REGULATIONS AND INTERNATIONAL
TREATIES OF INTEREST TO THE
WILDLIFE BIOLOGIST

In the United States Title 16, *Conservation,*
and Title 43, *Public Lands,* of the *United States
Code* will provide the wildlifer with statements of
appropriate Federal law governing these two
areas. The *Code of Federal Regulations,* Title 50
revised as of January 1, 1967 with annual cumulations provides the wildlifer with an up-to-date
compilation of the Federal administrative, i.e.
from the various governmental agencies, regulations affecting wildlife and fisheries. The *Code
of Federal Regulations* covers such things as the
hunting and possession of wildlife, the national
wildlife refuge system, management of wildlife
research areas, and federal aid to states in fish
and wildlife restoration.

New laws appear separately as slip laws until
they can be incorporated into the *United States
Code.* New administrative regulations appear in
the *Federal Register* until they can become part
of the *Code of Federal Regulations.* The new
edition of Camp (Trefethen and Miracle 1966)
includes an historical resume of Federal laws
and regulations on p. 1011-1029 and a list of game
regulations for each state (U. S.), Canadian
province, and Mexico on p. 1033-1093.

In 1965 the Committee on Commerce of the
U. S. Senate, 89th Congress, 1st Session prepared a *Compilation of Federal Laws Relating to
the Conservation and Development of Our Nation's
Fish and Wildlife Resources.* This Committee
Print is a summary of the Federal laws relating
to fish and wildlife from the U. S. Code and the
U. S. Statutes at Large. It includes such things
as the Wilderness Act, the Dingell-Johnson Act,
Federal Aid in Wildlife Restoration Act, Fish and
Game Sanctuary Act, National Bison Range Act,
etc. A finding list for the popular and statutory
names of these acts is given in the front of this
booklet. A similar publication containing the texts
of international treaties was also prepared in
1965 as a Committee Print for this same Committee. The title of this publication is *Treaties
and Other International Agreements Containing
Provisions On Commercial Fisheries, Marine
Resources, Sport Fisheries, and Wildlife to Which
the United States is Party.* It covers multilateral
treaties, bilateral treaties and agreements which
were not yet in force in the U. S. as of Jan. 1965.

A bibliography of State and Territorial laws
for the United States with the Provincial laws for
Canada is given in Phillips (1930). He also includes a list of Executive Orders and Proclama-
tions, United States Statutes and Supreme Court
Decisions which have affected wildlife. Although
dated, this bibliography will be of help in locating
early state and provincial laws. Hayden (1942)
has written a history of international treaties for
the protection of the world's wildlife. Matthiessen
(1959) has a "Chronology of Representative Legislation Affecting North American Wildlife" from
1616 through the first introduction of the Wilderness Bill, which will give the reader some
historical perspective into this type of legislation. An earlier chronology by T. S. Palmer
(1912) is more detailed but stops with 1911.
Bethune Jones, 321 Sunset Avenue, Asbury Park,
New Jersey, publishes a reporting service called
From The State Capitols, one section of which is
a "Summary of Fish and Game Law Trends in
States." This is a news service discussing current legislation and judicial action at state or
local levels. The journal *Defenders of Wildlife
News* includes a section on Federal legislation
titled "Wildlife Interests in Congress." In 1960
the U. S. Fish and Wildlife Service published the
fish and wildlife regulations for the District of
Columbia in U.S.F.W.S. *Fishery Leaflet* No. 403.
Another important publication from the U.S.F.
W.S., *Wildlife Leaflet* no. 469, 472ff lists birds
protected by Federal law. Isaacson (1963) and
Sigler (1956) have written manuals for the conservation officer, outlining his role in enforcing
conservation regulations, presentation of testi-
mony, etc. Both include a list of fish and game
cases which will give the game officer some
precedent on which to work. Sigler has a glossary
of definitions and legal terms. Worrall (1964) in
a short chapter describes the laws relating to
game animals in Great Britain.

RESEARCH IN PROGRESS

Successful planning of a research project demands not only that one become aware of the
literature concerning his problem, but that he
also determine what related work is currently
in progress. For many years the lack of knowledge about work in progress has constituted a
major gap in our research effort and has resulted in much wasteful duplication. Today there
are a number of ways for an investigator to keep
himself informed about the research of others.
The Science Information Exchange was created
specifically to fill this gap in our knowledge. SIE's
purpose is twofold: to facilitate the exchange of
information between investigators with similar

interests and to prevent the duplication of research. The address of the Exchange is 300 Madison National Bank Building, 1730 M Street N. W., Washington, D. C. 20036.

Another way to keep aware of current research projects is to study the annual reports issued by governmental or private agencies interested in wildlife management and related areas. Patuxent Wildlife Research Center, the Wildlife Research Center in Denver, various U. S. Forest and Range Experiment Stations, the British Museum (Natural History), the Nature Conservancy (Great Britain), the Canadian Wildlife Service, the Wildfowl Trust, and the Game Research Association in Great Britain publish annual reports and/or reports of research in progress.

For many years current progress reports concerning research in the U. S. on wildlife restoration under the Federal Aid in Wildlife Restoration Act were reported in the *Pittman-Robertson Quarterly*. The *Quarterly* was replaced in 1955 by annual numbers in the series of U.S.F.W.S. circulars under the title *Survey of Pittman-Robertson Activities*. See U. S. Fish and Wildlife Service Circular nos. 38, 47ff. The activities of the Division of Wildlife Research of the Bureau of Sport Fisheries and Wildlife are also reported annually in this same circular series. See U.S.F. W.S. Circular nos. 104, 146ff. Each of the reports from the Division of Wildlife Research will also serve as a bibliography alerting the reader to publications by personnel in the Cooperative Wildlife Research Units, the various regional offices and research centers of the Division. In 1966 the Division of Wildlife Research of the Bureau of Sport Fisheries and Wildlife published a summary of *Wildlife Research: Problems, Programs, Progress* for 1965 as U.S.F.W.S. Resource Publication no. 23. Similar reviews of the *Progress in Sport Fishery Research* for 1965 and 1966 were published as U.S.F.W.S. Resource Publications nos. 17 and 39. In addition to its other work, the U.S.F.W.S. publishes surveys of research in specialized areas, notably the *Pesticide-Wildlife Studies* issued as U.S.F.W.S. Circulars nos. 15, 84, 143ff.

The Wildlife Management Institute has undertaken to report research projects operating under the Pittman-Robertson or Dingell-Johnson Acts in its annual publication *Federal Aid in Fish and Wildlife Restoration*. Many of these projects will also be reported at the State level in Progress Reports, Annual Reports, or Research Reports from the various State Fish and Game or Conservation Departments.

The Conservation Library Center in the Denver Public Library is providing reference service on all unpublished research reports from projects sponsored by the Federal government. The Center is also indexing and serving as the depository for such reports.

Although the research in progress under the auspices of the Office of Water Resources Research and the Public Health Service is not of direct interest to the work of the wildlife biologist, he should at least be aware of what is being done in these two agencies. The office of Water Resources Research of the U. S. Dept. of the Interior publishes annually a *Water Resources Research Catalog* describing Federally-supported, as well as non-Federally supported, research projects involving water. The U. S. Public Health Service issues annually a *Research Grants Index* for the purpose of disseminating information about current scientific activities supported by research grants from the P. H. S.

Many journals regularly issue short notes on research in progress or brief communiques summarizing preliminary conclusions. These may take the form of research briefs, short communications, notices of research grants, or letters to the editor. Examples of these are to be found in the *Journal of Mammalogy, BioScience, Science,* the *Journal of Wildlife Management,* and *Nature*. In addition to these short notices, a journal will often devote an entire article to describing the current and historical research efforts in a particular subject or area as Sladen (1965) did in a recent article on ornithological research in the antarctic or as Talbot (1965) and Jewell (1963) did on wildlife research in East Africa, or as Scott (1958) did for wildlife research in Illinois.

LITERATURE SEARCHING

Literature searching describes the process by which one makes use of the library tools covered in this guide in order to locate information. It involves both the selection of the most appropriate library tool for a given situation and the most efficient use of that tool. The discussion which follows will outline some of the problems encountered in literature searching, some solutions to these problems and a method of approach—a means of organizing and conducting a literature search.

The key to success in any literature search is to organize the search in such a way that each step follows in a logical sequence. Parke (1958) and Wilson (1952) contain excellent chapters on literature searching written for the novice. Although both are concerned primarily with the physical sciences, many of the principles and ideas they expound will merit reading by their colleagues in other disciplines.

Voigt (1961) has suggested that the use of information by the scientist arises from three identifiable needs, which he calls (1) the need to keep up-to-date with the current progress in one's field, or current approach; (2) the need for specific information relating to one's work, or everyday approach; and (3) the need for everything locatable on a subject, or the exhaustive approach. Voigt is very careful to point out that what he suggests is an over-simplification since these approaches often overlap. However, these ideas are useful when talking about literature searching for they help categorize the methods used in searching for material on a topic. For purposes of our discussion here the types of literature searches are current awareness, everyday, and exhaustive or retrospective. Of the three, the most difficult is usually the retrospective search since it involves the location and identification of everything pertinent to the subject. Because the retrospective search involves the same techniques and tools used in the other two, but to a much greater degree, the discussion which follows will be concerned primarily with this type of literature search. However, a discussion of library tools in this context should not be taken to imply that retrospective searching is their only function. The reader will find a discussion on current-awareness tools in the portion of this chapter covering the I/A services.

A literature search begins with a problem and works toward its solution. The first step is to put the problem into the concrete form of a statement, even writing it down if necessary. It is absolutely essential to verbalize the problem. It is also important that the problem be clearly understood and that all terms be defined in such a way that another qualified individual could understand and perform the search equally well if called upon to do so. Completion of this first step may entail some preliminary reading, but from this reading, related subjects under which the topic is indexed may be determined as well as the related terms to be used as key words. In all probability other individuals will be discovered who have already worked on this problem or have similar interests as well as societies, universities, museums, laboratories, foundations, journals, etc., known for their work in this field.

Next, clear boundary lines must be drawn and plans made to work within them. It is often possible in the sciences to establish very explicit boundaries for a literature search by not going beyond a certain date or by limiting the search to selected authors, journals, indexes, or books. Deciding what function the information is to serve will also help crystallize the problem. Essentially, the initial steps consist of (1) thinking and talking about the project with one's colleagues, (2) setting up objectives, and (3) establishing boundaries for the search. Library tools, should they be needed at this point, will consist of the basic dictionaries, handbooks, manuals, reviews, and encyclopedias. The wildlifer should be especially alert for a subject bibliography, since this will enable him to profit from the efforts of others in this area. Many people well versed in the techniques of literature searching no longer make a conscious effort to perform each of these steps. They have simply become part of the entire process of doing research and are no longer thought of as belonging just to the performance of a literature search.

The logical place to begin the search proper is at the card file in a library. It is at this point or while using the I/A serials that the searcher usually encounters the most critical factor in any literature search—the key word or phrase. These are the terms under which the information has been indexed. They are sometimes called descriptors or search words. Librarians sometimes call them subject headings and prepare lists of them in subject authority files. Such lists have been prepared by the Library of Congress (Quattlebaum 1966), the National Agricultural Library (1967), and the National Library of Medicine (1966). In 1966 the Department of the Interior Library prepared a two volume thesaurus of descriptors for the field of wildlife management. This list is composed of terms the wildlife biologist uses in his work. It serves as a list of terms which can be used in indexing the professional literature. One volume contains general terms and the other taxonomic terms. Yeager's (1940) short list of terms will be of additional help when attempting to arrange material in an orderly fashion. The Office of Water Resources Research (1966) has also prepared a thesaurus of terms which will be of some interest to the wildlife biologist.

Just how difficult the task of choosing a key word can be is better understood when one considers the large number of synonyms, homonyms, and hierarchies of related terms present in the English language. The literature searcher must constantly be aware of the generic and specific relationships between terms, of ambiguous, invalid, or rejected names, of variations in the spelling of a given term, of superseded formulas, as well as the various trade names of materials or drugs. The biologist searching for publications on an organism must decide whether to look for his material under the class, order, family, genus or species to which that organism belongs. Some indexes will arrange material under a single category, such as a family or species name. The literature searcher must also take into consideration the large number of perfectly acceptable scientific terms which mean one thing for discipline A, and something quite different when used in discipline B, for example, plasma, manifold, and radiation. Indeed, not only the words but the order in which these words appear can change the entire meaning of a sentence. Consider the classic example of blind Venetians and venetian blinds. Since all will agree that subject-matter indices are no better than the choice of words used by the indexer and the searcher, the problem of selecting and using the correct key word becomes a critical one. The searcher must use every related key word he can think of unless the index clearly does not accept a particular term. Thesauri and lists of subject headings will be invaluable in establishing the key words and their related terms. However, the individual's most important tools will be thoroughness and imagination combined with his knowledge of the literature to be covered.

That part of the search strategy concerned with establishing the validity of a key word for a particular search begins by testing the most specific key word known against the file. If no heading is found under one term, then a move is taken to the next higher generic term, continuing in this fashion until the necessary connections are made with a desired citation. The reason for proceeding from the specific to the generic level is that the more specific the search term, the less irrelevant references or "noise" will be encountered with a hit. This rule is particularly important in searching the I/A serials. The general terms usually have more citations to be scanned while a specific term enables the searcher to move directly to his objective. *Biological Abstracts* has offered the searcher an interesting variation on this search strategy with its new CROSS topical index. By using this internal index to BA, it is possible to select a general term and a specific term and seek the common reference number by comparing the numbers under each term for the number found in both places. This common number will then lead the searcher to the desired reference.

As soon as pertinent references are located, a personal card file should be started always noting complete bibliographic information for each item. This information should be transcribed the first time in exactly the style prescribed by the professional style manuals or journals.

The last problem encountered in a literature search will be deciding when to stop. Here the limits established when the search was initiated will help. However, stopping at the point where results no longer justify the effort requires the judgment which only practice can give.

It is impossible to obtain an adequate appreciation of literature searching by simply talking about it. Indeed, literature searching is considered by many to be an art, and one of the most important prerequisites for success is the feeling or intuitive appreciation for the literature of one's field, which comes only with practice in the use of that literature.

ORGANIZATION AND PREPARATION OF THE RESEARCH PAPER

Communicating the results of research should rank in importance close to, if not on an equal level with, the actual conducting of the research itself, for if one is inept at communicating his results to others the time, effort, and money spent in their accomplishment comes to naught. It is important that sufficient attention be given to the organization, preparation, and final publication of the research. As Beveridge (1957:135) carefully points out, writing should begin well before the work has been brought to a conclusion. Indeed, every experiment should be written up at least once a year, not only to refresh one's memory, but to bring out gaps or weak points in the work. This section along with Chapter 5 by Dr. Thomas G. Scott are intended to suggest for the researcher some of the aids which can assist him in this task. It does not treat the role of the hypothesis, experimentation, observation, intuition, or any of the other facets involved in research before the ideas crystallize in the mind of the investigator. The primary concern here is with the transfer of results from a state of mental understanding to their concrete form in the research paper. Brief mention will be made of one or two books on the philosophy of research and, because of their everyday usefulness, some examples of the better usage manuals for the English language.

There is an abundance of good material written on the preparation of the research paper. It can be found in many places ranging from the brief style guides of Campbell (1954), Turabian (1955), Pugh (1963), Hook and Gaver (1952) to the book-length manuals of Trelease (1958), Hillway (1964), and the Conference of Biological Editors (1960). Sanford (1958), Mosby (1963), and Nagel (1960) have written specifically for wildlifers. Each has useful ideas to contribute on the planning and writing of a scientific paper. However, their style and treatment differ. For this reason, attention will be given to some of the more salient features of these important guides.

Campbell, Turabian, Trelease, Pugh, and Hook and Gaver are strong on the mechanics and form which a good research paper or dissertation must follow. The last three also include a section on using the library. In addition, Trelease has included a section on photographs, drawings, tables, graphs, and slides which should be helpful to individuals concerned with their preparation. The material in Pugh, and in Hook and Gaver is very elementary and will be of little use to those with some experience in writing. Campbell is solely a guide to thesis preparation and is most valuable when used in this connection.

Quite often the journals themselves will provide suggestions for their prospective authors. These suggestions can appear either as part of the journal or as separates. In the latter form, they are often published as a society-sponsored booklet. Many societies follow this practice and the reader will find the AIBS style manual (Conference of Biological Editors 1964) of great value in his search for guidance in the preparation of copy and correct usage in the biological sciences. This manual has been accepted by more than 84 journals as their style guide. For these reasons and because of the number of excellent suggestions it contains, a prospective author should read this manual even before he begins his literature search. A careful reading will often prevent the worker having to go back over ground he has already covered in order to relocate a bibliographic citation or to correct improper usage.

Hillway (1964) covers the basic topics important to an understanding of research in an easy informal style. There are many helpful ideas scattered through his book on using the library, preparing the research paper, gathering a bibliography, and note taking. His ideas on research are fundamental and will be of interest to both the beginner and the mature investigator, although Beveridge will be more interesting to the latter group. Hillway makes little attempt to cover the actual mechanics of writing.

Beveridge offers the reader a sophisticated treatment of the entire topic of research methodology. Although he includes little on the actual preparation of the scientific paper, his discussion of the research process is erudite, provocative, and well worth the attention of both the beginning and mature scientist. The book reads easily and is replete with historical anecdotes written in a style which many scientists might well duplicate. His outline of how a research problem in biology may be tackled is thought provoking and, although some will not agree with him, here at least is a point of departure for a good discussion on research methodology.

One final source for guidance in the preparation of a research paper is a usage manual. There are several which merit attention and any prospective author should own one along with a dictionary and Roget's *Thesaurus*. Because individual styles and tastes differ, it would be wise to examine several before making a purchase. For many years Fowler (1965) has been the standard guide to correct usage although he stresses British as opposed to American usage. He follows a dictionary-type arrangement. The new Follett (1966) is more appropriate for authors in the United States although some will prefer Bryant (1962) and the much shorter Strunk (1959). No matter what the choice, authors should carefully select a usage manual and develop the habit of consulting it.

Since the early 1930's conferences of the U.S. Biological Survey and other wildlife research staffs have heard that "we have a tremendous quantity of accurately assembled statistics at our disposal, most of which we have not learned to use." In many other conferences statements akin to a conventional wisdom have been espoused that add up to: We need more generalists; we need synthesizers; we need to study and use the information we have before trying for the new.

It is passé to argue whether a literature search should come before or after a research effort. The probabilities that reading the work of others will channel the thinking of a good wildlife scientist are insignificant to the probabilities of avoiding duplication, gaining insight and direction, and progressively building on the work of others. Every investigation, program, employment of a technique, or speech should begin with literature study. Experience is a good teacher, all right, but there is not enough time, and resources are too critical for every wildlifer to make his own mistakes. The experiences of others are the best teachers and they are available in the literature of wildlife management.

CHAPTER FOUR

DEVELOPING AND MAINTAINING A SMALL PERSONAL REPRINT LIBRARY

ROBERT W. BURNS, JR.

Librarian for Research and Development
Colorado State University
Fort Collins, Colorado

and

HENRY S. MOSBY, PhD

Professor, Wildlife Management
Virginia Polytechnic Institute
Blacksburg, Virginia

NEEDS

THE MOSBY 3-CARD SYSTEM

MARGINAL NOTCHED CARDS

OTHER SYSTEMS

SECURING REPRINTS

NEEDS

A part of the continuing education of a successful wildlife manager is the development and use of a personal library. This library, besides its intangible values, can become a powerful working tool when systematically collected, adequately indexed, and consistently used. Personal libraries assembled by small groups of wildlifers who specialize but share materials, become even more useful because of the breadth added by the groups' interest. These literature pools of active wildlife managers and scientists, often spanning several continents, can provide additional motivation to keep up-to-date and can provide for each other current information.

A personal collection of books is rarely large enough to require indexing, but reprints, bulletins, booklets, tear-sheets, pamphlets, manuscripts, typed reports, and other similar materials require regular, systematic filing and indexing.

After the collection of the first several hundred items if not so catalogued, they will not be used effectively, if used at all. For convenience, all of these materials will be called "reprints" in this chapter.

The reprint library is usually thought of as that ubiquitous collection of papers on the bottom shelf, in the file cabinet, or on the floor in the office corner. It never seems to stop growing. The organization and indexing of this material varies from the complex edge-notched or internally punched peek-a-boo card to a miscellaneous collection of materials jammed in between alphabetic separators in a file drawer. Some individuals prefer to keep the actual reprints while others keep microfilms in envelopes. Some keep cards with only the citation and a three or four-line annotation, or extensive abstracts on cards. Some workers keep only a file of references, a bibliographic index, for the literature in their area of interest. In any event, the so-called "reprint" file is a highly individualistic affair with little uniformity in its preparation, use, or maintenance. At least one study has been made of the reprint file (Jahoda, Hutchins, and Galford 1966) and *Biological Abstracts* (Anon. 1966) recently completed a survey of the personal literature files kept by its users.

Many investigators who attempt to develop a reprint-filing system soon abandon the effort because they find the system which they selected too involved or complicated to maintain. Organization and indexing are, therefore, the most challenging aspects of maintaining and using the reprint collection.

Some individuals prefer a simple author arrangement for their file with little or no indexing. Others prefer subject categories in numerical or alphabetical order. Others develop complicated systems of their own by separating types of publications and combining the above categories.

Yeager's (1940) list of subject categories is still useful and is adaptable to many filing schemes. Some wildlifers simply use the table of contents of *Wildlife Review* as their subject index.

Numerical order of filing reprints is least expensive of storage file boxes and space. As the number of boxes grows with the collection there is never more than one partially empty box. An alphabetical order may require few or no file boxes at first but a moderate number will be required as the collection increases. Subject classification requires many file boxes, the number depending upon the extensiveness of the subjects listed. Each system has its advantages and disadvantages. Two systems which have been used very successfully by wildlifers are presented here.

THE MOSBY 3-CARD SYSTEM

Reprints are numbered serially, irrespective of subject, as they are acquired. Either three, bond-paper 3 inch x 5 inch "cards," or a templet (Fig. 4.1) to mark 3 inch x 5 inch cards on sheets of 8-1/2 inch x 11 inch paper are used. In either case, three copies of each bibliographie reference are made by typewriter or ball-point pen—one original and two carbons. Different colored paper may be used to good advantage for each carbon. The reference to each reprint is typed or written on the card as shown. The serial number is in the upper left and a complete citation follows. When template and pages are used the first two copies are cut to 3 inch x 5 inch

cards and the third left intact. The original card is filed alphabetically by author, the second copy filed by primary subject, and the third copy filed numerically. If the third copy is on a card, it is filed with occasional numerical tabs; if a sheet of 8-1/2 inch x 11 inch, then it is placed in a loose-leaf binder to give a complete record of the serial numbering of all reprints.

The filing of the author card is easy since it is filed alphabetically. Subject filing is and will continue to be a problem. This card is placed behind the most appropriate classification tab card. Cross-referencing can be done by writing the serial number of the reprint on the front of the tab card of other subjects.

Using this 3-card system, the investigator can locate the desired reprint either by author, subject, or by number. Since the reprints are filed serially, it is easy to find the reprint and just as easy to replace it after use. This latter characteristic is one of the best features of the 3-card system. From numerical cards or the notebook (third copy), missing items can be identified, errors corrected, and the sequence of receipt determined. While these cards are the least used of the three, they are of equal value. This system has been widely used, extensively tested for 97 small and moderate size (up to 4,500 reprints) research libraries (e.g. S. E. Forest Experiment Station, Ashville, North Carolina and several Cooperative Wildlife Research Units), and has many devotees.

MARGINAL NOTCHED CARDS

The marginal or edge-notched card is admirably suited for indexing the small (up to 10,000 cards) personal library.

While discussing the use of such cards, it is appropriate that mention be made of their capabilities for the organization of field or laboratory data (Van Gelder and Anderson 1967) as well as the preparation of keys. It is possible that either marginal-notched or cards of the Mosby system can be integrated with other similar types of record keeping on cards. Uniformity in card size and method have some advantages which should not be overlooked. Extensive bibliographies describing the many applications of marginal-notched cards are to be found in both Casey et al. (1958) and Scheele (1961). The advantages of using the edge-notched card for a personal file are (1) a single card can contain many indexing points, (2) when a card is lifted from the deck it does

A

2718

Forney, J. L.   1957.   Raising bait fish and
crayfish in New York ponds. Cornell
Ext. Bull. 986.   Ithaca.

2719

Hamilton, Max.   1957.   Weights of wild bobwhites
in central Missouri.   Bird Banding, v. 28.

2720

Weller, M. W.   1957.   An automatic nest-trap
for waterfowl.   J. Wildl. Mgmt., 21:
456:458.

Fig. 4.1. A. An example of a 3 inch x 5 inch templet-marked, letter-sized page with three serially numbered reprints cited. B. Examples of author and subject cards as filed for the Mosby 3-card system.

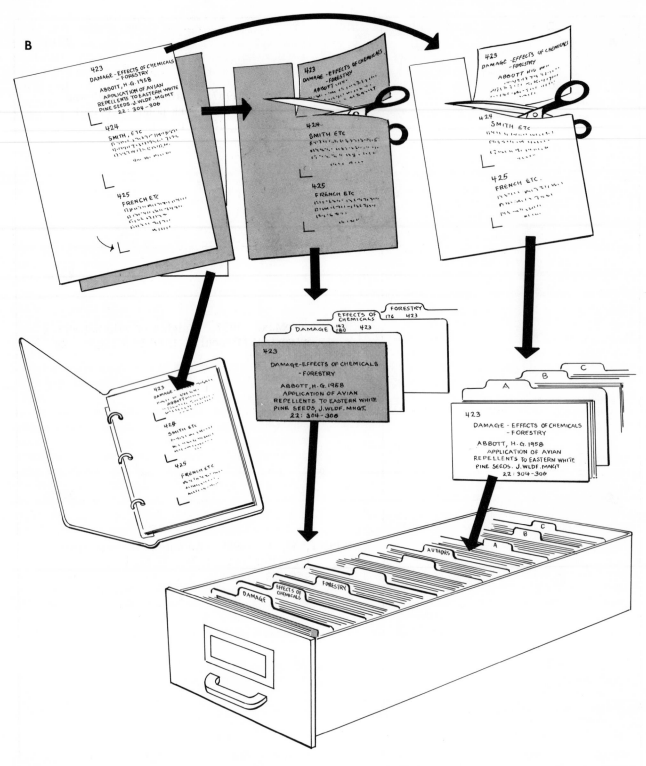

not have to be returned to the same alphabetical position, and (3) the file can be rearranged in any way the owner wishes with a minimum of effort. The disadvantages of edge-notched cards are (1) the size of the file which can be searched with one pass of the needle is limited, (2) the initial preparation of the classification scheme is extremely difficult, (3) the file is expensive in both direct and indirect costs, (4) each time a search is made the entire file must be handled, and (5) the size of a file which can be used efficiently is limited.

Books by Casey et al. (1958) and Scheele (1961), and an article by Bryan (1966) will provide the reader with a basic understanding of coding systems, files, edge-notched cards and how they may be designed and used to best advantage. Also worthy of special mention are articles by Adams on the creation of a file for vertebrate ecologists (1955) and on a file for use with small samples (1950); Schwabe and Davis (1954) on a file used for references in veterinary research; Levine (1955) on a file for parasitologists; Hill and Himwich (1957) on the preparation of a file for material on the central nervous system; and finally, an article by Milne and Milne (1959) giving "after-thoughts" on the preparation of an edge-notched card file. The latter article offers a number of useful hints and should be read by anyone contemplating the preparation of such a file. Although the experience of Milne and Milne is with a file involving literature covering vision in invertebrates, the mistakes they made are almost universal and a careful reading of their article will save the novice many wasted hours and cards.

OTHER SYSTEMS

The number of ways to organize one's personal file is subject only to the limits of the individual's ingenuity, available materials, and special interests. Hellmers (1964) has discussed what he calls a modified coordinate system. There are direct coding systems using a notch (Aldous 1947) or marginal dot (Larimore 1957), a peek-a-boo or see-thru system (Fowler 1965), uniterm coordinate indexing (Weil 1954), and even a code system based upon the phonetics of a word (Thoma 1962). Each of these can be adopted for individual use. However, great care should be ex-

ercised in selecting a filing system for one's personal library. Systems such as those described here should be rejected only after they have been carefully explored. Experience has often shown that more problems arise later in indexing and cross-referencing than were ever imagined possible and that all too often the feeling of the user is: "I have the wrong filing system, but I've gone too far to start all over now."

SECURING REPRINTS

Many wildlifers use printed postcards for requesting reprints of journal articles and other reprint material. Often authors will purchase reprints of their articles which they will supply free, as a courtesy to their colleagues. Theirs is a courtesy which should not be abused by indiscriminate requestors. Studying the literature, using *Current Contents*, *Wildlife Review*, and literature sections in current journals as well as browsing in the collections of others will also provide titles for requests.

Studying the journals as recommended in Chapter 3 provides titles and addresses for desired reprints. U. S. Government Printing Office publications, for which there are minimal costs are also a large part of most personal libraries. Some state agencies have mailing lists and most organizations and agencies will supply lists of available publications, many of which are free or have a nominal cost. Many articles not otherwise available can now be reproduced readily on a copy machine. Many materials in this category are not retained by even large libraries since they are "ephemeral." The personal reprint library, then, is essential for having close at hand the pertinent, local, specialized information necessary for successful performance by many wildlife managers.

CHAPTER FIVE

WRITING THE SCIENTIFIC REPORT

THOMAS G. SCOTT, PhD

Head, Department of Fisheries and Wildlife
Oregon State University
Corvallis, Oregon

and

JAMES S. AYARS

Chairman, Committee on Form and Style
Council of Biology Editors
Urbana, Illinois

BASIC REFERENCES
THE AUTHOR'S PROCEDURE
PREPARATION OF COPY
PROOF
EDITORIAL LIFE HISTORY OF A MANUSCRIPT
SUGGESTIONS FOR EFFECTIVE SCIENCE WRITING

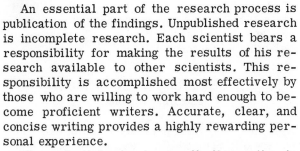

An essential part of the research process is publication of the findings. Unpublished research is incomplete research. Each scientist bears a responsibility for making the results of his research available to other scientists. This responsibility is accomplished most effectively by those who are willing to work hard enough to become proficient writers. Accurate, clear, and concise writing provides a highly rewarding personal experience.

The scientist who is an effective writer is largely self-trained. Courses in rhetoric are helpful; so are useful references on writing. Beyond these, the scientist is largely on his own. The degree of effectiveness he attains will depend largely upon his intelligence and his desire to excel.

BASIC REFERENCES

The scientist-writer will find the following references indispensable:

1. A good style manual, for example, *Style Manual for Biological Journals*. Second edition.

2. A good dictionary. It will be well to arrange access to Webster's *Third New International Dictionary,* unabridged.

3. A handbook of English rhetoric.

4. Thesaurus. The following is recommended: *The New Roget's Thesaurus in Dictionary Form.*

THE AUTHOR'S PROCEDURE

Let us assume that an investigation has been terminated and that the results must be prepared for publication. What is the most effective procedure? Many scientists have adopted the following plan, or one fairly close to it.

The First Step (Preparing Outline)

The first step in the preparation of a manuscript is the formulation of a working outline. The outline helps to insure fidelity to the assignment and to give unity to the paper. Trelease's (1958:36) advice is appropriate: "A scientific paper should be a unit, treating a single definite subject. . . . Include only what is necessary, but omit nothing that is essential."

The task of preparing an outline has been simplified for scientists because most investigational reports fit a standard format. Some papers may be too short to justify format headings, but the presentation of information will still follow the format sequence.

The standard format leads the reader from an understandable description of the subject, or a clear statement of purpose, through the investigational techniques used, to the results of the study and an objective discussion of the findings. The parts of the standard format provide a skeleton for the author's working outline.

In the order of their physical arrangement, the principal divisions of the standard format are:

1. Title
2. By-line
3. Abstract
4. Introduction
5. Acknowledgments (usually included with the introduction)
6. Study Area (used only when a detailed description of the study area is an essential part of the report)
7. Materials and Methods
8. Results (sometimes called "Findings")
9. Discussion (sometimes combined with Results)
10. Literature Cited

Title.—The title, which serves as an index to the content of the paper, should include key words that facilitate machine processing and retrieval. It should be short, specific, and accurate. A 10-word limit is a guide to length. Where appropriate, include the nature of the study, the principal species involved, and the geographic location.

By-Line.—The by-line identifies the author(s) and the institution(s) where the investigation was made. The relationship of the author and institution is best understood where the author's name is followed by that of the institution. The author should be consistent in the form of his name.

Abstract.—The abstract should be written to stand alone as a condensed report of a paper's contents. It should not be longer than 3 percent of the paper's length.

Introduction.—The introduction should be used to state the objective or purpose of the investi-

gation or paper. It may include a review of the literature pertinent to the investigation.

Materials and Methods.—This section should be detailed enough to allow other scientists to check on the authenticity of the work or to duplicate the procedures used. At times *materials* may not be pertinent enough to merit listing; in such instances the heading becomes "Methods."

Results.—The observations and data resulting from the investigation are described here. Great latitude is possible in this section. In some papers the results and discussion sections can be combined.

Discussion.—This section is a possibility, not a necessity. It is more easily justified for some papers than for others. It relates the results to the pertinent findings of other scientists and attempts to evaluate the meaning of the findings. It should not be merely a convenient depository for afterthoughts. If it is to justify the space it occupies, it should be more than a rehash of results. The section may be regarded as a convenient place for (1) broadly interpreting the facts presented in the paper and relating them to the pertinent findings of other scientists, (2) taking a refreshing, wide-eyed look at the width and depth of the problems involved, and (3) projecting whatever thinking may be induced by the paper at least a little way into the future.

Literature Cited.—This section lists only the literature that has been cited in the text. It documents the author's interpretations of the literature and provides the reader with a means of evaluating this interpretation.

The Second Step (Planning Tables and Illustrations)

Tables essential for presentation of data must be carefully planned. Carelessness in early tabulations can result in errors that may not be found until it is too late to correct them except in an errata sheet. Errors in tables may result in errors in the text and in the conclusions.

Graphs, charts, maps, and photographs essential to presentation of the findings should be available for reference during the writing stage. At this stage, graphs may be in rough form but with all points accurately plotted.

The Third Step (Assembling References to Literature)

Consultation of pertinent literature is a continuous process throughout the investigation. The library research should be as nearly up-to-date as possible before the writing is undertaken. The results of this research will be available for ready reference if you have maintained a file of cards, all the same size (4 x 6 inches or 3 x 5 inches), on which you have accurately copied pertinent ideas and data from the literature and have indicated their sources. If you have limited each card to a single item, you will be able to assign any card you use to a part of your outline and can arrange the cards in the order in which you will refer to them. Some writers follow the practice of writing their first drafts from cards; they write their own ideas and data, as well as those of other authors, on cards and arrange the cards in the order dictated by the outline.

The Fourth Step (Writing)

When you are ready to begin writing try to determine the time of day in which you do your clearest thinking, for this will be the best time for you to write. For many people this time comes early in the day.

Prepare your first draft section by section. Your outline should be detailed enough so that at least one section can be written at a sitting. For many authors it is far better to write a little every day than attempt to write the entire paper at one or a few sittings. Prepare the abstract last.

In the preparation of the first draft, concentrate on the subject matter and do not allow yourself to be stopped by mental blocks over such things as the right word. If nothing more, leave a space and continue writing down your ideas as rapidly as possible. In subsequent drafts, you can refine the phraseology and select words having a more precise meaning.

After preparation of the first draft, examine it section by section and paragraph by paragraph to determine whether the information presented is in the right section and in a logical sequence to permit an understanding flow of thought. A common shortcoming in science writing is the inclusion of information on methods and materials in the Results and Discussion sections when it should have been presented in the Materials and Methods section. Examine the draft also for topical sentences introducing ideas to be discussed, and for transitional sentences or paragraphs between major parts of the manuscript; if well constructed, these contribute to ease of reading and readiness of comprehension.

Study each sentence to determine whether it conveys the correct meaning, whether it can be shortened, and whether it can be omitted. Go about this with the same attitude that you might expect from your severest critic or professional competitor.

After you have revised the manuscript several times and have reached the point where you are no longer effective in making improvements, invite the criticism of a colleague who is a good writer and is knowledgeable in your field. You will find that a rest from intensive work on a paper will clear your vision for mistakes that you could not see earlier.

PREPARATION OF COPY

When your manuscript is nearing completion, read or reread the "Instruction to Contributors" in the journal to which you plan to submit your work. Your manuscript will be ready for its final typing only after it conforms to those instructions. Any of the following suggestions that are not in disagreement with the style of your chosen journal may prove useful in the preparation of your copy.

Paper and Typing

Type all copy—text, footnotes, legends, tables, and table headings—doublespaced on one side of good quality white paper, 16-pound or 20-pound for ribbon copy, 13-pound or 16-pound for the two or more carbon copies.

The ribbon copy and one carbon copy are for the editor of the journal. Your institution may want one or more carbon copies. Retain one copy for yourself.

The copies should be kept identical, changes in one being made in the others.

Leave margins of at least 1 to 1-1/2 inches on each page, the left margin slightly larger than the others.

Type copy in each of these categories—text, tables, legends, and literature cited—on separate sheets, as copy for each may be set on a different machine or at a different time. Whenever possible, avoid the use of footnotes. If you use them, type them with the text, indicating clearly the material to which they apply and that they are footnotes.

Number pages of the final typescript consecutively. If you wish to insert a page give it a number and a letter. Then on the pages immediately preceding and following indicate the position of the page. For example, if you insert a page between pages 10 and 11, number the new page "10A." Indicate at the bottom of page 10 that "Page 10A follows" and at the top of page 11 that "Page 10A precedes."

Headings

Use headings and subheadings descriptive of the text matter to which they apply. If possible, make each short enough to be set in one line of type. Most articles of journal length need heads of no more than three categories or levels of importance. Indicate for each head the level to which it belongs. For example, indicate the most important head by capital letters, the second most important by lower case letters except for a capital for the first letter of each important word, the third most important by run-in heads in italics.

Examples:
Most important: WATER AREAS
Second most important: Floodplain Lakes
Third most important:
Lake Chautauqua.—The most important lake in the Illinois River valley is

Follow the head style of the journal to which you intend to submit your paper.

Numbers

Use numerals for all measurements, including measurements of time: 1 inch, 3 days, 5 months.

In expressing large numbers ending in zeros, combine words and numerals. Example: $7 million.

Otherwise, spell numbers one through nine and use numerals for others.

In a category (as seeds, birds, insects) containing some numbers under 10 and others over, use numerals for all.

Example:
Of the 35 prairie chickens, 5 were eating seeds.

In sentences containing some categories with numbers below 10 and other categories with some numbers above nine, spell out the numbers in a category having all numbers under 10 and use numerals throughout a category having some numbers above nine.

Example: Of the seven prairie chickens, three ate 7 seeds each and four ate 33 seeds each.

Citations and Quotations

Use the date system in citing published works. If you wish to be especially helpful to readers and editors, include with the date the page number or numbers on which the cited material can be found.

Examples: Schoolcraft (1822:67-69) reported prairie chickens in Illinois.
Prairie chickens were reported in Illinois more than a century ago (Schoolcraft 1822: 67-69).

The page number is helpful to the editor or the serious reader in locating a direct quotation. It is even more helpful in locating material that has been paraphrased.

In citing a paper by two authors, name both: Brown and Black (1967:28). In citing a paper by more than two authors, name only the first and add et al. For example, instead of Brown, Black, Green, White, and Goodhue (1935:67), write Brown et al. (1935:67). Alternatives for citing several references on one topic follow: (1) Brown (1963), Black (1964), and Green (1965) have contributed to refinement of the concept of plant succession; (2) From 1962 to 1965, three Americans (Brown 1963, Black 1964, Green 1965) made important contributions to our concept of plant succession; (3) In recent years, the concept of plant succession has been expanded (Brown 1963, 1964*a*; 1964*b*; Black 1962, 1963; Green 1966); (4) Rabid bats can transmit rabies by biting (Reagan et al. 1957, Tierkel and Arnstein 1958, Bell 1959).

There is no preference with respect to whether the author(s) name is outside or within the parentheses. The manner in which the author's name is used depends entirely upon the nature of the expression which the writer elects to use.

In quoting material consisting of more than one paragraph, use double quotation marks at the beginning of each paragraph and at the end of the last. Do not use double quotation marks at the end of the first or interior paragraphs. Use single quotation marks to indicate quotations within quotations.

Place periods and commas in quoted material within the quotation marks, regardless of logic.

If you omit one or more words from the interior of a quoted sentence, indicate the omission by ellipsis marks (three spaced periods . . .). If you omit words at the end of a sentence, place the ellipsis marks ahead of the period. Do not use ellipsis marks for words omitted from the beginning of a sentence, or with single words or phrases lifted from a sentence.

Enclose in brackets any changes you make in words or spelling of quoted matter. Otherwise, quote exactly, including errors. You may use [sic] following an error to indicate that you know it is an error.

Tables

Because tabular matter is expensive, use tables only when the cost can be justified. Make each table (with its heading) complete. Do not depend upon the text to tell what, when, and where.

Study the style of tables in the journal of your choice and, as far as possible, make your tables conform to that style.

Do not submit a table larger than a page of the journal will accommodate, unless you have persuaded the editor to run your table across facing pages. Break long tables into two or more smaller tables, each complete in itself.

Do not repeat in the text the material shown in your tables, except to interpret or to call attention to unusual data.

Photographs

Submit only such photographs as will contribute to an understanding of your paper.

Photographs should be of medium contrast, on glossy finish paper, and slightly larger than they will appear in the journal. Matte finish paper is unacceptable.

In having your photographs made, tell the photographer what you wish them to show. By lighting and other devices, he may be able to emphasize the features you want your readers to see.

Do not include too much in a single photograph. Learn when to use macro- and when to use micro-photographs.

Do not expect black and white photographs to show what can be shown only in color.

Graphs and Maps

Submit only such graphs and maps as will contribute significantly to the reader's rapid orientation to the problem and the results of your work. They should be an integral part of the paper. Do not repeat in graphs material already in the tables you are submitting; some tables have graphic qualities.

Use imagination and judgment in your selection of types of graphs. Bar graphs are sometimes used when line, pie, 3-dimensional or other types would be more useful.

Submit graphs and maps on good quality white paper or drawing board. They should be about one and a half times the size you expect them to appear in the journal.

Lines, dots, circles, Zip-a-Tone (see Fig. 22.3) and lettering should be large enough to take the necessary reduction. A reducing lens is helpful for these determinations.

Letters and numerals should not be freehand, and, to remain legible, they should be at least 1/16 inch tall when reduced for printing. Those carefully made with mechanical lettering devices usually are satisfactory. Applied letters (as Craft-tone, Zip-a-Tone) are also usually satisfactory.

Literature Cited

In the literature cited section, list only works cited in your paper. Do not list unpublished works, except theses that are available in one or more libraries.

Arrange cited works alphabetically by family names of authors, or of senior authors (in cases of joint authorship). Arrange cited works by the same author (or authors) chronologically.

Invert the family name and given names or initials of the author of a paper, but only of the senior author in a paper with joint authorship.

List elements of a journal citation in the following order: author or authors, date of publication, title of article, name, volume, and number of journal, page or pages.

Example: Hiller, E. J., and R. Brown. 1948. Influence of some carbon compounds on growth of plant tissues. Anat. Rec. 70(5):68-75.

Abbreviate the titles of journals as in the *Style Manual for Biological Journals*.

List elements of a book citation as follows: author or authors, date of publication, title of book, publisher, place of publication, number of pages.

Example: Menzel, D. H., H. M. Jones, and L. G. Boyd. 1961. Writing a technical paper. McGraw-Hill Book Co., New York. 132 p.

Type citations with hanging indentations, as shown above.

Final Examination

Many authors make the mistake of not examining the final draft, relying on the accuracy of the typist. It is advisable for the author to check the final work for typographical errors and to verify the correctness of technical terms and names of persons. There is a proneness to use names of persons carelessly in acknowledgments. Check the Literature Cited section against original sources for accuracy and, at the same time, verify the accuracy of quotations. Make certain that the dates used with citations in the text agree with those listed in the Literature Cited section. Determine that the correct abbreviations have been used in the references. Finally, check the numerical data in the tables for typographical errors.

Make certain that you have cleared the manuscript for submission to an editor. Failure to obtain administrative approval for publication can prove extremely embarrassing to everyone concerned. This is true especially where a thesis is involved, and particularly when the thesis has not yet been accepted by the educational institution for which it is written.

PROOF

When you receive galley proof from the printer, read it carefully against your original copy. Read it again for meaning and accuracy. Correct inaccuracies, but refrain from making the "second thought" type of changes that should have been made in the copy. You may be charged for the cost of making changes that do not involve errors of the printer.

Indicate corrections on the margins of the proof sheets. Most printers are blind to corrections within lines unless their attention is called to them by marks in the margins. Use printer's symbols if you know them. If you do not, write notes to the printer that leave no doubt of your meaning. Draw a line through each word you want omitted and use a caret ($\wedge$) to indicate where you want a word or words inserted. In each case do not fail to make appropriate marks in the margin.

Mail the proof promptly to the place to which you are directed to send it.

EDITORIAL LIFE HISTORY OF A MANUSCRIPT

An understanding of the editorial process and of the responsibilities of the editorial staff will be helpful to the writer-scientist.

The editor supervises the editorial process, and a good editor is more than the custodian of a collection station for manuscripts. His job is demanding and complex. He must work on an exacting time schedule with overlapping deadlines. He must possess skill in several technical fields and be constantly sensitive to details. He must be staunch in his defense of excellence in scientific and editorial standards. He cannot afford indecisiveness. He is the final judge in accepting or rejecting a manuscript.

The following is a list of the steps in the editorial life history of a manuscript:

1. The manuscript is submitted by the author.
2. The editor acknowledges receipt of the manuscript.
3. The manuscript, with a covering letter, is sent by the editor to a number of referees. This is for the author's protection as well as that of the readers and the editor. The referees are qualified by training and experience in the subject area of the manuscript.
4. The referees make comments and suggestions and return the manuscript to the editor. The referees are concerned with scientific accuracy and the value of the contribution made.
5. The editor reads the manuscript and the comments of the referees. A decision is made to accept or reject the manuscript.
6. If the manuscript is found acceptable, an editorial assistant, or the editor, checks the manuscript for rhetorical irregularities, errors of syntax, spelling, grammar, mechanics of style, clarity, arrangement of material, and logical presentation of data in the text and in the tables and figures. Sentences are recast, revisions are made or are suggested, and corrections are made. Every citation is checked against the original reference, if available.
7. The manuscript is sent to the author with a covering letter of suggestions and comments from the editor, and with the referees' reviews of the article.
8. With suggested changes, corrections, and comments in mind, the author revises his manuscript.
9. The manuscript is retyped and returned to the editor.

10. An editorial assistant and the editor check the revised version for possible errors of omission or commission.

11. If necessary, the manuscript is returned to the author for further work and again returned to the editor.

12. The manuscript is marked for the printer and sent to him.

13. Proofs are forwarded to the author for reading, marking, and return to the editor.

14. The editor and assistants read and mark the proof sheets and send them to the printer for corrections.

15. The printer sends revised proof sheets to the editor, who, with his assistants, checks and returns them to the printer for publication.

SUGGESTIONS FOR EFFECTIVE SCIENCE WRITING

Application of the following simple guidelines should improve upon the effectiveness of your writing:

1. Feel free to use personal subjects such as "I," "we," "Jones."
2. Avoid too many polysyllabic words.
3. Avoid the use of long and involved sentences.
4. Use the active voice unless the passive voice is clearly preferable.

5. Avoid the excessive use of nouns as adjectives.
6. Avoid excessive hedging.
7. Avoid the use of Latin abbreviations, especially "etc."
8. Avoid using scientific nomenclature throughout a paper if suitable common names are available.

Some common faults in scientific papers are:

1. Illogical grouping of ideas. (A good working outline will minimize this shortcoming.)
2. Omission of vital facts or steps in procedure, interpretation, or conclusion.
3. Needless repetition of facts.
4. Inaccurate paraphrasing of facts or copying of quotations from references.
5. Inaccuracies in the Literature Cited section.
6. Inaccuracy in making computations.
7. Imprecise use of words, use of words in senses peculiar only to the author or a small group, or use of words for the sake of the use of words.
8. Drawing conclusions unsupported by the facts presented.
9. Inclusion of data favorable to a desired conclusion, and exclusion of equally valuable data unfavorable to the conclusion.
10. Use of obscure or doubtful antecedents for pronouns.
11. Failure of authors to read their manuscripts with thoughtfulness, thoroughness, objectivity, detachment, and patience.

CHAPTER SIX

MAKING OBSERVATIONS AND RECORDS

HENRY S. MOSBY, PhD

Professor, Wildlife Management
Department of Forestry and Wildlife
Virginia Polytechnic Institute
Blacksburg, Virginia

It has been stated that "The strongest mind is weaker than the palest ink." Those facts which are left to memory are usually questionable; if a written or photographic record is made, this record when properly filed becomes of permanent value. The wildlife investigator should develop the habit of making accurate observations, recording his field and laboratory data in written or photographic form, and classifying and filing these records in such a manner that they may be efficiently consulted.

FIELD NOTES

Nothing will force all individuals to observe accurately the same event and report this event in the same precise detail and manner. Various techniques have been used to train an individual to observe events accurately and to interpret correctly what is seen. The power to observe

may be developed by constant and diligent practice. Further, the observational ability may be developed by reducing to writing the events observed. For example, should an observer be in an automobile traveling parallel to a flying duck he might observe in a general way that the duck was flying at a rather high rate of speed. Such an observation would hardly be worth recording. However, if he had developed the habit of making a written record of all such events, he undoubtedly would record the species of duck, note the speed of the automobile from the speedometer, observe if there was a tail or head wind, and determine if the duck was being pursued. Thus, making recordings of such observations increases the precision of the observation.

· Distinguishing what is worth recording is a major problem. No hard and fast rule may be stated. Usually, the more detail, the better. The keen observation of what appears to be a trivial event in the field may direct attention at some later date to some phase of a problem that has been completely overlooked. For example, it has been noted that ring-necked pheasants "crow" in response to any sudden noises such as fire-crackers, banging a piece of metal, or blowing a car horn. As a result of this observation, which may have appeared trivial at the time, further investigations were made to determine if this method of locating male pheasants could be utilized in estimating pheasant populations.

Predation, dead or diseased animals, and similar events are observed in the field only at rare intervals. They should be recorded in as great a detail as possible, preferably with measurements of distances, notes on weather conditions (depth of snow, time since last rain, and related data), marks on the animals observed, location of these marks, and all other data. Such events usually shout for careful observations and recording, but less spectacular happenings are more frequently observed in the field and often are of equal or greater importance.

It is quite impossible to keep notes on everything; when discoveries are being made, the full meaning of each event may not be realized until the observer has been exposed to his subject for a long time. If there is a skeleton of basic facts in the notes, a framework for understanding is present.

Taking Field Notes

The mechanics of taking field notes has considerable bearing on their systematic indexing and filing. Any method of recording field data that suits the personal preferences of the game investigator is satisfactory so long as it is simple enough to be convenient and workable in the field and permits easy indexing, filing, and recovery of all types of field records. Personal preferences vary widely on the type of paper, size of paper, type of field-form holder, the amount of printed matter on the field form, and type of pencil or ink used. Some investigators prefer 8-1/2 by 11-inch paper, with a printed form for recording all types of field data. Others use slightly smaller sized, permanently-bound printed forms. Still others make good use of detachable-sheeted, pocket-size notebooks. For certain types of field investigations, marginal-notch and IBM-type

cards are used. Whatever the personal preference, the mechanics of how and upon what the observer records field data is not important. The important consideration is getting the data recorded and then indexed and filed in such a manner that these records are easily available for future reference.

Both continuous and discrete field data, such as tagging records, kill information, field-plot data (Sincock and Powell 1957; Overton and Sincock 1956), and similar measurements, may be recorded efficiently on edge-punched (key-sort) or mark-sense (machine sort) cards (Casey 1958). Edge-punched cards are used frequently for recording and filing literature abstracts and references (Hood et al. 1953; Adams 1955).

Edge-punched cards (Fig. 6.1A) are available in single- to four-holed form and in a variety of sizes. A hand punch is used in coding and a needle sorter is employed to hand-sort and select the desired cards by rejection. For example, a hand-operated punch may be employed to punch out a "V" at the proper hole(s), thus recording the data on key-sort cards. A needle sorter is inserted through a stack of cards and all cards with the hole(s) punched out are rejected and the cards with intact holes are removed. Standard printed cards, such as literature abstract cards, are available in any practical size from 3 by 5 inch to 8 by 10-1/2 inch. The cards vary in cost (1962) from about $15.50 to $61.50 per thousand. The hand punch costs about $5.00 and the needle sorter about $1.50 (E-Z Sort System, Ltd., 45 Second St., San Francisco, California). See Casey et al. (1958:30 ff.) for a description of the various types and manufacturers of edge-punched cards and accessories.

If the field investigator has access to a Mark Sensing Reproducer and other electronic data-processing equipment, the use of mark-sense cards offers an ideal way of recording a large quantity of data with a minimum of effort. This method of recording field data offers maximum flexibility since the data may be electronically punched, tabulated, and analysed. Mark-sense cards are marked, in the appropriate code block, using a special electrographic pencil (Fig. 6.1B). The special pencil lays down a heavy graphite coating which is detected electronically by three brushes of the Mark Sensing Reproducer and, after detection, the marked area is punched on a key-

Fig. 6.1. Edge-punched (hand- or key-sort) cards (*A*) are available in a variety of sizes and code combinations. Mark-sense (machine-sort) cards (*B*) are code-marked by means of special electrographic pencils. The marked areas are punched by electronic machines. The Porta-punch (IBM) card (*C*) is punched by means of a portable hand-operated machine which is transported into the field and data punched on specially-printed cards as collected.

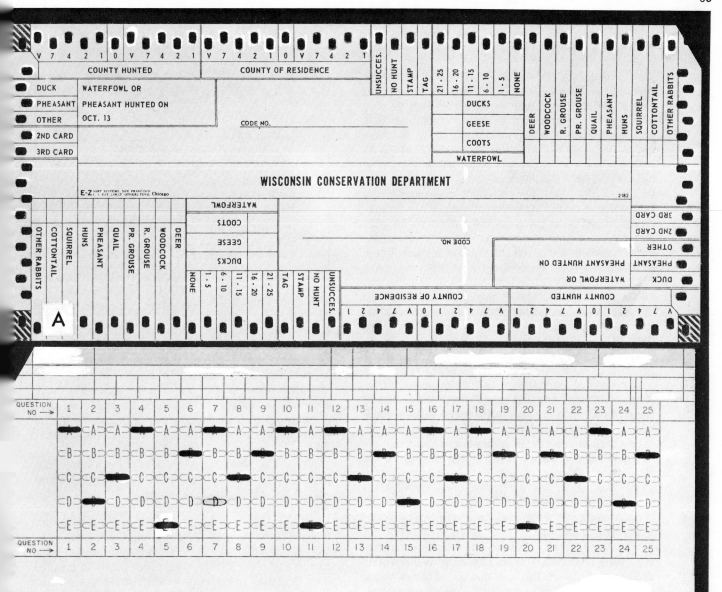

punch machine. Cards coded (Fig. 6.1C) in this manner or by means of the Porta-punch (Rogers and Fleming 1963) may be tabulated in a variety of ways by electronic processing machines (IBM and Remington Rand). Special printed mark-sense cards, printed on both sides, cost (1962) about as follows: for the engraved plate, $90.00; printing set-up charge, $20.00; and cost per thousand for cards, $1.50. Any investigator who anticipates collecting a large quantity of either continuous count or discrete data should examine the possibility of using either hand-sort or machine-sorted punch cards as these techniques offer efficient ways of recording, tabulating, and analyzing information.

Loveless et al. (1966) describe the use of a standard 8-1/2 x 11 inch Page Reader sheet having 800 marking positions on which to record data. These forms are read electronically by an IBM Optical Mark Page Reader and can be punched directly onto cards. Page "reading" progresses at a maximum of 2000 pages per hour. Rubber-styrene overlay templates on the standard form held on a wooden clip-board indicate the proper position to make marks. One sheet is marked for each series of observations, then inserted beneath the stack of 30-40 sheets on the clip board. Extra sheets can be carried. The Page Reader has a maximum capacity of 1000 mark positions, the Mark-sense card has 540 (employing both front and back of card), and the Porta-punch has 480.

Loveless et al. (1966:522) make the point that field note collections should avoid as much as possible copying, editing, grouping, and translation. These operations are tedious, expensive, time-consuming, and often introduce errors into the data. Use of Optical Mark Page Readers provides for data to be directly converted to machine language for tabulation and analysis.

AN EXAMPLE

One method of taking, indexing, and filing written field notes is outlined below. It is preferred by the writer after much testing and study of alternate methods.

Field notes are recorded on 4 by 6-inch cards. This size field-note form was selected as it is about as large as can be carried conveniently in the pocket, and still afford a reasonable amount of writing space. Such forms can be carried in a metal datum holder; this holder will preserve them from bending and will keep the field records in good condition. A form is printed on the top of the card for recording the minimum

Fig. 6.2. Field note observation card and recorded field note.

amount of information necessary for all types of observations. An example of this field-note form, with field note #1254, is shown in Fig. 6.2. Lengthy observations are continued on the back side of the card. If needed, a second card may be used, with the second form being assigned the same observation number. When filed, the original and second card are stapled together.

All field notes are typed as soon as possible after returning from the field. The original notes are typed on letter-size paper (8-1/2 x 11 inch), making at least two copies of the letter-size records. The cards should be arranged in the numerical sequence in which they were taken in the field (that is, by observation numbers as assigned to each field-note card) prior to typing. The original typed copy of the field notes should be filed in a fire-proof file and the carbon copy should be filed in some other fire-proof container. Thus, if one copy is lost or damaged, the second copy is available for use. After the data on the original field-note cards have been typed, each original field-note card is filed under the appropriate heading.

A practical alternative personal field note method is to make one field card (4 x 6 inches, bond paper) in ink, file it in numerical order, and record its number on an appropriate subject file-guide card as described in Chapter 4. There is then only one card per observation filed in order, and a set of file-guide cards. The advantages are that time is saved by not copying cards, each guide card "topic" can be easily divided (or grouped), and all observations on a topic can be pulled for use, and refiling can be accurately done by anyone. The system is more flexible than marginal-notched cards in that it can be easily modified as interests change, certain subject areas are expanded, and as whole groups of cards are discarded. Index words in the upper right corner of each observation card allow secretarial aid in filing and in maintaining the file-guide card cross index.

When a large number of field observations must be recorded in a short period of time, portable recorders have proven of considerable value (Crissey 1953, Bartlett 1954, Miller et al. 1965). Battery-operated recorders (Fig. 6.3) are available in a variety of models, makes, and sizes; they range in price from about $30.00 to $250.00. Observations recorded on tapes or wire may be transcribed, typed, and filed. The tape or wire may be filed or reused as the investigator desires. Many workers now use this technique for almost all field survey work, even in place of the Porta-punch or Optical Mark Page Reader sheets. Secretarial or recording facilities in combination with telephone, radio, or intercom systems should not be overlooked, especially with animal behavior studies.

Field notes on which data are recorded should be planned for rapid key punching onto data cards. Brotzman and Giles (1966) present one example. Planning considerations should be for ease of placing each number, letter, or "bit" into each numbered column of the card, (each card con-

Fig. 6.3. Battery-operated recorders are especially useful for collecting a large quantity of descriptive or mathematical information in a short period.

tains 80 columns); ease of sequentially and rapidly punching each data line; clarity of numbers and letters; and recognition that the key-punch operator will do little or no interpretive, organizational, or decision-making as to "what numbers go where." Engineers of data-processing companies should be consulted early in research and management planning for the greatest efficiency in data collection as well as processing.

Filing Field Notes

Two methods of filing the field notes have been outlined above. The classification under the most appropriate file heading, the filing, and the cross-referencing of the field notes are all as important as the taking of field notes. An accurate and detailed field note which is lost in the file is of little or no value.

A general outline of file headings which may be used in classifying "general" field observations (including laboratory and literature data if desired) is shown in Fig. 6.4 or the Content page of *Wildlife Review* may be used for the file categories. The index of this book also can be used as a guide. It will be noted that these file headings are very general; each sub-heading could be expanded considerably. When the available data warrant, any section of the file can be subdivided further by the addition of other appropriate file headings. See also Anderson (1966) and Needy (1966).

When the wildlifer is concerned with a specific topic, species, or project, he should prepare a detailed outline of the classifications, or file categories, under which he wishes to collect data. The investigational plan outline shown in Chapter 2 and the outline in Chapter 5 are useful major headings for some types of filing. Such a detailed outline, if prepared at the beginning of the investigations, will serve to direct the investigator's attention to the topics for which data are required. The simpler the file outline, the more workable it will be; if a complicated file system is attempted, it probably will not be maintained unless the wildlifer has competent office assistance.

It is not necessary to assign the observation number and file classification when the data are recorded on the field-note form in the field. This can be done when the field notes are typed in the office. An observation may refer to more than one file heading (classification) and cross-referencing may be necessary. In cross-referencing, the original field-note card is filed under the most appropriate heading and the observation number

Field Note File Classification

Antelope	Furbearers—General	Quail
	Fur Farming	
Bats		Rabbit
Bear	Goat—Mountain	Refuges—Wildlife
Bibliography—Wildlife	Grouse	Research—Wildlife
Big Game—General		Restocking
Birds—General	Hawks and Owls	Rodents
	History—Wildlife	
Chicken—Prairie		Sheep—Mountain
Conservation—Wildlife	Insects	Skunk
Control—Wildlife		Snakes
Coyote	Laws—Wildlife	Soils
	Livestock—Wildlife	Squirrel
Damage—Wildlife		
Disease—Wildlife	Mammals—General	Techniques—Wildlife
Dogs	Management—Farm Game	Trapping
Dove	Management—Forest Game	Turkey—Wild
Deer	Management—Land	
	Mink	Utilization—Wildlife
Ecology	Muskrat	
Economics—Wildlife		Waterfowl
	Opossum	Weather
Fish—General		Woodchuck
Fish Ponds	Partridges	Woodcock
Feed and Cover—General	Pheasant	
Foods—Food Habits	Plants—General	
Forestry—General	Predation	
Fox	Propagation	

Fig. 6.4. General file classifications used in filing field notes. This simplified filing system can be expanded for any subject when sufficient data are at hand to warrant such an expansion.

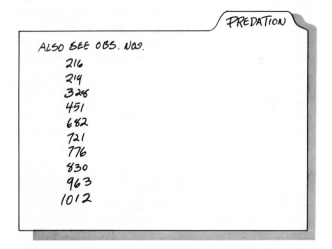

Fig. 6.5. File-guide card for the classification "Predation." All original field notes classified "Predation" are filed behind this file guide card. The observation numbers of other field notes which refer to predation filed elsewhere are recorded on the front of the file-guide card.

is listed on the front of the file guide card(s) (see Fig. 6.5) of the other subject(s) to which it may refer. If this is done, and if the field notes are typed in numerical sequence, it is easy to obtain access to all field data bearing on any file subject. In the example shown in Fig. 6.5, the majority of the field note data on predation will be found on the original field cards filed directly behind the "Predation" file guide; observation numbers 216, 219, 328, 451, 682 etc. also refer to predation in some form. These latter observations can be consulted by referring to the typed file notes.

Many beginning filers are over-ambitious in setting up their filing system. If a system is too complicated, the wildlifer is prone to put off filing his data and eventually he is convinced that it is a hopeless task. When this is the case, all types of data are filed under "Miscellaneous." Bitter experience has demonstrated that the category "Miscellaneous" should not appear in any filing system, even the very simple one outlined here.

Daily Journal

Every serious game investigator should maintain a field journal in which he records his general field activities. Most investigators prefer a bound journal, usually 8-1/2 by 11 inches, in which to record a condensed "diary-type" entry of each day's activities. These summary records are permanent and are most helpful in preparing monthly, quarterly, and annual project reports; they also are useful in many other ways. The utility of such records has to be experienced to be fully appreciated. It should be emphasized that journal entries should be made *daily*—not periodically.

Special Field Forms

The wildlifer usually has need for special forms upon which to record specific types of data. Examples of such special forms are: trap-record forms, vegetative-survey forms, food-habits forms, form maps (see Chapter 12), and hunting pressure forms. Such special forms, if carefully prepared, facilitate the recording of data and, perhaps more importantly, they assure that complete and uniform data are collected. They can also simplify coding for data processing.

These special forms may be printed, if required in quantity (Loveless et al. 1966). Offset equipment for duplicating forms is usually available to most game investigators, as is mimeograph equipment; both of these types of equipment may be used for quantity duplication. For the duplication of small quantities of forms on 4 by 6 inch cards, the hand-operated Multistamp set (which operates on the mimeograph principle) is very convenient. If the special forms are not exposed to damp conditions, ditto duplication is one of the quickest and simplest methods. Therefore, the duplication of special field-record forms should offer no problem to the wildlifer who learns the capabilities of and how to use office duplicating equipment.

PHOTOGRAPHIC RECORD TAKING

The camera can be one of the most useful tools of the wildlifer for making permanent records. A familiarity with photographic equipment and techniques will permit the investigator to present field, laboratory, and public relations information more quickly and with greater clarity than can be done in any other way. Also, photography can be utilized to facilitate office record duplication.

Both still and motion pictures can be utilized to excellent advantage but the still camera has the greater utility for the wildlife worker under most circumstances. Therefore, the following discussion will be concerned only with the general techniques of using still cameras. No effort will be made to list all of the various types of equipment, procedures and techniques that may be used by the wildlife investigator. The following elementary discussion will be confined to outlining some of the more obvious uses of the camera in the field of wildlife management.

Photography is mastered only by first-hand experience. Perhaps the best way for the beginner to learn how to use the camera as a field tool is to: (1) review a general publication on photography; (2) get a camera, take photos, develop the negatives, make prints; and then (3) critically examine each print for errors in picture taking, developing, and printing. There is a considerable amount of literature available (much of it free) on all phases of photography but the beginner should start with a general treatment of photography (e.g., Mess 1951; Baines 1958) before advancing to the more specialized publications (e.g. Miller 1942; Sprungman 1951). Current photography publications (Popular Photography, Modern Photography, etc.) usually contain in each issue a number of articles of value both to the beginning and the advanced photographer. Each photographer has to develop his own preferences for photographic equipment and technique by trial and error. The job of taking good photographs is made simpler if the photographer decides what specific equipment suits his purpose best and then concentrates on as few types of films, chemicals, cameras, and gadgets as possible.

Fox (1959), after conferring with several magazine editors, listed their consensus of what makes a good picture. These attributes of a good story-telling print refer primarily to public-relations photographs but they are equally applicable to technical photographs. The main points listed by Fox are:

1. Plan each picture carefully.
2. Get people or animals into the picture.
3. Avoid stiff, posed, photographs.
4. Make the photograph illustrate the point you have in mind.
5. Take pictures from several angles; film is the cheapest part of photo-taking costs.

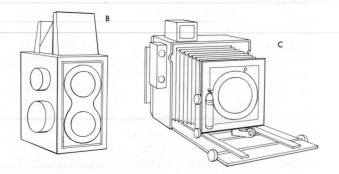

Fig. 6.6. Types of cameras: (A) single lens 35 mm.; (B) twin lens 2-1/4 x 2-1/4 reflex; and (C) press type, coupled rangefinder—ground glass focus 4 x 5.

6. Avoid long-range, panoramic shots; include close-ups, preferably within 6 to 8 ft.

7. To show scale, use a person or animal; avoid lifeless objects to show size.

8. Watch the background; remove such articles as cars, equipment, and other movable objects.

9. Use fill-in flash when natural light won't reveal the detail you desire.

10. Crop the picture to remove unwanted objects or harsh lighting effects.

Types of Cameras

The number of cameras and camera attachments are bewildering in their variety (see Ziff-Davis Pub. Co. 1962). However, the general types of cameras are: (1) fixed focus (box), (2) manual focusing (distance estimated and set manually), (3) coupled range finder focusing including (a) roll film or (b) pack-cut film, (4) twin lens reflex and (5) single lens reflex. Examples of several of the various types of cameras are illustrated in Fig. 6.6.

As emphasized previously, the choice of cameras and related equipment is based on personal preference. It should be obvious that each type of camera has certain advantages and disadvantages and *no single type of camera will perform all functions equally well*.

Listed below are the writer's personal camera preferences:

For color slides:
    35 mm single lens reflex
For general field use:
    Twin lens reflex, 2-1/4 x 2-1/4, roll film

For field use, copying, and general record taking:
    Coupled rangefinder-ground glass, press type; 4 x 5, role or pack-cut film

If only one field camera had to be selected, the writer's preference would be a twin lens reflex (with parallax correcting portrait lenses) as it can be used to perform all of the above functions, but with definite limitations. Again, it is emphasized that no single camera will serve all photographic purposes just as no single type of firearm may be used successfully for taking all forms of game.

Field Records

In the hands of a reasonably competent photographer, field events can be recorded photographically with considerable clarity. In many instances, a good photograph is the only satisfactory way in which such events can be recorded in an easily used and permanent manner. For example, the general description of an area is easily depicted photographically (Fig. 6.7A) and ecological succession can be shown in a manner difficult to accomplish with equal clarity by any other technique (see Bump 1950). The camera offers an excellent medium for recording habitat improvement practices (Fig. 6.7E), habitat changes (Fig. 6.7C and D), specimens (Fig. 6.7B), cover density changes, field techniques or equipment, field structures, animals (Shaub 1951) and their homes, food (Greenewalt and Jones 1955), signs (Gysel and Davis 1956), animal damage, legal evidence (Rollmann 1962), and many other field and laboratory phenomena.

Fig. 6.7. The camera may be used to record (A) general habitat conditions; (B) biological specimens; (C and D) cover density changes; (E) habitat improvement practices and (F) other field phenomena.

70

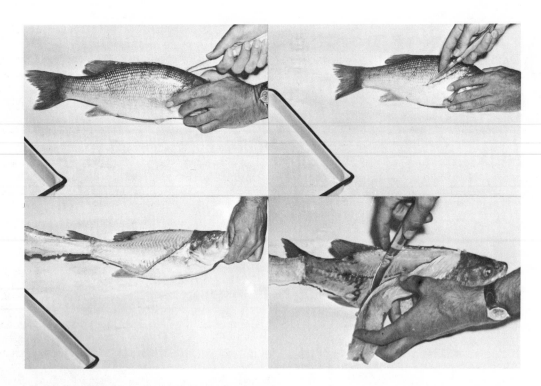

Fig. 6.8. The camera can be used to present a "step-by-step" procedure with a minimum of written explanation.

The good field photographer often is stimulated by his camera to be a closer observer and a better recorder. The greater the familiarity of the field worker with the technique of making both written and photographic records, the better field investigator he is likely to be.

Laboratory Records

The camera is equally as useful in the laboratory as in the field. Records of biological specimens (Fig. 6.7B), laboratory equipment, laboratory techniques, biological events and reactions, growth of organisms and related matters are recorded with permanence and clarity by means of the camera. Often a procedure or technique can be shown photographically step by step, with practically no written explanation being required (Fig. 6.8). The use of the camera in the laboratory often extends over the fields of "regular" photography, microphotography, and macrophotography. Micro- and macrophotography are rather specialized aspects of photography that normally require special equipment and critical attention to lighting, depth of field, and related matters. It is recommended, therefore, that the techniques of "regular" photography be mastered before venturing too far into specialized photography.

Office and Public Relations Photography

Office record duplication can be simplified by the use of photography. Black and white material such as maps (8-1/2 by 11 inches), forms, personnel records, and related documents can be reproduced by office duplicating equipment using the photographic principles of contact printing. Where copies in small quantities (6 to 10) are required, this method of duplicating is rapid and satisfactory for most purposes. Likewise, similar sized (up to 8-1/2 by 14 inch) records can be duplicated by the Kodagraph process in which a paper negative is prepared by contact printing. This negative can then be reproduced, by contact printing, to make as many copies as may be required.

The use of a camera often is a satisfactory way of enlarging or reducing maps (see Chapter 12), or, in fact, any similar records for report purposes.

The camera is an indispensible tool in public-relations work. Most state conservation magazines and similar avenues of publication will not give serious consideration to a paper for publication unless it has photographic illustrations. In many instances, a series of photographs may be used to tell a rather complete story (see Schwartz 1944) or explain a procedure (Fig. 6.8). Such photographic "essays" are highly sought after in public-relations periodicals. Likewise, color slides (usually 35 mm but larger sizes are rapidly becoming more universally used) permit the explanation to public gatherings of research and management programs in a manner that is difficult to accomplish in any other way. Such slides should be taken with the presentation of the full topic in mind. A miscellaneous collection of slides seldom, if ever, will include all of the illustrative material necessary to present a logical sequence. For this reason, it is recommended that the topic be outlined and that each slide necessary to present the various aspects of the problem be stated. Then, the photographer must go out and secure all of the photos necessary to present the topic in a full and orderly manner. Some of the "shots" may be in the file, but in most instances it will be necessary to take additional slides on specific aspects of the subject to complete the series in a logical manner. (See Haugen 1964.)

Filing Negatives and Prints

The filing of slides, negatives, and prints often presents quite a problem. Elaborate techniques of filing photographic records are available. Experience indicates, however, that the simpler the filing system, the greater is the probability that it will be used and maintained. The following simple system has proven fairly satisfactory for individual use or for use in an office with a moderate number of slides, negatives, and prints on records.

SLIDES

Slides may be 35 mm or larger. Each size slide has its own file numbering system under the method outlined here. These numbers are arranged in numerical sequence, with a prefix numeral to designate their size classification. For example, the 35 mm slides would be numbered 35-1, 35-2, 35-3, etc., the 2-1/4 x 2-1/4 slides, as 22-1, 22-2, 22-3, etc., the 3-1/4 x 4-1/4 slides as 34-1, 34-2, 34-3, etc. The slides in each size classification are numbered without regard to subject and in the order in which they were taken. A card is prepared on each slide, giving the file number, date, subject, and any other pertinent data. These cards are then filed by subject, with the slide number recorded on the front of the file-guide card of any additional subjects to which cross-referencing is desired (see Fig. 6.5 for the method in which this may be done). Thus, when assembling slides on a given subject, all slides can be located by number by consulting the file cards.

The slide itself is then ready for filing. The slides are filed by the serial slide number. Write on the slide itself the major subject (under which it is filed in the slide card file). Any additional data should be written on the slide in as great detail as space will permit. Of course, it is the usual practice to indicate (by a dot, punch, or other means) the upper right hand corner of the slide as it would be inserted in the projector.

The above system works satisfactorily for small slide collections, (500-2,000). The slides in each size classification are numbered without regard to subject and in the order in which they are to be filed. A 4 x 6-inch card is prepared for each slide, giving the file number, date, subject, other pertinent data, and key words for filing. These cards are filed numerically. A number is written on the slide mounting with any additional information desired. The upper right-hand corner of the slide as it would be inserted into the projector should be indicated by a dot or punch. The slide number is listed on a file-guide card just as for filing field notes and cross-referencing reprint citations (Fig. 6.5). Thus when assembling slides on a given subject, all slides can be located by number for inspection for appropriateness. Since all slides are filed numerically, there are no waste spaces for subject areas not yet filled, re-filing is simple, and the cards provide data on slides not possible to write on the mounting. In addition these cards identify missing slides and provide a device for noting borrowed slides or slides in current use. When infrequently used by others, their name and date can be penciled on the card; otherwise a borrow-slip can be clipped to each card. The clips showing in the file indicate at a glance the slides that are out and provide a measure of use. This system works satisfactorily for collections of up to several thousand slides. Smaller collections may be filed by subject only, with no card file, and large collections may require a more complex filing system.

Other indexing systems such as marginal notch, should not be overlooked. The compatibility of the field note, reprint, and slide filing systems described in this book should be noted as an advantage. Advantages are in similar filing cases, forms, and ease of learning the system.

NEGATIVES

Negatives (irrespective of size) may be filed by "packs," irrespective of subject. This may be done by collecting a convenient number of negatives (from 10 to 20 negatives), assigning a pack number and a sequence number to each negative,

72

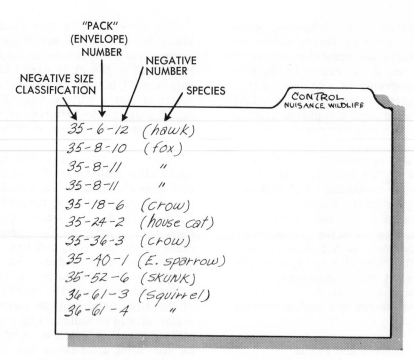

NEGATIVE SIZE
CLASSIFICATION

"PACK"
(ENVELOPE)
NUMBER

NEGATIVE
NUMBER

SPECIES

CONTROL
NUISANCE WILDLIFE

35 - 6 - 12 (hawk)
35 - 8 - 10 (fox)
35 - 8 - 11 "
35 - 8 - 11 "
35 - 18 - 6 (crow)
35 - 24 - 2 (house cat)
35 - 36 - 3 (crow)
35 - 40 - 1 (E. sparrow)
35 - 52 - 6 (SKUNK)
36 - 61 - 3 (squirrel)
36 - 61 - 4 "

Fig. 6.9. Negative file-guide card showing the file number of all negatives relating to the control of nuisance wildlife.

and writing this pack-sequence number on each negative in ink. The pertinent data are typed, in two copies, on regular 8-1/2 by 11 inch paper, one copy of which is cut and pasted on the envelope containing the pack of negatives and the second typed copy is filed. For example, suppose that a group of 14 negatives of various subjects are ready for filing. Assume that the next "pack" number is 86. Thus, the negatives would have the numbers 86-1, 86-2, 86-3, etc., written on each respective negative in ink. Detailed, typed data on each negative would appear on the front of the envelope containing this pack of negatives. Likewise, each print would have the corresponding negative number recorded on it as will be explained later. A subject file card is prepared and the number of each negative referring to this subject is recorded on the front of this file card (Fig. 6.9). Each negative can be cross-referred to as many subjects as desired. If this is done, all the negatives on a given subject may be located (and the data on each determined) by consulting the subject file card and noting the number of each negative filed under this subject.

PRINTS

Each print is stamped on the back (using a rubber-stamp form). Required data, including

the exact number of the negative from which the print was made, is entered in the proper spaces (Fig. 6.10). The print is then filed under the most appropriate subject heading. If it is desired to file prints under more than one subject heading, it will be necessary to prepare a print for each file heading.

Virginia Cooperative Wildlife Research Unit
V. P. I.
Blacksburg, Virginia

No. 36-1 Date APRIL 4, 1968

Location NEW RIVER, GILES CO., VA.

Legend FISH KILLED BY

POLLUTION — CATFISH, CARP

BREAM & SMALLMOUTH BASS

Author JOHN A. SMITH

Fig. 6.10. A rubber-stamped outline on the back of each photographic print insures that all necessary data relating to the print are recorded.

CHAPTER SEVEN

INSTRUMENTATION

ROBERT H. GILES, JR., PhD

Associate Professor, Wildlife Management
Department of Forestry and Wildlife
Virginia Polytechnic Institute
Blacksburg, Virginia

POWER SOURCES
AUDIAL INSTRUMENTS
VISUAL INSTRUMENTS
ACTIVITY RECORDING INSTRUMENTS
WEIGHT MEASUREMENT AND ESTIMATION

Within 50 years wildlife research has moved from subjective field observations to highly complex, precise, objective measures of mammal and bird morphology, physiology and behavior. Though recent trends are to greater use of instruments for obtaining quantities of valid numerical data, the researcher must continue to seek perfection in making observations of field events and in taking records that can be compiled and analyzed. The tendency toward gadgeteering is strong; the means can easily shadow the end, which is knowledge of wildlife, its relation to its total environment, and ways of influencing this relationship.

Instrumentation is the use of any device for studying and analyzing natural phenomena more objectively, practically, or efficiently than can be done by the unaided human. Instruments are an extension of man's perceptual abilities. Instrumentation encompasses almost every device from knotting a string for counting birds flushed, to an electronic computer for processing data.

The advance of instrumentation in wildlife research has been hampered not only by limited funds for proper equipment, but also by field transportation difficulties, lack of power sources, and adverse environmental factors. The great mobility and secretiveness of wildlife has also retarded the use of instruments. Besides having been expensive, some instruments such as radio transmitters and ultra-sensitive infra-red aerial films have been unavailable from governmental agencies.

Only recently have wildlifers plunged deeply into the previously remote but interrelated fields of electronics, radioisotopes, light physics, and communications. This chapter is a literature review of some special investigational instrumentation developed for, or applied to, wildlife problems. There are few biological or physical techniques that will not eventually be applied to problems of wildlife management and investigation. The chapter attempts to show only some of these uses, to stimulate modifications of and additional use of instruments to obtain more accurate observations and more reliable data. Davis (1954) provides the precautionary word for the need for knowledge of being able to acquire statistically adequate samples of observations of animal activity before investments are made in instrumentation. Chapters 8, 9, 10, and 11 also deal with instrumentation.

General books on instrumentation useful for those seeking advice on a particular problem or background on advice given are by Lion (1959), Considine and Ross (1964), Kay (1964), Aronson (1960), Studer (1963), Lenhoff (1966), and Dewhurst (1966).

The series, *Physical Techniques in Biological Research,* edited by W. L. Nastuk, provides fundamental guides and discussions. This series is largely for fundamental biological research. It covers topics of electrophysiological methods pertinent to some current wildlife research efforts. Newman (1964) and Alt (1966) also treat these and related topics.

In *Science* (1967, Vol. 158A No. 3804A) there appeared 1967-68 *Guide to Scientific Instruments* an important resource. In addition, a scientific instrument information service was described that would provide information, referral to a salesman, and make efforts to locate a source of supply for items not listed in the *Guide*. Most departments of Universities and natural resource agencies have catalog libraries of their specialties that are available to investigators. A publication of potential usefulness is *Instrument and Apparatus News* (Instruments Publishing Co., 845 Ridge Street, Pittsburg 12, Pa).

POWER SOURCES

Field sources of electrical power create problems where portability or accessibility is a factor and where instruments must be operated for long periods.

Gasoline-operated generators have the disadvantages of being expensive, noisy, and heavy. With adequate extension wires they can be removed from the site of instrument operation. Hand-operated generators may be suitable for some purposes. Instruments operating on direct current (DC) can be attached directly to a storage battery for short runs (depending, of course, on the drain). Most instruments are designed for AC and so require a DC to AC converter (e.g. Terado Co., Raymond Ave., St. Paul 8, Minn.) when operated from a storage battery or from an automobile lighter jack. Loveless et al. (1963) reported on the use of an AC to DC converter in a remote situation to operate an 8-day strip chart recorder. Dry and wet cell batteries can be connected to provide the exact energy requirement with minimum size, weight, and cost. Rechargeable D-size "flashlight" batteries can be purchased. Minature batteries are now available through electronics dealers. Taylor and Taylor (1964) reported on recharging batteries used for wildlife photography.

Workers should consult a textbook for basic electrical considerations, definitions, and answers to such practical problems as wire sizes, current requirements, and minor adaptations in instruments. Cornsweet's book (1963) may also be helpful.

AUDIAL INSTRUMENTS

Bird songs have attracted much attention in the field of instrumentation. When word descriptions of bird songs failed and even musical notations were unable to handle the complexities of bird notes, other methods were sought for studying and recording sound.

The phonographic recording of bird song was unsatisfactory for detailed study of song but has proven of benefit in learning bird identification, producing sounds repellent to crop pests, hunting and predator calling, and other uses. "Photographing" bird songs on motion picture film was the first technique allowing detailed bird song study (Brand 1935). Microscopic examination of the sound track allowed measurement of the length of a song and of individual notes accurately to 1/500 second. It allowed determination of details of rhythm and frequencies of the fundamentals but nothing could be measured on harmonics or the other frequencies present. Notes inaudible to the human ear and the pitch of a note could be accurately measured. Microscopic examination and manual recording were very time consuming; amplitude or tone intensity were difficult to measure accurately.

Recently these major disadvantages have overcome by devices that automatically transfer recorded sounds to a stylus marking a cylindrical drum. Borror and Reese (1953), Collias and Joos (1953), Thorpe (1954), Bennet (1961), Saunders (1961), Collias (1962), Davis (1964), Lanyon and Gill (1964), and Dewolfe (1967) utilized a vibralizer or sound spectrograph. These devices allowed measurement of high and low tones, time, rhythm, amplitude or loudness, sound quality, and fundamental frequencies and overtones inaudible to the human ear. Vibrograms are made electrically on 5-5/8 x 12-3/4 inch facimile paper on a rotating drum.

Garber and Cochran (1959) used a 72-1/2 inch diameter parabolic reflector with 14-1/2 inch maxium depth to "collect" and study the calls of nocturnal migrant songbirds (See Hamilton 1962). Sounds were amplified and recorded using the system shown in Fig. 7.1. The use of a horn instead of a parabola was suggested as a less expensive possibility. The maximum distance of sound detection will vary directly as the diameter of the parabola. Doubling the diameter may more than double the detection distance. The range depends on the size of the parabola, the sensitivity

Fig. 7.1. Equipment used for flight-call detection of night-migrating birds. From l. to r.: recorder, recorder timer, high-pass filter, parabolic reflector surrounded by straw sound baffle, and preamplifier with speaker (photo courtesy R. R. Graber, Illinois Natural History Survey).

of the microphone and amplifier, and the amount of external noise. This fourth factor will be limiting. Garber and Cochran used a 4-inch permanent magnet speaker with voice-coil-to-grid matching transformer. A pre-amplifier instead of a self-contained amplifier found with most tape recorders was used. The power source, 110 AC, was a 6-v storage battery and 90-v drycell battery for the amplifier. In personal correspondence Graber speculates that if the parabola were turned on edge, the range for detecting game sounds, e.g., pheasant's crowing, would be over 5 miles. Gans and Bonin (1963) have developed an acoustical activity recorder for burrowing animals.

Sound has been used to attract and repel animals for centuries by man. Game calls for "bugling up" elk or moose, calling waterfowl, or calling predators and other animals have a long history. "Squeaking" animals out of cover or causing them to freeze is easily done with the mouth and hand or blade of grass between the thumbs (Anon. 1946). Kinne (1960) suggested calling animals for photography.

In 1954 Frings and Jumber reported on use of tape recorded calls to repel starlings (Sturnus vulgaris) from roosts. In the same year Diem reported the use of deer calls for locating fawns which, if they were present were always seen within 150 yards of the doe. Doe behavior at the sound of the call clearly indicated whether fawns were present. Bohl (1956) used recorded calls of chukkar partridge in the field to attempt census, but was only partially successful in stimulating a calling response. Frings et al. (1955) and Frings and Frings (1958) were successful in using tape recordings of gull and crow vocalization to attract and repel flocks. They used a continuous-loop cartridge in a special player ("Bird-E-Vict") with amplifiers and speakers. By playing a food-finding or assembly call at high sound intensity they attracted birds; distress or alarm call at low intensity repelled birds.

Nesbit (1959) used a modified goose call operated by a 12-v battery to increase the waterfowl use of Powell Marsh in Wisconsin from 82 geese to 12,000. The player stimulated feeding and flight calls which attracted geese. The flight call was more attractive.

Morse and Balser (1961) reported on the use of a portable battery-operated, high fidelity record player with amplifier and loud speaker to call foxes for hunting. They reviewed the literature on game calling as a hunting technique for coyotes, wolves, deer, raccoon, bobcat, and fox.

Sterling and Bendell (1966) used recordings of the pre-copulatory calls of blue grouse hens for censusing birds and suggested use for searching, detecting, censusing, observing, and capturing male and female grouse. Levy et al. (1966) recorded the calls of Mearns' quail during the breeding season. The best calls were transcribed to another tape. By moving over a route and playing the calls at stops, males and their territories could be located. They also developed tapes for Gambel's, scaled, and masked bobwhite quail. On some occasions birds flew to the recorder. They suggested uses of locating birds in an area (e.g. the rare masked bobwhite) for relative population density estimates and trend counts (see Chapter 21), for observing movement in territory, for relating mated to bachelor males, for determining breeding season behavior, and, thus, to improve call-count census techniques.

VISUAL INSTRUMENTS

No one field glass or binocular can serve all needs. By knowing the requirements for and the characteristics and capabilities of the glasses, a wise selection can be made. Reichert and Reichert (1961) presented a comprehensive treatment of the selection of binoculars and scopes. Binoculars differ from field glasses by having internal optical prisms, adjustments for opthalmic differences, reduced length, increased field of view, and improved clarity. Binoculars are usually "named" by two numbers, e.g. 7 X 50. The magnification, 7 X, specifies that objects will appear seven times normal size or that objects will appear one-seventh as distant. However, a higher magnification also magnifies movement so that the resolving power of a 10 X glass when hand-held is only 6 X or 7 X. The second number is the diameter in millimeters of the objective lens (the larger lens). The larger this lens, the greater will be the light-gathering capabilities and consequently the brightness of the image. The field of view is governed, not by the objective lens, but the angular degrees and focal length of the binoculars which is a function of the number and arrangement of internal prisms. Wide fields of view are desirable for keeping moving objects such as warblers in view. Coated lenses are generally more desirable than uncoated lenses, for they reduce internal reflection and thereby increase the brightness and detail of the image.

The light-gathering power of a binocular is numerically the square of the diameter in mm of the exit pupil (the white spot seen in the eye lens when the binocular is held at arms length and pointed toward a light). The diameter of the exit pupil is obtained by dividing the diameter in mm of the objective lens (D) by the magnification (M). Thus the light-gathering efficiency equals $\left(\frac{D}{M}\right)^2$. This figure should be increased by 50 per cent for coated lenses. For example the light efficiency of a pair of 6 x 30 coated binoculars is $\left(\frac{30}{6}\right)^2 = 25 + 50\% = 37.5$ per cent light efficiency.

The significance of the exit pupil size (usually 3-8 mm) is that its diameter need be no larger than the size of the observer's pupil (approximately 2 mm in daylight, maximum of 7 mm in darkness) to obtain the maximum light efficiency, not the diameter of the exit pupil lens. The 7 X 50 glass was adopted by the armed forces as a "night glass" because its large exit pupil works extremely well in poor light. Characteristics of some common glasses are shown in Table 7.1.

One easily made check on binocular quality is the sharpness and regularity of the exit pupil. The relative field of 2600 to 2700 is considered "standard"; 3400 and above, "wide." The difference in relative fields of 8 X 30 glasses, for example (See Table 2) is due to focal length.

Center-focus and individual lens focus are largely matters of preference. Focusing is needed for all binoculars at distances of less than 300 ft. Objects moving rapidly toward or away from the observer require rapid focusing such as provided by a center-focus mechanism that adjusts both lenses by the turn of a single knob. The construction of center-focus glasses is not as moisture or dust proof as individually focusing glasses and they are usually more expensive.

Telescopes follow the same general characteristics of binoculars. Due to their variety, expense, limitations in mobility, and adaptability for photography, they must be carefully tailored to the research job.

Richter (1955) used a five-cell flashlight to spot rabbits tagged with Scotch-lite ear discs. A spotting head lamp fitted to a battery unit combined with coated 7 X 50 binoculars should provide a near-maximum in night-observation capabilities.

Though many animals seem unaffected by artificial light or photo flashes, some are. Since this light prohibits extensive observations of animals

Table 7.1. Characteristics of some binoculars commonly used in wildlife research

Magnification (M)	Objective lens diameter (D)	Exit pupil diameter $\left(\dfrac{D}{M}\right)$	Relative[1] brightness $\left(\dfrac{D}{M}\right)$	Angular degrees	Field in feet at 1000 yds. (F)	Relative field (MxF)
6	30	5.0	25	8.5	450	2700
7	35	5.0	25	7.3	380	2660
7	50	7.1	50	7.3	380	2660
8	30	3.75	14	6.3	330	2640
8	30	3.75	14	7.4	390	3120
8	30	3.75	14	8.5	450	3600
8	40	5.0	25	7.2	375	3000
10	50	5.0	25	7.0	370	3700

[1]Add 50% for coated lenses.

at night under "normal" conditions, infra-red lighting has been used. Southern et al. (1946:198) used an infra-red light apparatus to study a wild rat *(Rattus norwegicus)* population. The apparatus was similar to the "snooperscope" used by the armed forces with a carbine and called a "sniper-scope." It was used in a building and operated at a range of 9 ft. Observations were made by use of a telescope and infra-red apparatus with spot 200 watt photoflood lights used for picture taking. These allowed focusing on the subject without illuminating the entire surroundings and eliminated problems of flash bulb changes.

Seubert (1948) used a snooperscope with additional infra-red filters to reduce the red glow from the lamp, to provide greater "visual security." He used a 6-v battery power source. Limitations of the system were power-pac hum, some light, and some heat. He obtained good resolution up to 150 ft. He noted that an infra-red heat lamp gives enough light for observations to be made on the snooperscope screen. Since animals and birds have little color perception, Seubert (1948) concluded that the color of the light was not a limiting factor in the use of infra-red equipment for observations of "natural" animals, but that some other factor of artificial light, e.g. heat, was limiting. Seubert (1948) studied infra-red photography of wildlife. See Clark (1946) and the works of Hollaender (1954).

Colwell (1964, 1967) presents the prospect and current feasibility of infra-red aerial photography for thermographs for detecting fires, evaluating potential productivity of each part of a forest property, soil and vegetation moisture differences, plant disease or nutritional differences (plant vigor), plant species differences, and successional stages of plant community formation. He makes the point that "multi band spectral reconnaissance," that is, the use of many photos taken with different types of film or sensings (recorded photographically or electronically at different wave length bands of the electromagnetic spectrum), can yield more ecological information than any one type of photograph studied alone. Colwell (1968) discussed and illustrated the equipment and its potentials. This equipment includes the conventional aerial camera, the panoramic camera, the multi band camera, the optical-mechanical scanner, side-looking airborne radar, and the gamma ray spectrometer. Milton, Darling, and Watson (St. Joseph 1966) presented general uses and potentials of aerial photography in wildlife and natural resource management.

Ultra-violet light has some possible applications in wildlife research. When invisible ultra-violet light or black light irradiates certain substances they absorb the light and reflect it at longer wave length. The light is visible then as fluorescence. Ultra-violet sources are available in mercury, fluorescent, filament and glow lamps with filters (e.g. General Electric, Cleveland 12, Ohio, Pamphlet LS-141, *Black Light*). The use of fluorescent materials and ultra-violet lamps has possibilities for special tagging and banding, for feces coloration and location at night (Brown and Conoway 1961), tracking, verification of predators and scavengers on prey dusted with fluorescent powers, and many other uses. The spot bulb of a Blak-ray B-100 unit (Ultra-Violet Products, Inc., Walnut Grove Ave., San Gabriel, California) will effectively cover a 15 ft wide area at 30 ft. Insects are greatly attracted by ultra-violet light which may be a field disadvantage. The property of ultra-violet attractiveness is used in insect light traps (e.g. Gardner Manufacturing Co., Horicon, Wisc.). Such traps might be used in measuring the effectiveness of habitat management programs in producing insects for game food.

Research results can be very effectively presented using fluorescing charts, maps, and diagrams illuminated with ultra-violet light.

Ability to make observations is not entirely a function of light and magnification but also of position. Aircraft, towers (Klett 1965), or moving observation platforms are useful.

ACTIVITY RECORDING INSTRUMENTS

Besides direct visual and audial observations of animals, many simple and complex devices and techniques have been devised for getting expressions of animal presence and activity. Simple devices for collecting hair samples of animals using specific areas have been suggested by Hartesveldt (1951). Radio-location telemetry is presented in Chapter 9.

Between these extremes, sophisticated techniques have been developed. Extensive use has been made of photography in wildlife studies since 1927 (Gregory 1927). Publications of general interest are by Ledley (1964), Blaker (1965), Herzfeld (1962). Gysel and Davis (1956), Pearson (1959), Osterberg (1962), Buchner (1964), Abbott and Coombs (1964), Cowardin and Ashe (1965) and Gans (1966) have explained use of 35 mm and motion picture cameras and triggering devices with photoelectric flashes. Green and Anderson (1961) and Amos (1965) have used time-lapse and pre-set interval photography in entomological studies. These techniques have some application in caged or confined animal studies and habitat studies. Dodge and Snyder (1960), like Pearson, circumvented the variable-producing problems of return-

ing to reset such devices as described by Gysel and Davis. They used an electronic flash gun, a 16 mm movie camera and a photo-electric actuating mechanism operated by a pack of five 67 1/2-v batteries. The unit was portable and independent of an AC source. About 2000 flashes could be obtained from one set of batteries. The cost was approximately $150 with used equipment.

Loveless et al. (1963) reported on a photoelectric cell device which they developed and installed in 20 areas in Colorado. They were able to record deer activity and relate it to measures of environmental variables at the same sites. Their paper is particularly valuable because of a literature review of uses of photoelectric cells with animal studies.

Dane et al. (1959) used moving pictures to examine and describe the actions of the goldeneye. Watt (1967) described computer analyses of behavioral patterns taken from film. Novacek (1961) and Cowardin and Ashe (1965) describe equipment they used in studies of bird behavior.

Many ingenious devices have been developed for studying animal activity. Justice (1961) has reported on the use of smoked kymograph paper in studying small mammals. Papers are placed in open, empty milk cartons and put out on an area after a brief period of trapping and marking by toe-clipping. The animals can be further studied without recapture as they leave tracks on the carton-protected papers. A similar technique was used earlier (Mayer 1957) for determining activity at mammal holes.

In order to obtain an activity pattern of moles, Arlton (1936) used many box-housed alarm clocks with a weighted lever that stopped the clock when a mole passed through a tunnel. Ozoga and Gysel (1965) used a similar mechanical device for measuring deer activity along a trail. Their modified alarm clock rotated a spool of paper tape into which was punched a hole when a trip wire was activated.

Godfrey (1954) (See Chapter 11) used a Geiger counter to trace field voles carrying sub-cutaneous radioactive gold wires. Godfrey (1953) also used radioactive nest material for finding vole nests. Godfrey (1955), Gifford and Griffin (1960) and Breckenridge and Tester (1961) have also reported on use of radioactive tags for studying animal movement.

Other types of movement studies, (besides those possible through capturing, marking, or similar studies) are those of Sowls and Minnamon (1963) who used glass-beads for marking feces, Brown and Conaway (1961) who used several fluorescing dyes, and Gast (1963) who used Rhodamine-B dye.

Gast (1963) used the dye which could be detected to 1 part in 10 billion to stain feces which, once collected, fluoresce under a flurometer.

Heath (1961) developed an ingenious spool which he attached to the tail of Gila monsters. During the animals' travels they unwound behind them fused nylon thread which provided a record of their movement. Activities such as burrowing and resting along the route were determined from sign. The device was originally designed for studies of the physiological ecology of small animals.

Nesting activity has been recorded by a thermocouple and recording potentiometer (Baldwin and Kendeigh 1927, Kendeigh 1963). Body heat activated the thermocouple, and presence and departure were recorded. Klonglan et al. (1956) modified a device of Fant (1953) and used an electrical switch projecting into a pheasant nest to activate a pen marking on a rotating chart to record the movements of the nesting hen. An itograph and electro-magnetic devices were used by Kendeigh and Baldwin (1930) and Bussman (1933) to record nest activity of birds. Marples and Gurr (1943) used an electrical mercury-contact device. Gurr (1955) used a pneumatic device. He fit a copper tambour with a sheet rubber membrane snugly into the bottom of a nest. The movements of the bird depressed the membrane. A similar tambour nearby on which rested a recording pen was activated by the air pressure created by the nesting bird. The pen recorded on a clock-operated kymograph. Kendeigh (1952) reviewed the automatic nest recording instruments used in songbird study. Farner and Mewaldt (1953) obtained caged bird activity from birds activating a 2-way microswitch attached to a perch. Recordings were on kymograph paper. Kessler 1962 used Yates' (1942) method of photoelectric cells (with an infra-red filter) to record nest attentiveness to ring-necked pheasants.

Salter (1966) presented a device for recording the activity within intact game bird eggs. The laboratory device is a vibration transducer.

Animal activity in the laboratory has been extensively studied by animal behaviorists. Kavanau (1961) used ferromagnetic collars on mice to unbalance an excited inductance bridge thus triggering recording circuitry. He later described (1963) a device for continuous monitoring of the activity of a single animal using a system of electromechanical transducers and electric eyes. He had available 22 independent channels of information. Edwards' (1962) note on the actograph and Kavanan's reply shed further light on animal activity instrumentation. A series of treadles with electrical contacts has been used by Dice (1961) to study animal activity in cages and in the field by Voisey and Kalbfleisch (1962). Behney (1936) used swinging wire doors whose electrical contacts were recorded on an itograph. He studied the 24-hr activity of mice, *Peromyscus leucopus*, caged indoors. Hendrick (1963) reported on a mechanical counter for bird activity. Lawrence and Sherman (1963) reported on a resistor-capacitor traffic counter unit for recording the burrow use of the mountain beaver. The device was operated by a 30-v battery. Weiland (1964) wrote of trap activation by solenoids.

Fallon (1965) described an "eatometer," a device for recording the feeding behavior of caged animals. It was less refined than the drinkometer (Wessman 1962) in that it simply measured animal contacts with the feeding cup. Morton (1965) employed strain gauges as the principal tranducer of continuous feeding activity of caged birds. He was able to detect weight changes in supplied food of 0.05 g in 15 g with 99% accuracy.

Harned et al. (1952) presented a method for studying the movements of individual small caged animals. The animal was suspended in a cage and its movements (from respiration to jumps) were transmitted by a silk thread to a heart lever equipped with a wooden stylus. Recordings were made on smoked kymograph paper.

WEIGHT MEASUREMENT AND ESTIMATION

One of the most taken but least used observation of wildlife is total body wieght. The field notes of hundreds of workers are filled with thousands of weight observations of animals but rarely are these presented in reports or used in research conclusions. There are several reasons for this lack of use. Mammals and birds vary widely in weight with sex, age, migration, seasons, time of day, breeding condition, molt, range conditions, length of time since death, and cause of death. One meal can frequently vary the weight of a mammal over 20%. Daily fluctuations of from 3.5 to 10.8 per cent occur in birds' weights (Nice 1938). With such great variances within relatively small numbers of animals examined at any one time, conclusions based on total body weights must be general and cautiously made.

Nevertheless, weights, particularly live weight, are a major concern of biologists, ecologists, and game managers. They are interesting to sportsmen, used by those studying bioenergetics and production, and used in appraising population vigor through age-weight correlation. Facilities for weighing large animals in the field are often lacking (Smith and Ledger 1965). Murie (1928) described weighing the sections of butchered moose and elk to determine total weight. With this approach, loss of body fluids creates an error usually well within the significant figures needed or obtainable. Doutt (1940) described the ingenious use of a tripod and gallon container of water (about 8 lb.) as counter-weights on a lever arm to measure big game weight. He employed only a 25 lb. capacity spring balance.

Craighead et al. (1960) described weighing bear in a culvert trap by putting the trap on a trailer, then rolling trap, bear, and trailer onto portable scales. The weight of the bear was gained by subtraction.

Beam scales, approximate cost $10, have a capacity of 400 lb. and are more accurate than large capacity spring scales. They weigh only several pounds and can be lifted with the animal to be weighed with a sportsman's nylon rope hoist.

Support for scales in treeless or open areas may be difficult to find. Talbot and Talbot (1962) developed a truck-mounted hand-winch for their work with big game. Greer and Howe (1964) used a 500 lb. Chatillion spring scale suspended from the 15-ft boom of a hoisting truck for weighing elk carcasses. Smith and Ledger (1965) described a 3-inch iron-pipe tripod for suspending spring balances for weighing whole large African animals. They suspended five spring balances each with a 1200 lb. capacity across a bar suspended from a chain-hoist attached to the apex of the tripod. They preferred a chain hoist to a block and tackle because it gave greater control.

Talbot and Talbot (1962) and Pan et al. (1965) devised supports or sling harnesses useful for suspending dead animals or weighing experimental animals (pigs) alive.

Greer (1965) developed for a metabolism cage an attachment useful for easily weighing a small pugnacious animal, a grison, *Galictis cuja.* Geese (Beer and Boyd 1962) can be placed in a sack and weighed suspended from a spring balance. Sherwood (1965) presented a photo of an efficient goose weighing station and tripod.

Tension spring scales with direct reading gauge or geared, circular gauge are available from 20 g to 1200 lbs. The smaller scales have accuracies to the nearest 1/2 ounce.

Single, double, and triple balances have increasingly greater weighing capabilities without accessory weights. They cost approximately $25 and vary widely in make and construction. Their capacities range from a single-beam 10 g to 0.1 g, to a triple-beam 610 g to 0.1 g. With additional weights their capacities are 2600 g. A triple-beam is most satisfactory for weighing live small mammals but is bulky, needs a carrier for field use, and must be level for accurate readings. Movements of animals add to inaccuracies.

Bookhout and Harger (1964) recommend the use of a modestly priced power and bullet scale that reads up to 21.06 g. Its units are grains but easily converted (grams = grains x 0.0648).

Analytical balances are well known and, depending on quality, have measurement capabilities of from 200 to 0.05 mg. Semi-micro balances have capacities from 100 to 0.005 mg. Prices range from $100 to $1000 depending on quality and characteristics. More recently developed are electrical analytical balances that cost approximately $800 to $1700. Although four to eight times more expensive than an "adequate," general-purpose analytical balance, they allow accurate weights to be very rapidly obtained to 0.005 mg. Where many small, accurate weights must be obtained, these balances are economical.

Although the weights of body organs do not show the extreme variability of total body weight, their collection, just as the collection of total body weight, must be guided by the principle: seek a measuring instrument that will allow observations within one's ability to express and analyze them in mathematically significant figures.

Weights of large animals are difficult to take no matter what the conditions or techniques. Halloran (1961) presented impressive measurements of over 200 bison made under near-slaughterhouse conditions. Rapid field use estimation equations are needed. Because of the great variability in weights previously discussed, efforts to convert hog-dressed weights to live weights have been largely unsuccessful.

Three terms often used are *live-* or *whole-weight,* with self-evident meaning; *field-dressed* weight, a gross measurement meaning the weight of an animal with vicera removed but with heart and liver (and often lungs) included in the weight; *hog-dressed* weight is weight of animals with all organs removed but with hide, feet, and head intact i.e. whole weight minus all vicera and blood; then there is *skinned-weight,* which is hog dressed weight minus the hide only, and *skinned-dressed weight,* self evident.

Blood and Lovaas (1966) reported that hog-dressed weights of Rocky Mountain elk was 67% of live weight and that Manitoba elk on the average weighed 75% of live weight but ranged from 67 to 81%. Jonkel (1964) reported that black bear hog-dressed weight was 84% of live weight and varied from 79 to 88%.

Table 7.2. Single leg-weight/ live weight regression equations, where $y = \bar{y} + b\,(x - \bar{x})$ and y = live weight in kilos and x = leg weight in kilos (adapted from Smith and Ledger 1965:507)

Species	Regression Equation	
	Hind leg/live weight	Fore leg/live weight
Uganda kob	y = 67.2 + 10.9(x - 7.8)	y = 67.2 + 26.4(x - 2.6)
Thompson's gazelle	y = 18.7 + 10.4(x - 2.1)	y = 18.7 + 21.8(x - 0.8)
Waterbuck	y = 163.8 + 10.7(x - 18.2)	y = 163.8 + 21.4(x - 7.0)
Wildebeest	y = 149.8 + 12.9(x - 13.5)	y = 149.8 + 28.4(x - 7.1)
Wart hog	y = 60.0 + 13.3(x - 5.0)	y = 60.0 + 17.4(x - 1.8)
Hippopotamus	y = 1109.2 + 16.0(x - 71.0)	y = 1109.2 + 3.1(x - 38.8)
Oryx	y = 169.1 + 9.4(x - 17.1)	y = 169.1 + 16.6(x - 8.1)
Lesser kudu	y = 92.1 + 10.0(x - 10.2)	y = 92.1 + 24.8(x - 4.2)
Brahma steers	y = 403.1 + 11.1(x - 35.3)	y = 403.1 + 27.0(x - 14.9)
Brahma cows and heifers	y = 312.0 + 9.9(x - 26.5)	y = 312.0 + 25.7(x - 10.7)
Brahma bulls	y = 375.0 + 11.1(x - 32.6)	y = 375.0 + 22.7(x - 14.2)

Patrick (1961) developed two regression equations relating skinned weight of black bear to total weight, y = 1.86 + 0.86x, (where x is total weight) and skinned dressed weight to total weight, y = 2.10 + 0.699x. Correlation was strong and no differences were noticeable in the weight relationship between the sexes.

Hamerstrom and Cambus (1950) also found no significant difference between equations from animals of different sex or age. With their equations, they concluded that one could predict live weight within plus or minus 5 lb. from hog dressed weight of Michigan white-tailed deer two-thirds of the time. However, one might miss the true figure as much as 18 pounds and possibly even more. The average for a large series, such as at a checking station, could be calculated from the equation. Their equation for 1941-42 (males and females) was x = 2.62 + 1.251y (where x = live weight and y = hog-dressed weight), and for 1942-43, x = 8.55 + 1.265y. The equation for skinned dressed weight, y_1, was $y_1 = -1.48 + 0.538x$.

Other correlations have also been found useful. Smith and Ledger (1965) found that the weight of a single leg was closely correlated to live weight. Prediction is limited by the amount of body fat, but the method has use for large and small animals that are evicerated in the field, then brought to a place where they can be weighed. Their regression equations are shown in Table 7.2.

Bandy et al. (1956), Talbot and McCullock (1965), McCullock and Talbot (1965), and McEwan and Wood (1966) used heart girth as a reliable predictor of live weight. Heart girth is the circumference of the chest immediately behind the axilla, usually measured with a flexible steel tape. Talbot and McCullock (1965) found their equations (Table 7.3) independent of stomach content and concluded that heart girth may provide as close an estimate of the true mean live weight as the single spot weighing of animals at the time of collection.

Bandy et al. (1956) found the live weight (w) of Columbian black-tailed deer as related to heart girth (HG) was as follows

$$W = 0.0037HG^{2.64}$$

McEwan and Wood (1966) found a similar equation for caribou of

$$W = 0.0016HG^{2.51}$$

Table 7.3. Equations of the relation of live weight (w) to heart girth (HG) from Talbot and McCulloch (1965)

	W = wt. in lbs., heart girth in meters correct to 5 mm.
Uganda kob	W = 468 x HG - 276
Thompson's gazelle	W = 175 x HG - 62
Wildebeest	W = 646 x HG - 519
Oryx	W = 495 x HG - 318
Grant's gazelle	W = 319 x HG - 156
Hyena	W = 274 x HG - 117
Impala	W = 309 x HG - 149
Topi and hartebeest	W = 347 x HG - 132
Zebra	W = 645 x HG - 325

CHAPTER EIGHT

USING COMPUTERS IN WILDLIFE MANAGEMENT[1]

LOWELL ADAMS, ScD

Associate Research Ecologist
The George Williams Hooper Foundation
The University of California Medical Center
San Francisco, California

Electronic computers and their uses touch the daily lives of nearly everyone in America. Bills, advertisements, applications, and many other communications come to us on the now-familiar cropped-corner card. Almost everyone knows, at least vaguely, that computers do mathematical computations, but relatively few know that computers also are important tools for biological research in a way that transcends their use in solving mathematical equations. This phase of computer technology spans only the past 10 years of the computer's 25-year history.

Computers are useful to ecologists because they can handle large amounts of complex relationships rapidly. Life is a large number of complex relationships, whether examined at the level of the cell, the organism, the population, or the community. Before computers became available, the complexities of life could not be studied except by simple, isolated pieces. The realization was always that the pieces should not be studied alone but with all their many working relation-

ships to each other as well. Now biology is beginning a period of rapidly-growing ability to deal with complex living processes. This ability is made possible by computers. The wildlife manager and researcher needs to know how to obtain the use of a computer and how to use it.

The purpose of this chapter is to describe the kinds of computers available, to introduce methods of using them, and to illustrate some of the uses wildlifers are making of them. Reading this chapter will not make anyone an accomplished user of computers, for that comes only with actual practice, but it will provide an introduction.

KINDS OF COMPUTERS

There are two main kinds of computers—analog and digital. Other kinds are combinations of these (hybrid computers), and special purpose computers. Analog computers work by a set of electronic components (resistors, capacitors, transistors, amplifiers, etc.) which act upon a voltage. The voltage is the analog of the biological quantity involved, e.g. the number of animals in

[1]This work was partly supported by Research Grant GM11993 from the National Institute of General Medicine.

a population. The actions by the electronic components are analogs of biological effects, e.g. births and deaths. Births are represented by voltage increases (amplifiers), deaths by voltage decreases (resistors). The solution is displayed as a curve of the changing voltage, over time as the independent variable, drawn by a strip-chart, an x-y recorder, or by an oscilloscope. The voltage curve is converted to a population curve simply by labeling the coordinates "population" instead of "voltage" with proper scales to represent animal numbers instead of voltage. This conversion is much like a slide-rule in which the distance along a rule can be added to, subtracted from, divided, or multiplied by a number. Distance along the rule is the analog of the quantity being manipulated, and corresponds to voltage in an electrical conductor.

A wildlifer does not have to be an electronics engineer to operate an analog computer, any more than he needs to be one to use a radio or television set. He does have to know mathematics, because the machine can perform only mathematical operations.

The digital computer works with digits (numbers), not voltages. To operate the machine, numbers are put in together with instructions about what to do with them, and numbers are produced printed in tables on paper, punched on cards or paper tape, or stored on magnetic tape.

How the digital computer manages to push numbers around to achieve the mathematical computation is a problem best left to the computer engineer with his circuits, gates, pulses, registers, etc. (Evans 1966). The user needs to know only how to "talk to" the machine. This skill will be discussed later.

The hybrid computer is a digital computer, an analog computer, and interface equipment to transfer information and controls between the two. The use of such a tool requires intimate and sophisticated knowledge of computer technology. Therefore any detailed description of hybrid computers is out of order here. For an excellent review of the subject, see Siler (1:86, in: Stacy and Waxman 1965). The main point is that analog and digital computers each have certain strong points and weaknesses, and the hybrid assembly provides for use of the best features of both.

Special-purpose computers are used in the automation of manufacturing processes, aiming guns, landing aircraft on carriers—wherever logical decisions and consequent adjustments are required in the course of an operation. These special machines are also beyond the scope of

this review, since wildlife biologists will rarely use them.

COMPARISON OF ANALOG AND DIGITAL COMPUTERS

Because of administrative, budgetary and other constraints the question of comparison of computers may be useless. Many working biologists are "stuck" with the type and size computer that is available. It is important, nevertheless, that lack of awareness of computers, their types, capabilities, and local availability not be an impediment to the wildlifer.

The choice of computer usually lies between the analog and the digital types. Which should be used? It is impossible to say because the answer depends on what use is to be made of the computer and what kind is available. However, the prices and the good and bad points of each type can be compared. The technology of computer hardware (machinery) is developing rapidly and some things written here will be outdated by the time they are published. As Lederberg (1965) has said, "Any writing on computers faces the hazard of instant obsolescence."

Analog computers cost less than digital ones. It may be financially feasible to have an analog computer in the laboratory or office of the wildlifer for as little as $2500. For only $200 an analog computer can be bought in kit form. The assembled equipment is the absolute minimum in cost and usefulness. The lowest-priced digital computer costs about $10,000. In both classes, instruments having these costs are limited in capacity and efficiency. More commonly the reader may think of large computers costing hundreds of thousands of dollars. These are usually found in industrial, university, and governmental computer centers where they are available to scientists, engineers, management personnel and for private lease. Purchasing or renting any computer or the establishment of a computer center must be based on intensive consideration of the use to be made of the facility in relation to its capabilities.

In some ways analog computers can be used more flexibly than digital ones. For example, certain parameters of a model can be changed while the computer is in operation to see what effect the change has on the model. To illustrate, in a study of the effects of different birth rates on the size of a population of animals, it is possible to use any birth rate of interest to set up the model on the analog computer and determine the resulting population size. Then by simply turning the dial of a variable resistor, the birth rate can be varied and the population levels resulting from a large array of comparative birth rates immediately found. Similarly, death rates and other parameters can be varied at will, either independently or in conjunction with each other. This facility for "playing with the model" by twirling dials and watching effects on the recorder chart has considerable heuristic value for better comprehension of the parameters' effects. The digital computer can also be used to test various hypothetical parameters, but this is done either by manually re-running the program with the test parameters as new input or by programming a set of inputs to be used automatically in sequential cyclic runs of the program. This process takes more time (possibly including much waiting time if you are awaiting your turn between runs at a computer center). Also, the operation does not have the illuminating effect on the wildlifer obtained by the manipulation of the dials of the analog computer and the direct cause-effect observation.

Another flexibility of the analog computer is its ability to accept electronic-signal data directly from the experiment in progress and to process the data while the experiment is in progress. Such "on line" or immediate analysis might be useful, for example, in computing heart rate during the administration of cardiac drugs to find out whether to inject more drug, or less, or to drop back to some intermediate level which needs to be filled in for complete results. Similar on-line analysis is also possible with digital computers. Analog data can be handled only with considerable difficulty involving intermediate steps to convert to digital form. The analog computer, on the other hand, handles both analog (e.g. electro-encephalogram) and digital data.

Usually, the analog is faster than the digital computer. Its superior computing rate results from the fact that it does not have to find numbers and instructions in its memory block and restore results to memory for every computational step as the digital computer does.

For the foregoing the analog computer would seem superior to the digital type. This is not true. The analog computer is less accurate. It can present results with only approximate precision and accuracy, just as one can estimate results on a slide rule only to a few significant figures. This limitation is due in part to the fact

that electronic components are subject to drift with temperature and other environmental changes. The digital computer is designed to present correct results in spite of environmental changes and accomplishes this by using the all-or-one principle of circuitry. For example, a switch is either open or closed in a digital computer, while in an analog computer the capacitor may be charged to a given level that can be only relatively exact, depending on the momentary physical condition of that capacitor.

Another disadvantage of the analog computer is that it accepts only mathematical models based on linear differential equations. In engineering, where such models are frequently used, the analog computer is especially valuable. The computer is valuable, to a lesser degree, in other fields of science. But relationships are non-linear in many biological models and often must be handled by numerical means, rather than by formal calculus.

In general the digital computer is used much more extensively than the analog computer because it has proved superior for most uses. But this does not mean that the use of the analog computer is declining. On the contrary, it is being used more and more as computer-use becomes more common. Its ultimate fate is the subject of much debate among computer users, but apparently there will always be a place for it, though probably subordinate.

Greater attention will be paid in the remainder of the chapter to the digital computer.

HOW TO WORK WITH COMPUTERS

This section will describe how to decide whether you need a computer, how to obtain the use of a computer, and how to use it.

When is a computer needed? Of course, no clear-cut answer is possible because the need depends upon the nature of the job plus the availability (location, cost, and time) of a computer. However, some guidelines are available.

The decision to use a computer hinges on the amount and repetitiousness of computing to be done. You may have a large computing job to do once or a relatively simple computation to be repeated often with new data.

What determines if small jobs that are to be done only once (or only a few times) should be done by a computer? The key to this decision is the amount of time required to do the mathematics on a hand calculator versus the time required to program it, plus the cost of computer time. The choice of strategy can be stated thus:

If: $\dfrac{tc}{TC} > 1$, use the computer

$\dfrac{tc}{TC} < 1$, do it by hand or desk calculator

Here t = time required to compute by hand.
 c = salary of person doing the computing.
 T = time required to program the computer.
 C = salary of programmer + cost of computer-time.

Many modifying factors could be included in the above inequalities. Is there already a considerable investment in computer and programmer facilities whose time would be idle if not used for this job? Is the time, t, the biologist's time which might be better used in other aspects of the project? Which method will meet the deadline? And very importantly, are the chances and consequences of errors great when computations are done by hand? If so, perhaps C, the programmer and computer cost, should be discounted to achieve accuracy of results.

Some sample applications of the above principles: Annually, data are collected on the furbearer harvest in a state, as a basis for management decisions. This data includes the species of fur-bearers, number of trappers, sales prices, etc., by management districts. In any one year it costs less to work up the data by hand than by computer, but the same analysis procedure is used every year. In about 3 years the programming time pro-rated over the 3 years reduces to the break-even point where it is equally expensive to do the job by hand or by computer. From the third year on, the computer is the cheaper way. Therefore the computer should be chosen in the beginning. Computers might be used in annual analyses of creel censuses, game-range forage surveys, hunter questionnaire analyses, and similarly repetitious tasks. Once set up for such computer work, organizations may find it profitable to use the facilities for such distantly-related tasks as making pay-rolls, bookkeeping, equipment inventory, procurement, and the like.

Another situation for deciding on computer use may be a complex analysis of a multi-factorial experiment involving, for example, the effects of weather, fertilizers, degree of use, and seasons on forage production on winter deer range. This is a one-time study, but involves a large set of computations. Other factors permitting, the wildlifer may elect to program the job for a computer rather than use the desk calculator, to save time or to avoid computational errors, or both.

In essence, then, the job is a candidate for the computer if it is to be accomplished repeatedly in the same way or if it is highly complex. Choice of computing method is an administrative decision based largely on relative costs, the time available for the computations, and accuracy of computer versus hand computation.

GAINING ACCESS TO COMPUTERS

Having decided to use the computer, how do you gain access to one?

Computer availability is undergoing rapid change at the present time. A brief review of computer history will place the present trends in perspective. The early, "first generation" computers were developed and built during World War II. These (ENIAC, Harvard's Automatic Sequence-Controlled Calculator, MIT's Differential Analyzer, Bell Laboratory's general purpose relay calculators, and others) demonstrated the feasibility of performing complex calculations automatically (Berkeley 1949). In the following 20 years many others were built and used, each one an improvement over the preceding. Improvement was primarily aimed at making the computers more available to more people. Computers have continued to be too expensive for most institutions to own outright. So a pattern evolved for sharing computer centers by constellations of associated laboratories and research institutions. This arrangement has the disadvantage that the scientist does not have the computer immediately at hand. Often he must take or send data and programs to centers a few blocks or a few miles away. There the job must await its turn to be processed, then be picked up by courier and returned to the researcher.

Computer designers are approaching the solution to this problem of computer accessibility in two ways. The computer can be placed at the researcher's elbow either by making a small computer that will sit by his desk in its entirety, or by placing there a control console connected to a computer center. Both these approaches are producing results. The "miniaturized" desk-top computer became feasible with the advent of transistors, and with integrated circuitry, a technology developed in the last 5 years and growing rapidly. Micro-miniaturized electronic components have reduced the packaging of electronic machines from many cubic inches into only one or two cubic *millimeters* of space! As the component size shrinks, so does the computer size, and we can expect a large room full of computers to be condensed into a desk-top box. This miniaturization is currently happening, but not so rapidly as to cancel the need for the alternative—consoles remote from computer centers.

Computers are made of four different blocks of components: An input-output block, a memory block, an arithmetic and logic block, and a control block (Maley and Skiko 1964:24). Although very expensive to do so, the input-output block and part of the control block can be located remotely from the rest of the computer, so long as they are connected by a wire circuit (or even by radio communication). This means that input-output-control consoles can be placed at strategic locations in laboratories or offices for immediate access to the wildlifers. It would be as if each group of wildlifers had its own large computer, eliminating courier time between project and computer center. Accompanying this convenience is a technological development called time-sharing which reduces waiting time at the various remote consoles. Not all blocks of the computer work at the same speed. The input-output block, for example, takes much more time than the other units. As a result the arithmetic and logic block, for example, may stand idle awaiting completion of the input or output process. So computer designers have inserted a storage compartment in the data channels between the remote consoles and the rest of the machine. Now inputs are entered in these storage compartments and are all ready to be dumped quickly into the main memory block at the instant the arithmetic and logic block complete the preceding job. The resulting speed-up is so great that the respective users are serviced almost as quickly as if each one were the sole user.

These facts of computer life simplify use but complicate the problem of deciding what computer facility to use. Where formerly the small-project researcher had to find a computer center to handle his computations or do them on a desk calculator, now he must decide whether to use an analog or digital desk-top computer, a remote control console, or the services or an analog or digital computer center. And, with the rapidity of technological developments a right choice today may be second best tomorrow. However, the frequency of such difficult decisions in today's rapidly changing technology is such that wildlife managers are becoming accustomed to them, primarily by accepting uncertainty as a built-in aspect of living.

USE OF COMPUTERS

Assuming a decision has been reached about the computer facility to use, how do you go about it? The answer is computer programming. The program, or set of instructions, activates or "tells" the computer what data is available and how it is to be analyzed. Learning to program a computer is like learning to knit or to weave cloth, to find a book in a library, or other similar tasks requiring a knowledge of a process and how to proceed with it. Learning to program is an intriguing experience and, with present simplifications, is not a great task if one has a competent instructor.

The task of programming at first looks formidable. The wildlifer can't visualize how the machine works and cannot see how it is possible to learn to operate it unless he knows how it works. The same fears apply to learning to drive an automobile or operate any complex machine. The use of a computer involves a set of knowledge and skills quite distinct from the knowledge and skills required to know how a computer works and how to keep it operative. Just as mechanics keep automobiles in running condition, so electronic technicians keep computers in working order. Wildlifers are usually concerned with using the computer, not with its workings.

Should the researcher know how to program, or should he hire a programmer? If the project can afford a programmer, the researcher need not do his own programming. Nevertheless, the researcher should know how to program for two reasons. First, a knowledge of programming technique aids in communicating with a programmer; and, second, programming can be a way of thinking scientifically, once it is learned. Just as statistical techniques can teach one to "think statistically," so programming teaches him to "think computer wise." In some areas of thought (e.g. simulation, neural anatomy) this "computer thinking" is a valuable mental tool.

Many texts purport to teach how to program. All those studied so far by the author have proved confusing. (Some not seen may be otherwise.) It is strongly recommended that beginners take a course in programming from an instructor doing actual programming and using the computer in the course. "Learning by doing" applies particularly to programming. Fortunately, computer manufacturers, computer centers, and most universities now present courses in programming.

Computer programming is step 2 in a sequence of procedures involved in computer use. Step 1 is the formulation of the problem and step 3 is the operation of the computer. Fig. 8.1 illustrates the entire system which will be discussed.

Here, the first step is skipped, assuming that the problem is already organized in mathematical form. Frequently, however, there is back-and-forth interplay between steps 1 and 2 because the investigator may not be sure he has the right mathematical formulation until he has programmed and run it on the computer. Then revision may be necessary.

Programming is the process of stating the solution to a problem or the steps of a process in a form the computer will accept. Usually the programmer first constructs a flow-chart. The flow-chart is a device for organizing the se-

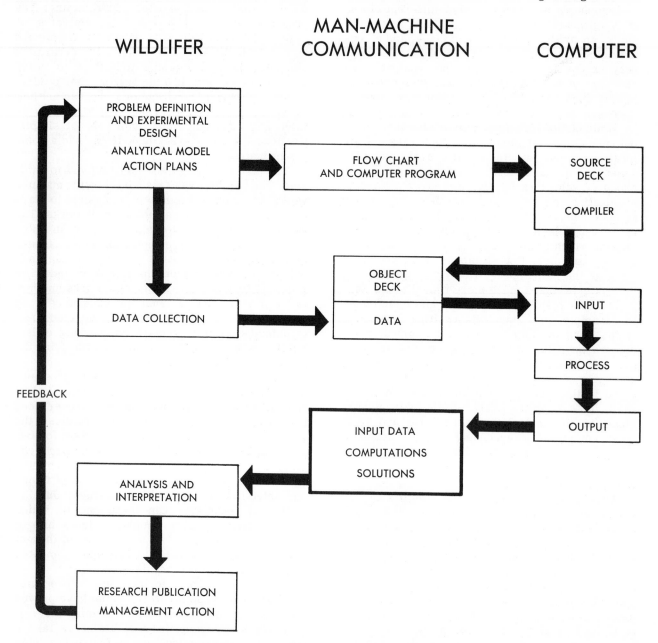

Fig. 8.1. Generalized flow-chart diagram of the computer-wildlife management research system.

quence of computational operations in a pattern acceptable to the computer. A simple example best illustrates the use of the flow-chart.

Suppose the problem is to compute the locations of points on a graph for the mathematical formulation,

$$Y = BX.^2$$

The flow-chart might look like this:

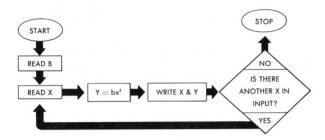

This very simple program has only one branch and one loop. The branch, or two-paths that go to "Yes" or "No," is the major decision-making capability of the computer. The loop is the circle of procedures that goes from READ to WRITE, to the branch, to READ, to . . . etc. until the particular set of instructions is complete. When the program becomes more complicated with many branchings and loops (including loops within loops), the need for the flow-chart becomes more apparent.

Next the flow-chart is converted into computer program language. Each block (circle, rectangle, oval, etc.) of the chart is considered in sequence and translated into programming language. In the early years of the automatic computers, the programmer wrote his instructions in "machine language." That is, he worked with the computer's memory in mind, placing specific "bits" and "words" in selected locations in memory whose "addresses" were recorded. When an arithmetical procedure was to occur, the computer called forth the "words" by their "addresses." This method of programming placed great responsibility on the programmer to keep track of the information in the various localities in memory.

Computer technologists soon overcame much of this burden by programming the computer itself to keep track of the location of information in memory and to find correct "words" as needed. With this development, it was also possible to let the machine translate instructions from more nearly human to machine language. Programming

is now done as a two-step process. First the programmer writes a "source program" which is fed into the machine along with a "compiler program." The compiler program causes the machine to translate from the programmer language to an "object program," to produce a translation of the "source program" into machine-language. The "object program" is then fed back into the computer, along with the data to be processed. Although this has introduced the additional step of translation by a "compiler program," it has reduced programming time and made programming methods easier to learn.

Many different programming languages, together with their compiler programs, have been developed. Some are for general purpose computation (FORTRAN, ALGOL, PL-1, etc.), others for special purposes (LISP, SIMSCRIPT, etc.). A language is selected with the aid of a computer operator based on the operations to be performed, abilities of the programmer available, compiler programs, and other considerations. The following program (in FORTRAN) for the simple computation, $Y = bX^2$, illustrates the use of programming language:

	PRØGRAM EXAMPLE	(1)
	READ 1, B	(2)
1	FØRMAT (F 10.2)	(3)
2	READ 3, X, IEND	(4)
3	FØRMAT (F 10.2, I5)	(5)
	Y = B*X**2	(6)
	PRINT 4, X, Y	(7)
4	FØRMAT (F 10.2, 10X, F 12.4)	(8)
	IF (IEND) 2, 2, 5	(9)
5	CØNTINUE	(10)
	END	(11)
	END	(12)
	0.5	(13)
	0.2	(14)
	0.5	(15)
	1.0	(16)
	2.0	(17)
	2.5	(18)
	3.0	(19)

The index numbers in parentheses at the right are to explain the purpose and effect of each statement. (These index numbers are not part of the program as actually used.)

(1) Name of the program for identification and billing.

(2) Causes the machine to read the constant B on a data card and put it in memory according to format instruction No. *1* (next card, card (3)).

(3) Format instructions describing the positions of the digits and decimal point on the input card. The F is a code that causes the machine to accept B in the "floating point" form commonly used in many scientific applications. The number is expressed, in the computer, as some number multiplied by a power of 10, e.g. 150 in floating point is 1.5×10^2. In computers this is an efficient form to use. The 10.2, in the format statement (3), indicates that B (13) is allowed enough space to be a 10-digit number in which the decimal point is 2 places to the left of the last digit.

(4) The index number, 2, is used to find this instruction when the machine comes back to it in (9). This instruction causes the machine to *read* the next data card according to format *3*. This is the first X-value. It also causes a *read* of the space on the card designated *IEND* whose location is also designated in (5). This is the indicator of the end of the run as will be explained under (9).

(5) Format for reading and storing X and IEND. It also causes a *read* of the next five columns to see whether anything (IEND) is punched there (see (9) below).

(6) Instruction for the actual computation (all other instructions before and after this one are "housekeeping" instructions for getting the data into and out of the computer). Instructions: "Find the value previously stored ((4) and (5)) at the address for X, square it (**2), find the stored value of B, multiply B times X-squared. Store the result in memory at the address for Y.

(7) Instruction to *print* X and Y according to format 4.

(8) Instruction to print X in the first column on the print-out page. This column is spaced for *10* digits, 8 to the left of the decimal place and *two* to the right. Next, skip 10 spaces (*10X*), then print Y in a column within a space with *12* places, 8 to the left and *4* to the right of the decimal point. Thus the X's and Y's are printed in two straight columns as follows:

‡‡FORX 4

00404 CORES USED
39999 NEXT COMMON
END OF COMPILATION
EXECUTION

.20	.0200
.50	.1250
1.00	.5000
2.00	2.0000
2.50	3.1250
3.00	4.5000

The hand-plotted results are shown in Fig. 8.2. Some computers have automatic plotters or cathode-ray tube displays for such data.

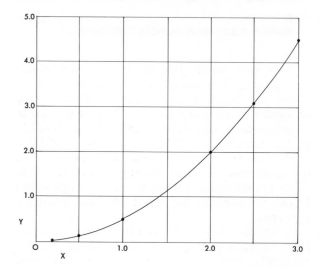

Fig. 8.2. A plot of X and Y as generated by the computer are shown. These are hand-plotted, but can be generated on an oscilloscope, or automatically plotted on paper.

(9) Instruction to return to instruction *2* if the space for *IEND* on the last data card was unpunched, i.e., was less than, or equal to, zero. If a number greater than zero is punched in the *IEND* space, go to instruction *5*. In punching the X data cards the IEND space was left unpunched (= zero or less than zero) until the last X card. This card was punched with a "one" in the IEND space, thus signalling the end of the run.

(10) Instruction merely to send the process on to the next instruction. In some FORTRAN languages the machine cannot go from an IF in-

struction to an END instruction, so here is introduced a *CØNTINUE*.

(11) & (12) *END* instructions. Two are needed for some FORTRAN compilers because one indicates the end of the preceding sub-program (which may occur in the middle of a continuing program), and the other indicates the end of the entire program.

(13) The value, 0.5, was assigned to B. This coefficient could have been assigned an array of different values by using a so-called DO statement, which would cause the machine to repeat the computations for each of the sequential values of B.

(14) The remaining (14)-(19) cards are data specifying the values of X.

Now the program is ready for use. The first step to put it into action is to convert the typed or hand-printed page(s) into a form the computer can accept. This form is usually a set of cards, or a punched paper tape. It can then be transferred to magnetic tape. The cards are punched on a key-punch machine, usually one line of program per card. The key-punch machine has a key-board much like that of a typewriter and is operated the same way. Pressing a key causes a hole or holes to be punched in the column of the card in position under the punch-head and also activates the spacer, bringing the next column into position. The operator does not need to know in what position(s) in a column the hole(s) need to be to designate the number; the machine takes care of that. The machine can also type the punched letter or number at the top of the column, so the entries in the card are typed across the top.

Often in wildlife work data can be placed on mark-sensing cards and then converted directly to punched cards by a special machine. See chapter 6 and 7 for additional discussions of ways of efficient conversion of data to machine-useable form. Such conversion is a major problem that should be solved early in research planning.

The punched cards constitute a "source deck." This deck is placed in the computer hopper which processes one card at a time. First the machine translates the source-deck instructions into machine instructions using a "compiler," which is a set of instructions permanently available to the computer on magnetic tape, discs, or punched cards. (Programs and compilers for different program languages are called "software" in contrast to "hardware"—the computers key-punches, sorters, etc.) The translated machine-language program, the object deck, may be punched on

cards or stored in magnetic-tape memory. In the larger modern computers the operator need not be concerned with the compiler and object decks; the computer automatically handles all processes from input to output. The computer and its print-out device return the data-object deck and a printed copy of the results arranged in whatever form the program prescribed.

Many supplementary details are omitted here in presenting the general procedures. For example, the computer often encounters instructions that it cannot execute because they are improperly written, or for other reasons. The computer may then write a message to the operator explaining the error, and either proceed with the rest of the compilation or stop. It is then up to the programmer to correct programming mistakes and resubmit the program. This is called "de-bugging" the program, sometimes a tedious and exasperating task. Methods of de-bugging and the many other details not covered here must be learned from instructors and references. O'Neal's book (1964) is an excellent instructional reference on data processing with automatic digital computers. It covers the entire process from input to output, including programming (machine language). Various manuals exist for programming techniques using the many programming languages. Novice programmers should use these in conjunction with a competent instructor and a computer available for practice while learning.

Data processing by analog computer is strikingly different from that by digital computer. Instead of the human-language approach, the problem is stated in mathematical form. Then using plug-in connecting wires, the various components of the computer are wired together in proper configuration to solve the problem. In planning the program a diagram slightly resembling a flow-chart is used with conventional symbols representing components (summing amplifier, potentiometer, etc.). Lines connecting the components represent the connecting wires.

The details of data processing by analog computer are presented in elementary, introductory form by Strong and Hannauer (1962) and by Olson (1963).

COMPUTER USE IN WILDLIFE RESEARCH AND MANAGEMENT

Probably most departments of wildlife of state or provincial and federal governments use computers in one way or another, at least for payroll and personnel processing. There has been no survey to determine how wildlife researchers and managers are using computers.

Actually, the use of computers by wildlife biologists is extremely limited, despite a rapid increase of computer use by society at large. The greatest use of the computer has been for statistical analyses and data processing. Apparently wildlife biologists are not "rising with the tide." (One reason why this presentation has been addressed to the beginner is that most wildlife biologists seem strangers to the computer.) In the following review of projects using computers only those examples are included that have come to the author's attention from a survey of the literature and personal contacts.

Mr. O. G. Tracewitz, Manager of Woodlands, International Paper Company has kindly sent the author unpublished information about their Wildlife Survey. The computer was used essentially as a management tool in handling extensive data on wildlife resources of the Company's lands in ten southern states. This use is applied research because the information is used in evaluating the effects of land-use practices on the wildlife resource. It is primarily a running inventory of forest and wildlife resources for use in making management decisions.

First an inventory was made of the resources by management tracts. This covered information on the geographical, physical, biological, and cultural conditions, and on wildlife populations and their use for each tract. All this information was suitably coded and entered on punch cards. An IBM 1620 computer was used to give each tract a score, based on descriptions fed into the machine on three cards per tract. The score was an index of the tract's potential desirability for game management. Finally, the computer printed out all pertinent information for each tract, listed in order of its potentiality score, plus summaries for various aggregations of tracts. Future resurveys compared with the records on hand will show the effects on the wildlife of the new game and forest management methods applied.

Dean and Galloway (1965) developed programs on the IBM 1620 computer to simulate big game populations. Most wildlife students have attempted at some time or other to compute with pencil and paper the generation-to-generation changes in the sex, age and numbers of animals in a wildlife population. The job becomes tedious after a few generations. With the Dean and Galloway program various rates of reproduction and death, sex ratios, etc., can be analyzed over any desired number of generations in minutes or less of machine time. Also a parameter (e.g. the death rate as affected by postulated changes in hunter pressure) can be changed and re-run to obtain effects on the population under the new conditions. It is in this type of inquiry that computers have been of great value in many fields, for example, in the use of simulated manufacturing processes to test alternative methods and systems. The computer often replaces a more expensive pilot plant. Similarly biologists can test the effects of alternative game management strategies without waiting for new laws on seasons and bag limits to do so in actual practice.

The Dean and Galloway type of computer program is also valuable in the education of wildlife biologists. It gives them practice in the use of computers and the "feel" of population dynamics as they manipulate parameters from one computer run to the next.

Brotzman and Giles (1966) have written a program for the IBM 7090 computer to compute populations using capture-recapture data. The computations are in three forms according to methods developed by Schnabel, by Schumacher and Eschmeyer, and by Petersen and Lincoln. The program, which prints out the population estimates, variances and standard errors for each method, is available from the junior author. As computer use becomes more general, we can expect to find "standard" programs such as this developed by wildlife researchers and managers and made available to members of the profession.

Physiologists are the prime users of computers in biology. The organism as a chemical-physical system naturally lends itself to the computer technology that has developed to meet the needs of systems of manufacturing, business, and the physical sciences. The wildlife biologist who develops his computer skills should find great help from applications in biomedical science: computer simulations of the blood and respiratory systems, neuro-physiology (where physiology and computer technology sometimes blend into one), and in general, the process-balancing, feed-back mechanisms of the organism (Stacy and Waxman 1965). Computers are also used in biomedicine in the mathematical analysis of body potentials (electromyograms, electrocardiograms, electroencephalograms).

Of still greater interest to wildlife biologists are recent developments in dynamic ecology. Computers are unshackling community ecologists, who have been chained to the enormous complexities of ecological systems. Although the community has long been recognized as an "organism"—a functioning system whose interacting parts are kept in concert by internal stabilizing forces—heretofore it has been possible only to describe the parts and some of their isolated interactions. The term "eco-system" was as much an expression of frustration as of enlightenment until the recent beginnings of eco-systems analysis began to emerge. Its beginnings and its development can be traced in the publications of Holling, Odum, Olson, Slobodkin, Van Dyne, Watts, and others listed in the Selected Bibliography and Literature Cited. Van Dyne (1966) presented an excellent recent review and introduction to this exciting new development. On the importance of computers now and in the future, he said,

"Computers are essential in studying . . . systems ecology . . . The role of computers in the future of systems ecology is too readily underestimated. Computers in tomorrow's technology will have larger and faster memories, remote consoles and time-sharing systems. Some may accept hand-written notes and drawings, respond to human voices, and translate written words from one language into spoken words in another. There will be vast networks of data stations and information banks, with information transmitted by laser channels over a global network. This network will be used not only by researchers but also by engineers, lawyers, medical men, and sociologists as well as government, industry, and the military. Computers could become tomorrow's reference library used by students in the university; they are already starting to revolutionize our present approaches to certain kinds of teaching. To utilize computers effectively in ecology we will have to state precisely what we know, what we do not know, and what we wish to know. Also, it will be necessary to assemble, analyze, identify, reduce, and store our ecological data and knowledge in a form retrievable by machine."

SELECTED BIBLIOGRAPHY

In addition to the literature cited, the following references are of value in relating use of computers to wildlife research and management.

Angelton, G. M., C. D. Bonham and L. L. Shannon. 1966. Direct processing of field data. J. Range Mgmt. 19: 143-144.

Benson, D. A. 1964. A wildlife biologist looks at sampling, data processing, and computers. Canadian Wildl. Serv. Occ. Papers No. 6. 1-16.

Berry, G. T., T. J. Cleaver, J. A. Nelder, and P. J. Salter. 1966. Methods of recording data in the laboratory and field. Exp. Agr. 2: 68-80.

Carmer, S. G. and J. A. Jackobs. 1964. A computer program for correction of visual estimates of botanical composition in forage mixtures. Agron. J. 56: 243-44.

Computing Reviews. Published by Assoc. for Computing Machinery, 211 E. 43rd St., N. Y. 10017. (A journal of reviews of papers on computers.)

Garfinkel, D. 1962. Digital computer simulation of ecological systems. Nature 194: 856-857.

Hammidi, I. B. 1965. Survey of life science computer programs. U. S. Air Force Tech. Doc. Rep. AMRL-TR 65-113. 1-123.

Holling, C. S. 1965. The functional response of predators to prey density and its role in mimicry and population regulation. Mem. Ent. Soc. Canada No. 45. 1-60.

Larkin, P. A. and A. S. Hourston. 1964. A model for simulation of the population biology of Pacific salmon. J. Fish. Res. Bd. Canada 21: 1245-1265.

Ledley, R. S. 1965. Use of computers in biology and medicine. McGraw-Hill Book Co., N. Y. xxiii + 965 p.

Menshutkin, V. V. 1964. A study of fish population dynamics on the basis of a fish population regarded as a cybernetic system. Vop. Ikthiol. 4: 23-33. [In Russian]

Odum, H. T. 1960. Ecological potential and analogue circuits for the ecosystem. Amer. Sci. 48: 1-8.

Orcutt, G. H., M. Greenberger, J. Korbel and A. M. Riulin. 1961. Microanalysis of socio-economic systems. Harper and Bros., N. Y. xviii + 425 p.

Patten, B. C. 1966. The biocoenetic process in an estuarine phytoplankton community. Oak Ridge National Laboratory, ORNL-3946. iv + 97 p. (Oak Ridge, Tenn.)

Siniff, D. B. and J. R. Tester. 1965. Computer analysis of animal-movement data obtained by telemetry. BioScience 15: 104-108.

Slobodkin, L. B. 1965. On the present incompleteness of mathematical ecology. Amer. Sci. 53: 347-357.

Sterling, F. D. and S. V. Pollack. 1965. Computers and the life sciences. Columb. U. Press, N. Y. x + 342 p.

Swingle, W. E. and H. S. Swingle. 1966. Population analysis programs, IBM 1620, Fortran Format. Trans. Amer. Fish. Soc. 95: 232-33.

94

Van Dyne, G. M. 1965. Application of some operations research techniques to food chain analysis problems. Health Phys. 11: 1511-1519.

Various Authors. 1966. Information. W. H. Freeman, 660 Market St., San Francisco. (An excellent introduction to electronic data processing. It is a reprint of the September, 1966, issue of Scientific American which was devoted entirely to 12 articles on digital computers.)

Watt, K. E. F. 1961. Use of a computer to evaluate alternative insecticidal programs. Science 133: 706-707.

_____. 1964. Computers and the evaluation of resource management strategies. Amer. Sci. 52: 408-418.

_____. 1964. The use of mathematics and computers to determine optimal strategy and tactics for a given insect pest control problem. Canadian Entom. 96: 202-220.

_____. (Ed.) 1966. Systems analysis in ecology. Academic Press, N. Y. xix + 276 p.

_____. 1968. Ecology and resource management: a quantitative approach. McGraw-Hill, N. Y. xii + 449 p.

CHAPTER NINE

RADIO-LOCATION TELEMETRY

ROBERT B. BRANDER, PhD

Assistant Professor, Wildlife Management
University of Massachusetts
Amherst, Massachusetts

and

WILLIAM W. COCHRAN

Associate Wildlife Specialist
Section of Wildlife Research
Illinois Natural History Survey
Urbana, Illinois

PRELIMINARY CONSIDERATIONS
TRANSMITTERS
RECEIVING SYSTEMS
ACCURACY
DATA REDUCTION
FCC REGULATIONS

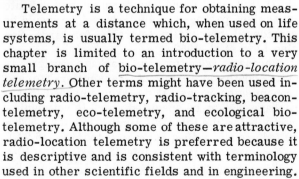

Telemetry is a technique for obtaining measurements at a distance which, when used on life systems, is usually termed bio-telemetry. This chapter is limited to an introduction to a very small branch of bio-telemetry—*radio-location telemetry.* Other terms might have been used including radio-telemetry, radio-tracking, beacon-telemetry, eco-telemetry, and ecological bio-telemetry. Although some of these are attractive, radio-location telemetry is preferred because it is descriptive and is consistent with terminology used in other scientific fields and in engineering.

The scope of the chapter is further narrowed to a review of the literature readily available to biologists. Numerous progress reports with limited circulation are considered too preliminary to be included in this manual.

A history of the development of bio-telemetry and its recent off-shoot, radio-location telemetry, may be traced in Slater 1963, Adams and Smith 1964, Adams 1965, Caceres and Cooper 1965, Mackay 1965, and Galler 1965. Here it is important only to note that advances in electronics have been exceedingly rapid since the first free-ranging animals were tracked around 1962 and it is now feasible to track all but the very smallest vertebrate animals.

PRELIMINARY CONSIDERATIONS

Before a telemetry system is acquired, other techniques for obtaining the required data should be given strong consideration. Radio-tracking should be construed as no more than a technique ". . . to extend the range of man's observational powers" (Craighead and Craighead 1965). In this sense, field glasses might in some instances yield information as quickly and efficiently as a costly and complex telemetric system.

In studies of animals which range in remote areas, animals with cryptic behavior, animals whose behavior is easily influenced by an observer, etc., justification for the use of telemetry would appear to require only a statement of "biological need." However, all factors considered, the simplest radio-tracking equipment represents a significant financial investment which may require another kind of justification.

Tracking equipment is now available from various suppliers (BIAC, 1967) for prices in the $1,000 to $2,000 range. If justification for such an investment is necessary it is perhaps best done through an analysis of alternative methods and costs.

The usual alternative to radio-tracking has been to trap, mark, and retrap (or observe) animals. Trapping and marking are also done in the telemetric method. The cost of the initial trapping effort should be similar in either case but cost of markers is quite disparate, being a few cents per animal in the trap-retrap method and $50 or more for each animal equipped with a transmitter-package. After a marked animal is released, the return per unit-investment is weighed heavily in favor of radio-tracking. Adams (1965) pointed out that efforts to study animal movements by the trap-retrap method commonly cost $1 to $5 per unit of information whereas the increased observation rate of radio-location reduces per unit cost to one or two cents.

TRANSMITTERS

A transmitter *package* typically includes a transmitter, a power cell, and a harness. An engineer usually builds the transmitter but the biologist should specify shape, size, weight, and harness arrangement for the package. The biologist often works from limited dictates but he should attempt to achieve a design which will least interfere with "normal" behavior of an animal.

Therefore, the package should be designed to conform closely to the contours of the animal. If, for example, the transmitter is to be attached to a neck-collar, it should be shaped to curve with the collar; transmitters built to ride on a bird's back should be narrow enough to ride between the scapulae. While earlier transmitters were necessarily bulky and angular, it is now possible to obtain a smoothly contoured unit of the proper size to conform to almost any game animal.

Circuits and physical transmitter designs are numerous in the literature (Cochran and Lord 1963, Cochran 1966, 1967, Dodge and Church 1965, Ellis 1964, Mech et al. 1965, Moore and Kluth 1966, Slagle 1965, Southern 1964, Tester et al. 1964, Verts 1963, DeVos and Anderka 1964). A comprehensive review of batteries and their application for bio-telemetry has been prepared by Kuechle (1967). See also Caceres (1965).

Earlier in the development of the technique the weight that a "normally behaving" animal would support was not known. Since 1962 several empirically determined data have been reported and it is now possible to suggest fairly safe guidelines (Table 9.1). Animals as large as a grizzly bear will carry considerable weight (up to a kilogram) without an apparent change in their behavioral patterns. This is probably so because even a heavy package is relatively insignificant when compared to the total weight of a large animal. However, package-weight does become a critical matter when the weight of an animal is 10 kg (raccoon sized) or lighter.

As indicated in Table 9.1, many mammals raccoon-sized and smaller have carried packages weighing less than 6% of body weight. Mammals as small as *Peromyscus* (about 25 g) will carry a package of 10% of the bodyweight, but this proportion is not recommended if the mammal is to be truly "free-ranging."

Because birds are aerodynamically fragile, the proportion of body weight that they will support is probably less than that for mammals. Most studies on free-ranging birds (Table 9.1) have indicated that a favorable weight proportion is less than 4%. However, recently a robin carried a package of 8% of body weight for 32 hours (Graber and Wunderle 1966) and similarly equipped Hylocichlid thrushes have flown 200-400 miles during a single night of migration (Cochran et al. 1967). But until more long-term studies indicate otherwise, packages of 4% body weight should be considered maximally tolerable for birds. See also Lord et al. 1962.

Because reduction in package weight is quite costly in terms of transmitter-life and transmission-range, it is recommended that a package weight be specified which is not significantly below the tolerable limit. Thus for a 600-g ruffed grouse, a 40-g package is too heavy (6.7%), a 20-g package is tolerable (3.3%), and a 10-g package is unnecessarily light (1.7%). On the other hand, even a 10-g package is too heavy for a 160-g bobwhite (6.3%) and further reduction is needed to keep package-weight below a tolerable 4%.

More determinations of tolerable weights are needed and indeed might be reported here if authors would specify *package weight*. Too frequently reports in the literature give *transmitter weight*, leaving the reader in doubt about total or package weight.

Several methods have been devised for attaching packages to animals (see Table 9.2). There are five methods that appear to be most feasible:

Table 9.1. Weights of transmitter-packages used in animal-tracking studies.

Study	Species	Wt. of animal, g.	Wt. of x-mitter package, g.	Package: % Body wt.
MAMMALS				
Rawson & Hartline (1964)	*Peromyscus sp.*	10-35	2.6	26.0-7.4
Beal (1967)	*Sciurus carolinensis,*	340-680	21	6.2-3.1
	S. niger	545-1,360	21	3.9-1.5
Cochran et al. (1965)	*Sylvilagus floridanus*	900-1,800	32	3.6-1.8
Mech et al. (1965)	*S. floridanus, Lepus americanus*	900-1,800	50	5.6-2.8
Merriam (1963, 1966)	*Marmota monax*	2,300-4,500	45	2.0-1.0
Moore & Kluth (1966)	*Dasypus novemcinctus*	3,400	40	1.2
Cochran et al. (1965)	*Vulpes fulva*	4,500-6,800	130	2.9-1.9
Cochran et al. (1965)	*Taxidea taxus*	5,900-11,300	140	2.4-1.2
Mech et al. (1965)	*Procyon lotor*	5,400-15,900	115	2.1-0.7
Tester et al. (1964)	*Odocoileus virginianus*	34,000-91,000	180	0.5-0.2
Cochran et al. (1965)	*Odocoileus virginianus*	34,000-91,000	300	0.9-0.3
Craighead & Craighead (1965)	*Ursus arctos*	147,000-385,000	906	0.6-0.2
BIRDS				
Cochran et al. (1967)	*Hylocichla spp.*	30-40	2.5	8.3-6.3
Graber & Wunderle (1966)	*Turdus migratorius*	70-90	6	8.6-6.7
Southern (1965a)	*Colinus virginianus*	140-180	6	4.3-3.3
Michener & Walcott (1966)	*Columba livia*	240-290	30	12.5-10.3
Marshall (1965)	*Bonasa umbellus*	500-700	20	4.0-2.9
McEwen & Brown (1966)	*Pedioecetes phasianellus*	700-900	22	3.1-2.4
Southern (1965)	*Larus spp.*	900-1,100	40	4.4-3.6
Southern (1964, 1965)	*Haliaeetus leucocephalus*	4,100-6,300	80	2.0-1.3

subdermal implantation, slip-on collar, fitted collar, fitted neck-antenna, and harness. A schematic representation of these devices (except subdermal implantation) is given in Fig. 9.1.

A recent innovation yet to be widely tested is attachment by an adhesive. Graber (1965, has had some success glueing packages to the back plumage of the gray-cheeked thrush (*Hylocichla minima*). Graber and Wunderle (1966) successfully glued packages to the backs of house sparrows (*Passer domesticus*) with Duco cement, but

they also noted that common grackles (*Quiscalus quiscula*) and starlings (*Sturnus vulgaris*) would not tolerate such a "harness." Cochran et al. (1967) removed 15 to 20 feathers from the dorsal tracts of various Hylocichlid thrushes and attached a transmitter to the bared skin with Eastman 910 adhesive. Their technique yielded variable results. One transmitter remained attached for 5 days, whereas several came off within a few hours of release. However, many thrushes thus marked did continue their migratory flights in

Table 9.2. Attachment of transmitter-packages used in animal-tracking studies.

Study	Species	Attachment
	MAMMALS	
Rawson and Hartline (1964)	*Peromyscus sp.*	Subdermal implantation.
Williams and Williams (1967)	*Phyllostomus hastatus*	Glue.
Sanderson and Sanderson (1964)	*Rattus spp.*	Harness.
Gentry (1965)	*Rattus spp.*	Harness.
Beal (1967)	*Sciurus carolinensis* *S. niger*	Fitted collar. Fitted collar.
Dodge and Church (1965)	"Mt. Beaver" "Hare"	Fitted neck-antenna. Fitted neck-antenna.
*Mech et al. (1965)	*Lepus americanus* *Sylvilagus floridanus*	Fitted neck-antenna. Fitted neck-antenna.
Holmes and Sanderson (1965)	*Didelphis virginianus*	(1) Slip-on collar. (2) Slip-on girth.
*Verts (1963)	*Mephitis mephitis*	Fitted collar.
Merriam (1963)	*Marmota monax*	Subdermal implantation.
*Storm (1965)	*Vulpes fulva*	Fitted collar.
Marshall et al. (1962)	*Erethizon dorsatum*	Harness.
Moore and Kluth (1966)	*Dasypus novemcinctus*	Glue.
*Ellis (1964)	*Procyon lotor*	Fitted collar.
*Mech et al. (1965)	*Procyon lotor*	Fitted neck-antenna.
Tester et al. (1964)	*Odocoileus virginianus*	Slip-on collar.
*Craighead and Craighead (1965)	*Ursus arctos*	Slip-on collar.
	BIRDS	
Cochran et al. (1967)	*Hylocichla spp.*	Glue.
Graber (1965)	*Hylocichla minima*	Glue.
Graber and Wunderle (1966)	*Passer domesticus* *Turdus migratorius*	Glue. Harness.
*Southern (1965)	*Colinus virginianus* *Haliaeetus leucocephalus*	Slip-on collar. Harness.
*Southern (1965)	*Larus argentatus*	Harness.
*Brander (1965)	*Bonasa umbellus*	Harness.
McEwen and Brown (1966)	*Pedioecetes phasianellus*	Harness.

*Illustrated in the original paper.

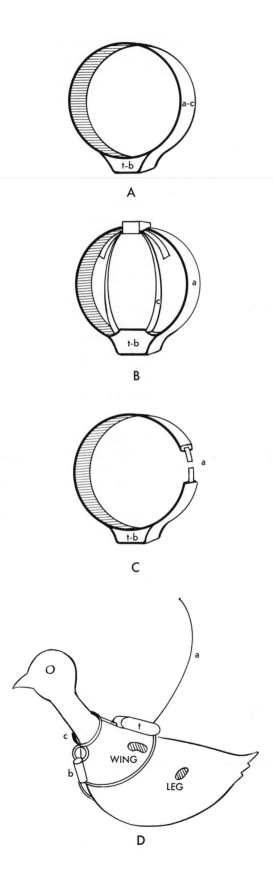

Fig. 9.1. Attachment methods: A—Slip-on collar; B—Fitted collar; C—Fitted neck-antenna; D—Harness; a—antenna; b—battery; c—collar; t—transmitter. The collar of the fitted neck-antenna is adjusted to the neck of the animal and then the antenna ends are soldered, therefore its transmitter must be returned.

an apparently normal manner and, without doubt, the utility of the adhesive method for birds was adequately proved. In the case of mammals, Williams and Williams (1967) used *parlodion* to attach a transmitter to the back of a large (75 g) neotropical bat, *Phyllostomus hastatus*, and Moore and Kluth (1966) attached a transmitter to the base of an armadillo's (*Dasypus novemcinctus*) with epoxy cement; both efforts led to notable successes.

It is not possible to specify a universal attachment device for tracking studies because the "ideal" will vary with the physiognomy and locomotive habits of the species type. Fossorial mammals such as the woodchuck would probably best carry a subdermally implanted package (cf. Merriam 1963) while non-fossorial mammals appear to be most tolerable of collar-packages. Weight distribution is quite critical in birds and therefore it is advisable to distribute package-weight with regards to the center of gravity; in this case some type of harness, usually plastic tubing, is required to support the power supply and transmitter along a particular axis.

While it is not possible to specify a universal it is appropriate to consider the "ideal" attachment device which, according to Mech et al. (1965), would have the following characteristics: (1) minimum weight, (2) minimum effect on the animal, (3) maximum protection for the transmitter, (4) permanence of attachment, and (5) maximum protection of transmitter from animal mortality factors such as predation and accident. A cogent discussion of these criteria and an evaluation of an attempt to achieve the "ideal" is included in the report of Mech et al. (1965).

RECEIVING SYSTEMS

The simplest system for radio-location makes use of a radio (beacon) transmitter attached to a subject animal. If the objective is to locate the animal for visual observation, the observer simply homes on the signal with a receiver and directional antenna until experience indicates that a spotting scope should be used in the approximate direction indicated by the radio equipment. Other

100

uses for homing include recovery of dropped transmitters, exact location of den or nest sites, recovery of dead subject animals, and determination of "flushing" distances. Most users of the radio-location technique have utilized homing in some aspect of their studies.

Locations of radio-tagged animals may be determined remotely (without homing) by triangulation of bearings (or azimuths) obtained at two or more locations. Considerable work has been done by single operators using one receiver which is moved to obtain bearings from different locations (cf. Verts 1963, Cochran and Lord 1963, Marshall et al. 1962, Ellis 1964, and Sanderson and Sanderson 1964). A source of error with this method is animal movement while the operator is changing his location. Verts (1963) used three to five bearings for each "fix" thereby providing a safeguard against this error; for if the animal were moving the probability would be very low that three of the three or more bearings would cross at or near the same point.

To avoid errors due to animal movement and disturbance due to operator movement, some workers have utilized two or more stationary or semi-stationary operators who obtain near simultaneous bearings by synchronizing their observations by two-way radio or by a continuous or pre-set observation schedule (cf. Sanderson and Sanderson 1964, Marshall 1965, Gentry 1965, and Southern 1964).

Operational procedures may be carried out by using a relatively small directional antenna (Fig.

9.2C) carried by the operator or installed on a vehicle, (Fig. 9.2B) or numerous larger and more directive antennas (Fig. 9.2A) may be semi-permanently installed at advantageous locations throughout a study area and utilized as the general locations of the radio-tagged animals dictate. Advantages of the semi-permanent antennas are that their locations and reference bearings can be accurately determined (Fig. 9.3) and that larger antennas at greater height yield greater accuracy and reception range (Marshall and Kupa 1963).

A next step in ascending order of complexity is the installation of permanent antennas at considerable heights (50 to 100 ft) and their control from a centralized location where a single operator can take numerous near-simultaneous bearings to radio-tagged animals. The cost of cabling and antenna installation is partially offset by the increased range and bearing accuracy afforded and the reduction in man-hours per animal location. However, the principle disadvantage of this system is that the useful study area is rigidly defined. This latter limitation requires some *a priori* knowledge of the range and habitat use of the animals to be studied in order that optimal antenna locations may be selected. A system of this type with automatic control of antennas and recording of signals is described by Cochran et al. (1965). In their system, signal strength and angular antenna position information are recorded on photographic film from which bearings must be taken manually.

Savage (1966) discussed what might be termed

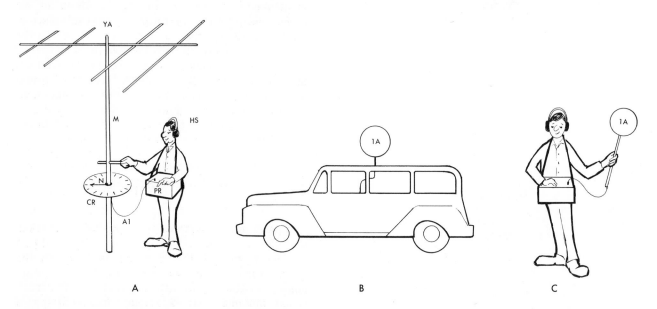

Fig. 9.2. Some receiving systems: (A) semi-permanent; (B) mobile; (C) hand-carried. *ya*, Yagi antenna; *la*, loop antenna; *m*, mast; *n*, needle; *cr*, compass rose; *pr*, portable receiver; *al*, antenna lead; *hs*, headset.

the ultimate triangulation system in which signal information from rotating antennas is analyzed automatically to determine bearings which are stored in digital form on magnetic tape. The tape may be used as a digital computer input with the computer performing all location calculations as well as other analyses of the location data.

Merriam (1963) used a system employing low-frequency beacon transmitters subdermally implanted in woodchucks (*Marmota monax*) with locations determined by a signal from one of 47 loops varying in diameter from 10 to 30 ft. The loops encircled the burrows, and analyses were in terms of movements into, out of and between loops (burrow areas). The location data were

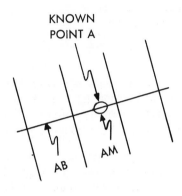

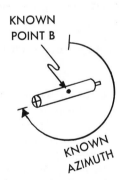

Fig. 9.3. Alignment of a semi-permanent station. A spotting scope at known point B is oriented on point A—the antenna mast (AM). The antenna beam (AB) is then positioned so that its long axis aligns with the long axis of the scope. The azimuth of the beam now equals the scope-azimuth and the antenna needle is positioned to indicate this azimuth on the compass rose (Fig. 9.2).

recorded on punch tape. Moore and Kluth (1966) described a similar system using 100, 24 x 24 ft loops distributed uniformly over their study area. Their system employs circuitry which gives an improvement in data reliability over that achieved by Merriam (1963). Advantages of these "grid" systems include well-defined and uniform accuracy and relatively low cost recording of the data in computer compatible form.

At least two other systems are being developed for animal radio-location. Baldwin (pers. communication) is developing a doppler system featuring relatively long range performance. Patric et al. (1965) reported that they were about to field test an active transponder system on deer. Although both these systems hold promise of advantages over the triangulation method, their cost and complexity will probably restrict their application to problems where these inherent advantages far outweigh the cost factor.

General system design considerations are well summarized by Adams and Smith (1964):

"The choice of the wave length at which a telemetry system will operate is affected by many considerations. In order to generate adequate energy in a radio field, the circuit producing the energy must have a linear dimension which is an appreciable part of the wave length. This is the reason we use transmitting antennas—to spread out the generating circuit over an effective part of the wave length. It follows that the higher the frequency we choose, the shorter the wave length and the smaller we can make the generating circuit, our transmitter. Conversely, the lower the frequency the larger the antenna. Since we are limited as to the size of antenna we can attach to an animal, we tend to choose to work with higher frequencies and smaller antennas. But the higher the frequency the greater the absorption, refraction, and reflection of the signal by obstacles such as terrain and vegetation. So we are forced to compromise, choosing the lowest frequency possible considering the animal's antenna carrying ability. Many other factors influence frequency-antenna choice—the kind of antenna (loop or whip) which depends in part on which type is best adapted to the animal; and the nature of the terrain and vegetation hazards. These hazards cannot be characterized with any certainty except by field tests. . . . Practically all parameters — transmitter - to - receiver range, battery life, weight, type of modulation, and many others—are subject to compromise

102

in design and to cut-and-try in development. Thus the simplest of transmitter-receiver systems is one of an almost infinite set of such systems from which the engineer must select specifically for the purpose at hand. The biologist must not expect the selection to be made quickly, nor should he expect the final design to be the best. Optimum design covers a range of designs, not a particular one."

Cochran and Lord (1963) and Pienkowski (1965) discuss both theoretical and empirical system design considerations.

ACCURACY

While some tracking studies utilize radio-telemetry as a means of bringing an animal under visual observation, often the animal is remotely located or "fixed" by triangulation. In the latter case there is the important question of accuracy in the tracking system. Three critical studies of this aspect of radio-telemetry have been reported in the literature (Slade et al. 1965, Mech et al. 1966, and Heezen and Tester 1967).

The accuracy of a system is any measure of closeness-of-fit of the true location of a transmitter and the telemetrically determined location. Slade et al. (1965) give an accuracy term which is stated in feet and degrees as a function of distance, a depiction similar to the "error-zones" of Mech et al. (1966). These are perhaps awkward means of describing errors which mount with distance and angular change.

A better representation is the "error polygon" of Heezen and Tester (1967). In their study, *system-error* (errors due to antenna referencing, factors of weather, etc.) and *reading errors* (errors made in reading and recording bearings) combined to dictate an accuracy of $\pm 0.5°$. System and reading errors are fixed factors, but the location of a transmitter in relation to the receiving antennas compound this initial statement of accuracy into what they termed an *error polygon*—a geometric figure whose size varies continuously with angular change.

Examination of error polygons resulting from plots of intersects (Fig. 9.4) will demonstrate that accuracy of a fix is highest at the *optimum position*—a right-angle intersect. As the acuteness of the intersect-angle increases precision falls off rapidly, and with two receiving-antennas oriented along the base line there is no chance of achieving an acceptable fix.

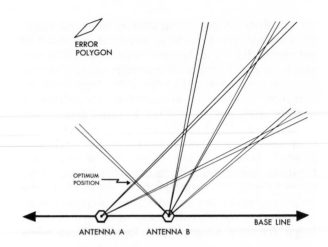

Fig. 9.4. Relative sizes and shapes of error polygons in relation to two tracking antennae. Any true location within an error polygon would be recorded at the center of that polygon. (From Heezen and Tester 1967).

Other factors also may affect accuracy. Signal reflection or refraction by vegetation is an example. The nature of such phenomena is extremely variable and should be evaluated for each study area.

The most plausible method of increasing accuracy, it would seem, is to decrease the chance of acquiring small angle (less than 30°) intersects. This could be done by erecting more than two fixed receiving antennas (at considerable added expense) or by utilizing portable antennas (less expensive but also less accurate).

DATA REDUCTION

The most primitive tracking system will yield locational data of considerable volume. If, for example, an animal were tracked for 90 days and three locations were acquired each day, 270 locations would be known. It would take a biologist several hours to place these data on a map of publishable quality. Some "automatic systems" yield data far in excess of three locations per day (Siniff and Tester 1965), so much that it may become totally impractical to manually process locational data.

For this reason *any* radio-tracking study of animal movements should include an appropriate budgetary request for computer analysis. The computer program proposed by Siniff and Tester (1965) produces publishable maps from the basic field data of animal number, date-time, receiving-station location, and azimuths. In addition other analyses may be simultaneously produced. Tester and Siniff (1965), e.g., used computer analyses to examine the concept of home range in relation to center of activity, activity radius, and the relationship that time interval between fixes bears to distance traveled and area used.

The cost of computer analysis of tracking data has not been stated but it almost certainly is less than a purely manual effort. However, more important than cost considerations are the analytic approaches which would not be undertaken without recourse to a computer.

FCC REGULATIONS

The Federal Communications Commission (FCC) controls all radio transmission in the United States as stated in its *Rules and Regulations*. Anyone contemplating construction of a radio-telemetry system should be familiar with three publications which may be purchased from the

Superintendent of Documents
U. S. Government Printing Office
Washington, D. C. 20402.

These publications include certain FCC Rules and Regulations given in

Vol. II - Part 5, Experimental Radio Services (other than broadcast);
Vol. II - Part 15, Radio Frequency Devices;
Vol. VI - Part 95, Citizens Radio Service.

Part 15 states, in general, that non-licensed operation in the FM band (88-108 mc) is permissible if transmitters meet certain specifications and produce *low power*, i.e., less than 1000 ft range. Because of the range limitations, few tracking systems would benefit from the dispensations in Part 15.

Part 95 deals with the so-called "Citizens Band", 26-27 mc. At these frequencies a license is required but its issuance is practically assured any U. S. citizen possessing equipment acceptable to the FCC. While it is possible to construct perfectly adequate tracking systems in the 26-27 megacycle range, the band is extremely crowded with voice transmission, and voice transmission can effectively mask signals from a tracking transmitter. For this reason it is best to avoid the Citizens Band and request a license under Part 5.

It is not possible to list here all of the pertinent Rules and Regulations covering Experimental Radio Services (Part 5). However, it is important to note that most tracking systems would qualify as experimental and that contrary to Haahn (1966), Part 5 does often cover radio-tracking. In general, the applicant selects a frequency (covered in Part 2 of the Rules and Sections 5.203, 5.253 of Part 5) and then prepares two forms:

(1) FCC Form 440, Application for New or Modified Radio Station Construction Permit under Part 5 of FCC Rules.
(2) FCC Form 403, Application of Radio Station License.

According to Section 5.57 of Part 5, a formal application requires that supplemental statements be submitted with each application. These statements (called "exhibits") usually have to do with the scope of the research involving transmitters and with details of transmitter construction. Fees are not required with experimental applications. License renewals are requested periodically (usually annually) on FCC Form 405, together with a brief experimental report pursuant to Section 5.204.

CHAPTER TEN

USES OF RADAR IN WILDLIFE MANAGEMENT

M. T. MYRES

Assistant Professor of Zoology
University of Calgary
Calgary, Alberta, Canada

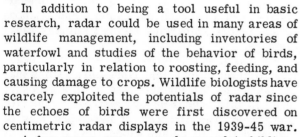

In addition to being a tool useful in basic research, radar could be used in many areas of wildlife management, including inventories of waterfowl and studies of the behavior of birds, particularly in relation to roosting, feeding, and causing damage to crops. Wildlife biologists have scarcely exploited the potentials of radar since the echoes of birds were first discovered on centimetric radar displays in the 1939-45 war.

A few years ago, a nearly complete bibliography of radar-migration studies was published, along with technical and organizational details of all bird-radar studies up to that time (Myres 1964). Myres suggested that high-powered, long-range, fixed-location surveillance radars (e.g. 500 KW, 23 cm radars at airports) should be used in combination with low-powered, short-range mobile radars (e.g. 50 KW, 3 or 10 cm naval or aircraft radars) to carry out waterfowl studies. Eastwood and Rider (1966) suggested using a 23 cm L-band radar, together with radar signature analysis by a 3 cm X-band high resolution radar aimed vertically upwards to determine the number of birds in each echo. The principles of microwave radar, its use in studies of bird migration, and the use of radar signature analysis have been explained in a recent book, *Radar Ornithology* (Eastwood 1967). Schaefer (1966, 1968), using radar signature analysis, has studied fluctuations in the amplitude ("wing beat patterns")

of individual radar echoes, which he interprets as being due to changes in the shape of the bird's body as it flaps its wings in flight. He expects that it will be possible before long to identify the species producing a radar echo by its WBP; he states that this is best done by a 10 cm S-band tracking radar.

Surveillance with one or more types of radar could, and perhaps should, become routine for state and provincial as well as federal agencies responsible for waterfowl inventories. On the one hand radar is a tool that can enable a wildlife biologist to watch the movements of flights of waterfowl simultaneously over a circular area greater than 100 miles in diameter, at all altitudes, thus adding to his understanding of the directions, form, and phenology of migration. On the other hand radar can be used to study local concentrations of birds at wildlife refuges, or in roosting or feeding areas. In both cases it will shortly be possible to make quantitative assessments of the numbers of birds producing the radar echoes, and even to identify them with some degree of accuracy, by means of radar signature analysis.

Reports of waterfowl being observed with radar have been published by a number of scientists: Bergman (1961) and Bergman and Donner (1960, 1964) for Finland; Svärdson (1959) and Mascher et al. (1962) for Sweden; Lee (1963) for Scotland;

Graber and Hassler (1962), and Bellrose (1964, 1967) for the United States. Dr. F. C. Bellrose of the Illinois Natural History Survey has been analyzing radar films taken at 20 U.S. Weather Bureau stations with 10 cm radars in the central and eastern United States, though most of his studies since 1960 have been carried out with 3 cm aircraft-type radars. In Canada, since 1964, a team working for the National Research Council of Canada's Associate Committee on Bird Hazards to Aircraft (Chairman: Mr. M. S. Kuhring) has been analyzing radar films taken at up to 20 Department of Transport and Royal Canadian Air Force 23 cm radar stations across Canada from British Columbia to the Maritime Provinces, under the direction of Dr. W. W. H. Gunn of the Canadian Wildlife Service. The program has required the cooperation of experienced ornithologists in interpreting the radar films. A radar study of the migration of whistling swans over Lake Erie and southwestern Ontario by W. John Richardson and M. E. Haight, and an analysis of a goose flight over Fort William, Ontario, by J. Murray Speirs and two co-workers, will be published shortly by the Canadian Wildlife Service.

Wildlife biologists are often responsible for population manipulation, and for alleviating damage from nuisance birds such as European starlings, blackbirds, grackles and, in some areas, waterfowl, gulls, cranes and shorebirds (and in Africa, *Quelea*). Local flights to and from roosts of such birds have been studied extensively with radar by Elder (1957), Ligda (1958), Harper (1959), Eastwood, et al. (1959), Eastwood et al. (1960, 1962), Rider (1961) and Dyer (1964). In Canada roosts and roosting-feeding movements of European starlings, ducks, blackbirds, and gulls in the vicinity of airports have recently been a major concern, as in other parts of the world.

Waterfowl, gulls, shorebirds, and passerines are not only a hazard in the approaches to airfields but also on occasions present major hazards to aircraft in cruising flight. The main purpose of the Canadian radar program has been to develop a means of forecasting when the numbers of birds in the air on migration is great enough to present a real hazard to military and civil aircraft, so that evasive action may be taken by pilots or air-traffic controllers (Kuhring and Gunn 1965, Gunn and Solman 1968). Among the major hazards are the densely-packed movements of geese, ducks, whistling swans, sandhill cranes, some birds of prey, and gulls. These movements are usually brief in time but long in linear distance, and their passage across the airlanes and over airports presents great hazards. The films that have been taken from coast to coast across Canada are likely to increase enormously our understanding of the weather factors associated with the initiation of migration (Gunn 1966, Myres 1966). Much of the analysis will be carried out by computer. It has already been suggested that duty biologists should be appointed to selected airfields where they would produce an operational bird-hazard forecast similar to a thunderstorm warning (Gunn and Solman 1968). Using FIDAC (Film Input to a Digital Automatic Computer), in which a cathode-ray tube spot generator and film-scanning photocells extract data directly from movie films into a computer (Ledley 1965, Watt 1966), an almost completely automatic bird-hazard warning system is ultimately possible.

Procedures for filming the radar display to reduce arduous direct observation, and to permit restudying of past events, have been described by Phelp (1963), Gunn (1964) and Gunn and Solman (1968). Dyer (1967) developed a system for quantifying analyses of the density of bird echoes using photo-electric cells. Since considerable trouble was experienced with the cameras used in the Canadian radar program, wildlife biologists should seek advice on the camera and methods to use before embarking on the filming of radar displays.

Basically, still photographs (Polaroid or negative film) or 16 mm time-lapse movie films may be taken. In the former case a time exposure leads to bird echoes making a streak on the still photograph. The direction of movement may be indicated if a 10 minute exposure is followed by a 2 minute pause with a final minute of further exposure. The interruption in the streak caused by closing the shutter indicates the direction in which the echo was traveling (Gunn and Solman 1968).

Still photographs can also be made from 16 mm time-lapse movie films. The examples shown in Fig. 10 were made available through the courtesy of the Associate Committee on Bird Hazards to Aircraft, National Research Council of Canada, and were selected by M. T. Myres.

Each frame of the 16 mm movie film was a 9.5 second exposure for the duration of one full rotation of the radar antenna. If the phosphor on the display is a long-lasting one, each echo will appear to have a fainter "tail" attached to it, indicative of its position during earlier sweeps of the antenna, and these "tails" therefore indicate the direction of movement of the echoes. When, however, the phosphor fades rapidly (as in the examples shown) a flock of birds appears only

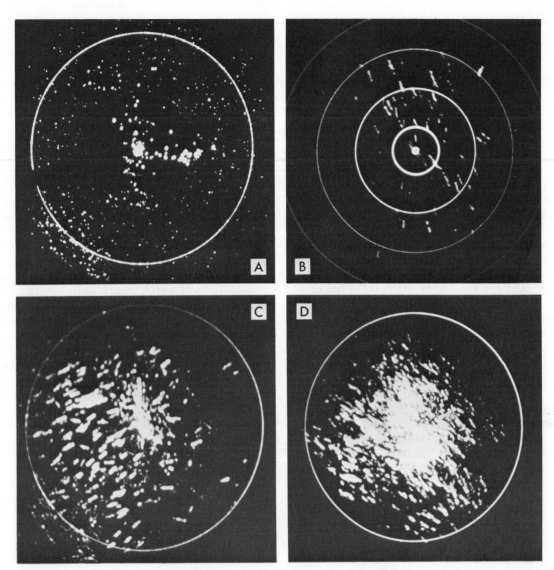

Fig. 10.1. *A. Local movement of a nuisance species.* A single frame of 16 mm radar film showing the pattern made by gulls (mainly Franklin's gulls) when leaving a municipal garbage dump only 3 n.m. south of an airport in the evening (North is in top center of each photo). The airport is at the center of the circle. The birds are travelling in a line eastwards to a breeding colony some 40 n.m. away. The birds remain visible for more than 25 n.m. Such feeding-roosting movements are a hazard to aircraft. The bright range-ring is 40 n.m. from the antenna. Ignore the numerous background echoes. (Calgary, Alberta. 15 May 1965. 1916 MST.) *B. Variation in the orientation of migrants.* Nocturnal migration of large echoes (probably waterfowl). Note the variation in direction of movement of some echoes on either side of the SE orientation of the majority of the echoes. Large numbers of similar photographs can be used for an analysis of migratory orientation. Range-rings are at 10 n.m. intervals. (Edmonton, Alberta. 7 November 1964. 0100-0104 MST.) *C. Broad-front migration across mountains at great height.* Large unidentified echoes (perhaps arctic shorebirds), which had evidently been travelling at night higher than the maximum 9,000 ft elevation that mountain peaks reach in the vicinity, are arriving ENE in Alberta over the Rocky Mountains from British Columbia on a broad front shortly after sunrise. The eastern slopes of the Rocky Moutains extend NW-SE across the west and south sectors of the display; ridges and valleys are visible as ground echoes beyond 30 n.m. to the SW. The bright range-ring is at a range of 40 n.m. from the antenna. (Calgary, Alberta. 27 May 1965. 0507-0511 MST.) *D. The complexity of migratory movements observed with radar.* The high ground of the Missouri Coteau in southwestern Saskatchewan runs SE-NW across the southern and western sectors of the display. Within 20 n.m. echoes (probably passerines) are moving WNW, but their number is so great that they cannot be separated from each other in this superimposition of several frames of movie film; hence one must study the actual movement they produce on the projected film itself. Beyond 20 n.m., except over the Missouri Coteau, large echoes (probably waterfowl) are moving NW/NNW. Beyond 30 n.m. to the SW, over the Missouri Coteau, large echoes, probably soaring sandhill cranes, are moving NW more slowly than the other echoes and sometimes in clumps, so that smears are produced in a time-exposure of the movie-film. The bright range-ring is at a range of 50 n.m. (Regina, Saskatchewan. 19 April 1965. 1144-1150 CST.)

as a round white dot on a single frame of film (Fig. 10A), so that the direction of movement is not indicated. Prints from single frames nevertheless have their uses, for they can be used to demonstrate recognizable configurations of echoes which are repeated each day. Such is the case with local roosting and feeding flights of nuisance species.

To show the direction of movement of migrants, 16 mm film may be projected onto a screen and a time-exposure made onto a single still 35 mm negative of a section of the film, as in Fig. 10B, C, and D. Exposure for 1 second results in superimposition of 24 frames, representing 4 minutes of live radar. A moving bird echo, therefore, appears as a white streak. Comparing the length of the streak produced in 4 minutes with the distance between the 10 nautical mile (n.m.) intervals between the range rings (cf. Fig. 10B) allows an estimate to be made of the speed of the bird echo (in knots).

The altitudes at which birds fly on migration have been studied by Lack (1960), Bellrose and Graber (1963), Hassler et al. (1963), Nisbet (1963), Eastwood and Rider (1965) and Bellrose (1967). The maximum altitude recorded appears to be about 20,000 feet.

Studies on the quantitative physical aspects of radar surveillance of bird echoes have been made by Caws et al. (1958), Coultas and Houghton (1959), Edwards and Houghton (1959), Rider (1961), Houghton (1963), Nisbet (1963), Dyer (1964), Schnell (1965), Eastwood and Rider (1966) and Schaefer (1968). Radar has been used to provide estimates of the numbers of European starlings (Rider 1961) and red-winged blackbirds (Dyer 1964, 1967) entering roosts, and will undoubtedly be used increasingly in the future to estimate numbers of birds on migratory movements, particularly when automated quantitative analysis of echoes and echo densities is more generally available.

From time to time it has been suggested that birds are sensitive to radio waves. A recent review shows that there is no positive evidence of this, aside from thermal effects (Eastwood and Rider 1964). Studies by Tanner (1962, 1965) nevertheless suggest that in the future it might be possible to use microwave radiation to inactivate birds in the flight paths of aircraft so that they fall below them, and it might also be possible to use it as a means of diverting nuisance species from sites needing protection from them. With all new technological developments wisdom lags behind skill, so if such things become feasible it will be necessary to establish strict legislative controls on the use of the apparatus *before* prototypes are converted into field equipment, if abuses are to be prevented.

CHAPTER ELEVEN

RADIOISOTOPES AND THEIR USE IN WILDLIFE RESEARCH

TONY J. PETERLE, PhD

Professor, The Ohio State University
Columbus, Ohio

INTRODUCTION
ISOTOPES AND TYPES OF RADIATION
MEANS OF MEASUREMENT
COSTS
EXAMPLES OF USE

Techniques of wildlife research must become more sophisticated and precise to assure their more beneficial application to broadening questions of resource management. The use of radioisotopes can meet some of these research and management needs.

The growing application of radioisotopes (or nuclides) to a wide spectrum of physical and biological research suggests that unique areas of wildlife research might also benefit through the intelligent application of radiological methods. A careful appraisal of the benefits should precede any incorporation of these techniques since, in many instances, standard chemical methodology is simpler, cheaper, and less hazardous.

Special training is desirable for laboratory personnel prior to the use of isotope or tracer techniques in a research program. Courses are available at many colleges and universities; at the Oak Ridge Institute of Nuclear Studies, Oak Ridge, Tennessee; and at Argonne National Laboratories, the University of Chicago, Chicago, Illinois. Many foreign nations have also developed Nuclear Institutes where training in the biological aspects of tracer methodology and radiology is readily available at low cost. Significant general books on the subject include: Atomic Energy of Canada Ltd. 1960; Overman and Clarke 1960; Overman 1963; Sheppard 1962; Shilling 1964; USAEC 1962, 1962, 1964; and Wolf 1964.

ISOTOPES AND TYPES OF RADIATION

There are about 102 chemical elements occurring, either naturally or artificially, as approximately 1,200 isotopes. Isotopes are collections of nuclei with the same number of protons (hence belonging to the same chemical element) but with different atomic weights, indicating a different number of total particles in the nucleus. Examples are C^{12}, C^{13}, and C^{14} which are all isotopes of the element carbon with the same atomic number 6, but differing atomic weights indicating 6, 7, and 8 neutrons, respectively. The first two are stable, but C^{14} is an unstable, or radioactive, isotope with a half life of 5,760 years. Radioactive isotopes are called nuclides assuming they are capable of more than transient existence. Half life is a term denoting the time required for one half the nuclei in a collection of radioactive atoms of a particular isotope to decay to a stable state. Thus, to start with 1,000,000 C^{14} nuclei today, there will only be 500,000 in 5,760 years. As isotopes decay to their stable daughter elements, characteristic types of radiation are emitted as a result of the energy loss.

Alpha Radiation

There are about 100 isotopes which emit charged alpha particles while they are decaying to more stable daughter isotopes with 4 less mass units and 2 units lower in atomic number. Polonium^{210} having a half-life of about 138 days decays to lead^{206}, a decrease of 4 mass units and two less positive units.

$$_{84}Po^{210} \xrightarrow[\text{138 days}]{} {}_{82}Pb^{206}$$

The emitted alpha particle is much heavier than the particles from beta emissions, has an electrical charge of +2, an energy of 4 to 10 Mev (million electron volts), a range in air of only up to about 9 cm, and a very limited range in tissues. High specific ionization over a short distance makes alpha radiation very hazardous. Tissue damage might be 20 times greater than for either beta or gamma radiation. Although alpha particles will not penetrate the skin, they are dangerous when inhaled or ingested. Some common alpha emitters are actinium, bismuth, polonium, and radium. The alpha emitters (uranium, plutonium, and thorium) are becoming more common as nuclear energy programs progress. It is unfortunate that the unique characteristics of alpha particle radiation, of great potential for select research projects, have been of only limited use in biological research to the present. This is due, in part, to the difficulty of measurement and possible tissue damage.

Beta Radiation

Beta particles are lighter and emerge from the nucleus with much higher velocities (some close to the speed of light) than alpha particles. They are physically similar to orbital electrons. Some isotopes decay to more stable isotopes through the emission of a beta particle which increases the atomic number by 1, but the mass number remains the same. One of the commonest beta emitters, C^{14} decays to N^{14} through the change of one neutron to a proton and a beta particle with the subsequent emission of the beta particle.

$$_{6}C^{14} \xrightarrow[\text{9.9 m}]{B + {}_{1}e^{0}} {}_{7}N^{14} \qquad {}_{6}C^{14} \xrightarrow[\text{5.6 x 10}^{3}\text{y}]{B + \text{neutrino}} {}_{7}N^{14}$$

The mass number remains at 14, but the atomic number increases from 6 for carbon to 7 for nitrogen. A wide range of maximum energies (E_{max}) are available to the researcher since each element has a characteristic energy. Beta particles can emerge from any given nucleus with a range of energies from nearly zero up to the maximum energy which is characteristic of the isotope under consideration. Some characteristic E_{max} values from common beta emitters potentially useful in wildlife research are: P^{32}, 1.7 Mev.; C^{14}, 0.155 Mev.; Ca^{45}, 0.25 Mev.; S^{35}, 0.167 Mev.; and Cl^{36}, 0.714 Mev. All have varied half-lives ranging from hours to thousands of years. As beta rays pass through matter they lose energy by the formation of radiation and ion pairs (ionization). It is this energy loss which is so important, since the ability to use isotopes is directly related to their energy and its measurement. Typically, beta particles can penetrate about 100 times farther than alpha particles with the same energy and are capable of passing through about 1 cm of tissue. As with alpha particles, inhalation and ingestion are considered the greatest safety hazard. Some beta emitters (e.g. P^{32}) are important in many phases of biological research and are commonly used in clinical medicine studies of humans. Beta emitters are of limited use for field application and detection. Their low energy makes measurement problems complex. Field beta detectors (see Fig. 11.1) are delicate and the results variable. Applications combined with laboratory analyses, however, have great research potential.

Gamma Radiation

Gamma radiations are emitted by the nucleus and are of short wave-length. They are similar to X-rays, radio waves and visible light. They are part of the electromagnetic spectrum and are of high energy ranging from 0.01 to 10.0 Mev. Gamma ray emission is usually accompanied by alpha and also beta radiation. While photons are emitted from the nucleus, the radioactive element decays to a less energetic form of the same nuclide. Alpha or beta energies are emitted from a parent nucleus to form the excited state, then the emission of gamma rays reduces the excess energy and the nuclide decays to the ground state of the daughter nucleus. Gamma ray energies are dissipated in three major ways as they pass through matter. These are: the Photoelectric Effect, in which the gamma-ray gives up *all* of its energy to an orbital electron; the Compton

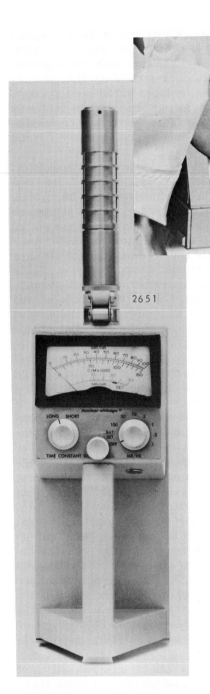

2651

Fig. 11.1. The portable Geiger Mueller survey meter is useful for measuring hard beta and gamma radiation. Probes are available for alpha, soft beta, and gamma measurements. Radiation is detected from the dial or from earphones.

are Cs^{137}, 0.662 Mev.; Zn^{65}, 1.12 Mev.; Co^{60}, 1.33 Mev.; and Na^{24}, 2.7 Mev. Half-lives of these isotopes range from 15 hours to slightly over five years. Gamma emitters should be used only under carefully controlled conditions. They have widespread and important use in biological research.

MEANS OF MEASUREMENT

Because of the unique amounts of energy and mode of decay of isotopes, each requires electronic assay equipment especially designed for highest efficiency. A probe or survey meter designed to measure gamma radiation (Fig. 11.2) would not be very useful for assessing the levels of alpha particles with limited penetrating power. Conversely, gamma rays would pass undetected through some survey equipment with very low counting efficiency. The industrial development of assay equipment has been rapid and quite competitive. As with the automobile, an assay instrument is outdated when it leaves the manufacturer. Sophisticated scintillation detectors or pulse-height analysers with built-in computers cost thousands of dollars. These may not be needed, for as with the automobile, progress can be made with the Model-T as well as with the Cadillac, only it takes a little longer.

Effect in which the ray collides with an electron and gives up *part* of its energy; and Pair Production, in which positron-electron pairs are formed as the gamma ray is annihilated near the nucleus of the absorbing atom. X-rays are comparable to gamma rays but originate from electron orbits, not the nucleus. Gamma rays have high penetrating power, produce secondary ionization, and are consequently very dangerous to animal tissue. Some common gamma emitters and their energies

Portable Survey Meters

Portable survey meters (Fig. 11.1 and 11.2) and some laboratory survey equipment (Fig. 11.3) are designed to collect the ions produced along the path of radiation particles or rays as they interact with matter. Frequently, these meters are designed for better geometric efficiency as a cylindrical probe. These probes have a central wire as one electrode and the outside case as the other. As ionizing radiation passes through the tube charged ions are formed. These ions are collected and as a quantity of electricity are measured and displayed either on a meter, or with some type of digital scaler. Frequently, the efficiency of the collection of ions is enhanced by filling the tube with mixtures of gasses, e.g. commercial Q gas, usually a mixture of helium and butane. The windows of the probes for survey meters are variable. Some probes have very thin windows to admit alpha particles or less energetic beta particles, while others, designed for gamma ray assay, do not have windows. Some meters are made with interchangeable probes, where the suitable probe is attached for measuring specific kinds of radiation. In biological research, beta emitters are most commonly used, so a probe with a thin window is desirable. Usually detecting equipment must be within two or three feet of the animal to determine any radioactivity.

Laboratory Systems

Two main types of laboratory assay systems are the gas flow or Geiger-Mueller counting devices, similar in operation to the portable meters, and the scintillation systems, (Fig. 11.4) where phosphors (a phosphorescing substance) are used to permit the measurement of the radiation by photoelectric tubes. Gas systems are usually tubes housed in shielding to reduce background radiation and to which an external gas supply is attached. Results are recorded on a scaler which can be read directly or attached to a print-out device. (See Fig. 11.5) Various levels of sophistication are available in these systems. Automatic sample changing devices are available (Fig. 11.6) which can handle over 100 plated samples. The operator is able to pre-set the time or total count of the assay. Background subtractions and the data can be printed on tape providing sample number, time of count, total counts, counts per minute, or counts per minute minus background. Thin windows can be purchased for separating the gas from the sample itself. Windowless counters are available where the sample is inserted in the gas chamber, as are gas assay systems where the radioactive gas is directly mixed with the Q gas for assay. Each particular type of system has advantages for specific types of radioactive assay. The selection of a versatile system, which is suitable and efficient for a wide range of measurements is difficult and should be given careful consideration.

Scintillation detectors or assay systems detect ionization by measuring the scintillation produced in a phosphor. These scintillators may be crystalline (such as sodium iodide), liquid, plastic, or gaseous. The substance to be assayed is placed within or near a scintillator which is itself placed in intimate contact with a photomultiplier tube. The resultant light measured by the tube is proportional to the energy of the radiation causing the scintillation. Some systems are housed in freezer cabinets to improve the efficiency of the photoelectric tubes but others are operated at ambient temperatures. Shielding and anticoincidence circuitry reduce the background level from cosmic and other types of radiation. Liquid scintillation systems are most efficient for low energy beta emitters such as carbon and tritium. The sample is mixed directly into a liquid phosphor and the vial inserted between two photomultiplier tubes to improve efficiency. Assay problems occur because many biological materials act as quenching agents to the phosphor, but newer counting systems (Fig. 11.4) have an external standard which automatically provides a correction ratio for each sample. The external source of radiation is moved to the vicinity of the sample vial at the termination of the preset counting period and a standard one minute count rate is printed on the tape, allowing corrections for quenching. Liquid phosphors or "scintillation cocktails" can be mixed according to the dictates of the isotope characteristics. Suspendors or emulsifiers can be added to keep particulate matter from settling in the vials, and samples of various consistancies can be assayed. Strips of paper cut from chromatograms can be successfully assayed for radioactive content when immersed in the scintillation liquid. Normal precautions for preparation efficiencies, standards, peak electronic responses and effects of quenching must be taken in determining the most expedient and satisfactory method for sample preparation.

Solid crystals, primarily thallium-activated sodium iodide, are directly coupled to photomultiplier tubes to provide a high efficiency for transferring the photons of light produced by the

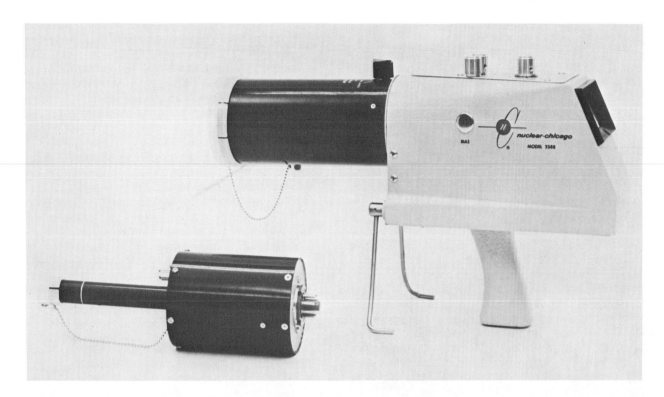

Fig. 11.2. The "cutie-pie" portable battery operated survey meter can be fitted with chambers (lower left) having different measurement capabilities.

radioactivity from the crystal to the tube. Housings for the crystals are coated with reflectors to enhance the collection of light. Sodium iodide crystals are primarily used to assay gamma radiation, since each element provides characteristic radiation pulse heights. Pulse-height analysers are available which assign the various voltage pulses to a series of channels or addresses ranging from 100 to several thousand. As the equipment scans the pre-set energy range, the counts per minute, reflecting the radioactivity of the sample, are reproduced visually on an oscilloscope, graphically on a chart, or numerically in printed tabular form. Other equipment is available to record this information directly on magnetic or punched tape or on machine data cards for subsequent analysis.

Recently, solid state semiconductor detectors providing higher resolution between gamma-rays of nearly equal energy have become available. Higher costs must be balanced against greater resolution and lower efficiencies. Technological developments in this area of radiation detection are being made very rapidly and most equipment is soon outdated, but by no means no longer useful. Resolution for crystal detectors is about 5-10%, while for solid state semiconductors, the range is 0.5 to 3%. Current costs of semiconductors are about five to ten times higher than crystal scintillators.

COSTS

Equipment

There is such a wide variety of equipment available and prices are so temporal that any estimates of cost would be out of date immediately. But if radiological methods are to become an integral part of an established laboratory, modern automatic equipment is not only desirable but necessary. Minimum basic assay equipment could be purchased for under $1,000. Automated sample changers, printouts and built-in calculators could increase the cost to $5-10,000 for gas flow systems. Automated liquid scintillation systems (Fig. 11.4) are available for $6-18,000. Multichannel analysers and other computational and print-out equipment with new semiconductor detectors would cost $20,000 and higher. The scope of the research, the estimated results, the predicted life of the laboratory, and the available

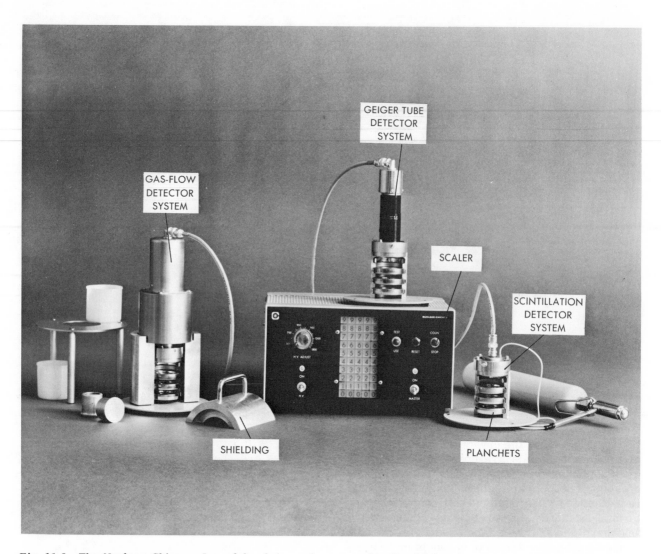

Fig. 11.3. The Nuclear-Chicago, Inc. alpha, beta, and gamma educational laboratory system includes Geiger, gas-flow, and scintillation measurement systems.

and predicted financial support are all important considerations in the selection of assay equipment. If a single limited application of isotopes is anticipated, the expenditure of large sums of money for highly automated equipment cannot be justified. Obtaining rental equipment or contractual services may be feasible.

Labeled Compounds and Isotopes

There are a number of reputable commercial firms both in the U. S. and abroad which supply a wide variety of isotopes in various forms and can supply a remarkable number of labeled compounds. One commercial firm recently listed over 1,200 labeled compounds (radiochemicals) incorporating the use of 170 isotopes. Many firms will specially synthesize labeled compounds requested by researchers at added cost. Since prices vary widely it is desirable to get several estimates for the purity and specific activity required.

EXAMPLES OF USE

Extensive bibliographies have been prepared on the uses of radioisotopes. Several of importance are: Dahm's (1957) on use in pesticide research; Hooper's et al. (1961) on use in hydrobiology and fish culture; Jenkins' (1957) on use, generally, in etomology; McCormick's (1958)

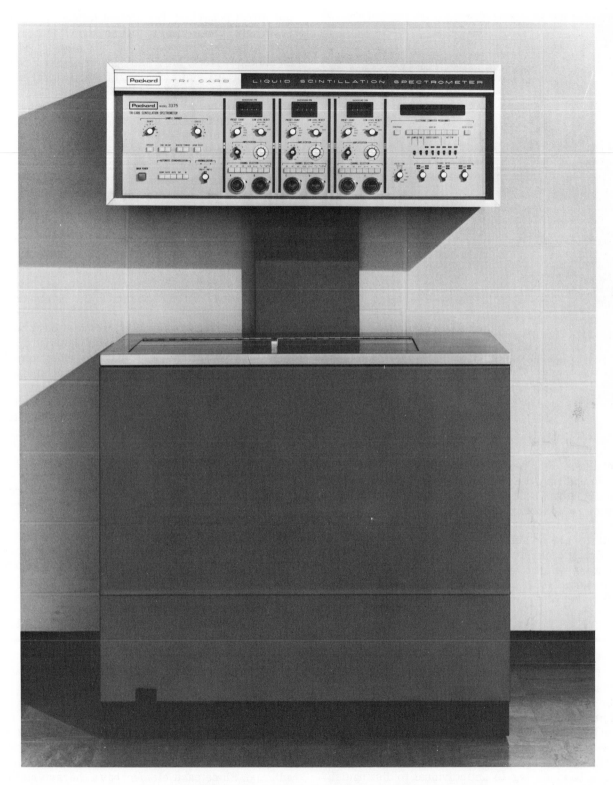

Fig. 11.4. The Packard Tri-Carb liquid scintillation spectrometer automatically or manually handles up to 200 samples in a continuous belt. Counting is by two photomultiplier tubes.

Fig. 11.5. The Packard Instrument Co. radiochromatogram scanner measures and records the beta-emitting nuclides deposited on thin-layer plates or paper strip chromatograms. The scanner employs two Geiger detectors for 4-pi scanning of both sides of the paper strip.

select list on use in animal physiology; and Schultz's (1963) on use in ornithology.

In addition, the select bibliographies of Klement and Schultz (1962-66) on terrestrial and freshwater radioecology and the annotated bibliography of Klement (1965) on natural environmental radioactivity are notable.

Early expectations for isotope-tracer solutions to many wildlife problems have not materialized (Pendleton 1952, 1956; Godfrey 1954; and Griffin 1952), but other uses have developed.

Tracers

Tracer methodology dates back to the 1920's when lead was used in studies of plant physiology. The many isotopes available from controlled atomic fission since that time have greatly expanded this area of research. (See Schultz and Klement 1962.) Using a radioactive label in a compound or in an animal is the same as attaching a band or tag to an individual to distinguish it from the group. It is assumed that the behavior of the labeled or tagged individual is the same as the rest of the group. Most isotopes, except for tritium and carbon[14] (Buchanan et al. 1953) will

not affect behavior. The atomic weight of tritium is nearly three times higher than for normal hydrogen. In some reactions this might produce an isotope effect. Most isotopes of higher atomic weight are little affected by this small difference. Tracers, such as P^{32}, Ca^{45}, S^{35}, Fe^{59}, Cu^{64} and others, can be used as single elements in nutrition and metabolism studies. Clinical diagnosis for certain diseases and glandular function are possible through the use of isotopes such as I^{131}. A number of isotopes have been used to label or mark individual animals. Grouse, ducks, fish, toads, reptiles, and a number of mammals have been labeled with radioactive gold, phosphorus, cobalt, silver, tantalum, and others. The potential anatomical or physiological effect on the animal must be assessed, and the possibility of human ingestion, particularly of game animals, must be weighed against advantages of use before some of these strong gamma emitters are used in the field.

Nest materials, as well as animals, have been marked, movements studied by radioactive excrement, parent-offspring relations determined, predator-prey and food-chain relations studied, all by radioisotope tracers.

The advantages in marking with a radiolabel are that the animal does not have to be handled to sense the mark, a number of individuals can be scanned quickly, the label is easy to apply, and can be useful for a limited time if desirable.

Recently one of the most important uses of isotope-labeled compounds has been to study the distribution, translocation, and bioaccumulation of pesticides in natural environments as well as within closed laboratory systems. Ease of pesticide sample preparation and residue determinations are major advantages, but a serious drawback is that sophisticated assays of metabolic products are not possible. As an example, Cl^{36} ring-labeled DDT could not be used to assay for DDE, DDD, or the other metabolites by using only radioassay procedures.

Neutron Activation Analysis

The determination of minute quantities of various elements is possible by bombarding a sample of the unknown with neutrons or charged particles and subsequently analyzing the induced radiation. Since each element has a characteristic energy spectrum, the composition of the unknown can be determined quantitatively and qualitatively. Using this method, mercury, bromine, sodium, and other elements can be determined at nano-

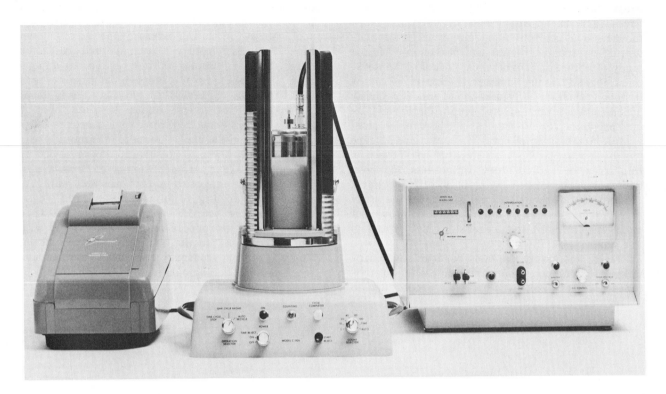

Fig. 11.6. Automatic sample changer (center) with gas-flow, thin-window, or scintillation detector heads automatically count the activity of 35 solid beta samples for a preset number of counts, and have the number of the sample and the time required to reach the counts printed on the timer (left). A binary scaler is at the right.

gram (10^{-9} gm) levels. Gold can be measured at levels of 10^{-11} grams. Radioassay of trace elements can be an aid in taxonomic work, residue determinations of various pollutants, and in tracer studies.

Isotope Dilution Analysis

Dilution analysis (Radiochemical Center 1965) is an additional means for determining low levels of specific compounds in mixtures. A known radioactive quantity of the compound to be measured is mixed with the unknown mixture. The compound to be measured is then extracted and the total radioactivity of the extracted portion is measured and compared in ratio to the original mixture. The total quantity in the unknown mixture can then be computed. This method can produce a considerable savings in time since only a small quantity of the original mixture need be extracted for the compound to be measured. Some pesticide residue work has been developed using these methods.

Miscellaneous

Autoradiography can be an important adjunct to research projects where radioactive compounds are already being used. Macro or micro sections of animal tissue can be placed in contact with X-ray film and exposed for adequate periods of time. Some exposures require a month or longer when residues in tissues are low and the isotope is a weak emitter. As an example, the location of pesticide residues within cells can be determined by feeding labeled compounds to the animal. Techniques for microautoradiography are quite exacting and considerable experience is necessary to produce and interpret results that are meaningful. Instruments in which the whole body of specimens as large as a human can be put for counting are now available. The whole-body method of measuring essentially gamma radiation is unique in that it permits periodic assay of a single living individual, facilitating the study of bioaccumulation and excretion rates of various elements and compounds. Radioactive dating of fossils and biological materials which is based on the ratios of various isotopes and known decay rates has been useful in the study of geologic time. Such dating might also be used in a more modern context for taxonomic studies or predicting environmental trends, particularly in the study of pollen and invertebrates from lake sediment cores. The use of naturally occurring radioisotopes such as K^{40} and those more recently added to our environmental contamination as fallout products (Sr^{90}, Cs^{137}, I^{131}) can be most useful in the study of natural ecosystems. There has been a great body of literature developed in this area of radioecology which has not been generally appreciated by most wildlife workers. Information, techniques, and data from the study of radioisotopes can be useful for solving current problems in pollution research. The parallels are clear.

Health and safety are considerations and practices of paramount importance in the use of isotopes. Ward (1952) wrote of the proper design of laboratories for safety. The *Radiological Health Handbook* (U. S. Dept. Health, Ed., and Wel. 1960) is an important general reference. Most installations require a trained radiation safety officer, employed by licensee, to supervise those aspects of research programs where quantities of radioactive materials are used. Licensing requirements are clearly set forth by the Atomic Energy Commission and requests for use of materials above certain minimum levels (C^{14}, 50 uc; P^{32}, 10 uc; H^3 250 uc) reviewed by that agency. (See Atomic Energy of Canada Ltd. 1961). Waste disposal in both air and water is regulated according to published standards. These standards are set and enforced by the USAEC to protect both the people in intimate contact with radioactive materials and the general public. They do not materially hamper use of radioactive materials in ecological or laboratory research.

CHAPTER TWELVE

RECONNAISSANCE MAPPING AND MAP USE

HENRY S. MOSBY, PhD

Professor, Wildlife Management
Virginia Polytechnic Institute
Blacksburg, Virginia

Maps are the most convenient and universally understood means yet devised to show graphically the spatial relations between the various features and structures on the earth's surface. These relations are expressed so that it is possible to determine from a map the distance and bearing (angle) from any point on the map to any other point. In wildlife management, as in other activities dealing with areas of land, a map is indispensable for recording and communicating the information relating to a specific area (War Department 1939 and 1944).

Recording on a map all data about a specific area would result in such a jumble of symbols that the map would be unintelligible. For this reason, a map is normally prepared to show a specific set of data. Thus there are many types of maps showing, for example, cover types and distribution, land use patterns, soil types and characteristics, distribution and abundance of animals, topography, future plans, and even field-note locations.

In most instances wildlifers prepare reconnaissance-type maps that do not have to be of a high order of accuracy. If great accuracy, such as distances accurate to one foot or less are required, standard surveying instruments and techniques must be employed. The preparation of maps of such accuracy will require considerable training and experience in surveying and therefore the services of a professional surveyor should be used. Thus, this chapter is concerned only with the preparation of reconnaissance maps or the utilization of available maps.

The wildlifer, when working in new and unfamiliar country, should first assemble maps of the area. Adequate and satisfactory maps can usually be secured. Highway maps are usually available from the state highway department or the district highway engineer's office; soil maps

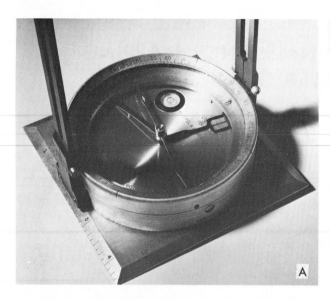

Fig. 12.1. The most frequently used reconnaissance-mapping tools are the staff held, or forester's compass *A*, and the Abney level *B*.

for those areas which have been mapped usually are available from the state agricultural extension service, located at the state college, or from the local office of the Soil Conservation Service; topographic maps are available for many sections from the Map Information Officer of the U. S. Geological Survey or the Superintendent of Documents, Washington, D. C., and often are in stock at local stationery stores; local offices of the Soil Conservation District can supply information on the availability of aerial photographs; local and state planning commissions usually have various types of maps which they will make available to interested individuals and, finally, the Army Map Service, Washington, D. C., acts as a map coordinating agency for the federal government. They have available for sale a vast number of maps for most regions of the United States.

It may be necessary to prepare special maps or to redraft, enlarge, or reduce existing maps for particular uses. These techniques will be discussed briefly.

RECONNAISSANCE-MAPPING INSTRUMENTS

Perhaps the mapping tools most often used by the wildlife worker who prepares his own maps in the field are the hand-held (box) or staff-held (forester's) compass (Fig. 12.1A), Abney level (Fig. 12.1B), and tape (either 100-ft or Gunter's chain—66 ft). Details of the construction of the compass and Abney level are supplied in the manufacturers' manuals. Kjellstrom (1955) presented an excellent discussion of the compass and its use; deMoisy (1949) described both the compass and Abney level and their use. Table 12.1 shows the accuracy in distance which may be expected with these instruments.

MAP DISTANCES

All map distances are horizontal, not ground, measurements. The ground measurement, the hy-

Table 12.1. Distance accuracy expected using reconnaissance-mapping techniques (Virginia Polytechnic Institute, Dept. of Forestry and Wildlife).

Measurement Technique	Allowable error in feet
Pacing	1 in 80
Hand-held compass (box)	1 in 80
Staff-held compass (forester's)	1 in 300
Abney level—elevation	1 in 500
Taping	1 in 5000

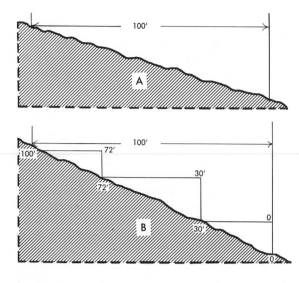

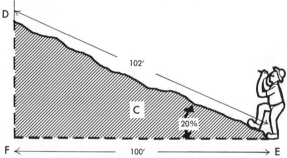

Fig. 12.2. Measurements along a slope may be corrected to horizontal distances by holding the tape horizontally A, by "breaking tape" into smaller horizontal measurements B, by a special "trailer" tape (see text), or by tape and Abney level C.

potenuse of a triange, (see Fig. 12.2) is greater than map distance. Slope measurements may be reduced to horizontal measurements for mapping by holding the tape horizontal (Fig. 12.2A), by "breaking" the tape (Fig. 12.2B), by formula, or by the use of a "trailer tape." Since the first two methods are illustrated, slope correction by formula and by the use of a trailer tape will be discussed.

Several formulae for reducing slope distances to horizontal distances may be used when a tape and Abney level are employed (Fig. 12.2C). An Abney level may have a topographic, degree, or a percent scale, each of which has advantages in certain situations. When employing the topographic scale on the Abney, a chain tape should be used with built-in graduations on the back showing the difference between slope and horizontal distance at various Abney level readings. The use of the topographic Abney and surveyor's chain tape is described and shown in Forbes

(1956:17:30-31). The degree Abney measures to the nearest degree the angle between the slope and the horizontal. Normal geometric calculations and trigometric tables are then used. The percent Abney scale measures the number of feet rise per 100 ft of horizontal distance. The percent reading expressed as a decimal is also the tangent of the slope angle.

The distance FE in Fig. 12.2C is obtained from the approximate formula

$$C = \frac{P^2}{200} \quad \text{where C = correction}$$

$$P = \text{percent slope}$$

where the slope is 20%, $\quad C = \frac{(20)^2}{200} = 2.0$

Therefore 100 ft on the 20% slope is equivalent to 98 ft; 102 ft equivalent to 100 ft. This equation is approximate and suitable generally below slopes of 23%.

The precise method is:

The cosine of the angle A whose tangent is 0.2 (20%) or 11° · 20' is 0.98.

Table 12.2. Corrections for Abney level measurements.

Abney Reading	Percent Arc Correction in Feet per 100 Feet	Topographic Arc Correction in Links per Chain
5	0.2	0.3
10	0.5	1.0
15	1.1	2.5
20	2.0	4.5
25	3.1	6.9
30	4.4	9.9
35	6.0	13.2
40	7.7	16.9
45	9.7	21.1
50	11.8	25.3
55	14.1	30.3
60	16.6	35.2
65	19.3	40.4
70	22.1	45.7
75	25.0	51.4
80	28.1	57.0
85	31.2	62.9
90	34.5	69.0
95	37.9	75.0
100	41.4	81.8

122

Horizontal Dist. = Slope Dist x Cosine A
FE = 102 x 0.98 = 100 ft

Table 12.2 provides similar corrections for the percent and topographic Abney arcs.

Most tapes are two (or more) Gunter's chains in length (132 ft) and are equipped with a "trailer" to facilitate the reduction of slope to horizontal distances. At the one chain length (66 ft), these slope conversion units are found on the backside of the second chain; at the two chain length, they are attached to the tape as a trailer, extending beyond the two-chain mark. These units, which represent the difference between slope and horizontal distance at various Abney topographic arc readings, are used as follows:

The head chainman with the zero end of the tape goes up the slope a distance of two chains. The rear chainman reads +20 on the Abney. The rear chainman finds the 20 reading on the trailer, and has the head chainman move out this distance. The rear chainman again reads the Abney. If the reading is still +20 (if elevation change is great, the reading could be greater than +20), the head chainman locates that point on the ground as being two chains of horizontal distance.

MAKING RECONNAISSANCE MAPS

All maps should include scale, date, surveyor's names, descriptive title, North (magnetic or true), and, if applicable, the contour interval.

Sketch Maps

A sketch map is nothing more than a sketch of an area to give the approximate location of various land and structural features. Such maps may involve no measurements of distances and no accurate determinations of bearings. All features are placed on the map in their approximate relationship by eye and by estimation. A map made in this manner should be clearly labeled as a sketch map. Such sketches, despite their limitations, are far superior to resorting to a written description of the location of various features. An example of a sketch map is shown in Fig. 12.3.

Compass-Traverse Maps

Traverse-survey maps may be prepared by the wildlifer with reasonable accuracy by: (1) staff compass and taped distances or (2) hand-held (box) compass and paced distances or, variations on these combinations. In the preparation of a compass traverse map, the use of the forester's compass and Jacob staff is a more accurate method of determining the bearings than by means of a box compass held in the hand. The box compass and paced distance method of preparing a map is much more rapid, of course, than forester's compass and taping, but less accurate. However, an experienced worker can prepare a surprisingly reliable and usable map by compass and pacing.

The bearings and distances can be recorded in field notes, and these notes can be plotted later in the office. This method of preparing a compass-traverse map is not recommended if it can be avoided. Rather, the map should be prepared in the field as the survey progresses. When the latter method is utilized, as errors become apparent they can be corrected immediately. Plotting a map in the office from field notes does not offer this opportunity.

Plotting the map in the field on coordinate paper is highly desirable for the vertical lines may be used as the north-south bearing. Thus coordinate paper, a rule, pencil, protractor, and clip board or datum holder are required when preparing the map in the field. A rubber band placed across the bottom of the paper on the clip board or datum holder prevents the paper from flopping in the wind. The Redy-mapper (deMoisy 1949) employs this concept and is an efficient field device for reconnaissance maps.

The scale of the map should be adjusted so that it can be plotted on a single sheet of coordinate paper. After the scale is determined, care must be exercised to locate the known starting point on the coordinate paper so that the plotted map will be contained on a single sheet of paper. With a known starting point established, set up the compass over this point, determine the bearing to some other prominent object (turning point), such as a tree, stake, or building. Plot this bearing on the coordinate paper, and then tape or pace the distance to that point. Turning points may be established at any convenient interval desired. Other points to be located within the traversed areas may be determined by intersection from two known points or by running a traverse line to them. Normally, determination by intersection of the bearings from two or more

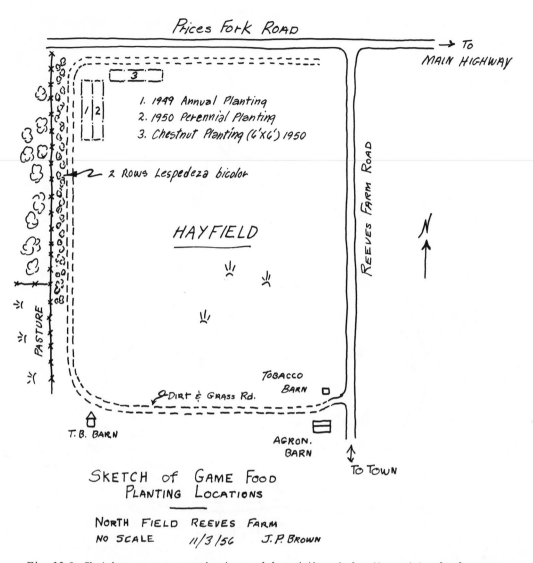

Fig. 12.3. Sketch maps are superior to word descriptions in locating points of reference.

known points is the quickest and easiest method of locating such objects as trees, buildings, and similar features. Other data such as cover type, fence rows, types of crops in the fields, and related data should be recorded on the map as the survey progresses.

An example of a field map prepared by the compass traverse and compass intersection method is shown in Fig. 12.4.

Topographic Maps

Topographic maps graphically show the differences in elevation of a specific area. Normally, these differences in elevation are shown by means of contour lines, which are lines which pass through points of equal elevation. The vertical interval between the contours may vary widely, depending upon the accuracy desired. Usually these contour intervals are 5, 10, 20, 50 and 100 feet in most reconnaissance maps.

Many sections of the United States have been topographically mapped by the U. S. Geological Survey and, near navigable water, by the U. S. Coast and Geodetic Survey. Many of the earlier Geological Survey topographic maps were prepared by means of aneroid barometers. For this reason, a high degree of accuracy is not claimed for these earlier maps. Both the Geological Survey and the Coast and Geodetic Survey maps should prove of great value to the wildlife manager, especially when he is concerned with large areas. The Geological Survey maps usually are prepared

124

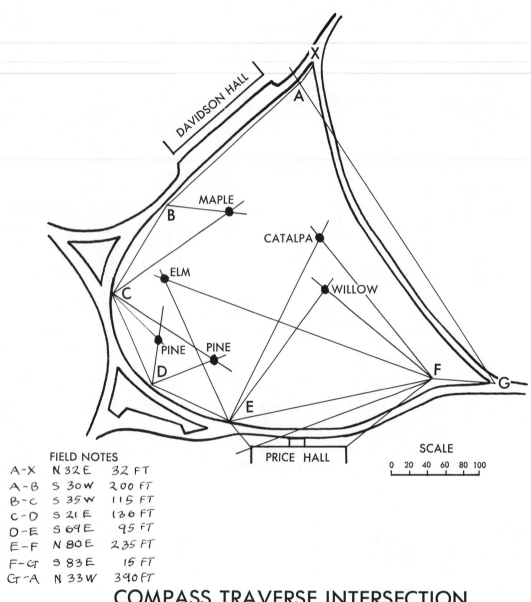

FIELD NOTES

A-X	N 32 E	32 FT
A-B	S 30 W	200 FT
B-C	S 35 W	115 FT
C-D	S 21 E	136 FT
D-E	S 69 E	95 FT
E-F	N 80 E	235 FT
F-G	S 83 E	15 FT
G-A	N 33 W	390 FT

COMPASS TRAVERSE INTERSECTION

LOWER TRIANGLE V.P.I. BLACKSBURG, VA.
MAY, 1957   PARTY: J.C. BROWN
T.E. WRIGHT

Fig. 12.4. Field map prepared on coordinate paper by the compass traverse and intersection method. For report use, this field map would have to be redrafted, usually by tracing.

as quadrangles, and an index map is available for most states showing those sections of the state which have been mapped and the quadrangle name of each mapped section. Common sizes are 7-1/2'' and 15'' latitude and longitude. When ordering topographic maps, the name of the quadrangle desired should be stipulated. If the quadrangle name is not known, give the specific locality desired by naming the county or parish, a post office in that specific locality, and the state.

The wildlife manager who is concerned with manipulating the habitat on a relatively small area may find it desirable to prepare his own topographic map. For example, he may wish to lay out a farm pond, drain or flood a marsh, or determine the difference in elevation on various parts of a watershed. The accuracy desired will vary widely, and it will be the responsibility of the wildlife manager to determine the contour interval and accuracy necessary to meet the requirements of his specific problem.

Contour maps may be prepared by various methods, such as by the stadia method with a plane table and alidade, from aerial photographs, by the use of aneroid barometers, by level surveys, and by hand levels. For a discussion of the procedures, advantages and disadvantages, and accuracy of each of these methods, consult any standard surveying text (e.g., Brinker and Taylor 1955).

Perhaps the hand level is the instrument most often used by the wildlifer in the preparation of topographic maps. The accuracy, while not high, is satisfactory for normal uses by wildlifers. A discussion follows of the topographic mapping technique using a K & E Abney level (Fig. 12.1B) having both a topographic arc and a percent arc. Other instruments employing the same general principles may be used. In any event, the instrument maker can supply a manual which explains the uses and applications of the individual instrument (e.g., Keuffel & Esser Co., n.d.).

Abney Level Surveys

The Abney level is an instrument used to measure slope, to determine the height of trees, to measure differences in ground elevation, to run lines of elevations, and to reduce slope measurements to horizontal equivalents. The instrument discussed in the following pages is the Abney level having an arc graduated on one side in percent of grade and the opposite side graduated in rise or fall per 66 ft on the horizontal. The arc is reversible so that either type of reading

may be used. (see Calkins and Yule 1935 and deMoisy 1949.)

The Abney level normally is read by the observer from the top of a rod (such as the top of the Jacob staff or, for tall observers, a higher rod), reading the top of a similar-height rod held by the rodman. The reading by the instrument man is then in feet of rise or fall if the horizontal distance is 100 ft and the percent arc is being used; the reading would be in feet of rise or fall if the horizontal distance is 66 ft and the topographic arc is being used.

Topographic maps of reconnaissance accuracy can be made with an Abney level and Jacob staff and compass. A two-man field party, with only a moderate amount of experience, should develop sufficient accuracy and speed to map in the field from 20 to 30 acres of rolling to hilly terrain per field day. With additional experience, it is possible to double this acreage in favorable country. Of course, the acreage mapped per day would vary widely, depending upon such factors as the amount and type of cover, extremes in elevation, and the accuracy (contour interval) employed.

In the following discussion, a reasonable familiarity with the construction and operation of the Abney level and the Jacob staff and compass (Fig. 12.1) is assumed. Those who do not possess such information should consult the manuals supplied by the manufacturers of such instruments (cf. deMoisy 1949).

The equipment needed by a two-man field party engaged in topographic mapping should include: Abney level with either a percent arc or a topographic arc, Jacob staff and compass, chain tape, pins, stakes, protractor, rule, clipboard, cross-section paper, flashlight (for signaling) and field notebook. An axe may be needed in heavy cover.

If the topographic map is to be tied in with other existing topographic maps, it will be necessary to run an elevation line from a bench mark of known elevation to a turning point, or temporary bench mark, located on the area to be mapped. In some instances, such as topographic maps to be used in laying out a farm pond, the exact elevation may not be necessary and an assumed elevation may be assigned to the starting station of the control traverse.

There are several methods of making surveys with the Abney level and compass, but the following procedure has proven to be satisfactory. The variations in the procedure need not be discussed here. In the following description it is assumed; (1) that an elevation line must be run from a known benchmark to the area being mapped; (2) that the Abney level used has a topographic arc; (3) that all slope distances are reduced to horizontal distances, either by breaking the tape or by the use of the tape trailer; (4) that the field party is sufficiently experienced to choose a scale of such magnitude that the map can be plotted in the field as the survey is made; (5) that the above listed equipment is available; and (6) that the instrument man will make all readings and the rodman will plot the data.

Set up the Jacob staff and compass over the reference benchmark and determine the bearing to be taken in running the line of levels to the area to be mapped. Have the rodman place a reference stake at a convenient, but not necessarily a measured, distance along this bearing. Locate the reference benchmark on graph paper in such a manner that the entire area can be plotted on a single piece of paper if at all possible. The rodman plots this bearing on the graph paper by means of a protractor. The rodman then goes to Station 1, which is a measured distance from the reference benchmark. The instrument man places the Abney level on the compass housing and by tilting the compass on its swivel head, aligns the reference crosshair on the top of a rod, which is exactly the same height as the level. The arc is adjusted until the bubble in the level is centered on the crosshair; then the arc is locked by means of the turn screw. The instrument man reads the arc scale and if the distance between the instrument and the rod is one horizontal chain, the arc reading is the actual difference in elevation between the two points. If the distance between the two points is a multiple or fraction of a chain, the arc reading must be multiplied by this whole or fractional number for the elevation change. The instrument man should call the difference in elevation to the rodman who plots the distance and elevation at the appropriate point along his bearing line. In addition to the data plotted by the rodman, it is advisable for the instrument man to record field notes, such as the station number, arc reading, distance between stations, difference in elevation between the two stations, and the bearing reading between the turning points. Such data permit the instrument man to check the plotted data of the rodman and facilitate the location of errors should the traverse fail to close or the elevations fail to check out due to mathematical mistakes.

After recording and plotting the information at the first location, the instrument man moves and places his Jacob staff and compass at Station 2. The rodman moves a measured distance along the bearing line and is aligned by the instrument man. At Station 2, and until Turning Point No. 2

(TP-2) is reached, it is unnecessary for the instrument man to take another bearing reading from the compass. Thus, the Jacob staff and compass are used only as a support for the Abney level between the several TPs. This process is repeated until a traverse line, with elevations, is run around the area to be mapped and the traverse is closed on either the original reference benchmark or on a turning point. Both the traverse and level lines should close within the accuracy which would be acceptable for the purposes of the map. The traverse should close within at least one-half chain for every 80 chains of line and the level should close within at least one contour interval. If this degree of accuracy is accepted, the error of closure, both in the traverse and level lines, can be distributed equally among each of the turning points.

After the traverse line, with elevations, has been established, level lines can be run between the several turning points. The number of level lines necessary would vary with the differences in elevation and must be determined by the survey party. In any event, a sufficient number of elevations must be determined to permit the survey crew to put in the contour line with reasonable accuracy. If possible, these contour lines should be placed on the map before the survey crew leaves the area. By doing this, it often is possible to check the contours by a visual inspection of the area. Figure 12.5 shows an example of a field map plotted in the above manner.

The Abney level can be set at 0 on the arc and used as a lock level to stake out contour lines. If this is to be done, the exact location of the contour must be determined and with this known point, the instrument is set up over this point. From this known point he can direct the rodman to points of the same elevation and the rodman can indicate these points by stakes. Staked contour lines are often used in locating the water level of a proposed pond or in the establishment of farm contour strips.

Mapping by Intersection

Fairly accurate maps of small areas may be made by intersection even when crude instruments are used. This type of mapping is especially suited for areas of one or two acres, the entire area being visible from some vantage point. For example, the area of a farm pond can be determined rather rapidly by this method. Mapping a pond by intersection using readily available instruments will be briefly described

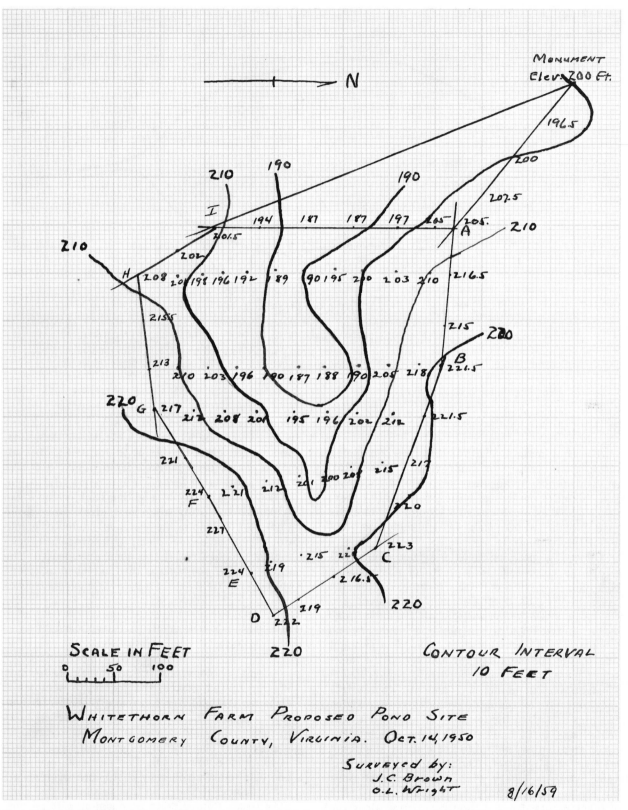

Fig. 12.5. Field copy of topographic map prepared by the compass traverse and Abney level method. The map was plotted on coordinate paper and then the contour lines were sketched on the field map.

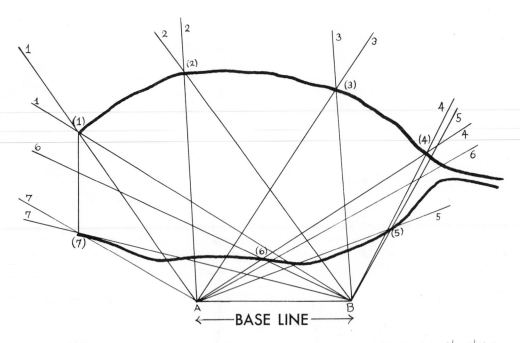

Fig. 12.6. Farm pond mapped by the intersection method. The base line (points A and B) is a measured distance. The plane table is placed over point A, aligned on point B, then the numbered points are located by sighting along an alidade or triangular scale. The plane table is moved to point B, aligned on point A, and each of the numbered points fixed by a second intersection line.

as an example. Reference should be made to Fig. 12.6.

The equipment needed for this type of mapping is: a plane table, (or improvised plane table); an alidade or triangular scale; straight pins; tape to measure the base line; coordinate paper; pencil; and several stakes. A compass to indicate North on the map is desirable, but not absolutely essential.

Choose a position near the pond which will afford as unobstructed a view of the pond as possible. Lay out a carefully measured base line (A-B in Fig. 12.6) of a measured distance and choose a scale which will permit the entire map to be plotted on a single piece of paper. Set up the plane table over point "A," choose a straight line on the coordinate paper and lay off the measured base line on the coordinate paper. Insert straight pins at points "A" and "B," place triangular scale on the table with one edge touching the pins and align the table by turning it until the scale edge is in line with the stake at point "B." After so aligning, set table securely so it will not jar out of alignment. Choose convenient points around the periphery of the pond and sight along the top of the triangular scale or alidade to each of these points. Draw a light pencil line along the edge of the alidade or ruler, making this line ex-

tend well beyond the point being located. These points should be located in a clockwise direction, numbering each line as it is located. After all points have been marked from point "A," take up the plane table and move it to point "B." Align, as described above, by sighting back on the stake at point "A." After alignment, draw lines from point "B" to each of the previously selected points along the pond shore. Thus, by intersection, convenient points around the pond are located. The shore line of the pond is then sketched in by eye while in the field.

MAPS FROM AERIAL PHOTOGRAPHS

Aerial photographs are now available for most of the United States and for large sections of Canada; the wildlifer can make good use of these photographs. The interpretation of aerial photographs will yield a vast amount of data to the experienced photo-interpreter (Dalke 1937, Leedy 1948, and Spurr 1948). The various techniques and equipment utilized by photo-interpreters will not be discussed here as this is a large and complex field. Rather, this discussion will be concerned only with the use of aerial photographs as a convenient way of preparing reconnaissance base maps.

Reconnaissance maps can be prepared from aerial photographs by: (1) the use of the individual photograph itself for small areas (2,000 acres or less); (2) blue prints made from photographic negatives (Moessner 1963); (3) making a mosaic from several aerial photographs for larger areas; (4) making a direct tracing of individual prints or of a mosaic; (5) a tracing made by equipment designed for this purpose, such as the aerial sketch-master or radial-planimetric plotter, and (6) tracing the desired data in India ink directly on the aerial photograph, then bleaching the photo, leaving the inked record.

Aerial photographs are often available to the wildlife investigator through loan from local public agencies. Prints also may be purchased. The identification number on each print, as well as the source from which it may be purchased, usually is available from the local office of the Soil Conservation Service, County Agricultural Agent, U. S. Forest Service, or Production and Marketing Agency.

If the wildlife investigator acquires his own copies of aerial photographs, the individually-owned prints make excellent field maps. Making an accurate mosaic of a series of aerial photographs is rather involved (Kelsh 1940; Am. Soc. Photogrammetry 1962) but the wildlife worker can put together a serviceable mosaic if high accuracy is not required. Such mosaics often serve as excellent reconnaissance maps (Fig. 12.7). The mosaic itself may be traced to give an inked map.

If the field worker does not have time to wait the several months normally required to purchase prints, many public agencies will permit the direct tracing of specific aerial photographs if the prints are not removed from the office. Such tracings frequently afford the field worker the best method of quickly securing reconnaissance maps from aerial photographs which are not his property.

Fig. 12.7. Composite aerial photos, or mosaics, are of limited accuracy but serve as excellent maps for many areas.

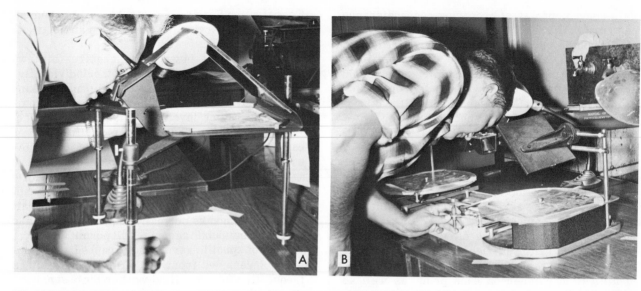

Fig. 12.8. Maps may be drawn from aerial photographs by means of *A* the aerial sketch-master (camera lucida principle) or *B* by means of the radial-planimetric plotter (stereoscopic principle).

Base maps are drafted from aerial photographs by means of the aerial sketch-master (Fig. 12.8A) and the radial-planimetric plotter (Fig. 12.8B). This equipment is available in many public land-use agencies and the wildlife investigator may prepare the map he requires by borrowing the use of this equipment and the necessary photographs.

The scales used in aerial photographs will vary

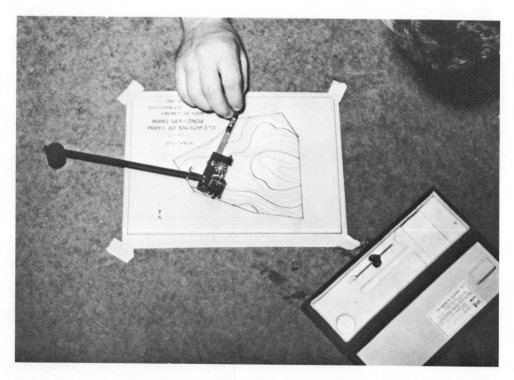

Fig. 12.9. Compensating polar planimeters are used to measure the square inches (or centimeters) within a given area. This measurement is then translated into acreage figures according to the scale of the map.

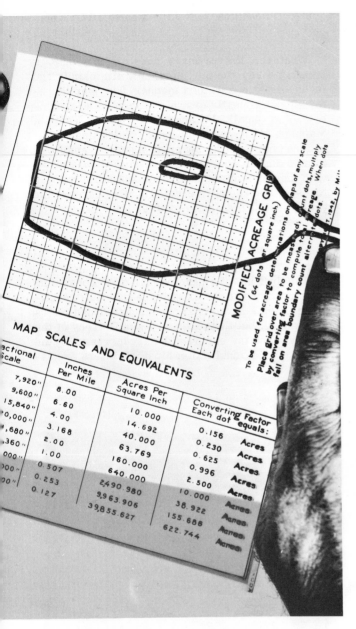

MODIFIED ACREAGE GRID
(64 dots per square inch)

To be used for acreage determinations on maps of any scale. Place grid over area to be measured, count dots, multiply by converting factor to compute total acreage. When dots fall on area boundary count alternate dots. T. 1942, by M...

MAP SCALES AND EQUIVALENTS

Fractional Scale	Inches Per Mile	Acres Per Square Inch	Converting Factor Each dot equals:
7,920"	8.00	10.000	0.156 Acres
9,600"	6.60	14.692	0.230 Acres
15,840"	4.00	40.000	0.625 Acres
?0,000"	3.168	63.769	0.996 Acres
?,680"	2.00	160.000	2.500 Acres
?360"	1.00	640.000	10.000 Acres
?000"	0.507	2490.980	38.922 Acres
?00"	0.253	9,963.906	155.688 Acres
?00"	0.127	39,855.627	622.744 Acres

Fig. 12.10. The Bryant transparent grid is a quick and reasonably accurate method of determining acreage. See text for explanation of how this grid is used.

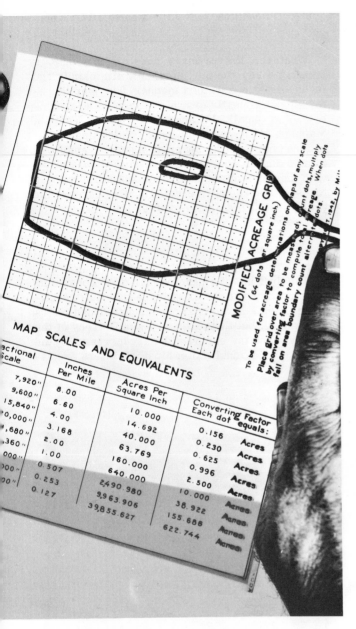

horizontal distance on the ground between these two points. The scale is expressed as follows:

$$\text{Scale} = \frac{\text{Distance in inches on aerial photograph}}{\text{Distance in inches, measured on ground}}$$

Whenever possible, maps should be prepared and traced from the center of aerial photographs, due to distortion near the edges of all prints.

If access is available to a photographic darkroom, the following technique may be useful under special circumstances. Take a photograph of an aerial print; enlarge the copy negative to the approximate size print desired; trace directly on the copy print in India ink those features which are desired; bleach the photograph in Farmer's solution (ferricyanide and hypo), leaving only the outline in India ink.

In addition to offering a convenient way of preparing reconnaissance maps, aerial photographs afford an excellent source of data for the preparation of cover maps (Nixon 1964). When used for the preparation of cover maps, the aerial photographs supply data for the base map and for the cover present on the area (See Dalke 1937, Leedy 1948, and especially MacConnell 1957).

ACREAGE DETERMINATION

The size of land areas is best described by acreages (1 acre = 208.71 ft square; 3.16 chains square; 43,560 sq. ft., 1/640 sq. mi. or 40.468 ares). Even approximate acreage figures are better than such terms as "a large boundary of land" or similar expressions. Rough acreage figures can be determined by dividing the map into convenient rectangles and measuring the two sides of each rectangle. From these measurements it is a simple matter to determine from the map scale roughly the square feet or square miles in the area. Of course, if the data so calculated are in square feet, the number of acres can be determined by dividing by 43,560.

A compensating polar planimeter is an instrument designed to measure area from maps (Fig. 12.9). Planimeters measure (1) the number of square inches or (2) number of square centimeters. In each case, it is necessary to determine from the map scale the area of a square inch or square centimeter. A square drawn to one unit of the map scale and planimetered will provide a useful factor for converting the planimeter readings to areas. When this information is

with the size of the print (degree of enlargement). Since there is a change in scale from the center to the edge of aerial prints (and with rough topography), it is advisable not to accept the listed scale for the prints of aerial photographs. The scale should be checked on the ground. This is done by selecting two conspicuous landmarks on the aerial photograph, measuring the distance in inches and tenths on the photo, then measuring the

132

available, the reading from the planimeter dial can be translated into area measurements.

On small areas, acreage can be determined by plotting the map on coordinate paper and, with the number of square feet per block of coordinate paper known, it is a simple matter to count the blocks or fractions and thus determine acreage.

The transparent grid developed by Bryant (1943) is a simple and reasonably accurate method of determining acreage (Fig. 12.10). This grid is marked in blocks and dots, which are fractions of a square inch. The grid is placed over the map, the number of blocks and dots counted within the area being measured, and the area determined from the scale of the map (acres, or square miles per square inch).

Acreage may be determined mathematically from the bearing and distances of a traverse survey. This method is more complicated and achieves a level of accuracy rarely needed by wildlifers. For a description of the method used in calculating the acreage mathematically, see a standard surveying text (e.g., Brinker and Taylor 1955).

Whatever the primary purpose of a map, it should convey the pertinent data with clarity and in an easily understood manner. The map therefore must be neatly drawn, use conventional symbols, and usually be acceptable for duplication. Mappers must have knowledge of drafting and an understanding of the several techniques employed in map duplication. If the field worker is familiar with the technique of duplication which he proposes to use, this knowledge will greatly decrease the time spent at the drafting table.

Drafting

The drafting of a neat map is a time-consuming matter that requires experience to acquire proficiency. Some persons are more gifted than others in drafting, but the neatness and efficiency of the neophyte and the expert alike are increased by the use of conventional tools. Most wildlifers are fa-

Fig. 12.11. A pantograph is useful in copying, enlarging, or reducing maps. The enlargement or reduction is determined by selecting the appropriate holes in the four perforated ruler arms.

miliar with the normal drafting instruments such as the ruling pen, compass, speedball pens, protractors, crow quill pens, T-squares, and triangles. Mechanical lettering and numbering sets, glass-top tracing tables, mechanically-printed types of hatching and lettering (such as Zip-A-Tone), and related equipment of the draftsman are very helpful. Such equipment, if available to the casual mapper, may be used to excellent advantage.

Usually, the working copy of a map is redrawn on tracing paper or tracing cloth before it is reproduced or filed. Such tracings may be made on a tracing board or a glass-top tracing table. If a mechanical lettering set is available, this instrument will greatly speed up the lettering of maps. Black waterproof ink is used in preparing tracings, especially if the tracings are to be reproduced photographically, photostatically, by B & W or blueprint processes, or by any of the engraving processes.

Enlarging and Reducing

Most maps prepared by the wildlifer will be used in reports or in manuscripts submitted for publication. The maps should be prepared and submitted in such a form that either the superior officer or the publisher can use them without time-consuming adjustment or redrafting of these maps. For example, if the map is to be used in a report on standard-size paper (8-1/2 x 11 inch), the map should be submitted in this size, or multiples of this size, so that it may be folded and fitted into the report. Likewise, if the map is to be used in mimeograph form, it should be submitted on a mimeograph stencil, thus saving trouble, as well as avoiding the possibility of errors if copied by inexperienced clerks. If the map is to be reproduced by photography or engraving, it should be drafted in a size that will permit a 50% reduction.

Adjusting the scale of the work map to a suitable scale for the finished map often presents a problem. For example, if the map is for use in an administrative report, the finished map should be of such size as to fit on a letter-size page (9 x 6 inches). On the other hand, this scale is not always acceptable in the field map and it may be necessary either to enlarge or reduce the field map. Enlargement or reduction may be accomplished by the use of a pantograph, or by photography. The pantograph is a mechanical device for either copying a map or diagram in the same scale, enlarging the scale, or reducing the scale (Fig.

12.11). This instrument is available in an inexpensive form or as a very elaborate and costly piece of apparatus. The pantograph may be adjusted, by means of perforated adjustable rules, in such a manner as to copy, enlarge, or reduce according to the scale desired. The following method of determining the most suitable scale may be used: Assuming that the work map is to be reduced from a larger size to a tracing which will fit on 8-1/2 x 11 inch tracing paper; estimate the percentage reduction which will be necessary and set the adjustable arms at this estimated reduction scale as printed on each pantograph rule face. Then, select a specific section of the larger map, and measure the distance in inches and tenths. Put the pantograph in place and, on a piece of scratch paper, trace the above-measured distance. Measure the line as reduced by the pantograph and use this figure as the numerator and the distance traced on the larger map as the denominator of a fraction. With this reduction fraction determined, measure the outside measurements of the larger map and multiply these measurements by the reduction fraction. If the resulting figures are less than 8-1/2 by 11 inch, this scale is satisfactory; if it is not, adjust the scale on the pantograph, either up or down, and repeat this procedure.

Drawings made with an inexpensive pantograph are not finished products and will have to be "dressed-up" before they can be inked. Most of the lines made by the pantograph will be wavy and of unequal density. Thus, it is well to locate accurately the important points on the reduced map by means of dots so that they can be checked when making the final inked tracing.

Maps may also be reduced, copied, or enlarged photographically. The map must be photographed, using special film and developer (e.g., Eastman Contrast Process Ortho film and D-11 developer), and the resulting negative printed contact or projected to secure either a reduction or enlargement. It is important that a map which is to be photographed for reduction should be inked with heavy lines and the lettering should be of such a scale that it will be legible (at least 1/16 inch) in the reduced copy of the map. This latter point cannot be overemphasized as it often causes trouble. A reducing lens is useful for checking such scaling.

Reproducing Maps

Maps may be reproduced in a number of ways, including blueprinting, blue-line or black-line

134

printing, mimeographing, lithoprinting, photostating, dittoing, line-cut printing, or photographic printing. In all instances, except when maps are to be reproduced by mimeographing or dittoing, the map should be on tracing paper or tracing cloth in dense waterproof ink. It is possible to make a blueprint and blue or black-line print from a penciled tracing on opaque paper, but such prints are not entirely satisfactory. Most engravers prefer that the maps from which they prepare line-cuts be made on white bond paper although they will accept inked copy on tracing paper or cloth. Likewise, they will accept clear and sharp photographic copies of maps, but their preference is for copies made in black ink on white bond paper.

Lithoprinted or multilithed maps can be copied, by a photographic process, from inked tracings, or the map may be drawn directly on a special lithoprint or multilith stencil. Maps to be reproduced by the mimeograph or ditto process should be copied directly on the stencil used in the respective process of reproduction. Experience is necessary in making a reasonably good tracing on a mimeograph or ditto stencil and the amount of fine details which may be included on these stencils is limited.

Maps for use in reports may be contact reproduced by several commercial "blueprint" processes. Many offices now have duplicators (xerox, Verifax, etc.) that will reproduce contact prints of inked maps in sized 8-1/2 by 11 inch or 8-1/2 by 14 inch. The photostat process can reproduce maps either the same or enlarged-reduced size. Whatever method of map reproduction is used to secure multiple copies of field maps, a thorough understanding of *how* the maps are to be reproduced should be determined before the final tracings are made. If the exact method of reproduction is determined, considerable redrafting time probably will be saved.

CHAPTER THIRTEEN

HABITAT ANALYSIS AND EVALUATION[1]

ANTOON DE VOS, PhD

Department of Entomology and Zoology
The Ontario Agricultural College
Guelph, Ontario, Canada

HENRY S. MOSBY, PhD

Department of Forestry and Wildlife
Virginia Polytechnic Institute
Blacksburg, Virginia

Wildlife is a product of the land. The abundance and well-being of any animal population may be used as an indication of the productivity of the land (Crawford 1950), its misuse (Graham 1944: 52), or both. It logically follows, therefore, that the wildlife manager must be able to evaluate—at least to some degree—the habitat of any animal population he proposes to manipulate. A review of Graham (1944) and Grange (1949), for example, will show that the real contributions to regulating

[1]Editor's Note: Due to circumstances beyond my control I was unable to secure a timely revision or alternate chapter on the difficult topic of habitat analysis and evaluation. "Chapter 4—Evaluation of Habitat" was reproduced from the 1963 *Wildlife Investigational Techniques*. The first part of the chapter is by Mosby; the section "Permanent Condition-Trend Transects" by Paul A. Shrauder, Staff Assistant, Jefferson National Forest, Roanoke, Virginia; and "Farm-Game Habitat Evaluation" and subsequent sections by Antoon de Vos.

The reader is encouraged to utilize Chapter 3 of this text to extend the usefulness of this chapter. Especially pertinent are works by Greig-Smith (2nd ed. 1964) and Kershaw (1964).

One extra comment seems desirable in order to make clear the need for distinction between "analyses" and "evaluations." Analyses are observations of habitat as it has or does exist. They are reports of the characteristics of habitat. Evaluations on the other hand, are analyses plus value judgments made based on a set of

our wild animal populations are made only when the wildlife manager correctly evaluates the habitat. Then, if ecologically feasible, he may manipulate the habitat so as to influence the animal population as desired.

The phrase "evaluation of wildlife habitat" as used herein implies both intensive and extensive efforts to estimate or appraise the value of various segments of the environment for an animal population. This includes the adverse influence which animal populations such as deer and rabbit, may exert on their habitat. Generally, vegetation is the most important aspect of the environment for most forms of game animals. Therefore, the following discussion will be concerned primarily with techniques of vegetation appraisal and analysis.

Obviously, it is necessary for the wildlife biologist to possess some knowledge of the situation being evaluated. The following discussion presupposes that the wildlife investigator has knowledge of the general habitat requirements and biology of the animal species involved, for without such knowledge, it is impossible to determine the importance (value) of various habitat factors.

It is impossible to apply intelligently any technique for measuring habitat unless the objectives of such measurements are clearly stated. Evans (1959:141), in commenting on the statistical aspects of the various papers presented at a recent symposium on vegetative analysis, said, "It seems abundantly clear that we understand the need for unambiguous objectives. It would seem that we are quite conscious of the dangers of gadgeteering and peering into small places. But we seem to have spent an appalling amount of time discussing what might be done on a variety of plots, without much consideration of whether or not we belong on the plot to begin with." As Gates (1949:1) points out, habitat evaluation may unintentionally become so involved with instrumentation and procedure that the latter two considerations are of major concern, rather than the ecological question under investigation. The field investigator, therefore,

must constantly keep in mind the main objective(s) and guard against the danger of over-emphasizing instrumentation and gadgeteering in his efforts to assess wildlife habitat.

For simplicity of presentation, the following discussion is separated into (1) reconnaissance-type techniques and (2) vegetative analysis techniques of habitat evaluation. Such a division is arbitrary but of practical value in keeping the techniques used in *line with the objectives of the investigation*. Detailed vegetative analysis techniques, due to practical considerations, are not suitable to large area habitat evaluation; reconnaissance-type techniques will not produce detailed data suitable for statistical testing. Each approach is valuable but they should not be confused.

Perhaps one of the most significant facts to emerge from the symposium (USFS 1959) on techniques and methods for measuring understory vegetation is that each habitat evaluation investigation problem should be individually designed and executed. For example, techniques that are designed for measuring forage rarely can be adapted for measuring shrub vegetation. Further, forage measuring techniques used in semi-arid range lands of the Southwest are not as suitable as might be desired for use in the humid Southeast. Such observations should be obvious but many errors of this kind have been committed in habitat investigations.

Any investigator planning habitat investigations should review recent literature on this subject (Brown 1954, Greig-Smith 1964, USFS 1959, Gates 1949, Phillips 1959, McLean and Cook 1946, Oosting 1958) and, if detailed sampling is involved, should seek assistance of a statistician in designing the investigation.

RECONNAISSANCE-TYPE EVALUATION OF HABITAT

Most wildlife investigators have—or should acquire—an appreciation of the general habitat requirements of the species with which they are concerned. Often a visual inspection of a given area will reveal its general suitability, or deficiency, for the wildlife species in question. In the following paragraphs, several techniques will be discussed which may be used to supply reconnaissance-type data that can serve as a basis for evaluating a given area for a given species.

---

human criteria. "Over-browsed" is an evaluation; "20 pounds of browse, production per acre" is an analysis of observations of browse and space. Whether "20 pounds of production" is good, bad, desirable or undesirable, can only be determined by a host of criteria such as: where is the area, next to an orchard? in a wilderness?; what was the production last year, is it increasing?; and how much production is needed to achieve the desired population (see Chapter 24). Habitat manipulation (Chapter 14) at its best, follows careful, objective analyses *and* evaluations based on well-articulated criteria.

Cover Maps

Cover maps are extremely useful for assessing general habitat conditions. If the cover mapping technique utilizes an ecological approach, such maps can be projected for a period of years to give the wildlife investigator a better understanding of the current habitat conditions and those that likely will prevail some years in the future. Conversely, if the cover mapping technique does not utilize an ecological approach, at least to a large degree, the value of the map is limited to a comparatively short period of years.

The following cover mapping technique is cited as an example of a method based on the ecological approach. K. E. Hungerford, University of Idaho, has pointed out that Graham's code is not applicable to western conditions but he, too, has used the ecological approach in his method of extensive cover mapping (Fig. 13.1). Other investigators (Arnold 1946, Alexander 1959) have proposed variations in detail. MacConnell (1957) has used the general ecological approach to cover mapping and applied it on an extensive scale; under this technique, the State of Massachusetts has been cover mapped from aerial photographs with ground checking of details.

Wight (1934 and 1938), Dalke (1937 and 1941), and Graham (1945) have pointed out the need for using cover map symbols based on ecological succession. Graham's paper, upon which the following discussion is largely based presents this technique in detail.

Perhaps the greatest problem encountered in cover mapping is: How much detail should be included on the map? No definite answer can be given to this question as the amount of detail mapped will vary widely, and will depend upon: (1) the use to be made of the map; (2) the area, or acreage; (3) the time available for mapping; (4) the principal animal species under consideration (e.g., sedentary small rodents or migratory caribou); and (5) related factors. Graham (1945) proposed a system of cover mapping which is based on ecological succession and his major cover symbols are arranged accordingly. These symbols may be expanded to include as much detail as may be required, or they may be abbreviated for extensive cover mapping. The cover map symbols may be placed on a base map prepared by any one of the several techniques discussed in Chapter 12.

The term "cover" is interpreted differently by various individuals (cf. Elton 1939 and Soc. Am. Foresters 1958). In the restricted interpretation as used here, we are concerned only with vegetative cover which may be divided into (1) the overstory, (2) understory, and (3) ground cover. Extensive cover mapping may be concerned with only the overstory; intensive, small acreage, cover maps may consider in great detail all three of the above cover components.

Fig. 13.1 shows the ecological classification of cover types as proposed by Graham (1945:184). As Graham points out, not all of the stages of each of the ten major classifications will occur in the various sections of North America. Thus, the proposed general system of classification may be shortened or lengthened as required.

The cover types are shown in the form of a fraction, with the numerator indicating the overstory and the denominator showing the ground cover conditions. For example, applying this system to an abandoned field ten years after cultivation in the Virginia Piedmont, the overstory cover might be indicated somewhat as follows:

$$A_e8\ 44''\ 4\text{-}6$$

which would show a clay soil (A), eroded (disturbance factor "e", subletter) seeded into an intolerant tree (8), Virginia pine (SAF type 44)[2], with medium stocking (''), ranging in diameter from 4 to 6 inches.

Ground cover may be denoted as the denominator of the above group of symbols. Assuming that the symbol for broomsedge (Andropogon virginicus) is "a" and the symbol for blackberry is "r", the above may be written as:

$$\frac{A_e8\ 44''\ 4\text{-}6}{a = r^-}$$

which would indicate a medium-dense ground cover of broomsedge and scattered blackberry. Anyone acquainted with the ecology of such an area in central Virginia could surmise with fair accuracy that this cover type[3] is likely to pass, within 15 years, to:

$$\frac{A_e8\ 44'''\ 4\text{-}12}{\theta}$$

[2]The overstory is designated by the forest cover-type number as described in detail by the Society of American Foresters Committee on Forest Types (Soc. Am. Foresters 1932).

[3]When both overstory and ground cover are indicated, in the form of a fraction, it is suggested that the absence of understory and ground cover (denominator) be denoted as: ground cover, understory absent = θ.

Eastern and Mid-U.S. Cover Types Code

A

Upland types—Terrestrial origin			Transition types		Lowland types—Aquatic origin			
					Bogs		Marshes	
Porous soils	Nonporous soils	Rock outcrops	Flood plain	Transition belts	Seepage	Stagnant	Seepage	Stagnant
P	A	R	F	E	BS	B	MS	M
1 Bare soil	1 Bare soil	1 Bare rock	1 Bare soil		1 Saturated soil or water	1 Water	1 Saturated soil or water	1 Water
2	2	2 Crustose lichens	2		2	2 Submerged vegetation	2	2 Same as B2
3	3	3 Foliose lichens and moss	3	3 Same as corresponding water or dry land type	3	3	3	3
4 Moss and annuals	4 Same as P4	4 Same as P4	4 Annuals		4 Sphagnum sedge mat	4 Same as BS4	4 Emergent aquatics	4 Same as MS4
5 Grass & other perennials	5 Same as P5	5 Same as P5	5 Same as P5		5 Sphagnum sedge and heaths	5 Same as BS5	5 Emergents & sedge-grass	5 Same as MS5
6 Mixed herbaceous	6 Same as P6	6 Same as P6	6 Same as P6	6 Same as P6 or BS6	6 Heaths predominate	6 Same as BS6	6 Same as P6	6 Same as P6
7 Shrubs	7 Same as P7	7 Same as P7	7 Same as P7	7 Same as P7 or BS7	7 Swamp shrubs	7 Same as BS7	7 Same as BS7	7 Same as BS7
8 Intolerant trees	8 Same as P8	8 Same as P8	8 Same as P8	8 Same as P8	8 Same as P8	8 Same as P8	8 Same as P8	8 Same as P8
9 Mid-tolerant trees	9 Same as P9	9 Same as P9	9 Same as P9	9 Same as P9	9 Same as P9	9 Same as P9	9 Same as P9	9 Same as P9
10 Tolerant trees	10 Same as P10	10 Same as P10	10 Same as P10	10 Same as P10	10 Same as P10	10 Same as P10	10 Same as P10	10 Same as P10

"Same as" means ecologically equivalent, not necessarily identical species.

Rocky Mountain Cover Type Code

B

Vegetative Zone (*Prefix Number*)	Successional Stage	UPLAND TYPES				LOWLAND TYPES	
		Rock outcrops (Bare rock) R	Porous soils P	Non-porous soil A	Marsh or pond M	Stream bottom non-porous soils F	Flood plain porous soils F
1. Arctic – Alpine	1	Bare rocks	Bare soil	Bare soil	Open water	Bare soil	Bare gravel
2. Spruce – Fir	2	Crustose lichens	Bare soil	Bare soil	Submerged vegetation	Bare soil	Bare gravel
3. Cedar – Hemlock	3	Foliose lichens, moss	Bare soil	Bare soil	Floating aquatics	Bare soil	Bare gravel
4. Douglas Fir	4	Pioneer shrubs or moss and annuals	Same as R 4	Same as R 4	Emergent aquatics	Annuals	Pioneer shrubs
5. Ponderosa Pine	5	Perennials and grass	Same as R 5	Same as R 5	Sedge-grass meadow	Perennials and grass	Perennials and grass
6. Fescue Wheatgrass	6	Mixed herbaceous	Same as R 6	Same as R 6	Same as R 6	Same as R 6	Same as R 6
	7	Shrubs	Same as R 7	Same as R 7	Same as R 7	Same as R 7	Same as R 7
	8	Intolerant trees	Same as R 8	Same as R 8	Same as R 8	Same as R 8	Same as R 8
	9	Mid-tolerant trees	Same as R 9	Same as R 9	Same as R 9	Same as R 9	Same as R 9
	10	Tolerant trees	Same as R 10	Same as R 10	Same as R 10	Same as R 10	Same as R 10

Symbols for use with A and B above

Physiographic Conditions (*Exponential letter*)
o – outwash or alluvial fan
b – loess
d – dunes
s – shale or talus slope
l – calcareous origin
g – igneous rock
k – kettle hole
m – glacial drift

Disturbance Effects (*Sub-letters*)
d – drained
p – pastured
g – seasonal grazing
a – wild animal browsing, grazing
c – cropland
f – flooded
y – cutover
x – burned
e – severely eroded
b – blowdown

Grass and Timber Stocking and Size (*Symbols and Numerals*)

		Diam.
'	Scattered	in inches
''	Medium	4–6, 6–12, etc.
'''	Dense	or basal area

Shrub Density
- Scattered
= Medium
≡ Dense

Fig. 13.1. A. Codes for ecological classification of cover types as proposed by Graham (1945:184) and B. K. E. Hungerford and P. D. Dalke (pers. communication) based on Daubenmire (1952). For example, a symbol with numerator of 5–Pg–5 designates an area in a ponderosa pine zone having porous soil of igneous origin and, at the time of observation, covered by perennials and grass.

As pointed out by Graham, the amount of data plotted on the cover map may vary widely. However, in wildlife management the disturbance factors and ground cover are of considerable importance. The use to which the map is to be put will determine the detail which should be plotted. Caution must be exercised, however, to avoid expanding the symbols employed to a point where the map becomes unintelligibly complex.

The plotting of the symbols denoting agricultural crops on the permanent, inked, copy of the cover map is not recommended, as such crops may change from year to year. Denoting the particular crops being grown on the field map is recommended as these data are of considerable, though temporary, value in wildlife management planning. The recommended procedure for indicating cultivated land in corn would be $\frac{C}{cn}$ on the field map but only as C on the inked tracing.

The above system of cover mapping may appear complicated to those who have not used it. Its use in the field for only a short period of time will demonstrate that it is not nearly as complex as it first appears. The amount of information which may be presented about the cover on any area by this system of cover mapping is indicated in Fig. 13.2. Note in this illustration that only the cover symbols appearing on the particular map need be given in the map legend.

Cover Density Evaluation

In the preceding discussion of cover mapping, reference was made to indicating cover density by the symbols: - Scattered or light; = Medium; and ≡ Dense. The following discussion is concerned with methods of measuring cover density, at least to the degree that the above symbols may be designated identically by different field investigators.

So far as is known, there is no acceptable measure of cover density that will consider adequately all of the factors involved for all species of wildlife (Webb 1942, Trippensee 1934, Braun 1941, Allard 1947). Vegetative cover will diminish light intensity or obstruct vision, both horizontally and vertically. For the purposes of the following discussion, it will be assumed that either light intensity beneath the cover being measured or the obstruction of vision is a function of cover. If this assumption is valid, then the measure of either, or both, constitutes a measure of cover density.

Techniques for evaluation of cover density include: (1) ocular estimation, (2) counting the number of stems per sample quadrat, (3) measuring the obstruction of vision, (4) measuring, by photoelectric devices, the influence of cover on exclusion of light, and (5) photography.

OCULAR ESTIMATING

Any experienced field worker who is familiar with the requirements of a specific wildlife species has his own ideas as to the required cover density for that particular species. The experienced observer can readily designate, by ocular estimate, almost any cover into one of three categories: scarce, medium, or dense. Often this is done and there is no actual measurement made of cover density.

Webb (1942) has suggested a measure of cover density using an ocular estimate of the relative amount of the sample area which is covered by leaves of the plants in each of three cover components: overstory (tree), understory (shrub), and ground cover. The cover density classes which he used are:

1. Density T (Trace)—leaves cover less than 1/80 of the area of the plot.
2. Density 1—leaves cover 1/80 to 1/3 of the area of the plot.
3. Density 2—leaves cover 1/3 to 2/3 of the area of the plot.
4. Density 3—leaves cover more than 2/3 of the area of the plot.

The sizes of the sample plots as used by Webb are: for estimating tree cover, plot radius of 66 ft (1 chain); for estimating shrub cover, plot radius of 9 ft; for estimating ground cover, plot 3 ft by 3 ft. Webb suggests a numerical rating which seeks to express both density and abundance of each plant species on the area being examined. Obviously, Webb's method of denoting cover density would be limited to that period of the year when the plants were in full foliage. This is a serious weakness, for that period of the year is one in which cover is abundant; cover for concealment and for protection against the elements is of most value to wildlife during the period of the year when leaves are absent.

NUMBER OF STEMS PER SAMPLE PLOT

A method of indicating cover density for the ring-necked pheasant by counting the number of stalks per quadrat was proposed by Wight (1938). Trippensee (1934), in measuring cover for the

SCALE

LEGEND

P	Porous soil
A	Nonporous soil
p	Pastured
M	Marsh
C	Row crop
CH	Pasture and hay
O	Orchard
bg	Bluegrass
cn	Corn
Cl	Clover
gr	Grazed
m	Mixed vegetation
t	Trees
s	Shrubs
h	Herbs
v	Honeysuckle
wh	Wheat
▱	Degree of tree stocking
10	Tolerant trees
9	Mid-tolerant tree
50	S.A.F. forest type 50
10-40	d.b.h.
″	Degree of stocking or grazing intensity

Fig. 13.2. Field map of general cover types on an approximately 2,200-acre area.

142

Fig. 13.3. Cover "density board" used in measuring cover by obstruction to vision. The reading here is (3 + 4 + 6) 13. This board also may be used to measure cover height up to 6 ft.

cottontail rabbit, also used the stem-count technique. Any procedure which entails the counting of a large number of stems is time-consuming; some more rapid method of indicating cover density is desirable, if feasible.

MEASURING OBSTRUCTION OF VISION

Wight (1938) proposed a system of indicating cover density by the use of a "density board." This board (Fig. 13.3) is 6 ft tall with each foot marked off and numbered from 1 to 6. It is used in the following manner: the rodman places the density board in the cover to be measured and an observer reads the figures which are unobscured by cover at a distance of 66 ft. If there is no cover, the reading is 21 (1, 2, 3, 4, 5, and 6 added together); if cover completely obscures the entire board the reading would be 0. In this manner, a measure of the obscuring qualities (or density) of the cover is indicated. Thus, a series of readings—

or the average of these data—would give some measure of the density of the cover.[4]

A suggested classification of such readings in a manner which would render them amenable for use on cover maps is:

Per cent obscurity	Classification	Map Symbol
16	Scarce	-
33 to 66	Medium	=
66 and over	Dense	≡

MEASURING COVER DENSITY BY PHOTOELECTRIC EQUIPMENT

Sather (1950) described in detail the construction of a photoelectric device designed especially for the measurement of light which is excluded by

4Editor's Note: The reader is cautioned that vegetation obscuring panels 1+2+3 produce results equivalent to vegetation obscuring panel 6.

various types of cover. The function of this instrument is to measure light conditions under various types of vegetation and to compare these measurements with simultaneously or identically taken readings of light conditions in open situations. This instrument consists of a phototronic cell, diffusion disc, a microammeter, and a three-way switch to obtain ranges of low, middle, and high. If desired, measurements taken with this instrument may be converted to readings in foot-candles by constructing the necessary graphs. Sather concluded that readings from seven mechanically selected 1 ft by 4 ft quadrats would provide an adequate sample for the most complex types of herbaceous and shrubby growths.

Allard (1947) used a standard Weston Illuminator Meter, Model 603, to measure the illumination beneath various types of cover and in full light under no cover. He expressed his relationship between the amount of light under various cover types and in the open as a ratio; e.g., 1:0002 for a reading of 2.2 ft-c in shade as compared to 10,000 ft-c in full sun.

A method used at the Virginia Cooperative Wildlife Research Unit is simple and consists of making simultaneous photoelectric readings of the light conditions beneath various types of cover and in full light. The instruments used are two photographic exposure meters, supported on a frame 8-inches above an 8-inch square board which has been painted with aluminum paint. The light reading is taken with the photoelectric cell facing downward; therefore, the reading is obtained from light reflected from the base of the frame. The details regarding this simple instrument are evident from Fig. 13.4. This system of measuring cover density has one disadvantage in that it requires a two-man crew. One of the two instruments is placed on the ground beneath the cover to be measured and the second instrument is located in full light. At a given signal, each instrument is read and the measurements are recorded as a fraction:

$$\frac{\text{Reading under cover}}{\text{Reading in full light}} = \frac{\text{Per cent of light admitted}}{\text{by cover}}$$

The rating of the cover density according to these measurements is the same as that proposed by Sather (1950):

Per cent of Light Admitted	Classification	Map Symbol
More than 75	Scarce	-
51 to 75	Medium	=
0 to 50	Dense	≡

Fig. 13.4. Photoelectric exposure meter on aluminum-painted frame used to measure cover density as expressed by its obstruction of reflected light.

PHOTOGRAPHIC EVALUATION

Frequently, it is desirable to depict the cover conditions in as graphic a manner as possible. One method of showing the changes which take place in cover composition from one season of the year to another (Fig. 13.5), under different land uses or abuses, and as a result of normal ecological succession, is by means of photographs. Such photographs often tell the story, especially to the lay public, in a way that is superior to all other methods (see Bump 1950). If photographs are used for this purpose, care should be taken to frame the sequence pictures in as identical a manner as possible. The placing of white stakes at intervals throughout the area being photographed is an excellent method of giving some recognizable points of reference within the photographs. A small chalkboard with area name and date shown within the picture is desirable for identification.

Soil Evaluation

There is a growing realization of the interrelationships which exist between animal populations and the soils upon which they are produced (Van Dersal 1937, Crawford 1946 and 1950). The nutritive value of plants varies widely with soil conditions, as the chemical composition of a plant is affected by the chemical elements available in the soil. Apparently wild animals can detect this dif-

Fig. 13.5. Seasonal changes of cover can be shown by means of photography. A. September fencerow cover. B. March fencerow cover.

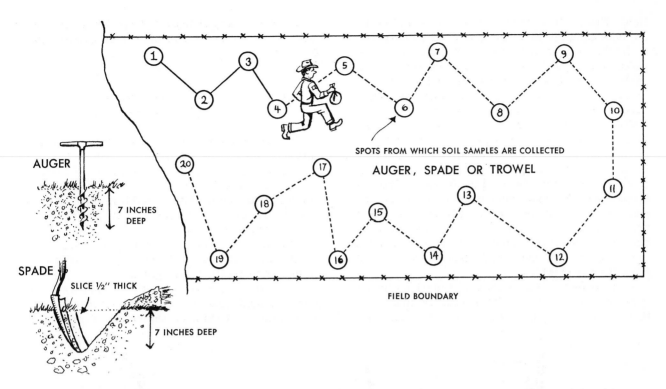

Fig. 13.6. General instructions for collecting soil samples for analysis by a government soil-testing laboratory.

ference, for experiments in New York State showed that in a 40-year-old oak stand 80.7% of the plants of flowering dogwood were fed upon in a plot heavily fertilized with nitrogen, while in the adjoining untreated plot only 3.6% were browsed (Mitchell and Hosley 1936).

The types of soils present on areas being managed for wild game may be used as an index of the wildlife productivity of the area. Soil maps are the best source of information for such an evaluation. Published soil maps are available for many sections of the U.S. on a county or parish basis. Those soil maps prepared since 1930 are of the greater accuracy. Where published maps are not available, it is often possible to secure detailed, but unpublished, information on the soil types of a specific area by consulting the local Soil Conservation Service office or the State Soil Scientist of the Agricultural Experiment Station.

It is unlikely that the wildlife manager will be called upon to make his own soil map although he should be acquainted with the procedures used in preparing such maps (Ableiter 1938). Local soil scientists should be consulted for evaluating soil conditions on any wildlife management area. If the advice of soil specialists is not available, it is possible for wildlife managers to make simple soil tests with commercially available kits to determine the major plant foods present. Such tests

are of value in indicating the treatment that may be necessary to produce satisfactory plant growth on areas being managed as food-producing areas.

Most state (and some county) governments have well-equipped soil testing laboratories. A simple procedure for collecting soil samples suitable for individual or laboratory testing is shown in Fig. 13.6. Important things to remember about sampling soil are as follows: 1. Use a clean bucket in which to gather soil samples. Send samples to laboratory in boxes provided by your county agent, Soil Conservation Service technician, vocational agricultural teacher, or other agricultural workers. Write the name and address of the owner and sender on each sample. If more than one sample is being sent for an individual, be sure to number or letter each sample. 2. Take from 10 to 30 small samples from every part of field. Combine samples of soil from parts of field which have the same type of soil and which have received the same fertilizer and lime treatments.

Soil samples must be taken carefully and properly if the results of the test are to be of any value since a sample represents many million pounds of soil. For a sample to represent a whole field, a large number of samples must be taken and thoroughly mixed; then a sample from this mixture is sent in for testing. How many samples to take from a field will depend on the size of the field. From 10 to 30 places may be sampled. Do not take samples when the land is extremely wet.

If the soil in the field is of different types, make a composite sample for each type. Or if parts of the field have been used for different crops or have been treated differently in the past, make a composite sample for each part.

Take samples with a trowel, shovel or spade. Make a vertical cut to the desired depth and push the soil aside. Then cut a thin slice from the face of the cut and collect it carefully for the sample. A soil auger or a tube can also be used. The desired depth for crop land is plow depth and for pasture land, 2 inches. Do not take samples from under manure, decaying organic matter, corn shocks, small grain shocks, or litter, because those places will have extra plant food leached from the material.

A composite sample should be not less than a quart of soil. It should be thoroughly mixed and then a half-pint of the mixture sent in for analysis.

Do not send samples in paper bags. If regular containers are not available, ice cream cartons may be used.

Evaluation of Food Production, Availability, and Consumption

Increasing emphasis is being given to the evaluation of the ability of habitat to produce food for wildlife and of the use made of this food by various wildlife species. The techniques which have been employed to obtain data on wildlife food production, availability, and consumption are diverse; no uniformly acceptable procedures have been evolved at this time. In the following discussion, examples of the general types of procedures used in such investigations are given.

As used here, food *production* includes all food grown or synthesized in one growing season (e.g., the total crop of mast grown during the preceding

Fig. 13.7. Oak twigs with leaves removed showing (1) black oak acorns set on second-year wood, good yield; (2) white oak acorns on current-year wood, good yield; (3) chestnut oak acorns on current-year wood, bumper crop (photo courtesy W. M. Sharp).

period of plant activity). Food *availability* designates the quantity of food present and within reach of the animal in question (e.g., the amount of mast on the ground at a specified time which might be taken as food by the eastern wild turkey). Food *consumption* may be defined as the proportion of the available food which has been utilized by the animal species in question (e.g., the proportion of the available browse which has been eaten by white-tailed deer).

FOOD PRODUCTION

Mast production in the black oak group can be predicted about 1-1/2 years in advance (Allen and McGinley 1947, Sharp 1958). The black oaks require 1-1/2 years to mature their fruit, whereas mature acorns are produced the same year of flowering in the white oaks (Fig. 13.7). Thus, an inspection of the oaks in July will give general in-

formation on the quantity of acorns which may be produced the following fall for both white and black oaks. Such an inspection would also give information on the amount of black oak mast which might be expected the second fall.

Sharp (1958) recommended inspecting, between August 10 and 25, the outermost 24 inches of the lateral and terminal branches of oaks. A branch tip of black oak bearing 32 or more acorns is ranked as 100%; in white oaks, 24 acorns are ranked as 100%. He recommends selecting 10 specimens of each species for mast examination and presents details for rating mast yield based on these examinations.

Petrides et al. (1953) counted the number of acorns on the first 25 twigs of oaks as they were encountered. Gysel (1958) utilized a telescope to count immature acorns. Downs (1944) and later workers (Reid and Goodrum 1957, Gysel 1956 and 1958) used acorn traps to get an index of production of various oaks. Crawford (1959) reviewed

Fig. 13.8. Exclosures, such as the Hickory Run (Pennsylvania) deer exclosure shown above, may be used to measure vegetative production in the absence of animal feeding. The results can be shown dramatically by photographs or by detailed vegetative analysis as shown in Table 13.1 (U.S. Forest Service, Northeastern Forest Experiment Station, photo by Ted. J. Grizez).

the work of a number of investigators in their efforts to determine seed production of woody and herbaceous plants.

Bishop and Spinner (1946) examined a number of corn fields to determine weed seed production. Ten milacre plots were systematically selected in each field according to a predetermined plan so that all sections of each field would be sampled. The number of stems of each species of weed was counted on each plot. The average number of seeds-per-stem was calculated by collecting, cleaning, and weighing the seed from 100 stems of each species. Brookhout (1958) investigated plant seed production in nine major land-use divisions in Southern Illinois. Samples were collected by tossing a metal ring with a diameter of 6 inches into the cover type under investigation. All seed within the 6-inch ring were separated from the soil, identified, and classified.

In agronomic work, the production of various crops is determined by collecting seed (or other portions of plants) from sample plots. Similar studies in wildlife investigations are often made, especially on forage crops planted for such species as ungulates and geese. Production of forage crops may be measured by means of exclosures and clipping studies. For example, in an exclosure in a ladino clover planting heavily used by deer, the production in pounds-per-acre may be determined by clipping and weighing the clover produced within the exclosure. Similarly, the utilization of clover by deer may be determined by a comparison of clippings taken outside and inside such exclosures (see Stoddart and Smith 1955). The production of various species of browse for deer and the degree of utilization of each species may be indicated by clippings studies made within and outside larger "deer exclosures" (Fig. 13.8). Table 13.1 shows one type of data which may be secured from deer exclosure investigations.

FOOD AVAILABILITY

In field studies dealing with native foods it is often difficult to measure production completely and even more difficult to distinguish, with certainty, between production and availability. There are good reasons to think that food availability is the more practical consideration of the two, at least so far as wildlife is concerned.

Haugen and Fitch (1955) determined the availability to bobwhite of bicolor and large partridge pea seeds by collecting at random square-foot samples from the ground throughout plantings of these species. Their technique in determining the

Table 13.1. Per cent of total area under 5 ft occupied by woody plant crowns inside and outside the Hickory Run (Pennsylvania) deer exclosure (Grizez 1959)

Species	Per cent of area occupied	
	Inside	Outside
Red pine	46	3
Red oak	2	0
Black cherry	1	*
Aspen	9	0
Gray birch	16	13
Other tree species	2	*
Willow (shrubs)	4	0
Meadowsweet	2	*
Blackberry	6	1
Dwarf sumac	2	0
Blueberry	16	6
Bush-honeysuckle	4	0
Wild raisin	1	0

*Observed but did not occur on sampling points.

availability of bicolor seed included the collection of samples of 1 ft of litter, down to mineral soil. Each ground sample was placed in a paper sack to dry, and when dry, it was run through a seed cleaner. After the first run, the sample was recrushed by hand to break up clods of soil and rerun. The sample was rerun until all that remained was bicolor seed and a few pebbles. The seeds were separated from the pebbles by flotation, using a liquid of the proper specific gravity, such as carbon tetrachloride.

Any technique to determine food availability is time-consuming and tedious. Clipping studies—as a technique for determining forage for cattle and browse for deer—are no exception. Studies of livestock food production clearly indicate that no single technique will supply data that will fully meet all needs for scientific range management (see Brown 1954). This is equally true for similar studies dealing with the evaluation of food production and food utilization for such species as deer and elk (see Dasmann 1948).

Wildlife investigators have experienced difficulty in attempting to use techniques designed primarily for one geographic region in other areas of completely different ecological conditions (i.e., the use in the humid East of forage studies developed for the semi-arid sections or the use in the deep South of deer browse techniques developed for northern deer yard conditions). Thus, it is unsound to use such techniques unless they are modified intelligently to apply to conditions existing in the area under investigation. Likewise, it is unreasonable to condemn the technique in question if it must be "jammed" in order to be used under unusual or unique conditions.

FOOD CONSUMPTION

Oftentimes it is impossible to separate completely food availability and food usage. Many techniques seek to determine both with the same procedure. Schwan and Swift (1941) suggested the use of clipping studies to check estimates of the air-dried weight of forage available for big game. They pointed out that refinement in ocular estimation of density is difficult but, if weights are taken periodically (by clipping each 5th plot, or portion of a plot), such measurements permit the investigator to refine his ocular estimates of weight. This system also makes it possible for one investigator to compare his results with other workers. These writers recommended the following general procedure:

1. Transects are established through each cover type and randomized plots are taken in proportion to the importance of cover type to big game. At least 10 plots should be taken for each 640 acres, under western conditions. The size of the plot may be varied according to local conditions but they suggest plots with radii of 2.82 ft (25 sq. ft) or 5.64 ft (100 sq. ft) for ease of conversion of the weight data to pounds-per-acre.

2. The investigator should clip a plot, or a portion of a plot, immediately upon entering a new cover type. The clipped material is weighed, preferably separated by species, and the material saved for determination of the air-dried weight. The weight of browse or forage present on subsequent plots is estimated using the clipped plots as a guide. Approximately each fifth plot is wholly or partially clipped.

Casebeer and Rognrud (1949) suggested a technique which, if applied over a period of years, should produce data of considerable interest as to the use by deer of selected or "key" browse species (Fig. 13.9). This technique involves the linear measurement of the annual growth of twigs of four plant specimens at a number of stations, such measurements being made both in early fall and in late spring. The stations are located by traversing from a known benchmark along a predetermined course for a predetermined distance. At each station (marked by a colored stake), four browse specimens are selected for measurement. The specimens to be measured are selected according to the abundance of the key species in that particular area. For example, if maple is reasonably common in one area but is not abundant in another, the investigator may select maple for measurement where it is abundant and measure another species in the second locality. A representative branch on each specimen is selected and marked with a tag. The linear lengths of all twigs on the branch measured and recorded according to length classes. Thus, a comparison of the linear lengths recorded in the fall with similar measurements made in the spring will permit a percentage calculation as to the amount of each species taken by deer during the winter. There is now, however, some evidence that deer are attracted by the tags.

Aldous (1944) developed a browse survey method mainly for use in northern winter yarding areas, but it has been used widely in the East with modifications. Fig. 13.16 shows an example of this technique, described later in the chapter, for measuring deer food availability and consumption.

Plant Indicators

The vegetation which develops in any given situation indicates a great deal about habitat conditions. Those plants which dominate the habitat may be used to evaluate habitat conditions as indicators of climate, soil conditions, moisture conditions, past disturbance, and agricultural potentials. Indicator plants and plant communities have received considerable attention, especially in the western states; perhaps the most exhaustive treatment of plants as indicators is given by Clements (1928). Some papers that are of interest to the wildlife biologist include those by Shantz (1950), Barnes (1948), Kellogg (1948), Graham (1944), Stoddart and Smith (1955), and Weaver and Clements (1938).

It is true that plant indicators and what they tell of habitat conditions are difficult, if not impossible, to reduce to instrumental measurement. They do permit the observant field worker to deduce a great deal about conditions in the field *provided* he has a good grasp of the ecology of the area in which he is working. Care must be exercised in translating too freely ecological experience obtained in one region to a new field of work.

CLIMATE

Plant growth and vigor is a good indication of the general climate of the area. It is common

BROWSE UTILIZATION STUDIES

Field Data Sheet

Dates: Fall: 10/27/48 Species Maple Stake # 1 Tag # 92 190

Spring: 5/18/49 District: Spotted Bear Drainage Horse Ridge

Location of Stake: 300 yds. on 190° from blazed tree 2.4 miles below Spotted Bear Ranger Station on main road

Location of Tag: (In relation to stake) 15' S.E. of stake

Crew: Fall Darling Spring Rognrud

Overman Casebeer

Length Classes	Length of stem available				Length of stem left			
	Unused		Used		Unused		Used	
	Tally	Total	Tally	Total	Tally	Total	Tally	Total
0 to .4	::	2			;	0.5		
.5 to .9							::	4
1.0 to 1.4	⬚ ::	19			,	1		
1.5 to 2.4	.	2					::	6
2.5 to 3.4	. .	6						
3.5 to 4.4								
4.5 to 5.4	.	5						
5.5 to 6.4	.	6						
6.5 to 7.4	. .	14						
7.5 to 8.4								
8.5 to 9.4								
9.5 to 10.4	. .	20						
10.5 to 11.4								
11.5 to 12.4	.	1 2						
12.5 to 13.4	.	1 3						
13.5 to 14.4	; :	56						
14.5 to 15.4	. .	30						
15.5 to 16.4								
16.5 to 17.4	. .	34						
17.5 to 18.4								
18.5 to 19.4								
19.5 to 20.4	.	20						
20.5 to 21.4								
21.5 to 22.4								
22.5 to 23.4								
23.5 to 24.4								
24.5 to 25.4								
Others	23, 24, 25	72						
Totals	44	311			3	2	6	10

Total growth available 311 Unused stems available 44
Total growth left 12 Unused stems left 3
Total growth utilized 299 - 96% Stems used 41 - 93%

knowledge that deciduous forests indicate an abundant annual rainfall distributed throughout the year, that tall grasslands indicate moderate rainfall, that shortgrass areas normally occur in areas of low and periodic rainfall, and that savannas usually occur in areas of periodic precipitation (with some exceptions). Arid climate is immediately indicated by such species as the cacti while a spruce-fir forest indicates a cool climate.

SOILS

Plants reveal a great deal to the observant field worker. Hardwood forests indicate chernozem soils with a dark surface and usually with a high organic humus content. Pine normally occurs on sandy or gravelly soils which are well drained or have inferior water holding capacity. They occur on areas with a rather equitable distribution of rainfall throughout the year. Even within the pines the predominance of a certain species in a given area will give additional information. In Virginia, for example, the loblolly pine (Pinus taeda) is found on the deeper sandy soils in moist situations whereas shortleaf pine (P. echinata) occurs on heavier and drier soils of the ridges of central and eastern Virginia. Cove hardwoods, such as tulip poplar (Liriodendron tulipifera), basswoods (Tilia spp.), and black walnut (Juglans nigra), are found on deep soils, often transported, of high fertility. Red cedar (Juniperus virginiana) generally occurs as a practically pure stand on basic soils. In western Virginia, red cedar communities are associated with outcropping limestone or with a thin soil-layer over limestone bedrock. These juniper barrens are often quite dry due to the low moisture retaining ability of the thin soil. In most of the Southeastern U.S., broomsedges (Andropogon spp.) occur on areas of moderate to low fertility. This plant is considered to be indicative of soils with a low availability of phosphorus.

MOISTURE

Throughout the Appalachians, rhododendron (Rhododendron maximum) is usually found on the north slopes and mountain laurel (Kalmia latifolia) is often more abundant on the south slopes, thus indicating differences in soil moisture and temperature. In this same area, other ericaceous plants such as the huckleberries (Gaylussacia spp.) and blueberries (Vaccinium spp.) are found on dry, often sandy, soils which are low in fertility and pH. In the West, sagebrush (Artemisia spp.) occurs on good soil in areas of low rainfall whereas the pinon-juniper type of forest cover occurs on rocky, shallow soils.

DISTURBANCE AND PAST HISTORY

Any successional plant stage other than the climax type normally indicates disturbance in one form or another. For example, Maxwell (1910) records that pine in eastern Virginia was reported to be very scarce in the 1600's, but now it is perhaps the most extensive forest cover, certainly throughout Tidewater Virginia. Sheet erosion is often indicative of past cultivation or excessive grazing. Gully erosion suggests slope cultivation or excessive grazing; both types of erosion often confine the plant growth to more aggressive pioneering plant forms. "Weedy" cattle range—those pastures which contain such species as everlasting (Antennaria spp.), mouse ear hawkweed (Hieracium pilosella), long-bracted plantain (Plantago aristata) or broomsedge—are usually typical of over-grazing. In Virginia, the bear oak (Quercus illicifolia) community is generally indicative of the destruction of the organic layer of mountain forests by severe forest fire. Similarly, longleaf pine (P. palustris), lodgepole pine (P. contorta), and jack pine (P. banksiana) are found in areas where fire has been a disturbing factor; this is also true of aspen and birch. Ring counts of trees afford a good index to periods of good and poor years of growth.

One approach to the use of plant indicators as a means of evaluating big game range is indicated in Fig. 13.10. This figure shows a portion of a form used to assign specific values to plant abundance, desirability, and vigor in regard to big game. Similar forms can be designed for the evaluation of any game habitat provided the investigator has knowledge of the value of various indicator plants to the specific form of wildlife with which he is concerned.

The evaluation of wildlife habitat by means of plant indicators is far from a precise technique. In fact, it is so dependent upon the judgment and experience of the individual investigator that there is some question as to its being designated as a technique. However, it has been used with such good results (e.g. Stoddard 1932, Grange 1949, and Graham 1944) that all wildlife investi-

Fig. 13.9. Form used to record data on marked twigs examined in fall and again in spring to determine their usage by deer (from Casebeer and Rognrud 1949).

152

Preliminary Score Card
VEGETATION CONDITION GUIDE

Vegetation Type _____ Soil Type _____ Cluster No. _____

CHECK ONLY INDICATORS
WHICH APPLY

	Adj. Rating	Point Rating**

COMPOSITION

(a) **Better perennial herbaceous plants abundant. Palatable browse species represented in normal amount. Age classes represented for perennial herbaceous plants and browse. Secondary forage plants inconspicuous or scarce . . . .   E

(b) Better plants, including desirable browse species, moderately abundant to abundant. Secondary plants may be moderately abundant. Low value or worthless plants scarce . . . .   G

(c) Secondary plants may be conspicuous and abundant. Better grasses and weeds may be scarce, or if present in normal amount, the palatable browse species are generally below normal. Low value or worthless plants may be abundant. Shrubs such as big sagebrush, snowberry and rose may form a third or more of the plant cover . . . .   F

(d) Better grasses and weeds scarce, or if present in normal amount, the palatable browse species are generally scarce, hedged and highlined. Secondary grasses and weeds may be moderately abundant to scarce. Less desirable shrubs and weeds may form half or more of the plant cover . . . .   P

(e) Low value or annual plants abundant to scarce. Better and secondary plants scarce or absent from the cover. The better plants, if present, occurring as relics or confined to brush clumps out of reach of grazing animals. Palatable shrubs, if present, are hedged and highlined. Shrubs such as big sagebrush, snowberry and rose may make up 90 percent of the plant cover . . . .   VP

VIGOR*

(a) Palatable perennial plants high in vigor. Grasses with numerous seed stalks. Abundant production of foliage. Palatable browse with profuse flowers or fruits . . . .   E

(b) Palatable perennial plants are vigorous. Grasses usually have numerous seed stalks. Foliage production is normal—plants well formed and not stunted. Crowns of palatable browse species loose and open. . . . .   G

*Relate to cluster summary.
**To be assigned.

A-15

(R-4 1954)

Fig. 13.10. A portion of a form designed to assist an investigator in his examination of vegetative conditions of livestock and big-game range.

gators should make all possible use of this discipline—if the term "technique" is unacceptable.

PERMANENT CONDITION-TREND TRANSECTS

The U.S. Forest Service is using on certain of its eastern forests a reconnaissance-analysis technique to measure present conditions of the vegetation and, with later measurements of the same transects, to determine long-range trends. This technique employs permanent line transects to provide measurements of certain range indicators. Understory indicators, when related to overstory characteristics, provide a basis for estimating the condition and trend of understory vegetation, as well as a basis for rating the relative abilities of different understory types to support game, particularly deer. The method was developed by Shaw and Stiteler (1962) for use on eastern National Forests. It is an adaptation of Parker's three-step method (Parker 1954) used on rangeland in the west.

Briefly, the technique involves establishment of permanently located transect-clusters on management area, at an average spacing of one transect-cluster per 3,000 acres. The number of clusters may vary from one per 2,000 acres if a wide range of understory conditions occur, to a spacing of one per 5,000 acres if more uniform conditions exist. In major deer yards, one cluster per linear mile of drainage is used.

The location of each cluster is recorded on a

gridded map (preferred scale; 1 inch = 1 mile), numbered, and transferred to an aerial photograph of the area under investigation. The location of each transect-cluster is permanently marked on the ground, and labeled to include starting point, bearing, and distance from some easily located point found both on the ground and on the aerial photograph. The starting point and course to the transect-cluster is witnessed and marked. Cluster locations in the field are identified by painted angle-iron stakes for easy relocation by a remeasurement crew at a later date. Two parallel transect "A" and "B" are established in each cluster (Fig. 13.11). A third transect ("C") is added if the density of vegetation encountered along transect "A" or "B" is greater than three times the other or if the difference exceeds five times the density.

By means of a suspended plumb bob, vegetation "hits" are recorded at 6-inch intervals along the right side of a stretched 50-ft metal tape held in place by tape holders. The taut metal tape is aligned on the same bearing as that used in establishing the starting point of the cluster. Vegetation "hits" and related data are recorded at each 6-inch interval for each transect (Fig. 13.12, left). Production and utilization of woody browse in an area 13 inches on each side of the

transect is estimated and recorded on another form (Fig. 13.12, right). Available browse and utilization figures are obtained through an independent twig-clip study (Shafer, n.d.) made during the dormant vegetation period. Photographs of each transect are taken and general-view photographs may be taken if they aid in relocation or show points of interest.

The condition of the vegetation and current trend are rated by referring to a score card especially designed for the purpose. As vegetative trends are determined through remeasurement, a basis is established for recommending whether animal numbers, primarily deer, should be increased, kept stable, or be decreased to maintain the range in a productive condition on a sustained basis. This technique also can be used to determine the characteristics of different condition-classes of understory vegetation as they relate to such factors as site index, crown closure, and basal area.

Ripley, Johnson, and Thomas (1960) describe a 4-1/2-ft "browse rod," equipped with a ring bubble for leveling, which they have used to measure more accurately the vertical sides of the belt transect (above the taut tape) in which occurs the vegetation to be recorded.

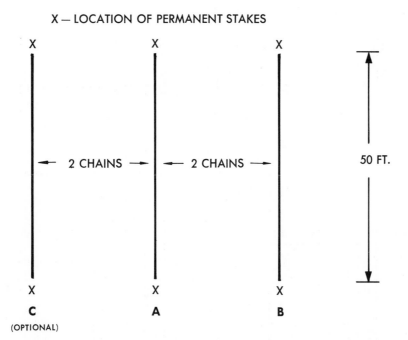

Fig. 13.11. Arrangement of a typical cluster used in laying out condition-trend transects.

PRODUCTION AND UTILIZATION OF WOODY BROWSE

Forest _Blacksburg_ Ranger District _J·D_ Unit _J·28·61_ Date _B. Leichter_ Observer

Cluster & Transect _W/L #1-2B_ _70_ Site _E86-4-89_ Aerial Photograph Stand Size Class _3_

	UNBROWSED				BROWSED		
	Sprout	Seedling	(1)		Sprout	Seedling (2)	
Species	No. of Tot. Wt. Twigs Wt.	No. of Tot. Wt. Twigs Wt.	Tot. Wt. Unbrowsed		No. of Tot. Wt. Twigs Wt.	No. of Tot. Wt. Twigs Wt.	Tot. Wt. Browsed
Salb		4					
Vtz		10					
Arub		18					
Fraz		2					
Robi		4					
Ctlo		20					
Total.		58					

Twig Weight (Grams)*

Species	Sprout	Seedling

*Utilized portion only.

1. Available Browse _____ lbs. per A.
   (Total wt. (1) x .88)
2. Total Forage Utilized _____ lbs. per A.
   (Total wt. (2) x .88)
3. Forage Production _____ lbs. per A.
   (Item 1 + Item 2)
4. Utilization Factor _____
   (Item 2 ÷ Item 3)
5. Total Forage Production _____ lbs.
   (Item 3 x area (acres) of unit.)
6. Deer Days of Browse per A. _____
   (Item 3 ÷ 5)
7. Carrying Capacity _____
   (Item 7a ÷ c ÷ Item 6)
   a. 360 days - 1 deer per _____ acres
   b. 270 " - " " = " "
   c. 180 " - " " = " "
   d. 90 " - " " = " "
   e. 45 " - " " = " "

R7-2600-4
(Rev. 5/61)

Record of Permanent Line Transect

Forest _Blacksburg_ Ranger District _J·D_ Unit _J·28·61_ Date _B. Leichter_ Observer

Cluster & Transect _W/L #1-2B_ _70_ Site _E86-4-89_ Aerial Photo Stand Size Class _3_ Forest Type _Overhardwoods_

Tape Height at Stakes _0' 2½8 50.5' 2' 3½"_

Summary

	Symbol
Bare Soil	P
Erosion Pavement	R
Rock	L 81
Litter	M-F 13
Moss & Fern	Total 100
Plant Density Index	6
Forage Density Index	100
Ground Cover Index	

Key Indicator Species not recorded. _____

Pellet Group Count _____
Vigor Measurements _____
Age Class _1_
Form Class _2_

Crown Description

Closure _84_ % Height _30_ Ft.
Profile: (Check)
  Low
  High
  Flat
  Mod. Irreg.
  Very Irreg.
Foliage Density:
  Light
  Med.
  Heavy

Basal Area

Species	DBH	Sq. Ft.
Arub	1-6	
Prit	1-6	
Qril	6-12	
Qcoc	12+	
Qbor	12+	
All		607

Reproduction

Stocking Frequency _75_ %

Sketch and notes on reverse side.

R7-2600-2
(Rev. 5/61)

Fig. 13.12. Forms used in recording condition-trend data. _Left_ Field Data form used to record data collected at 6-inch intervals along each 50-foot transect. _Right_ Production and utilization record form and data.

VEGETATIVE ANALYSIS

Reconnaissance appraisal of wildlife habitat may not meet completely the requirements of the wildlife investigator and more detailed data may be required. As here used, vegetative analysis implies a detailed examination of the vegetative aspects of wildlife habitat. In vegetative analysis, what has been stated previously may bear repeating: (1) the objective(s) of the investigation must be clearly stated; (2) care must be exercised to avoid devoting most of the effort to gadgeteering and instrumentation; and (3) *each* investigation must be *designed* to attain the specific objective(s).

Units of Measure

Vegetative analysis investigations usually include some measure of one or more of the following: presence-absence, basal area, cover, frequency, density, dominance, and importance. These terms (see U.S. Forest Service 1959, and Soc. Am. Foresters 1958) may be defined as follows:

• *Presence-absence* is merely a statement of the presence or the absence of a given species in a given area.

• *Basal area* is "a measure somewhat similar to cover, being the proportion of ground surface occupied by a species" (Greig-Smith 1957).

• *Cover* is the "vertical projection of above ground parts onto the ground" (Brown 1954). Foresters (Soc. Am. Foresters 1958) have recognized the following categories of cover: crown cover, forest cover, ground cover, range plant cover, refuge cover, and vegetative cover.

• *Frequency* is an expression of the percentage of sample plots in which a species occurs.

• *Density* is the number of individuals per unit area.

• *Dominance* indicates the "effect of competition and environmental factors on the position occupied by a species in a stand (U.S. Forest Service 1959:99). The term dominance has been variously used by investigators (see Greig-Smith 1957:4) and for this reason, a clear interpretation of the term should be stated.

• *Importance* is a weighted expression to designate the value of a given plant for a given purpose. This expression may consist of a simple averaging of frequency, density, and dominance.

Sampling Vegetation

Most wildlife investigators are concerned with large areas of land and it is impractical to measure in detail the vegetation on the entire area. Therefore, most vegetative analysis investigations are concerned with sampling. As pointed out by Oosting (1958:41), statisticians interested in detailed vegetative analysis problems have emphasized that mathematical computation can not be substituted for judgment either in the selection of the communities for investigation or in the interpretation of the data collected. The principles of sampling are covered fully in many publications (for example, Schumacher and Chapman 1948). All field investigators employing any form of sampling procedure should be acquainted with sampling principles.

Vegetative sampling normally is done by means of quadrats or sample plots. A quadrat, as originally designated, is a square-sided sample, but in recent years this definition has not been applied too rigidly. Often the term quadrat is used to designate a circle, a rectangle or other-shaped area (Gates 1949:13). Quadrats and sample plots as used in vegetative analysis studies are discussed in a number of publications (Gates 1949:13-41, Greig-Smith 1957, Phillips 1959, and U.S. Forest Service 1959).

TYPES OF QUADRATS AND SAMPLE PLOTS

The types of quadrats normally used in ecological studies of vegetation include the list quadrat, basal area quadrat, clip quadrat, chart quadrat, denuded quadrat, and the permanent quadrat. It is possible to use the same quadrat for two or more purposes. Other sampling units include the belt transect, line transect, point transect, and enclosures and exclosures. The latter two are used both in vegetative studies and in the appraisal of the influence of animals on their environment. Each of these sampling units has its advantages and disadvantages; the wildlife investigator must use his own judgment in determining the type or types of sampling units which are best suited to his needs.

SHAPE OF SAMPLE PLOTS

Recent investigations have shown that the shape of the sample plot is of much greater importance than was originally assumed (Oosting 1958: 41-43). For low, herbaceous (less than waist high) vegetation, the circular plot has distinct advantages. Circles can be quickly and accurately marked in the field (Fig. 13.11). In general, rectangular units are more efficient than square plots of equal size. Short strips give less variable results than do squares but short strips are more variable than long strips.

The point quadrat (Clarke, Campbell, and Campbell 1942, Parker and Harris 1959) has been developed principally for determining cover values and relative abundance of forage-type plants. In point surveys, pins are lowered vertically at spaced intervals; all plants touched by these pins are recorded. In grassland surveys, a rimless wheel, with pins for spokes, has been used in point-plot surveys.

Currently, plotless sampling is receiving increasing attention, especially in forest surveys. This technique of investigating vegetation is used primarily for measuring vegetation (trees) 4 inches d.b.h. or greater.

In summary, the most efficient shape of plots is of great importance and the shape of the sampling unit will vary with the type of vegetation being investigated.

SIZE OF SAMPLE PLOTS

The size of the sample plot will depend very largely on the homogeneity of the plant community, the intensity of the investigation, and the type (trees, shrubs, or herbs) of vegetation or animal that is of primary concern. Gates (1949:13) has suggested the use of 1/2-acre plots for the study of trees, 1/25-acre plots for the study of shrubs and 1/100-acre plots for the investigation of herbs. The dimensions of various-sized quadrats,

Table 13.2. Dimensions for various-sized sample plots

Size of study plot in acres	Square feet in plot	Length of one side of a square (in feet)	Length of radius of circle (in feet)
0.0001	4.4	2.1	1.2
0.0004	17.4	4.2	2.4
0.0010	43.5	6.6	3.7
0.0100	435.6	20.9	11.8
0.1000	4,356.0	66.0	37.2
0.2500	10,890.0	104.3	58.9
0.5000	21,780.0	147.6	83.3
1.0000	43,560.0	208.7	117.8

Table 13.3. Acreage in belt transects of different lengths and widths

Width of transect in feet	Acreage per 100 feet	Acreage per 100 yards	Acreage per mile
1	0.0023	0.0069	0.121
2	0.0046	0.0137	0.242
3	0.0069	0.0206	0.363
4	0.0092	0.0275	0.484
5	0.0115	0.0344	0.605
6	0.0138	0.0413	0.726
7	0.0160	0.0481	0.847
8	0.0183	0.0550	0.968
9	0.0206	0.0618	1.089
10	0.0230	0.0687	1.21
20	0.0458	0.1374	2.42
30	0.0688	0.2064	3.63
40	0.0916	0.2748	4.84
50	0.1145	0.3435	6.05
60	0.1375	0.4125	7.26
70	0.1603	0.4809	8.47
80	0.1832	0.5496	9.68
90	0.2061	0.6183	10.89
100	0.2296	0.6887	12.10

either as square or circular plots, are given in Table 13.2. The approximate acreage in belt transects of different length and width is given in Table 13.3.

The size of the sample plot has considerable practical, as well as statistical, importance. In field surveys, the smaller the plot, the lower the cost-per-plot. Thus, a determination of the minimum size that will supply adequate data has received considerable attention.

One of the methods used to determine minimum size of sample plots is by means of a species-area curve (Fig. 13.13 A left). This technique was first used by European ecologists and has been tested under a variety of conditions. The curve is constructed by plotting the number of species (absolute or per cent of total) accumulated in the sampling on the y axis and the number or size of the sample on the x axis. The curve formed by plotting these data rises abruptly and then levels off. The break in the curve indicates the approximate point beyond which added sampling effort produces diminishing returns. It was generally assumed that sampling was adequate when a 10% increase yielded additional species equal only to 10% of the total number of species present. This point on the curve can not be located by inspection

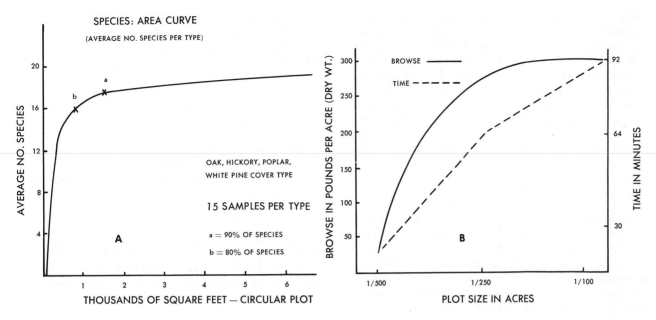

Fig. 13.13. Nested plots may be used in making a judgment regarding plot size. A. Species: area curve constructed from a group of "nested" plots in sampling shrub vegetation. This curve indicates that 90% of the plant species would occur on a plot (point "a") with a 22.56-ft radius, or about 1,600 sq. ft. For the technique used in locating points "a" and "b", see Oosting 1958. B. Nested plots used to indicate the variation in dry weight of browse and time per plot in relation to various-sized sample plots.

and a mechanical method of determination has been proposed (Oosting 1958:46). The species:area curve method of determining minimum plot size has a number of deficiencies; these have been summarized by Oosting (1958:46-48) and Ursic and McClurkin (1959:71-73).

Another technique used to determine adequacy of plot size is to "nest" the plots, increasing from smaller to larger plot size and keeping the data separate for each size plot. These data can be plotted (Fig. 13.13) on the species:area curve (Oosting 1958:47-48) or the variance between plots of different sizes can be tested statistically.

A few examples will illustrate some of the considerations which enter into the selection of the type and size of sample plots as used by various wildlife workers. Davison (mimeo dated Feb. 19, 1953) suggests the use of boxes with inside measurements of 24 inches by 12 inches (2 sq. ft) for determining seed production in bicolor lespedeza stands. He states that every four seeds in the box equals about 1 pound per acre. Bishop and Spinner (1946) in their investigation of weed seed production in corn fields in Connecticut used milacre plots (Table 13.2) and placed 10 plots in each field. These plots were located systematically in each of 20 fields that averaged approximately 2.25 acres in size. Haugen and Fitch (1955) periodically collected ground samples of 1 sq. ft, down to mineral soil, throughout plantings of bicolor lespedeza and

large partridge pea. By this technique they determined the availability of seeds of these two plants to bobwhite throughout the year. Aldous (1944), in his study of deer browsing, recommended a sample plot of 1/100 acre (circle with a radius of 11.8 ft). Smith (1949) used a series of 100 sq. ft plots to compare the influence of deer and livestock on two adjoining areas.

There is no general agreement as to a single technique that will determine adequately the plot size needed to sample all types of vegetation. Each plant community must be considered individually or, at least, the field investigator must use sound statistical counsel as well as judgment in selecting the plot size best adapted to his specific needs.

SAMPLING BIAS

Bias—or an error that affects all observations alike—is of importance in all sampling procedures. Hayne (1952) demonstrated, for example, that bias existed in the choice of samples when eight investigators selected in a non-random manner "representative samples" from a group of fish to be measured. Thus, the location of plots should not be made on a "representative" basis; they should be designated, if possible, in a random manner if detailed statistical analysis is planned. Feasible procedures for locating sample plots

158

include: (1) in a systematic or predetermined and mechanical manner (i.e. along a given compass course and spaced a designated distance apart), (2) using method (1) but by randomly selecting the azimuth and distance, and (3) by dividing the total area to be sampled into numbered plots and then selecting the individual plots to be investigated from tables of random numbers (e.g., a total area of 100 plots with plots 1, 18, 26, and 53, selected from a table of random numbers).

SAMPLING INTENSITY

Determining the number of samples required to give reliable information is of great importance in any habitat sampling procedure. If the number of samples is too small, the data obtained may give inaccurate results; likewise if the sample is too large, valuable time has been wasted when a smaller number of samples would have given equally reliable information. Consequently, a technique which will enable an investigator to obtain some idea of the number of samples that will be needed is of great help.

If the cover type or population is homogeneous and therefore is suitable for simple random sampling, it is necessary to decide upon the accuracy desired before sampling intensity can be determined. It is also necessary to know: the confidence level limit (e.g., 0.05, 0.10, 0.25, etc.), margin of error (d), and the normal deviate (t) corresponding to an acceptable confidence limit.

The size of the sample (n) cannot be determined without some previous knowledge of the standard deviation (s) of the population. Preferably, s is estimated from previous sampling of the same or of a similar population; however, the value of s may be chosen by estimate.

If the total population being sampled (N) is very large (n/N being less than 0.05), a formula (see Snedecor 1950:456-458) for estimating the approximate size of the sample (n) is:

$$n = \frac{s^2 t^2}{d^2}$$

in which n = number of samples required

s = standard deviation

t = normal deviate at confidence limit level and given degrees of freedom (from t table)

d = margin of error (arithmetic mean times designated accuracy)

For example, suppose we desire to determine the available browse by clipping studies and want to know the number of 1/100-acre plots which should be taken. It would be necessary to know (or assume):

(1) That cover type is homogeneous so far as the particular investigation is concerned.
(2) The size (acreage) of the cover type.
(3) The acceptable accuracy.
(4) The acceptable confidence limit.
(5) The acceptable degree of freedom, which is n minus one.

Let us assume that the cover type being sampled is 100 acres and that a 10% accuracy at a 0.05 confidence limit level is satisfactory. In order to estimate the variation, suppose we randomly sample 10 plots which are 1/100 acre in size, and that these samples supply the following data:

$\bar{x}$ = 42.3 = arithmetic mean of the pounds of browse-per-acre.

s = 5.6 = standard deviation.

n = number of plots required.

t = 2.26 = (9 degrees of freedom [n - 1] at 0.05 confidence level).

d = designated accuracy (10% times $\bar{x}$).

Then, solving for n under the above conditions:

$$n = \frac{s^2 t^2}{d^2}$$

$$n = \frac{(5.6)^2 (2.26)^2}{(42.3 \times 0.10)^2}$$

$$n = \frac{160.17}{17.89} = 8.9$$

Under the above assumptions it may be concluded that 10 plots "probably" (i.e. 95% +) will give a "reasonable" (i.e. within 10% +) estimate of the available browse in this cover type.

FARM-GAME HABITAT EVALUATION

On cultivated land the need for food or cover, or both, by wildlife is often acute. This has been intensified by gradually increasing human pressure on the land; there are fewer weeds, less waste, and less idle land. There is little doubt that habitat changes have greatly reduced population of some game species, for example, pinnated grouse. Therefore, considerable attention has been given to habitat improvement by the wildlife manager.

Wildlife managers have considered the artificial improvement of wildlife habitat by the establishment of food and cover plants as one of the most effective approaches. Since the farmer is reluctant to make good land available, most improvements have been made so far on apparently worthless areas, such as badly eroded places, deserted strip-mines, gravel pits, and banks of streams. As these areas are also given attention by the soil conservationist, there is the chance of improvement both for soil condition and wildlife. It should be realized, however, that habitat improvement on worn-out soils has its limitations. On fertile soils a gradual loss of cover usually occurs; hence the food which does exist is largely unavailable to those species reluctant to venture far from cover.

Wildlifers involved in habitat improvement programs have often ignored the question of is the average farmer prepared to maintain wildlife practices. Habitat development for wildlife may become generally acceptable when hunters are willing to make management of farm land profitable to landowners. Ideally, artificially established vegetation must be capable of permanent maintenance with little effort on the part of the landowner. However, plantings, whether annuals or perennials, often require frequent care such as cultivation, fertilization, mowing, and protection from livestock. Further requirements for wildlife plantings are listed by Edminster and May (1951). These include: hardiness, site adaptability, growth habits, form and character of growth, use of products (other than for game), lack of obnoxious qualities, and ease of establishment.

Although evaluation of artificial improvements of wildlife habitat will be emphasized, it should be recognized that natural habitats, such as ponds, can also be very productive of wildlife.

Habitat Appraisal

Although considerable time and money have been spent in the U.S. on habitat improvement for wildlife, relatively little effort has been made to analyze habitat conditions. Generally, conditions were not adequately evaluated before improvements were made. Habitat improvements through natural regrowth of shrubs and trees have been studied by some, e.g. Bump (1950) in New York. So far, no satisfactory procedure of habitat appraisal has been developed from which useful inferences might be drawn as to whether a given habitat is suitable for the support of a given species of wildlife.

Only few long-range studies have been undertaken to determine the effect of habitat improvement on wildlife populations and these concerned themselves mainly with an aquatic environment. Because a need was felt to step up such fact-finding programs, Evans (1954) prepared a blueprint for evaluating upland-game habitat developments. Two principal concepts provide the basis for these projects. These are that:

- Habitat development programs should result in increased game populations and harvest, and

- The cost of extensive application of the work should be in line with the results obtained.

With reference to the first point it should be interjected that programs directed at maintaining a population in a good condition through habitat management are also worthy of support by the wildlife biologist.

Projects can be enlarged to obtain additional data such as what types of development are most effective, and what patterns of interspersion and juxtaposition produce the best results. An evaluation of all these factors would be extremely costly and time consuming.

In setting up evaluation studies, two problems should be looked into: first, the extent, size and selection of study areas, and second, adequate population sampling techniques. Details for planning such studies are presented by Evans (1954).

The duration of studies varies with the type of cover and species of game to be evaluated. For evaluation of woody winter cover, a period of not less than 10 years may be required; for evaluation of nesting cover, periods of 5 years may be adequate.

The first overall assessment of farm-game habitat restoration programs was made by Marshall (1953), who visited 15 states mainly in the northeast and midwest. In summing up his appraisal of conditions, he remarked that basic research studies into habitat evaluation have been far too few and that research projects are under-manned, under-financed, and under-equipped compared to development projects. In his opinion, the following questions should be considered when evaluating wildlife management programs:

1. Are the programs sound in regard to basic plant and wildlife ecology?

2. What is the permanence of the improvement practices?

3. What are the real costs in terms of game produced over a period of years?

4. Are these questions understood and analyzed objectively by the agencies carrying out the programs?

The forces of plant succession are rapidly working against shrub and herbaceous plantings in many cases. Small stands of a desirable plant scattered here and there may not replace the larger loss of a changing land-use pattern that eliminates the intermixture of various cover types found under more primitive farming. Whitlock (1961) in his appraisal of problems facing state agencies in farm-game habitat management came to the conclusion that efforts to evaluate extensive small-game habitat improvement programs have failed to come up with quantitative evidence to prove their value. Intensive efforts on small areas where cover is markedly deficient will produce more game but at a fairly high cost per unit of game. A shotgun approach should be dropped in favor of pin-pointing efforts on smaller areas where deficiencies in cover and food are glaringly apparent. Large-scale habitat management by state agencies for the ring-necked pheasant, ruffed grouse, and snowshoe hare appears to be a losing proposition. Rabbits and quail offer more promise.

In Virginia, Gehrken (pers. communication) has assembled information on a long-range evaluation project. His technique consisted of:

1. Censusing bobwhite with a trained dog on an approximately 1,200-acre farm previous to improvements;

2. Establishing food and cover plantings (primarily food) on one-half of the acreage;

3. Recording the changes, if any, in the bobwhite population on the improved section.

Later, the plantings on the experimental area will be destroyed and the control and experimental areas will be reversed; the investigation will then be repeated for a period of years.

Shaffer (1953) reported upon a technique of evaluating a statewide planting program designed to improve farm-game habitat. The form used in evaluating each planting from a sample drawn from the planting stock distributed each year is given in Fig. 13.14.

Smith (1956) assessed the value of conifer plantations as wildlife habitat. He studied 60 conifer plantations of various types and ages near Ithaca, New York, and found that the wildlife potential of conifer plantations depends on a great number of variables, including site, coniferous species, height, size, openings, and management. According to him, plantations of more than 10 acres have created favorable habitat for certain species of wildlife in areas where no suitable habitat existed before. The diameter of large plantations is of little significance as long as openings occur within them.

Sharp (1957) reported on an evaluation of experimental forest management to improve wildlife populations. Half of a tract of 1,470 acres was improved by cutting and bulldozing areas scattered over the tract, mostly 1/2-to 1 acre in size, with varying degrees of intensity. Ruffed grouse, white-tailed deer, cottontail rabbits, and eastern wild turkeys all responded well to the habitat changes.

Food Plantings for Wildlife

A basic consideration is that agricultural practices can produce specific high-quality foods better than undivided nature. Ideally plant species used for improvement of conditions for wildlife should provide food and cover whenever such is in most demand. It is during the later winter and early spring that deficiencies generally occur. Unfortunately, relatively few species of plants have been found so far which adequately meet these dual requirements. If single plant species that provide both food and cover cannot be found, it is desirable to use several species of food plants and of cover plants in combination.

As a general rule, the farther north one tries to improve wildlife habitat, the more difficult it becomes to locate suitable species of plants.

Before making any efforts to improve habitat conditions by the establishment of food and cover plants, one should try to analyze whether it is food or cover or possibly both which is in short supply.

A successful food planting requires: (1) selection of one or more food plants which rate as "choice" to the species under management; and (2) further selection to meet favorably the local agricultural factors such as soil, rainfall, temperature extremes and competition with unwanted fauna.

There are some 150 species of leguminous shrubs and herbs belonging to the genus *Lespedeza* native to North America and Asia. Only 5 or 6 of these species have proved adaptable to North American use (Davison 1945). Among these, the

FARM GAME EVALUATION SHEET

County _____ Grade _____

Name of Cooperator _____ Address _____

Route to and exact location of farm _____

Type of planting _____ When planted _____

Method of planting (check) rows _____ broadcast _____ plants _____

Has planting been cultivated? _____ Has planting been fertilized since? _____

How much fertilizer? _____

Wildlife utilization (signs) _____

Was planting censused (dogs)? _____ Results _____

Did landowner receive planting instruction? _____ Written _____ Verbal _____

EVALUATION

1. Survival or germination (check) less than ½ (1) _____;
   ½ to ¾ (2) _____; ¾ to ⁹⁄₁₀ (3) _____; ⁹⁄₁₀ plus (4) _____ .

2. Competition (check) heavy (1) _____; Moderate (2) _____; light
   (3) _____; nil (4) _____ .

3. Seed production (check) heavy (4) _____; Moderate (3) _____; light
   (2) _____; nil (1) _____ .

4. Location of planting (grade) (4) _____; (3) _____; (2) _____;
   (1) _____ (Land use, relation to farm practices, relation to cover)

5. Size of planting (grade) 1 or 4 _____

REMARKS

Ratings
A   19–20
B   17–18
C   15–16
D   13–14
F   Below 13

Inspected by _____ Date _____

Fig. 13.14. Form used in evaluation of farm-game plantings (Schaffer 1953).

shrub lespedezas (principally *Lespedeza bicolor* and varieties) are the most important species in terms of numbers of plants distributed. Lespedezas introduced from Asia do not do well on soils of low fertility, and even on moderately good soils artificial fertilizer is desirable.

There are several limitations to the long-time values of *Lespedeza bicolor:* first, border plantings 10 years old and over give ground rapidly to woody plant invasion. Second, many plantings lose seed production by their fifth year, and third, a considerable investment in time, fertilizer, and farm equipment seems to be necessary (Rosene 1952). Other disadvantages of bicolor are that it will not grow next to timber, and will not stand continued grazing (Durell 1955). According to Blackwell (1955) this species is too costly, too slow to produce, too quickly choked out by honeysuckle, too unpopular with landowners and hunters, and too little used by wildlife to warrant further establishment.

The benefit which upland game, particularly bobwhite, derive from this lespedeza seems to have been overrated. Durell (1955) states that bicolor is used by bobwhite chiefly in late winter after favorite foods are gone. Rosene (1956) showed that where native foods were plentiful, bicolor failed to increase bobwhite populations. To enable comparisons, he attempted to match each experimental area having bicolor strips with a

162

similar area to serve as a control. The vigor and productivity of bicolor plantings, and the degree of weed growth in the planted strips were noted periodically. At each inspection, the strips were rated as good, fair, or poor. Bobwhite censuses were taken from fall to spring. Resulting information on covey locations, size of area used by each cover, and numbers of birds before and after the hunting season were recorded on aerial photographs. Gehrken (1956), who followed bobwhite population trends on 14 farms in Virginia for the years 1948-53, concluded that plantings had no practical benefits in increasing bobwhite populations.

Among the several herbaceous perennial species, only sericea *(L. cuneata)* has been found useful. It is considered to provide low, dense nesting or roosting cover for bobwhite and cottontails, but it provides poor food. Shrub lespedezas are becoming well known as a source of food that can be depended on. All the shrub lespedezas are perennials that grow from 4- to 8-ft high.

Thickets or rows of autumn olive plants furnish cover and food for many species of wildlife. Bobwhite, ruffed grouse, and ring-necked pheasants find the berries highly attractive food but songbirds often leave very few for these game species (Allen and Skeiner 1959).

Hedgerows and Other Cover

The recent trend in clean farming has been towards the elimination of fencerows. The reasons given for their elimination include that they harbor noxious weeds and insects, shade out crops, and cause a reduction in the yield of crops. Also, modern mechanized agriculture requires larger fields.

Fencerows supporting vegetation more than 6-ft high may cause a material reduction in the yield of adjacent cultivated crops. However, well managed fencerows are less than 6-ft high, and they seem to have little or no adverse effect on adjacent crops (Dambach 1945). Moreover, the roots of fencerow plants can be confined by digging a trench alongside the row. Advantages of fencerows, other than to wildlife, include a change in the local microclimate (Geiger et al. 1951), resulting in increased soil moisture, and decreased evaporation. Water runoff is slowed, and soil loss reduced. Hedgerows serve also as windbreaks. Contour hedges used for soil conservation also aid wildlife populations. Insect population studies conducted in the summer (Dambach 1945) indicate that few insects injurious to grain and forage crops occur on woody vegetation adjacent to crop fields. Many beneficial insects, however, do frequent such areas. Breeding bird populations in crop field borders containing woody vegetation greatly exceed those of borders composed of herbaceous plants. Several hedge species are sources of pollen for bees, and provide nesting places for bumble bees.

A well planned and properly maintained hedge has several advantages to wildlife. These include increased cover for travel ways and nesting or den sites, and increased and more varied food supplies.

Activities of both birds and mammals are greatest in low, shrub-stage hedgerows where fruit, browse and cover are most abundant (Petrides 1942). The ideal hedgerow should be composed of shrubs and vines which provide food as well as cover for wildlife, such as wild plum and black berries.

Multiflora rose *(Rosa multiflora)*, a native of Eastern Asia, has been advertised and planted widely, because it was considered a suitable species for improving wildlife habitat on farmlands. Hedges of this rose were praised because of their quality of being stock-proof. The longevity of plantings also appears to be no problem.

Klimstra (1956), after surveying the literature on the values of this rose, came to the conclusion that there is actually little evidence of its value to wildlife, except where adjacent food supply was readily available. He suggested that use of multiflora might be limited to areas where no other cover exists.

More than one species should be used in any one hedge. The species should be planted in rows, and arranged so that the tallest forms are located in center. Utmost care must be exercised in the choice of species to avoid difficulties arising from the use of plants conflicting with agricultural practices.

Dense cover near the ground gives best protection to wildlife. This also assures a minimum amount of weeds. A well-managed fencerow should have fewer weeds than a "clean fence." Shading of adjacent crops may be reduced to a minimum by selecting species of a low height growth. Conifers may occasionally be used to advantage but they should be cut back when attaining excessive height.

After a well-planned shrub border has become established, generally only little upkeep is necessary. At any rate maintenance is less costly than cutting trees and shrubs along field margins.

Wildlife Borders

Wildlife borders are strips of vegetation between woodlots and cultivated fields, or between fields planted for the purpose of encouraging wildlife. The value of a wildlife border varies with the type of food and cover planting used (annual or perennial), the amount and approximity of permanent cover, the interspersion and juxtaposition with other cover and food, and the species benefitting from the improvements.

Wildlife borders may be just a seed drill wide, or they may be as much as 25-ft wide, all depending on local conditions and requirements. The plantings may consist of one species only, two or more rows of different species, or a mixture of two or more species.

Food Patches

The establishment of food patches of annuals has been given more attention during the past few years. Blackwell (1955) compared the costs of the use of bicolor with the costs for an annual food-patch seed mixture, and found that annuals are superior to perennials, because they are cheaper, utilized by more species of game, and will produce some seed even in adverse years. Moreover, annuals will produce the same year that they are planted, and the farmer will devote better land on his farm to temporary plantings than he will to permanent ones. A little of the crop should be left unharvested near good cover. Unharvested strips of seed crops are as good as food patches. Also, a strip of unmowed hay provides food and cover. Davidson (1961), however, points out that there is severe competition of flocking nongame birds that rob the ground-feeding game birds of seeds from such plantings as grain sorgum and millet. He further refers to the serious rate of deterioration of such foods in the humid climate of the southeastern United States. He suggests alternate plants that deteriorate less and that are not choice foods of flocking birds; i.e., annual or perennial lespedezas for bobwhite, green-grazing plants for deer and turkey, pokeberry for mourning doves, and smartweeds, or other plants that can be flooded to protect the seeds from unwanted birds, for ducks.

Several food patch mixtures have been tried. Commonly corn, sorghum, and millet are used. Hungerford (1956) suggested a mixture for winter game bird food on Idaho farms consisting of 5 parts safflower, 2 dwarf sunflower, 1 Idaho amber sorgo, 1 squaw corn or flint corn, and 1 of field peas, barley, wheat, or millet. Safflower is the most important seed in this mixture.

FOREST RANGE EVALUATION

When evaluating range conditions in forested habitats for Artiodactyla, to which this discussion is restricted, one should keep in mind that range requirements of different species vary greatly. Therefore, a wildlife manager should have an intimate knowledge of the habitat requirements of these animals and particularly of their need of food and cover in the various seasons. Some species, such as the white-tailed deer, are largely browsers; others, such as the elk, are largely grazers. Moose, although browsers throughout most of the year, utilize aquatic plants widely during the summer. Caribou feed to a considerable extent on lichens. Deer may die on a winter diet on which elk thrive.

Another important consideration when appraising range conditions is whether this is done for one particular species, or for several species which are more or less using the same food.

The condition of the range in terms of food and cover basically determines the relative abundance of hoofed game. Since cover evaluation has been discussed, no further reference will be made to it here. A range should be considered a dynamic entity, changing continually with fluctuations in precipitation, temperature, evaporation, and varying use-patterns.

Usually only a portion of the vegetative production of a range is available for use by artiodactyls. Topographic features and distance from cover and water influence usage. Furthermore, the behavior of certain deer species restricts them to only certain parts of the range: deer often stay on overused range, while good range, close-at-hand, is left untouched.

Influence of Browsing on Vegetation

The degree of use that plants will withstand without a reduction of satisfactory production significantly affects the carrying capacity of the range. There is a wide variation in the amount of browsing pressure that various species can endure. Gill (1957) listed the resistance to browsing of several northeastern shrubs and trees. If the range is in good condition, utilization of about 50% of current annual growth may be considered reasonably safe for several palatable species. The optimum browsing rate of white cedar is considered, however, to be less than 25% of the annual growth (Gill 1957). Some browse species react to browsing pressure by sprouting. Aldous (1952), conducted a clipping study of browse plants during a period of 6 years. He imitated heavy, moderate, and light deer browsing by clipping off various amounts of annual growth from selected species. In the case of hardwoods, the clipped samples were weighed and measured. He concluded that several species of trees and shrubs will produce well and will continue to grow under moderate to heavy usage and should be used at least moderately if the plant growth is to be kept within reach. Ranges depleted by past heavy use need a greater percentage of the annual growth reserved to allow for recovery. Dieback is worse on over-utilized plants than on less heavily browsed vegetation. Twig mortality as a result of browsing is an important factor to consider in judging utilization.

Graham (1954) investigated the influence of deer browsing on forest reproduction in Michigan by means of a series of milacre plots on a variety of soils in partially-cut forests. These plots were examined at intervals throughout an 11-year period. On these 6.6-ft radius plots, the species present, number of stems of each species, height, and other data were recorded. He found that the more desirable browse species (including hemlock, white cedar and yellow birch) had all but disappeared, whereas red maple and hard maple were stunted in growth by excessive browsing. Balsam fir, lightly browsed, if at all, increased in density. Similar plots were laid out on recently-logged areas, on scalped and unscalped plots. Further, plots were examined inside and outside of deer exclosures. In these exclosures, height growth of forest reproduction was more normal, with many species reaching a height of 8-ft 4 years after construction of the exclosure.

Range Condition and Plant Successional Stages

One of the most important indications of the condition of a range is the successional stage of its vegetation. Fires retard plant succession, produce suitable browse, and usually a few years after a fire deer and moose populations build up rapidly because of increased food production. In the slow stages of forest succession from newly burned areas to the climax condition, a progressive deterioration in food values and carrying capacity of the range can be observed. The closing of the forest canopy brings gradual reduction in quantity and marked lowered quality of woody food plants. The amounts of proteins, carbohydrates, fats, and minerals gradually decrease (Cowan, Hoar, and Hatter 1950). The following sampling procedure was used by these workers: the collector, walking across the area, removed not more than one small branch from each tree or shrub encountered. When an adequate sample had been accumulated, it was bundled, quick frozen, and shipped by air to the laboratory where it was either processed immediately or again frozen. Collections were made only on days preceded by a 36-hr period without precipitation.

In the laboratory, the growth of the current was trimmed from the twigs, chopped, dried to constant weight at 80° - 90°C, and then stored in sealed jars. For each sample the following determinations were made: total minerals, moisture, protein, carbohydrates, nitrogen-free extract, ether extract, carotene, and ascorbic acid.

The distribution of various forest types, as well as age-classes within these types, is also of importance to ungulates. Ideal range consists of a proper distribution of various age-classes of different timber types. Large areas of uniform plant cover do not maintain high populations of ungulates.

In Oregon, Einarsen (1946) found substantial differences in the percentage of protein in preferred deer foods taken the same day from burns of different ages. On a recent, 3-month-old burn, the percentage of protein averaged 12.1, while on a 6-year-old burn the percentage of protein averaged about 6.8. Various species of ungulates seem to be able to detect the higher food values of recent burns.

In order to improve range conditions, it will be necessary to know more about how palatability, succulence, and nutrient content of game food vary with stand structure as well as with other factors.

Productivity and nutritive value of food plants influence the carrying capacity of a range. The principal task of research in respect to productivity and nutrient value of game foods is to provide techniques for measuring the usable volume, nutritive value, and seasonal variation of game food in relation to forest type and site, and to relate these to game management objectives and silvicultural practices (Burke 1956). The nutritive value of food should preferably be determined for the critical season.

Plants utilized are not always the most highly nutritious ones available. White cedar, the most preferred northern browse species for white-tailed deer, may contain less protein than balsam fir, jack pine or speckled alder, all of which rate as poor food (Anonymous 1937).

The correlation between palatability of food and its nutritive value, as established by chemical analysis, is poorly understood. It is also difficult to explain why the palatability requirements of two ungulates inhabiting the same range may differ substantially.

Chemical analyses of foods indicate their value for wildlife species only in a general way and fail to explain why some plants are palatable and others are not. Controlled experiments on digestibility seem to give a better understanding of the values of certain foods. Few coefficients of digestibility for food plants utilized by deer are known. Chemical composition varies with different species of plants and soil conditions. It usually also differs in the same species under different range conditions, and at different seasons. During spring months, or when plants are in the first stages of rapid growth, protein content of vegetation is adequate for growing animals. Later during the summer, and on through autumn and winter, the herbaceous plants characteristically lose in crude protein more rapidly and to a greater degree than do the shrubs. From November to April the percentage of crude fiber in browse species increases, while that of nitrogen-free extract and protein decreases. According to this, calcium and phosphorus in palatable shrubs on the winter range are adequate to meet minimum requirements of deer, and ample at other seasons of the year.

Generally, winter ranges furnish only survival rations. Stored body fats are essential to bring the deer through cold winters. Not only is good winter range necessary, but the summer range must provide forage in quantity and quality that will build adequate storage reserves within the animals' bodies.

The amount of food intake required by various ungulates varies with season of the year and carrying capacity on the range. Browsing sometimes stimulates twig production. The amount of food required per hundred-weight of white-tailed deer varies from a little more than 2 lb to 7 lb (Taylor 1947). On heavily-used ranges greater food intakes will be necessary than on ranges in good condition because of the low quality of food. When food is adequate in quantity, but of such poor quality that the animals are unable to eat and digest enough to obtain the necessary nutrients, malnutrition will result.

Relationship Between Food Abundance and Herd Condition

Deer preferably eat only a few highly palatable plant species, even if many species are available. When these "key" species are overused, deer must resort to secondary species, on which they are generally unable to sustain life.

Range conditions affect the weights of ungulates. The white-tailed deer has been studied most thoroughly in this respect. Johnson (1937) stated that the average weight of bucks killed on one area in Pennsylvania was 127 lb, while on a second tract having two and one-half times as many deer, the average weight was 92 lb.

It has been shown for various members of the family Cervidae that range conditions affect reproductive rates. This has been studied in the greatest detail for the white-tailed deer: lower rates of reproduction on overbrowsed ranges has been demonstrated by Morton and Cheatum (1946), and various later workers. Further studies should be undertaken to establish the relationships between nutrient requirements and the production, growth, and survival of young.

Methods of Measuring Browse Conditions

Range conditions, or the state of health or productivity of a range, vary greatly from place to place and season to season, and no system has been developed so far which may be equally useful everywhere. Research must determine the ecological relationships and standardize descriptions which may be used as guides for establishing the "food" carrying capacity of the range (Burke 1956).

Obviously, a browsed-out range can carry fewer deer than a range, similar in other respects, but in good condition. Drought can seriously affect the available amount of food, and so can deep snow. It is therefore essential to know the carrying capacity of a range, and how various environmental factors affect it.

Hoofed game are not the only animals using a range. Insects, rabbits, rodents, birds, etc., all compete for the available food. This should always be considered when running a browse survey for ungulates. Peak populations of snowshoe hares may utilize more browse than deer, for example.

Cover evaluation indicates that in the southern part of the U.S. there is generally an adequate supply for most indigenous deer species. The need for cover becomes more critical to the north where white-tailed deer are often concentrated in areas on winter range which have good coniferous cover and little food (Webb 1948).

A wildlife manager needs to be more concerned with the fraction of woody vegetative growth that range animals leave than the fraction they take, since the condition of the range at the time of examination determines the future production of game. This is not true for forbs. In certain areas forbs comprise a high percentage of the deer diet, regardless of other forage present.

If deer eat more browse than is produced, they may so thoroughly destroy certain food plants that it may take decades for the range to regenerate. As a result of continuous protection of deer herds, many ranges have been damaged so severely that the first and most important step is to decrease the populations to or below the proper stocking level (Leopold et al. 1947).

Range improvement or deterioration is often a slow process, and is therefore difficult to measure. Moreover, a trend may be modified by the influence of good or poor growing seasons. A range can be considered on the uptrend if there is a general return to good growth. Conversely, if palatable shrubs show no recovery, if whole plants or branches are dying, and if better forage species are not reproducing, the trend is down.

Considerable literature has accumulated on range appraisal for wild ungulates during the past 10 years. In the methods developed so far, consideration is given to why present conditions exist, and how the cause and effect of availability and use are weighted against each other. Different nutritional influences of site, browse species used, and successional stages should be investigated, but relatively little is known about this subject. Preferably methods of analysis should be tied in closely with soil, forest, and forage types.

Range analysis has an ecological implication, and one should try to analyze range conditions in terms of plant succession and community interrelationships. Over most of the West, the original climax vegetation is used as the standard from which to judge the current plant community, even though the vegetative cover sought in management is not the climax (Burke 1956). Range conditions are also closely tied up with edaphic factors, moisture regime, slope and site conditions. More research towards the development of better systems of range analysis is still needed.

Range-condition surveys seek to appraise the status of the range and to determine whether the trend in plant and soil development is up, down, or in approximate balance. Range condition is a reflection of the accumulated effects of past use; range trend is an expression of the effects of current use and of plant succession.

In evaluating range conditions, one should realize that no two situations may be considered identical; over-and-above mere physical availability and palatability of food, the distribution and density of food and cover are important considerations.

The following specific requirements for analysis methods may be listed:

1. They should relate availability and utilization of food so that it is possible to realize whether a range is at, above, or below carrying capacity and whether the trend is toward over- or underutilization.

2. The methods should be ecologically sound.

3. If possible, the analysis should provide statistically valid data.

4. The method used should not be so involved or time-consuming that expenditures become prohibitive.

5. Large enough samples should be collected to be meaningful in terms of management.

6. The anlaysis should be made preferably during that time of the year when food or cover are in short supply; e.g., the winter in northern latitudes.

It should be stressed that range analysis for management purposes does not need to be nearly as detailed or precise in approach as for research purposes. Analyses should be as quantitative as possible.

What kinds of techniques are going to tell us what we want to know? In order to obtain specific facts about a relatively small area, use an intensive analysis; but if one wants to have general facts about a relatively wide area, use an extensive analysis.

EXTENSIVE METHODS

When work on range analysis was initiated a decade or more ago, insufficient competent personnel could be found to run state-wide surveys that would provide statistically accurate results. Extensive methods, such as the one described by Dahlberg and Guettinger (1956) had to be employed. This survey, which restricts itself to an inventory of deer yards, consists of a random walking-cruise of as large a portion of the total area of one yard as the cruiser feels is desirable. He notes the distribution, composition, density and availability of the various deer browse plants as well as the evidence of current and previous browsing pressure and the degree of yarding.

When he has completed the survey, he makes a report about the present range conditions, classified into three categories; "poor," "medium," and "good," based on the following appraisal:

- Poor: range probably not capable of supporting its present number of deer.

- Medium: range currently capable of supporting the deer population, but range condition changing.

- Good: no immediate browse shortage, and no shortage foreseeable for several years.

Next, the present browse utilization is classified in relation to the carrying capacity of the range, or a determination is made of whether the amount of browse eaten by deer is greater than the annual amount of browse produced, about as much, or less than might be removed without endangering the future food supply.

Dasmann (1948) reviewed the literature on methods of browse analysis and evaluated some extensive methods. These methods also describe general distribution, composition, and availability to deer of food plants on winter range and the degree of current utilization by deer. He suggested that a reconnaisance method based on range indicators be used where rapid, extensive utilization checks are wanted.

A disadvantage of extensive methods, in which the surveyor makes estimates only, is that they will be no better than the experience, memory, and judgment of the man making the survey. However, qualified observers will produce faster results from a management standpoint when using these surveys than when using intensive methods.

INTENSIVE METHODS

Intensive methods of range analysis point toward a more clear-cut assessment of the factors of availability and utilization. Intensive quantitative methods are discussed by Dasmann (1948). These survey methods can be classified into three categories:

- forage inventories
- range condition surveys
- forage utilization checks.

In these methods, individual bias and personal errors are eliminated to a greater extent than in extensive analyses. Various approaches have been used to measure availability and utilization. These include a calculation of the proportion of the twig length eaten or the number of twigs browsed, or methods of weighing available browse after clipping same. When evaluating forage inventories, one should realize that density measurements alone, without making allowance for height, ignore the three dimensional aspect of plant growth, and are a poor index of forage yield (Smith 1944). One way to eliminate the troublesome density element from forage inventories is to substitute actual weight of forage on randomized plots as determined by clipping and weighing, but this method is very time-consuming. No matter how perfect the inventory method, interpretation of results must finally be based on the local pattern of use by big game.

Parker (1954) developed a three-step method of determining range condition and trend. This procedure, which involves point-sampling on transects, was formulated by Varner et al. (1954) as a detailed set of instructions for the analysis of big-game ranges in Utah. The latter authors also describe a twig-measurement method of determining browse utilization. This method consists of tagging branches on selected browse plants along a transect to measure the percentage of utilization. It is most effective with browse species where the seasonal growth tends to be linear.

The recommended procedure to follow in establishing browse-utilization transects is as follows:

1. Locate the transect to obtain a representative sample of the key area.

2. Establish the transect along a compass course or a line described by meets and bounds tied into recognizable landmarks or map points.

3. Tag only branches that are available to the game animal under study. In addition to tagging two twigs to be measured on each plant, tag or flag each plant in an identical place for ease in relocating.

4. Classify each tagged plant according to its form- and age-class.

Figs. 13.9 and 13.15 show tally sheets used in the twig-measurement method.

Varner et al. (1954) also described a modification of the above method in which whole plants are tagged instead of individual twigs.

One method for taking data on browse use which has found wide application was developed by Aldous (1944). This is a plot system along transect lines by which use of food species as browse is compared with the amounts available. In addition to measuring degree of use, the method also indicates relative palatabilities among the species present. These estimates are practical when all the browsing is being done by one species, but not where other browsers exert pressure on the vegetation.

The method consists of making a percentage sample survey of an area in which data are obtained regarding the occurrence and density of all browse species under 6 ft in height and the degree of utilization of each species. This survey is normally made in late spring following the browsing season and before new growth starts. The number of plots examined may be varied to obtain any degree of sampling intensity desired depending on time available and degree of accuracy required. Standard sample areas are circular plots with a radius of 11.8 ft (1/100-acre plots) at predetermined intervals on a compass course. The survey should take into consideration cover types so that a representative sample of the area is actually obtained.

Prepared tally sheets are used to record the results of all plots. On each plot, density and utilization (degree of browsing) are determined for each species of browse plant present. Density is determined by visual estimation of the percentage of ground covered by each browse species under 6 ft tall. This percentage of ground cover is listed as the numerator on the form and the median of each 10% bracket of cover density is used; i.e., 5% (0-10%), 15% (10-20%), etc. Since each species is projected on the ground from above and there may be several layers of browse species in the area, the total density (as measured by the percentage of ground covered) for the aggregate of all species could total over 100%. Utilization is listed as the denominator in brackets of 10% starting with 5% if any degree of browsing is evident on species. In determining degree of browsing, only current year's growth between the ground and 6 ft is considered, but removal by deer of *any* or *all* of the current growth of a twig is considered to be "browsing." A fairly rapid method of estimating the percentage of browsing is to count the total number of stems on all specimens of each species within the plot and divide this number into the number of stems actually browsed (i.e., 86 stems present and 30 browsed would be recorded as 35% browsed). Fig. 13.16 shows an example of field data collected using the Aldous browse survey technique.

Dasmann (1948) suggested the actual-weight method for intensive studies of yield and utilization: on one set of randomized plots the crop of ungrazed forage is clipped and weighted; on the other the stubble remaining after the season of use is clipped and weighed.

Hoskins and Dalke (1955) describe an intensive-sampling method, in which the composition and density of the vegetational cover were determined by the line-interception method (Canfield 1941), as follows:

"The interception of all perennial vegetation along a 100-foot cable was measured and recorded in feet and tenths of feet by species. Relative composition of the vegetation can be determined by totaling the measurements of each species along a sufficient number of lines. The amount of each species or forage class can then be expressed in terms of percentage of the ground cover and represents the relative amount of space completely covered with perennial vegetation. Shrubs were measured on the crown spread as intercepted by the vertical projection of the line. Single-stemmed forbs were measured on the stem diameter, whereas forbs of rosette form were measured on the intercept of the basal leaves. Grasses were measured at ground level and include only the intercept of living grass at that level.

"Utilization of a browse plant is based upon the percentage of leaf and annual twig growth removed by browsing animals. . . Percentages of annual growth utilized were determined by measuring twigs beyond a tagged point in the fall and then again in spring after the animals had left the winter range."

Passmore and Hepburn (1955) described a method which is so designed that errors in judgment and estimation are precluded as far as possible. The authors try to determine the relationship between the number of deer using a range and the "food" carrying capacity of the area in question by comparing the proportion of the available twigs which are used and the effect of this use on the plants producing them. A rectangular plot 66.0 x 2.0 ft (1/330 acre) at ground level was found to be most conducive to accuracy in the counting of both stems and twigs. Sampling is confined to the limits of concentration areas. Rate of sampling was arbitrarily established as 64 plots required to sample an area of 1 square mile or less. In large areas, a sampling intensity of 64 times the square root of the area in square miles is applied. Positioning of sample plots is by a line-plot method,

Fig. 13.15. Tally sheet used to determine browse utilization by the twig-measurement method (from Varner et al. 1954).

Period of Use

W
STUDIES _____ (Forest)

Area used by:
_____ Cattle _____
_____ Sheep _____
_____ Deer _____
_____ Elk _____
_____ (Specify) _____

_____
(No. and Name of Game Herd)

Examiner_____
Species _____
Age and Form Class _____
Shrub No._____
Branch No._____
Date examined fall (aftergrowth) _____

(Current Growth Only)

Name and Location of Transect_____
_____
_____
Date spring examination _____

(Optional – Old Growth between tag
and current growth)

Shoot Length Inches	Before Browsing		After Browsing			Before Browsing		After Browsing	
	Number of Shoots	Total Growth Inches	Number of Shoots	Total Length Inches		Number of Shoots	Total Growth Inches	Number of Shoots	Total Length Inches
1									
2									
3									
4									
5									
6									
7									
8									
9									
10									
11									
12									
13									
14									
15									
16									
17									
18									
19									
20									
Totals									
Average	XXXX			XXXX		XXXX		XXXX	

Estimated total inches removed, fall (if any) [____]

Old growth removed, fall (if any) [____]

Notes:

Percent Utilization

	Current Growth		Old Growth	
	Summer	Winter	Summer	Winter
Cattle				
Sheep				
Deer				
Elk				

Other
(Specify)

170

DEER BROWSE SURVEY

Species	Plot Numbers (Density over Browsing)												Total
	1	2	3	4	5	6	7	8	9	10	11	12	
Acer rubrum	5/0						5/0		25/0	25/0			3.1/0
Azalea sp.	15/0	10/0	5/0		25/25	25/25			15/15	25/25	15/15		8.18/14.8
Carya ovata	10/0	10/0	5/0			7.5/0							2.72/0
Castanea dentata					5/0		5/0			5/0			.45/0
Cornus florida	25/0	5/0		25/25				5/0		5/5			6.36/6.25
Betula lenta		5/0		5/0	5/0								.91/0
Ilex montana	5/0	5/0	5/0	5/0									3.64/0
Kalmia latifolia	5/0	5/0	5/0	5/0			85/0	85/0	80/0	35/0			28/0
Liriodendron tulipifera							5/0						.45/0
Nyssa sylvatica					5/0	5/0		5/0	25/25	25/25	5/0		6.36/6.25
Oxydendron arboreum	5/0						No/0						1.36/0
Pinus rigida	5/0												.45/0
Pinus strobus	5/0					5/0							.91/0
Prunus serotina	5/0												.45/0
Quercus alba	5/0			5/0	15/15	15/0			35/0				10.0/0
Quercus velutina	25/15	10/0			15/15	15/0			5/0	5/0	5/0		.45/0
Robinia pseudoacacia	5/0												.45/0
Rubus sp.	5/0	5/0					5/0	5/0	5/0	5/0			5.9/0
Sassafras albidum	5/0	5/0	5/0	5/0	5/0	5/0	5/0		5/0	5/5	5/5		2.72/7.8
Smilax sp.	5/0	5/0	5/0	15/0	35/0	15/0	15/15	25/25	15/15	15/15	15/15		2.4/1.9
Vaccinium sp.		1/0											1.34/.25
Viburnum sp.		2.5/0	5/0										1.25
Vitis sp.		5/0	5/0										1.36

Area analyzed West Side Potts Mt. Location Borders Deer L. Cony Co.
Date plots examined 4/24/53 Total number of plots 11 Size per plot 0.01 ac.
Plots examined by L. R. Hundley Analysis by L. R. Hundley
Remarks:

PLOT ANALYSIS FORM
Aldous Method Browse Survey

Browse species	Percent of plots present (1)	Average density (2)	Average degree of browsing (3)	Utilization factor (4)	Percent food eaten (5)	Percent browse available (6)
Acer rubrum	27.2	3.18	0	0	0	0.788
Azalea sp.	34.5	8.18	16.8	12.9	54	7.4
Carya ovata	36.4	2.72	0	0	0	2.46
Castanea dentata	9.1	.46	0	0	0	.46
Cornus florida	36.4	6.36	6.25	39.8	16.65	5.761
Betula lenta	18.2	.91	0	0	0	0.824
Ilex montana	36.4	3.64	0	0	0	3.30
Kalmia latifolia	72.7	28.00	0	0	0	25.46
Liriodendron tulipifera	9.1	0.46	0	0	0	0.416
Nyssa sylvatica	54.5	1.36	0	0	0	5.76
Oxydendron arboreum	9.1	1.36	0	0	0	1.23
Pinus rigida	9.1	.46	0	0	0	0.416
Pinus strobus	18.2	.91	0	0	0	0.823
Prunus serotina	9.1	.46	0	0	0	0.416
Quercus alba	18.2	.91	0	0	0	0.823
Quercus velutina	54.5	10.00	0	0	0	9.05
Robinia pseudoacacia	9.1	.46	0	0	0	0.416
Rubus sp.	81.8	5.90	7.8	45.4	19.0	5.35
Sassafras albidum	36.4	2.72	0	0	0	2.46
Smilax sp.	100.0	24.00	0.9	21.6	9.05	21.70
Vaccinium sp.	9.1	1.36	25	340	12.6	1.23
Viburnum sp.	27.2	1.36	0	0	0	1.23
Vitis sp.						

Calculation of Data: (1). No. plots with species present divided by total no. plots; (2) Ave. percent of plots covered by indicated species; (3) The average percent of species browsed by deer in all plots; (4) Product of columns 2 and 3; (5) Total of (4) divided into the utilization factor for individual plant species; (6) Total of (2) divided into the average density for individual species.

Area analyzed West side Potts Mt. Location Borders Deer L. Cony Co.
Date plots examined 4/24/53 Total number of plots 11 Size per plot 0.01 acre
Plots examined by L. R. Hundley Analysis by L. R. Hundley
Remarks

Fig. 13.16. Forms used in collecting and analysing data collected by the Aldous deer-browse survey (adapted from Aldous 1944).

with a 5-chain interval between plot centers. Cruise lines are drawn on a field map in positions designed to give even distribution of the sample.

Plot records are made on tally sheets, which list plant species commonly browsed by deer. Entries for each species are:

K   Number of stems killed by browsing.

M   Number of stems mutilated by previous browsing.

L   Number of living stems providing twigs available to deer under average winter conditions.

B   Percentage of twigs which have had some part of their length removed by deer.

The numbers of stems tallied as K, M, and L are determined by actual counts. The percentage of twigs browsed (B) is calculated from figures obtained by counts of browsed and unbrowsed twigs.

Harlow (1955) devised a forage-weight method of range inventory which is applicable to all forms of green vegetation available as deer food. He used sample plots 3.1 ft square. The quantity of vegetation is obtained by weighing for each plot that portion of each plant species considered edible to deer. Only those portions of a plant which are within reach are counted. The green-weighed samples of each species of vegetation clipped are saved in paper bags and dried in order to obtain the percent moisture loss. Utilization of grasses and herbaceous material is determined by the use of a descriptive scale.

To check on range trends, fenced plots from which browsing animals are excluded are most helpful. These, together with a photographic record, take much of the guess-work out of range evaluation.

EVALUATION OF WETLAND HABITAT

Wetlands serve an important role in the protection and production of wildlife, particularly of waterfowl and aquatic mammals. However, other species such as pheasants, rabbits, woodcock, Hungarian partridge, raccoon and deer, as well as non-game species, also require such lands for food and cover. It may even be stated that acre for acre, wetlands exceed all other land types in wildlife productivity. McCabe (1956) presented a description of the values of wetlands to wildlife.

Wetlands are lowlands covered by shallow and sometimes temporary or intermittent waters, including marshes, swamps, bogs, wet meadows, potholes, sloughs, and river-bottom lands. Small, shallow lakes and ponds are usually also included in this group, as well as waterlogged soils. Wetlands may be covered by a great diversity of vegetative types.

As most wetlands can be either drained or filled, a large percentage of them has been converted into some other form of land use. Particularly in the "duck factory" of the prairie states and provinces, but also in other parts of the United States and Canada, drainage of wetlands has destroyed much wildlife habitat.

The U.S. Soil Conservation Service has estimated the original wetlands of the U.S.A. at 127 million acres, of which some 45 million acres have been drained. These figures conform closely to findings of a wetlands survey by the U.S. Fish and Wildlife Service. As a basic step to wetlands planning, this Service, with cooperation of State wildlife agencies, undertook an extensive wetlands inventory in the U.S. (Shaw and Fredine 1956) to determine: (a) the location and extent of wetlands, (b) the wetlands types in each area, and (c) their relative usefulness to wildlife.

In this survey emphasis was placed on wetlands considered susceptible to drainage or other land-use changes. The aim was to make the coverage as complete as time and manpower would permit. Aerial photographs, topographic maps, soil maps, and land use maps were used as sources of information on the locations of wetlands. In regions inventoried, most wetlands of less than 40 acres were excluded. Wetlands were recorded on county maps either as specific units or as general areas. In some states acreage data were collected on small scattered wetlands. In each county estimates of the amount, type and quality of the wetlands were obtained. Twenty ecologically different wetland types were recognized, grouped in four categories, namely: inland fresh areas, inland saline areas, coastal fresh areas, and coastal saline areas. Value categories of high, moderate, low, and negligible were used to indicate the relative importance of wetlands to waterfowl. Wetlands in the breeding range of waterfowl were appraised as to their suitability for production purposes, those in the South as to their values as wintering habitat. Inventory data can serve as an effective starting point for wetlands improvement as well as for wetlands preservation. The completed inventory encompasses only natural wetlands, and not seasonally flooded lands presently used for crops or pasture. The value of the survey arises from a standardization of types of wetlands and a focusing of attention on the wildlife values of these areas.

The U.S. Fish and Wildlife Service inventory does not contain sufficiently quantitative data for a detailed habitat analysis. It has also been argued that wetlands smaller than 40 acres are the most important habitat for some game species in certain sections of the country. Therefore, more detailed surveys have been undertaken in Wisconsin (Dahlen 1955). Wetlands down to 1/4 acre in size were evaluated. Information obtained by the Wisconsin inventory will make available accurate acreage figures of all remaining wetlands and will enable a close estimate of acreage drained. The distribution, the degree of grazing, as well as the types and amounts of existing wetlands, will be determined.

Relatively few evaluations have been made so far of the habitat of individual wetlands and their value to wildlife. Beard (1953) developed a system for measuring the amount and composition of emergent vegetation along transect lines. Density estimates of the vegetation were based on the ease with which ducks could penetrate it. A series of 32 stem counts, each along a 36-inch line, were made at random. Three degrees of density were set up:

- Sparse—growth offers no hindrance and only scant cover to waterfowl. Stem counts from 0 to 160.
- Medium—growth allows easy penetration by waterfowl and provides abundant escape cover. Stem counts 160 to 290.
- Dense—vegetation cannot be penetrated by waterfowl. Stem counts above 290.

Interspersion of vegetation types was expressed numerically by dividing the total number of occurrences in a specified unit by the number of cover types present in that unit.

Results of the artificial establishment of aquatic vegetation perhaps have not been studied as much as they should have been. Progress has been made recently by U.S. federal agencies in techniques to benefit waterfowl through artificial plantings and agricultural practices. Dillon (1957) pointed out the dependence of ducks in Louisiana on agricultural lands which are flooded in winter. Davison and Neely (1959) described the management of farm fields, wetlands, and waters for ducks in the South.

Few studies have been made so far of the physico-chemical conditions of soils and water in wetlands. Cook and Powers (1958) have studied the early biochemical changes in the soils and waters of artificially created marshes in New York. One of their findings was that marshes surrounded by good agricultural soils were more productive of food and cover plants than those surrounded by degraded lands.

CHAPTER FOURTEEN

HABITAT MANIPULATION PRACTICES

JIM YOAKUM

Wildlife Management Biologist
U.S. Bureau of Land Management
Reno, Nevada

and

WILLIAM P. DASMANN

Chief, Wildlife Management Branch, Region 5
U.S. Forest Service
San Francisco, California

173

Aldo Leopold's list of "cow, plow, fire, and axe" as major habitat management tools has been expanded with new understandings, technological advances, and under current pressure to develop specialized habitats. All of the land-use tools available to the farmer, rancher, forester, construction engineer, orchard grower, poultryman, or fur farmer are available. Most have been employed in some way to manipulate wildlife habitat. All these practices and techniques cannot be described in one book, consequently, a guide for selection of projects and ways to "get the job done" is presented. Each method must be judged critically for each site and for the goal to be accomplished. Many of the methods discussed here are from the following major periodicals on game range restoration: (a) *Western Browse Research* published annually by various western State Fish and Game Departments from 1955 to 1963; (b) *Game Range Restoration Studies* published annually by the Utah State Department of Fish and Game from 1956 to date; and (c) *Range Improvement Notes* published by the Intermountain Forest and Range Experiment Station, Logan, Utah. By far the most important compendium on habitat manipulation is the U.S. Forest Service's "Wildlife Habitat Improvement Handbook" currently being edited. The document is the best available compilation of State, Federal, and private findings regarding various practices of food, cover, water, and space manipulation for the benefit of wildlife in North America. Consequently, the authors have incorporated much of the information in this chapter.

FOOD PRODUCTION

Mast and Fruits

Mast is the fruit of oak, hickory, beech, gum, cherry, ash, and other tree and shrub species. Mast occurs on a wide variety of understory plant species such as flowering dogwood, wild grape, haws, blackberries, blueberries, crabapples, persimmon, serviceberry, sumacs, wild plums and cherries, and many others. The three major methods of improving mast and fruit production are propagation, release, and protection. Propagation is the direct planting of desirable seeds or transplants. Release encompasses such practices as mechanical crushing, controlled burning, and creating forest openings by mechanical or chemical means to favor increased production of desirable species. Protection includes the preservation of mature mast producers, protecting

trees until they reach mast producing age, and protection of the mast itself from consumption by undesirable organisms.

PROPAGATION

Relatively little is known about propagation of many wild native mast and fruit producing plants. Several, such as dogwood, persimmon, grape, and crabapple are available commercially. Experiences in developing shelterbelts, windbreaks, living fences, and gully or waterway plantings provide much helpful information on propagation. These practices not only serve their original purpose of reducing soil movement and decreasing water runoff, but often provide an abundance of wildlife food. A number of plant species such as Russian olive, juniper, ponderosa pine, squawberry, and wild plum are available for these practices.

The arid and semi-arid lands of the west are characterized by alternating warm and very cold periods during typical winters; consequently many of the fruit-bearing shrubs and tress of the East will not successfully grow. Russian olive and native berries may be used in the western high plains and mountain plantings. Russian olive is an example of one adaptable species that thrives throughout the west from Canada to Mexico. The fruit is eaten by more than 50 species of birds and mammals (Borell 1962). When planting this tree in gullies, borrow pits, or waste areas, spacing of the seedlings should be 3 to 6 ft apart if the plants can be irrigated or will have adequate moisture. On drier sites, seedlings should be spaced 6 to 8 ft apart. Where there is adequate moisture, Russian olive can be used as a living fence. Spaced 2 ft apart, the plants will form a living fence within 2 to 4 years. There is no need for trimming the fence; however, pruning back will make it more bushy and produce more branches near the ground. Tall tree growth can be encouraged by spacing at 10 ft intervals and trimming the central trunk annually. Russian olive for windbreaks or use along streambanks, can be planted with a mechanical tree planter or by digging a hole for each plant. The plants should be set at the same depth, or slightly deeper than they were in the nursery. If the nursery stock is not too large, it may be satisfactorily planted by plowing a deep furrow with a 12- or 14-inch plow. Place the plants in the furrow at the desired spacing and plow back over the roots. Firm the earth by running the wheel of the tractor close to the new plantings. Often it is necessary to straighten each plant by hand and firm the earth by foot to hold the plants erect.

Habitat managers in the East desiring to increase food production for wildlife will find the autumn-olive a highly beneficial species to consider for propagation. The tree's small berries provide fall and winter food for many kinds of wildlife as well as nesting sites and protective cover (Allan and Steiner 1959). Its production is outstanding. For example, four 150-ft rows in southern New York yielded 2 tons of berries yearly with regularity. Generally dormant seedlings 1 or 2 years old are transplanted either in the fall or spring. Plantings in strips are more successful if the site is plowed, harrowed, and allowed to settle before planting is done. Block plantings may be made in deep plow furrows or in spots from which sod has been scalped.

Seedling roots must be kept moist until planted. A hole for a plant should be deep enough to take the full unbent root. Unusually long roots on many plants may be pruned back to 6 inches and the tops also cropped to 6 inches. Soil must be packed firmly around the roots and stamped down. On poor soils a scant handful of 5-20-5 or 10-10-10 fertilizer (Nitrogen-Phosphorus-Potassium) per plant, well mixed with the soil, helps plants get off to a good start. On dry sites mulches of straw, sawdust, or wood chips are helpful. Cultivation around plants often helps speed established seedling growth.

Autumn olive seeds should be planted the latter part of October in wet, cold soil to germinate in the spring. Desired seeding areas should first be plowed, then 600 to 800 pounds of 10-10-10 fertilizer per acre applied if needed, followed by harrowing, and then packed down to give a smooth, moderately firm seedbed. Beds for broadcast seeding should be about 4 ft wide to make hand weeding easy during the growing season. For every 48 square feet of bed, 8 ounces of clean seed should be evenly sown. The seeds are covered 1/4 to 1/2 inch with a layer of sand or very light sandy soil. A pound of seed thus broadcast usually yields about 3,000 useable year-old seedlings. For row plantings, the seed can be drilled 8 to 10 inches apart with a mechanical garden-type seeder. The seedbed should be prepared as mentioned above. Seed should be planted 1/2 inch deep at the rate of about 25 seeds per linear foot of row. With the row method, mechanical cultivators or a hand-pushed wheel hoe can be used for weeding. About the same number of plants will be produced in a given area by either the broadcast or the row method.

RELEASE

On many sites, growth and production of mast species may be improved by release from competition from less desirable species. Dense mature woodlands seldom produce a variety or abundance of desirable food plants. One method to open a forest is to clearcut the timber from 1/2- to 2-acre strips. The strips can be of any shape, but those 30 to 60 ft wide generally running east and west are best. Clearcutting is not needed in timber stands which are open enough to permit the growth of blackberries, blueberries, and similar plants. Once shading out of plants in previously made openings has started, new openings can be cut.

Another method of increasing fruit production by providing openings, is to select trees, such as apple (wild or in abandoned orchards), wild cherry, hackberry, oak or hickory, and apply one of the orchardist's methods for producing more fruit. This method involves measurement of the diameter of the tree in inches at 4-1/2 ft above ground. The diameter is multiplied by 3, and feet are then substituted for inches. The resulting figure is the length of each side of a square from which all trees are to be removed except the fruit tree to be favored. Not only will this give the tree an opportunity to produce more fruit, but the interspaces are open for increased production of grasses, forbs and shrubs (Shomon et al. 1966).

With many fruit producing chaparral species in the West such as manzanita, California red berry, and toyon, decadent stands can be renewed by mechanical crushing, chemical spraying, and especially by controlled burning. These practices are discussed in further detail under "Controlled Burning."

Browse

Browse is defined as leaves, shoots and twigs of shrubs and trees used as food. In some situations, such as a range recently burned by wildfire, there may be a need to plant desirable browse to introduce or restore a supply of forage. Elsewhere increased food production may be a goal. Browse manipulation practices can be grouped into the following categories:

(a) Release through thinning to remove competition from less desirable species.
(b) Rejuvenation through breaking, crushing, herbicide spraying, pruning, or burning rapidly regenerating species.

(c) Planting in areas of need either to introduce seed stock or to provide for additional browse production.

In planning such projects, such factors as temperature, precipitation, humidity, geological formation, soil, slope, aspect, plant ecology, and biological agents should be considered. Methods and species suggested below may need to be modified to fit situations other than those described.

RELEASE

Many of the procedures used to release desirable browse plants from the competition of less desirable species are the same as those used for complete removal of existing vegetation. The results of such treatments depend upon the intensity of application. For example, chemical sprays may be used to dessicate only the crowns of woody species, or to completely kill the plants, dependent on strength of the mix and the number of applications (Pechanec et al. 1954, Plummer et al. 1955).

There are four general methods of eliminating competition—mechanical and manual treatment, chemical sprays, and planned burning. Often these methods are used in combination to meet specific needs. Mechanical methods and hand methods are more expensive than either chemicals or burning, but have much wider application.

Mechanical and Manual Methods

The *Range Seeding Equipment Handbook* (USFS 1965) contains rather complete descriptions of equipment that may be used to treat areas for release of competition, together with the advantages and limitations of each method. Only a few of the more common procedures will be described briefly here. Other important references on these practices include Plummer et al. (1955), Sampson and Jesperson (1963), Pechanec et al. (1954), Box and Powell (1965).

● Anchor Chaining

Chaining consists of dragging a heavy chain through vegetation in order to break off or uproot plants (Kerr and Hoffman 1964). The general procedure is for two tractors, one attached to each end of the chain, to travel on parallel courses 60 to 100 ft apart. The spacing is dependent upon density of vegetation, weight, and length of the anchor chain, size of tractor, bite of tracks, and slope. Ordinarily, tractors with a minimum of 110 horsepower on the draw bar are used. The chain

size is dependent upon the degree of kill desired. For dense stands of target species with little desirable understory, a heavy anchor chain weighing near 100 lb. per link achieves the best results. Dense young stands of trees or brush require a heavier chain than older stands, because of the need to have the chain ride close to the ground. Links of 27 to 40 lb. are used on areas where it is desired to leave a fairly dense residual stand of browse plants.

A better kill can be ensured by chaining when the soil moisture is at a minimum or when the first several inches of the soil are frozen. Chaining efficiently removes young, willowy trees. Chaining can create a good seedbed for aerial broadcast seeding. In areas planned for twice-over chaining along with aerial seeding, the second pass should be timed so it will cover the seed.

● Cabling

Cabling is suited to areas where it is planned to save residual stands of desirable shrubs and herbaceous cover and where the target species are not young and willowy (Plummer et al. 1955). Cabling is carried on essentially the same as the procedure described in chaining except that a 150- to 200-ft long, 1-1/2-inch cable is used in place of a chain.

● Hula Dozer

This mechanical device is a 100 to 125 drawbar-horsepower crawler-type tractor with a "hula dozer" blade. The blade consists of hinged pusher bars and hydraulic tilting attachments. The pusher bar is used to tip trees, while the corner of the blade is used to lift them from the ground. Hula dozing is economically advantageous in areas where target trees are clustered and clusters are widely spaced, or where trees do not exceed 100 per acre. This method is used primarily where stands of browse plants are present and it is desired to leave them undamaged.

● Scalping

Scalping consists of scraping off the plants and part of the top layer of soil from planting sites. It is a simple and highly effective method of removing vegetation as well as most of the seed in the soil beneath it (Brown and Martinsen 1959, Holgren and Basile 1959, Box and Powell 1965). The scalping of broad areas often leads to soil losses from erosion.

There are a number of methods for scalping. The simplest is with a hand hoe. The fastest and least expensive is with mechanical equipment. However, mechanical scalping is limited to terrain that can be negotiated by a tractor or jeep. A practical method for scalping and planting gentle slopes fairly free of rocks involves the use of a Hansen seeder equipped with a wide mold-board plow. Hand scalping is effective on steep slopes and rocky areas. Scalps 2-ft square and at least 2-inches deep or deeper than the effective depth of the annual roots are cleared with hoe. Heavier, narrower hoes are required for rocky, compact soils with perennial vegetation. In scalping, the material scraped off is piled on the lower side of the plot to form a catch basin. Care should be taken to avoid dirt spilling over the top of the blade back into the plot, since this may contaminate the seed-bed with annual weed seeds. Sloughing of the soil into the scalp from its upper edge is common on slopes steeper than 50%. This sloughing can be minimized by gradually increasing the scalp in depth as the hoe is pulled downhill rather than by vertically chopping.

• Conventional Tillage Implements

Where soil and vegetative conditions permit, plowing is a desirable method to eliminate competitive vegetation (Plummer et al. 1955, Pechanec et al. 1954). Disk-type plows, such as heavy offset disk or wheatland plow, are good for controlling nonsprouting species on soils with relatively few rocks. The brushland plow is best for rough, moderately rocky areas.

Plowing to a depth of 3 to 4 inches is recommended for most nonsprouting plants such as sagebrush. Depths of 4 to 6 inches are required to eradicate plants which spread by underground root stocks or from the crown. A heavyduty root plow is required to eliminate root-sprouting species.

The Holt plow is effective in reducing competition on slopes up to 40% where watershed measures are also needed. It will construct a continuous furrow in either direction. This double disk furrower is attached to a crawler-type tractor by means of a specially built 3-point hitch. The depth and angle is controlled by a hydraulic ram. The tractor must have in excess of 100 horsepower on the drawbar to effectively handle the Holt furrower.

Chemical Sprays

Herbicides offer possibilities for improving wildlife habitat (Sampson and Jesperson 1963:28, Kearl 1965, Krenz 1962, Oregon State Univ. School of Forestry 1967). Selective spraying may be used to reduce stands of undesirable browse plants.

Basal sprouting of browse species that have grown too high or dense for deer and elk can be stimulated by killing the aerial crowns with chemicals (Wilbert 1963, Mueggler 1966). The variable sensitivity of different species to the formulation, concentration, and time of application of herbicides should enable discriminating manipulation of the habitat, once these sensitivities are known. Unfortunately, not a great deal is currently known about this subject. Most big game ranges, for instance, support a mixture of shrub species that differ in sensitivity to chemicals. This often makes the effects of sprays unpredictable. It is known, for instance, that mixed stands of big sagebrush and bitterbush may be sprayed with 2, 4-D butyl or isopropyl ester at the standard sagebrush control rate without serious loss of bitterbrush, provided spraying is done while bitterbrush is still in bloom. On one California project, a 2-lb. acid equivalent 2, 4-D spray with diesel oil as a carrier, at a volume of 3 gal per acre, resulted in 95% removal of sagebrush and 18% kill of the most severely hedged and decadent bitterbrush plants. The remaining bitterbrush plants, however, rapidly developed good form and vigor. Leader growth of treated plants was 1.11 times greater than that on controls two seasons after treatment even though crested wheatgrass had been planted in the treated area. However, until more is learned about selective sensitivities, caution is needed in application of chemical sprays on mixed browse stands. Opportunities to observe effects of forest or range management spraying on plants of various species should not be overlooked. The advantages of hand- or power-operated ground sprayers for control of individual undesirable species could be considered.

Planned Burning

Planned or controlled burning is one of the more economical procedures for removal of a stand of vegetation for a prescribed purpose (Sampson and Jesperson 1963:27, Pechanec and Stewart 1948, Hiehle 1961, Biswell and Gilman 1961, and Cushwa 1968). It can be used as a first step in seedbed preparation to reduce competing plant species, to create openings in dense stands of brush, to break seed dormancy in some species, and for other purposes. The wildlifer responsible for burning must insure that the fire remain controlled. Fireline preparation, season, time of day of burns, and firing and manning plans should be gauged to insure this objective.

REJUVENATION

Many species of shrubs and trees can regenerate through spouting either from adventitious buds on the stem or from the root crown. With chaparral species and some others the seed is heat resistant and heat responsive and germinates in abundance after fire. When such species have grown too tall, dense, or decadent to produce available browse forage, it is possible to rejuvenate the stand by controlled burning (Biswell et al. 1952, Hiehle 1961). With many species, it has been found that the sprouts and young plants are considerably higher in protein and other food values for several years after burning than in older growth stages. Some species of shrubs and trees are killed by fire and may not reestablish on an area naturally for decades after a hot burn. Often, however, these kinds of plants will respond to a rejuvenation treatment by crushing, rolling, cutting, or mowing by high production of adventitious growth. Chemical spraying, where it burns back the tops but does not kill the shrubs has a similar effect on many kinds of woody plants. The root systems remain largely undamaged; the plants respond to the reduction of aerial growth by rapid and expansive shoot and leaf development. However, there is evidence that deer are reluctant to browse heavily on plants where a multitude of dead stems are intermingled with new growth. Dead stems may be a disadvantage if moderate to heavy browsing is needed to hold the growth at heights available for browsing (Macgregor et al. 1967). Crushing of brush either before or after burning results in better utilization of regenerated forage.

Special Considerations

The size and pattern of rejuvenation treatments planned for an area should be geared to the requirements of the target animal species involved. With non-migratory deer, for instance, many small treated spots or strips scattered over a large area will benefit more deer than a large single project. There are several reasons for this. In the first place, the home ranges of bucks or doe-yearling-fawn family groups can be quite small. Only the deer whose home ranges impinge on or are immediately adjacent to the treated area will move into and use the rejuvenated forage stand. In addition, deer often are reluctant to travel more than 200-300 ft from cover and may use only the circumference of a large opening. Of prime importance, also, is the need to gear the amount of forage produced to the number of animals that will use it. If use is too light, the rejuvenating spouts and young plants may rapidly grow out of reach or become as dense as the original untreated stand. But if the treated areas are small enough so that moderately heavy browsing of forage holds plants in desirable forms, value will be prolonged over much longer periods. If deer respond to better forage conditions by increase in numbers, the frequency and size of treated areas can be increased. Treatments can be rotated so that no one area will be manipulated more often than once in 10-20 years. In any case no more than 50% of the area should be treated to create better forage areas and the other 50% left in cover, with size of cover patches at least 40 acres or more (Taber and Dasmann 1958).

The prescribed treatments for key portions of migratory deer winter range will necessarily differ from those described above. Since key areas are parts of the range where heavy snows and other conditions force deer to concentrate during mid-winter, deer densities and the demand for food tends to be high. For this reason, it is essential that treatments be large enough to prevent decimation of rejuvenating forage. But even here, the most productive patterns will be in extensive broad strips or openings interspersed with patches or strips of cover rather than in single large projects. Retention of cover, certainly, should not be neglected in such projects and should be given special emphasis where winters are severe. In northern Maine, for instance, dense conifer winter cover for deer should be alternated with open feeding areas at intervals not exceeding 100 yards.

This brief description of requirements for deer will show the need for analysis of the requirements of the wildlife species to be favored and the importance of tailoring the program to fit these requirements.

Rejuvenating Bitterbrush

Bitterbrush is an important browse species on deer winter ranges in several Western regions. Many procedures have been used to rejuvenate tall, decadent stands of bitterbrush (Ferguson and Basile 1966, Driscoll 1963). Results from railing or by crushing with a bull-dozer, with blade 1 to 2 ft above the ground, indicate a great increase in growth the first year after treatment. But this increase has been followed by a decline in growth the second and third year and by an actual loss of forage production. The evidence at hand indicates that dozing and railing cause severe mortality and diminishment of the total area of crown.

Rolling bitterbrush with a heavy log covered

with rubber tires and pulled by a rubber-tired tractor shows promise for plant rejuvenation. Although there was little response the first year after rolling on a California project, bitterbrush leader growth averaged 54% greater than that on the control area the second year, and most of the treated plants showed excellent vigor. Only 2% of the rolled plants failed to resprout. Cost of the California project was $11.50 per acre.

Roto-cutting bitterbrush in early spring with blade set 18 inches above the ground level resulted in a 47% increase in leader growth the same year on one project. But long-term results have not yet been evaluated. Pruning from an average height of over 5 ft to heights under 4 ft coupled with removal of all shrub competition, resulted in an increase in leader growth 2.08 times over that on an adjacent control area, after two growing seasons. Again, long-term evaluation has yet to be made (Schneegas and Zufelt 1965).

Crushed Browse-Ways

Many chaparral-type brushfields are practically impenetrable to deer and offer little habitat to other wildlife. Such brush ranges can be improved for wildlife by creation of interspersions of brush sprouts and herbaceous vegetation through development of small openings connected by lanes (Biswell et al. 1952, Hiehle 1961). The primary objective of such work is the development of both food and access.

PLANTINGS

The planting of browse species is expensive and the results are commonly not predictable. Planting is no easy cure-all. From the standpoint of costs, there is no good substitute for natural regeneration. Where possible, browse management should aim at maintenance or improvement of existing stands. Where it becomes necessary to plant in order to introduce or to restore browse species, this may be done by direct seeding or use of transplants (Plummer et al. 1955, Plummer et al. 1966, Brown and Martinsen 1959, Holmgren and Basile 1959, Hubbard 1964).

The most important considerations leading to a successful browse plantation are: site selection, site preparation, planting depth, and soil moisture. The best results may be expected on sites which are known to have supported the browse species concerned in the past. A knowledge of plant requirements including answers to the following questions is essential: Should the soil be coarse or fine textured; should it be well-drained or poorly drained, acid or alkaline? At what depth should seed be planted?

An important cause of plantation failure is the competition for soil moisture given the young seedlings by established vegetation. Whether planting is done on selected spots or over a broad acreage, care must be taken to eliminate, or at least reduce, competition by existing herbaceous and woody vegetation. With spot planting, reduction of competition can be secured through either hand or mechanical scalping. For broad plantations, the best results follow the preparation of the site by regular farming methods. The objective is to plant in a clean, firm seedbed. This may involve plowing or disking as well as the drilling of seed.

Direct Seeding

There are several procedures commonly used for direct seeding. The kinds of equipment are described in the *Range Seeding Equipment Handbook* (USFS 1965) and are discussed briefly below.

● Deep-Furrow Drill
The deep-furrow drill provides a furrow 2 to 3 inches deep, spaced at 14-inch intervals. Wider spacing is achieved by removing drops. The 21- or 28-inch spacing is regarded the most practical for planting browse. Spacers in the seedbox can be quickly provided to permit seeding of different species in alternate rows. The drill is mounted on rubber tires and can be pulled by a light tractor or jeep. It was not designed for seeding rough rangelands. On the more level lands, the drill does an excellent job of seeding as well as leaving a good seedbed for emergence. The machine can be hauled on a 1-1/2 ton truck. Maneuverability of the drill limits its use. It is not a practical tool for seeding small openings.

● Hansen Browse Seeder
The Hansen browse seeder can be equipped with either 16- or 32-inch scalping wings. Whether equipped with one or two scalpers, the seeder can be pulled by a jeep or small tractor (either with wheels or tracks). The equipment is small enough to operate in small spaces as well as larger areas. Arrangements can be made to pull two drills at a time for large scale seeding operations (see Fig. 14.1). Successful plantings have been effectively made with a variety of shrubs, broadleaf herbs, and grass.

● Cutout Disk
The horse-drawn cutout disk used a decade ago

Fig. 14.1. Two Hansen browse seed drills hooked on a tandematic bar behind a tractor. The purpose of this arrangement was to drill over 4,000 acres burned by wildfire on critical deer ranges. (U.S. Bureau of Land Management photo by Jim Yoakum.)

has been satisfactorily used in rocky and partially brushy areas. This small disk pits the ground with many small impressions or gouges. The seed is broadcast either ahead of the disk or behind it. The gouges or impressions aid in retaining moisture in the soil. The disk is light in weight, compact and rugged. It can be pulled by a single horse or by a team (Fig. 14.1).

● Seed Dribblers

Observations in the past have indicated that soil disturbed by tractor tracks are excellent seedbeds for browse, forb, and grass species. Some of the best stands are often obtained in these tracks of crawler tractors. Apparently the soil disturbance, compaction, and seed coverage are effective in improving the establishment of new plants. Because of the availability and high cost of native browse, forb, and grass seed, it is important that an effective method be used in seedings. To meet

this need an experimental seed dribbler was constructed (see Fig. 14.2). This attachment dribbles seed into the track-pad just as it breaks over the front idler. The seed drops off the pad and is imbedded in a compacted seedbed.

Seed dribblers are mounted on the deck of a D-8 or similar size tractor. The seed-drop mechanism has a direct drive from a rubber-tired wheel riding on the tracks or the tractor. The seeders may be mounted as a pair, one on each side of the tractor, and are adaptable to various types of seed. The hopper holds enough seed for approximately 1-1/2 hr of operation. With some modifications, it could be used to broadcast in front of plows or pipe harrows.

● Aerial Broadcasting

One approach used in seeding extensive ranges, especially in conjunction with chaining of juniper-

Fig. 14.2. A seed dribbler mounted on a large tractor. Although not portrayed in this photograph, an extension tube is usually attached to the seed dribbler for the purpose of dropping the seed to the leading edge on the track (Utah Fish & Game photo by Clark Davis).

pinyon and mountain brush types, couples aerial broadcasting with a treatment to cover the seed. Aerial seeding may be the solution for seeding irregular, rocky, and steep terrain where drills cannot be used. This is also true of areas where a heavy litter of smashed trees and branches makes the drilling method difficult and expensive. Best results for this method are achieved when the seed is covered after aerial application. For chaining projects, this would mean a second chaining treatment.

• Hand Broadcasting

Hand broadcasting is an effective method of dispersing seed on small areas or in selected sites. Seed can also be hand-broadcast in disturbed sites or in pits which are left after juniper-pinyon tree removal.

Cyclone seeders can be used for broadcasting small areas that are uneconomical for aerial seeding or where the terrain or physical obstacles prohibit mechanical ground methods. Excellent results have been obtained by seeding up to 80-acre areas by hand with a five-man crew. Two days are required to seed such an area with 12-15 pounds of seed per acre.

Shrub seeds, such as bitterbrush, can be planted in three or four spots on 2-1/2 ft. diameter cleared areas from which 1/2- to 1-inch of topsoil has been scraped away. This method has proven to be successful even on areas where cheatgrass brome or other annual weed cover occurs.

Use of Transplants

The transplanting of nursery stock, wildings, and seedlings has been an effective method of establishing browse. Transplanting should be done as early as possible in the spring to take advantage of the residual moisture.

In some areas, early spring transplanting has proven successful where direct seeding methods have failed. The transplants are generally planted in a similar manner to that of tree planting. Individual planting sites are prepared by scooping away an area of earth prior to digging the hole. This is normally constructed in the same manner as a scalp, the size of which will depend upon the amount of existing competing vegetation. Normally, the scalped area should be 14 inches in diameter and 1 to 4 inches deep. In contour-trenched terrain, planting is normally done at the bottom of the trench for smaller trenches, and just below the crest of the larger trenches and individual baffles. Each planting hole is dug in the center of the cleared area with a shovel or pulaski. The depth of the hole should exceed the root length. The seedling is then removed from the planting bucket and placed in the hole with the roots spread in normal position. Holding the crown in place, the planter should place soil free of organic litter and rocks against the roots. This soil should then be firmly packed. The planting bucket should have a perforated bottom and the seedlings should be packed in material such as peat moss.

Herbaceous Plantings (Grasses and Forbs)

The diet of almost all game animals and birds includes herbaceous plants and seeds. The establishment and improvement of interspersions of herbaceous plant cover is a wildlife habitat improvement measure of broad application (Plummer et al. 1955, Hungerford 1965, Sampson et al. 1951, Edmunson and Cornelius 1961). Since there are opportunities for herbaceous cover improvement frequently available through coordination of the wildlife resource with other resource activities, it is important that such opportunities be recognized and used when available.

Some other land management activities which offer opportunities to establish herbaceous cover at low costs are timber stand improvement, type conversion, power and gas line clearings, soil stabilization after wildfire burns, road-fill stabilization, restoration of borrow-pits, ski-slope stabilization, skid-tail stabilization, patch cutting of timber, and range re-seeding. It is often possible to choose desirable wildlife foods for the entire mixture or part of the seeding mixture for these areas. Coordination of this kind is an economical way to achieve herbaceous plant improvement.

Thousands of pounds of seed have been needlessly wasted in random broadcasting over areas not having seedbed preparation. Unless the broadcast seed has all the characteristics of an aggressive weed, the chances of establishment under such conditions are very low. Seed may be broadcasted successfully on burns, particularly if the seeding is made before the rains pack and wash the ashes. Broadcast seeding has often been successful on disturbed soils, but even here some treatment is desirable to insure that seed is covered with soil. Ordinarily, regular farming methods provide the best chance for successful establishment of grass or forb plantations. Given adequate soil moisture, the three essential steps needed in grass seeding are (1) removal of competition, (2) planting seed at proper depth and (3) good cover of seed. The species to be chosen will vary by region, climate, elevation, and soil type. Desirable native seed when obtainable reduces the gamble on most sites (Plummer et al. 1955, Hungerford 1965, Hankla and Verts 1948).

SEEDBED PREPARATION

The first step ordinarily will be to get rid of woody vegetation by crushing and burning or other disposal. It is necessary to have a seedbed of exposed mineral soil for the seed to germinate and grow. This job is best accomplished by disking as many times as needed to get the desired seedbed and to eliminate as much of the residual vegetation as possible. The type of equipment needed will vary with site and cover conditions. If free-ranging domestic livestock are in the area, they will need to be fenced from wildlife food plots. Some wildlifers recommend that when hog-proof fencing is used around turkey food plots, poles should be placed above the top strand of wire, at intervals, to allow the turkeys to jump to the poles before dropping into the plot. It is their opinion that without the poles, turkeys will not enter.

FERTILIZATION AND LIMING

It is advisable to secure a soil test as a basis for deciding about the need for fertilizer and lime.

The County Agent can assist in getting the soil test and the interpretation of the results.

In some regions, grasses will require generous amounts of nitrogen fertilizer for best growth. Nitrogen should be added during or just before periods of active growth since a single application is effective only 1 to 3 months. Fertilize warm-season species with nitrogen in the early spring and summer. For cool-season annuals overseeded in the fall, nitrogen should be applied at time of seeding and again in midwinter. Phosphate additions may be needed in some regions to improve stand density, height growth, and success of legumes.

SEEDINGS AND PLANTINGS

Drill or broadcast summer grasses and legumes in late winter or early spring. Since results of sowing on bare soil without packing or covering seeds is often unsuccessful, it is a good practice to follow with a cultipacker. Winter legumes and winter annual grasses must be seeded in the fall, even though the soil is dry.

CEREAL PLANTINGS

Small plots of unharvested grains will provide food for a variety of upland game. The additional winter food supply can be particularly valuable to such upland game birds as pheasants, bobwhite quail, Hungarian and chukar partridge, sharptail grouse, turkeys, geese, and ducks. In some areas in the eastern United States, grain plantings are used also to provide valuable food for deer, squirrels, raccoons, and other small game. Grain plantings may be justified if it is desired to maintain higher numbers of one or more species of wildlife than can be expected to survive with natural winter food supplies. Plantings are used also as buffers in some areas to help prevent depredation of agricultural crops.

Grain plantings for upland game need not be large. Plots one-eighth to one acre will suffice. Long and narrow or irregularly shaped plots are preferred. The plantings should be adjacent to good cover of the type and amount necessary for the wildlife species involved. Steep slopes should be avoided because the soils will be unprotected from erosion after plowing and before the grain crop is established. Even on slight slopes, strips of grain should be alternated on the contour with strips of grass or native cover to minimize soil erosion.

For most wildlife species, the food should be available in later winter and early spring; therefore, avoid planting where excessive snowdrifting will occur. However, drifting is usually not a problem in grain seedings made for waterfowl. Normally, these seedings will be used in the fall before or during migrations. Plots should be planted every other year in order to permit volunteer grains and weeds to develop during alternate years.

Plant grain varieties suitable to the locality and site. County agents and seed supply houses can be consulted for local recommendations.

Small grains, as wheat, oats, rye, barley, buckwheat, sorghum, millet, and soybeans, can be seeded in mixtures or as separate species. Buckwheat, millet, and barley are valuable for waterfowl, especially where the site will be flooded for part of the year. Seeding rates will vary depending upon locality and site. Row plantings are generally preferable to broadcast seedings.

Standing corn is especially valuable to many wildlife species because corn has high food value and the ears are available in most winters. Field corn is preferred to sweet corn because the stalks stand better during the winter. Wide spacing is better than narrow. Seeding soybeans and buckwheat is a good wildlife practice and will provide additional soil protection as well. Seedbeds should be thoroughly prepared as in any normal agricultural operation using standard farming practices. Liming and fertilization should be done if soil tests indicate the need.

Mixture Seedings

WESTERN INTERMOUNTAIN REGION

On most lands in the Intermountain Region of the western United States, the use of mixtures of two or more adapted species is advisable (Plummer et al. 1955, Hungerford 1965). Soil and moisture conditions often change so markedly within short distances that there may be great variation in the success and productivity of a single species within a seeded area. If one species does poorly because of an unfavorable site condition, or is killed by rodents, insects, disease, or frost, one or more of the others may take its place. Another advantage of mixtures is that some species develop stands quickly and supply forage while slower developing species become established. Mixtures also produce vegetation with a more varied and often higher food value. Plants should be chosen which best supplement native ranges.

If adapted legumes are available, their use with grasses usually increases total production and improves the nutritive value of the forage. They also help increase soil nitrogen through the action of associated nodule bacteria which converts free nitrogen from the air into available soil nitrogen.

Browse species can be mixed with grass and forb seeds and drilled or broadcasted concurrently. Over 75,000 acres of rangelands in Utah alone have been planted by such methods. On one 4,000 acre project in central Utah, there was a seven-fold increase in forage production 3 years after treatment. Forage increased from about 100 lb. per acre to an average of nearly 700 lb. per acre. Deer day-use per acre averaged 4 deer days per acre on the adjacent untreated lands and 83 deer days of use per acre on the seeded areas 3 years after treatment—about a 20-fold increase. It was noted that deer were attracted to the seeded areas from adjacent untreated ranges. While the degree of deer use apparently had not damaged the forage plants at the time of inspection, such heavy use might if continued over many years. Average deer use of seeded range over the State of Utah is much less than reported here, but it appears possible to increase the carrying capacity on many thousand acres of critical deer winter range by seeding and planting (Plummer et al. 1966).

Forage on seeded areas is generally available earlier in the growing season and is more palatable than that on untreated ranges. The adequate supply of green forage on seeded areas during the critical early spring period, when fetuses are developing rapidly in pregnant does, is of special value. The improved forage reduces winter and early spring mortality and increases fawn production. Seeded ranges have also been especially helpful in keeping deer off cultivated fields. Experience and knowledge gained from seeding projects to date discloses that the game range manager obtains greatly increased livestock grazing capacities and watershed values—both of which greatly add to multiple-use justification.

The adaptation and relative value of 56 most promising species for seeding lowland ranges with annual precipitation below 8, 8 to 12, and above 12 inches; salty lowlands; and mountain brush, aspen, and subalpine zones, are shown in Table 14.1.

EASTERN MOUNTAIN REGION

The practice of planting mixed seedings to improve habitat for wildlife has been success-

Table 14.1. Adaptation and recommended use[1] of species for seeding in various precipitation and vegetation zones on lowland and mountain areas in the Intermountain region (Plummer et al. 1955).

GRASSES

Species	Lowlands				Mountain lands		
	Below 8 inches precipitation	8-12 inches precipitation	Above 12 inches precipitation	Salty soils	Mountain brush[2]	Aspen[3]	Subalpine
Sand dropseed	C	C	....	....	....	....	....
Bottlebrush squirreltail	C	C	....	....	....	....	....
Indian ricegrass	C	C	C	....	C	....	....
Russian wildrye	C	B	B	B	C	....	....
Crested wheatgrass (Standard)	B	A	A	....	B	....	....
Crested wheatgrass (Fairway)	B	A	A	....	A	C	....
Bulbous bluegrass	....	X	X	....	X	....	....
Bluebunch wheatgrass	....	B	B	....	B	C	....
Beardless wheatgrass	....	B	B	....	B	C	....
Pubescent wheatgrass	....	C[4]	A	....	A	B	....
Intermediate wheatgrass	....	C[4]	A	....	A	B	....
Western wheatgrass	....	C[4]	B	....	C	C	....
Beardless wildrye	....	C[4]	B	C	C	C	....
Big bluegrass	....	C[4]	C	....	C	....	....
Mountain rye	....	....	X	....	X	....	....
Great Basin wildrye	....	....	B	....	B	C	....
Tall wheatgrass	....	....	B	A	B	C	....
Tall fescue	....	....	....	B[4]	....	C	....
Bulbous barley	....	....	....	....	B	C	....
Blue wildrye	....	....	....	....	B	B	....
Bearded wheatgrass	....	....	....	....	B	B	....
Smooth brome (southern strain)	....	....	C[4]	....	A	A	B
Smooth brome (northern strain)	....	....	....	....	C	A	B
Slender wheatgrass	....	....	....	....	B	B	C
Mountain brome	....	....	....	....	B	B	C
Meadow brome	....	....	....	....	B	B	B
Kentucky bluegrass	....	....	....	....	X	X	X
Tall Oatgrass	....	....	....	....	A	A	A
Orchardgrass	....	....	....	....	B	A	C
Reed canarygrass	....	....	....	....	B[4]	B	B[4]
Timothy	....	....	....	....	B[4]	A	B
Meadow foxtail	....	....	....	....	B[4]	A	B
Sheep fescue (Sulcata)	....	....	....	....	....	C	C
Red fescue (sod-forming)	....	....	....	....	....	C	C
Subalpine brome	....	....	....	....	....	....	B
Winter rye	....	X	X	....	X	....	....

Table 14.1. Continued.

LEGUMES

Species	Below 8 inches precipitation	8-12 inches precipitation	Above 12 inches precipitation	Salty soils	Mountain brush[2]	Aspen[3]	Subalpine
	Lowlands				Mountain lands		
Alfalfa	....	C^4	B	....	B	C	....
Sicklepod milkvetch	....	C^4	B	....	B	C	....
Chickpea milkvetch	....	C^4	B	....	B	B	C
Yellow sweetclover	....	....	X^4	B^4	X	C	....
Strawberry clover	....	....	....	X^4	....	....	....
Birdsfoot trefoil	....	....	....	....	C	C	....
Mountain lupine	....	....	....	....	....	C	B
Alsike clover	....	....	....	....	....	C^4	C^4

OTHER BROADLEAF HERBS

Species	Below 8 inches precipitation	8-12 inches precipitation	Above 12 inches precipitation	Salty soils	Mountain brush[2]	Aspen[3]	Subalpine
Summercypress	....	....	....	X	....	....	....
Fivehook bassia	....	....	....	X	....	....	....
Palmer penstemon	....	X	X	....	X	....	....
Wasatch penstemon	....	....	....	....	X	X	....
Showy goldeneye	....	....	....	....	X	X	X
Common cowparsnip	....	....	....	....	C	C	C
Sweetanise	....	....	....	....	C^4	C	C

SHRUBS

Species	Below 8 inches precipitation	8-12 inches precipitation	Above 12 inches precipitation	Salty soils	Mountain brush[2]	Aspen[3]	Subalpine
Winterfat	C	C	C	....	C	....	....
Fourwing saltbush	C^4	C	C	....	C	....	....
Antelope bitterbrush	....	C	C	....	C	C	....
Oldman wormwood	....	....	X	....	X	X	....
Blueberry elder	....	....	X	....	C	C	....

[1]A—Proved to be productive and widely adapted for seeding throughout the zone or type.

B—Valuable over much of the zone or type, but value or adaptation either more restricted or not as well determined as species designated A.

C—Value or adaptation more restricted than those species designated B, but useful in some situations.

X—Recommended for special uses or conditions, usually as pure stands.

[2]Applicable also for seeding openings in the ponderosa pine zone.

[3]Applicable also for seeding openings in Douglas-fir and spruce timber.

[4]Adapted only to better than average sites in the zone or type.

fully accomplished for many years in the eastern states (Leopold 1933, Grange 1949, Riley 1963, Shomon et al. 1966). Stoddard (1946) was one of the earliest wildlifers to use this method when he began the practice of plowing, or disking, and planting narrow strips in, around, and through every accessible and conceivable upland type of habitat, so that at all seasons of the year quail would be near abundant food. These food strips, planted to various mixtures, are widened year after year for several seasons, planting the newly turned soil each year but leaving most of the plantings made in former years unplowed. The purpose of this combination planting-fallowing is (1) to secure the benefits of different succession stages, and (2) to diversify freshly seeded cropland with fallowed strips. These areas provide high-grade cover and food consisting of both planted and naturally seeded mixtures. Food strips in the south planted for quail include such species as: cowpeas, sorghum, millet, clover, and vetch. Food strips in the north should usually include yellow corn, rye, sweet clover, vetch, millets, buckwheat, and soybeans. This does not mean that each strip must include all of the species listed; the best guide as to what to plant is gained through knowledge of which crops are locally most successful. The kinds of plants employed in game food strip use, however, should aim to provide spring, summer and winter greens (clover and rye), late summer seeds (millets, buckwheat), and winter grain (corn, buckwheat, rye) as local conditions permit (Grange 1949).

On reclaimed surface mining or strip mining areas, Riley (1963) planted mixed seedings totaling 57 species of trees, grasses, legumes, and shrubs, all of which became successfully established. He tested these various species on different soil types having critical site factors such as extreme acidity, high total salts, and compacted surface spoil. Successful seedings grew on soils having a range of pH values from 3.4 to 7.2; and most of the sites exhibited acid to extremely acid soil reaction. Many species of shrubs, grasses, and legumes displayed a tolerance to very acid soils, high concentrations of trace elements, sulfates, and soluble salts.

For reclaimed areas on which forest plantations presently grow, the technique of seeding strips of grass and legume through the plantations has proven highly beneficial to wildlife. Older forests often consist of hardwoods with a high percentage of black locust, often in a decadent condition. For such areas, a bulldozer can create seeding strips having a recommended minimum width of not less than 50 ft and a maximum of 100 ft. On strips less than 50 ft wide black locust usually invades and closes the area within 5 years, therefore, often making treatment of such areas uneconomical. Seeding strips through hardwood plantations, other than black locust, have remained open for 6 years with practically no invasion by tree species. Large, non-forested areas supporting grasses and legumes can be improved for wildlife by planting strips not over 20 ft wide with shrub species such as Scotch broom, autumn olive, and multiflora rose. Such woody plants, along with selected tree species, may be used around the perimeter of croplands, on slopes of mine-strip lands, or in abandoned fields. Species of shrubs such as listed above plus bush lespedeza, memorial rose, crown vetch, conifers, and willow can be planted within or at the edge of large depressions or rock dumps.

Mowing strips 30 to 40 ft wide through seedings of smooth brome grass, orchard grass, lespedeza, and sweet-clover, not only enhances the habitat for wildlife, but also makes the area more accessible to hunters. If such strips are mowed during September and early October, the

Table 14.2. Food patch mixtures for planting in spring for the eastern United States region (Shomon et al. 1966).

Mixture #1 for five acres:	lbs.
Buckwheat	10
Grain sorghum	9
Foxtail millet	15
Proso millet	15
Kaffir	9
Sudangrass	5
Soybeans	15
Cowpeas	13
Vetch	9
	100

Mixture #2 for five acres:	
Buckwheat	15
Foxtail millet	15
Sudangrass	15
Soybeans	25
Cowpeas	30
	100

Mixture #3 for five acres:	
Proso millet	17.5
Grain sorghum	25.0
Sunflower	7.5
	50.0

Table 14.3. Seeding guide for wildlife plantings in the eastern United States (Shomon et al. 1966).

Seed	Rate of Seed per Acre	Lime	Fertilizer	Size of Patch	Planting Time
Food patch mix #1, #2	20 lbs. per acre	according to lime requirement test for 6-6.5 pH	300-400 lbs. per acre 5-10-10	1/4-1 acre	spring
Food patch mix #3	10 lbs. per acre	Same	Same	Same	spring
Rye	3-4 pecks per acre	Same	Same	Same	early fall
Wheat	1-1 1/2 bu. per acre	Same	Same	Same	early fall
Soybeans	1/2-2 bu. per acre	Same	Same	up to 5 acres	late spring
Corn	10 lbs.; 40" between rows	Same	400-500 lbs. per acre 5-10-10	up to 5 acres	late spring
Japanese millet	25 lbs.	Same		1/4-1 acre	late spring
Buckwheat	1-1 1/2 bu.	Same	300 lbs. per acre 5-10-10	1/4-1 acre	early summer
Birdsfoot trefoil with grass	6 lbs.; with 3 lbs. orchardgrass	Same	at seeding 300 lbs. per acre 5-10-10. Annual top dressing 300 lbs. 0-14-14.	1/4-1 acre	early spring or late summer
Sericea lespedeza	15 lbs.	maintain pH 5.8	Same	long strips	spring
Bicolor lespedeza	16 lbs.	maintain pH 5.8	Same	long strips	spring

resulting new growth provides more palatable food for certain species. Tables 14.2 and 14.3 provide some general guidelines for planting seed mixtures in the Eastern states.

Ten Basic Principles for Successful Plantings

There are 10 fundamental principles or "commandments" for making ranges[1] more productive by plantings of browse, forbs, and grass. They are based upon over 15 years of research and

[1]Editor's Note: Although this section deals primarily with semi-arid range, it has been included because the principles have wide utility, because more millions of acres of land for which these principles apply are manipulated for wildlife than any other land type, and because of the need for making this information available to wildlifers and land managers in the U.S. and abroad where semi-arid land management is critical.

field-tested procedures developed at the Intermountain Forest and Range Experiment Station (Plummer et al. 1960). Recommendations usually cover broad areas and need to be modified to fit local conditions, availability of seeds, and facilities for doing the work. Such modifications will usually be satisfactory if they conform to the following 10 rules:

(1) *Reduce competition.*—Seedlings and suppressed plants must have moisture to develop. Established plants that use all or most of the available moisture must be greatly reduced before seedlings can develop into satisfactory game forage.

(2) *Eliminate overgrazing.*—Young plants and seedlings do not develop well when cropped off or severely trampled by large or small animals. Livestock use of planted areas should be eliminated until the seeded stand has been established. Where there is heavy big game pressure, excess animals should be reduced to a population level at which use is not damaging. This can usually be done by increasing the harvest during the hunting seasons. Excessive numbers of rabbits should be controlled by use of poison baits. Alfalfa or fresh apple segments dusted with strychnine powder put out in the winter period when snow is on the ground are effective means of controlling rabbits during high population cycles when the animal may kill stands of young plants. Mice, chipmunks, kangaroo rats, and ground squirrels also can cause similar devastation if control measures are not employed. Personnel in the Division of Wildlife Services of the Bureau of Sport Fisheries and Wildlife, as well as county agricultural agents, can give up-to-date information on animal control methods. (See Chapter 23.) Care in placement of poison baits is essential to prevent loss of other than target species.

(3) *Determine when and where planting will improve the range.*—Where good forage plants are present, reduction of competition may be all that is necessary for the desired restoration. On Western ranges usually one shrub on the average to each 100 square feet and one herb to each 10 square feet is an approximate minimum. Sometimes, there is need to round out an existing forage resource by introduction of a scarce element. For example, there may be ample browse on a big game winter range, but a lack of grasses and broadleaf herbs. Departure of deer and elk from their native ranges to cultivated fields in later winter and early springtime in search of succulent plants, is a particular problem in some western states. A good balance of browse and

herbaceous plants on the winter range may help to reduce such depredation. The establishment of early spring growing herbaceous species, such as crested wheatgrass, Russian wildrye, intermediate wheatgrass, a range type alfalfa, small burnet, and balsamroot can provide desirable succulent herbs on inter-mountain big game winter ranges.

(4) *Annual precipitation should be adequate.*— Ordinarily, artificial seeding should not be undertaken on sites where precipitation is less than ten inches. The amount of precipitation, along with occurrence of indicator species, is the important guide in selection of the species which may be used. Where precipitation is near the lower limits, species which may be successfully seeded are limited in the West to such plants as crested wheatgrass, Russian wildrye, and range alfalfa. As precipitation increases the species that may be successfully established increase.

(5) *Terrain and soil should be suitable to support the desired forage species and to permit restoration treatments.*—Shallow, infertile soils naturally produce little forage and may not justify restoration. While some improvement is usually possible on unfavorable sites, similar effort on favorable tracts will usually be more effective and more productive. With improvement of forage on good sites, game animals may shift use to the better forage and as a result more severe sites will improve naturally. There will be instances, of course, where poor sites may require restoration treatment solely to fill a critical need such as control of soil erosion.

(6) *Plant adapted species and strains.*—Returns on the investment for restoration and seeding depends on a lasting improvement. It is essential that the planted species be able to maintain themselves and, preferably, to spread by natural means. Sometimes it may be wise to include rapidly developing short-lived species to meet a planned objective, such as a nurse crop or a quick forage supply. Such species as mountain rye, small burnet, short-lived perennials, and yellow sweetclover, a biennial, are useful in the West for this purpose. A low seeding rate of annual winter rye may achieve the same goal. Planting rates of transient species in the mix should not be so great as to offer serious competition to more desirable and persistent species. Usually 3 to 5 lb. per acre is adequate for the short-lived perennials and sweetclover, and 15 lb. of winter rye per acre is adequate. Slower developing but more persistent plants such as antelope bitterbrush, fourwing saltbush, balsamroot, crested wheatgrass, and bluebunch wheat-

grass, will gradually replace the short-lived plants. Where there is no need for the rapid developing species, then only long-lived perennials should be used.

It is particularly important that adapted sources or strains be used. Ordinarily seed from plants growing on greatly different soils, or in different climatic zones, are much less preferable than seed from sites similar to that planned for treatment. For example, it has been observed that antelope bitterbrush seed collected from acid granitic soils may develop chlorotic plants on basic soils originating from limestone. Fourwing saltbush collected in the blackbrush type in southwestern Utah has failed to survive well in the higher elevation mountain brush type. Similarly, Indian ricegrass from salt desert shrub types has failed to survive on mountain brush and higher elevation juniper-pinyon range. It appears that sources from colder areas with greater precipitation can survive better in warmer and drier areas than the reverse. There may be exceptions, but these are rare.

(7) *Plant mixtures, especially on variable sites.*—A major reason for using mixtures is to put different species in the site conditions to which they are best suited. Site characteristics can change often and dramatically within a limited area. Another advantage of mixtures is that they provide a variety of forage. The total production of a well chosen mixture is considerably greater than of single species stands. Where possible, seeds of slower growing shrubs and herbs should make up the initial seeding and fast growing, aggressive species introduced later. Thus, grasses drilled in alternate rows with shrubs permits better establishment of the slower establishing shrubs than when both changes of seed are planted in the same rows. Also, broadleaf herbs generally establish better if they can be similarly separated from the grass. The planting of shrub seeds and certain broadleaf herbs into pits left after cabling juniper and pinyon trees permits more adequate establishment in such suitable spots than if planted in a mixture broadcast over the whole range from an airplane or by hand. If some species, such as smooth brome or orchard grass, are better suited to north slopes and shady areas it may be best to confine them to such sites. Of course, the practicability of separating species for localized condition depends on the size of the area. Often it is not practical to segregate sites, so mixtures are used.

(8) *Use sufficient seed to insure a stand.*—One reason to avoid heavy seeding is the unnec-

essary cost entailed. Stands are usually not materially improved by excessive seeding. Usually, 8 to 20 lb. per acre of total mixture is adequate, depending on the sites involved and the method being used. Ordinarily, when drilling, 8 to 10 lb. per acre are advised and in broadcasting 15 to 20 lb. are recommended. With proper planting, 3 to 8 lb. of shrub seed per acre is usually sufficient. Proper planting depths and spacing of seed by drilling is often far more effective than heavy broadcast seeding. However there are many sites where, because of terrain and obstacles, broadcasting must be used in spite of its being more wasteful.

(9) *Proper planting and coverage of seed is essential.*—Provision for some seed coverage must be made. Seeds placed under 1/4- to 3/4-inch of soil are usually satisfactorily covered. A few species with large seeds may emerge from depths deeper than one inch, but most are suppressed by excessive planting depths. Seeds which are very small should be sown no more than 1/4-inch deep. Planting on slopes too steep for machinery makes hand methods necessary. Here a corn planter or a specially built "Schussler"[2] bitterbrush planter can be used to advantage to gauge the depth and plant the seed of most species. Such equipment speeds up the hand seeding operation. Establishment of seedlings from uncovered seed, as from broadcasting, requires unusual moisture conditions for successful establishment.

(10) *Seed usually in late fall and early winter but transplant in early spring.*—Seeding in October, November, December, and even January is best for most species and is essential for those that need to lay over winter to break dormancy. With a few species, notably alfalfa, fourwing saltbush, and winterfat, spring planting is superior to fall. This results from their tendency to germinate during a warm period in winter or early spring only to succumb later as a result of freezing temperatures. The major advantages of late fall or winter seeding are that (1) inherent dormancy is overcome; (2) some stimulative effects are provided by the cold temperatures and seedlings are induced to more rapid growth; (3) a longer period of adequate moisture is available so that seedlings are larger and better able to withstand the drought and heat of summer; (4) many seed collecting rodents tend to be inactive after late fall so seed loss from this factor is reduced.

[2]Bitterbrush seed planter designed by Mr. Howard Schussler and is sold by Crookham Seed Company, Caldwell, Idaho.

Where spring planting is necessary, treatment of seeds is needed to break dormancy. This may be done by stratification methods or by chemical treatments. A 3% solution of thiourea overcomes dormancy in some shrub species. Spring planting should be done as soon as moisture conditions permit getting on the land. This is usually before May 1 and preferably before April 15. In the blackbrush type in southwestern Utah, spring seeding should be completed before March 15.

In contrast to direct planting of seed, transplanting of nursery stock, seedlings and wildlings is most successful if carried out in the early spring while the ground is still moist from snowmelt. Usually the ground is so dry in the fall period that roots dry out. There are some exceptions to the requirement for spring transplanting. In trials, late fall planting of wildlings of bud sagebrush and common iris, even into dry soil, survived nearly 100%; whereas, similar planting of big sagebrush and rubber rabbitbrush failed completely.

WATER DEVELOPMENTS

The amount, availability, quality, and presence throughout the year of water can be improved for purposes of increasing wildlife numbers or expanding the use of habitat. Water can be "removed" to reduce animal numbers and feeding in areas where they are undesired. More frequently than for wildlife, water is developed for various other uses. When these uses are properly planned, then the water can provide benefits to wildlife. Consequently, the habitat manager should be familiar with the various techniques for development of water including natural springs, seeps, and water holes; and man-made structures such as reservoirs, "guzzlers" and wells.

Water Holes

Water holes are open water storage basins, either natural or artificial. Water is such a basic requirement to some species in some areas that water holes are often the hub of wildlife activities; therefore, they should be designed and maintained to be usable for all species of wild animals.

Natural water holes are often found in playas and rocky areas where run-off waters are accumulated in a depression. At times such holes can be improved by deepening the catchment or by trenching run-off waters directly to the basin.

In the southwest, cement embankments have been added to large flat rock surfaces, thereby channeling water to a nearby hole. Storage has been increased by raising the lowest level of the basin's edge.

Man-made structures can be adapted to provide water holes for wildlife. Examples are the side basins on pipelines as illustrated in Fig. 14.3. One such pipeline development in Nevada provided three new water holes along a 15 mile stretch which formerly had no natural waters for chukar partridge (U.S. Bureau of Land Management 1964).

Springs and Seeps

No two springs are alike as to developmental needs, however, there are several different planning techniques that can be applied. Before a spring or seep is developed, the reliability and quantity of its flow should be checked. Generally it is necessary to install a protective box to catch and store the water. Sometimes it is advisable to provide large capacity storage at sites where waterflow is intermittent so that stored water will be available after the spring or seep quits flowing. These waters should be dug out of firm ground, hardpan, or rock to obtain maximum flow. The source, whether one or several, should be conducted to a collection basin and thence piped to a trough. It is usually necessary and desirable to fence the water source and collection basin from human or livestock use.

In the central and western U.S., many springs are found in canyon bottoms and when developed, often become a maintenance problem due to storm flood damage. Flood damage can be reduced for canyon bottom projects by burying a short length of perforated asphalt soil pipe in packed gravel at the water source from which the water is piped to a basin out of the canyon bottom. This technique allows storm water to flow over the buried source of spring water without damage to the development work (Weaver et al. 1959).

For wildlife water developments, plastic pipe is usually preferred to galvanized iron pipe since it is lighter and easier to transport and lay. The pipe should be buried deep enough to escape damage by freezing, trampling by livestock, or washing out during floods. The pipe should also be laid to grade, in order to avoid air blocks.

The development of a spring is not just a simple matter of collecting a maximum flow of water and making it available. The development should be planned to achieve a purpose with a minimum of detrimental effects. Spring developments planned primarily for wildlife use, as well as those planned for other purposes, should do the following:

1. Provide at least one escape route to and from the water. Take advantage of the natural terrain and vegetation where possible.

2. Provide an alternate escape route where feasible.

3. Fence water developments from livestock. Fences can serve the purposes of preserving the water source and protecting food and cover needed for small species of wildlife. Protective fences should be negotiable by wildlife except where trampling or wallowing by big game will damage the spring source. Fence posts should be pointed to discourage perching by avian predators.

4. Provide a natural drinking environment.

5. Provide safety from wildlife drowning by construction of gentle basin slopes or ramps in tanks.

6. Maintain or provide adequate cover around the watering area, either by saving the natural cover or by means such as plantings, brush piles, and buried drain pipes.

7. Provide, where applicable, an information sign to inform the public as to the purpose of the development.

8. Provide water developments of sufficient capacity to supply water at all seasons of the year during which it is needed for wild animals.

9. Provide public access to water by piping it outside of fenced water developments. Where shy animals are involved, pipe water for human consumption some distance from wildlife water. For example, it is recommended that sustained camping be discouraged within 1/2-mile radius of waters for desert bighorn sheep.

Reservoirs and Small Ponds

The term "reservoir" as used here refers to water impounded behind a dam. It may be formed by building a dam directly across a drainage or by enclosing a depression to one side of a drainage and constructing a diversion ditch into the resulting basin. Reservoirs should be designed to provide maximum storage with a minimum of surface area to reduce evaporation loss. Following are some major points to consider in the selection of a reservoir site:

1. The most suitable soils for dams are clays with a fair proportion of sand and gravel (one part clay to two or three parts grit). Soils with a high proportion of clay crack badly upon drying and are apt to slip when wet.

2. The watershed above the dam should be large enough to provide sufficient water to fill the reservoir, but not so large that excessive flows will damage the spillway or wash out the dam.

3. The most economical site is one along a natural drainage where the channel is narrow, relatively deep, and the bottom is easily made watertight. The channel grade immediately above the dam should be as flat as possible.

4. Wildlife should have easy access to the water.

5. The dam should be located, if possible, to take advantage of natural spillway sites. Otherwise, an adequate spillway must be incorporated into the development.

The dam site should be surveyed and staked prior to construction. If there is any question as to the suitability of material for dam construction, an examination should be made by a soil scientist. Trees and shrubs should be cleared from the dam site and flooded basin. The foundation area of the dam should be plowed or scarified in the direction of the main axis of the dam so there will be a good bond between the foundation and the fill material. On sites where stability and permeability of the foundation material is questionable, a narrow core trench should be dug lengthwise to the dam, then refilled and packed with damp clay soil. Where suitable material is available above the dam, it should be obtained there so the borrow pit will become part of the reservoir and add depth to the impoundment. General specifications for the construction of dams should include these items:

1. The base thickness of the dam must be equal to or greater than 4-1/2 times the height plus the crest thickness. The slopes of the dam should be 2-1/2:1 on the upstream face and 2:1 on the downstream face.

2. Minimum width of the top of all dams should be 10 ft.

3. The fill of the dam should be carried at least 10% higher than the required height to allow for settling.

4. Freeboard (depth from the top of the dam to the high water mark when the spillway is carrying the estimated peak run-off) should be not less than 2 ft. The spillway should be designed to handle double the largest known volume of run-off and should be constructed at a level

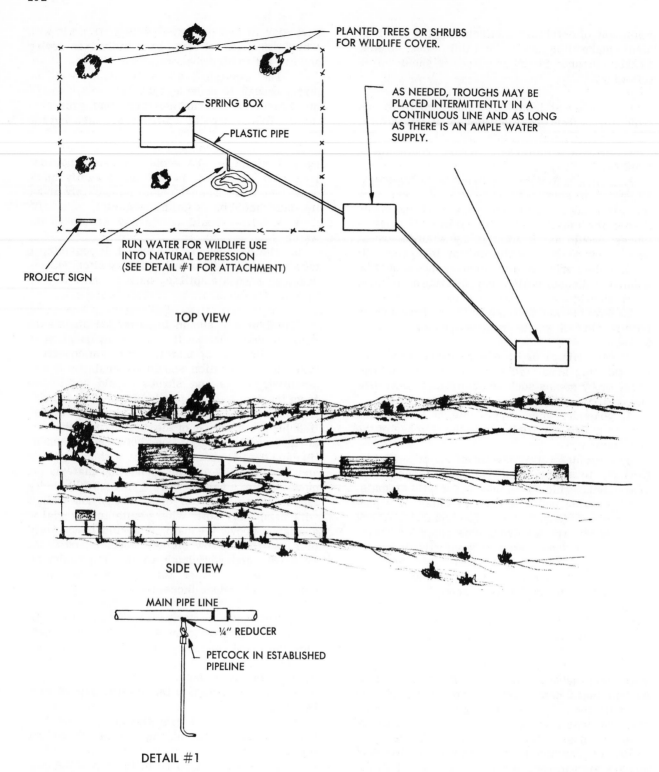

PLANTED TREES OR SHRUBS
FOR WILDLIFE COVER.

SPRING BOX

PLASTIC PIPE

AS NEEDED, TROUGHS MAY BE
PLACED INTERMITTENTLY IN A
CONTINUOUS LINE AND AS LONG
AS THERE IS AN AMPLE WATER
SUPPLY.

RUN WATER FOR WILDLIFE USE
INTO NATURAL DEPRESSION
(SEE DETAIL #1 FOR ATTACHMENT)

PROJECT SIGN

TOP VIEW

SIDE VIEW

MAIN PIPE LINE

¼" REDUCER

PETCOCK IN ESTABLISHED
PIPELINE

DETAIL #1

Fig. 14.3. Water developments for many uses can be modified for the benefit of wildlife. This drawing of a spring improvement for livestock in Nevada included a side basin installation for chukars. (Nevada State Office, U.S. Bureau of Land Management.)

which will prevent the water from ever rising higher than within 2 ft of the top of the dam. A natural spillway is preferred. It should have a broad, relatively flat cross section; take the water out well above the fill; and re-enter the main channel some distance downstream from the fill. When a spillway is built, it should be wide, flat-bottomed, and protected from washing by rip-rapping (facing with rocks). The entrance should be wide and smooth and the grade of the spillway channel mild so the water will flow through without cutting (Hamilton and Jepson 1940).

New reservoirs usually do not hold water satisfactorily for several months. It may be necessary to spread bentonite over the bottom and sides of the basin and face of the dam to "seal" the impoundment so it will hold water. Samples of soil from the reservoir, the dam material, and the bentonite can be laboratory tested to determine how much bentonite should be applied. Another method of sealing reservoirs to prevent excessive loss of water is to line the basin with polyethylene (U.S. Bureau Land Management 1966). After the basin has been made, it is covered with plastic sheets, then 6 to 8 inches of dirt rolled evenly over the plastic. Where there is the possibility of damage to the plastic by animals, 12 inches of soil must be placed over the liner.

While working in the southwest, biologists for the U.S. Fish and Wildlife Service found that water-cut canyons offer suitable sites for small concrete dams and reservoirs to provide water for desert bighorn sheep (Halloran and Deming 1956). These small reservoirs were most effective where canyons narrowed down with steep, vertical sides of bedrock (Fig. 14.4). Such arroyos make good construction sites particularly on east or north facing drainages which provide protection from the sun and reduce evaporation. Dams should be firmly keyed into the bedrock on both sides and bottom. A pipe outlet should be incorporated into the dam. Water loss will be prevented if rock formations are checked for cracks and fissures. Rock sealing is, at times, an important phase of sound construction. Commerical sealers can be quickly applied to the dam after completion. Usually, such canyon dams should be under 40 ft long and not over 10 or 12 ft high. During the first several years after construction, the small ponds formed behind the dams will provide water for wildlife. After the reservoir becomes filled with gravel and sand washed in by rain floods, the water soaking into the gravel and sand is stored and protected from excessive evaporation. The stored water is piped through the dam

to natural rock basins below or to cement troughs constructed away from the main water course (U.S. Bureau of Land Management 1964).

Water Catchments

During the past couple decades, there have been several types of self-filling watering devices designed for the use of wildlife. Probably the greatest numbers have been constructed for primary use by quail. However, many of these structures have been built specifically to benefit other wild animals, including antelope, bighorn sheep, deer, sage grouse, and turkeys. The California Department of Fish and Game (Glading 1947, McLean 1962) has constructed over a thousand catchments on quail and partridge ranges. Since so many of these devices were installed for upland game birds (Galliformes) they have been referred to as "Gallinaceous Guzzlers," or recently, just "Guzzlers."

"GUZZLERS"

The guzzler is a permanent, self-filling water catchment similar to a cistern. The whole structure is so simple there is very little that can get out of order, and so a minimum of maintenance is required. Essentially, the guzzler installation consists of a water-tight tank set in the ground which is filled by a rain-collecting apron. This apron collects rainwater and drains it into a tank where it is stored for use by wildlife. Where the device is intended for watering birds or small animals, these may enter the covered tank through an open end and walk down a sloping ramp to the water level. If the birds and other animals drink directly from the storage tank, all floating valves or other mechanical devices that are subject to failure are eliminated. (see Fig. 14.5)

The most important step in the installation of a guzzler is locating an adequate site for its placement. A guzzler should not be placed in a wash or gully where it may collect silt or sand, or be damaged by flood waters. The size of the water-collecting apron should be proportioned so that the cistern will need no water source other than rainfall to fill it. Since the cost of digging the hole for the cistern is one of the largest items of cost, a site should be chosen where digging is comparatively easy. The tank should be placed with its open end away from the prevailing wind and, if possible, facing in a northerly

194

direction in order that a minimum of sunlight will enter the tank. Such placement will cut down the growth of algae, temperature of water, and evaporation.

The cisterns used for guzzlers usually are made of either concrete or plastic. Occasionally steel tanks are used. The plastic guzzler is a prefabricated tank constructed of fiber glass impregnated with a plastic resin. If the construction site is a long distance from a source of washed aggregate, or if labor costs are high, the plastic guzzlers offer savings in transportation and labor costs. In California, for instance, plastic guzzlers have been obtained at a cost of $240. Quantity orders have cost less. In 1966, 50 units were purchased at a price of $167 each.

With concrete guzzlers, only washed gravel aggregates should be used for construction; otherwise the concrete may start to disintegrate after 5 or 10 years. Tanks made of steel are used for guzzlers in some areas and are reported as giving satisfactory service.

Collecting aprons have been made of many materials. Concrete sealed with bitumul, galvanized metal sheet roofing, glass mat and bitumul, rubber or plastic sheets, asphalt, and plywood have all been used successfully. From the standpoint of maintenance costs, however, durable materials such as concrete or metal have proven most satisfactory.

The size of the water collecting apron or surface needed to fill a guzzler will depend on the size of guzzler and the minimum annual rainfall that can be expected at the construction site. Actually, the size of the needed interception area will prove surprisingly small because nearly 100% of the rainfall is collected. Calculation of the potential yield of the rainfall collection surface can be determined by the following formula:

$$\frac{\text{Surface area (sq. ft.) of apron}}{12} \times 7.4$$

= gallons per inch of rainfall

It is important that calculations be made on the basis of the minimum of precipitation expected, rather than the average or maximum, to prevent guzzler failing during drought years. The Table 14.4 gives the size of aprons in square feet needed to fill 600, 700, and 900 gal tanks at different minimum rainfall rates.

General instructions for installation of a concrete guzzler are summarized as follows:

1. Select the site and clear the apron. Lay out the excavation site for the guzzler. To square the outline, measure diagonally from each rear corner to opposite front corner and adjust stakes until these distances are equal. Excavate the rear portion to required depth, slope ramp at front to ground level. Line excavation with laminated Kraft paper.

2. Assemble re-usable plywood forms for inner walls and hang in position with 4-inch clearance between forms and walls and floor. Level the forms and pour concrete between forms and walls of excavation. Tamp and vibrate walls. Pour enough concrete to complete floor and ramp. Trowel smooth, allowing 1/2-inch clearance between edge of form and ramp.

3. Remove wall form carriers, assemble re-usable roof forms, place in position and cover with three thicknesses of Kraft paper. Place dishpan in position for manhole. Cover roof with 3 inches of concrete, place 3 inches of concrete inside of the dishpan. Insert a loop of heavy wire or 1/4-inch reinforcing rod at center of manhole cover to serve as a handle. Provide a 6-inch curb at front end of guzzler roof. Pour a 3-inch skirt 3 ft wide in front of guzzler ramp and provide a 6-inch trash wall.

4. Outline apron. Excavate a settling basin 18 inches in diameter and 8 inches deep in front of skirt. Cover entire apron and basin with Kraft paper and pour concrete 3-inches thick. Trowel smooth and provide a 6-inch trash wall around circumference of apron. Provide a hole of 3-inch diameter through trash wall for screened inlet to guzzler. Make holes for 1/2-inch diameter iron coyote guard at 4-inch intervals across front of guzzler. Cover all fresh concrete with paper to ensure proper curing.

5. Allow to set for 24 hr, remove paper and forms, wash inside of guzzler with cement and water. Apply asphalt emulsion to apron. Install coyote guards. Cover roof with 10 inches of dirt to stabilize temperature within cistern. If domestic livestock graze the area, fence the entire guzzler against stock so there will be no chance of damage to apron, tank, or lid. When guzzler is constructed after the rainy season, it is best to fill it with water to aid in curing concrete and to develop bird or animal acceptance.

Although incorporating the same general principles as the concrete guzzler described above, the quail guzzler illustrated in Fig. 14.5 is dissimilar in many respects. This illustrates the flexibility and diversity of design that has been characteristic of guzzler development in various regions. The iron roof should have a gentle slope

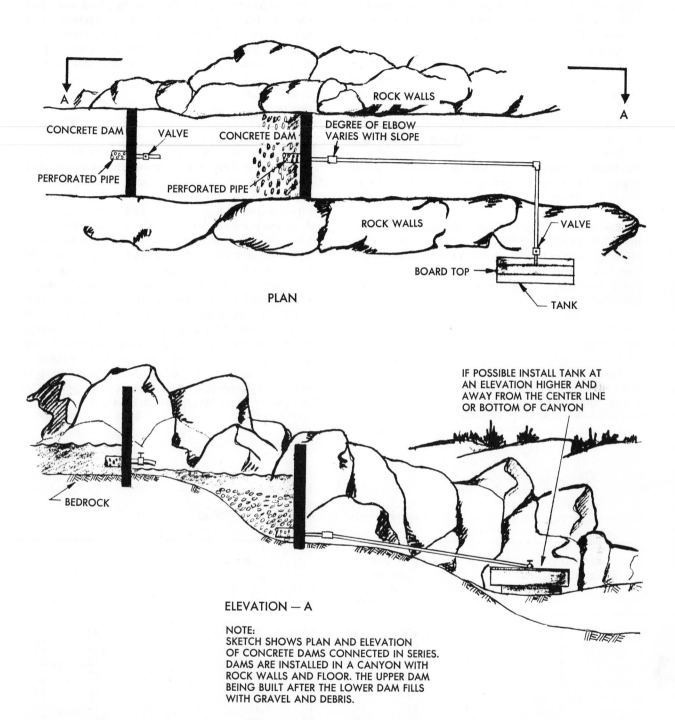

ROCK WALLS

CONCRETE DAM   VALVE   CONCRETE DAM   DEGREE OF ELBOW
VARIES WITH SLOPE

PERFORATED PIPE   PERFORATED PIPE

ROCK WALLS   VALVE

BOARD TOP

TANK

PLAN

IF POSSIBLE INSTALL TANK AT
AN ELEVATION HIGHER AND
AWAY FROM THE CENTER LINE
OR BOTTOM OF CANYON

BEDROCK

ELEVATION — A

NOTE:
SKETCH SHOWS PLAN AND ELEVATION
OF CONCRETE DAMS CONNECTED IN SERIES.
DAMS ARE INSTALLED IN A CANYON WITH
ROCK WALLS AND FLOOR. THE UPPER DAM
BEING BUILT AFTER THE LOWER DAM FILLS
WITH GRAVEL AND DEBRIS.

Fig. 14.4. Schematic drawing of reinforced concrete dam constructed by the U.S. Bureau of Sport Fisheries and Wildlife to collect and hold water for desert bighorn sheep on the Desert Game Range. (Nevada State Office, U.S. Bureau
of Land Management.)

196

of around 5% for best performance and should be relatively smooth to prevent water from standing on surface. Run-off is caught at the bottom of the aprons and carried in pipes to the storage container.

In some localities the storage tank has been closed at all ends, or a storage bag is used, and the water piped by gravity flow to a small trough (Lauritizen and Thayer 1966). Here the flow is regulated by a float valve. Where such valves are in use, a regular schedule of maintenance checks should be made to make certain valve is functioning during the season when water is needed. The general lay-out for such an arrangement is shown in the sketch below and in Fig. 14.6.

The most fool-proof deer guzzlers are those in which an arrangement has been conceived to allow the animal to drink directly from the storage tank. More commonly, for deer and other large animals, a trough with float valve has been provided.

DUGOUTS

As cattlemen moved into the West, they constructed large earthen catchment basins to collect water for livestock. These excavations were commonly called "dugouts" by early pioneers and "charcos" by early settlers along the Mexican border. Lately, government agencies have been constructing many of these charco pits on public lands. Deer and antelope make use of such improvements frequently and rely heavily upon their use during critical dry summer months. Bighorn sheep are not frequent users of these projects, but do benefit occasionally during seasonal movements to and from their ranges in rocky, mountainous terrain.

Dugouts may be located in almost any type of topography. They are, however, most satisfactory and commonly used in areas of comparatively flat but well-drained terrain. Flat slopes facilitate maximum storage with minimum excavation. A natural pot hole or dry lake bed is often a good location for a dugout. Dugouts should not be located in wet or muddy areas because of the difficulty for large animals to get to the water.

Fig. 14.7 shows a small rectangular dugout with specifications. For larger dugouts the length, width or depth may be increased, but the side slopes should be about the same. All sides should be sloped sufficiently to prevent sloughing (usually 2:1 or flatter) and one or more relatively flat side slopes (4:1 or flatter) should be provided for livestock or big game entrances (U.S. Bureau of Land Management 1964).

Table 14.4. Size of apron needed for 600, 700, and 900 gal "guzzlers."

| Minimum Annual Rainfall (inches) | Square Feet of Collecting Surface Required | | | Apron Dimension in Feet | | | | | |
| | | | | Square | | | Circular | | |
	600g.	700g.	900g.	600g.	700g.	900g.	600g.	700g.	900g.
1	965	1,127	1,453	31	34	38	36	38	43
2	482	563	726	22	24	27	25	27	31
3	322	376	485	18	19	22	20	22	25
4	242	282	365	16	17	19	18	19	22
5	192	225	290	14	15	17	16	17	19
6	162	189	243	13	14	15	15	16	18
7	138	161	208	12	13	14	13	14	16
8	121	141	182	11	12	14	12	13	15
9	107	125	161	11	12	13	12	13	14
10	97	113	146	10	11	12	11	12	14
11	87	102	132	9	10	11	10	11	13
12	80	94	121	9	10	11	10	11	12

Other Developments

The habitat manager may construct water developments, such as tanks, troughs, or wells strictly for the benefit of wildlife. More commonly water development will be constructed for other purposes, i.e. for livestock, campground water storage, and fire suppression. Often a slight modification or addition to such developments can be made that will make surplus water available to wildlife. Wildlifers desiring additional information on specifications, plans and construction details for water improvements will find the following sources of value: "Range Improvement Standards Handbook" (U.S. Forest Service 1960), "Engineering Handbook and Construction Manual" (U.S. Bureau of Land Management 1967), and "Stock-water Developments" (Hamilton 1940).

Safety Devices in Water Developments

Where water is not present in nature, birds and mammals will come to man-made water improvements. The hazard of drowning can be reduced by floats, ramps, or ladders in the facilities that will allow avenues of escape. The best design will incorporate such escape facilities into the improvements. Where this has not been done, it becomes necessary to improvise. Any float, ramp, or ladder placed in a water development should be relatively maintenance free and designed so that it neither interferes with nor can be damaged by livestock. Some suggested approaches are shown in Figs. 14.8, 14.9, and 14.10.

COVER IMPROVEMENT

Cover fulfills varied needs in the total wildlife habitat. Cover is important to wildlife like food

Fig. 14.5. Water catchments for small wildlife species have been constructed in all the western states. They have been an important factor in increasing suitable habitat. (U.S. Bureau of Land Management photo by Ed Smith.)

198

and water, for without all three wildlife will not inhabit an area. The absence of cover, its sparceness, or its poor distribution can be the factor limiting the use of an area by wildlife. Therefore, the habitat manager can improve wildlife numbers or area of use by improving cover quality or quantity. When manipulating food or water, wildlifers should be careful to assure enough cover of various kinds is left to meet wildlife needs.

Protective Cover

Protective cover includes escape, winter or refuge cover. It is most often vegetation offering

hidding places or mechanical protection from driving rains, winds, or snows, the sun in the summer, or vegetation from which game cannot be driven by hunters, either animal or human.

HEDGEROWS

Hedgerows provide desirable escape, refuge, and travel lanes for many songbirds and game birds and mammals. Low, woody vegetation can be planted along fence rows, in gullies, and along streams or around ponds, springs, food patches, nesting grounds, and breeding grounds. Such plantings are established with seedlings or wild-

Fig. 14.6. A water catchment constructed in the southwest for the purpose of water on a critical summer range inhabited by desert bighorn sheep. (U.S. Bureau of Land Management photo by Jim Yoakum.)

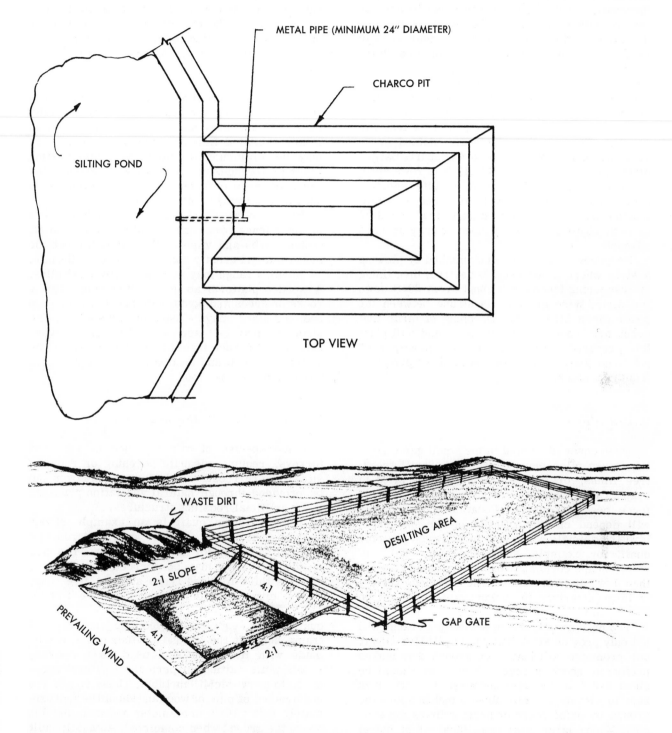

METAL PIPE (MINIMUM 24″ DIAMETER)

CHARCO PIT

SILTING POND

TOP VIEW

WASTE DIRT

2:1 SLOPE

4:1

DESILTING AREA

PREVAILING WIND

4:1

2:1

GAP GATE

Fig. 14.7. Schematic sketch of a "dugout" or charco pit used in the west for providing water on the ranges for livestock and wildlife. (Nevada State Office, U.S. Bureau of Land Management.)

lings. Site preparations consist of reducing competition by means such as plowing, contour furrowing, or scalping. Planting can be done by hand or with a mechanical planter depending upon the size of the project. Three to four rows of varying size plants should be planted in a stairstep method so that varied degrees of cover exist. For instance, rows of Russian olive, squawbush, and Siberian pea spaced appropriately will provide travel lanes, nesting, and food for many wildlife species. Spacing of plants varies with species. The smaller plants are planted every 18 to 24 inches in rows 3 to 4 ft apart. Larger plants are planted every 8 to 12 ft in rows about 8 to 10 ft apart. For most wildlife species, hedgerows 15 to 20 ft wide are adequate. Row lengths will vary to different purposes. One strip to each 20 to 25 acres in open country appears adequate.

Hedgerows can also be established by plowing a strip where a hedgerow is desired, then lining or staggering fence posts about every 20-ft down the strip. Wire or twine is strung between the posts for a bird perch. Dropping of birds that perch are laden with viable seed and will plant the prepared seed bed. These "plow-perch" plantings grow almost as fast as those produced from root stock.

BRUSH PILES

When cover is limited in the small game habitat, brush piles may be provided. Small trees, tree limbs, or shrubs can be loosely piled in heaps. Other materials, such as cull logs, and old fence posts are useful. Location of such cover will depend on the mobility of the species of birds or animals which use them. Brush piles for quail, for example, should be within 200 ft of other escape cover and (for western quail) no more than 1/4 mile from water. The carrying capacity of large clearings for upland game birds can be increased by providing brush pile cover.

Top pruning of trees on scaled quail range will not only provide slash that can be piled for cover, but promotes a bushy tree growth that makes preferred roosting cover. Such piles should be about 5-6 ft in diameter and about 3 ft high. It is best to elevate the pile about 6 inches above the ground by using rocks or heavier limbs for support. Where large clearings (100 acres or more) are made on quail range, brush should be piled occasionally at an optimum rate of about one pile per acre.

Long brush piles placed in the upper portion of broad arroyos or low-profile ravines may be used to increase cottontail rabbit population. For rabbits, the pile may be 25 to 50 ft long, 5 ft wide, and 4 ft high. The orientation of the axis of the pile can be alternated to facilitate hunter access and visibility (Shomon, Ashbaugh, and Tolman 1966).

Turkey nests have been found in slash piles, thickets, fallen tree tops or at the base of bushes and trees. There are indications that carefully located brush piles may provide nesting sites in turkey habitat deficient in nesting cover. There may be advantages to simulate turkey nesting cover preferences by piling brush or slash at the bases of trees or around logs. Such brush piles should be within 1/2 mile of water.

Brush or trees piled loosely in field corners or along fence rows may extend pheasant habitat. Grass, forbs and vines will grow up through the brush and add density and permanence to the pile.

Javelina range may be extended by brush piles. A wooden platform about 3 ft high supported by rocks or creosoted posts, with brush piled on top and on 2 sides, may be used for this species. The structure may be placed against a bank or overhanging cliff. Such javelina brush piles should be at least 6 x 6 ft and located in an area protected from wind and near food.

NATURAL AND ARTIFICIAL ROOSTS

Some species of wildlife, such as quail and turkeys, require adequate perching or roosting sites. Where roosts are lacking, such cover can be provided through natural vegetation plantings or by artificial roosting structures.

The California quail is an example of one species that needs at least one good roosting site per 30 acres for desirable habitat. The lack of adequate sites may be corrected by planting suitable thick-foilaged trees such as live oaks, olives, citrus and juniper trees. Where it is not practical or feasible to plant trees, artificial quail roosts, e.g. brush piled on a wire-covered frame held off the ground by four posts, can be made with little cost and used as temporary roosts while waiting for permanent natural vegetation to grow (McMillan 1959). These roosts are constructed of pipe or wood and should be approximately 8 ft x 16 ft in diameter and installed 6 ft above the ground when completed. An easily built roost is made from 2-inch pipe (Fig. 14.10). The supports consist of four 8-ft lengths of pipe, the ends of which are flattened and bent at right angles. One end is set about 2 ft deep in a post-

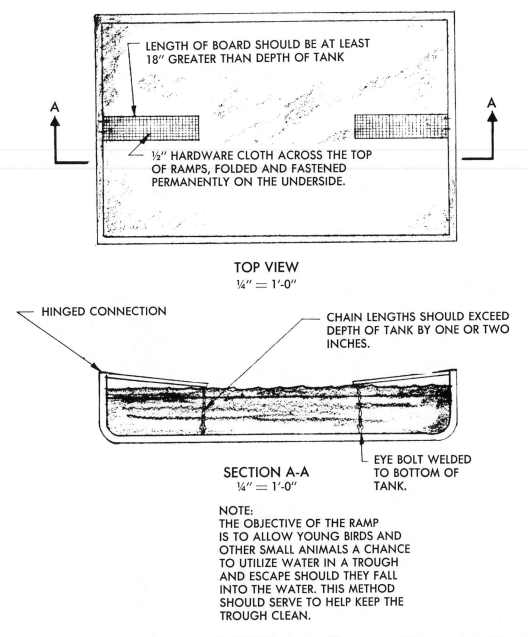

LENGTH OF BOARD SHOULD BE AT LEAST 18" GREATER THAN DEPTH OF TANK

½" HARDWARE CLOTH ACROSS THE TOP OF RAMPS, FOLDED AND FASTENED PERMANENTLY ON THE UNDERSIDE.

TOP VIEW
¼" = 1'-0"

HINGED CONNECTION

CHAIN LENGTHS SHOULD EXCEED DEPTH OF TANK BY ONE OR TWO INCHES.

SECTION A-A
¼" = 1'-0"

EYE BOLT WELDED TO BOTTOM OF TANK.

NOTE:
THE OBJECTIVE OF THE RAMP IS TO ALLOW YOUNG BIRDS AND OTHER SMALL ANIMALS A CHANCE TO UTILIZE WATER IN A TROUGH AND ESCAPE SHOULD THEY FALL INTO THE WATER. THIS METHOD SHOULD SERVE TO HELP KEEP THE TROUGH CLEAN.

Fig. 14.8. Troughs installed for livestock can be modified by the installation of "ladders;" thereby allowing young birds and other small animals a chance to utilize the available water. (Nevada State Office, U.S. Bureau of Land Management.)

hole filled with concrete, and a 1/2-inch hole is drilled in the flattened part of the other. The framework is made of flattening the ends of two 8-ft and two 16-ft lengths of pipe and drilling 1/2-inch holes through the flattened portions. The framework is fastened together and attached to the supports by 3/8-inch bolts. Hog wire is then fastened to the framework and brush piled on top of the wire. Large, crooked limbs should be used so the brush will not pack down and thus allow maximum density use (Mcgregor 1950).

Another method to improve protective roosting sites for quail is by cutting the limbs of large trees above the primary forks and piling these same limbs in the forks. This also causes the tree to bush out, which creates good dove nesting cover as well as quail roosting cover (Bauer 1963).

202

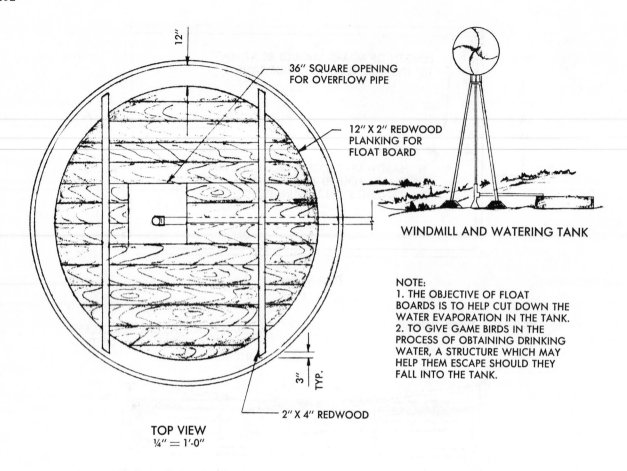

12"

36" SQUARE OPENING
FOR OVERFLOW PIPE

12" X 2" REDWOOD
PLANKING FOR
FLOAT BOARD

WINDMILL AND WATERING TANK

NOTE:
1. THE OBJECTIVE OF FLOAT
BOARDS IS TO HELP CUT DOWN THE
WATER EVAPORATION IN THE TANK.
2. TO GIVE GAME BIRDS IN THE
PROCESS OF OBTAINING DRINKING
WATER, A STRUCTURE WHICH MAY
HELP THEM ESCAPE SHOULD THEY
FALL INTO THE TANK.

3" TYP.

2" X 4" REDWOOD

TOP VIEW
¼" = 1'-0"

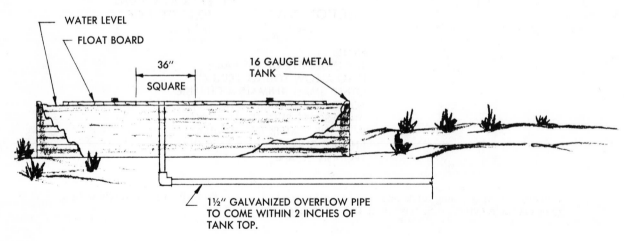

WATER LEVEL
FLOAT BOARD

36"
SQUARE

16 GAUGE METAL
TANK

1½" GALVANIZED OVERFLOW PIPE
TO COME WITHIN 2 INCHES OF
TANK TOP.

SIDE VIEW
¼" = 1'-0"

Fig. 14.9. The simple round float board illustrated in these drawings has saved hundreds of wild birds by providing an area for them to drink at round water troughs. One such trough without the board flat contained 13 sage grouse carcasses, however, after the "wildlife saver" had been installed, no further mortalities were observed. (Nevada State Office, U.S. Bureau of Land Management.)

Nesting Cover

GROUND NESTING COVER

Finding cover in ample amounts is by far the most critical problem for many ground nesting wild animals. Some suggestions for maintaining or improving nesting cover are (Shomon, Ashbaugh, and Tolman 1966) as follows:

1. Maintain permanent undisturbed cover along fences, ditchbanks, roadsides, railroad rights-of-way, and in waste areas (such as cattail sloughs) and odd corners, where possible.
2. Encourage farmers and ranchers to enter into one or more of the several government programs which provide financial aid for planting vegetation which is suitable for wildlife cover.
3. Work with state and local highway departments to discourage burning of cover along roadsides during the winter and spring; encourage the delay of mowing until after July 1; and encourage the planting of grasses and legumes for use by nesting pheasants.
4. Refrain from dryland fallowing operations between the period of April 15 and June 20 to enable ground nesting birds to hatch in the important stubble field nesting areas.
5. Use flushing devices on mowers to save nesting females during the first cutting of alfalfa.
6. Fence nesting cover to prevent grazing by livestock.
7. Plant shrubby thickets along gulleys and draws for use as cover. Techniques for such plantings are discussed in this Chapter under "Food Production."

DEN AND NESTING TREES

Man should husband important existing den or nesting tree areas, and should look to artificial nest structures only as a secondary technique after full evaluation of the need. It is more realistic and justifiable, in view of the many human and ecological values at stake, to make ample den or nest trees continuously available as a natural and vital component of the living forest.

An example of how the all important, but seldom understood, technique of protection is currently being practiced, is the U.S. Forest Service's system of managing nesting trees for rare and endangered native wildlife such as the bald eagle, ivory-billed woodpecker, and osprey. The following are practiced:

1. Maintain an inventory of all nest sites identifying in detail the location of each.
2. Check nests periodically and record a cumulative nest history of use.
3. Development activities, within 5 chains of any nest tree, will be limited to management measures beneficial to maintaining the nesting site.
4. A special buffer zone, 10 chains in radius, will be established and marked on the ground around each nest site.
5. Timber cutting, timber stand improvement, prescribed burning, road construction, recreation construction, and other disturbing activities will not be allowed within the buffer zone during the period from November 1 to April 15.
6. All practices such as insecticide spraying, aquatic plant control, and the use of fish toxicants, will be critically evaluated regarding their effects on nesting sites within the Forests and areas outside of the Forest, but within 1/2 mile of the Forest's boundary.
7. Three to five old-growth trees will be reserved as roosting and potential nest trees within the buffer zone surrounding the nest.
8. The location of all nests and their buffer zones will be shown in the Forest's "Multiple Use Atlas." These special management considerations will stay in effect until it has been conclusively determined that the nesting site has been abandoned.

NEST STRUCTURES

Artificial nest structures can substitute for natural sites found lacking in otherwise suitable habitat. Nest boxes have been useful for wood ducks and squirrels, whereas nest baskets and platforms have been readily used by waterfowl.

Nest Boxes

Nest boxes must be properly designed, located, erected, and maintained for beneficial results. They must also be durable, predator proof, weather tight, lightweight, economical to build, convenient to erect and maintain. Besides these, the boxes must meet the biological needs of each species, if they are to be practical for habitat management purposes.

● Specifications for Wood Duck Houses.
The basic requirements for wood duck nest cavities are that (1) a hen can enter, (2) the base will hold a clutch of eggs, and (3) there is

Fig. 14.10. Installation of an artificial quail roost in southern California (photos by I. McMillan).

enough debris to form a base and cover the first few eggs. Any wood duck house meeting these requirements might be used. Refinements and improvements have evolved for improving acceptability to the birds, reducing predator losses, and reducing costs per unit per year of use. Critical factors in the construction of houses are size, weight, depth, entrance hole, mounting fixtures, and provision for exit by ducklings. Since young ducklings must clamber up the steep interior wall of the house using sharp toenails and beaks for support, it is essential that the interior have a rough surface. A recommended design for general use calls for galvanized 12-inch stovepipe with conical roof and lined with auto undercoating (Fig. 14.11). A disadvantage of metal houses is that ducks must be conditioned to using them by the prior use of wooden houses. Provision must be made for exit by ducklings. One technique is to apply a strip of rough material 1/2- to 1-inch thick and 6 inches wide from entrance to bottom of house. The recommended material to use is a mixture of auto undercoating and vermiculite applied with a trowel.

A design for a wooden house is shown in Fig. 14.12. Wooden houses may be left unpainted but should be treated with a preservative such as pentachlorophenol. Use of creosote should be avoided. It may be esthetically desirable to paint metal boxes with a rustic shade of outdoor paint.

Recommended guidelines for the placement and maintenance of wood duck nest boxes include the following (Bellrose, Johnson, and Meyers 1964):

1. Houses may be erected within 1 mile of suitable breeding habitat waters; however, placement fairly close to such waters reduces duckling loss during the trek from house to brood habitat and may enhance initial acceptance by ducks.

2. Houses should be securely fastened to prevent excessive motion by wind, but in such a manner, if hung in a tree, as to permit tree growth and expansion.

3. Cracks or holes in boxes should be sealed or covered, but bottom drains should be provided.

4. Nesting material in the form of 2 to 3 inches mixed sawdust and shavings should be provided in base of each box.

5. Houses should be 10 to 30 ft above ground if in trees, or above flood level if on posts over water. If in trees, they should be in open woods with no branches shielding the entrances. Wood ducks fly straight into a box and do not need to alight first. Branches shielding entrances merely enhance the chance of predation.

6. Erect board nesting houses, with 3 x 4 inch elliptical entrances, in areas where the only important predators are yearling and old raccoons weighing 10 lb. or more.

7. Erect metal nesting houses, with raccoon-proof entrances and 24-inch high conical roofs, in areas where small raccoons, fox squirrels, and large snakes are potential predators.

8. Erect board and metal houses in the same area to promote initial use of metal houses.

9. Erect houses in groups, to attract returning yearlings as breeding birds.

10. Space houses according to habitat and potential breeding population. A desirable density appears to be 2 to 3 houses per acre for areas where nesting in natural cavities is at the rate of one pair per 10 acres.

11. Place some nesting houses in each unit in large trees at heights over 20 ft (the higher, the better) to secure optimum initial use.

12. Where houses are erected on posts over water, post sites should be selected to avoid possible damage by shifting ice flows or wave action. Houses should be high enough to prevent flood damage or inundation and posts should be provided with predator guards. Ideally, if flood conditions permit, houses erected on posts should be low enough (5 ft) to permit easy maintenance from boat or canoe.

13. Annual maintenance just prior to nesting season is required. Remove leaves or nests if squirrels or birds have gained access. Check box mounts and replace nest box base materials. At this time, entrance holes should be checked against enlargement by predators. Posts may require straightening or boxes may need to be repaired if damaged by storms, ice and snow, and falling branches and trees. Tree limbs affording predators access to the boxes should be removed.

● Specifications for Squirrel Nest Boxes.

The ideal squirrel box for management purposes should (1) attract maximum squirrel use, (2) be durable and require little maintenance, (3) exclude predators, (4) be inexpensive, (5) be simple to construct and erect, and (6) be protected as much as possible against accidental damage from storms and human vandalism.

Design specifications for a squirrel box are shown in Fig. 14.13. It is important that the entrance hole be just large enough to permit squirrel use but small enough to exclude larger predators. A round hole 2-1/2 inches in diameter is satisfactory for grey squirrels; one 3 inches in diameter is required for fox squirrels and possibly the larger northern races of grey

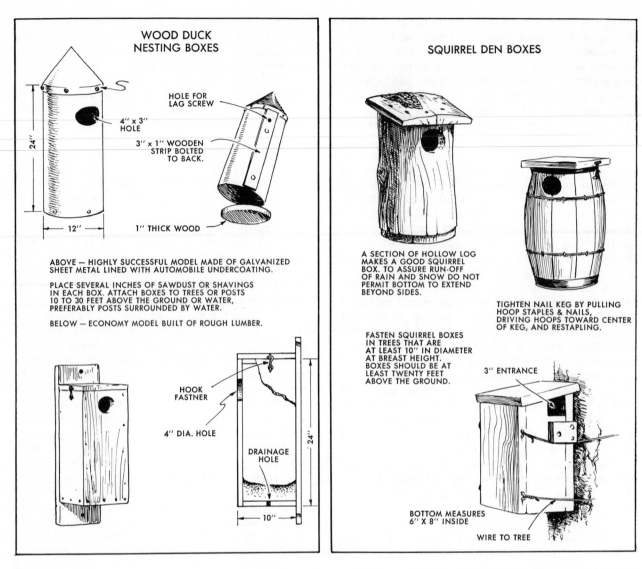

Fig. 14.11. Plans for constructing nesting and den boxes for wood ducks and squirrels (Shoman, Ashbaugh, and Tolman 1966).

squirrels. If entrance holes are excessively gnawed, the size should be slightly increased until the acceptable opening size is found. A box depth of 14 inches or more below the entrance hole assures that nestlings will be beyond the reach of raccoons and opossums.

A sloping roof with overhanging sides reduces water seeping into the box. By using cleats, roof warping may be minimized. The roof should be removable. The bottom should be constructed of 1/2- by 1/2-inch hardware cloth made of 14-gauge iron wires and galvanized after welding. A tough material is required to prevent tearing and entrance by raccoons. The wire is bent in the form of a basket fitting the interior dimensions of the box and stapled in an inverted position, 1/2 inch from the bottom of the box. The wire mesh permits drainage, ventilation, and the gradual deterioration and loss of decaying material. The minimum interior dimensions of a predator proof box appears to be 7 x 7 x 17-1/2 inches.

One-inch pentachlorophenol treated pine boards or untreated heart cypress or cedar boards fastened with rust-proof nails can be expected to last 20 to 25 years. If treated boards are not used, heart cypress or cedar should be used. It is not necessary that boxes be painted, but rustic painting may camouflage boxes from vandals and be more esthetic.

A density of one box per acre will result in a

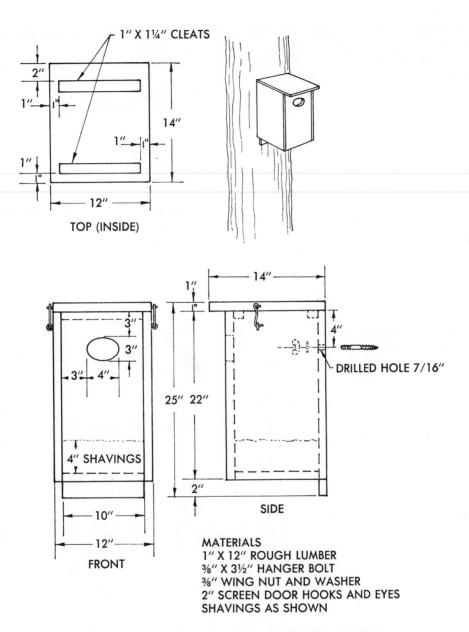

MATERIALS
1" X 12" ROUGH LUMBER
⅜" X 3½" HANGER BOLT
⅜" WING NUT AND WASHER
2" SCREEN DOOR HOOKS AND EYES
SHAVINGS AS SHOWN

Fig. 14.12. Plan for a wood duck nest box (Naylor 1962).

significant increase in populations after two breeding seasons (spring and summer) have elapsed as compared with unboxed areas. Nest boxes should be hung 10 ft or more above the ground, the higher, the better, giving due consideration to worker safety and increased cost of hanging and maintenance. It is advisable that boxes be hung above, but not directly on, one or more large limbs providing shielding to the box from vandalism. Placing a box directly on a limb increases breakage due to tree sway and may increase predation by tree climbing snakes, such as the black rat snake.

Boxes should be suspended from the tree with two 20d-40d zinc coated or aluminum nails with ample clearance left for tree growth—at least 1 inch. In the interest of timber values, trees of low merchantability or cull value should be selected for boxes. To prevent rocking or excess movement, a single strand of No. 10 solid polyethlene-coated conductor wire should be tied around box and tree. This arrangement of nails and wire is adequate to secure a box yet flexible enough to slip with tree growth or if knocked by falling limbs. Tightly fastened boxes are more apt to be demolished by falling objects. Maintenance of properly constructed boxes is reduced to periodic rehanging to permit tree growth, cleaning, and renailing if nails have worked loose. Bottoms should be inspected for predator damage.

Nest Baskets

The following specifications have been used in the construction of durable and economic nest baskets for use of waterfowl.

Materials needed include:

  4 - 21 inch x 1/4 inch black metal rods
  1 - 7 ft x 1/4 inch black metal rod

  1 - 36 inch x 36 inch x 1/4 inch hardware cloth
  1 - 18 inch x 1-1/4 inch galvanized pipe (I.D.)
  1 - 3/8 x 1 inch machine bolt and nut
12 - medium pig rings
  4 - sticks welding rod
  1 - 10 ft x 1 inch galvanized pipe (I.D.)

Recommended procedures for construction of nest baskets are:

1. Cut cone from hardware cloth according to pattern "A" in Fig. 14.14, bend to shape, and fasten with 4 pig rings.
2. Bend 7 ft rod to form a hoop and weld.

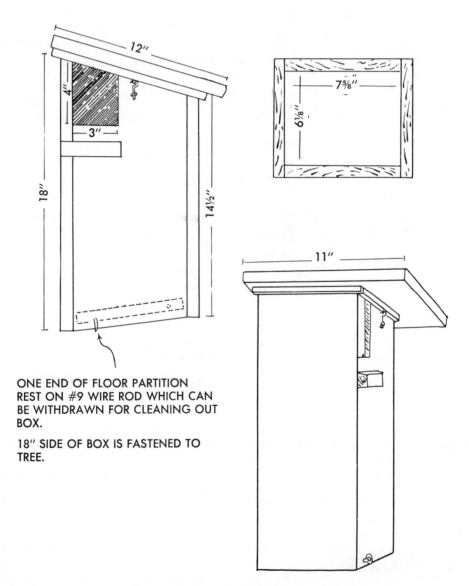

ONE END OF FLOOR PARTITION REST ON #9 WIRE ROD WHICH CAN BE WITHDRAWN FOR CLEANING OUT BOX.

18" SIDE OF BOX IS FASTENED TO TREE.

Fig. 14.13. Plans for construction of nest boxes for squirrels (Allen 1952).

3. Bend the four 21 inch braces according to pattern "B" in Fig. 14.14 below.

    a. Bend short hook in one end to fasten over hoop.

    b. Bend other end of rod to lay flat against pipe for welding.

4. Drill one 7/16 inch hole in 1-1/4 inch I.D. pipe 2 inches from end. This will be referred to as the bottom of the pipe.

5. Weld nut to pipe over hole and insert 3/8 inch machine bolt as set screw.

6. Weld braces to top end of 1-1/4 inch I.D. pipe according to pattern "C" in Fig. 14.14 below. (One brace is welded inside to serve as a stopper in case the set screw loosens allowing the basket to slip on the pipe stand.)

7. Hook braces to hoop and weld in place.

8. Place hardware cloth cone inside of hoop according to the diagram of the basket. Attach to braces and hoop with pig rings.

9. The constructed basket is attached to the 1 inch I.D. galvanized pipe at the time nesting structure is erected.

Procedures for placing nesting material in basket include the following:

1. Fill the baskets with a desirable nesting material prior to being erected. Suitable material may be flax straw, sedge grass or upland "wild" hay.

2. Place a large handful of nesting material in the bottom of the basket.

3. Line the inside of the basket with nesting material and secure it in place with stovepipe wire woven loosely through the straw and hardware cloth.

4. Completely fill the basket with loose nesting material leaving a slight depression in the middle of the basket to simulate a nest.

5. Spray the hardware cloth with light brown or olive color paint to reduce reflection.

6. Replenish the supply of nesting material as needed.

Care should be exercised to insure proper procedures for erecting the nest baskets. General guidelines to consider are:

1. Baskets should be erected in a minimum of 1 ft of water on a 1-inch I.D. galvanized pipe. Length of pipe will vary with type of soil. In many types of lake bottoms it may be necessary to lengthen the stand-pipe by attaching it to a pole and push the pole further into the muck.

2. The rim of the basket should be 30 inches above the normal water level.

3. Baskets should be erected in sheltered areas to reduce damage from ice.

4. Baskets should be located (to the extent possible) in or close to emergent vegetation.

5. Baskets should be erected in diamond shaped clusters of four with one cluster per mile of shoreline. Spacing of the nest baskets is shown in Fig. 14.15.

6. Baskets will be checked for ice damage immediately after spring breakup.

Nesting Platforms

Structures such as illustrated in Fig. 14.16 have been constructed for the benefit of geese in the West (Saake 1968). Their value is especially great in areas where predation by feral dogs is a problem. Many construction variations to this technique may be empolyed, i.e., one stout pole instead of four, four bales of hay instead of the tire, and a large metal washtub instead of the wooden platform. The one pole specification is better than the four steel posts in regions where ice movement is a problem.

Nest Cones

Mourning doves generally build a loose, flimsy platform of twigs for a nest and many are destroyed by heavy winds and rains. Artificial wire cone nest structures have proven successful in improving nesting survival (Cowan 1959). These wire cones are made of 1/4- or 3/8-inch mesh hardware cloth. They are easy to construct and install (Fig. 14.17).

The best location usually is along limbs where branches have forked off and where there is moderate shade. Most doves seem to prefer a height of 6 to 16 ft above the ground for their nests. Sites must command good visibility and have enough clearance of brushy limb growth so that the birds can escape danger easily. After the nest cone is properly secured, bend the outer rough edges down slightly so as to form a smooth place for the birds to alight. Best results are obtained by installing the wire cones in late February, March, and April, before most doves have chosen their nesting territories.

Periodic checks should be made to see that the wire cones remain securely fastened and that they are not obstructed by new branches. Brush out old nest material from the cone each year and let the birds make a nest with new twigs.

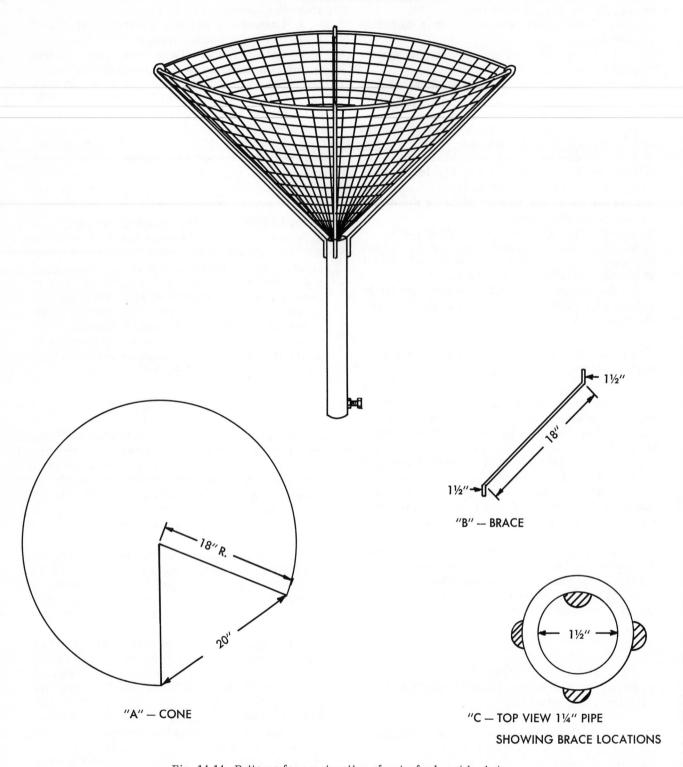

"D" — DIAGRAM OF BASKET

1½"

18"

1½"

"B" — BRACE

18" R.

20"

1½"

"A" — CONE

"C — TOP VIEW 1¼" PIPE
SHOWING BRACE LOCATIONS

Fig. 14.14. Patterns for construction of waterfowl nest baskets.

WETLAND IMPROVEMENT

Development of Water Areas

Techniques for improving wetlands will vary and are dependent to a large degree on the prior structural development of the area, water, water level management, soil, climate, topography, and plant succession. Sometimes wetlands can be manipulated by the use of biological and physical forces to develop an improved environment for wildlife.

A biological need should be established before any plans for wetland improvements are made. The chief use or uses of the area should be the prime consideration in judging its potential development, although these uses are also largely determined by the location of the area and physical characteristics. Some areas may best be developed primarily for waterfowl, others for muskrat or other fur production. There will be other areas where these two features can be com-

bined. The habitat manager can often use various practices to create interspersion of open water with marshland, interlace ditches and high spoil lands, plant desired vegetation for food and cover, and thereby create wetlands favorable to ducks and geese, to beaver, muskrats, mink, and to warm-water fishes. For the habitat manager seriously concerned with techniques of preserving, managing, or manipulating wetlands, the authors recommend the "Waterfowl Techniques Handbook" published by the Atlantic Waterfowl Council (1963). A sizeable portion of this book is devoted to making preliminary evaluations prior to development in order to establish need. There are also sections on improvements techniques, many of which are incorporated in this Chapter.

SHALLOW MARSHES

Marshes provide nest sites, cover, and food for waterfowl and for muskrats and other fur-bearing mammals, such as mink and otter.

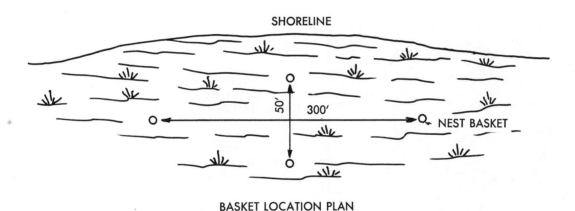

BASKET LOCATION PLAN

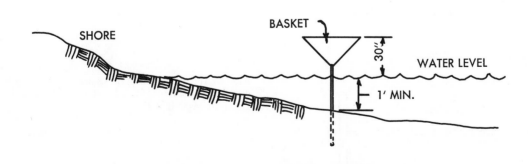

SIDE VIEW OF BASKET

Fig. 14.15. Diagram of cluster placement of waterfowl nest baskets.

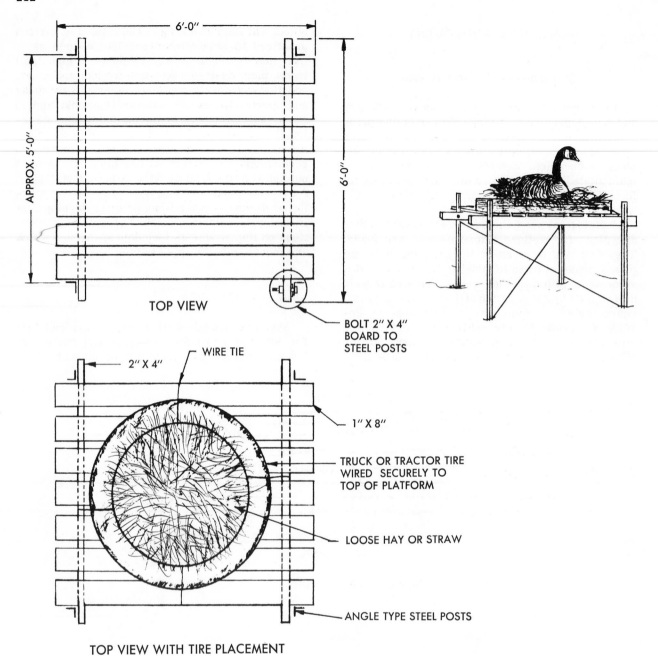

TOP VIEW

BOLT 2" X 4"
BOARD TO
STEEL POSTS

WIRE TIE

2" X 4"

1" X 8"

TRUCK OR TRACTOR TIRE
WIRED SECURELY TO
TOP OF PLATFORM

LOOSE HAY OR STRAW

ANGLE TYPE STEEL POSTS

TOP VIEW WITH TIRE PLACEMENT

6'-0"

APPROX. 5'-0"

6'-0"

Fig. 14.16. Diagrammatic plans for constructing a goose nesting platform. (Nevada State Office, U.S. Bureau of Land Management.)

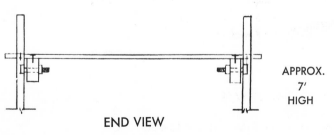

END VIEW

APPROX.
7'
HIGH

Herons, cranes, rails, plovers, and sandpipers are the chief bird families that require marshes. Many forms of reptiles, amphibians, and fish complete the vertebrate fauna. A marsh should have open water areas if it is large, or an adjacent pond, if small, for maximum wildlife value.

Artificial impoundment is a common practice used to improve existing marshes or to create new ones. The objective is not merely to flood an area, but to control water levels after impoundment as a method of managing food and cover conditions. Stop log controls should be designed so that water level can be manipulated, including complete draw-down when needed. In most instances the average water depth should be 18 to 24 inches depending on site condition and amount of edge.

Ditching marshes increases the variety of

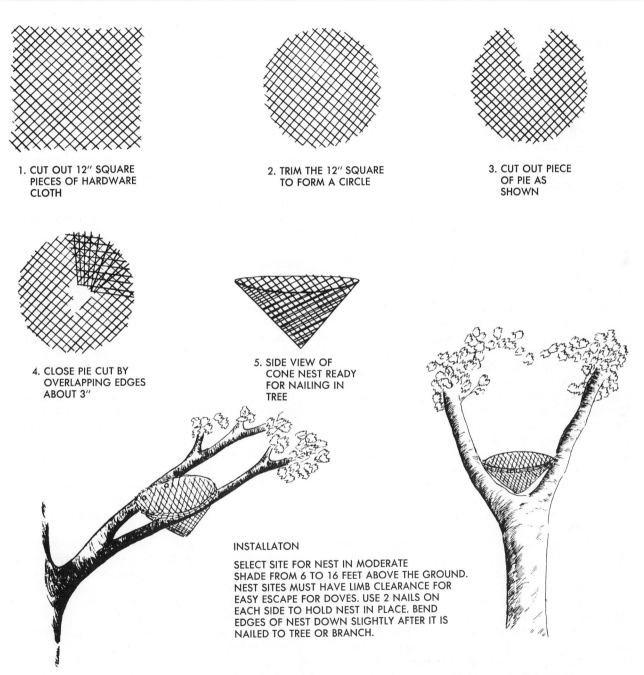

1. CUT OUT 12″ SQUARE PIECES OF HARDWARE CLOTH

2. TRIM THE 12″ SQUARE TO FORM A CIRCLE

3. CUT OUT PIECE OF PIE AS SHOWN

4. CLOSE PIE CUT BY OVERLAPPING EDGES ABOUT 3″

5. SIDE VIEW OF CONE NEST READY FOR NAILING IN TREE

INSTALLATON

SELECT SITE FOR NEST IN MODERATE SHADE FROM 6 TO 16 FEET ABOVE THE GROUND. NEST SITES MUST HAVE LIMB CLEARANCE FOR EASY ESCAPE FOR DOVES. USE 2 NAILS ON EACH SIDE TO HOLD NEST IN PLACE. BEND EDGES OF NEST DOWN SLIGHTLY AFTER IT IS NAILED TO TREE OR BRANCH.

Fig. 14.17. Construction and installation of wire nest cones for mourning doves (Cowan 1959).

214

habitat for furbearers as well as waterfowl. Deeper water in ditches helps animals find food and cover during dry periods. The spoil banks, on the other hand, offer dry resting sites, feeding areas, and shelter during flood periods. Ditches also facilitate access for hunters and maintenance crews.

Dredging has been found superior to blasting as a method of ditch construction. Blasted ditches tend to be shallower and loosened muck along the edges of the ditch is highly susceptible to wave and wind erosion. The lack of high spoilbanks desired for waterfowl nest sites and muskrat dens further reduces the value of blasting.

In constructing improvements in shallow marshes, the use of scoops, draglines, bulldozers, or combinations of the three, are recommended so that the material removed may be piled along the edges. The high areas should be planted to a grass-brush cover.

POTHOLES OR SUMPS

Potholes may be defined as small shallow open water retention areas or basins with surface areas usually under 4 acres in size. These areas, when developed in conjunction with large permanent water areas, can be a particularly valuable tool in waterfowl management. The purpose of making potholes is to create or increase water area lost to geological change and plant succession. An ideal wetland for waterfowl has one-third open water and two-thirds marsh.

Draglines and bulldozers have been used in construction of potholes, but they are of most use when ditching, damming, and diking are required. The use of a blasting agent is the most expeditious and economical method to employ in creating new small potholes. Recent experience has shown ammonium nitrate to be a very effective agent. It is less expensive and safer than dynamite. It has recently been discovered that best results are obtained with commercially prepackaged ammonium nitrate fuel oil charges. In pastured areas potholes should be fenced. Fences should be located at least 25 ft and preferably 40 ft or more feet back from the waterline (Mathiak 1965).

Beavers, when skillfully managed, can create much desirable habitat. Their ponds in intermediate stages of development are major attractions, not only for waterfowl, but also for other wildlife. But the typical beaver impoundment is a changing affair that evolves through several stages. For this reason, the manager should not be as concerned with maintenance of individual ponds as he is with rotation of favorable habitat elements within the entire area of beaver influence.

GREENTREE RESERVOIRS

Greentree reservoirs are bottomland hardwood areas shallowly flooded for short periods during the dormant growth period for the purpose of attracting waterfowl. Short-term flooding makes possible attractive feeding conditions on mast from various oaks (pin, willow, Nuttall, and cherrybark) supplemented by understory food plants, such as wild millet and smartweed. Flooding may be scheduled so as not to adversely affect tree growth or plant succession.

Acorns are the staple wildlife food item for which such areas are managed. Ducks (mallards and wood ducks) are the principal target species, but greentree reservoirs are also good for turkey, squirrel, deer, quail, raccoon, other furbearers, and many species of nongame mammals, birds, reptiles, amphibians, and fish.

Water depth of 1 ft to 18 inches is considered most suitable for "puddle duck" feeding. It is not necessary that the ground be completely flooded; narrow ridges may remain dry and still be utilized by waterfowl.

The selection of a site for a greentree reservoir should be based on three main considerations:

1. Select the proper site. The area should be flat and contain impervious clay soils and be close to a low gradient stream to prevent excessive diking cost.

2. There must be mast-bearing oak timber that can be flooded and is adapted to flooding. The opportunity for this appears to be limited to broad, geologically old-age valleys such as those of the South Central and Southeastern United States.

3. There must be an ample and dependable water supply which can be removed from the area before tree growth starts in the spring.

In the operation of a greentree reservoir, it is desirable to begin flooding sufficiently early in the fall to attract early flights of waterfowl. Drainage of flooded areas should be accomplished during the late March to mid-April period to prevent loss or damage to timber stands.

An open marsh constitutes an ideal supplement to a greentree reservoir. Such marshes add to the variety of habitat conditions and probably increase nesting and brood rearing values.

Marshes may be improved by the methods suggested in the "Shallow Marshes" section of this chapter. Technical engineering guidance and planning are needed for all proposed greentree reservoirs. A detailed plan of the area to be flooded should be made prior to construction including proposed water levels, soil samples, and location and design of levees and diversion channels or dams. Engineering features that should be included in the plan include:

Levees

a. Levees should be wide enough for small vehicles, a minimum of 4 ft wide at top.

b. Levees should have a 3 to 1 slope downstream, 4 to 1 slope upstream.

c. Levees should be seeded or sodded to permanent vegetative cover including wildlife food plants.

Borrow Areas

Areas from which soil is taken should be outside the greentree reservoir, preferably on high ground where the spillway will be located. Borrowing from within the greentree reservoir creates a deep water hazard for hunters.

Spillways and Drainage

a. The borrow area, if properly located, may be incorporated into the spillway. The spillway should flow onto undisturbed earth.

b. When a system of levees is needed to make flooding possible or to divide large areas into management units, the spillway may be incorporated into the structures.

c. Spillways built into levees must be stabilized by using soil cement, concrete, or paving material.

d. Flooding of the feeding range may be accomplished by several methods, all of which require use of low contour levees with control structures.

● Retention of Rainfall or Floodwaters

This method is best adapted to flat bottoms with low gradient. It requires minimum investment and is economical to operate. This method depends on rainfall for flooding at the proper season. Since soils on these sites generally are heavy clay and difficult to drain, sites should be chosen which will allow draining the impoundment early in the spring to guard against loss of tree growth.

● Diversion of Inflowing Streams

This method may be used where small streams enter terraces and well drained bottomlands. It consists of a gate-type structure in the stream to permit diversion of the stream-flow into the diked area at the proper time. Initial cost is largely governed by the size of the diversion structure and extent of facilitating levees. Flooding by this method, however, is not dependent on rainfall.

● Pumping

Pumping is used where ground water is readily available and where other water sources are unreliable. Flooding, of course, is completely controlled, but requires a relatively fixed annual cost for pumping. Pumping costs usually range from $2.50 to $5.00 per acre foot.

Habitat Manipulation Practices

WATER LEVEL CONTROL

Production of submerged aquatic vegetation will generally require stable water levels. Actual depths will depend upon topography, clarity of the water, plants used, and species of wildlife involved. Operating depths will usually vary from 1-1/2 to 12 ft, with the optimum being about 4 or 5 ft. Water levels of 1 or 2 ft during the production season for submerged aquatics proved most beneficial to waterfowl on the Montezuma National Wildlife Refuge. Depths greater than this were of little value to dabbling ducks. Water levels should be managed so as not to allow freezing to occur in the bottom soils. It should be pointed out, too, that where sufficient water level control is possible to permit growth of wet-soil plants, food production usually exceeds that of submerged aquatics. In all improvement projects, means should be incorporated in the control structures to allow maximum flexibility in manipulating water levels.

For management of emergent vegetation, the drawdown practice of water level controls is used in areas where waters are acid, turbid and light penetration is inhibited, and also where soils are of low quality. Perennial and annual food plants may be managed by drawdown dependent upon whether the objective is to encourage permanent muskrat populations, or to provide needed habitat requirements for waterfowl. Drawdown should be as late as possible yet still early enough to allow seed production for such fast growing acquatics as wild millet, rice cutgrass, and annual smartweeds which may become established on moist mud flats. The drawdown date will vary according to latitude. In the Middle Atlantic states, June 20 is the approximate drawdown date. Reflooding is usually done by September 1 in order to serve early migrating waterfowl.

If the impoundment is in an estuarine area, tide gates should be in operation during the period of drawdown to prevent ingress of saline waters. For most marshland plants drawdown is to meadow level in order to furnish subirrigation waters. For millet, the water level should be raised above meadow level after the growing millet has attained a height of 6 or more inches. As the millet grows, water levels can be raised accordingly, but in no case should the water be allowed to flood over the top of the growing plants. Preventing over-flooding has the advantage of inhibiting the growth of undesirable and perennial plants.

Reservoir drawdown is an effective method of manipulating cover around waterfowl impoundments. Species composition of cover can be controlled by time and length of drawdowns. If the soil remains wet, cattail and bullrush are favored. If it is allowed to dry, sedges and such species as woolgrass (*Scirpus* sp.) are likely to invade. Late spring and early summer drawdowns favor submerged plants; mid and late summer drawdowns favor weedy growth. In some regions, willow and red-osier dogwood may invade rapidly where the drawdown is sustained for 2 years or more. Drawdowns also improve the growth of submerged aquatic plants once the area is re-flooded because of both physical and chemical improvement of soils.

Although water drawdowns are a valuable tool in marsh management, they must be used with care, and should be predicated on knowledge of physical and biological characteristics of the marsh. Bottom topography, soils characteristics, existing plant communities, current waterfowl use and productivity, and seasonal water supplies, are all important factors that will affect the decision to use drawdown as a habitat manipulation technique.

PLANTINGS FOR FOOD AND COVER

Efforts to propagate plants for waterfowl food should be undertaken only after thorough survey of existing conditions. The important native species first must be identified and inventoried. Consideration needs to be given to the distribution and environmental requirements of all the important duck food plants that are, or should be,

present on the area. Planting, the last step in the program, is done only when it is known that important species are missing and that conditions for their introduction are right. A very important first step in providing food plants for waterfowl is covered in this Chapter under "Shallow Marshes." This is to create the kind of shallow, marshy-edged type of impoundment that encourages the favored flora. A constant, stabilized water level is very important for growth and reproduction of most aquatic life, whether it be plant or animal. This is especially true during late spring and summer.

Artificial introductions are of most value to small areas where the site can be managed and controlled intensively. Planting of large marshes, river bottoms, or extensive impoundments is frequently very costly. When starting a planting program, small plantings should be made, thereby determining the adaptability of test species for the site.

To realize best results from a planting program, the work must be conducted at the proper period of the year, usually during spring or early summer months. Second, the planting site must be of a nature that promotes growth. If the site is already supporting a cover, there is little reason to expect planting success, as the plants growing on the site will be much more adapted than introduced species (Singleton 1965).

The job of the habitat manager is similar to that of the farmer as he implements the principles and practices of crop production. In order to insure successful growth, the crop producer first removes all competing growth from the land and tills the soil in an effort to create conditions favorable to the growth and production of the target crop. Recommended sources of good information pertaining to plantings, especially for waterfowl, include the following: for the Gulf states (Singleton 1965), for the eastern states (Atlantic Flyway Council 1963), for the Pacific northwest (Scheffer and Hotchkiss 1945), for the Great Lakes areas (Pirnie 1935), for the Pacific southwest (George 1963, Miller et al. 1960), and in general for North America (Addy and MacNamara 1948).

For immediate reference, the following are some of the more important food plants for waterfowl and suggested techniques for planting them:

● Pondweeds

Pondweeds can best be introduced into new waters by transplanting of the rootstock early in the spring season. Whole plants should be pulled or dug, the roots balled with mud, and immediately transplanted. Soft, muddy bottoms make the most satisfactory growth sites.

● Smartweed

Smartweed is best propagated by transplanting rootstocks. Successful establishment has also been accomplished by 12-inch long stem cuttings. About one-half of each cutting should be stuck into mud bottoms in shallow water. Rootstocks or cuttings should be transplanted during late winter or early spring.

● Duck Potato

This species may be established by transplanting the entire plants in the spring or early summer. The transplants should be set in water equally as deep as that from which they were collected. Soft, muddy bottoms make the best growth sites.

● Spike Sedges

Rootstalk or entire plants can be propagated. All transplanting should be completed in the spring or early summer months.

● Duckweeds

Transplant the entire plant. This is done simply by collecting the floating plants in a bucket or basket and then scattering the material in the site to be planted. Duckweed makes its best growth in sites having emergent vegetation which will protect the duckweed from excessive wind or wave action.

● Coontail

New plants grow from fragments of coontail stems. The stem fragments may be planted at any time during the growing season and can be transported whenever it may be gathered, either from the masses of live plants in the fall or by rakes and drags used on the bottom in winter or spring. They may be planted in packages or merely pushed by hand into the soft soil.

● Grasses

There are hundreds of grasses, both natural and domesticated grains, used by waterfowl in North America. Two native species commonly planted are wildrice and wild millet. Wildrice is broadcasted and requires no covering, for each good seed sinks at once and becomes embedded in the bottom soils. Best planting sites are those that have shallow, fresh, non-stagnant water; mud bottoms; and are open to the sunlight. A great deal of wildrice seed has been wasted in water too deep for the young plants to reach the surface or on sludge bottom into which the seed worked down too deep by means of its tiny slanting barbs.

Wild millet, or watergrass, will not sprout if the water depth exceeds 6 inches. Usually no seedbed preparation is necessary if the wetlands are newly formed on agricultural land or on annual grassland. The seed can be broadcast and the pond flooded. The same treatment can be given bare pond bottoms. However, a seedbed must be prepared if the bottom is covered with cattails, tules, and saltgrass, or rushes and spikerushes, since millet cannot compete with these plants. In such cases the soil must be plowed or disced two or three times and then harrowed to break the sod. The seed may be planted by a field broadcaster, airplane application, or by use of grain drills. When using drills, plant the seed no more than 1/4-inch deep since deeper plantings often fail to germinate. The usual planting rate is 20 to 30 lb. of seed per acre. May and June plantings producing the best yield. Millet germinates rapidly when soaked and must not be left dry afterwards or the germ will die (Miller and Arend 1960).

● Alkali Bullrush

For many of the southwestern salt wetlands, alkali bullrush may be established. Generally seedbed preparation is not needed unless competition is severe with other plants such as cattails, tules, and saltgrasses. Spring seedings are recommended at a rate of 30 lb. per acre. Seeds may be aerially broadcast (seed should be presoaked for 5 days) for large areas or a standard 20 x 6 grain drill used for operations smaller than 25 acres. If drilled, be sure not to cover the seed more than 1/2 inch, otherwise germination will be retarded or lost. Very small areas (of less than 1 acre) can be hand transplanted by digging up the entire plant, including rhizomes and tubers.

Proper water management is exceedingly important to establishing this species. First, as much of the field as possible should be preflooded to a depth of 1 to 3 inches. After seeding, the water should be held at this 1- to 3-inch level for 2 to 3 weeks, then the water should be drawn down to a mud flat stage for 2 or 3 days. This allows the seedlings to emerge and firm their rudimentary root systems. The wetland should then be reflooded to the original depth (1 to 3 inches) and maintained at this depth until the plants have full mature seed heads. After this plant has become established, it may be flooded to almost any depth without adverse effects (George 1963).

NESTING AND RESTING SITES

Often it is necessary to create loafing islands or nesting sites on wetland development projects for waterfowl. Brood-rearing territories can be increased on improved marshlands exceeding 2 acres by partitioning the tract. Partitions are made by ridging or building chains of islands across the project. Ridges and islands can be constructed with a bulldozer or dragline during dry periods or by depositing rocks and boulders on the ice in winter. Snow fences strung across potholes is another practice to serve as temporary partitions (Atlantic Waterfowl Flyway 1963).

Floating "islands" can be anchored in shallow low water ponds. Metal barrels are sometimes attached underneath to adjust the height of flotation. The "islands" can be constructed from green logs with rough mitred corners made by a chain saw and held together with lag screws. Each "island" should be landscaped with grass or willows to provide shade and protection from predators (Shomon, Ashbaugh, and Tolman 1966). For suggested techniques on nest boxes, nest platforms and cones, see "Nesting Cover" in this Chapter.

Loafing and resting places may also be made by anchoring a couple of logs or 4 ft x 4 ft rafts in open water, or by stacking rocks, old straw or hay bales in shallow water.

Constructing Water Control Devices

There are various development structures used to control water to improve wetlands for wildlife. A general list of techniques is presented here with references on construction methods and specifications. The importance of working with expert engineers in developing construction requirements cannot be overemphasized.

DIKES AND EMBANKMENTS

All discussions relating to earthen water impounding embankments are limited to fills 10 ft high or less. If higher embankments are required, detailed soil studies must be undertaken in order to design and construct a safe structure for the most reasonable cost.

For a well-documented review of principles and methods of making dikes or impoundments, see the excellent *Waterfowl Habitat Development and Management Techniques Handbook* compiled by the Atlantic Waterfowl Council (1963). The material presented here was obtained from that book. The handbook describes the following types of embankments:

Simple Embankments

Simple embankments are those consisting of reasonably uniform material throughout. They are generally located in marsh or swamp areas where on-the-site soils must be used. They generally involve the least expenditures for construction and in many instances are the only feasible type to use (Fig. 14.18).

Core Type Embankments

Core type embankments are those whose central portion or core is constructed of selected soil, usually the least pervious material. The outer surface is comprised of on-the-site, more pervious soils. This type of embankment seldom is used on low head fills unless the supply of less pervious materials is readily available or unless the soils of different permeability are separated naturally distinct layers, readily available to the earth-moving equipment being used. However, on-the-site soils can be so poor that stability of the embankment will be questioned by competent engineers. In such cases it may be economically sound to haul the core material from some distant borrow pit (Fig. 14.19).

Diaphragm Type Embankments

Diaphragm embankments are those which incorporate a relatively thin section of concrete, steel or wood to form a barrier to percolating water. The "full diaphragm" type has the barrier extended from the level of the impounded water down to a seal in an impervious foundation. A "partial diaphragm" or cutoff wall type is one which does not meet the conditions of the full type (Fig. 14.20).

Although the need for complete, detailed investigations of the properties of soils and subsurface conditions is less on the low-head fills, on-the-site inspections must be made and rule-of-thumb criteria, based on experience, must be used in designing the embankment and selecting the type earth moving equipment for the job.

All earthen embankments should meet the following recommended criteria:

The dam shall be designed so that destruction through erosion is prevented. In order to meet this condition: (a) the spillway should have sufficient capacity to safely pass the expected peak flow for the drainage area, and (b) freeboard should prevent overtopping by wave action at maximum high water. The final top elevation of the embankment, after settlement, in areas of runoff water should be designed by adding to the maximum high-water elevation (resulting from flood flows) an amount at least equal to the wave height plus wave run up the slope. These amounts are determined by standard construction formulas. In areas of deep frost, an additional amount must be added to allow for damage from frost action. The elevation so determined considers over-topping by water originating upstream from the embankment.

For construction of sites in tidewater areas, overtopping by storm waters from outside the impoundment should be given consideration. The type management within the impounded area, type of material available, and the cost of construction will have to be weighed to determine whether or not embankments in these locations will be constructed to exclude such storm waters. If it is decided not to exclude them, provisions must be made in spillway and control structure sizes to admit the storm water into the impoundment in such quantities that the water surface elevation within the impoundment rises at approximately the same rate as the water outside. Then, when overtopping occurs, dike erosion will be reduced to the minimum.

For some wildlife management purposes, extremely low fills may be desirable to temporarily impound shallow water. Under these conditions, a comparison of construction cost plus annual maintenance must be made between dikes which would allow for overtopping and those which would prevent overtopping.

The foundation should be able to support the load imposed by the embankment and live-loads placed on it. Foundation soils will usually be stable enough to support the load of the embankment and live-loads for low-head fills. In some areas, however, the soils may be highly plastic so special precautions must be taken to insure stability. If such soils are not too deep they can be removed and replaced with more stable material. In other areas, however, it may not be feasible to remove and replace them and some method of treating them in order to realize stability will have to be devised. Rows of sheet piling or round piling can be used, but the cost per foot of dike is high. If extensive areas of such unsuitable foundation soils are encountered it may be wise to abandon the site.

The resistance of the embankment and foundation to the passage of water is dependent on the imperviousness and compaction of the material used. Loss of water is not dangerous if the supply retained in the impoundment is sufficient for operational needs and the seepage of water does not cause flotation of soils. Care must be taken to establish the minimum slopes and top width of dike which will provide this embankment safety and bury the seep line. While impervious soils will be stable on much steeper slopes and on embankments with narrower top or crown widths than are recommended for operation and maintenance. A 3.5 or 4 to 1 slope is considered the minimum for maintenance because tractor mowing equipment usually cannot safely operate on steeper slopes. Any embankment which will be used for travel, or on which maintenance mowing will be performed, should have a minimum 8 ft crown width, with 10 ft preferable.

The sites for habitat impoundment projects cannot always be limited to those having suitable foundation and fill materials. It is frequently

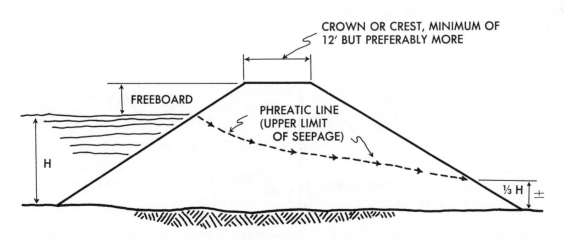

Fig. 14.18. Plans for construction of a homogenous fill typical dike (Atlantic Flyway Council 1963).

220

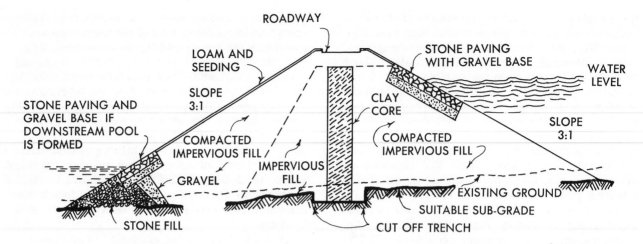

Fig. 14.19. Plans for construction of a typical clay core dam (Atlantic Flyway Council 1963).

necessary to compensate for poor on-the-site materials by safe design and construction of the embankment. However, under such conditions, the initial construction cost and future annual maintenance costs will increase proportionately with the decrease in soil stability. In all cases, the typical section (slopes, crown width and freeboard) should be such as to keep the impoundment seep water line within the fill. Wet spots on the downstream slope of any embankment could indicate the seepage line is not covered and remedial action should be taken. The type of embankment will be governed by the depth of water to be impounded, the materials available and the cost of both the initial construction and maintenance. All of these factors are interrelated but any one of them can outweigh the others on a specific project.

SPILLWAYS

Spillways are provided in major wetland developments to release surplus or floodwater which cannot be contained in the impoundment basin. Inadequate design of the spillway structure may result in failure of the retaining dam and possible downstream damage. The spillway design should be considered in relation to the management potential of the marsh and to drawdown or stable pool operation. A spillway design of maximum flexibility of water levels will, in most cases, be the best suited to the management of a wetland impoundment. Flexibility should be carefully judged against its benefits as related to structural costs. Standard types of spillways include the following:

● Free Overfall or Straight Drop

This type is used most frequently in the northeast in low head design, common to most large shallow area impoundments. It is necessary to provide artificial protection below the spill crest, as scouring and structural damage is likely to occur. A concrete or plank apron combined with cutoff walls is, therefore, an integral part of the free overfall design. The free overfall spillway

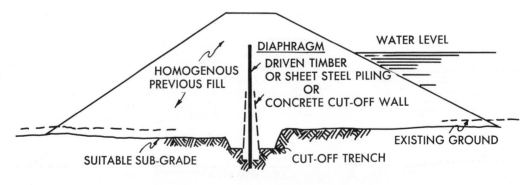

Fig. 14.20. Plans for construction of a typical diaphragm embankment (Atlantic Flyway Council 1963).

of reinforced concrete or wood planking is usually designed for fixed water level impoundments. In low head waterfowl impoundments, the design is usually modified to provide for drawdown or limited increase in storage capacity.

The reinforced concrete spillway is usually the most satisfactory design. The initial cost of concrete design is higher than log cribbing or Wakefield piling, but maintenance of the structure is minimized since concrete longevity is much greater than other materials. The location of the impoundment site and availability of material may warrant use of material other than concrete. The spillway should be designed for access so structural maintenance can be performed.

● Ogee

The Ogee spillway, usually designed of reinforced concrete, has a weir that is ogee or (S) shaped in profile. The flow is over the crest and along the profile of the structure with minimum interference and therefore attains near maximum discharge efficiency. In many low-head designs for waterfowl, storage of water is important and discharge efficiency is not a factor limiting design. The ease of construction and cost-related considerations may limit construction of ogee spillway design. In cases where ogee designs are contemplated for waterfowl impoundments, consideration should be given to incorporating drawdown features. This may involve drop boards, gates, or valves, so that water levels may be dropped below normal operational levels. Drawdown features should be considered even where management planning is based on stable pools. The installation cost of a drawdown feature may will pay for itself by improving the future maintenance of the prime structure.

● Natural

This spillway is one that provides for impoundment runoff over natural undisturbed ground. A spillway of this type is unusual in a large fresh water impoundment design. The possibility of locating a natural spillway with runoff capacity, soil type, and vegetative cover, that will meet design criteria, is unlikely. If a design can take advantage of such a spillway, substantial savings in development cost may result. It should be noted that maintenance of this type spillway may in some instances be rather high. The obvious disadvantage is that unless this type is supplemented with gates or other mechanical devices, it is not possible to provide for drawdown or drainage.

● Pipe or Culvert

A culvert spillway is a simple type spillway with the inlet opening placed either vertically or inclined upstream, with a uniform profile grade. The approach to the conduit may have flared or tapered sidewalls with a level or sloping floor. Conduits are usually metal, with a bituminous coating, and may have paved inverts. Concrete or fiberglass conduits have been used some. In lowhead design, this type spillway is adaptable for either part or full capacity operation. Construction is simple and economical.

There are disadvantages, however, in the use of culvert-type spillways in managed wetland impoundments. The capacity does not increase greatly with increased head, and there are limitations imposed in drawdown unless a gate valve is incorporated.

● Log Crib

The log crib spillway used in wetland impoundment is limited to location where the use of permanent materials would be too costly. Logs should be selected that have uniform taper and are highly resistant to deterioration. Logs treated with preservatives such as coal tar creosote or pentachlorophenol solution, are desirable where longevity is important. The abutments and spillway are usually faced with 3-inch treated planking. The maintenance of this type spillway is often very high in relation to cost of a more permanent type installation.

Since standard design plans are not often used in these structures, it is important that a plan be designed to meet local needs. The plan should be based on competent engineering standards. In general, log spillways are constructed of toe piling driven on the upstream face of a bed log and the spillway having a maximum incline of 30°. All bark should be peeled from logs not completely underwater. It may be desirable to include a stop-log section if drawdown is a consideration in the impoundment.

● Drop Inlet

A drop inlet is one in which the water enters over a horizontal positioned lip, drops through a vertical box or shaft, and is discharged through a pipe or conduit. In waterfowl impoundments, a concrete drop inlet in conjunction with reinforced metal pipe may be suited to small drainage areas. The most usual design is a monolithically reinforced concrete box, with stop-log slots on the upstream side. Provisions may be made for trash screens to prevent pipe constriction. Emergency spillways are incorporated in the design.

● Stop Planks

Stop planks provide a means of adding flexibility to an ungated spillway. These are planks spanning horizontally between grooved recesses in supporting piers. Stop planks may be removed during floods to pass excess waters and also when partial or complete drawdown of the pond is desirable. This type control is the most economical and provides adequate area to pass debris. The passage space should be a minimum of 4 ft wide on larger dam structures. A lifting type device may be desirable if the stop planks are to be removed frequently since manual removal may entail considerable time and work. If water loss is to be minimized, stop planks should be planed four sides and free from warp. Leaks between planks can be easily sealed by placing soft coal ashes in small quantities (handful) immediately upstream and over the leak. Dry cinders are best as they float more quickly into the leak. Planks should be a minimum 2 inch naturally-resistant or treated planking.

● Gates

Gates are used in spillways where a higher frequency and greater control of drawdown may be desirable. Lift gates span horizontally between guide grooves in supporting piers. Gates are usually cast iron or steel and raised or lowered by an overhead hoist device. Radial gates are usually constructed of steel (prefabricated). Water thrust operates the radial type of gate which may be set at a predetermined level so as to operate automatically. Cost of the installation of radial gates may be appreciably higher than lift gates, stop logs, or drop inlet installations. If continual drawdown in the impoundment is contemplated, gate installation should be considered.

LEVEL DITCHING

Level ditching means constructing ungraded ditches on lands having a high water table. These ditches are installed to improve water distribution, provide open water for waterfowl, furnish nesting sites, and aid in increasing or maintaining aquatic food and cover plants for waterfowl and furbearers (Mathiak and Linde 1956). This practice is applicable on wetlands where soils are suitable for ditch construction and require a minimum of maintenance for a long period of time. Suitable soils include peats, muck, clays, and silt. Sands, sandy loam, and clay high in salt content generally are not suitable. Generally, ditching is applied to marshes exceeding 2 acres.

It is helpful to consult with soil scientists, hydrologists and agricultural engineers for planning level ditching. On large wet areas, an aerial photo or topographic map is useful in locating natural drainage patterns and in laying out ditch systems. A sufficient number of levels should be run to determine the general slope of the wet area. Where slopes exceed 0.5% the ditches must be laid out on the contour level. The ditching pattern is designed to avoid interception of natural channels except where desirable for circulating systems. Usually blocks are left between level ditches and the natural channels, but these are designed to allow flood or high tide flows into the ditches or else water circulation is regulated by means of control devices. As a rule, level ditches are installed at approximate right angles to natural channels.

Level ditches are generally constructed with a dragline or with ditching dynamite. Occasionally a backhoe or a bogharrow may be used. In the use of ditching dynamite, the supervision of a licensed and experienced explosive expert is recommended. When a dragline is employed for ditching, spoil material is stacked 10 ft from the ditch edge in piles alternated from side to side at 50 ft intervals. This spoil serves an important function in providing nesting areas. The breaks between piles are said to reduce nest predation. In small marshes ditching usually is done in straight lines or, where there is a slope, on the contour. Whether straight or curved, these ditches must not have a fall. On flat marshes exceeding 10 acres, the ditch is constructed in zigzag pattern, with each reach about 100 ft long. Such a design reduces influences of wave action during high winds. Multiple ditches are laid out with parallel reaches 200 to 400 ft apart.

Minimum dimensions recommended for level ditches are 4 ft depth and 12 ft top width. Such ditches provide, at intervals given above, about 1200 square ft of open water per acre.

PLUGS

Plugs are usually recommended for marshes where diking is not a feasible management tool due to either improper physical conditions of the area (size, location, water, or terrain) or economic reasons.

Plugs can prevent the fluctuation of water levels in existing water areas or increase the water area in the marsh. Various types of plugs as defined by the Atlantic Flyway Council (1963) include the following:

1. *Non-spilling earth plugs* are usually used to repair marsh damage caused by mosquito or other drainage marsh projects. The same principles

are used as in building a dike across a tidal creek. The plug must be keyed in to both sides of the ditch and a good bond must be made between the fill material and the bottom of the ditch.

2. *Non-spilling wooden plugs* serve the same purpose as the earth plug type. Wakefield piling of creosoted lumber is used. Care must be taken to use piling long enough to prevent undercutting and the wing walls must be of sufficient length to prevent water from cutting around the end of the plug.

3. *Spilling gut plugs* are designed to reduce water fluctuations due to tidal action and thereby to make more food available to waterfowl for longer periods. The most common material used in this type of construction is creosoted lumber.

STRUCTURAL IMPROVEMENTS

Fences

FENCE DESIGNS FOR LIVESTOCK AND WILDLIFE

Wildlife populations often live today in environments which have been modified by man's development and use of the land. Fences are part of this modified environment with which wildlife must contend to survive. Fences that may impede movements of wild animals should have characteristics that insure passage with the least possible hindrance. The following designs will provide the land manager with fences which have these characteristics and yet are livestock proof. Construct net wire fences a maximum of 32 inches high. Construct barbed wire fences so the bottom wire is at least 16 inches from the ground. Where deer, elk, or moose are the target species, construct fences not more than 40 inches high. Where possible, poles should be used in place of the top wire. Poles have proved effective in reduction of game damage to range fences.

ANTELOPE FENCE SPECIFICATIONS

Livestock range fences can be a factor affecting antelope movements. However, modifications of fence construction can be made that will control livestock and at the same time provide minor interference to antelope.

Net or Woven Wire Fences

In 1963 and 1964, an intensive domestic sheep-antelope fence relationship study was conducted in Wyoming (Spillett, Low and Sill 1967). After conduction many trails in various fenced enclosures, recommendations for fence specification to allow sheep control with the least interference with antelope movement were: (1) 32-inch net, or (2) 26-inch net with 1 barbed wire 4 inches above.

Apparently a fence 32-inches high was the maximum most antelope readily crossed. The Wyoming study indicated antelope possess an inherent learning ability to cross fences, however, herds living in wide open ranges were reluctant to readily cross most fences. Extensive fencing projects should, therefore, be spaced over as long a period of time as possible in order to provide an opportunity for antelope to adjust to fenced ranges.

When fences located across well-used antelope routes are not being used to control livestock, let-down gaps should be left open to prevent hindrance of antelope movement. These openings should be located in low places rather than on ridges because although the antelope generally use the ridges for normal travel, they seek the protected washes and draws during seasons of heavy snows (Spillett, Low, and Sill 1967).

Barbed Wire Fences

Antelope prefer to go under barbed wire fences in almost all cases. The Interstate Antelope Conference (1962) recognized this characteristic and recommended the following two specifications for range fences that would aid in the control of cattle and not seriously affect antelope movements:

● Three-wire Fence
A 40-inch total height, with wires spaced 18, 28, and 40 inches above the ground for range fences (see Fig. 14.21).

● Four-wire Fence
Where greater cattle pressure is exerted (i.e. around water holes), wires should be spaced at 16, 22, 30, and 40 inches above the ground.

Both these recommendations incorporate two major specifications for the benefit of wildlife: the bottom spacing of a minimum of 16 inches to allow antelope to go under the fence, and the maximum height of 40 inches to allow deer to jump over.

224

Passes, Ramps, and Cattleguards

Standard cattleguards will permit the movement of adult antelope. Fawns, however, have some difficulty in crossing them. They must be placed where antelope can readily locate them. Advantages have been realized by placing cattleguards in fence corners. The fences then act to "drift" the antelope to the pass opening. In long sections of fence, it is helpful to build a jog in the fence line in which to install the cattleguard. Care needs to be taken in locating the placement site to minimize the cattleguards filling with debris and silt.

Structures described as "antelope passes" were developed and tested in the Wyoming sheep-antelope-fence study (Spillet, Low and Sill 1967). These consisted of a horizontal panel placed in a corner of a net wire fence (Fig. 14.22). The panel was constructed by laying a steel wire fence with 6-inch square openings over a rectangular frame of 2 x 4-inch lumber. The frame was held 9 inches above the ground level by bolting it to short posts. A modified panel 6 ft wide instead of 4 ft can be placed at ground level with an 18-inch excavation below, rather than being placed 9 inches above the ground. Both these structures were readily used by adult antelope but there is some question as to their affect on fawn movements.

Another device used to aid antelope movement in net wire fenced range pastures is dirt ramps (Fig. 14.23). These structures were built on both sides of a net wire fence by driving steel posts into the ground 12 inches from the fence on each side. Railroad ties were stacked against the posts to a height of 22 inches. Dirt was then pushed up against the ties to form a ramp on either side of the fence. Ramps may also be located at corners and have been observed to be used by both adult and fawn antelope.

INTERSTATE HIGHWAY FENCES

Movement of big game over county roads and low standard highways has not been a serious problem. Normally, the fences previously described in conjunction with traffic management will take care of most situations.

With the creation of the federal interstate highway system, a serious problem is developing. Highway construction is cutting across important big game migratory and access routes. It is important to maintain these big game travel routes, yet the human hazard caused by animals seeking

"SPECS" NO. 1:

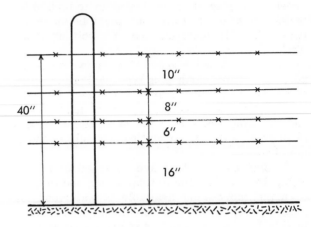

"SPECS" NO. 2:

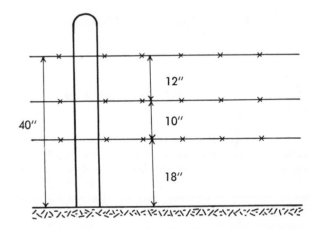

Fig. 14.21. Recommended specifications for barbed wire fences to control cattle and allow antelope movement (Interstate Antelope Conference 1962).

to cross high-speed highways must also be given consideration. When fences are constructed to reduce hazard to life and property on super-highways, alternate methods of allowing game to cross need to be devised. Otherwise, highway fences can have a serious detrimental effect on big game. In some instances, migratory habits may be impeded sufficiently to eliminate a complete big game herd. Mitigation of wildlife losses due to fence barriers must be done through State Fish and Game agencies. The following approaches to the problem should be considered:

Traversable game fences are described in this section in "Fence Designs for Livestock and Wildlife." These fences will hold livestock but

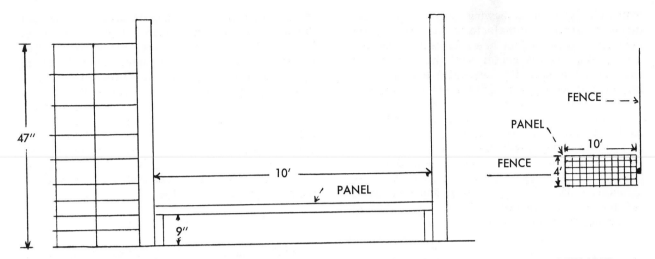

Fig. 14.22. Suggested plans for the construction of an antelope pass structure (Spillet, Low, and Sill 1967).

will allow game relatively free crossing. They should be used only in areas of light automobile traffic and in stretches where there are no center or island fences. They should be wide enough to allow game to make crossings without entrapment.

There are many areas where game normally winter or summer adjacent to interstate highways. While highways present no barriers to wildlife, the 7-ft high woven wire fences used in some areas not only block game from crossing the right-of-way, but commonly entrap any animals that manage to get inside. Also, in narrow canyons, interstate highways sometime abandon the separate opposite lanes of traffic and place

roadways adjacent to one another, separated by a chain-link fence to reduce collisions and headlight glare. The fence may or may not have a space at the bottom and may exceed the maximum height game animals can jump. This type of fence not only creates an unnatural barrier to wildlife, but a hazard to the driving public as well, because it holds animals in the traffic zone. Where chain link fences are used, a 4-inch space should be left on the bottom to allow small animals to cross. The maximum height should not exceed 40 inches where consistent with highway needs.

Underpasses and overpasses will need either

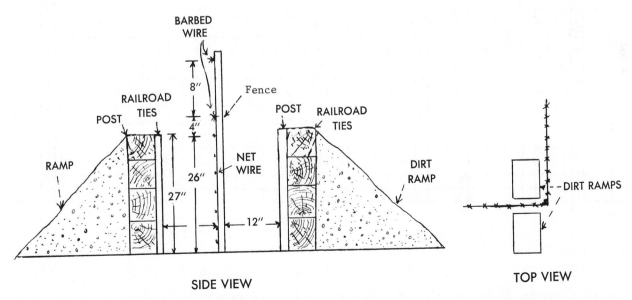

Fig. 14.23. Plans for construction of dirt ramps to help antelope cross woven wire fences (Spillet, Low and Sill 1967).

natural terrain or else wing fences to guide and funnel migrating animals to them. Preliminary evidence indicates deer are reluctant to use long underpasses unless center skylights reduce the dark tunnel effect. It is essential that the floor be covered with soil or gravel. Overpasses may be used if they are short and relatively wide. Overpass use by game shows a marked reduction as the structure increases in length or decreases in width. Floors should be covered with soil to reduce resonance and simulate natural conditions. Fenced wings to guide big game to these structures have been used with some success, but more study is needed to discover ways of improving their effectiveness.

FENCES FOR CONTROLLING DEER

Properly constructed fences can provide good protection against deer depredations to various agricultural crops, high concentration winter ranges, and areas of timber reproduction (Longhurst et al. 1962). Although the initial cost of installation of fencing for depredation controls is often high and continued maintenance is necessary, the expense can, in many cases, be justified.

Fences can provide economic protection against damage that deer can cause to high-value crops. Deer control fences are also being constructed for the purpose of rotating deer use of forage in range pastures on critical bitterbrush winter ranges in California and protecting critical areas in Washington. Under most circumstances the upright style of fence has proven most satisfactory but under some conditions the slanting fence is cheaper to construct and is advantageous because of its lower height. Specifications for both these types of fences are presented here as adapted from Longhurst et al. (1962).

Upright Fences

While a height of 6 ft is usually adequate for upright fences on level ground, a 7-ft fence may be necessary against larger deer (Fig. 14.24). Deer normally will not jump a 6-ft fence for food but if pressed they can jump an 8-ft fence on level ground. When fences are to be located on sloping ground, it may be necessary to build them 10 or 11 ft high to guard against deer jumping from above.

Woven mesh wire is preferable for the full height of the fence; if economy is necessary, two

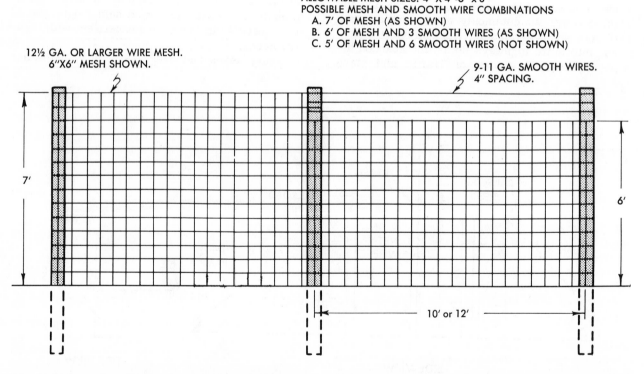

Fig. 14.24. Drawing showing two methods of using wire, either mesh above or combinations of mesh and smooth, to construct an upright fence for controlling deer damage (Longhurst et al. 1962.)

or more strands of 9 or 10 gauge smooth wire can be stretched at 4 to 6 inch spacings above a 5-ft mesh. There is no advantage in using barbed wire for this purpose, and it is more costly. Welded mesh wire is less expensive than woven, but it is too rigid to conform readily to irregularities in the ground surface and is most useful on even ground. Wire lighter than 12-1/2 gauge is not recommended. Vertical stays should not be over 6 to 8 inches apart, and line wires not over 4 to 6 inches apart. Because deer will crawl under a fence when possible, mesh wire should be secured and kept close to ground level. An extra strand of barbed wire stretched along the ground will help prevent them from crawling under. In any depressions between posts, wire should be staked firmly to the ground or depressions should be filled with materials which will not deteriorate or wash away. A 3- to 4-ft piece of angle-iron post makes a good permanent stake to hold wire close to the ground.

Wooden or steel posts may be used, the choice depending on availability and costs. Wooden posts are usually somewhat cheaper, with sawed ones being more expensive than split posts. Their dimensions at the ends should not be less than 4 to 5 inches across. If fences are to be moved from time to time, steel posts are preferable because of the greater ease with which they can be installed and removed. Steel posts can be purchased in three types: T-shaped, channel, and angle. The T-type is more rigid and is perhaps preferable, with channel next and angle last in order of strength; prices also decrease in that order. Posts should generally be set about 10 to 12 ft apart, but extra posts may be necessary to hold the wire to the contour of uneven ground. When building with steel posts it is often advisable to intersperse them with wooden posts in order to strengthen the fence—one wooden post for every three to five steel posts is the approximate ratio. Proper bracing along fence lines is important to give sufficient strength. Wooden corner posts should be at least 6 inches across the ends and are preferable to steel posts unless the latter are in concrete and are well braced.

With upright fences the gate height should be approximately equal to fence height. Weight should be kept to a minimum. A light wooden frame over which mesh wire is stretched is often satisfactory. If factory-made aluminum gates are used, metal extensions may be bolted or welded on and mesh wire stretched over them. It is always advisable to sink a metal or treated wooden base frame in the ground below the gate to give a

uniform surface and to prevent deer from working under the gate.

Overhanging or Slanting Fences

This type of fencing is less expensive to construct than upright fencing because fewer and shorter posts are needed and lighter gauge wire can be used. Slanting fences are particularly suitable for temporary fencing, as the few posts can easily be removed and the wire more readily rolled. This type of fencing is also suitable for locations where an upright fence would be unsightly or otherwise unsuitable.

The slanting fence is effective because it acts primarily as a psychological barrier to deer. Deer usually first try to crawl under such a fence and then, finding this impossible and with the wire extended above them, they are discouraged from jumping. For this reason slanting fences are effective in *one direction only*.

Overhanging woven wire mesh fences are not recommended in heavy snowfall areas since the fence is subject to being crushed by the settling snow pack. Under such circumstances the fence can be modified by using smooth wires stretched horizontally at 4-inch spacings.

The basic design for the slanting fence consists of approximately 6 ft of mesh wire supported by a guy wire stretched between widely spaced posts (Fig. 14.25). The high side of the fence is the side away from the area to be protected.

For temporary installations, light chicken wire or stucco mesh may be used. For permanent installation, wire no lighter than 12-1/2 gauge is advisable. If woven wire is used, vertical stays should not be over 6 to 8 inches apart and horizontal line wires should not be over 4 to 6 inches apart. Six ft steel posts are recommended, spaced up to 30 to 40 ft apart.

A hinged gate is needed if there will be considerable traffic. Adequate side wings should be provided. If little traffic is expected, a panel consisting of a light wooden frame with wire mesh stretched over it is often satisfactory. For easy access where no gate is needed, a stile is simple to construct.

Study Exclosures

Exclosures are constructed for a number of purposes, but mainly to exclude or control livestock or game use on the fenced area. These exclosures provide a basis for comparison of

228

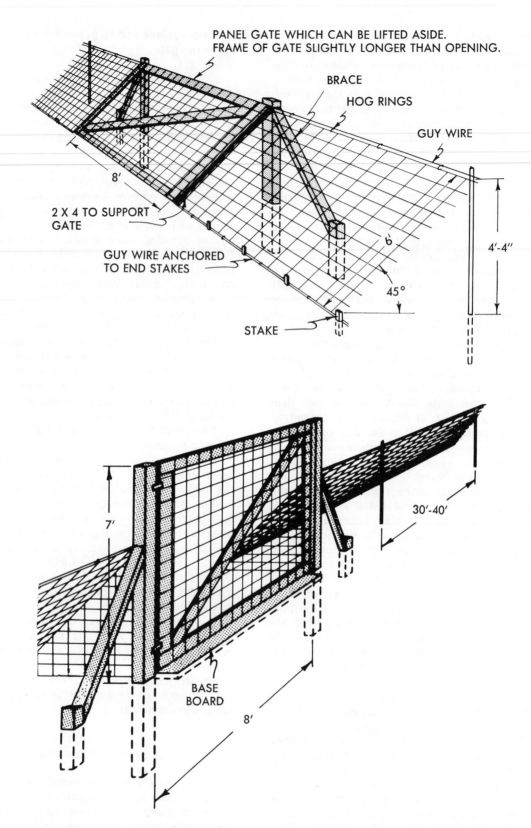

PANEL GATE WHICH CAN BE LIFTED ASIDE.
FRAME OF GATE SLIGHTLY LONGER THAN OPENING.

BRACE

HOG RINGS

GUY WIRE

8'

2 X 4 TO SUPPORT
GATE

GUY WIRE ANCHORED
TO END STAKES

6'

45°

4'-4"

STAKE

7'

30'-40'

BASE
BOARD

8'

Fig. 14.25. Typical slanting deer fencing with examples of placing the gates either slanting or vertical (Longhurst et al. 1962).

grazing or browsing with that on adjacent open range. Exclosures also serve as a method to determine proportionate use on ranges grazed by both game and livestock.

Permanent exclosures should not be less than 1 acre in size—2-1/2 to 5 acres are frequently more desirable. Extra strong construction is needed on all parts of the fence to withstand heavy pressure by animals against these small, fenced areas of better forage. Gates will not be constructed in exclosure fences. Stiles, steps, or ladders will provide access to the plot.

Three-way exclosures are often used to compare big game and livestock use of vegetation in an area (Fig. 14.26). These exclosures are constructed with two fenced plots and one unfenced or open adjacent control plot. They are generally not less than 1 acre each. One fenced exclosure is game and livestock-proof (a); and, the second livestock-proof (b); but readily accessible to game. The third plot (c) or control, is established on open range nearby. This unfenced control plot (c) should be an equal-sized area marked on the ground. The following specifications apply to the fenced plots.

A 7-ft fence is usually adequate to exclude both elk and deer. However, if the exclosure is so located or of such a size that it forms a barrier to concentrated game movements, the fence should be at least 8-ft high. If snowdrift areas cannot be entirely avoided, it will be necessary to construct a higher fence through the drift zone. Fences should not be located on steep ground unless necessary. This will minimize the influence of water drainage from outside the plot.

A square exclosure with wire fence 7-ft high with 210-ft sides, will enclose slightly over 1 acre and will require the following materials:

20 corner posts	6-inches diameter at small end and 10-ft long, peeled and penetrated
48 steel line posts	"T" stud, 10-ft long
16 line posts, wooden	6-inches diameter at small end and 10-ft long, peeled and penetrated
8 braces, horizontal	5-inches diameter at small end and 8-ft long
8 braces, diagonal	5-inches diameter at small end and 11-ft long
2 spools, barbed wire	80-rod spool
No. 9 smooth wire, galvanized	300 ft

20 lbs staples	1-1/2 inches
4 lbs nails	40 d.
hog wire	42-inches, galvanized, 840 ft or 51 rods
Rabbit-proof wire	2 x 4, galvanized, 840 ft or 51 rods
200 hog rings	Heavy duty, galvanized

The livestock-proof plot (b) will be enclosed with 38-inch fencing; 13-ft spacing between posts (210 ft to a side). On livestock range, four barbed wires shall be spaced 5, 11, 18 and 26 inches from the ground with a smooth wire on top, 10 inches above the top strand of barbed wire.

The following is a bill of materials for a livestock-proof plot having one side in common with a game and livestock-proof exclosure:

8 corner posts	6-inches diameter and 6-ft long, peeled and penetrated
6 brace posts	6 inch diameter and 6-ft long
6 wood line posts	6 inches diameter and 6-ft long
36 steel line posts	"T" stud, 6 ft long
2 spools barbed wire	Standard (12-1/2 gauge, 2 points), 80 rod spools
5 lbs staples	1-1/2 inches
2 lbs nails	40d.
No. 9 smooth wire, galvanized	80 ft

A ladder should be constructed in one corner of the plot with the high fence to facilitate workers access in and out. Following is a list of materials needed to construct the ladder:

4	6 x 6 inches	10 ft long
10	2 x 4 inches	9 ft long
6 lbs of 40 d. nails		

Consideration should be given to the construction of a large attractive sign denoting: (1) name of exclosure plot; (2) terse statement on purpose of plot; (3) and a list of cooperating agencies responsible for construction.

Plot (c) should have two steel 6-ft stakes placed at the two exterior corners for location purposes. In some areas, it may be desirable to construct buck pole fences or else worm fences around exclosures.

230

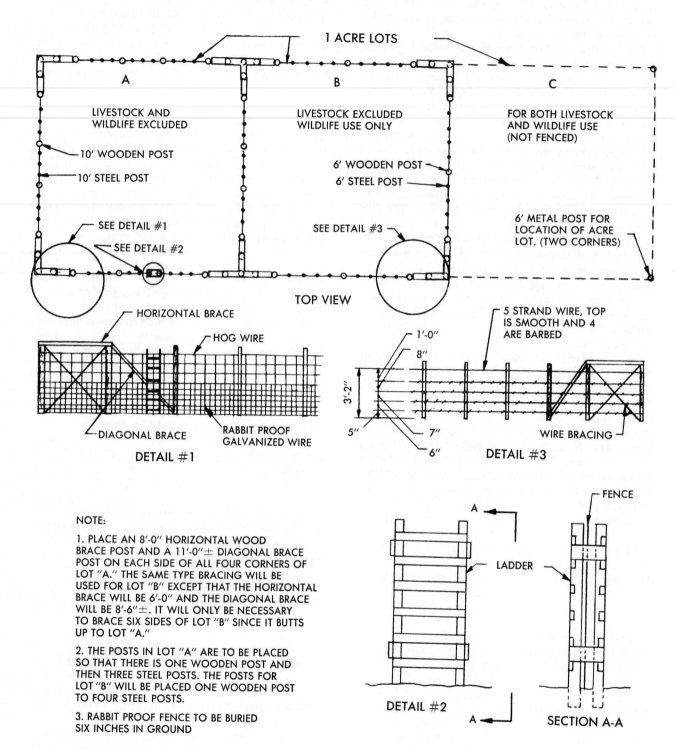

1 ACRE LOTS

A   B   C

LIVESTOCK AND
WILDLIFE EXCLUDED

LIVESTOCK EXCLUDED
WILDLIFE USE ONLY

FOR BOTH LIVESTOCK
AND WILDLIFE USE
(NOT FENCED)

10' WOODEN POST

10' STEEL POST

6' WOODEN POST

6' STEEL POST

SEE DETAIL #1

SEE DETAIL #2

SEE DETAIL #3

6' METAL POST FOR
LOCATION OF ACRE
LOT. (TWO CORNERS)

TOP VIEW

HORIZONTAL BRACE

HOG WIRE

DIAGONAL BRACE

RABBIT PROOF
GALVANIZED WIRE

DETAIL #1

5 STRAND WIRE, TOP
IS SMOOTH AND 4
ARE BARBED

1'-0"

8"

3'-2"

5"

7"

6"

WIRE BRACING

DETAIL #3

NOTE:

1. PLACE AN 8'-0" HORIZONTAL WOOD
BRACE POST AND A 11'-0"± DIAGONAL BRACE
POST ON EACH SIDE OF ALL FOUR CORNERS OF
LOT "A." THE SAME TYPE BRACING WILL BE
USED FOR LOT "B" EXCEPT THAT THE HORIZONTAL
BRACE WILL BE 6'-0" AND THE DIAGONAL BRACE
WILL BE 8'-6"±. IT WILL ONLY BE NECESSARY
TO BRACE SIX SIDES OF LOT "B" SINCE IT BUTTS
UP TO LOT "A."

2. THE POSTS IN LOT "A" ARE TO BE PLACED
SO THAT THERE IS ONE WOODEN POST AND
THEN THREE STEEL POSTS. THE POSTS FOR
LOT "B" WILL BE PLACED ONE WOODEN POST
TO FOUR STEEL POSTS.

3. RABBIT PROOF FENCE TO BE BURIED
SIX INCHES IN GROUND

A

FENCE

LADDER

DETAIL #2

A

SECTION A-A

Fig. 14.26. Plans and specifications for the installation of a 3-way Wildlife-livestock exclosure.

SUMMARY

This chapter on wildlife habitat improvements has set forth numerous ideas and suggestions on how to manipulate food, water, cover, and living space for the benefit of wildlife. Techniques will, of course, vary throughout the regions of North America, however, below is a list of the main principles and methods:

1. Develop as much "edge" as possible because wildlife is a product of the places where two habitats meet. Examples are the borders of woods, fields, ponds, orchards, meadows, rivers, potholes, marshes, brushlands, clearings and swamps.

2. Plant small food patches or strips containing mixtures of a variety of foods.

3. Leave nut trees in woodlots when cutting.

4. Encourage fruit trees; also woody cover in hedgerows and fence rows.

5. Leave small patches of field crops standing and unharvested for wildlife.

6. Favor trees and shrubs with high wildlife value, especially heavy seed-, berry-, and fruit-producing species like autumn olive, Russian olive, dogwood, and thornapple.

7. Erect wood duck nest boxes in suitable sites.

8. Erect squirrel nest boxes in wooded sites, in parks, nature centers, on school grounds.

9. Favor tall nesting trees, especially tall tree clumps, for eagles, ospreys, other hawks and herons.

10. Save den trees in wooded areas to provide homes for woodpeckers, squirrels and raccoons.

11. Construct brush piles where needed for protection and nesting sites.

12. Leave netsing cover undisturbed wherever practical, i.e. plow land before large-scale nesting; mow after nesting is over.

13. Plant areas not suited for farming to trees, shrubs and permanent cover crops so as to have an interspersion of cover types.

14. Maintain existing low-growing shrubs to provide natural food and cover.

15. Establish living hedges around field boundaries to reduce soil erosion and provide nesting cover, travel lanes and food.

16. Establish windbreaks along roads, around homesites and between fields and crop strips.

17. Establish and maintain openings in woods.

18. Maintain ditch banks with cover of grasses and weeds.

19. Encourage cattail sedge and reeds in marshes and sloughs.

20. Maintain fence corners, borders, highway median strips, and interchanges with natural cover.

21. Keep certain fields open on old farmland by mowing hayfields or keeping certain areas in cultivation.

22. Vary cover as much as possible. The more varied the cover, the more wildlife.

23. Mix evergreen plantings with hardwoods for cover; do not plant in extensive solid blocks at the very least, reserve the bottoms for hardwoods.

24. Control excessive weed growth in canals, streams, lakes and ponds.

25. Provide floating logs or rafts as loafing sites for waterfowl.

26. Establish water holes at springs or in seepage areas.

27. Provide potholes and other small open-water areas for nesting or resting waterfowl.

28. Develop ponds and lakes for waterfowl, water birds, and aquatic mammals.

29. Protect forests, marshes, swales and fields from uncontrolled fires.

30. Avoid spring burning of fence rows, marshes, swales, woodlots, and croplands since fire destroys humus, wildlife food, cover, nests and sometimes the young of wildlife.

31. Perpetuate sand and small, natural gravel along roads and trails to supply birds with grit.

32. Provide small clearings as dusting and sunning areas.

33. Fence woodlots and planted areas against uncontrolled grazing to protect food and cover.

34. Stabilize stream banks with willow, shrub and conifer plantings.

35. Reserve undisturbed buffer strips of vegetation along streams to provide shade, insect food for fish, and dens for aquatic mammals.

36. Control water levels in marshes to favor habitat for waterfowl and other water birds.

37. Establish wildlife watering places in the arid parts of the country; build "water guzzlers."

CHAPTER FIFTEEN

PROCEDURES FOR FOOD-HABITS ANALYSES

LEROY J. KORSCHGEN[1]

Research Biologist, Game Research Section
Missouri Department of Conservation
Columbia, Missouri

GENERAL PRINCIPLES
MATERIALS AND METHODS
ANALYTICAL PROCEDURES
NUTRITION AND BIOENERGETICS
FIELD STUDIES OF FOOD HABITS
RELATED ACTIVITIES

GENERAL PRINCIPLES

History and Importance

The exact beginning of wildlife food-habits studies is obscure, but it is likely that prehistoric hunters employed a knowledge of the feeding habits of wild animals as an aid in capturing their daily sustenance. The scientific study of wildlife foods and feeding habits, however, is of comparatively recent origin. Field observations of what animals fed upon, where, and when, have been recorded and reported through the centuries and evolved into our present-day knowledge of food habits with its associated specific field and laboratory methods.

Kalmbach (1934) reviewed the early history of stomach analysis and credited Prof. S. A. Forbes as the founder of modern food-habits study because of his 1880 publication on the food of Illinois birds. Federal recognition of food-habits studies occurred in 1885 when Congress authorized the Section of Economic Ornithology in the Division

of Entomology, U. S. Department of Agriculture, "for the promotion of economic ornithology, or the study of interrelation of birds and agriculture, an investigation of the food, habits, and migration in relation to both insects and plants and publishing reports thereon" (McAtee 1933).

Many meaningful food-habits analyses were performed by professional biologists prior to official recognition of the subject. Results appeared in reports by Warren (1890), Fisher (1894), Beal (1895, 1897), and Beal and Judd (1898). Additional pioneering data were published by Judd (1903, 1905, 1905), Oberholser (1906), McAtee (1908, 1911), and Beal (1911). Results often were derived by both field and laboratory methods and each report was important.

Early studies were exclusively of birds, largely non-game birds, and particularly of the economic importance of their feeding habits upon agricultural crops, poultry and livestock. Later emphasis was placed on food studies of game species, particularly waterfowl and upland game birds, but included fur, game, and predatory mammals. Greatest activity in food-habits research occurred during the decade from the early 1930's to early 1940's. Technicians were trained or self-taught by experience, techniques were developed, reference collections expanded, and the quality and quantity of wildlife foods information was greatly

[1]The extensive use of reference materials presented by Martin (1949 and 1960) are gratefully acknowledged.

improved. Kalmbach (1934) emphasized the importance of stomach analysis for directly solving certain practical problems in wildlife management.

Improved facilities and equipment became available with the opening in 1940 of the Food Habits Laboratory at the Patuxent Wildlife Research Refuge, Laurel, Maryland. The new laboratory shared the work load with a western counterpart at Denver, Colorado. Sufficient funds were provided for many significant studies destined to affect game management across the nation.

It is regrettable that in 1942 the caustic comment was made in Congress that "every small boy knows what a robin eats; it eats angleworms." This was advanced as a reason for the termination of formal food-habits studies by the Fish and Wildlife Service (Kalmbach 1954). Legislators have repeatedly failed for more than two decades to appropriate funds for this important phase of wildlife management. These facts are not generally known by many persons who look to the Fish and Wildlife Service as a source of factual information on the foods and economics of wildlife. Fortunately, the 1942 budgetary restrictions of Congress did not totally eliminate food-habits research and thus its contribution to the management of game and other wildlife. Some of the early work of the Service is summarized in Martin, Zim, and Nelson (1951). Many state conservation departments and educational institutions have continued studies of wildlife foods, often with less well equipped and staffed laboratories than were previously available.

Wildlife food-habits investigations have lost none of their significance within the scope of wildlife research, but rather have become more important through new applications. Information needed for modern game management often is obtained only through properly designed and carefully executed food-habits studies.

Purposes and Types of Study

The primary purpose of food-habits investigations is to learn which foods are utilized by wild animals, and how, when, and where such foods are obtained. Depending upon objectives and methods, these investigations are classified basically as either "natural history" or "management studies."

Natural history food-habits investigations are conducted to determine the foods and feeding habits of all kinds of animals. These studies are time-consuming and investigators require a considerable amount of technical information to identify properly the many biological organisms. Analyses must be meticulously performed to produce complete lists of all foods, irrespective of quantities present. Counts of specific food items, percentage of each in the sample, and other measurements are normally taken. In the results are revealed the important foods of an animal species by bulk and frequency of occurrence, and also the number or bulk of items taken for a single meal. Most of the early food-habits studies were natural-history investigations to determine beneficial or harmful feeding habits of a species, the impact of birds upon insect populations, or predator-prey relationships.

Management food-habits studies provide practical and immediately useful information for management of a particular species and occasionally provide aids to law enforcement. Management studies include obtaining information of the principal or preferred foods of game birds and mammals, assessing damage to crops by wildlife, observing predation upon managed species, observing wildlife selection for and utilization of food-plot plants, or the detecting baiting practices to lure animals for hunting. Recently, management-oriented studies have provided bases for more sophisticated investigations of seasonal variability and availability of important foods, incidence of disease as related to food supplies, and population dynamics as related to nutritional factors such as nutritive quality of foods, dietary influences upon reproduction, and establishment or maintenance of game populations. Studies of metabolism, energetics, and pesticide-wildlife relationships are served by results from food-habits examinations.

Food habits analyses techniques are virtually all alike. Rough management-oriented food-habits studies, however, often may be simplified by the practical short cuts suggested by Davison (1940) for quail and doves, by Sperry (1941) for field examination of coyote stomachs, and by Korschgen (1962) for laboratory examination of deer stomach contents. The foods present in greatest quantity seem to be of greatest significance to management, and minor foods seldom are listed. All foods should be identified during analyses, however; and complete listing, naturally, kept in files of original data.

Food-habits studies include coordinated field and laboratory work. Precise, long-term knowledge of the ecology of a study area is desirable and survey-type information on relative food supplies provides a basis for laboratory analyses. Kalmbach (1934), Cottam (1936), and Davison and

Hamor (1960), said that results from laboratory studies cannot be adequately interpreted without correlating them with field conditions. Knowledge of the availability of a food is essential in order to rate properly the importance of that food. It also aids in evaluation of the effects of one animal population upon another, and of the economics of wildlife feeding as related to other interests of man.

Sampling

The quality of food-habits data is dependent upon quantity and quality of the sample. Precision in the techniques of analysis has little meaning unless an adequate number of samples are collected to show local, seasonal, or annual changes in diets. Adequate sampling is just as important for studies with limited objectives. Inadequate samples often prompt misleading conclusions (Errington 1932:77, Hartly 1948:365-366).

Sample size requirements will vary with different species of wildlife, scope and objectives of study, diversity in habitat, and kind of material available for analyses. Statistical consideration normal to most other situations apply (Cochran 1963). As an example, because of greater variability a greater number of samples will usually be needed to show year-round versus seasonally important foods, statewide versus regional wildlife feeding habits, or foods of far-ranging versus sedentary species. Generally the number of stomach samples from big game will be fewer than the number needed for game birds (crops, gizzards, droppings), predators (scats), or birds of prey (pellets).

Sampling needs are difficult to establish prior to the investigation. They must be determined by noting the extent of changes that occur when additional units are analyzed and added during the study. Three criteria have been used to judge the extent of these changes with increased samples: (1) uniformity of volumetric percentages, (2) the rate of appearance of important new food items, and (3) the overall uniform percentages of individual food items. The sample size is large enough when new samples add no significant new information to that obtained from previous samples.

Davison (1940) showed that 100 crops can serve as an adequate sample for bobwhite quail in a county-sized area of similar plant composition. Results from a smaller number of crops showed wide divergence in proportions of food, while those from a much larger number were substan-

tially the same as information from the first 100 crops.

Korschgen (1948:50) arrived at similar conclusions by a different method. He considered a sample as adequate when a cumulative total of crops showed little difference in important foods. Thus, 50 samples from a several-county region contained the important bobwhite quail foods that comprised 92.8% of the volume in 1,200 crops; 100 contained 97.1%; 200 contained 98.8%; and 300 contained foods that comprised 99.5%. It was concluded that 100 samples (bird crops) obtained from a region of similar plant growth were representative, while 200 or more were preferable. Occurrence of food items proved an unsatisfactory measure for determining sample size.

A statistical method for determining the number of samples required to estimate the food habits of a population was reported by Hanson and Graybill (1956). The method was based on the variance of data for the single most important food in a series.

To show the principal or most representative foods of a species, the span of sampling time often is more important than the number of samples. Only rarely can the principal foods be determined by analyses of samples collected during a single season or year. Food desirability, availability, and use vary with food production, quality, abundance, and other factors. Many plant species do not set seed or fruit heavily each year, and populations of prey species often fluctuate annually. Samples should be collected over a minimum period of 2 years to show the most representative foods for any wildlife species. Unfortunately, the food-habits literature abounds with studies based upon inadequate sample sizes or an inadequate number of collection periods.

Equipment

Equipment needed for performing food-habits investigations varies considerably and depends in part on where the primary analyses are made and the objectives of the studies. Field studies for determining relative amounts of foods for management purposes require a minimum of simple equipment: a hand lens, graduated cylinders, screen sieves, forceps, scalpel or knife, tray or heavy paper squares, pencil and tablet or cards for record keeping. Field examination of predator stomachs requires even less equipment, since food amounts usually are estimated.

Greater accuracy can be attained by laboratory analyses, and equipment needs are proportionately

236

greater. Laboratory space equipped with a sink and washing facilities are basic requirements. Good microscopes are essential. The best type for low magnification work is the wide-field, parfocal dissecting binocular with good quality lenses. A useful adaptation for examination of large quantities of material in pans, as in studies on deer or large game birds, is a microscope mounted on a horizontal, swinging arm and supported on a heavy base. Compound binocular microscopes are essential for high magnification examination of hair and feathers and for histological studies.

Other useful equipment includes: pans or trays of various sizes, petri dishes, small forceps, scalpels, dissecting needles, sieves of several screen sizes from approximately 12 to 40 meshes per inch, glass measuring graduates, metal scoops, and tamping rods to fit various sized graduates (Fig. 15.1). A 6-inch section of wood dowel, square-cut on one end and sharpened to scalpel form on the other, provides an excellent tool for sorting and tamping items such as seeds and gravel. A small spoon is useful for removing items segregated from a sample for measurement. Funnels covered with bolting cloth may be used to strain off fine materials. A drying oven and squares of blotting paper are useful for drying large wet samples before examination or storage. Scales or balances suitable for ascertaining weights of foods are necessary for gravimetric measurements, such as are required in nutritional studies. A moisture-determination balance is useful for evaluating succulent foods in bird crop samples. Reference texts, photographs, and collections are essential for both the beginning and the experienced food-habits investigator.

Reference Collections

Small, personally developed reference collections are useful for local investigations, but usually are too limited for broader studies. Materials included in reference collections must be correctly identified to be useful and accurate. Plant parts, such as seeds, should be collected from correctly identified whole plants.

Extensive reference collections are needed for more intensive studies requiring identification of both major and minor items. Seed, fruit, plant, mammal, bird, insect, and other invertebrate collections and photographs of these are essential for complete investigations.

The cost of collecting and curating extensive

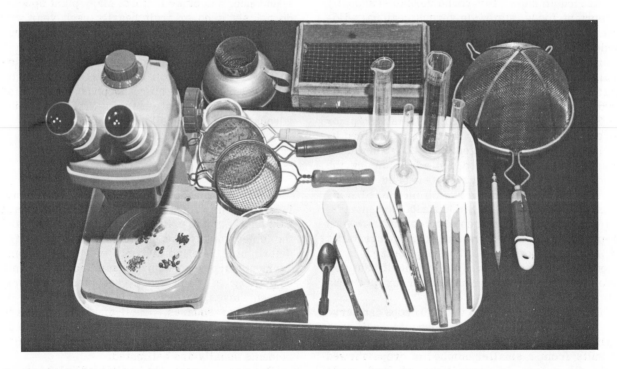

Fig. 15.1. Some equipment used in food-habits analyses: dissecting microscope, enamel tray, petri dishes, glass graduates, screen sieves, forceps, scalpel, dissecting needle, scoop, spoon, and tamping rods.

reference materials is very great, and includes the expense of cabinets, boxes, vials, or other containers. Large collections often represent the work of many people over several generations. Universities and research stations often have large reference collections and are staffed with specialists who can identify plant and animal items. These are logical centers for food-habits studies.

Personnel Qualifications

Attitudes and work habits of the investigator have great bearing on achievements from food-habits studies. A successful investigator must commit to memory the detailed characteristics of many kinds of specimen materials. He must be thorough, patient, and persevering at routine work. There is no substitute for experience and hard work and, as pointed out by Latham (1951), good food-habits technicians are made, not born. Success requires an intimate knowledge of the flora and fauna of the region where samples were collected, and techniques for their identification. The technician must be a taxonomist, anatomist, botanist, mammalogist, ornithologist, entomologist, and herpetologist to recognize plant, mammal, bird, insect, reptile, and amphibian remains. Full accomplishment in all these disciplines is virtually impossible to attain in a lifetime. Therefore, the assistance of subject specialists often is required during food-habits investigations.

MATERIALS AND METHODS

Kinds of Study Materials

Many kinds of materials serve for food-habits study. Specimens commonly are obtained from three sources: animals killed during hunting seasons, accidental kills, and samples collected specifically for study. Commonly used study materials from birds are crops, gizzards, and droppings. Crops are always preferable to gizzards or droppings because of the comparative ease and reliability in identifying and measuring foods in proportion to amounts consumed. A flushing tube, as described by Vogtman (1945), may be used for obtaining crop contents without killing the birds. MacGregor (1958) also made effective use of this apparatus to extract food from the crops of nestling mourning doves. Studies of gizzard contents may be used to supplement data from crops, or to determine the kind and quantity of grit, occurrence of lead shot, or retention of hard seeds.

Stomach (gizzard) contents have been used almost exclusively as source material from waterfowl, crows, and other birds which lack a true crop. Waterfowl gullets occasionally contain a sufficient quantity of food for satisfactory analyses. Since the foods are relatively undigested, they are more easily identified than gizzard contents.

Droppings of birds can be used successfully as sources of food-habits information, as shown by Dalke (1935) for pheasants; Swanson (1940) for sharptailed grouse; Wilson and Vaughn (1944) for bobwhite quail; and Korschgen (1962) for prairie chickens. This method requires a greater degree of skill in identification, but it is particularly useful when stomachs or crops are unavailable, such as for rare or depleted species. Some workers think that only frequency-of-occurrence observations should be taken with droppings; however, principal foods can be determined from droppings for all periods of the year. In a controlled feeding test on bobwhite quail, Jensen and Korschgen (1947:43) found that droppings were equal to stomachs in reliability, but crops were superior for study.

Stomachs are preferred for food studies of predatory birds which consume animal foods, but they are difficult to obtain in sufficient numbers. Regurgitated pellets of undigested food have been used extensively. Errington (1930) concluded that pellets from owls are faithful representations of the birds' diets. Pellets also can supplement stomach analyses, observation, or nest studies of hawks. However, bony materials do not survive digestion of hawks, and pellets are widely scattered. Because of these factors, hawk pellets are more difficult to obtain and analyze than owl pellets. Errington (1932:78-79) found that food of nestling hawks was temporarily retained in the esophagus, and by squeezing their gullets he prompted regurgitation and obtained undigested food for analysis.

Food studies of small and medium-sized mammals are dependent largely upon stomach contents. The large intestine sometimes contains more food than the stomach, especially in trapped animals. Use of both may result in obtaining data from more than a single meal.

Mammal scats may be used as primary or supplemental sources of information. Scott (1941) found a close correlation between food fed to captive foxes and residual evidence in the scats. Murie (1946) showed that the number of rabbit-sized animals can be judged from scats, but mouse-sized animals may be considerably under-estimated. Fitch (1948:74-75) assumed one average-sized adult of the species in question for each occurrence in coyote scats.

Special knowledge is required for positive scat identification. The field guide by Murie (1954) contains many clues for identification of spoor, including scats. Careful consideration of size, conformation, and composition of scats, along with related evidence such as location and tracks, usually will establish identity of the animal concerned. Odor of a dampened specimen may be distinctive for a species and can be an important aid in identification of some predator scats, especially those of the red fox. If the identity of a scat is questionable, it must not be included in any food-habits investigation. Clues to the identity of droppings from rodents and rabbits were reported by Webb (1940). Reference collections of correctly identified scats may be useful.

Hildebrand (1955) described the skeletal differences between deer, sheep, and goats. The mammal skull keys prepared by Brainerd (1939), Driver (1949), Glass (1951), and Brown (1952), and the keys provided by Eddy and Hodson (1961) will help to accurately identify many biological specimens.

Additional sources of food habits information are available for certain species of wildlife. They include food caches and cheek pouches of rodents, and den debris of carnivores. Feeding platforms of muskrats have been used (Takos 1947:334-335).

Data for Collections

The accumulated data from laboratory analyses may be affected greatly by methods used during collection, handling, and storage of specimen materials. While the highly variable types of materials require different treatments, a few basic rules apply for all.

Accurate information should accompany all samples intended for laboratory examination. Pertinent information includes: name of animal, time (date) and place (locality) of collection, sex of animal, collector's name, and collector's number or acquisition number when a large series of specimens is anticipated.

Additional information often is helpful during laboratory examinations. This includes age of animal, hour of capture, method of capture, kind of bait used, etc. Information on abundance and kinds of food available, cover conditions, and associated plant species will help the investigator interpret the findings from food-habits examinations.

Primary collection data should be recorded at the time study materials are obtained and attached to each sample (Fig. 15.2). Labels of vulcanized-fiber paper withstand preservatives well. The starchy covering on some paper or cloth tags disintegrates and reduces or destroys the legibility of recorded data. Medium-hard, lead pencils or carbon ink (not India ink) should be used to record data on tags to be placed in preservative solutions. Labels may be glued to

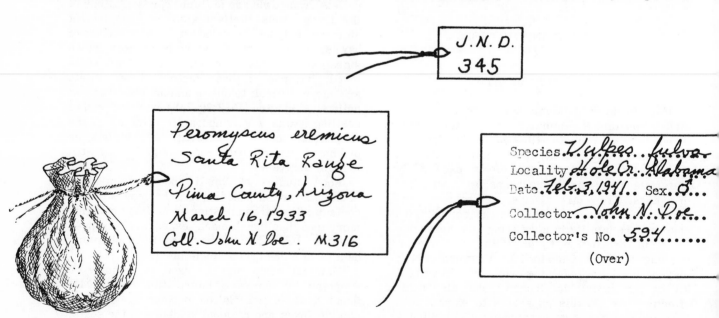

Fig. 15.2. Tags for labeling materials in food-habits studies.

the outside of large, single sample containers that are protected in carrying cases. Supplementary information may be recorded chronologically in a notebook or on a check sheet for ready reference.

Preservation

The container best suited for holding a sample depends largely on the moisture content of the sample and whether moist conditions must be maintained. Small envelopes, paper bags, plastic bags, shell vials, screw-top glass bottles, or fruit jars of 1/2 pint to 1/2 gal have proved satisfactory for collecting and transporting food-habits samples. The method of preservation will indicate the kind of container needed.

Three methods are commonly used to preserve study materials in usable condition: wet, dry, and frozen. Materials to be examined within 24 hr after collection generally do not require preservation. Usually examinations require a much longer time, so preservation of samples is necessary. The most practical, reliable, and economical preservative for samples containing flesh is a formalin solution prepared by diluting commercial formaldehyde with tap water. Alcohol (70%) is satisfactory for small samples of flesh, but alcohol (which extracts chlorophyll) should not be used if green plant material is present. Small to medium-sized stomachs can be preserved adequately with a 5% solution of formalin (1 part commercial formaldehyde in 19 parts of water). A 10% solution is recommended for large specimens. Bear- or deer-sized stomachs preserved intact should be injected with, and then submerged in, formalin solution. Small slits cut through the walls will insure penetration of the preservative. Entire stomach contents of large herbivores rarely are preserved for study. Instead, a quart-sized sample is collected after thoroughly mixing the stomach contents. This material may also be preserved in a 5% formalin solution. Some workers find ruminant stomach samples much more pleasant and easy to work on if the samples are washed on a fine screen soon after collection and then dried in the sun. About 5 gal of water is needed for each quart of sample.

Special precautions are recommended to prevent spillage and mixing of food contents when a number of stomach samples are preserved in a single large container. The severed ends of the esophagus and intestine should be tied to prevent loss of contents. The entire unit should be wrapped in cheesecloth or muslin and a label attached to each sample.

Material collected for shipment should be kept in the preservative solution for at least 5 days, after which it can be removed, drained, and shipped in moist packing. When preserved in permanent containers, such as sealed glass jars, specimens may be stored indefinitely.

Caution: Formaldehyde gas is irritating to the eyes and respiratory tract. Formalin solutions tend to dry and shrivel the skin. When removing specimens from formalin solution, use forceps or rubber gloves.

Specimens preserved in formalin can be handled safely after deformalizing for 3 to 5 min. in solution prepared as follows:

> One gallon of tap water
> 252 g of sodium bisulfite (NaHSO$_3$)
> 168 g of sodium sulfite (Na$_2$SO$_3$)

Dry preservation has proved satisfactory for a variety of materials. Without special handling, some would require the more cumbersome wet preservation. All predatory mammal scats, regurgitated pellets from birds of prey, and droppings from birds are suited to air-dry storage in paper or plastic bags. Samples should be thoroughly dried before containers are tied or sealed. Oven drying should be done at 80-85° for several hours or a time appropriate to the size of the sample. Moist samples tend to mold, especially in plastic containers. Stomach or crop contents consisting largely of dry seeds, fruits, leaves, and insects may be stored dry for years without harm. Material from large herbivore stomachs also may be held satisfactorily in dry storage, provided it is washed thoroughly to remove digestive juices and completely dried before it is packaged. In all cases of dry storage, materials should be checked and fumigated periodically. If stored in tight containers with PDB (para-dichloro-benzine) flakes or similar chemicals, insect damage is prevented.

Quick freezing of samples is a practical and convenient method of preservation. However, few laboratories are equipped to handle large quantities of material in this manner for extended periods. Freezing has the special advantage of not seriously impairing either color or texture of materials.

ANALYTICAL PROCEDURES

The best analytical procedure for any particular food-habits study depends upon the animal being studied, the dietary components, and the source of material available for study. Basically, complete examination includes (1) preparation of sample, (2) segregation of contents, (3) identification of food items, (4) recording of data, and (5) appraisal of results.

Preparation

Preparation of materials for analysis often is guided by previous handling and storage. Dry samples usually need little preparation. Washing may be omitted when contents of crops or stomachs consist mainly of seeds or other plant parts. Dry stored pellets of predatory birds and scats of mammals also require no preparation unless the analyst so desires. The material can be broken apart by hand, or picked apart with forceps. Some analysts prefer to wash pellets and scats to re-

Fig. 15.3. Removal of contents from predator stomach.

move mucus and to clean hair, bones, teeth, and other diagnostic parts partially. Washing has the disadvantage of mixing food remains when several kinds may form nearly distinct portions of the original sample.

Bird droppings can be examined dry after crumbling them. Washing of droppings in a 40-mesh sieve under the tap and then drying the sample is recommended for removing uric acid and fine particles not useful for identification.

Stomach contents from carnivores and predatory birds usually require thorough washing with hot water through a 12 to 20 mesh sieve to remove grease. The amount of grease removed by this process may be estimated and added to final measurements, or omitted when all samples are prepared in the same manner. Draining or squeezing the wet sample eliminates excess water and hastens drying on blotting paper.

Whole organs preserved in formalin solution should be thoroughly washed or placed in deformalizing solution before the contents are removed. Removal of an organ's contents can be facilitated by washing them into screen sieves with tap water under heavy pressure (Fig. 15.3). This wash further eliminates the objectionable formalin from the samples before analysis. The screens should be of proper mesh to retain food particles useful for identification. Specimens preserved in alcohol should also be washed.

Segregation

Objectives of the study, time required, ability of the investigator, and type of study material all affect the feasibility of item separation (Fig. 15.4). Some kinds of materials, such as stomach contents of waterfowl and gizzards of gallinaceous birds, do not lend themselves to complete separation of food items because some are broken or finely ground. Seeds, insects, and other items in crops can be separated with fair accuracy, and experience teaches many practical short cuts in foods analyses.

When seeds are in the study material, partial separations often can be accomplished by use of various mesh-sized sieves. Sorting time for seed samples also can be materially reduced by use of a wooden scalpel rather than a forceps. The principal component of a sample is judged by ocular comparison, and then drawn with the scalpel to the near edge of the dish. The sorted item is then removed for measurement, and the process repeated until complete analysis is achieved. Screening and scalpel work often can be com-

Fig. 15.4. Segregation of predator stomach contents.

bined for more rapid results. Mixtures of seeds, animal matter, and gravel, as found in waterfowl stomachs, often appear formidable to the analyst. Many food items in such samples can be segregated by decanting or floating off materials of lowest specific gravity. A simple procedure for removing gravel is to place the sample in a beaker of carbon tetrachloride, ethylene, or other cleaning solution. Vigorous stirring, or swirling, will cause the lighter plant and animal foods to float so they can be decanted into a fine mesh sieve held over a second beaker. Two or three such decantations will completely segregate the gravel from food materials. The latter then can be sorted after a few minutes of drying time.

A less effective method involves gently blowing food particles to the top of a tilted dish while gently tapping the container. Gravel and heavy food items will settle to the lower portion for a partial separation.

Samples from animals which grind or masticate their food often contain portions that are impractical to separate. The amount of this unsegregated part is determined by volume or weight and the proportions of its constituent items are estimated visually.

The volume of finely masticated wet materials may be accurately measured by centrifuging in calibrated centrifuge tubes. Green vegetation, even though finely masticated and thoroughly mixed with other food materials, can be easily separated out. For example, green vegetation can be separated from nut meat by mixing the sample thoroughly in a beaker of water and then directing a strong, fine stream of water from a wash bottle into the mixture. The fine bubbles of air carried into the mixture by the jet of water will stick to the vegetation and cause it to float to the top, but not to the nut meat (Dudderar pers. communication).

Segregation of food items in pellets, scats, and stomachs which contain hair, bones, or feathers can be accomplished best with the aid of forceps to remove diagnostic portions. Complete separation of items seldom is practical and a partial measure by visual estimate becomes necessary. Visual estimates of proportions also are commonly used in analysis of bird droppings and fecal pellets of both small and large mammals. Other methods of quantitative analysis may be used. Arata (1959) described a method for gross determinations of muskrat foods by differential sedimentation.

Screens of various sizes are commonly used for partial separation of materials when analyzing stomach contents of large herbivores. One method is to screen-sort and measure the larger, easily identified items, check the remainder for additional foods, and apportion the finer residues on the basis of all larger items identified (Korschgen 1962). Some investigators visually estimate all proportions; others identify, weigh, or measure the coarser items and leave unidentified the mass of finer items. If visual estimates are utilized, it is best to compare results with estimates made by a colleague. Dirschl (1962) recommended analysis of only that portion of the rumen contents retained by a screen of selected size. Adams (1957) used only diagnostic "recognition items" identified from fecal pellet analyses to appraise quantities of food consumed. Chamrad and Box (1964) described a method for rumen analysis based on a point frequency method in a large tray.

The choice of segregating material in a dry, moist, or wet condition is largely one to be determined by the investigator. The dry state is definitely advantageous for the analysis of most food-habits samples, but it may be necessary to work with moist materials when soft-bodied insects, spiders, or crustaceans are involved. The common practice of measuring dry food materials in graduated cylinders or beakers is satisfactory if uniform procedures are followed. Air space should be reduced by firmly tamping the material with a wood rod. Air space around irregularly shaped items may be reduced by filling the voids with measured amounts of small lead shot and subtracting their volume from final readings, or by water displacement. Inglis and Barstow (1960)

described a device adapted to measurement by water displacement, or a known volume of water can be added to the cylinder with a pipette. In water displacement, dry foods should first be moistened or accurate readings cannot be made.

Sorting materials from a liquid medium entails tedious effort with forceps because food particles tend to adhere to each other. Movement of floating materials and refraction of light from the liquid create additional problems.

Whatever the method used, uniformity of procedure is important. Results may be affected by sampling procedures, methods of analysis, standards of measurement, and comparisons with data from coordinated field investigations.

Samples which contain only minor amounts of food often are omitted from tabulated results, while items that comprise less than 0.1% of total food contents are listed as "trace" amounts.

Identification

The identification of items found in food-habits analyses becomes easier with experience, properly identified reference materials, pictorial references, field notes from the sampling areas, skin and skeleton materials of vertebrates, and whole specimens of invertebrates. Working with a specialist is the most rapid route to progress with identification of unknown items.

The easy course is best during the initial stages of an investigation. Instead of spending a lot of time trying to identify unknown items or fragments found in the first samples, it is advisable to number them properly or label them and put them aside until more and better specimens are found. Important items will occur repeatedly in a series of examinations and provide additional characteristics for identification. When gross analyses are completed, effort can be concentrated on items of unknown identity.

Accuracy of identification is particularly important. Total lack of recognition is better than reporting misidentified items. Limited amounts of unidentified materials in food lists need not reflect adversely on the analyst, for as Latham (1951:8) pointed out, a technician who presents a food habits table showing no unidentified materials is either exceedingly skilled, is working with a very simple diet, or is dishonest.

Reference materials should be consulted frequently, and important items that defy recognitions should be referred to specialists. Generally, the comparison of several characteristics will lead to positive identification of the specimen. Important aids to the identification of seeds used by wildlife include: *The Seed Identification Manual* (Martin and Barkley 1961); the 15-plate set of photographs of common "weed" seeds that occur on agricultural lands published by the Division of Photography, Office of Information, U. S. Dept. of Agriculture, Washington, D. C.; *The Comparative Internal Morphology of Seeds* (Martin 1946); *Identification of Crop and Weed Seeds* (Musil 1963); and *Woody-Plant Seed Manual* (USDA 1948). Other plant parts often can be recognized to genera or species by outline, texture, margins, midrib, veination, or pubescence of leaves using local or regional botanical texts. Final identification should be made from a reference collection, and, if possible, spot-checked by a specialist.

The identification of small mammal bones will be aided by keys and descriptions published by Brainerd (1939), Driver (1949), Glass (1951), Brown (1952), and Stains (1959). Conformation, muscle attachment ridges, and density are of greater importance than proportions or size for identifying bones. Surfaces of immature bones deteriorate rapidly from weathering or digestion, and show rough surfaces. Immature skulls often have milk dentition. Fish bones may be distinguished from mammal bones by their thin, folded structure. They often have radiating ridges or reticulations, and lack a smooth or rounded appearance. Amphibian limb bones are hollow, very light in weight and structure, and smooth. Bird bones are extremely light, but have a hard, highly polished surface. They often are thin walled, with the interior hollow or filled with a delicately reticulated mesh of bony material.

Identification of hairs usually requires high-powered microscopic examination (10 x oculars, 40 x objectives). Guard hairs are preferable to underfur for showing diagnostic characteristics. Although many hairs can be identified from banding patterns and general appearance under low magnification, others require special preparation.

Hausman (1920), Williamson (1938), and Spence (1963) described the structural and identifying characteristics of hairs. Mathiak (1938), Williamson (1938), Dearborn (1939), Williamson (1951), Mayer (1952), and Stains (1958) provided keys and aids to hair identification.

Williamson (1934) and Mathiak (1938) provide methods for cross-sectioning hairs. Permanent reference slides which show scale pattern, medulla, and cross-sections of hairs can be most helpful. Hardy and Plitt (1940) and Koonz and Strandine (1945) described methods for showing the cuticular patterns. Temporary mounts that show scale type and arrangement can be pre-pared rapidly by embedding hairs cleaned in carbon tetrachloride, in clear finger-nail polish, clarite, stencil correction fluid, or similar substance. Medullae and internal characteristics show well when clean hairs are immersed in cedar oil under a cover slip on a microscope slide. Procedure for making a semi-permanent cast of cuticular scales of mammal hair (Spence 1963) is as follows:

The medium is a 3% solution of glycerine jelly which is a gel when cool and fluid when warm. Glycerine, 3 cc, are mixed with 94 cc of warm water, and 3 g of gelatin are added. After stirring, 0.1 g of merthiolate or carbolic acid is added as a preservative. Repeated heating of the gel or heating at too high temperatures may prevent the medium from gelling. Heating the jar with the medium in a pan of water prevents over-heating. The medium and slides can be stored in a refrigerator indefinitely.

The procedure for the slides is as follows:

1. Rinse the hair in carbon tetrachloride for 10 to 15 min and let it dry.
2. Place 2 to 3 drops of the medium on a clean slide. With another slide, spread the medium evenly over the center 1/3 of the first slide.
3. Before the medium has begun to gel, place the clean hairs vertical to the long axis of the slide. Have one end of the hair projecting over the edge of the slide so it can be easily grasped for removal.
4. Let the slide set for 1 to 1-1/2 hr. The time depends on the condition of the medium and the temperature.
5. When the medium has become fairly solid, using forceps remove the hair with a fast jerk to prevent the hair from sticking to the solution. If the hair has stuck tightly to the medium, the cast will appear under the microscope to be an almost exact duplicate of the scales of the hair. If the medium was not completely set, or the hair not well imbedded, the cast will appear smudged or no scales will be visible.

Resins have also been used in a manner similar to gelatin and provide permanent mounts. Gelva V7 (Monsanto Co., St. Louis, Mo.) and Bakelite AYAF (Union Carbide Corp., N. Y.) are clear vinyl acetate polymers soluble in acetone, 95% ethyl alcohol, and 99% isopropyl alcohol. Gelva has a slightly faster dissolving rate but

244

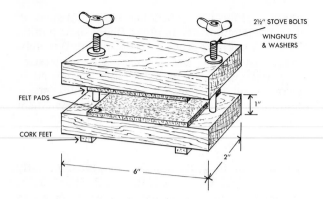

FELT PADS

CORK FEET

2½" STOVE BOLTS

WINGNUTS & WASHERS

1"

2"

6"

Fig. 15.5. A press for making hair impressions on microscope slides.

there seem to be no differences in the quality of slides prepared with either.

A resin solution is prepared and a thin film is spread over one-half of a slide using the same technique as for making blood smears (see Chapter 16). Allow to dry (40 min or less). Place the hairs across the hardened resin and cover with another slide. Insert in a press as shown by Williamson (1951) (Fig. 15.5) or apply an even pressure, release, and quickly pull the hairs away with forceps. Cover with a cover slip for a permanent collection.

The identification of feathers and other small bird remains is difficult without a good reference collection of study skins and skeletal parts, particularly feet and bills. Feathers of the Anatidae were pictured in Broley's article (1950). Chandler (1916) described microscopic techniques for examination of feathers.

Histological techniques may be necessary in food-habits studies of rabbits, squirrels and other rodents, and some large herbivores that finely masticate their foods. The microtechniques of Baumgartner and Martin (1939), Dusi (1949), Galt et al. (1966), Adams (1957), and Lay (1965) can be used to advantage, but they are time consuming and their use is limited for this reason. Preparation of reference slides to show distinctive structures or tissues of both suspected and known foods is required. Metcalf (1966) discusses methods for preparing such slides. Mr. O. B. Williams (pers. communication 1967) has used microscopic techniques for identifying plants from fecal materials. He prepares identification standards by boiling plant material in nitric acid until white as described by Metcalf then puts the specimens in 1% safranin and leaves them 3 days to a week. He then mounts the specimens directly from the 95% alcohol series in Euparal (R. I.

1.483) which shows the walls as well as silica bodies and associated structures. He uses a grid in a microscope eye-piece and counts areas of species. He favors area-counts to fragment-counts or percentage-counts due to the basic risk of differential fragmentation.

Phillip J. Urness (pers. communication 1967), U. S. Forest Service, has been studying quantification of forage plants in diets of wild deer. He reported that some plants have features more easily recognized than others. In addition he reported that all plants were degraded by the highly efficient digestive system of deer and that the fecal examination technique is limited since a large percentage of hits in any point-sampling scheme will remain unclassified. Fig. 15.6 shows a photomicrograph of silktassel (*Garrya wrightii*), an easily identified plant. To develop standards, caged deer were fed a single forage species for 3 days, after which fecal groups were collected and analyzed. Fecal groups were prepared by boiling in 10% NaOH for 10-15 minutes. Unstained mounts were most useful. The principal value of the technique is to confirm information obtained from field observations, although it may serve as a basic method for determining food use.

Data Records

Data from each food-habits investigation should become a matter of permanent record. Initial data from individual samples may be kept in temporary files. Record cards such as those used by the U. S. Fish and Wildlife Service are recom-

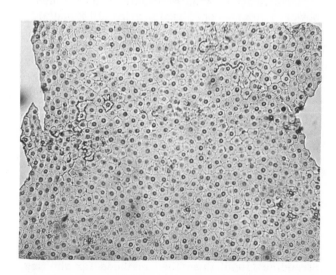

Fig. 15.6. Photomicrograph of silktassel*(Garrya wrightii)* from deer fecal material (photo from P. J. Urness).

Odocoileus virginianus — Sex M — No. M42909
State North Carolina — Co. Pender — Loc. Wallace Deer Club
Date 11-16-66 — Hr. 10:30 A — Collector W. D. Robbins — Coll. No. 7
Stom. ____ cc. Crop ____ cc. Anim. ____ % Veg. 100 % Grit ____ cc. ____ %
Examined by John N. Doe — Date 3-24-67

Cyrilla racemiflora	85%
Pinus sp.	10%
Ilex sp.	5%

Myrica cerifera
Vaccinium crassifolium
Smilax laurifolia

U. S. GOVERNMENT PRINTING OFFICE 16—15791 — 3-174a—(4-40)

Colinus virginianus — Sex Male — No. 550
State Missouri — Co. Boone — Loc. Ashland
Date 11-15-50 — Hr. ____ — Collector John Lewis — Coll. No. 5
Stom. ____ cc. Crop 6.0 cc. Anim. tr % Veg. 100 % Grit tr cc. tr %
Examined by L.J. Korschgen — Date 1-10-51

Lespedeza stipulacea	3.25 cc.
Rhus glabra	2.40
Strophostyles helvola	.25
Vitis sp.	.05
Rhus radicans	.05
Desmodium sp.	trace
Lespedeza striata	trace
Rosa sp.	trace
Acrididae	trace
Gravel	trace

9 — MISSOURI CONSERVATION COMMISSION

Fig. 15.7. Recommended type of food-habits record card.

mended for permanent files (Fig. 15.7). The record for each sample examined should contain pertinent collection data and a list of all identified foods recorded by the chosen unit of measurement: number, percentage, volume, or weight. Records of this kind are convenient for tabulating data from a particular study and for permanent reference. Marginal-notched card or computer-oriented file systems seldom are used for food-habits record keeping because of the great number of items that often are involved and because they ordinarily are tabulated only once into a master list of foods. Data from the cards may be tabulated by month or season, and then combined for all-season lists. The single use made of the permanent record usually does not merit the time required for establishing the punch-card or marginal-notched card systems.

Appraisal and Presentation

Appraisal of data necessarily is guided by the unit of measurement chosen by the investigator. Many methods have been used to express results obtained from food-habits analyses. Numbers, frequency of occurrence, volume, and weight are the common denominators employed to show food use or importance. All of these methods, sometimes in combinations, were employed in early studies (McAtee 1912, 1933) and there was little agreement on the best procedure. A single criterion usually is inadequate to provide meaningful results from a series of analyses. Numbers of prey eaten by a predator or seeds eaten by a game bird are of interest, but additional information on how often the item occurred and in what amount is more meaningful. Swanson (1940:433) suggested that the ideal method was to present two or more expressions of quantitative data (numbers, volume, occurrence) because each denoted a distinct and significant aspect of the findings.

Numbers of items eaten often are of little more than academic interest because size of food items is not taken into account. Measurements of frequency show that the item was eaten but fail to show a relationship to sustaining values in the diet. A single food item identified in a sample receives the same frequency rating as a full crop or stomach of the one item. However, frequency of occurrence becomes meaningful when used with volume or weight expressed as a percentage of the sample. High frequency and high volume indicate a food of high quality or preference. A high rating by one standard and low for the other may be reason to question quality,

quantity, or to suspect sampling biases when making an appraisal of food values.

Frequency data are derived from the number of samples in which a particular food occurred. Volume determinations are derived by various means. Originally, visual estimates of food volumes were recorded as percentages of the sample, but volumetric measurements are preferable. Percentages in individual samples are aggregated and averaged (see the precautionary article by Davis and Zippin 1954) to appraise importance by the "aggregate percentage method." Another method involves summing all volumes for each item in a series before calculating the percentage based upon the total food volume. This "aggregate volume method," reported by Martin, Gensch, and Brown (1946), now is standard procedure for routine food-habits summaries.

Gravimetric measurements may be substituted for volumetric data when sample contents are subject to complete segregation. Weight data are essential when studying nutrition or food energetics, but weight is often an impractical parameter to obtain for small items.

There is no ideal method of food analysis for all species or groups of animals (Hartley 1948). It is most desirable, however, that published records and summaries be in such form that they can be readily understood and combined with the results from other investigations. The many methods used in reporting data have resulted in chaos in the food-habits literature, and prevented the collation of results from many food studies on species of widespread distribution. For this reason it is recommended that the standard procedure for reporting food-habits data be by frequency of occurrence and volume, or weight. It is also recommended that the most important food items be shown at the beginning of tabular lists arranged in order of decreasing importance by a standard measurement. The total volume or weight of food contents and the number of samples examined should also be considered as essential data for any report. An example is shown in Table 15.1. These data enable other investigators to convert from percentages to original amounts for the purpose of combining them with information from similar studies. In long-term studies, it is a good practice to compute monthly averages of data based upon samples collected during each month. Yearly averages then are based upon the monthly percentages of principal items. This method may give more accurate yearly averages than when data are based upon the total number of samples collected for the year, especially if uneven monthly distribution of samples occurs.

Table 15.1. Principal fall foods of ruffed grouse in Missouri, 1961–1964 in percentages, by volume, from droppings analyses.

Foods	Months	Sept.	Oct.	Nov.	Season
	Samples	550	550	550	1,600
Wild grapes (*Vitis* spp.)		23.7	19.8	34.3	26.1
Acorns (*Quercus* spp.)		18.4	26.0	18.8	21.1
Tick trefoils (*Desmodium* spp.)		20.0	24.5	13.3	19.2
Green plant materials		15.6	5.7	2.8	7.9
Korean lespedeza (*Lespedeza stipulacea*)		9.8	0.6	–	3.4
Hop hornbeam (*Ostrya virginiana*)		1.3	0.9	6.8	3.0
Bush clovers (*Lespedeza* spp.)		0.2	5.8	2.6	2.9
Japanese rose (*Rosa multiflora*)		–	0.3	6.5	2.4
Flowering dogwood (*Cornus florida*)		1.3	3.8	1.3	2.1
Ladies' tobacco (*Antennaria* spp.)		–	0.5	4.2	1.6
Bittersweet (*Celastrus scandens*)		–	1.2	1.6	1.0
White avens (*Geum canadense*)		0.3	0.2	1.4	0.6
Galls		1.4	0.2	Tr.	0.5
Grasshoppers (Acrididae)		2.1	1.6	1.5	1.7
Walking sticks (Phasmidae)		0.6	2.5	0.5	1.2
Total Foods Examined (cc)		280.4	280.7	296.3	857.4
Percentage of Total Foods		94.7	93.6	95.6	94.7

248

Less precise methods have been used to appraise utilization of wildlife foods. Rankings of very high, high, medium, and low were used by Dalke et al. (1942). Wilson and Vaughn (1944) used percentage ranges from rough estimates of volume to designate food use as trace, scant, medium, or abundant. Martin et al. (1951) used a star system based upon percentage groups, while Clark (1957) employed a similar method using six percentage groups to estimate volumetric contents. Broad categories of choice, less desirable and extremely minor, were used by Davison and Graetz (1957) to express quality and acceptance of wildlife foods. This method was further refined by Davison and Hamor (1960) and Davison and Grizzell (1961, 1961) and Davison (1962, 1963, 1964), who showed that preferences indicated by stomach analyses were related primarily to availability and taste rather than color, shape, size, or texture of foods.

Index formulae methods of appraisal have been suggested to ascertain food importance by correlating amounts found in samples with amounts available (Glading et al. 1940, Bellrose and Anderson 1943, Beck 1952, and Hungerford 1957).

Related aspects of yield and availability of wildlife foods were studied by Davison et al. (1955), Haugen and Fitch (1955), and Korschgen (1960). Keeping quality of foods was reported by Neely (1956).

NUTRITION AND BIOENERGETICS[2]

Bioenergetics and nutrition research with wildlife species can effectively complement descriptive food-habits investigations. As the need for intensive wildlife management becomes increasingly great and the international search for unconventional protein and other food sources expands, the efficiency of management effort unavoidably is at a premium. To allow this efficiency a knowledge of how animals metabolize foods and the factors affecting metabolism is an obvious need. However, relatively little published information exists concerning the nutrition and energetics of wild animals.

The chemical composition of various wildlife foods first was investigated a quarter century ago. Early studies include those conducted with foods of pheasants and bobwhite quail (Wright

[2]The assistance of Mr. Ted D. McKinney, Graduate Fellow, Virginia Cooperative Wildlife Research Unit, with writing this section is gratefully acknowledged.

1941) and cottontail rabbits (Dalke 1942). Other research has been concerned with foods of the ruffed grouse (Treichler et al. 1946; Bump et al. 1947:845-849) and the wild turkey (Beck and Beck 1955). More generalized investigations of chemical composition were carried out by Wainio and Forbes (1941), King and McClure (1944), Spinner and Bishop (1950) and Caillouet (1960). Energy values of seeds were studied by Kendeigh and West (1965), and Robel and Harper (1965).

Proximate analysis (determination of crude protein, ether extract, crude fiber, ash and nitrogen-free extract) and evaluation of mineral composition have been applied widely in the study of forages eaten by ruminants, and a general discussion of pertinent data was presented by Dietz (1965). Both seasonal (Short et al. 1966) and possible daily (Kothmann 1966) variations in nutrient levels of plants have been reported, but these aspects of nutrition have received little attention. Dietz et al. (1962) compared nutritive constituents of foods on the seasonal ranges of a migratory mule deer herd.

Quantitative data on food intake by free-ranging animals are difficult to obtain. Short and Remmenga (1965) reported a ratio technique which utilizes fecal cellulose to estimate forage eaten by deer. Van Dyne and Meyer (1964) developed a method based on microdigestion which has potential for wildlife research. These latter workers also reviewed various methods which have been used to study forage intake by grazing animals.

Dietz et al. (1962) summarized digestion trials that have been conducted with deer. Various such studies have included comparison of browse species (Dietz et al. 1962; Ullrey et al. 1964) and the effects of different nutrient levels on apparent digestibility and on growth and reproduction by deer (French et al. 1956; Verme 1963, 1965; Murphy and Coates 1966; Short 1966). Techniques of rumen assay only recently have found use in wildlife research, and a review is presented by Short (1966).

Few investigations have been conducted on the nutritional requirements of non-ruminants. Korschgen (1964, 1966) presented evidence that birds select foods based upon their physiological needs, Schultz (1958) presented a bibliography on vitamin A nutrition in game birds, and Hungerford (1964) studied the importance of vitamin A in reproduction by Gambel's quail. Recent work by Golley et al. (1965) relates to the importance of food quality to bobcats.

Rumen microbiology offers a fertile area for nutrition research with wild ruminants. Rumen

microorganisms are essential in the conversion of cellulose to available energy for the host animal (Brock 1966, Hungate 1962). Fistulated animals of course could be used to obtain rumen samples for microbial study (Short 1962, Dziuk et al. 1963) but stomach tubes have been used satisfactorily (Hungate 1966, Ward and Nagy 1966). Samples can be taken readily from sacrificed animals (Pearson 1965), and this approach may have the broadest application for wildlife management. Techniques of analysis and identification of species of microbes are reviewed by Hungate (1966).

Estimates of the energy needs of free-ranging animals have for the most part been based on data from laboratory studies. Closed system respirometers may be used to determine "standard" metabolic rate (Buckner 1964) for small species. Though more expensive, respirometry also can be used in large animal research (Silver et al. 1959). Pfeiffer and Gass (1963) described a simple metabolism cage suitable for small mammals. Limited application has been made of techniques that show promise for measuring metabolism directly under field conditions (Golley 1966).

The relationship between body weight and energy metabolism (Kleiber 1961) has been used to estimate the energy requirements of animals. Short (1963) utilized this approach in considering the relative value of different diets in meeting the energy needs of white-tailed deer. Lamprey (1964) applied the concept to population studies of African herbivores. Conversions of biomass to energy based on average energy values can be of value (Petrides and Swank 1966), but this is justified only in extensive survey work (Golley 1961).

FIELD STUDIES OF FOOD-HABITS

Besides the direct study of samples of food taken from animals, knowledge of food-habits can be obtained indirectly in the field.

Large Herbivores

Many of the techniques for evaluating the food eaten by the large herbivores are described in Chapter 13. The amounts and species of plants eaten are determined by (1) direct observation of feeding, (2) evidence of feeding on plants, and (3) subtraction of remaining quantities from previous quantities to obtain the amount eaten.

Dixon (1934) and Hahn (1945) studied feeding by mule deer and white-tailed deer, respectively, using a "deer-minutes" technique. Observations were made through binoculars and the time spent by deer feeding upon particular plants was recorded. Feeding observations were followed by on-site inspection of the utilized plants to verify identification. Buechner (1950:321-322) discussed the merits and shortcomings of this procedure for the study of antelope feeding habits.

When ranges are inhabited by only one or a few species of herbivores, plants eaten can be observed, counted, and weighed; and amounts eaten by each animal in the population can be estimated. Amounts of feeding are also estimated by pellet-group counts as an index to the amount of feeding in a specific habitat type.

Utilization of browse plants has been described by many workers. Reports have been made on clipping studies on paired plots (Dalke 1941), twig length measurements (Shafer 1963), indicator species reflecting amount of range use, indices of occurrence and degree of use (Aldous 1944), and before-and-after animal-introduction comparisons within fenced enclosures (Davenport et al. 1944). Large and small exclosures (Robertson 1954) have been used to restrict the feeding of big game and demonstrate their effects upon native vegetation (Webb 1957; Ostrum 1937, 1942; Hough 1949), to show the differences between rodent, big game, and livestock feeding (Young 1955), and to ascertain the conditions of key browse plants within general range areas (Cole 1960, Hiehle 1964, Schuster 1965, and Stickney 1966).

Small Game and Other Wildlife

Certain methods for studying large herbivores in the field have been adapted for use with smaller wildlife species. The feeding habits of cottontail rabbits have been determined by direct observation, inspection of pellets in feeding areas, examination of vegetation near tracks in snow, and by analysis of stomach contents (Dalke 1942:47). Scarcity of a species or the need for food habits information during all seasons may necessitate use of non-laboratory methods for obtaining data. For example, the hourly and daily feeding activities of bobwhite quail may be observed with binoculars from an elevated blind (Wilson and Vaughn 1944:108). Diligent and conscientious field observations often provide information on the economic aspects of feeding by flocking birds, or to appraise the impact of birds upon insect populations such as spruce budworm in Maine (George and Mitchell 1948; Dowden, Jaynes, and Carolin 1953). Counts of predatory birds have been correlated with rodent catches to determine the nature of rodent distribution over a selected range (Neronov 1962).

Gibb and Hartley (1957) provided an excellent summary of observational methods for investigating the feeding habits of various kinds of birds. They indicated how to ascertain the time and duration of meals, how to determine quantities of food eaten, and how to record mechanically the visits of parent birds to nests. They also described an artificial nestling, perfected by Betts (1954, 1956), whose mouth opens automatically when a bird alights on the nest box perch. Food dropped into the gaping mouth falls down into a receptacle that contains preservative.

RELATED ACTIVITIES

The food-habits specialist often is called upon to make specific identification of meat by laboratory methods. Such an identification may be needed for food habits information or, more likely, for law enforcement purposes. The precipitin test, reported by Brohn and Korschgen (1950), has proved a useful technique as has paper chromatography (Brunetti 1965). Other methods for identifying meat and blood were reported by Winter and Honess (1952), Jackson (1958, 1962), and Pinto (1961).

CHAPTER SIXTEEN

POST-MORTEM EXAMINATIONS

I. McT. COWAN, PhD

Head, Department of Zoology
University of British Columbia
Vancouver, British Columbia, Canada

Revised by

LARS KARSTAD, DVM

Division of Zoonoses and Diseases of Wildlife
University of Guelph
Guelph, Ontario, Canada

A post-mortem examination may be designed to meet many different objectives. The investigator may wish to determine cause of death; to study the relationship between age, location, or nutritional state and parasite load; to determine the relative sizes of internal organs under different conditions; or any one of several other items. Thus the nature of the observations made will depend upon the objectives and these must be clearly determined in advance. It is highly desirable to have an autopsy-record sheet prepared to indicate the observations that are to be made (Fig. 16.1). Without this, certain observations will almost certainly be forgotten from time to time. Observations meticulously made and systematically recorded are of permanent value to students of animal biology (see Chapter 6).

It should be borne in mind that pathology is a highly specialized field and that whenever possible final determination of cause of death, when an animal has apparently succumbed to a disease, should be the responsibility of a pathologist. The part played by the wildlife technician is to make a complete and detailed examination that will narrow down the possible causes of death or illness, determine whether or not it is necessary to refer the case to the specialist, and to obtain the supporting details that will contribute to the pathologist's studies (see Chapter 17).

It is good practice to consult with the pathologist on the many special techniques that will render examinations more valuable.

Experienced biologists know the difficulty of obtaining carcasses in a suitable condition for autopsy. No opportunity should be lost, therefore, to examine even a single suitable carcass, since extensive mortality may occur in wild populations without numbers of dead animals being observed. Too often, extensive mortality is "diagnosed" in retrospect when only skeletons or putrified carcasses are found, or when population surveys indicate a puzzling reduction in numbers of animals.

The technician expecting to recognize condi-

252

Front

AUTOPSY REPORT
CARD No. _____

Animal No. _____ Species _____ Sex _____

Date of Birth _____ Date of Death _____

Skull and Skeleton No. _____ Body Weight _____

Bled Weight (if killed) _____ Eviscerated Weight _____

Heart-girth (1) Before evisceration _____ (2) Following evisceration _____

Hind leg length _____ Smallest circumference of tibia _____ Total length _____

Head length _____ Head width _____ Hip width _____ Height at withers _____

Organ	Weight	Check if Normal	Remarks	Specimen No.
Kidney (L)				
Kidney (R)				
Adrenal (L)				
Adrenal (R)				
Spleen				
Liver				
Stomach				
Intestines				
Heart				

Back

Organ	Weight	Check if Normal	Remarks	Specimen No.
Lungs				
Blood				
Thyroid				
Ext. Parathyroid (L)				
Ext. Parathyroid (R)				
Testis or ovary (L)				
Testis or ovary (R)				
Uterus				
Hide				
Lymphnodes				

PARASITES   Ident. by

Location _____ Specimen No. _____ Species _____ _____

_____ _____ _____ _____

_____ _____ _____ _____

Remarks: _____

_____

Cause of death: _____

tions of disease must familiarize himself with the normal appearance of organs in healthy animals. He should also examine the organs of healthy animals at various times after death, since the changes in appearance resulting from decomposition can be radical.

Wild animals seldom die of old age; starvation, diseases, accidents, and predation are the usual causes of death. In general, there is a high mortality rate among the young, followed by a much lower rate thereafter. Extremes of physical conditions such as drought, prolonged periods of extreme cold, or deep snow can alter the normal mortality rate. They can also alter the age specific or sex specific mortality rate so as to change the structure of the population. Much the same can be said of epizootic disease. It is important, therefore, to obtain as clear a picture as possible of the age and sex structure of the affected part of the population and the general environmental circumstances that may have contributed to the mortality.

When attempting to determine cause of death or illness of a wild animal, it is of first importance to seek clues offered by the immediate surroundings. Signs of struggle, signs of paroxysm at death, accumulation of feces, location of animal, condition of important food plants, and other observations should be noted. If the animal is seen alive, peculiarities of movement, respiration rate, and signs of distress should be recorded. Everything seen should be recorded; it is not necessary to be familiar with all the technical terms of pathology in order to make a useful record.

EQUIPMENT

A very compact autopsy kit can be assembled for field transport containing the following items in a rolled-up canvas kit: 6-inch fine forceps; 10-inch forceps; curved forceps; bone saw; bone forceps; boning knife; skinning knife; scalpel; small hone; surgical scissors; enterotome; 6-ft steel tape; spring balance to 25-lb. and equivalent grams; old scalpel for heating; 6-inch straight probe; several string tags; and several meters of strong string (Fig. 16.2). A light hatchet is also useful. In a lightweight, small, plywood box,

Fig. 16.1. Front and back of autopsy-report card. Such forms help to insure more complete recording of autopsy data.

can be carried six microscope slides for blood smears; four deep stab culture tubes for bacterial and fungus cultures; two 4-oz jars containing F.A.A. fixative; several small glass vials of F.A.A. or other fluid for preserving parasites (see Chapter 17); a small lightweight alcohol burner for sterilizing the old scalpel and probe and for flaming the edge of tubes when taking cultures (Fig. 16.3). Rubber gloves and a small tin of talc will protect the hands from unpleasant odors and the danger of infection. Several ounces of powdered borax are useful for the sterile packing of tissue for bacteriological study. The entire outfit weighs 7-lb. On long horse pack-trips, additional vials and jars of fixative can be carried on the horses and the field kit recharged as needed, while filled items are left in camp.

AUTOPSIES OF BIRDS

Later comments on examination of mammals apply here also. Many diseases of wild animals are transmissable to man and the investigator must always protect himself. The position and condition of the specimen when found may give important clues to cause of death. State of the plumage, soiling with feces, abrasion, or signs of lack of care will indicate long-standing illness. Fractures of the legs and wings will be obvious. Lesion of fowl pox may occur on the face or legs; scaly leg mite infections will distort the legs and cause sloughing of the claws in severe cases of long standing.

It is usually advisable to skin the bird to permit a closer examination for bruises and punctures by shot or by the claws and beak of predators.

To open the bird for internal examination place it on its back, part the feathers to expose the featherless area between the thigh and abdomen, cut through the skin of this area of both sides, then press the legs apart. Next, cut through the skin across the vent joining the two earlier cuts. Now peel the skin back from abdomen and breast and expose the neck. Free the esophagus and crop and examine them carefully. Now make a cut from the lower abdomen, along each side of the bird, severing the ribs and coracoid. Be careful not to cut into the viscera. Lift off the breast and expose the viscera (Fig. 16.4).

Take special note of spotting of the liver, indicative of degeneration, necrosis, or fibrosis. The presence of a whitish "bloom" on liver and other organs, usually accompanying a "strawberry"

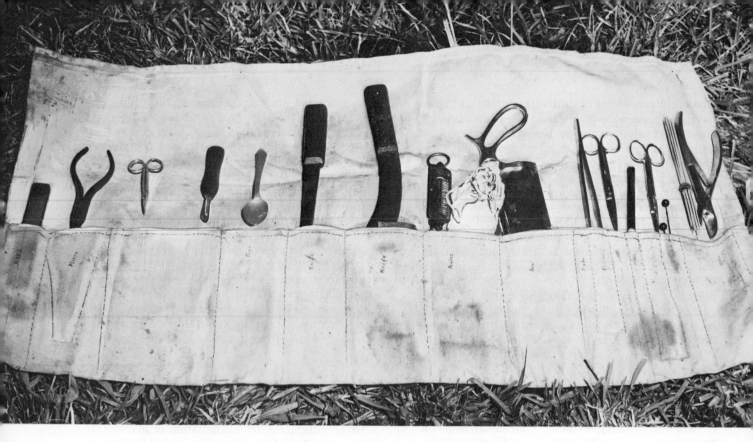

Fig. 16.2. A roll-up canvas field autopsy kit is easily transported for field use.

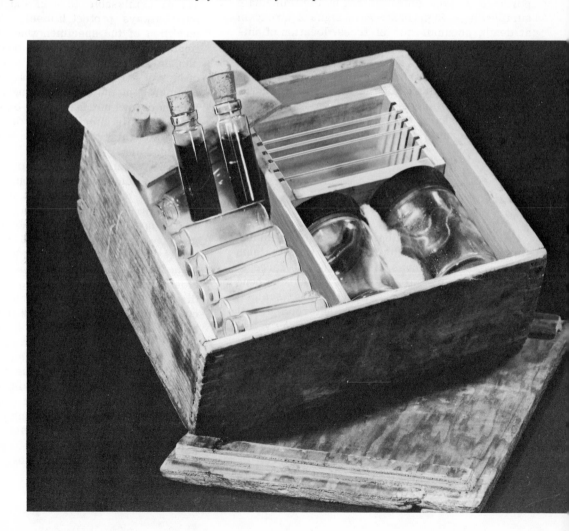

Fig. 16.3. A plywood kit is useful in transporting glassware, fixatives, and other material necessary for adequate field autopsy.

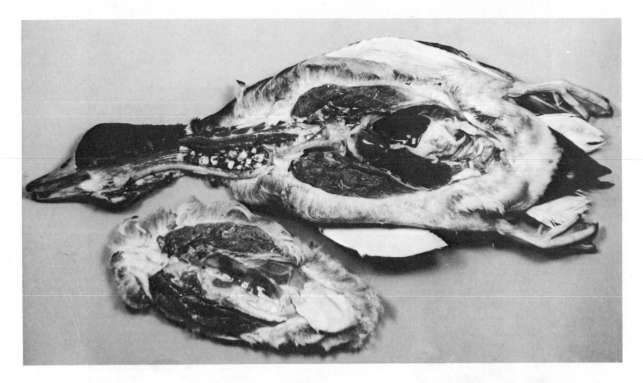

Fig. 16.4. Mallard autopsy. Vicera are exposed by cutting and laying aside the sternum and attached muscles.

appearance of the kidneys, indicates the presence of deposits of urates, as in visceral gout; cheesy or mouldy masses in the air sacs and on adjacent organs usually appear with aspergillosis; enlargements of the proventriculus may signify helminth parasitism; caeca may be enlarged or hardened, as in the disease called blackhead. A thickened, hardened intestinal wall may be indicative of severe parasite attack.

Examine the digestive tract for parasites and the organs generally for abscesses and inflamed areas. Some of the most damaging parasites are very small and may be embedded.

The contents of the gizzard of waterfowl should be washed out and carefully searched for lead shot. These may be hard to find if they have been in the gizzard for long and have been ground into irregular shapes.

If the specimen is reasonably fresh, blood smears should be taken (see Chapter 17 for technique) for later search for microfilariae and blood-inhabiting protozoa.

If there is a possibility of generalized viral or bacterial infection, the spleen and liver should be refrigerated or frozen for later culture. Refrigeration is preferred since unfrozen specimens can be used also for detailed parasitological, histological, and toxicological examinations. In most cases the proximity to a laboratory and the

availability of means of transportation will influence the methods of selection and preservation of specimens.

AUTOPSIES OF MAMMALS

First note the condition of the skin and pelage; skin the animal, examine for ulcers, shot holes or external injuries; note discharge from eyes, ears, or body openings; examine for external parasites. Certain ungroomed areas such as the groin, back of neck, and the chest are particularly prone to parasite attack. Preserve examples of these and note relative abundance.

A deer or other large animal should be turned on its side and measurements made. Measurements of total length, hind foot, tail, and girth behind forelegs are generally useful. Total length is taken in a straight line from tip of nose to tip of tail vertebrae with animal fully extended; hind foot is taken from tip of nail to point of hock. Next, raise the hind leg that is upper-most, cut through the joint at the hip and lay the leg on the ground (Fig. 16.5A). Repeat with the front leg (Fig. 16.5B). Now incise the abdomen along the midline taking care not to cut into the intestines and stomach. From the point of the breast

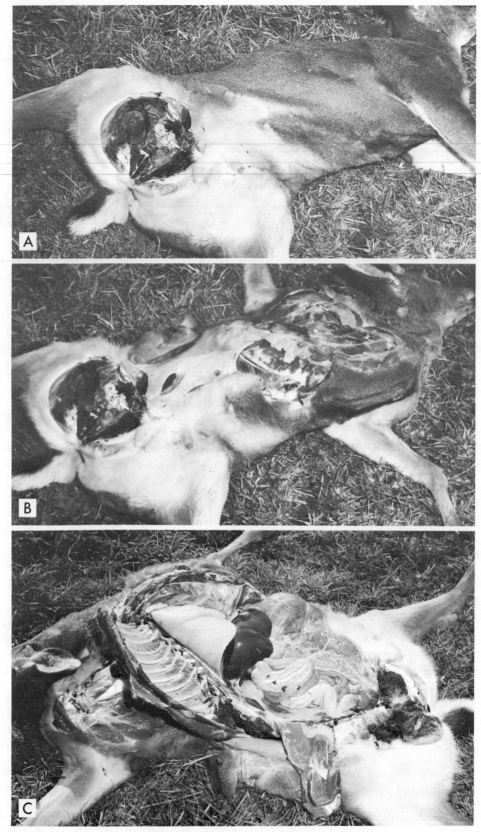

Fig. 16.5. Field autopsy of deer. *(A)* First cut joint at hip and let cut leg rest on the ground. *(B)* Next, cut front legs at joint and let all four legs lay flat on the ground. *(C)* Open abdominal and thoractic cavities, lay rib basket back to serve as table upon which excised organs can be placed.

bone extend the cut forward by cutting through the costal cartilages with the boning knife, hatchet, or saw. At the diaphragm end of the ribs, cut from the ventral incision up the side to the back bone. Reach in and carefully cut the diaphragm along the upper side. From the forward end of the chest, cut between the forward pair of ribs up to the back bone. Now sieze the cut edge of the rib basket and lift, breaking the ribs near the backbone. Lay this part of the basket over to serve as a table, upon which the organs can be placed for examination (Fig. 16.5C).

Now note the presence of fluid in the chest cavity, pericardium, or body cavity; the amount and color are important. Examine the membranes lining the chest cavity. Are they smooth, moist and glistening, or dull, or granular, or do they bear a fibrinous false membrane?

Have a large jar of 10% formalin at hand throughout the autopsy for fixation of small pieces of tissue for histopathology. Pieces of tissue larger than 1-inch cubes should not be taken. They do not fix properly. Take portions of all major organs for histology, whether they appear normal or not. Frequently, significant pathologic changes are visible only by microscopic examination. Fix also tissues which appear to be abnormal, or which contain lesions (scars, abscesses, necrosis, etc.).

A first inspection should involve the spleen and the lymph nodes of the inguinum. If the spleen is enlarged, swollen, inflamed; or if there is general inflammation of the visceral organs; or enlargement, inflammation, and perhaps abcessing of the lymph nodes, suspect an infectious condition and act accordingly.

If the spleen is as above, refrigerate a piece of it or place the piece in borax for later bacteriological examination. Other apparently infected tissues can be similarly treated but the spleen is of first importance.

Record the amount of fat and its location. Omental fat, kidney fat, and heart fat are important to record.

Lungs and Heart

Next examine the lungs, noting color and consistency where it departs from normal; feel them between thumb and finger for hardened areas that may indicate the presence of hydatid cysts or lungworm, or tubercular lesions; look for yellow spots or small abscesses. Remove the upper lung and open the air passages; check the hardened areas for parasites. Open the pericardium and check the heart, noting any abnormal condition; cut into the ventricles and determine the nature of the clot if one is present. Is the clot all one color or is there a separate, yellow clot of fibrin that indicates slow death? Remove the heart and open the aorta and carotids in search of filarid worms.

Digestive Tract

Turn to the liver and examine it for color, texture, presence of flukes or other parasites; open the bile duct and search for tapeworms. Remove the omentum and examine the stomach and intestines for inflammation. Now remove the entire digestive tract, tying the esophagus above the stomach and the rectum to prevent the escape of contents. If poisoning is suspected, keep at least a sample of the stomach contents, better still the entire stomach and contents.

Make two ties a few inches apart on the duodenum and cut the intestine between the ties. Open and examine the stomach, paying particular attention to the abomasum if the specimen is a ruminant. Very small worms may be found embedded in the lining of the abomasum, and the lining may also be ulcerated.

Stretch out the digestive tract by cutting or tearing the mesentery between the loops, then open the entire length with the enterotome and search for parasites and abnormal conditions of the lining or digestive contents. It is often convenient to divide the tract into separate regions for examination. This can be done clearly by tying it off above and below the point to be cut. Preserve samples of all parasites.

Urogenital Tract

The kidneys and bladder offer little evidence of cause of death. Note the condition of the kidney, whether inflamed, soft and pulpy, or otherwise abnormal. Special note should be made of the condition of the uterus, whether fetuses are present or scars of previous implantations (rodents and carnivores). The uterus may reveal inflammatory conditions and infection. The ovaries should be closely examined and note made of corpora lutea, or of any cystic conditions. If pertinent, the ovary should be preserved for more detailed examination.

The Head

All parts of the head should be examined. First, cut through skin and muscle at the angles of the mouth and remove the lower jaw. Examine the teeth and jaws carefully for advanced or irregular wear or abscessed alveoli. Open the nasopharynx and search for nose fly (bot) larvae in the retropharyngeal pouches. If the animal has been dead for some time, the larvae may have crawled into the mouth, nose, or down the trachea.

Skin the head and remove the muscle masses from the crown. When severing the ears, carefully explore the ear tube for spinose ear ticks. These may be attached to the ear drum and embedded in a mass of wax and tick feces. Now, using the saw, cut through the head transversely in front of the eyes. Examine the sinuses for infection, bot larvae, or nematode worms (in mustelids).

The brain can be removed by carefully sawing the cranium in half lengthwise or by sawing around the cap, prying this off, and removing the brain intact. Look for evidence of bruising, nematodes, tapeworm cysts, abscesses or inflammation of the brain tissue or surrounding membranes.

A most useful technique to determine the general nutritive condition at the time of death is to examine the marrow in the long bones of the legs. A well-nourished animal has firm, yellowish-white marrow, whereas an animal dead of starvation or badly debilitated by prolonged disease shows red gelatinous marrow, almost devoid of fat. All degrees between these extremes will be encountered. A useful account of the procedure with color charts can be found in *New York State Conservationist* (Cheatum 1949:19-22).

MAJOR WORKS ON WILDLIFE DISEASE

In order to become generally familiar with the pathology of disease processes in wild animals and the kinds of diseases so far discovered, the wildlife biologist will find it useful to consult such works as Halloran (1955), McDiarmid (1962), Wetzel and Reick (1962), and Karstad (1964).

CHAPTER SEVENTEEN

COLLECTION AND FIELD PRESERVATION OF BIOLOGICAL MATERIALS

HENRY S. MOSBY, PhD

Professor, Wildlife Management
Virginia Polytechnic Institute
Blacksburg, Virginia

and

I. McTAGGERT COWAN, PhD

Head, Department of Zoology
University of British Columbia
Vancouver, British Columbia, Canada

as revised by

LARS KARSTAD, DVM

Division of Zoonoses and Diseases of Wildlife
University of Guelph
Guelph, Ontario, Canada

All field investigators must preserve biological specimens from time to time. Valuable specimens often are wasted simply because the field worker has not equipped himself, or otherwise planned, for the preservation of specimens which come to hand. This chapter section is concerned with a brief discussion of the principal *field methods* which may be employed for the preservation of biological specimens. It is understood that if the wildlife research worker goes afield primarily for the purpose of collecting specific specimens, organs, or tissues, then he must be equipped to preserve properly such specimens until they may be cared for in the laboratory. No attempt will be made to catalogue the techniques for the preservation of all types of biological specimens; this discussion will be concerned only with certain techniques which might be utilized under normal field conditions, by a field biologist.

Refrigeration (approximately 35°F) is an excellent way to preserve most biological materials if the specimens are to be held for only a short period of time. For longer periods of preserva-

260

tion the popularity of communal and home deep freezers makes it possible for the field worker to utilize low temperatures (approximately 0° F) as an excellent method for the preservation of many specimens. Storage in deep freezers of such material as study mount specimens, hides, certain pathological material (but not all types, see Table 17.1), legal evidence, etc. is possible for short periods of time without any special treatment of the specimens. However, if such specimens are to be stored in deep freezers for more than several days they should be wrapped in freezer paper or placed in airtight containers to prevent the loss of moisture.

Fresh specimens may be sent immediately by mail or express to the laboratory. If this is to be done, the specimen should be placed in a watertight container and packed in a second container with either dry or natural ice surrounding the inner-most container. If dry ice (CO_2) is used, the outer container should not be completely airtight, as some ventilation is necessary to prevent a minor explosion due to the sublimation of the dry ice. If the specimen container is surrounded with natural ice, the outer container must be waterproof.

Recently, containers of rigid plastic foam have appeared on the market specifically designed for use in freezing and shipping biological materials. These containers come in a variety of sizes, from about one liter capacity to large square boxes which will accommodate a 50 pound block of dry ice. They are light and waterproof, yet their insulating properties are such that one filling of wet or dry ice will last up to a week under field conditions. They are usually protected

by outer boxes of cardboard. For repeated use in the field, light outer boxes of plywood can be constructed.

A variety of convenient plastic specimen containers are now commercially available. These include vials, bottles with snap-on or screw-on tops, bags with a variety of closures, and tightly closing dishes (Fig. 17.1). It must be kept in mind, however, that some types of plastic become brittle when cold and thus plastics must be carefully selected to withstand rugged use in cold weather or during frozen storage or shipment. Disposable plastic gloves also are available and provide convenient protection against accidental exposure to pathogenic organisms.

COMMON PRESERVATIVES

The chemical preservatives most often used for general field preservation include formaldehyde, ethyl alcohol, borax, and arsenic trioxide. Most of these materials can be obtained from drug stores or, in the case of borax, from grocery stores. Powder preservatives are inferior to liquids because they do not thoroughly penetrate tissues and therefore will not prevent autolysis nor bacterial decomposition if the specimen is contaminated before being placed in the preservative. Plastic and glass containers such as commercial screw-top jars and various sized ice cream containers can be obtained readily in most localities.

Table 17.1 presents a generalized summary of the more commonly used techniques for preserving several types of biological materials. For greater details regarding the preservation of entire specimens of vertebrates, reference is made to Anderson (1948), Anthony (1950), Hornaday (1929), Chapin (1946), Dice (1932), Burt (1948), Bishop (1947), and Howard (1942). For a summary of the methods used in the preservation of pathological materials, see Coffin (1953). Details regarding the preparation and limitations of the various preservatives and reagents are given in standard texts such as Guyer and Bean (1947) and Becker and Roundabush (1945). Knudsen (1966) discusses preservation of plants and animals and Post (1967) presents a complete field book for the wildlifer for specimen collection and preservation.

It will be noted in Table 17.1 that several concentrations of alcohol and formalin are required. When alcohol is stipulated in this table,

Fig. 17.1A. A sample of the sterile disposable plastic containers and instruments used in field collection of specimens for disease studies.

Table 17.1. Techniques recommended for preservation of biological material.

Biological Material	Recommended techniques, listed in order of preference	Reference
Mammals		
whole, small	Ethyl alcohol (70%) or 5% formalin*	
whole, large	Formalin (7-10%); also injection of preservative into internal organs by hypodermic—perfusion via circulatory route	Anderson 1948:21-22
Skins, pelts	(1) Clean thoroughly and air dry; (2) and salt thoroughly (NaCl); (3) use alum on pelts which appear to be "slipping"	(3) Anderson 1948:12
Skins, study**	(1) Borax (not to be used on skins having red pelage); (2) arsenic trioxide-borax mixture in equal proportions; (3) arsenical soap	Knudsen, 1966, Hall & Kelson, 1959, (3) Anderson 1948:12
Food material stomachs	Small stomachs—5% formalin; large stomachs—5-10% formalin (wrap stomachs in cheesecloth)	U. S. Fish and Wildlife Service 1941
Droppings	Dry quickly, fumigate with carbon disulfide	
Reproductive tracts	(1) AFA (preferably) or Bouin's fluid; (2) 10% formalin	Forbes 1941
Birds		
whole	(1) 70% alcohol; (2) 5% formalin, both with internal injection	Anderson 1948:21-22
Skins, pelts	(1) Borax; (2) arsenic-borax mixture	Anderson 1948:12
Skins, study	Borax; (3) arsenic-borax mixture	
Stomachs	5% formalin	Knudsen 1966
Droppings and pellets	Dry quickly and fumigate with carbon disulfide	U. S. Fish and Wildlife Service 1941
Reptiles & Amphibians		
whole	(1) 35-40% isopropyl alcohol or 70% ethyl alcohol; (2) formalin—specimens should be slit or injected	Knudsen 1966 (2) Anderson 1948:128-129
Snake skins	Rolled flat, placed in 70% alcohol	Anderson 1948:129
Salamanders	Kill with chloretone or 20% alcohol; harden with 5% formalin and store in 70% alcohol	Bishop 1947:15-16
Amphibian skins (to preserve color)	Kill with ether; skin and place skin in water; float onto cardboard; dry quickly	Anderson 1948:130
Fish	(1) 70% alcohol; (2) 10% formalin	Anderson 1948:132 Knudsen 1966
Insects		
Hard bodies	Kill with KCN bottle; store dry	Knudsen 1966
Soft bodies	Kill and store in 5% formalin or 10% alcohol	Howard 1942:401

Table 17.1. Continued.

Biological Material	Recommended techniques, listed in order of preference	Reference
Miscellaneous Skeletons--field	(1) Clean thoroughly and dry quickly; treat with arsenical soap† for shipment; (2) place in alcohol (formalin, unless neutralized, dissolves calcium of bones)	Anderson 1948:133-139
Skeletons--in laboratory ‡	(1) Boil gently in 3% hydrogen peroxide to remove meat and to bleach bones; degrease in carbon tetrachloride; (2) clean by use of dermestid beetles	(1) Anderson 1948:138 (2) Anderson 1948:140-142
Fumigants--for all specimens in pelt, study or standing mount form	Carbon disulfide as gas insecticide to kill insects; paradichlorobenzine as insect deterrent and DDT as insect contact killer	Anderson 1948:15-16
Pathological Material General	(1) Refrigerate (30°-40°F); (2) deep freeze and transport to laboratory as quickly as possible	
Hematological	(1) Make *several* blood or tissue smears; (2) Blood serum;§ (3) cell counts: either sodium oxalate 2-4 mg/ml or sodium citrate 2-4 mg/ml; refrigerate; (4) whole blood or serum dried on paper discs§	(3) Coffin 1953:122
Bacteriological	(1) Refrigerate entire specimens; (2) take blood, pus or fluids in sterile containers; refrigerate; (3) saturate cotton swabs with blood, pus, or tissue juices; transport in special medium;§ (4) make smears from blood, serous fluids, tissue juices§	
Virological Rabies	If possible confine the animal and wait until death occurs. Refrigerate and rush the head (if possible the entire carcass) to Public Health Laboratory	
Other Viruses	(1) refrigerate; (2) freeze; (3) put 1 cm. cubes of tissue in glycerol	
Parasitological Ectoparasites	Remove by hand or with aid of ether, chloroform, or sorptive silica powder (Dri Die). (1) ship live in non-airtight container with moist cotton, refrigerate if possible. (2) kill with ether, chloroform or HCN and ship dry between layers of cotton. (3) freeze and ship frozen.	

Table 17.1. Continued.

Biological Material	Recommended techniques, listed in order of preference	Reference
Helminths	(1) relax in cold water. Fix nematodes in hot 70% alcohol. Fix cestodes, trematodes in warm AFA. (2) alcohol 70%-95 parts glycerol-5 parts	Coffin 1953
Protozoa	(1) refrigerate tissues, feces, citrated blood (2) make smears of blood, feces, tissue impressions [§] (3) fix tissues in 10% formalin	
Histological	Fix *small pieces* of tissue in 10% formalin (10-20 X volume of tissue) *Do not freeze.*	
Toxicological	Refrigerate or freeze blood, liver, kidneys, brain, stomach with contents, small intestine.	
Plants Terrestrial	Place between folded paper, dry quickly between corrugated cardboards and with slight pressure in plant press	Lawrence 1951
Aquatics, or other plants with a mass of tissue	(1) alcohol-acetic acid-formalin solution; (2) 2 to 4% formalin	Johansen 1940-41

*See text for procedure in preparing dilutions of formalin and alcohol.
**Injection with embalming fluid (equal parts of formalin, glycerine, and phenol plus 85 parts water) will keep birds and mammals fresh enough to skin for study mounts for about a week without refrigeration.
[†]Poisons should *not* be used on skeletons which are to be cleaned by dermestids.
[‡]Clean large skulls and skeletons by boiling in 4 oz. sodium sulphate and 8 oz. ammonia to 6 gallons of water.
[§]See text for description of technique.

reference is made to ethyl[1] alcohol because methyl (or wood alcohol) is not a satisfactory preservative. Normally, alcohol is 95% strength, and formaldehyde solution is 40% strength in commercial quality. The formula used in diluting either of these chemicals is as follows:

$$\frac{\text{Desired concentration x desired volume}}{\text{Concentration of stock solution}}$$

$$= \frac{\text{Volume of stock solution to be}}{\text{diluted to desired volume}}$$

For example, suppose 200 ml of 60% alcohol is wanted and a stock solution of 95% alcohol is on hand. Then, according to the above formula:

[1]Isopropyl alcohol (35-40%) is preferred by some field workers as a preservative for fish, amphibia, and reptiles.

$$\frac{60 \times 200}{95} = 126.3 \text{ ml of 95\% alcohol}$$

to which is added 73.7 ml of water to make 200 ml of 60% alcohol. Likewise, 40% formalin is available from which to prepare 250 ml of 5% formalin. Then:

$$\frac{5 \times 250}{100} = 12.5 \text{ ml of stock formalin}$$

which is mixed with 237.5 ml of water.

Full information on all specimens should be attached to all specimens *when they are placed in the preservative.* Such data may be written on paper or cardboard (provided it does not have a starch filler) in soft lead pencil or with carbon (waterproof) ink. Regular ink should not be used as it will wash off in preservatives. It is a good practice to write full data on both sides of the label so that at least one set of data is preserved.

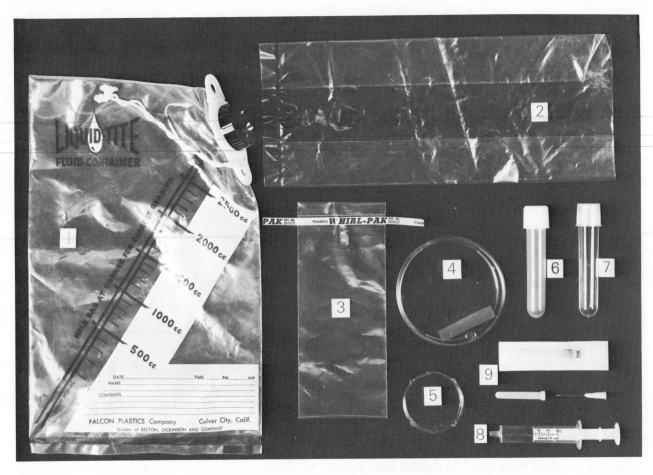

Fig. 17.1B. A variety of plastic bags, vials, caps, dishes, and syringes are available.

Some of the more commonly used preservatives, their composition and preparation and their principal uses are given in Table 17.2. Table 17.1 and Table 17.2 complement one another. Whenever possible specimens should be sent to the laboratory packed in ice. Freezing or fixing should be a secondary alternative.

PRESERVATION OF STUDY SKINS

Field workers often have the opportunity of preserving valuable study skins of mammals and birds because such specimens often become available from highway kills, accidents, trapping operations, sportsmen, and in many other ways.[2]

[2]Permits (federal and state) are required to collect or possess migratory birds, resident game birds, game mammals, and most furbearers out of season. Most birds except crows, grackles, English sparrows, starlings, jays, and certain hawks and owls are protected by federal laws. Game birds, game mammals, and most furbearers are protected by state laws.

Such specimens may be saved and put to good use if the wildlife worker is familiar with the simple technique of preparing study mounts—and is equipped to prepare such specimens.

Full descriptions of the techniques used in skinning and mounting mammal study skins are given in Anthony (1950), Anderson (1948), Burt (1948), and Hall and Kelson (1959). A label should be attached to the skin as soon as the specimen is completed. Identification is not necessary in field prepared mounts (positive identification may be made later), but sex, age, date, locality, collector, collector's number, measurements, and remarks should be entered on the label. This should be done *when the specimen is prepared* in the field and the tag should be attached to the specimen at that time. The original label tag should *never* be destroyed. It has been stated with some truth that a label without a specimen is of some value but a specimen without a label is relatively valuless. Steps in preparing mammal study skins are shown in Fig. 17.2.

The principal steps in the skinning of a bird

Table 17.2. Chemicals and compounds commonly used in the preservation of biological material.

Material	Composition	Preparation	Usage
Alcohol, ethyl	C_2H_5OH (95%)		Preservative; fix & harden organs; reptiles and amphibians
Alcohol-acetic acid-formaldehyde mixture (AFA)	50% (or 70%) ethyl alcohol acetic acid, glacial (CH_3COOH) Formaldehyde (40%) (CH_2O_3)	90 cc 5 cc 5 cc	Preservative and fixative
Alum	$KAl_2(SO_4)_2 \cdot 12H_2O$		Preservative; skins primarily
Alum-arsenic	$KAl_2(SO_4)_2$ and AS_2O_3	Equal parts	Preservative; skins primarily
Arsenical soap	White bar soap Powdered arsenic (AS_2O_3) Potassium bicarbonate ($KHCO_3$) Camphor ($C_{10}H_{16}O$) Alcohol (95%) ethyl	2 lbs 2 lbs 6 oz 5 oz 8 oz	Preservative; skins & skeletons
Bouin's fluid	Picric acid ($C_6H_2(NO_2)_3OH$) saturated aq sol Formaldehyde (40%) Acetic acid, glacial	750 cc 250 cc 50 cc	Fixative; organs tissues
Borax	$Na_2B_4O_7$		Preservative; skins primarily
Carbon disulfide	CS_2		Fumigant
Carbon tetrachloride	CCl_4		Degreaser; hides and bones
Dichlorodiphenyltrichloroethane (DDT)	$(ClC_6H_4)_2CHCCl_3$		Insecticide
Embalming fluid	Formalin Glycerin Phenol Water	1 part 1 part 1 part 85 parts	Whole body preservative
Ethylene dichloride-carbon tetrachloride mixture	CHCl:CHCl	4 parts	Fumigant
Formalin Regular	10% commercial formalin		Preservative and fixative for organs, tissues, and parasites as well as whole animals

Table 17.2. Continued.

Material	Composition	Preparation	Usage

Formalin Neutral-buffered	Formalin
	Distilled water
	Sodium phosphate
	  monobasic
	Sodium phosphate
	  anhydrous
		100 ml
		900 ml
		
		4 gm
		
		6.5 gm
			Fixative for tissues, organs, whole carcasses, parasites

Hydrogen peroxide	H_2O_2		Bleaching agent; bones
Potassium cyanide	Place a few lumps of KCN in bottom of wide-mouth bottle, add about 1/2 inch of semi-fluid plaster of Paris ($CaSO_4 \cdot 1/2H_2$); permit plaster to dry. Stopper bottle tightly.		Insect and invertebrate killing bottle
Glycerin (glycerol)			Tissue preservative for virus studies (not for histology)
Phenol (carbolic acid)			Preservative for serum (0.5%)
Merthiolate			Preservative for serum (.01%)

are given in Fig. 17.3. The major differences between skinning a mammal and a bird are: (1) the skull is left in bird study mounts (after the brain, eyes and the fleshy portions are removed), (2) wire is normally not needed to strengthen the legs and wings of birds as the flesh is removed from these appendages and cotton is wrapped around the bones, (3) a wire or small stick, usually inserted in the skull and extending to the tail, is used to strengthen bird mounts, and (4) finished bird mounts normally are wrapped in thin "sheets" of cotton or cheesecloth when left to dry. The same type of label is used to record the essential data for birds as is used for mammals.

The preparation of neat, quality mammal and bird study mounts becomes easier with practice. The beginner often requires from 1 to 2 hours per specimen, but an experienced individual can put up a neat small rodent or passerine specimen in about 10 minutes. Thus, it behooves the wildlife investigator to develop the art of preparing study mounts so that he can preserve such specimens in a reasonable manner and in a reasonable length of time. If the ability to work quickly and neatly is not developed through practice, the field worker is prone to discard the available specimens which opportunity presents him under the excuse that he does not have sufficient time to preserve them.

COLLECTING AND PRESERVING PATHOLOGICAL MATERIAL

Postmortem examinations (see Chapter 16) for pathological conditions are best made when the specimen is fresh. Decomposition of tissues due to autolysis and bacterial action begins at death. In warm weather a specimen may decompose within a matter of several hours to the point where it is unsuited for any pathological examination. Most pathologists prefer to make observations of an animal while it is still alive. For this reason, it is strongly recommended that, whenever possible, specimens be taken alive to diagnostic laboratories. Critically sick specimens should not be sent by express when more than a few hours (4 to 6 in warm weather and perhaps

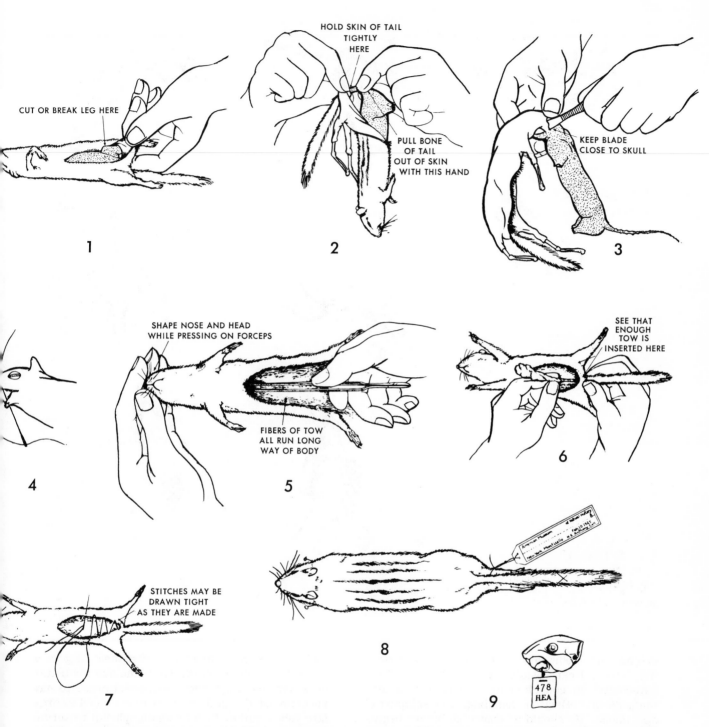

Fig. 17.2. Steps in the preparation of a mammal study skin: (1) The opening belly-cut and one leg freed from the skin at the knee; (2) removing the tail vertebrae; (3) cutting around the ears; (4) stitching the lips; (5) the start in filling the skin; (6) filling the tail with a covered wire; (7) sewing the filled skin; (8) top view of finished study skin; and (9) tagged skull (from Anthony (1950), courtesy of American Museum of Natural History).

double this time in cool weather) will be required for them to reach the laboratory. Should they die in transit—which most of them do—they usually arrive at the laboratory so decomposed that they are valueless. Such specimens should be killed and shipped packed in ice. Whenever possible

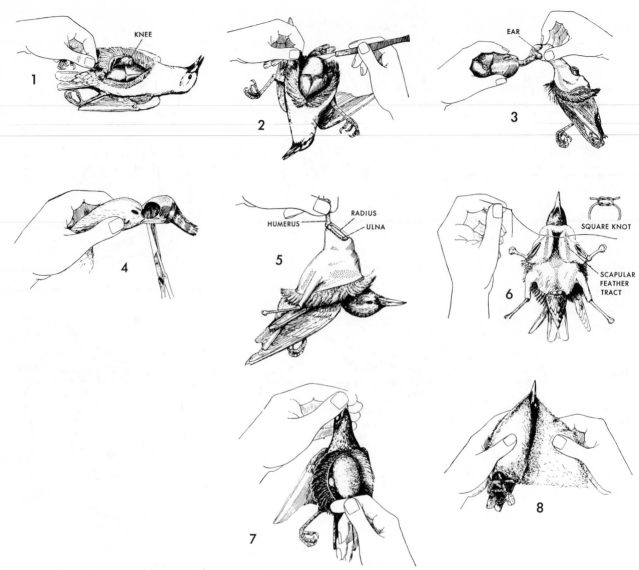

Fig. 17.3. Steps in the preparation of a bird study skin (after Chapin (1946) courtesy American Museum of Natural History).

contact the laboratory by telephone or by covering letter. Best results will be obtained if the pathologist is consulted by telephone regarding methods of collection, handling, and shipping of specimens. He should be consulted before beginning a field trip if specimen collecting is planned.

It is impossible to recommend any single preservative technique that would be suitable for use on all pathological specimens (see Coffin 1953:6-18). The preservatives recommended (particularly refrigeration) should save most specimens so that the pathologist can get a fair idea as to the cause of the disease. The patholo-

gist, with such information, can then suggest a more adaptable preservative technique for better preservation of any additional specimens. He may recommend the collection of fresh blood in oxalate tubes rather than by adding phenol to serum for example. In general, pathological material is best examined in fresh condition. If this is not possible, it should be refrigerated and gotten to the laboratory as quickly as possible. If refrigeration is not available, then chemical preservatives should be utilized.

The camera, especially when color film is used, is a valuable tool for recording observations on gross lesions of disease. A permanent, accurate, and natural-colored record may be secured that will be of considerable help to the pathologist. The color camera is especially useful to the field man for making such records of freshly-dead specimens that will change in color, size, and general appearance shortly after death.

General Rules and Recommendations

Caution must be exercised in making on-the-spot decisions as to cause of diseases or death. Rarely is it a matter of one-cause, one-disease. Illness and mortality in wildlife, as in man and domestic species, is usually a matter of multiple causation. Predation or road accidents, for example, may select for animals suffering from a disease condition. Parasitism, though it may be an obvious disease-producing factor, is rarely the sole cause of death in wildlife. The terms *infection* and *disease* are not synonymous. Most infections are not apparent; recognizable disease is the exception to the rule. Attention must be paid to clinically inapparent, or "silent" infections, in studying the longterm effects of infections on a population. Signs of disease may appear only under the super-imposition of several disease-producing factors.

The joint efforts of several specialists may be required to develop a true picture of multiple causation of disease.

General rules which should be followed in collecting and preserving specimens are:

(1) A live diseased animal is of most value to the pathologist.

(2) Submit entire carcasses if possible.

(3) When tissues or organs are to be examined, select for obvious structural or functional abnormalities; e.g. tumors, abscesses, lungs in cases of respiratory distress, intestine in animals with diarrhea, brain and spinal cord in cases of abnormal behaviour, incoordination, or paralysis.

Rules For Histology

Fix small pieces of tissue, 1-2 cm cubes, in 10% formalin, ensuring that the volume of formalin is 10 to 20 times that of the tissue to be fixed. Use a sharp knife. Dull instruments compress, distort and tear tissues. If immediate fixation is not possible, tissues may be refrigerated for a short period of time. Do not freeze, except as a last resort. Freezing causes disruption of tissues by ice crystals.

Rules For Bacteriology and Mycology

Refrigeration is an ideal means of preserving specimens for bacteriologic examination. Freezing is suitable for most bacterial organisms. Small carcasses should be sent to the laboratory intact. In removing organs from larger animals, avoid contamination with hair, soil, and gastrointestinal contents. If discrete lesions are present, they should either be carefully excised, including a margin of normal tissue, or if possible, submit entire organs. Sterile cotton swabs are useful for culture of feces, pus, blood or other body fluids. Saturated swabs are submitted to the laboratory refrigerated or immersed in a special semi-solid bacteriological transport medium.[3]

Rules For Virology

The best preservative for specimens intended for viral examination (blood, tissues, insect vectors, etc.) is refrigeration at ice box temperatures (4°C). Freezing should be used only if storage of more than a few days is required between the times of collection and laboratory examination. Repeated freezing and thawing must be avoided. Or, if it is found necessary to hold specimens for long periods of time at ice box temperatures, small pieces or cubes of tissue may be immersed in glycerine to prevent dehydration and bacterial putrefaction.

Specimens should be collected in clean or preferably sterile glass or plastic containers. Care must be taken to minimize contamination from the surface of a carcass or its gastrointestinal content. Specimens from an animal carcass must be collected as soon as possible after death because bacterial putrefaction begins at death. As it progresses it greatly reduces the chances of successfully isolating a viral agent. Clean, fresh specimens are suitable also for bacteriological and histological examinations—supporting studies necessary to the diagnosis of many viral diseases. Molded polystyrene containers are excellent for the storage and shipment of viral specimens. They may be used with either wet or dry ice.

[3]Stuart transport medium, prepared in sterilized screw-capped glass vials from dried medium obtainable from major microbiology supply houses.

Rules For Parasitology

Many ectoparasites and helminths are readily seen during postmortem examinations. Others are found only after extensive search by trained parasitologists. Tables 17.1 and 17.2 outline some of the methods and preservatives useful in collecting the larger parasites. Microscopic parasites, including protozoa, are demonstrable in specimens taken as for bacteriology and histology.

Arthropods (insects, ticks or mites) may be shipped either frozen or dried when packed between layers of cotton. Preferably, especially if they are to be examined for infectious agents, they should be transported alive. For this purpose they may be carried in small glass or plastic vials, the mouths of which are covered with cloth or gauze. The larger, overall container must allow some ventilation. Cardboard or screened containers are suitable. The outside container also should contain moistened cotton or sponge to prevent dessication of the arthropods enroute.

Rules For Blood

Blood for serum collection should be collected as cleanly as possible in sterile glass or plastic vials. It is allowed to clot. Normally, a fresh clot will contract during the first few hours after it forms, exuding clear straw-colored serum. This is to be expected if blood is obtained from the veins of a live or dying animal. In the field however, one must obtain blood whenever possible, often from a carcass where coagulation has already occurred. In such cases the blood collected may be partly clotted, partly serum, and usually contains free-floating cells. Sometimes hemolysis has occurred. Under ideal circumstances serum can be poured off a clot; centrifugation is an aid to remove free cells. Small hand operated centrifuges can be taken into the field. Small electric centrifuges are suitable for use in areas where electricity is available.

Hemolysis may render a sample unsuited for some serological tests, and therefore must be avoided. Some of the causes of hemolysis are: freezing, agitation, bacterial contamination, contamination with water or snow, and drawing blood under high vacuum.

If blood is collected before coagulation occurs, it should be allowed to clot at near body temperature and should be kept warm until serum has separated from the clot. Serum should then be poured off into a second vial and refrigerated or frozen. If serum cannot be removed at once, the tube containing serum and clot should be refrigerated (not frozen). Refrigeration of a blood sample immediately after it is collected will do no harm except to reduce the yield of serum. Blood collected from a carcass after death should be refrigerated promptly, since it is certain to contain bacteria.

TAKING BLOOD AND TISSUE SMEARS

Blood and tissue slides often offer a simple way of preserving evidence of blood-borne parasites and other disorders of the blood.

Blood smears (see Coffin 1953:123) should be made from fresh blood. Place a clean slide (Fig. 17.4) on a horizontal surface and put a drop of

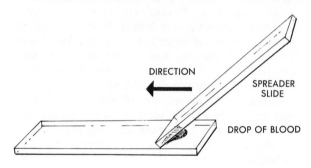

Fig. 17.4. Position of the spreader slide before the spreading of the smear. The final motion should be in the direction indicated by the arrow in a smooth, fairly rapid stroke (from Coffin 1945:93).

fresh blood on this slide near one end. A second (spreader) slide, held at an acute angle, is placed on the horizontal slide and drawn into the drop of blood. Allow the blood to spread evenly until it is distributed most of the way across the end of the spreader slide. Before the blood spreads to the ends of the spreader slide, push the spreader quickly across the bottom slide. This places a thin film of blood on the bottom slide.

A number may be placed on the specimen slide with a glass-writing pencil. The blood-smear slide should be dried as quickly as possible, and it may be stained immediately with Wrights or Giemsa stain, or stored in a dust-proof container for later staining and examination.

Tissue smears may be made by cutting fresh sections of such organs as the heart, liver, lungs, etc. and lightly dabbing these sections onto a clean slide. The blood and tissue smears should have as light a layer of blood on the slide as possible to facilitate staining and examination. Heavy smear slides are not suitable.

PAPER-DISC ABSORBED BLOOD SAMPLES

Recently, special 17 mm diameter paper discs have been used to collect and preserve (by air drying) specimens of both whole blood and serum (Karstad et al. 1959). These discs promise to be of great value to the field worker as they are simple to transport and store. They may be used to collect fresh blood from a live animal or blood from an animal that has been dead for several hours. This technique is recommended for epizootiological studies requiring the collection of blood samples from small mammals and birds.

Discs to be saturated with whole blood or serum are placed on a smooth non-absorbent surface, such as a glassine envelope or a plastic or glass petri dish. For quantitative tests each disc must be thoroughly wet (approx. 0.2 ml). Discs are dried by exposure to air, after which they may be stored without refrigeration in glassine envelopes or mailed directly to the laboratory. Each disc-absorbed specimen must be accompanied by a card bearing data on where, when and from what species collected, condition of animal, etc.

Fig. 17.5. Skinning out a buck deer head for mounting. *A* Make a longitudinal cut on the back of the neck from a point midway between the ears to the shoulder. Cut around shoulders. *B* Cut from between the ears to the base of the antlers, then around the antlers. *C* Sever the ears at their base (cartilage to be removed later). Skin out the head, cased, to tip of nose. *D* Saw off a portion of the skull with antlers attached.

PRESERVING GAME TROPHIES AND MEAT

The biologist should be familiar with the general techniques used in preserving game trophies and game meat because sportsmen will assume that he possesses such knowledge. In addition, the wildlifer can make a great contribution to conservation if he uses every opportunity to familiarize the sportsmen with the proper preservation and utilization of his trophies of the chase.

For purposes of illustration, the preservation of the meat and trophies of the deer will be used in the following discussion. For further details regarding the preservation of game meat, reference is made to Camp (1949), Rawley et al. (1950), Ashbrook and Sater (1945), and Low and Pierce (1950).

Preserving Big Game Trophies

The preservation of the head, hide, and feet of the deer will be briefly discussed to illustrate the general principles. Fish and birds require special treatment (see Hornaday 1929), but the general considerations are essentially the same.

To save a deer "head" for mounting by a professional taxidermist, make a cut through the hide along the top of the neck from the shoulder to about 3 inches from the midpoint between the base of the antlers (Fig. 17.5). Next, make a cut to and around each antler. This will leave a V-shaped flap of skin over the skull. Cut the ears free from the skull, making sure to cut as close to the skull as possible. Then, make an encircling cut around the base of the neck *at the shoulder*. Many hunters cut too far up on the neck, thus giving the taxidermist such a short mantle that he cannot prepare a good head mount. Pull the skin off the neck and over the head, cutting carefully around the eyes. Leave the lips attached to the mantle and leave the cartilage on the nose. Saw off a portion of the skull with antlers attached. Clean off all flesh and fat, salt liberally, roll up and ship the mantle and antlers to the taxidermist.

If the trophy can be delivered immediately to the taxidermist, case skin the neck (making an encircling cut at the base of the neck at the shoulders) up to the base of the skull. Sever the neck muscles at the base of the skull and then twist the head free from the neck vertebrae. The entire head, with antlers attached and the mantle can be turned over to the taxidermist for his immediate attention.

The hide can be removed by cutting along the inside of each leg from the first joint to the mid-belly line. Make an encircling cut around each leg at the first joint and pull the hide from the leg. The skin may be peeled off the body without the use of a knife. This is done by pulling with one hand and using the fist of the other hand to force the hide free from the body. This hide should be thoroughly cleaned of all flesh, fat, and tissue; all blood stains should be wiped off and then sponged with cold or lukewarm water. When possible, the hide should be tacked flat, but not stretched, to the side of a building in the shade and protected from rain. It should then be thoroughly salted and permitted to dry. When dry, it may be removed and rolled up. Do not fold a dry skin as folding will cause it to crack.

Preserving Game Meat

The primary objectives in all treatment of wild meat which is to be preserved for table use are (1) bleed as completely as possible (bleeding is not absolutely essential but it does make longer storage under refrigeration much more satisfactory); (2) cool the carcass as quickly as possible after the kill is made; and (3) clean (remove the viscera) immediately, exercising care to prevent contact of fur, intestinal contents, or other contamination with the meat.

If the hunter reaches the game, e.g. deer, before it is dead, bleeding should be attempted by severing the jugular veins on either *side* of the neck, making the cuts near the shoulder if the head is to be saved as a trophy. Bleeding should be done with the head as low as, or lower than, the rest of the body. After the animal is bled, the carcass should be shifted so that the head is up-hill or, preferably, the carcass should be hung by the head from the branch of a tree. Some individuals immediately cut off the scent-glands (metatarsal glands) from inside the hind legs and sever and remove the testicles of male deer. This is done under the assumption that these organs taint the meat, but other hunters, including the writer, have not found the removal of the scent glands necessary. After placing the carcass with the head higher than the hindquarters, carefully make an incision in the belly immediately below the sternum. Insert the fingers into this opening and press back the viscera so that the cut through the hide and belly wall may be extended to the anus. Extreme care should be taken not to cut the rumen, intestines, or the bladder because the contents of these organs will taint the meat. Extend the cut through the midline of the pelvis; a hatchet may be employed to cut through the pelvis if a stout knife is not available. Next, grasp the gullet and windpipe as close to the throat as possible, sever these two tubes and permit the viscera to roll downward by their own weight. It may be necessary to make some cuts with the knife to free the viscera from the attachments to the body wall. In this way most of the viscera may be removed from the carcass intact, leaving the heart, liver, and lungs attached to the carcass. A deer dressed in this manner is usually referred to as "field dressed;" if the heart, liver, and lungs are removed also, the carcass is referred to as "hog dressed." Some hunters leave the heart and liver attached to the carcass but remove the lungs, slit the throat (after saving the mantle if a trophy is desired) and remove the remainder of the trachia and esophagus.

The body cavity should be wiped as *dry* as possible with dry cloths, grass, leaves, or any other available material. Water should not be used to clean out the body cavity unless the body is badly contaminated. Cleaning of the body cavity with dry materials is recommended because it is desired to have a "blood glaze" form on the inside of the body wall to seal these exposed surfaces. Next, prop open the body cavity with several sticks so that air may circulate freely, thus hastening the cooling of the carcass. If flies are present, the carcass should be draped with cheesecloth or other similar material to prevent flies from reaching and depositing their eggs on the exposed surfaces. A carcass prepared in this manner may be hung out-of-doors for several days in temperatures which do not exceed 40° to 45°F. Deer which are not dressed (eviscerated) promptly after the kill is made may begin to decompose and bloat within 5 to 6 hours, even in cool weather.

Many individuals prefer not to skin their deer until it has aged for the proper period of time and is ready to cut up and store. They reason that the hide prevents the drying out of the meat. All deer meat should be "aged"—held in storage at a temperature of from 37 to 40 degrees F—and the time required to age various types of deer varies from 1 to 2 days for a young fawn up to 7 to 10 days for an old buck. Such aging permits a breakdown of the meat tissues by enzymatic action which "tenderizes" the meat. Aging may be done in a home refrigerator (temperature at about 40°F) for cuts of deer up to the size of a hindquarter. The aging of the meat should be done before it is frozen for storage; meat will not age when frozen.

PRESERVING PLANT MATERIAL[4]

The preservation of plants is a problem which confronts every field biologist. The proper collection and preparation of plants is not difficult and does not require elaborate equipment. The principal considerations in plant collection are (1) collect the entire plant (roots, stems, leaves and flowers) if possible, but if this is impractical, select those portions of the plant which are needed for identification, (2) clear roots of dirt, (3) press (or place in preservative) the plant specimen as soon as possible after it is collected, and (4) place only one kind of plant in a plant sheet. For greater detail regarding the collection and preservation of plants, see Lawrence (1951).

Most botanical specimens (herbs and grasses, for example) may be collected in the field using (1) a portfolio, (2) a vasculum (see Fig. 17.6), or (3) a large plastic bag. Pressing plants in the field in the portfolio is recommended because of the greater accuracy of recording field data. In addition, portfolio collected specimens, as compared with those collected using a vasculum, normally are in better condition when dried and they can be transferred directly to the drier with a minimum of handling.

The field portfolio may consist of a number of folded sheets of paper 18 by 24 inches, or newspaper folded to 12 by 18 inches, placed between two pieces of heavy cardboard or slat frames, and strapped together with two friction-buckle straps.

The slat frames (which also are used in the plant press discussed later) are 12 by 18 inches over-all and they are made by nailing together 1-inch x 1/4-inch strips of wood in a lattice-like arrangement as shown in Fig. 17.6D. Notes may be written directly on the sheet of press paper, and a wax pencil is recommended for this purpose. Care should be taken to arrange the plant specimens so that the various structures may be examined with a minimum of handling after the plant is dried. Thus, some of the leaves should be placed with their lower surfaces up and other leaves should lie with their top surfaces up. None of them should be folded. Likewise, the arrangement of the flowers and of the leaves on the stem should be apparent without having to handle the brittle, dried specimen. A careful arrangement of the fresh specimen at the time it is placed in

[4]Mr. Phil D. Goodrum, Wildlife Research Biologist, Bureau of Sport Fisheries and Wildlife, Nacogdoches, Texas, revised this section on plant materials.

274

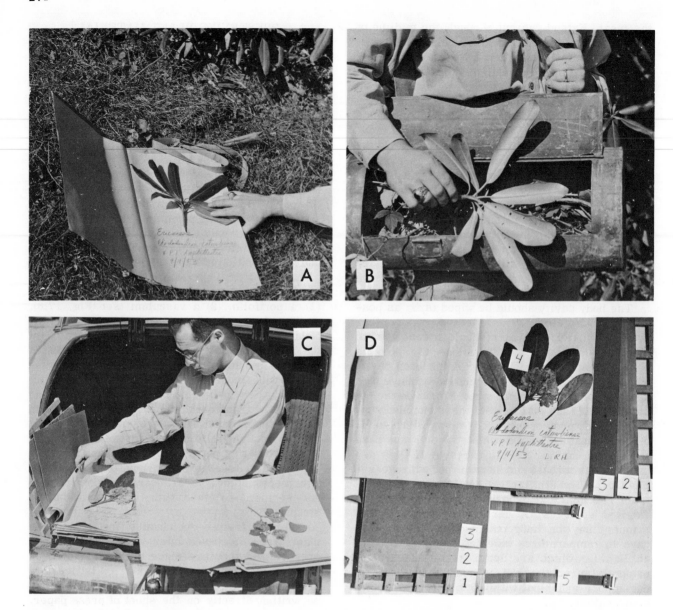

Fig. 17.6. Methods of collecting and pressing plants. *A* Plants may be collected and placed directly in a portfolio in the field. *B* If a portfolio is not used, a vasculum with moist paper in the bottom may be used to keep plants fresh until pressed. *C* Plants should be put in press—from portfolio or from vasculum—as soon after collection as possible. *D* Parts of a press include (1) lattice frames, (2) corrugated ventilators, (3) driers, (4) press sheets and (5) friction-buckle straps.

the portfolio in the field is recommended. After the fresh specimen is carefully arranged on the press paper, the folded paper is placed between the two cardboards, on slat frames, and put under slight pressure by means of the two friction-buckle straps.

Some field workers prefer to use a vasculum rather than a portfolio for the field collection of plants. Vasculums may vary in size, but the "normal" size vasculum is a hinged top, oval-shaped, metal container measuring approximately 5 by 8 inches cross-section and 20 inches in length, equipped with a hinged door, 17 by 6 inches, and two metal rings for the attachment of the shoulder strap. Specimens are placed in the vasculum as they are collected in the field; moist paper or damp moss often is placed in the vasculum to help keep the specimens in fresh condition. A large plastic bag, as previously mentioned, may be handy when collecting.

The plants collected in the field should be transferred to the plant press as soon as possible (Fig. 17.6D). The same type of slat frames as described for the portfolio are used in the plant press. Each folded paper containing a plant specimen is "sandwiched" with heavy felt paper driers, 12 by 17 inches, or with several sheets of paper. Felt-paper driers are recommended because they are more absorbent than paper. Corrugated boards may be used at intervals to permit air to circulate more freely. After the specimens are arranged one on top of the other, the top slat frame is placed on the pile and the entire bundle is placed under pressure by means of the two friction-buckle straps. The full press of plants is then stored where it will dry as rapidly as possible for 24 to 36 hours. At the end of this period, the driers are replaced with dry felt on corrugated driers, the press is put under as much pressure as possible, and the entire press is stored in a warm, dry place.

When the plant specimens are thoroughly dry, they are removed from the press and affixed by strips of white binding tape to sheets of stiff white paper, 11-1/2 by 17 inches. The lower right-hand corner is reserved for the label and the specimen is so arranged on the mounting sheet to accommodate the label.

Some workers now use a plastic glue to attach the specimens to the mounting sheet. One such glue is Gelva V 25, a polyvinyl acetate sold by Shawinigan Resins Corp., (Springfield, Massachusetts). Another substance which is purchased prepared and is handier is Archer's adhesive liquid (Caroline Biological Supply Co., Burlington, North Carolina) diluted 1:4 with a solvent made of one part alcohol, four parts xylene. A small hand grease-gun is an efficient applicator. Spot gluing works best but when mounting numerous specimens, the glue may be applied by first spreading the glue over a glass plate and then placing the specimen on the glue prior to attachment to the mounting paper.

Plants mounted in this manner are known as herbarium specimens, and they should be stored in tight boxes and protected from insect damage by means of suitable fumigants (see Table 17.2). Insect damage can be greatly reduced or prevented by immersing cured plants, before mounting, in a 1% solution of bichloride of mercury.

Aquatic plants and other plants having a large mass of fleshy tissue are difficult to preserve by pressing and drying. Such botanical specimens may be preserved by placing them in an alcohol-acetic acid-formalin solution (Table 17.1) or in 4% formalin solution. Graetz (1967) describes a plant mounting technique which presses fresh plants between a sheet of cardboard and a sheet of clear plastic with an adhesive coating on one surface.

MISCELLANEOUS PRESERVATION TECHNIQUES

Many techniques have been developed for the preservation of biological material for special uses. Some of the more common techniques include the use of plastics (Fessender 1949, and Specht 1950), stained sectional slides of tissues and organs, casts of plaster of Paris (or other media), Ricker mounts, photographic records, camera lucida drawings, and many other ways. The resourceful field worker can usually develop some method to preserve adequately most biological material if he is familiar with the general principles outlined in this chapter.

CHAPTER EIGHTEEN

CAPTURING AND MARKING WILD ANIMALS

RICHARD D. TABER, PhD[1]

Professor, School of Forest Resources
University of Washington
Seattle, Washington

and

I. McT. COWAN, PhD

Dean of the Graduate School
University of British Columbia
Vancouver, British Columbia, Canada

The wildlife manager must obtain wild animals, dead and alive, so often, and for so many reasons, that these reasons need not or scarcely can be listed here. The hunter's bag supplies dead game animals in abundance, but these are often eviscerated and are available only during a relatively short period of the year. For many purposes the wildlife manager must supply himself with animals, both game and non-game, during every season of the year. These animals must be taken alive and unharmed for purposes such as banding and tagging. This chapter deals with methods of capturing animals, handling them when caught, and marking them for future identification.

[1]Received for publication, August 1966.

CAPTURING WILD ANIMALS

The investigator should be thoroughly familiar with the habits of the species he is studying if he expects to enjoy consistent trapping success. It is much easier to capture animals, as a rule, if the trapping method is dove-tailed with the habits of the animals, than if the animal is expected to change its habits to suit the trapper. Ordinarily, trapping success is much higher if traps are set where animals or their sign is observed, rather than systematically or at random through the habitat (e.g. Melchior and Iwen 1965). However, the latter approach is often used when the investigator wants to use the results as an index of presence and abundance.

The first problem is to get the trap and the animal together. This may be done by putting out enough traps so that the animal is trapped "at random"; by placing the trap where the animal habitually comes; on its trail, at its nest, in its burrow; or by driving the animal to the trap. Where these approaches are not practicable, some method of attracting the animal is needed.

Baits and Scents

FOOD BAITS

Foods attractive to the animal are the most common form of trap bait. Baits are often preferred seasonal food, but may be entirely new substances. Bait attractiveness may be assessed by placing a variety of possible baits on the animal's range and measuring the use of each. Once a good bait has been found, the animals may be pre-baited to a trapping station to get them in the habit of feeding there. It is wise to create a track-bed in the pre-baiting area to be sure that the animal taking the bait is the species that the trapper wants. Food is the most common bait, but in dry areas water is good and, for some animals (especially herbivorous mammals not near the seacoast), salt is seasonally attractive.

The most commonly used food baits include grain, for most game birds; canned dog food, fish products, etc. for carnivores; apples, carrots, lettuce, etc., for rabbits and similar herbivores. For small mammals such as mice and rats, special mixtures of grain, fruits, and animal fat are often used. In this latter category, the following mixture is recommended (Anon., n.d.) for use as bait in the North American census of small mammals:

        2 lbs melted beef suet (i.e., beef fat)
        2 lbs peanut butter
        2 lbs raisins, ground
        2 lbs oatmeal
        1 lb of high melting-point paraffin

Verts (1961) pointed out that if this, or similar, baits are packed in a plastic "squeeze" bottle they are easier to carry and use, especially if the aperture of the bottle is about 0.25 inch in diameter and vegetable oil is added to viscous bait.

LIVE BAITS

Live bait may attract through an appeal to hunger, to sex attraction, or to territorial antagonism. As examples: mice confined with food will stay alive and give off scent which attracts a fox by appealing to hunger; a hen bobwhite, confined in the center of a multiple-compartment trap during the spring, will sexually attract unattached cocks, which enter the trap and are caught (Stoddard 1932) as is done with mallard ducks purposefully left in traps to attract others; domestic pigeons, starlings, owls, etc. are commonly used as live-food bait to lure birds of prey; a ruffed grouse cock, in the spring drumming period, will attack its own reflection in a mirror and cocks are captured in a mirror-backed trap set near their drumming place (Tanner and Bowers 1948); and, finally, quail (Levy, et al. 1966), woodcock, and other birds are often attracted by recorded calls or by stuffed skins of their own species.

CURIOSITY BAITS

Some animals are attracted by objects that resemble foods or appeal to the animal's curiosity. Thus a raccoon will feel for a bright piece of tin under the water; a weasel or a woodrat will enter an empty length of stovepipe; or a wildcat will approach a bird's wing fluttering from a bush. Many scents are effective because of their appeal to an animal's curiosity.

SCENTS

Scent is used only for mammals, for the sense of smell is acute in mammals but is poorly developed in birds. While food-bait appeals to an animal's hunger, and is attractive only when the animal is hungry, scent appeals to its sex-interest, antagonism, or curiosity and is attractive almost all the time. Mammals do much of their communicating by scent and so are constantly on the alert for it. For these reasons, scent is often superior to food as a lure for mammals.

Many mammals mark their home ranges with urine, feces, or secretions from special glands. Certain substances are attractive to the members of a whole family—such as valerian (*Valeriana*) for the Canidae and catnip (*Nepeta*) for the Felidae. Anise (*Pimpinella*) is attractive to the black bear. Beaver castor (*castoreum*) is found in the anal musk-sacs of both sexes. It is attractive to beavers and also is used in scent preparations for other species.

The scents below illustrate types of scent composition; specific, general, and food:

1. Coyote. Combine urine, gall, and anal glands of coyote. To every 3 oz of mixture add 1 oz of

glycerin, and 1 grain of corrosive sublimate. In several days it is ready for use. This scent is also effective for wolf if prepared from wolf materials (Young 1955).

2. Fox. Combine 1 pint of fox urine, 5 grains zinc valerate and 1 grain of beaver castor. This is ready for use after 12 hr (Garlough 1945).

3. Fox, coyote, etc. (putrid scent). Grind fresh fish and place in closed container with small, meshed air hole to permit escape of gas but to exclude flies. Leave for 1 to 4 weeks, until flesh has decayed. To each pint of liquid add 1-1/3 oz of glycerin and 1/3 teaspoon of beaver castor, mixing thoroughly (Garlough 1945).

Kill-Trapping Mammals

MECHANICAL MEANS

Small mammals—mice and shrews—are taken with ordinary commercial snap traps or mouse traps. Museum special traps (which are larger than the usual mouse traps) or ordinary mouse traps fitted with rubber tubing on the striking-bar should be used if it is necessary to take small mammals without damaging their skulls. Rat traps will kill larger mammals up to the size of a weasel or pine squirrel.

Gophers and moles, because of their burrowing habits, must be taken in special traps, well-known commercially.

For mammals from squirrel to beaver in size, a new trap has recently been reported (Collier 1957). This, the Conibear trap (Fig. 18.1) catches the animal around the neck or chest, killing it almost instantly. It has stood up successfully through extensive tests and promises to replace the standard leg-hold in some situations.

For capturing larger mammals and for game birds, a wide variety of snares and deadfalls is used. The basic element of a snare (Fig. 18.2) is a slip-noose which tightens around the animal's body or neck, and the basic element of a dead-fall (Fig. 18.3) is a weight that falls on an animal.

Snares are surprisingly effective for the capture of animals that move along well-defined trails. A fixed snare has the end fastened to a branch or stake; the forward momentum of the animal, and its struggles to escape, are sufficient to tighten the noose. Commercial snares (e.g. Fig. 23.7) have a special device which permits the noose to tighten but not loosen. Snares are most effective in capturing animals with large heads and small necks.

The trip-snare is attached to a spring (such as a bent sapling or a suspended weight) in such a manner that when the snare is sprung it is tightened about the animal and the upward pull carries the victim clear of the ground and out of reach of predators. The principal element in trip-snares is the trigger mechanism; several types of which are illustrated in Fig. 18.2 and 18.4.

A foot-snare currently used for large ungulates in Africa was described by Mossman and Reynolds (1962), and shown in Fig. 18.2.

DRUGS

Mammals may be killed by drugs but the use of poisons is dangerous. Unless the drug is quick to act, the animal may leave the area and not be recovered. At present, poisons are used on a large scale in rodent and carnivore control programs. Generally these programs are under the supervision of state (Agricultural Commissioner) and federal (U. S. Fish and Wildlife Service) agencies, which are alert to new developments and skilled in the safety precautions necessary in such programs.

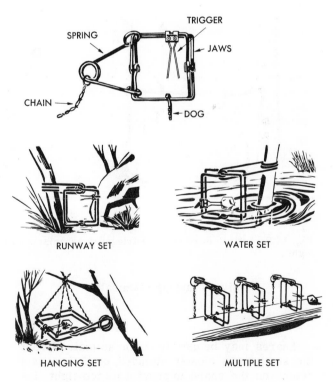

Fig. 18.1. The conibear trap.

280

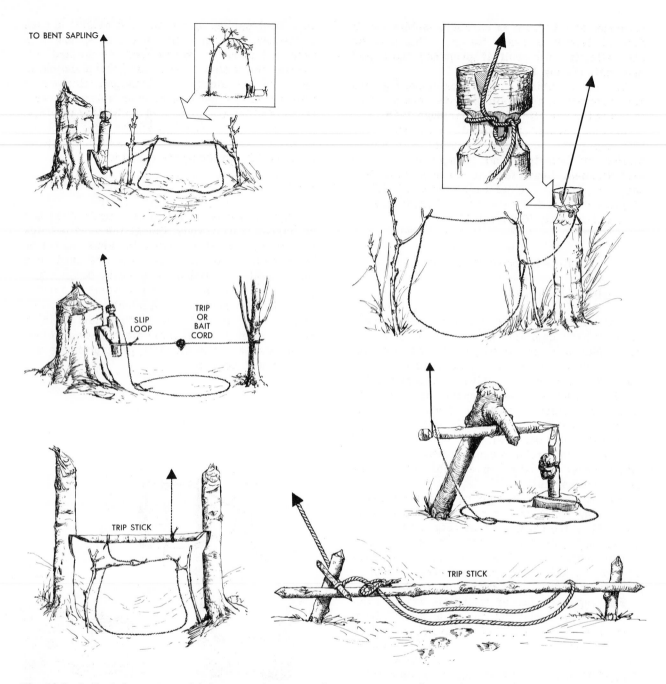

Fig. 18.2. Activated snares and trigger mechanisms (after Petrides 1946 and Mossman and Reynolds 1962 of lower right).

Live-Trapping Mammals

SNARES

Snares may be used to obtain animals alive if the snares are closely attended, or if there is a "stop" on the snare to prevent its too-tight closure. A stop is so designed that after the snare has tightened enough to hold the animal it cannot tighten further and kill the confined specimen. Mossman et al. (1963) describe the capture of African antelope alive with stopped snares. Keith (1965) used live snares successfully for snowshoe hare, preventing strangling by means of a stop-wire; however, he reports a higher mortality with this method than with box-traps.

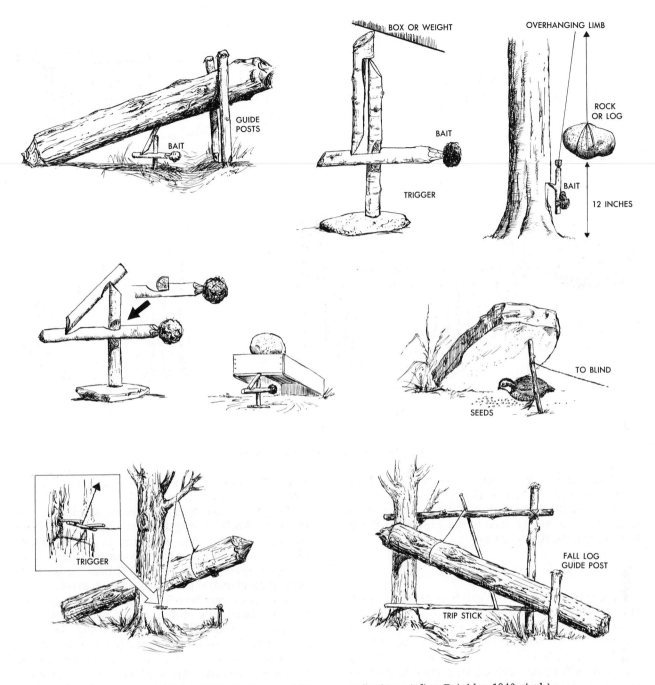

Fig. 18.3. Dead falls and types of trigger mechanisms (after Petrides 1946 et al.)

Deer, following well-defined migration trails, have been taken by means of snares in California. The snares are laid in clusters, without stops; they are so designed that when the deer strikes a trigger-string, the snares are pulled upward, catching the deer on one or more legs. The snares are fastened to a tree by means of stout rubber bands (from tire inner tubes) so that the deer, in its struggles to escape, does not have anything

solid against which to pull. Bells, attached to the snare, ring when a deer is caught, so that the trapper, who is camped nearby, can handle, mark, and release the deer before it hurts itself (see Fig. 18.5). This snare may be modified for use in a treeless area by means of a light, stiff 6-ft pole, which is horizontal when the snare is set. When it is sprung, the pole is jerked upright by a powerful rubber band; this upward motion throws

SMALL KINK IN WIRE

Fig. 18.4. Additional types of snares.

the loops of the snare up around the legs of the deer (Ashcraft and Reese 1957).

A foot-snare, including a triggering device (Fig. 23.7), is widely used in the capture of black bear in the Pacific Northwest.

BOX TRAPS

Box traps are used for catching animals which vary in size from mice to bears. They may be metal or wood or have screened sides. They may have a door at each end or at one end only. Open-mesh ends on box traps improve their efficiency for most mammals because bait scent is carried out on currents of air. Most animals will enter box traps more readily if they can look in one end and see out the other.

For mammals up to chipmunk-size, an effective live-trap (called the Scheffer trap) is made of two 1-quart oil cans, one with one end and the other with both ends removed. One is tapered, so that they can be wedged together. The door consists of a mouse-trap, fastened to the flattened top of one can, at the open end. A piece of hardware cloth fastened to the striking bar of the trap

forms the door. The trigger mechanism is illustrated in Fig. 18.6 (Davis 1956).

Traps of this type should be shaded in hot weather. While it might seem logical to include nesting material when trapping in cold weather, Llewellyn (1950) found that losses in *Peromyscus leucopus* were greatly reduced if bedding was left out and an abundance of corn was supplied.

A standard box trap for animals from chipmunk to small raccoon in size is illustrated, with construction and assembly guides, in Fig. 18.7 and Fig. 18.8. One used successfully for woodchucks was described by Trump and Henderickson (1943). A very sturdy box-trap, well anchored, is needed where domestic animals kick or trample the traps. A successful model was described by Edgar (1962).

Large mammals are taken in box traps of the same principle but adapted to the strength and trap-reaction of the species. For bears a very stout trap is necessary; it may be fashioned from sections of culvert-pipe, logs, or from wood and heavy wire. Deer may also be taken in box traps; the most efficient current design is the Clover single-gate portable, which is collapsible. It has a frame of 1/2-inch black pipe with the sides

283

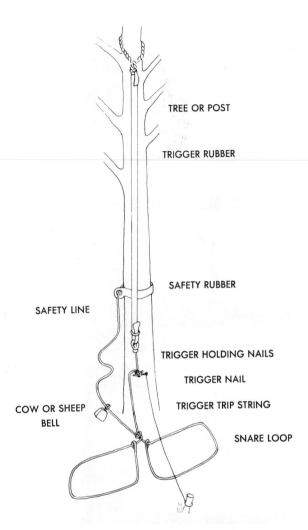

Fig. 18.5. Cluster snares for taking deer (after Ash-craft and Reese 1957).

and top of net, so that the deer will not injure itself in its efforts to escape (Clover 1956). This trap may be used in conjunction with a catch-net shaped like a bag. The opening of the net is hooked loosely around the opening of the trap and a 13-ft purse-line, threaded around the bag near the trap, is firmly attached to the trap. The gate is lifted and the deer dashes out into the catch-net. The impetus of the deer pulls the purse closed and the animal is bundled up in the netting bag and may then be handled (Clover 1954). Details of this trap are shown in Fig. 18.9.

Corral traps, used for deer, elk, sheep, goats, javelina, and other forms of big game which cannot climb sheer walls, are essentially large box traps without roofs (Fig. 18.10). The captured animals are either netted in the trap or shunted into a handling chute which opens off one side. Spillett and Zobell (1967) described innovations in pronghorn antelope traps and chutes using 3/8-inch nylon cargo netting with 2-inch mesh. Since corral traps are large enough to catch more than one animal at a time, the captured animals have room enough to run around if they are frightened. Therefore, care should be taken to have the corrals circular with no projections inside on which the animals can injure themselves. Such a trap for moose was described by Pimlott and Carberry (1958).

Mr. James Yorgason, Biologist, Wyoming Game and Fish Commission, Jackson, supplied the specifications for the corral trap, shown in Fig. 18.10, used at the Jackson Hole National Elk Refuge. He made the following observations which are typical of the considerations in all trapping operations; that is, the proper integration of

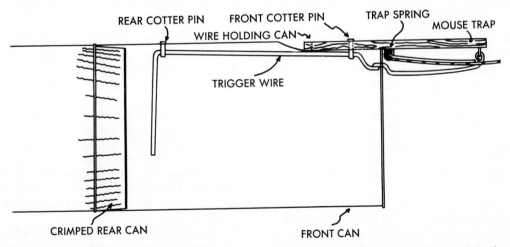

Fig. 18.6. Diagram of Scheffer trap. Note that the door swings down to throw mouse into the trap. To remove the mouse after capture, separate the front can from the back can (after Davis 1956).

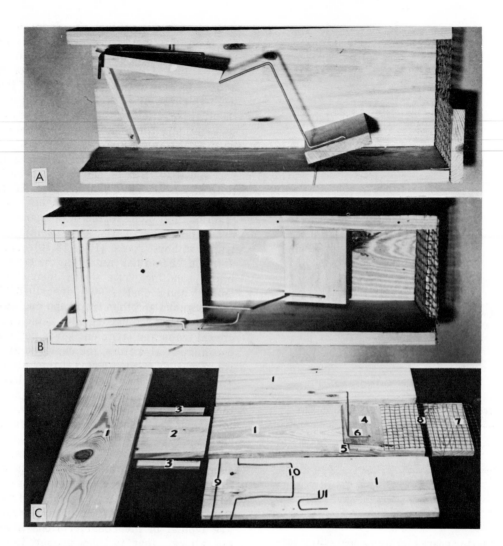

Fig. 18.7. Small mammal live trap, showing construction details. *A* Trap with side removed. *B* Trap with top removed. *C* Parts of trap, numbered as diagrammed in Fig. 18.8 (from Mosby 1955).

knowledge of animal behavior, technology, human resourcefulness, and a desire to improve the trapping efficiency and the well-being of the animals. The width between the pole sides of the trap is very important. If the width is too great, elk will try to jump through or escape between the poles. If too narrow, elk will hesitate to enter. Seeing animals outside the pen seems to allay some of their fears. The holding pens should be solid so elk will stand quietly while being worked.

Once inside, elk, according to Yorgason, "work exactly like domestic sheep." If the people working in the holding pen start from next to the chute and proceed to the rear of the pen, elk will run past them into the chute. If individuals stay on the high cat-walk outside the holding pen, elk tend to stand and watch rather than go into the chute. The low inside cat-walks are an important part of the trap. Workers should protect themselves when a bull gets into the holding pen (bulls are usually separated out and not handled), or when a cow "gets on-the-fight." Elk can be readily backed into the chute if they will not go head first. When they become irritated, they will face the worker who, by moving slowly and patiently toward them, will cause them, usually, to back right in. The person working the holding pen must get out after filling the chute or they will stand looking at him as he tries to work them.

The trigger wire on the trap may be lengthened or shortened to regulate the size of the catch. The longer the wire, the greater the probability of being tripped by even a few animals in the trap.

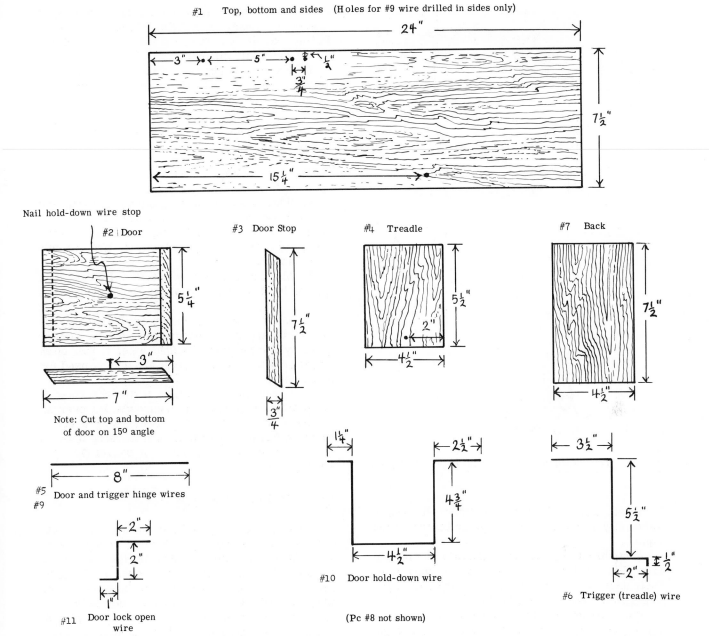

BILL OF MATERIALS FOR SMALL ANIMAL LIVE TRAP

No. Pieces	Dimensions	Part Name	Part No. (See Figs. 1 & 2)				
	ONE INCH DRESSED WOOD			FROM 9 GAUGE SMOOTH WIRE			
4 pcs.	7½" x 24"	Bottom, top sides	#1	2 pcs.	8"	Door and treadle hinges	#5, #9
1 pc.	5¼" x 7"	Door	#2	1 pc.	11"	Treadle Trigger	#6
2 pcs.	1" x 7½"	Door stops	#3	1 pc.	17 3/4"	Door hold down wire	#10
1 pc.	4½" x 5½"	Trigger Treadle	#4	1 pc.	5"	Door lock wire	#11
1 pc.	4½" x 7½"	Back of trap	#7				
	HARDWARE CLOTH OR WELDED WIRE				HARDWARE		
1 pc.	7½" x 9"	Back of trap	#8	18 - 6d box nails; 4 - 2¼ eye screws; 12 - 3/4" staples; 5 - 2d box nails			

Fig. 18.8. Parts diagram and bill of materials for small mammal live trap (from Mosby 1955).

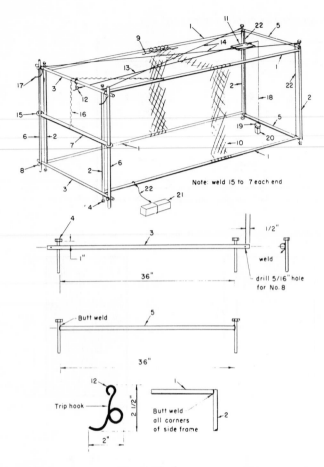

Fig. 18.9. The Clover single-gate deer trap (from Clover 1956).

In most cases, the catch is relatively small, especially in areas where regular feeding is not done.

A modified box trap for muskrats is a house-trap (Fig. 18.11) which leads the animals from their underwater runways up to a shaded platform above water level (Snead 1950).

For shrews it has been found that trapping mortality can be lowered by attaching a 5-gal can to the trap (Doremus 1964).

SPECIAL TRAPS AND METHODS OF CAPTURE

Beaver are live-trapped by means of both the Bailey and the Hancock beaver traps, both of which are set so that the trapped animals are kept partly out of water to avoid drowning. Where both of these traps were used by one crew, the following advantages and disadvantages of the Hancock trap, as compared to the Bailey trap, were listed (Grasse and Putnam 1950).

The advantages were:

1. Every time a Hancock trap is sprung, a beaver is caught and held. "Misses" with the Bailey trap are common and make future catches at the same site difficult.

2. Beaver caught in a Hancock trap are ordinarily held in less water and so suffer less from cold and exposure.

3. Sets may be made with the Hancock trap in deeper water, since it lifts the beaver when it springs.

The disadvantages were:

1. When the Hancock trap is properly set, most of the back face is out of the water. The exposed metal seems to repel beaver which are "trap-wise." Bailey traps, properly set, are entirely under water.

2. The Hancock trap is not as well adapted as the Bailey trap for setting in runs or channels.

Ordinary single- or double-spring steel traps may be equipped with padded jaws for the capture of many fur bearers. Padded steel traps, often offset or with teeth removed, are widely used for black bear.

Trapping small mammals under the snow is facilitated by placing a removable lid over an access-shaft (Fay 1960) and by using a string tied to the trap to steady it as it is being lowered into the shaft on the point of a shovel (MacKay 1962).

HERD AND DRIFT TRAPS

Some species may be herded with considerable success; others cannot be herded. Among game animals successfully herded is the pronghorn antelope. Current capture techniques involve preliminary herding by airplane into large net wings which funnel into a corral trap (Couey 1949). Elk are herded for up to 6-8 miles in winter in Yellowstone National Park by a pair of helicopters, and finally pushed into a trap similar to that for antelope. Jackrabbits may be herded in the same way but by men on foot or horseback. A peculiar form of herding is used in Europe for the capture of rabbits. Ferrets are released in the burrows of the rabbit colony and nets are set at each burrow entrance to catch the frightened rabbits as they bolt out.

Drift traps, consisting of hardware-cloth leads and funnel-entrance traps have been described by Imler (1945) as a method of taking snakes. A similar trap has been used to sample small mammals by Howard and his associates. It is

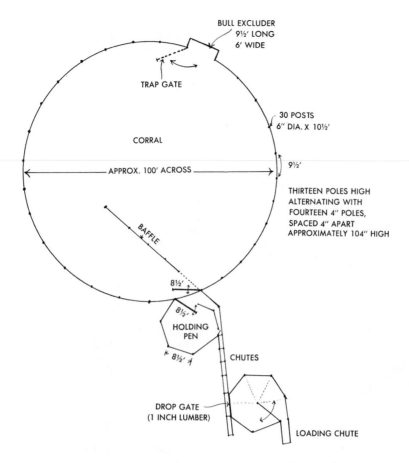

Fig. 18.10. Diagram of an elk trap at the National Elk Refuge, Jackson, Wyoming (courtesy James Yorgason, Wyoming Game and Fish Commission, Jackson).

especially effective in catching young rodents as they disperse from their nest areas (W. E. Howard, pers. communication).

Small mammals may be taken in a tin can buried with the top flush with the ground. The can should be of such size that they can neither jump nor crawl out. Cans may be conical for easier carrying and placement. Small mammals tumble into the cans in the course of their nocturnal excursions and cannot escape. However, these can traps cannot be used for mark-and-recapture studies, since it has been shown that shrews and *Peromyscus*, at least, avoid them after the initial capture. If a preservative liquid is kept in the can-trap, the captive will be pickled for future study. One satisfactory liquid is the fixative AFA (See Chapter 17) covered with mineral oil to reduce odor and evaporation. A combination drift and pitfall trap for small mammals, with use of a preservative, was described by Howard and Brock (1961).

INJECTED DRUGS

The capture of mammals alive by the use of drugs is in its infancy as a practical field technique. Crockford et al. (1957) discussed the problems connected with injecting a drug into an animal at a distance and listed the characteristics essential for such a drug. They are: effective dose contained in a small dart; drug stability; rapid absorption; fast onset of action; wide safety margin; no antedote required; rapid elimination; no gross effect on gestation; and no permanent damage to the recipient. Additional requirements must be met regarding the range, accuracy, and minimal expense of the method by which the drug is injected into the animal.

Early attempts involved the drug nicotine salicylate, powdered. This was made into a paste by admixture with honey, and the paste packed into the grooves of a drill-bit equipped with point and tail. This dart was fired from a CO_2-powered

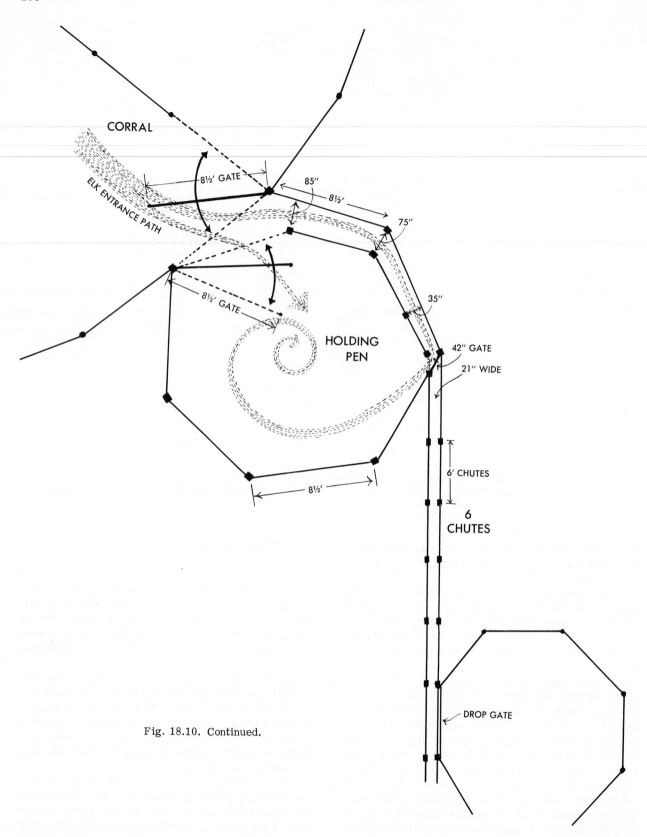

CORRAL

ELK ENTRANCE PATH

8½' GATE

85"

8½'

75"

35"

HOLDING
PEN

8½' GATE

8½' GATE

42" GATE

21" WIDE

6' CHUTES

6
CHUTES

8½'

DROP GATE

Fig. 18.10. Continued.

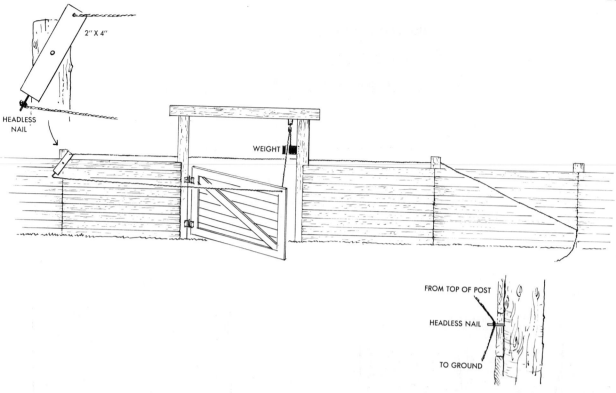

2" X 4"

HEADLESS
NAIL

WEIGHT

FROM TOP OF POST

HEADLESS NAIL

TO GROUND

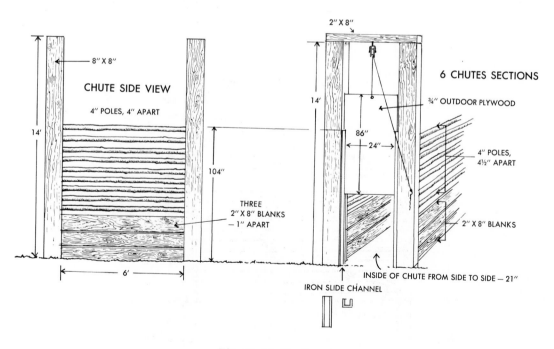

8" X 8"

CHUTE SIDE VIEW

4" POLES, 4" APART

14'

104"

THREE
2" X 8" BLANKS
— 1" APART

6'

2" X 8"

6 CHUTES SECTIONS

¾" OUTDOOR PLYWOOD

14'

86"

24"

4" POLES,
4½" APART

2" X 8" BLANKS

INSIDE OF CHUTE FROM SIDE TO SIDE — 21"

IRON SLIDE CHANNEL

Fig. 18.10. Continued.

290

HOLDING PEN SECTIONS

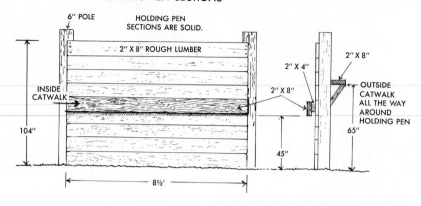

6" POLE — HOLDING PEN SECTIONS ARE SOLID.

2" X 8" ROUGH LUMBER

INSIDE CATWALK

2" X 4"

2" X 8"

2" X 8"

OUTSIDE CATWALK ALL THE WAY AROUND HOLDING PEN

104"

45"

65"

8½'

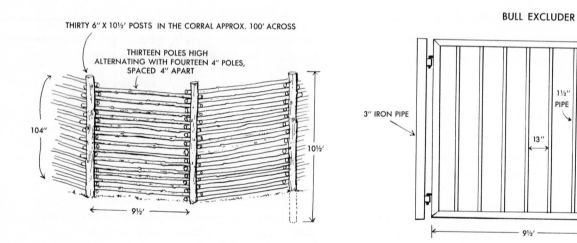

THIRTY 6" X 10½' POSTS IN THE CORRAL APPROX. 100' ACROSS

THIRTEEN POLES HIGH ALTERNATING WITH FOURTEEN 4" POLES, SPACED 4" APART

104"

10½'

9½'

BULL EXCLUDER

2" PIPE

3" IRON PIPE

1½" PIPE

13"

6'

9½'

LOADING CHUTE

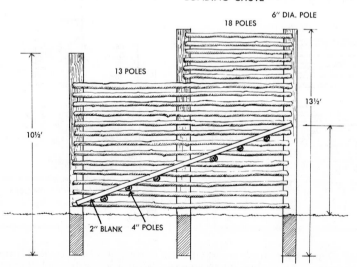

6" DIA. POLE

18 POLES

13 POLES

13½'

10½'

2" BLANK   4" POLES

Fig. 18.10. Continued.

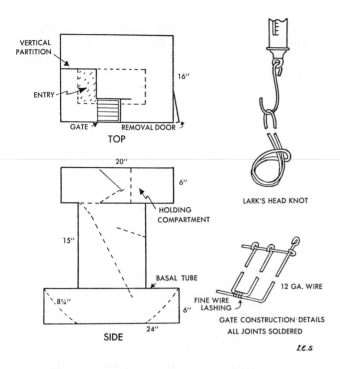

Fig. 18.11. The Snead family trap for muskrats, with weighing device (from Snead 1950).

gun (Crockford et al. 1957). Later, this same drug in liquid form was shot in a 0.50 caliber dart from a similar gun, the so-called Cap-Chur gun (Crockford et al. 1957) which was subsequently marketed commercially (Anon 1959). Most workers found this method too inaccurate for use beyond 35 yards, or at low temperatures (because of the loss of propulsive power). A much simpler dart was used with success as the head of an arrow shot from a long-bow (Anderson 1961). The

end of the shaft acted as a plunger to inject the drug (Fig. 18.12).

A return to the use of the drug in paste form was made by Montgomery (1961) who incorporated a commercial effervescent in the paste, so that rapid solution would follow upon contact with the body fluids. This paste was packed into a fenestrated tubular dart, equipped with point and tail. The dart was fired from a rifle of small caliber. This method of propulsion gave long range, high accuracy, and low cost but some darts penetrated too deeply to be recovered. African workers added the spreading agent hyaluronidase to the paste (Harthoorn 1965).

The two drugs most used currently for this purpose are nicotine salicylate and succinyl choline chloride. Some dosages for different species of mammals are given in Tables 18.1 and 18.2, respectively. It should be noted that fairly accurate estimation of weights of animals in the field must be made if proper dosages are to be administered.

More recently, improvements have been made in the gun, the projectile, and the drug. A special dart-gun is the 0.464 caliber "Paxarm," which is powered by 0.22 blank ammunition and has a velocity control (Taylor and Magnussen 1965). A conventional shotgun has been modified for dart-shooting by the insertion of a special sleeve in the barrel; black powder provides the propellant. It has been found that it is easier to use one powder charge and vary the range with darts of different weights than vice versa (Harthoorn 1965). The same author describes some improvements in dart design. Sowls and Schiveinburg (1967) modified a 0.38 cal. revolver to fire 2-cc darts for capturing *Pecari tajacu*. The range for uniform

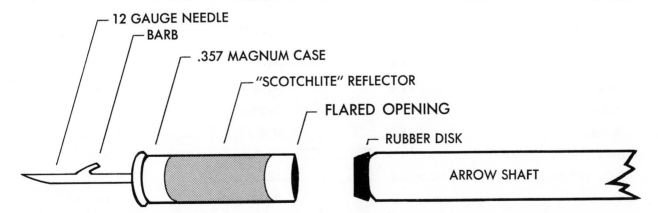

Fig. 18.12. A dart, or flying syringe, fitted over the shaft of an arrow, may be propelled from a long-bow of 45- to 55-pounds pull. The drug is loaded into the dart via the hollow needle after assembly and the arrow-shaft is slowly thrust forward until the drug is visible in the needle. This procedure reduces the danger of air-embolism (Anderson 1961).

performance was 10 ft, very suitable for anesthetizing animals in traps.

Chloral hydrate, dissolved in the water supply, has proven successful in the capture of kangaroos. It was dissolved at the rate of 5 oz per 8 gal of water. Ordinarily, the animals remained anesthetized for about 4 hr and little mortality ensued. However, this mortality could be virtually eliminated by giving the anesthetized animals a stomach wash via a rubber tube inserted down the esophogus (Marlow 1956).

Tranquilizer tabs, attached to conventional steel foot-traps, reduce damage to the feet of the trapped animals and facilitate their removal from the trap. These tabs are attached to the trap jaws and chewed by the trapped animal. The drug reported is *diazepam,* and the dosage is 1 g for coyote and 500 mg for fox (Balser 1965).

MISCELLANEOUS METHODS

In India, rhesus monkeys are captured in a baited trap consisting of two nets. These nets are shaped like two halves of a pup-tent and form a closed tent supported by four upright poles when the trap is sprung. The trap is set by staking one edge of each net and fastening a rope around the free periphery of the net. Short poles, attached to the free edge of the net, are flexibly tied to stakes driven at the center-line. Net and poles are concealed, the rope is attached to a pull-rope, and the area is baited. When the pull-rope is jerked and held tight, the two halves of the net are pulled upright and the trap is closed (Koford 1962).

Garst (1962) reported catching young black-tailed prairie dogs by the following method. A burrow was mined with a 1-inch length of dynamite, with an electric detonator, and wire leading to a nearby blind. The charge was set in a hole made for this purpose and located above the point at which the gently sloping tunnel turns sharply downward. When a young animal appeared at the burrow entrance, the charge was detonated. The young could then be caught by hand as it vainly attempted to retreat down the now-blocked burrow.

Other drugs may be used for immobilization and tranquilization. Tranquiline may be used on wild boars, 0.35 mg/kg (Zurowski and Sokowicz 1965); phencyclidine for fur seals, 0.10-0.20 mg/kg (Peterson 1965); and pentobarbital sodium for mountain lions, 24 mg/kg (Hornocker et al. 1965) and grizzly bears, 24 mg/kg (Craighead et al. 1960). Other usable drugs are atropine, flaxedil, M 99, and chlordiazoporide.

Capturing Birds Alive

The Manual for Bird Banders (Lincoln and Baldwin 1929; U. S. Fish and Wildlife Service 1961) and *Guide to Waterfowl Banding* (Addy 1956) contain much more detail on trap design than can be presented in this chapter. These publications are recommended to readers who desire more information.

BAITED BOX OR ENCLOSURE TRAPS

Many species of birds can be trapped, especially the gregarious seed-eaters. Traps differ,

Table 18.1. Recommended dosages of nicotine salicylate for immobilization (Anon. 1959).

Species	Approximate dose (mg per kg)	Species	Approximate dose (mg per kg)
Dogs	4.4—8.8	Cattle	1.7—4.4
Cats	2.2—4.4	Swine	6.6—11.0
Goats	4.4—11.0	Bears	6.6—8.8
Sheep	4.4—5.5	Horses	3.5—5.5
Deer (Black-tailed)	8.8 [1]	Monkeys	5.5—8.8
Deer (White-tailed)	3.3—5.5	Moose [2]	9.9—14.1
		Red Deer	4.4—6.6 [3]

[1] Koford (*pers. comm.*).
[2] Rausch and Ritchey (1961) report that moose under stress are often killed by this dose.
[3] Taylor and Magnussen (1965).

Table 18.2. Intramuscular dosages of succinyl choline chloride for immobilization of various mammals.

Family	Genus	Common Name	Dosage (mg/kg)	Comment
Cebidae	*Ateles*	Spider Monkey	2.23-8.81(T)	
Ursidae	*Ursus*	Grizzly Bear	0.74(C)	
		Black Bear	0.59(B)	
	Tremarctos	Spectacled Bear	0.30(P&W)	captive
	Helarctos	Malay Sun Bear	0.25(P&W)	captive
Felidae	*Panthera*	African Lion	0.24-0.55(P&W)	captive
		African Lion	0.75-1.50(T)	wild
		Tiger	0.75-0.92(T)	
	Felis	Mountain Lion	0.13(H)	wild
		Mountain Lion	0.17(H)	captive
Equidae	*Equus*	Zebra	0.19(Bu)	
		Horse	0.20-0.30(Bu)	
Rhinocerotidae	*Diceros*	Black Rhinoceros	0.13(Bu)	
Hippopotamidae	*Hippopotamus*	Hippopotamus	0.14(Ha)	♂♂ only
Cervidae	*Dama*	Fallow Deer	0.16(T)	
	Axis	Axis Deer	0.13(T)	
	Cervus	Sika Deer	0.09-0.12(T)	
		Barasingha Deer	0.07(T)	
		Red Deer	0.20(Ta)	
		Elk	0.11(F)	more for young range .008-.116
	Odocoileus	WT Deer	0.04-0.06(Co)	
		BT Deer	0.04-0.06(Co)	
	Rangifer	Newfoundland Caribou	0.10-0.14(Be)	
	Alces	Moose	0.04-0.07(Be)	
Giraffidae	*Giraffa*	Rothschild Giraffe	0.17-0.20(Bu)	in two doses at 15-min. intervals
Suidae	*Sus*	Wild Boar	0.60(Z)	range .27-1.34
Didelphidae	*Glironia*	Brush-tailed Oppossum	0.65(Ta)	
Otariidae	*Callorhinus*	Northern Fur Seal	0.30-0.37(P)	short duration
Antilocapridae	*Antilocapra*	Pronghorn Antelope	0.22(T)	

Table 18.2. Continued

Family	Genus	Common Name	Dosage (mg/kg)	Comment
Bovidae	*Hippotragus*	Wildebeest	0.06-0.07(O)	adult
		Wildebeest	0.08-0.10(O)	6-9 months
	Taurotragus	Eland	0.05(T)	
	Bos	Zebu	0.12(P&W)	captive
	Syneekos	Cape Buffalo	0.05(Bu)	with .1 mg/kg atropine
	Bison	Bison	0.08(T)	
	Kobus	Water Buck	0.35(Bu)	
	Adenote	Uganda Kob	0.35(Bu)	
	Alcelaphus	Jackson Hartebeest	0.30(Bu)	
	Hemitragus	Tahr	0.28(T)	
	Capra	Domestic Goat	0.55(T)	
	Ammotragus	Barbary Sheep	0.22(T)	

T—Thomas 1961; C—Craighead et al. 1960; B—Black 1958; P&W—Pistey and Wright 1961; Bu—Buechner et al. 1960; Ha—Harthoorn 1965; F—Flook et al. 1962; Co—Cowan et al. 1962; Be—Bergerud et al. 1964; P—Peterson 1965; O—Orr and Moore-Gilbert 1964; H—Hornocker et al. 1965; Ta—Taylor and Magnussen 1965; Z—Zurowski and Sokowicz 1965.

aside from size and shape, mainly in the type of entrance. The simplest trap, often used for small birds, consists merely of a mesh box, supported on one end by a stick. When the birds feed underneath the box, the hidden operator pulls a string attached to the stick and the box falls, imprisoning the birds. This principle has been used for capturing band-tailed pigeons by Wooten (1955), who used a 16-ft square wooden frame, tightly covered with 1-1/2 inch mesh, supported on one side by a 7-ft pole. A pull-wire ran from the pole to a blind. Weiland (1964) described the use of a solenoid for instantaneous springing of such traps.

In the funnel-trap, the wide portion of the funnel entrance is flush with the outer side of the trap with the narrow inner opening projecting well into the interior of the trap (Fig. 18.13A). Birds which enter then seek a way out around the inner face of the box and usually overlook the funnel. Usually horizontal wires are left to form a fringe around the inner entrance of the funnel, to discourage use of the funnel as an exit. Where traps are set on a fluctuating body of water, such as tidal marshes, the funnel is constructed tall enough to accommodate a bird at any level. The funnel entrance is the one most commonly used on waterfowl traps, being suitable for almost all species. If a trap is constructed of weak metal mesh, or fish-net, the funnel should be constructed of stout wire so that it will hold its shape.

The *swinging-wire* or *bob* entrance is often used in traps designed for taking birds such as the pheasant which are accustomed to walking through heavy vegetation. The principle is illustrated in Fig. 18.13B.

The *tip-top* entrance is a door in the upper surface of the trap (which may be buried in the ground). The door is balanced with a light spring, so that the weight of the bird will cause it to open. When the bird drops off within the trap it closes again (see Fig. 18.13C). This trap is not common, but has been used successfully for prairie grouse.

The *swinging* or *sliding door* entrance is most often used in song-bird traps. The door is supported by a device which is sprung when the weight of the bird depresses a bar or pan. This door is best used on a trap that is intended to catch only one bird at a time.

Trap size is usually a compromise between

efficiency and portability. If the trapped birds are drawn from a population which is migrating through the area, so that new individuals are constantly being caught, the trap may be large and permanent. Often, however, a trap must be moved frequently in order to catch birds previously uncaught. In trap construction, it is desirable to have the top of some soft material, such as fish-net, so that birds jumping or flying upward will not be injured.

If the body of the trap is large, a smaller catch-box is usually added. The birds are driven into this box and may then be removed through a door in the trap. Trapped birds are vulnerable to crowding, exposure, and predation. The best protection against trap mortality is prompt attention to the traps.

Waterfowl trapping is treated in detail in the *Guide to Waterfowl Banding* mentioned previously. However, some methods and considerations will be given here. If possible, traps set in water should be set over a firm bottom, so that the bait will not sink in the mud and so that trapped birds will not churn the bottom into a soupy mud which will mat their feathers. A swift current of water through the trap will carry away bait, while a lack of current will permit the water to freeze readily. Usually, vegetation should be removed from the vicinity of the entrance to waterfowl traps.

A "lily-leaf" portable trap useful for diving ducks where water-levels fluctuate daily was described by Hunt and Dahlka (1953). A portable rectangular trap with metal bait-pans and an improved gathering box, has been used for dabbling ducks, and was described by McCall (1954).

For upland birds, a variety of traps has been described, including (among others) the descrip-tion by Schultz (1950) for the bobwhite; Chambers and English (1958), Edwards (1961), and Gullion (1961) for the ruffed grouse; and Aldous (1936) for the white-necked raven.

BAITED NET TRAPS

For birds, such as the eastern wild turkey, that are too wary to enter an enclosure readily, a baited net trap may be used. A trap made of net and with a tubular metal frame may be suspended over the baiting place, concealed by overhanging foliage and dropped manually when the birds are underneath (Baldwin 1947).

The cannon, or rocket trap, now widely used for the wild turkey and for waterfowl, consists of a large, light net which is carried over the baited birds by mortar projectiles or rockets (Fig. 18.14). This is an especially good trap for geese, which are difficult to trap otherwise except during their flightless period (Dill and Thornsberry 1950; Salyer 1955). Although this method is still being modified and perfected, the following descriptions and comments may be made (from Addy 1956). Net sizes vary with the situation, but nets 30 ft x 60 ft up to 49 ft x 80 ft have been used; one 100 ft x 125 ft is being tried. Mesh cotton or nylon nets, 1-1/4 inch to 1-3/4 inch in size, have been used for geese. Cotton (#12 twine) nets should be treated to avoid damage by rodents and moisture; a mixture of gasoline and asphalt serves this purpose. The trailing edge of the net should be attached to stout rubber bands (cut from inner tubes) every 15 ft and staked securely. Stakes are set securely at the outer edge of the net's flight to lock it in place so that the birds cannot escape. One projectile per 50 ft is usually used. Each cannon is aimed about 20°

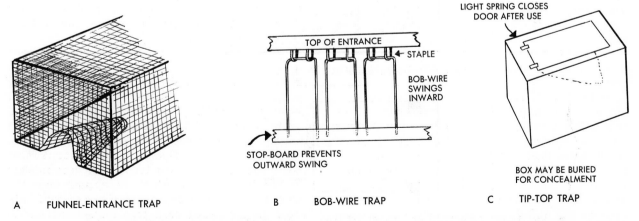

Fig. 18.13. Types of entrances for game-bird traps. *A* Funnel entrance. *B* Swinging or bob entrance. *C* Tip-top entrance.

296

from the horizontal, and the corner cannons are also aimed outward at about 45° from the edge of the net and set 5 or 6 m in from the end of the net. Cannon of various types have been tried. The propellant is usually FFG or FFFG black powder, loaded in a 12-gauge shell. A range of 120 to 170 grains of powder per load has been found satisfactory for nets of medium size. The cannon is loaded by inserting the projectile in the barrel, after coating the neoprene projectile-seal with powdered graphite. When the projectile has been rammed firmly against the breech, the shell is inserted in the breech, with electric squib (which acts as a primer) wires extending up opposite sides of the barrel. The barrel is then inserted in the tube holder. Firing is accomplished by use of regular electric cable and a blasting machine or by radio (Grieb and Shaldon 1956). Two-way radio units may generate sufficient static electricity to cause accidental discharge of electric blasting caps. Blasting machines may fail to operate on cold days and should be warmed before use. The blind should be built early, to accustom the birds to it, and is usually located 50 to 100 yards from the net, with a line of vision parallel to the folded net. The area under the net should be free of debris, and inconspicuous markers should be placed to show the location of the leading edge when the net is extended. Upon firing, the edges of the net should be lapped under or staked. If the net is shot over water, net and birds should be pulled ashore before birds are removed. With geese, up to 2 weeks may elapse before birds can again be brought into trapping position.

Miller (1957) described a type of cannon in which the propellent is bulk smokeless powder,

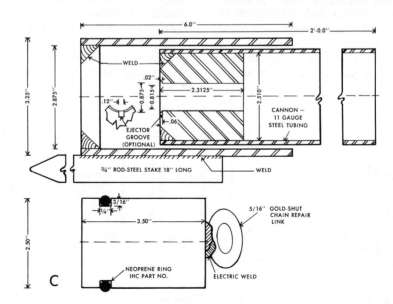

Fig. 18.14. Projection or cannon net trap. *A* Net and cannon ready for projection. *B* Cannons fired and net being thrown; note that cannon in lower right portion of the photo has not fired. *C* Dill cannon assembly and projectile [*C* from Addy 1956].

and the charge is protected from wetting. Marquardt (1960 and 1961) modified the Miller assembly for more powerful charges, so that larger nets could be propelled. He calculated muzzle velocities for different powder charges when used in the cannon. Lacher and Lacher (1964) described a cannon net trap mounted on the front of a jeep. Schlatterer (1960) fired two nets toward each other to capture sage grouse.

DRIVE AND DRIFT TRAPS

Waterfowl molt their wing-feathers all at once, in the summer, and while they are growing a new set they may be driven into traps. Currently a fyke-net trap is used in the pothole country for trapping flightless ducks and their half-grown young. Flightless geese may be taken, with care in herding, in a corral trap (Cooch 1953). Certain upland-game birds, although capable of flight, still generally run when herded. Large numbers of desert quail have in the past been taken by herding the birds into wings which lead to a tubular-enclosed cage. Tomlinson (1963) described catching dusky grouse hens and broods by driving them into a highly portable trap with 75-ft wings. Many upland-game birds are reluctant to fly if frightened by hawks; this fact might be utilized in inhabiting their tendency to flush while they are being driven into traps.

Rails and shorebirds have been taken with drift traps which consist of long chicken-wire leads directed into funnel-like openings. The leads cross the feeding areas, so that walking birds encounter them and are guided into the funnels. These funnels face in both directions and lead into the box of the trap (Low 1935; Stewart 1951). Drift traps also have been used successfully on sage grouse by placing traps at access points used by birds feeding in alfalfa fields (Pyrah, pers. communication).

MIST NETS

Bird netting, long practiced in Asia and the Mediterranean to catch birds for the market, has been introduced in the United States as a method of taking birds alive. McClure (1956) described the effective methods used in Japan. As described by Low (1957), the mist net itself is a fine black silk or nylon net, usually from 3 to 7 ft wide and 30 to 38 ft long. Two standard mesh sizes are 3/4 inch and 1-1/4 inch; the smaller is suitable for most small birds, while the larger is necessary to hold ducks, hawks, or ring-necked pheasants. A taut frame of stout twine

crossed by horizontal braces called "shelf-strings," is used in conjunction with the mist net. The net and shelfstrings are supported together by poles at the ends, the shelfstrings being tight, while the net is loose. The excess netting is arranged in a loose bag or pocket 3 or 4 inches deep below each shelfstring except the topmost one. A bird striking the net from either side carries the net beyond the shelfstring and hangs in the pocket of the net. A net properly hung, with 4 shelves, is about 6 ft. high.

In using nets, it is helpful to have a dark background. Wind interferes with netting. Birds should not be left over 1 hr in the net.

Phalaropes have been taken with a weighted mist-net suspended horizontally over the water and dropped when they are underneath (Johns 1963); this might well work for other water birds also.

Mist netting is particularly useful for those species which will not come to bait. It is also useful as a sampling device, taking all species in proportion to their abundance. Use of mist nets for the mourning dove is described by Harris and Morse (1958). In the U. S., special permission to use mist nets must be obtained from the U. S. Fish and Wildlife Service.

USE OF NETS AND LIGHTS AT NIGHT

Large, ground-roosting birds, such as the ring-necked pheasant and sagehen, can be taken at night on relatively flat terrain. An automobile equipped with a strong searchlight and seats on the front for the netters, frequently is used. When the birds are "fixed" in the light, the netters can pick them up with long-handled nets and swing them backward to the bed of the vehicle, where they are removed and placed in crates. This method is more effective if a rather steady loud noise is kept up throughout the operation. It can be used on waterfowl as well as ground-roosting birds. Labisky (1959) reported greatest success after birds have been roosting for 3 or 4 hr; he caught ring-necked pheasants (primarily) and also sora rails, Virginia rails, barn owls, screech owls, and common coturnix.

This combination of light and a loud steady noise has been applied successfully for capturing water birds by net from a boat at night (Cummings and Hewitt 1964).

NEST TRAPS

Ground-nesting birds, such as most waterfowl, may be caught on the nest with a manually-operated drop-net (Sowls 1955). A bow-net is a semi-circular frame, hinged at the ends, which was flipped over the sitting bird by a jerk on the pull-cord, carrying the net with it. Coulter (1958) developed a trap consisting of a circular frame, staked to the ground around the nest. A cylindrical net was fastened to the frame and the open end of the net laced with cord to form a purse-net closure when the cord was pulled. The cord led upward to a stake or limb and then on to the blind of the operator. When the trap was open the net was open and concealed around the frame; then a pull of the cord raised and closed the net simultaneously. Guide rods prevent the hen from disarranging the net while nest building and also insure that the net will not close until it passes over the hen.

Miller (1962) used the trap with an automatic activating mechanism. An alarm clock has also been used. The turning key on the alarm is used to spring a mouse trap which releases a rubber cord. The clock has the advantage that it springs the trap at a set time and the operator can promptly check to reduce possible harm to bird or nest. The trap has been used successfully on black ducks, mallards, blue-winged teal, ring-necked ducks, and common eider. An enlarged diving duck trap is most practical for eider hens at colonies on offshore islands (Coulter, pers. communication).

An iron frame, covered with 1-inch mesh netting, can be propped over the nest with a stick. Lead weights fastened to the front bar insure a good fall when the trap is tripped by means of a long string. A circular throw-net has been used successfully in capturing laying and incubating females. Also, a lightweight cotton net, 8 ft x 8 ft, stretched between two 12 ft poles, has been thrown over a previously marked nest. This "clap-net" requires two men for its operation. A blanket-net trap, measuring 12 ft by 12 ft, with 1 inch mesh, can be suspended over the vegetation around a nest. The edges are brought down loosely and attached. After the set has been left half a day, two persons approach from opposite sides and rush the nest. The hen usually flies straight up and hits the net (Addy 1956). Incubating diving ducks can be caught by setting a one-entrance funnel trap over the nest, with the entrance pointing along the path the female uses in coming to the nest (Addy 1956).

Mourning doves, nesting in trees, have been caught on the nest by manually-operated traps (Swank 1952) and with automatic traps (Stewert 1954). These are illustrated in Fig. 18.15.

MISCELLANEOUS METHODS

Newly-hatched chicks of ground nesting species with precocious young may be caught by hand if a low wire fence is placed around the nest before hatching.

Raptorial birds which perch on poles can be taken in steel traps with padded jaws set on top of poles. So that injury will be minimized, the trap should slide to the foot of the pole with the captured bird.

THE USE OF DRUGS IN TAKING BIRDS ALIVE

Tri-bromo-ethanol, a drug with the commercial name of Avertin (Winthrop-Stearns) was suggested as a method of catching wild birds by Wight (1953) who also pointed out the limitations imposed by the breakdown of this compound in sunlight. It has been tested as an oral anesthetic for the eastern wild turkey by Mosby, and Cantner (1956) who administered it as a liquid coating on grain. Success is reported providing the following steps are taken:

1. Prebait the birds and record the approximate time and number of birds using bait.
2. Place about twice the amount of grain which would be used at one feeding, coated with the undiluted drug. About 0.06-0.09 g per lb. of animal is the recommended dose. Sixty grains of whole corn will carry 0.75 g. Each cc of the undiluted drug contains about 1 g.
3. Allow 5-10 min for drug to take effect.
4. Approach drugged birds slowly and quietly and place them in individual crates.
5. Irrigate the bird crops to remove excess drug.

Using bait dosed with 1.5% by weight of alpha-chloralose, Murton (1962) was able to capture wood pigeons alive. Wood pigeons were successfully captured on the nest by baiting with 3% (by weight) alpha-chloralose on wheat. About 60 grains of treated wheat were placed just beneath where the head of the sitting bird would be (Murton et al. 1965). Williams (1966) used this same drug (2 g powdered/cup of cracked corn) to take wild turkeys. He found the first signs of narcosis in 20-30 min, sufficient uncoordination for hand-capture in 1 hr and general anesthesia in 2-5 hr.

Handling Live-Trapped Animals

In handling live-trapped animals, two objects must be kept in mind—the well-being of the ani-

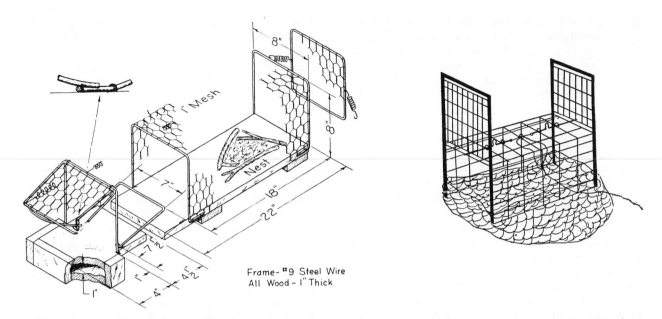

Fig. 18.15. Dove nest-traps. *Left*: Stewert (1954) substrate and nest trap. The central portion is set up as a nest site. If this substrate is used the doors are added to trap the dove on the nest. *Right*: Swank (1952) nest-trap. This trap is assembled around an occupied nest and is sprung manually when the dove returns to the nest.

mal and the safety of the trapper. Most birds present few safety hazards, although coots, raptores, herons, and egrets must be handled carefully. Most animals are quieter in the dark, so covering the trap, holding-cage, or head itself, according to the situation, will usually quiet the captive. Some species are quiet if placed on their backs.

In dealing with mammals, precautions to protect the trapper must be taken.

MECHANICAL RESTRAINING DEVICES

Grizzel (pers. communication), on the basis of considerable experience with mammals like squirrel, rabbit, woodchuck, mink and weasel, recommends a fish-bag of 1/2-inch mesh as the best handling aid. For skunks he recommends the use of burlap sacks. One is placed over the live-trap containing the skunk. The trap is opened and the skunk is allowed to run into a second sack. It may be handled in this sack, exposing the head for ear-tagging. Then, if the skunk is held firmly behind the head with the left hand, the right hand may be inserted in the sack to grasp the tail and hold it at right angles to the back. "The skunk may now be safely taken from the sack and examined for sex, age and other criteria. After examination, toss skunk lightly to ground and step back."

Crabb (1941) has devised a handling box espe-

cially for skunks, which present special problems. His box has solid sides and a glass bottom. The skunk enters the box, which is closed at one end, and a wooden block, with a handle, is inserted behind it to force it against the far end. It is held in place by this block while the trapper examines its feet and external genitalia through the glass. Then a slide is raised in front of it, revealing a hole through which it can stick its head. When the head emerges it is held in place with a leather strap while the operator examines or applies an ear tag. A similar method for black bear is described by Hiehle and Slosson (1961).

When small mammals of several sizes must be handled, as is often the case where there are adults or young, or several species being studied at once, the holder described by Erickson (1947) is useful. (See Fig. 18.16.)

Wire cones, fitted with a block to crowd the animal to the end are widely used for mammals of medium size. A simple cone of 1-inch wire mesh has been used with oppossum and raccoon. When the animals run from a trap into the cone, they become wedged in. Stepping on the cone at the rear crowds the animal and allows examination and tagging or the wire can be folded and the animal transported for a short while. Another cone with cloth adapter for traps is shown (Fig. 18.17) for use with animals the size of chipmunks to weasels. Mice may be handled in a cloth sack by grasping their skin behind the neck. Baumgartner (1940) describes a handling cage for the fox squirrel. This consists of a metal-framed box covered with 1/4-inch hardware cloth and contains a false or movable top. The squirrel enters the box from the livetrap and the door is closed behind it. Then the false top is lowered until the animal is pressed against the bottom and held still. The handles of the false top may be locked in any position while the animal is examined.

Large animals, such as deer, are often hobbled so that they will not kick while being examined. A hobble design is described by Barnes and Longhurst (1960), who also show and explain the use of a restraining bar used in weighing. Those animals with sharp horns or antlers may be rendered harmless by bending a section of garden hose and forcing one end over each horn. A simple harness with which to lift large animals for weighing is described by Pan et al. (1965).

Black bears, held in a steel trap with padded jaws, are handled by means of a chain loop, at the end of a 6-ft section of pipe. The loop is passed over the animal's head and twisted down snug, while the bear's legs are tied to trees; an anesthetic is then administered (Erickson 1957).

Trapped elk have been induced to leap over a low barrier whereupon they landed on a strong net raised just enough so that the elk would not injure themselves in their struggles (Boyd and Coghill 1964).

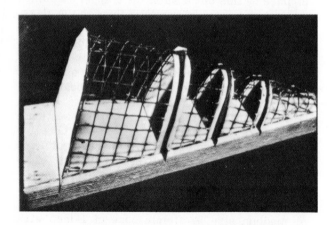

Fig. 18.16. Erickson adjustable small-mammal holder, with adjustable slides in place (Erickson, 1947).

THE USE OF DRUGS IN HANDLING BIRDS AND MAMMALS

The use of drugs to produce anesthesia, sedation, or muscle relaxation for the purpose of capture and handling wild animals has many advantages and a wide application in wildlife study.

The use of an appropriate drug will reduce the chances of damage to an animal resulting from forced restraint. Elimination of excitement reduces the physical and mental distress of an animal as well as the physiological and psychological complications arising from fright and shock. Furthermore, detailed measurements and the conduct of other research procedures on animals can frequently be carried out more effectively on animals that are not struggling.

The choice of an ideal drug for a particular animal and purpose involves several considerations. The drug should have a wide margin of safety; the duration of its effect is important; the potential means of administration is a major factor, as also is the time lapse between administration and onset of effect. See the discussion earlier in this chapter on the use of drugs for capture of wild animals.

Some of the terms used when working with drugs for altering the sensitivity of the animal nervous system will be unfamiliar to many zoologists and can be briefly defined:

Induction is the period of early administration. It may involve excitement and struggling and is usually accompanied by deepened respiration and accelerated heart beat. Urine and feces may be voided and salivation may occur.

Narcotic stage occurs when the animal loses volitional control. There may be exaggerated reflex response to stimuli. This second stage gradually or quickly gives way to the third stage.

Surgical anesthesia is the third stage in which there is a loss of consciousness, of pain sensation, and of the power of coordinate movement.

Analgesia refers to the reduction or removal of the pain sense without stupefaction or loss of consciousness.

Narcosis is a condition of analgesia accompanied by deep sleep or stupor.

Hypnosis is a condition of sleep produced by drugs.

Sedation is a mild degree of hypnosis, with the individual calmed and yet awake.

The method of administration is frequently of primary importance in the choice of a drug for use in wildlife techniques. Some can be administered by incorporation with food or water, some few can be administered by projectile, but by far the largest number require the handling of the experimental animal so as to anesthetize or sedate by injection or by inhalation.

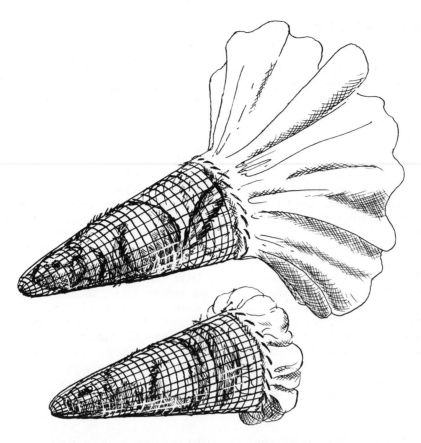

Fig. 18.17. An animal holding device can be made from a cone of hardware cloth or chicken wire attached to a dark-colored cloth adapter. The end of a live trap is enclosed with the adapter, the door or gate opened and the animal will usually run into the cone. They will escape once the cloth has been withdrawn.

Reptiles

Little published information on the anesthesia and sedation of reptiles is available. Details are summarized in Table 18.3. In general the venomous snakes are highly resistant to the curariform drugs, but many of the non-venomous species are more sensitive. Both drugs have proven satisfactory for some purposes, but the non-venomous species in particular often require resuscitation. Details of apparatus and technique are given by Brazenor and Geoffrey (1953). The reaction-time of reptiles, like other cold-blooded animals, may be greatly reduced by chilling. Of course, chilling makes handling venomous forms much safer.

Birds

In general, inhalation is to be avoided with birds. The air sac structure makes dosage control difficult. The lack of taste and smell discrimination in birds makes application in the food more practicable for birds than for mammals. There is much opportunity for research in this area. Table 18.4 lists the details of drugs used on birds.

Mammals

There is an abundant literature on the use of anesthetic, hypnotic, paralytic, and sedative drugs on mammals. These refer in particular to veterinary use with domestic species. Reference has been found for experiments with 22 drugs offering potential uses with mammals. Only a few of those of significance to the wildlife technician, with selected references and details, are given in Table 18.5.

Often, it is useful to administer drugs to mammals in traps to make it easier to handle them. A long aluminum pole carrying a hypodermic syringe on its end has been used successfully to immobilize skunks (Verts 1960) and foot-trapped big brown bears (Troyer, pers. communication).

MARKING ANIMALS FOR IDENTIFICATION

Basically, there are two reasons for marking animals; each requires a different sort of mark. One type of mark is for future identification of the animal in the hand (recaptured, shot, or found dead) and the other is its future identification, live, at a distance.

Marking Captured Mammals

For marking captured mammals there are three general systems; mutilation, tagging, and coloring.

MUTILATION

Mutilation involves toe-clipping, tail-docking, ear-cropping, hole-punching, fur-clipping, and branding. All forms of mutilation are open to the criticism that they maim the animal to some extent and so possibly affect its behavior or survival. Also, the marks applied by the investigator may be confused with those incurred by the animal in some other way. The main advantages of muti-lation are that marks may be readily applied with a minimum of equipment and the marks, in some cases, may be read at a distance. A standard system for marking small mammals by toe-clipping and ear-punching has been described by Blair (1941). Similar systems have been used on many mammals up to and including the opossum in size (Reynolds 1945). See Fig. 18.18. Sanderson (1961) even toe-clipped young opossums still in the pouch.

Dell (1957) describes the use of toe-clipping to mark varying hares for track identification. He recommends drawing back all the loose skin from the toe to be amputated, and cutting at the joint separating metatarsal and phalange. Only toes from the hind feet were taken, permitting a series of 24 if no more than one toe was removed from either foot. He found that tracks of marked snowshoe hares could easily be identified in the snow.

Ear-clipping and tail-docking both serve to draw the attention to the animal in the field and so can be used to draw attention to other, less conspicuous, markers.

Shearing, clipping, or singeing the tips of the hairs is especially useful when the hair-base, or

Table 18.3. Anesthetics and sedatives used with reptiles.

Drug	Species	Adminis-tration	Dosage (mg/kg)	Time to act (min.)	Duration (hrs.)	Remarks	Authority
Avertin (anesthetic)	Copper-head Snake	Orally	132.8	3	6+	Drug deteri-orates quickly in solution	Mosby and Cantner 1956
	Coachwhip Snake	Orally	176.3	3-5	6+		
	Snapping Turtle	Orally	176.3	5	48	Prolonged drowsiness	
Curare (paralysis)	Australian Tiger-snake	Intramus-cularly	6.0	72	1/4	Does not re-move pain sense	Brazenor and Geoffrey 1953
	Python	Intramus-cularly	1.8	55	3/4	Excessive dose-resp. failure	
Ether (anesthetic)	Many species of snakes and lizards	Inhalation	On demand			Artificial respiration often needed	Brazenor and Geoffrey 1953

Table 18.4. Anesthetics and sedatives used with birds.

Drug	Species	Administered	Dosage	Dangerous dose	Time to act (minutes)	Duration (hours)	Remarks	Authority
Avertin (anesthetic)	Eastern Wild Turkey	Orally (corn bait)	132-198 mg/kg 60 kernels of corn carry .75 ml of undiluted Avertin sol	0.10 gm/lb	5-17	1-3	Drug deteriorates rapidly (4 hrs.)	Mosby and Cantner 1956
	Ducks	Orally (corn bait)	132-198 mg/kg					Mosby and Cantner 1956
	Blackbirds	Orally (corn bait)	330.4 mg/kg		7	1.5		Mosby and Cantner 1956
	Starling	Orally (corn bait)	264.6 mg/kg		1	3+		Mosby and Cantner 1956
	Pheasant	Rectal	0.3 ml/kg in 3% solution					Balfour-Jones 1936
Equithesin (anesthetic)	Grackles & many others	Intramusc.	2-2.5 ml/kg	2.5+ ml/kg	1-2	1+		Gandal 1956
Nembutal (anesthetic)	Many species	Intramusc. (pectoral)	60 mg/kg					Durant 1953
	Domestic fowl	Intraven.	1 cc/5 lbs			1-2		Warren and Scott 1953
	Domestic fowl	Intraven.	0.5-0.75 grains (in 1 gr/cc sol)					
	Oregon Junco	Intramusc.	0.05 ml					Bailey 1953
	Song Sparrow	Intramusc.	0.05 ml					Bailey 1953
	White-crowned Sparrow	Intramusc.	0.07 ml					Bailey 1953

304

Table 18.4. Continued.

Drug	Species	Administered	Dosage	Dangerous dose	Time to act (minutes)	Duration (hours)	Remarks	Authority
	Brown Towhee & Robin	Intra-musc.	0.10 ml					Bailey 1953
	Domestic Pigeon		1.5 ml				Repeat injections 1/2 original	Bailey 1953
Reserpine (sedative)	Pigeons Rice birds	Parenter.	0.05-0.25 mg/kg		60-300	24+		Murphy n.d.
Chloral hydrate	Domestic fowl	Intraven.	12.9-38.9 mg/kg		1-2	1/3-1		Hole 1953

Table 18.5. Anesthetics used with mammals.

Drug	Species	Administration	Dosage	Dangerous Dose	Time to act (minutes)	Duration (hours)	Remarks	Authority
Nembutal (Sodium-pentobarbital)	Small mammals	Intra-venous	24-71 mg/kg			1/4 hour	Loss due to shock is a general hazard. 1/4 dose in 30-40 sec. Remainder slowly. Recovery long and violent	Wright 1952
	Rat	Intra-perit.	3-5 mg/100 gm in 6% sol.			1/4 hour		
	Mink	Intra-perit.	35.4 mg/kg		20	3-4		Mason and Kubin, pers. communication

Table 18.5. Continued.

Drug	Species	Administration	Dosage	Dangerous Dose	Time to act (minutes)	Duration (hours)	Remarks	Authority
	Raccoon	Intra-perit.	8-9.4 mg/lb.					Mech 1965
	Raccoon Marmot Fox Squirrel Rabbit	Intra-perit.	143 mg/kg				No ill effects	Rausch 1947 (important to see Mech 1965)
	Mice	Intra-perit.	81-174 mg/kg		6-15	1-5	1 gm in 10 cc water	Gates 1932
	Deer (White-tailed)	Intra-perit. / Intra-venous	0.44-0.74 mg/kg		15-29 / 5			Severing-haus 1950
	Sheep (lamb)	Intra-venous	28.6 mg/kg			1/2 hour	Admin. over 2 min.	Awad 1954
	Black Bear	Intra-perit.	0.44 cc/kg	0.55-0.74 cc/kg		2-1/2 hours		Erickson 1957
	Black Bear (juv. 24-32 lb)	Intra-perit.	28.6 mg/kg			3	Tends to lower temp. resp. and pulse	Youatt and Erickson 1959
Surital (thiamylal sodium)	Collared Peccary	Intra-perit.	7.5-9 mg/kg		15-60	1-12	Anesthesia only partial. No bad effects	Neal 1959
Avertin	Chipmunk	Orally	44.1 mg/kg		1	3-1/2	Lowers resp. rate	Mosby and Cantner 1956
	Opossum	Orally	242.5 mg/kg		6	10+		Mosby and Cantner 1956
	Woodchuck	Orally	198.4 mg/kg		2	1/2		Mosby and Cantner 1956
	Skunk	Orally	132.3 mg/kg		3	2-1/2		Mosby and Cantner 1956

Table 18.5. Continued.

Drug	Species	Administration	Dosage	Dangerous Dose	Time to act (minutes)	Duration (hours)	Remarks	Authority
	Cats	Rectally	300 mg/kg as a 2.5% sol		10	Lengthy recovery (24 hours)		Wright 1952
	Dogs	Rectally	500 mg/kg as a 2.5% sol					Wright 1952
Anavenol -K	Sheep and other ungulates	Intravenous	20 mg/kg			1/3 hour	Inject at 1 ml. per sec. Visual and audit function persists. Spinal block occurs. Inj. of additional 1/2 dose 10 min later prolongs action	Watson 1953
Chloral hydrate	Black Bear	Orally in honey	85 gm				Details not known	
	Kangaroo	Orally in water supply	3.9 gm/1 water			4	In the event of prolonged effect, use stomach wash	Marlow 1956
	Deer	Orally	55 mg/kg					
Paraldehyde	Beaver	Intramuscular	0.3 cc/kg	6 cc/10 lbs	6	1/2	Not satisfactory for deer	Hall 1955
Tubocurarine Chloride	Red Deer	Intramuscular	0.052-0.068 mg/kg	0.143-0.127 mg/kg	12-15	2-3		Jaczewski and Czaja 1959
Flaxedil	White-tailed Deer	Intramuscular	0.5-0.6 mg/kg	app. 4.0 mg/10 lb		1	Tensilon used as antidote (2.5 mg/10 lb)	Hall et al. 1953

Table 18.5. Continued

Drug	Species	Adminis-tration	Dosage	Danger-ous Dose	Time to act (minutes)	Duration (hours)	Remarks	Authority
	Elk	Intramus-cular	0.5-0.6 mg/kg			1/2	Overdose requires an anti-dote	Post 1959
Chloro-form	Collared Peccary	Vapor by nose	2 cc liquid (on cloth) per animal		Av. 1	5 to 15 min.	No bad effects on young or old	Neal 1959

underfur, is of a contrasting color, as it usually is. This technique has been used on fur seals (Scheffer 1950), newborn mice (Svihla 1934) and chipmunks (Yerger 1953), among others. This method is useful only until the next molt but has two cardinal advantages—it is easy and painless to apply and it constitutes a good mark for field identification. The possible series, however, is small. This problem was overcome by Chitty and Shorten (1946), who marked their Norway rats with a number drawn on the pelage with a depilatory. These marks lasted only two or three weeks.

Branding with a hot iron leaves a semi-permanent mark. It has been used principally on seals (Lindsey 1937; Rand 1950; Scheffer 1950). These brands have been successfully read 5-7 years after application in the Weddell seal (Perkins 1945) and 20 years after application in the Alaska fur seal (Scheffer 1950). In the beaver, the flat, hairless tail has been marked by branding (Bradt 1938) and by cutting (Hall, ms). Bradt (1938) found straight-line brands on the upper surface of the tail recognizable for at least 4 years. Cuts into the edge of the tail presumably last for life.

At present writing Dr. Keith Farrell of Washington State University is testing a promising method of branding with a copper branding instrument chilled to minus 94°F.; the application of 10 to 30 sec (for pigs and cattle respectively) on clipped portions of skin apparently inactivated pigment secreting cells, resulting in a permanent pattern of white hair.

Bighorn sheep have been branded with a numeral on each horn. A branding iron, heated copper-red, was used, with 7/8-inch numerals for ewes and 2-inch numerals for rams (Aldous

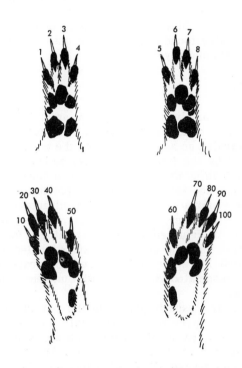

Fig. 18.18. A numbering system used in toe-clipping squirrels (from Baumgartner 1940 and Melchior and Iwen 1965) A Using only two clips, 1 toe per foot, numbers up to 108 can be obtained for marking 98 animals. By considering hyphenated numbers, e.g. 30-90, an additional 106 animals can be marked with the 2-toe constraint. B Using a constraint of clipping no more than two toes per foot the 1247 code, familiar to users of marginal-notched cards (upper left = units; upper right = digits; lower left = hundreds; lower right = thousands and thus 1+2=3, 7+2=9, etc.), has additional expansiveness.

and Craighead 1958). The authors suggest outlining the brand with paint for better visibility.

The webs between the toes have been punched as an identifying mark in beaver (Aldous 1940) and fur seal (Scheffer 1950). Such a mark is permanent and seldom duplicated in nature, but it is visible only at close hand and to a person consciously looking for it. Ear tattooing is a standard marking method for domestic rabbits which is suitable for any large-eared mammal or the membrane of bats. Tattooing is permanent when properly done but is most useful when used in conjunction with some other less durable, but more conspicuous, marking method.

Neal (1959) used tattoos on the ear of the collared peccary and found them ineffectual when dark ink was used on the dark skin. Craighead et al. (1960) tattooed a number on the lightly-haired axilla of the grizzly bear to facilitate recognition of hides after tanning. Robinson and Grand (1958) found tattooing to be unsatisfactory for bobcats and coyotes.

TAGGING

Tagging involves attaching to an animal a piece of metal on which is stamped an individual number and often an address to which the tag may be returned by the finder. Tags may be lost due to wear, infection, or even the gnawing or scratching of the marked animal but proper application will largely eliminate such loss. The advantages of tags are that they are easy to affix, easy to see, and may be returned to the investigator if found. Also, they may be discovered after the death of an animal in raptor pellets, predator scats, or may be associated with an otherwise unidentifiable carcass.

Tags are usually placed in the ear of most mammals. Where the ear is small, a fingerling tag is used. Even mice have been successfully ear-tagged (Scott 1942). In Wisconsin, 1500 beaver have been tagged (National Band and Tag Co. style 1005, #3) in both ears with over 400 returns. Even after 3 and 4 years most of these had both tags intact (Knudsen, pers. communication). A properly applied tag is, therefore, reasonably permanent. The tag must be placed so that it does not pinch and thereby interfere with the blood supply and subsequent sloughing. It is also desirable to place a tag low on the ear, where the cartilage is heavy, and on the inner edge, where there is greater protection. The tag should be as light as possible, since weight alone can cause a large tag to tear out.

Cattle and sheep ear-tags are often used on the ears of ungulates and bears. Cattle ear-tags of the strap-type have been used successfully on fur seals, being attached preferably at (a) the hind margin of the fore flipper at the junction of the furred and leathery parts, or (b) the hind flipper over the 1st or 5th digit, proximal to the claws. Tags should be of silver, monel, or stainless steel to avoid corrosion by sea water. Scheffer (1950) expected that by using duplicate tags an efficiency of about 94 per cent could be obtained at the end of 5 years.

In some mammals the ears are small, or tag losses through freezing or tearing are high, so tags are applied other than in the ears. Muskrats have been tagged by slipping a 5 by 24 mm aluminum tag through two slits in the skin of the back (Errington and Errington 1937). This technique of marking is most successful with muskrats not over 2 months old, due to the superior re-growth of blood vessels across the strip of skin between the two incisions in young animals (Errington 1944). There is evidence that this method is not satisfactory where the water is polluted, due to infection (Takos 1943). Permanent tagging of black-tailed deer was accomplished by Barnes and Longhurst (1960) who imbedded a plastic cylinder bearing an etched serial number beneath the skin close to the base of the ear.

Small bird bands have been used as loose-fitting bracelets around the hind legs of small mammals (Chitty 1937). On some species, however, leg-bands have been found to cause irritation, swelling, skin-puncture, and infection (Takos 1943). These difficulties may be overcome to a large extent by causing the band to encircle the Achilles tendon (*tendo calcaneous*) rather than the entire leg. Muskrats, foxes, opossums, and skunks have been successfully marked in this way (Cook 1943). Smaller bands have been clamped loosely around a hind toe on squirrels and kept in place by the toe pad (Cooley 1948).

Bats, also, have been marked with bird bands. Here it has been found that the most satisfactory location is "the distal portion of the forearm" and that if the band is loose enough to slide, the bat will not chew it (Trapido and Crowe 1946). However, a fingerling tag may be placed in the ear of the bat and has advantages, since it is easy to affix and, when bats are hanging head down, it is easy to inspect (Mohr 1942). At the other extreme of band-size is the spring-metal collar devised for the red fox (Fig. 18.19). This expands as the fox grows. It is large enough to bear a considerable legend and is conspicuous enough to attract the attention of an observer (Sheldon 1949).

Norwegian naturalists have tagged harp and hooded seals with paired disks joined by wires, one wire passing on each side of a tail vertebra (Sivertsen 1941).

A different type of marker applied to the muskrat, consisted of a waterproof plastic button, threaded through the loose skin on the back with a flexible steel needle and secured with another button (Hensley and Twining 1946). This plastic marker has the advantage of being visible from a distance on a swimming muskrat; there are as yet no data on its durability.

Sheep-bells have been strapped to the necks of deer (Hahn and Taylor 1950), and no doubt could be used on other big-game animals. In a California study, the bells were painted with the same colors and design as the ear-tag, so that the deer could be individually identified either from the front or the back (Jordan 1958).

Progulske (1957) used a collar made of leather for individually marking white-tailed deer. Individual designs in plastic of five different colors were used. This technique was not suitable for fawns but worked well on yearling and older deer. Craighead and his co-workers use braided collars of colored plastic with color-coded streamers and numbered tags for elk. When these are placed on calves a rubber band is used to keep them snug; this ultimately disintegrates as the animal grows larger (Craighead, pers. communication). Hewson (1961) used a similar collar to mark *Lepus timidus*. For male white-tailed deer, Hamilton (1962) used a collar with an elastic insert to accommodate the swelling of the neck during the rut. For the study of nocturnal mammals, a collar marked with designs in colored "Scotchlite" reflective tape was developed by Ealey and Dunnett (1956). It was found that designs could be recognized most easily if the design, but not the background, was reflective. Captive animals, marked for periods of 9 and 13 months respectively, had collars which showed some cracking of the reflective tape.

For the collared peccary, which has a neck too short and thick for marker-collars, a polyethylene braided rope harness has been devised. This has straps around both the neck and the body behind the forelegs, and carries an individual color patch on each side (Bigler 1966).

The jess, of colored plastic (Fig. 18.20),

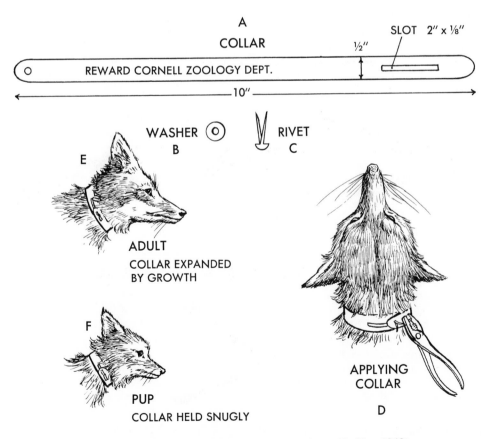

Fig. 18.19. Sheldon expanding fox collar (from Sheldon 1949).

310

has been fastened through a slit in the ear to mark deer, elk and mountain sheep, with good results (Craighead and Stockstad 1956). The same authors (1960) report fastening the plastic loop with rivets, instead of a jessknot; this permits use of a tail of contrasting color.

Mammals with large ears may be identified at a distance by means of a strap, or washer tag, holding a colored or numbered plastic disc (Thompson and Armour 1954, Labisky and Lord 1959). Ear-tags covered with colored reflective tape, which is visible when illuminated at night, have been used on rabbits (Richter 1955). Similar use has been made of glass beads (*Glo-beads*) imbedded in paint (Switzenberg, pers. communication). Care must be taken when all such materials are used that only inert metals come in contact with the flesh (not brass, for example) and that no pressure is exerted on the blood vessels. Impaired circulation leads to infection and sloughing. In tagging deer and rabbits it has been observed that if two plastic discs are used, one on the inside of the ear and one on the outside, too much pressure may be exerted on the blood vessels if a spacing gauge is not used. If

only one disc is used, less difficulty in retention is encountered.

Two methods of tagging employ devices which emit a signal. The leg-bracelet used on small mammals by Chitty (1937) has been modified to hold radioactive cobalt so that movements of marked voles could be traced with a Geiger-Muller counter (Godfrey 1954). The brown rat has been tagged radio-actively by being fed Ca^{45} in its food; this substance was transmitted from pregnant females to the young (Twigg and Miller 1963). A small radio transmitter has been placed under the skin of a woodchuck and its impulses picked up by a receiver (Le Munyan et al. 1959). Similar devices have been used in Canada in studying movements of wolves and to study movements of the black bear (Newby, pers. communication) in Montana. See Chapter 9 for a discussion of radio-tracking.

COLORING

Commercial fur dyes have been used successfully to color-mark wild animals. These dyes, however, are poisonous and must be used with

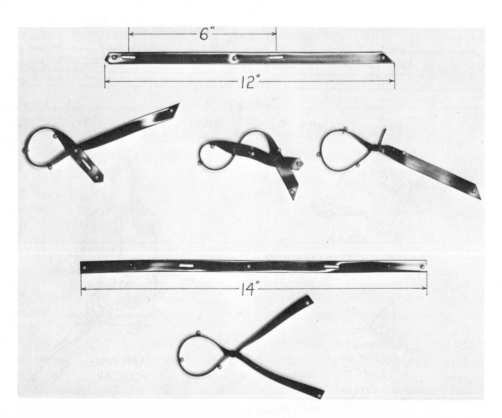

Fig. 18.20. The jess-marker used around the neck on birds and through ear-slits on big-game mammals (from Craighead and Stockstad 1956).

reasonable care. Examples are Nyanzol 4R (reddish-brown) and Nyanzol D (black). These may be fixed, after application, with hydrogen peroxide (Evans and Holdenreid 1943), or mixed with hydrogen peroxide before application (Fitzwater 1943). Dyes are useful for mammals of light pelage but the range of colors is small. The series can be increased by applying spots to different parts of the body. The coloring of pelage is dealt with in Table 18.6.

Brown (1961) embedded pellets under the skin and tough fascia of the back of the cottontail rabbit. The dyes used colored either the urine only, or both the urine and feces as follows: urine only—meta cresol purple, phenol red, and safranin; both urine and feces—cranol blue and fast green. Dye was administered in 80 mg pellets and 4 to 6 pellets were used per cottontail. Color was produced for from 4 to 7 days. Meta cresol purple was found to be of limited usefulness because its excreted color falls within the color range of normal cottontail urine.

A general consideration of the results of marking captive mammals leads one to conclude that most investigators tend to rely to too great an extent on a single marking method. It would seem a good investment of time to practice multiple marking. Where individuals need not be identified at a distance a practical system would be: small mammals—tag in each ear or ear-tag plus toe-clipping; bats—ear tag plus forearm band; large mammals—tag in each ear, ear-tag plus ear-tattoo, collar, or band around Achilles' tendon.

Marking Mammals Without Capture

It is the first thought of every big-game investigator to mark his subjects by means of bow and paint-tipped arrow but this is seldom practical. It is, however, possible. Elk, wintering on hay, have been so marked by Altmann and Simon (1952), while Kodiak bear have been marked by Clark (H. S. Mosby, pers. communication). Also, a marking dart has been developed for the Cap-Chur gun. On the whole it is usually preferable to use some mechanical device, tripped by the animal to be marked, to project paint or dye. A marking gun for small mammals consists of a mouse-trap, the striking-arm of which, when sprung, strikes the rubber bulb of an eye-dropper, forcing out the marking substance (Quay 1948). A marking gun for large mammals consists of a length of 1/2-inch pipe. At the rear is a nipple, drilled so that a nail—the firing pin—may slide through it. A 12-gauge shotgun shell, loaded with about one

dram equivalent of powder, is inserted in the pipe and the nipple screwed on. The hammer is the striking bar of a rat trap. When the trap is loaded, the pipe is full of coloring matter and a trip-wire crosses the trail and connects to the pan of the rat trap. When the victim presses the trip-wire the rat trap is sprung, the striking-bar hits the nail, the shell explodes, and the marking substance is propelled for several feet as a spray. The inventor has also constructed a multi-shot marking gun, powered by compressed gas (Clover 1954). Aluminum paint, sealed in the tube by a vaseline coated cork, has proven a good marking substance (White 1960).

A manually-triggered dye-spraying device, incorporating an electric solenoid for instantaneous action used successfully for desert sheep, was described by Simmons and Phillips (1966).

Two booby-trap devices have been used to mark moose and are suitable for any large, trail-using mammal. In both cases the object is to deposit the marking substance on the animal's back. It has been found that lead-base paint causes the hair to mat and fall out. Dye can be used to dark-color a light-pelaged animal but it is difficult to lighten the fur of a dark-colored mammal (Taber et al. 1956). See Table 18.6 for some dyes used in coloring mammal pelage.

If dyes are introduced into the food of mammals, the feces may be dyed. New (1958 and 1959) used various dyes (see Table 18.7) to mark fat, teeth, pelage, and droppings of small mammals. Kindel (1960) fed methylene blue, crystal violet, and basic fuchsin to elk in salt and found the feces vividly colored. Rhodamine-B, a fluorescent dye detectable in concentrations as low as one part in 10 billion, was applied to the food of meadow mice and detected in their feces from 2 hr to 2 days subsequently (Gast 1963).

Romanov (1956) reported on a self-affixing collar in the form of a snare which locks on the neck of an animal moving forward along a trail. Verme and Lowe (1961) have adapted this for use on white-tailed deer. Keith (1965) described a self-affixing snare marker for hares and rabbits. Although this method holds great promise, experience of several workers suggests that the following problems must be overcome before it can readily be used: the marker must lock tightly enough to stay on but not choke the animal, even if the neck swells, and yet it must not be so loose that the animal will stick a foreleg through it when feeding on the ground; it must lock in place before the animal becomes frightened and withdraws its head; it must come free shortly after locking so that the animal does not become injured

Table 18.6. Techniques for coloring the pelage of mammals.

Species	Coloring Agent	Special Techniques	Duration of Color	Authority
Pocket gopher	Human black hair dye with oil base: apply with equal part 3% hydrogen peroxide plus granulated soap until liquid is thick.	Recommended for light pelaged mammals	Until molt	Morejohn and Howard 1956
Pocket gopher	Ammonium hydroxide (4%)—1 part to 2 parts 3% hydrogen peroxide plus soap as above	Recommended for dark pelaged mammals	Until molt	Morejohn and Howard 1956
Squirrel	Picric acid in 5% formalin	Use on light pelage		Fitzwater 1943
Deer	Picric acid in saturated solution in alcohol or formalin	Applied to white rump area	Until molt	Webb 1943
Squirrel	Nyanzol A: 20 gm per 1 liter of water—hydrogen peroxide mixture in ratio of 2:1	Ring animal's body in broad bands	Until molt	Fitzwater 1943

in its struggles to escape. Romanov's model is shown in Fig. 18.21.

This idea has been carried further by Beale (1966), who set a collar-holding frame over water used by pronghorn antelope. When an animal put its head through the loop and touched a trigger just under the surface of the water, the elastic collar was released. This principle seems applicable to many mammals and also birds which will come to bait.

Marking Captured Birds

Captured birds are usually banded around the leg with an aluminum band, bearing a number and a return address. A band should move freely up and down the bird's tarsus, turn easily and smoothly, but should not fit loosely like a bracelet. It cannot be pulled down over the toes. The proper band size to use with various species of birds is shown in the appendix.

To keep order in the bird-banding field, the U. S. Fish and Wildlife Service and the Canadian Wildlife Service issue banding permits, furnish bands, and keep banding records (at Patuxent Wildlife Research Center, Laurel, Maryland) for all migratory birds. This standardization requires that all banders follow a uniform procedure for keeping records and a uniform nomenclature. *New birds* are newly banded; *returns* are recaptures at the original banding station 90 or more days from the time of banding or last date of recapture; *recoveries* are captures of birds trapped by someone else at another location; *repeats* are recaptures of birds banded or trapped at the same station less than 90 days before and includes "repeat" birds originally banded at a different station; *experimentals* are birds held for more than a few hours after removal from the trap, released other than in the immediate vicinity of capture, wing-clipped or pinioned, dyed, neck-banded, painted or subjected to anything more than being immediately leg-banded (numbered

Table 18.7. Some results of dyeing food for marking small mammals (after New 1959).

Dye	Species	Remarks
Alizarin red S	*Microtus pennsylvanicus* *Peromyscus leucopus*	Colors dentine surface of incisors and molars (*Microtus*—up to 5 days) or enamel (*Peromyscus*—up to 9 days)
Sudan III	*Peromyscus leucopus*	Colors fat salmon-orange to red for at least two weeks
Sudan black	*Microtus pennsylvanicus* *Peromyscus leucopus*	Colors fat blue-black
Water-soluble dyes	*Peromyscus leucopus* *Microtus pennsylvanicus* *Blarina brevicauda*	Dye on lips, paws, and pelage persists for 24 (*Blarina*) to at least 36 hours (*Peromyscus*).

and/or colored) and immediately released at the point of capture; *hand-reared* birds are those reared from eggs hatched in an incubator or under a setting hen, reared from domestic stock, or reared at any stage in captivity or from parents which are held, clipped, or pinioned; *sick* or *injured* birds are those not in good normal condition when obtained for banding and includes birds banded after recovery from sickness such as botulism; *wild* birds are normal healthy birds raised in the wild; *loc* or *local* birds are young which have not yet attained flight and can be considered as having hatched in or near the coordinate where the bird is banded; *I* or *immature*

birds are capable of flight but less than 1 year old as indicated by an immature penis, presence of the bursa, or an immature tail feather. (For puddle ducks, all birds after January 1, regardless of these three criteria, shall be designated *adults*.) The immature cloacal characters of Canada geese are retained to 2 or more years, so an *immature* shall be characterized as having at least one immature tail feather or an immature penis less than 10 mm long; *a* or *adult* birds are characterized by absence of bursa or presence of a mature penis. *Adult on territory* is an adult established on a definite breeding territory. *Flying adult not on territory* is not on territory or not

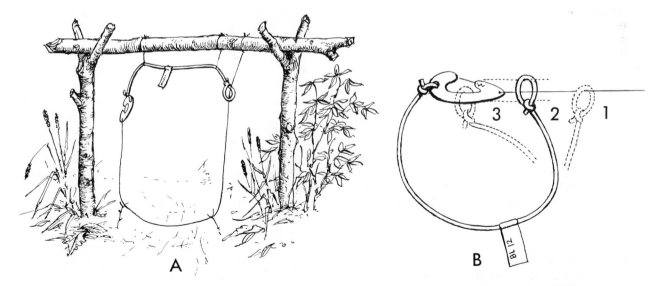

Fig. 18.21. A self-affixing collar which acts on the principle of the snare (from Romanov 1956).

summering. *Molting adult* refers to adults which have shed one or more primaries or secondaries. If the post-nuptial molt has not been completed, but the adult has regained flight ability, the adult is called *flying adult not on territory. Adult with brood* and *adult on nest* are self-explanatory (Addy 1956).

While most of these terms refer to waterfowl, many of them can be used for other birds, thus adding to the usefulness of the banding record.

Many states use their own bands for resident game birds.

Bands are usually strung, in numerical order, in units of 100. Bands must be opened to be placed on the leg and then closed so that the ends are flush and tight against each other. Needle-nosed pliers may be used for both these operations, although where many birds must be banded various devices for holding bands and opening them increase the ease of banding (Addy 1956).

Colored aluminum or plastic bands have been used to identify prairie grouse, geese, and other birds at a distance. The most durable plastic is "plexiglas," which must be molded in place while hot (Balham and Elder 1953). Frankhauser (1964) reported that colored plastic adhesive tape, wrapped twice around the leg, lasts a year or more on caged birds. The same tape, placed over ordinary aluminum bands on free-living sparrows, lasted at least 2 years (Gullion 1965).

A combination leg-marker and band has been reported by Campbell (1960). A strip of plastic is held parallel to the tarsus by the conventional leg-band, which passes through a slot in the plastic and around the tarsus.

For birds which stand with their legs in the grass, some marker higher on the body is necessary. Borrowing a technique from medieval falconers, brightly colored feathers may be "imped" to the wing or tail (Wright 1939). The imping process is illustrated in Fig. 18.22.

Similarly, colored feathers or a plastic marker may be wired or glued to the tail feathers (Trippensee 1941). The feathers themselves may be painted or sprayed with quick-drying lacquer or "airplane dope" (Swank 1952).

The feathers may be dyed instead of painted. Dye penetrates better and does not cause matting like paint but dyes are not bright unless applied to white feathers. Some methods are summarized in Table 18.8.

Ross's geese have been dyed in entirety as an aid in tracing migration routes. The use of any sort of marking on migratory birds is now, like banding, under the supervision of the U. S. Fish and Wildlife Service and the Canadian Wildlife Service, so that sightings may be recorded systematically and duplications avoided.

An ingenious method has been developed for dyeing duck embryos in the egg, so that they hatch with colored down. The dye, in a concentration of 5-15 g per 100 ml of water, is injected through the egg shell about 2 to 8 days prior to hatching. Care must be taken to seal the opening and to maintain sterile conditions. Two dyes used in the field were Ponceau SX (scarlet) and Fast Green FCF (bright green). Optimum dosages were found to vary according to the size of the egg and amounted to about .01 ml per 2.4 g of egg weight (Evans 1951).

More permanent color markers are of several kinds. One type consists of two tags joined by a silver plated safety pin, surgical clip, or monel wire. This is fastened to, or through, the loose skin of the back at the base of the neck (Taber 1949, Wint 1951, and Nelson 1955).

These permanent-type color markers have proven successful for upland game birds but not for waterfowl. For coots, it was found necessary to enclose the colored tag in hard waterproof plastic and to fasten the marker high on the neck (Gullion 1951).

Strips of colored plasticized nylon fabric fastened to the patagium of the wild turkey with button-tags are highly visible from the side (Knowlton et al. 1964).

Another permanent back-marker consists of a single tag held in place by a loop around the base of each wing. As used on English partridges, the tape is made of polyvinyl chloride with the crosspiece and harness loops of chrome-tanned horsehide. Numbers are painted on the tag with Vynafor black paint (Blank and Ash 1956). These markers are replaced annually when the birds are retrapped.

Markers hung around the neck have been used with considerable success on geese. These may be held in place by staples (Helm 1955) or the jess knot (Craighead and Stockstad 1956). Jess-markers have not proven satisfactory for ducks, as ducks tend to get their bills caught under the marker. They have, however, been used successfully on ring-necked pheasants, scaled quail, and several other species (Craighead, pers. communication).

A similar plastic neck-marker with a simpler looking device has been developed by Downing and Marshall (1959). This consists of a piece of plastic tape with a hole at one point and a pair of notches at another (see Fig. 18.23). The folded end of the marker is passed through the hole to the point where the notches allow it to unfold and

Table 18.8. Methods for coloring the plumage of birds.

Species	Coloring Agent	Special Techniques	Duration of Color	Authority
Waterfowl (in egg)	Amaranth, Brilliant Blue FCF, Croceine Scarlet MOO, Fast Green FCF, Patent Blue, Ponceau SX: 5-15 grams per 100 ml water	Inject 0.1 ml per 2.4 grams egg wt. 2-8 days before hatching, under sterile conditions	Field obs.: 23-32 days. Hand: up to 7 wks.	Evans 1951
Waterfowl	Picric acid: saturated solution in water	On undertail coverts	Field obs.: 2-3 weeks	Helm 1955
Snow and Ross Goose	Rhodamine B, Malachite Green and picric acid in alcohol	Dipped wings and tails in dye	Field obs.: 3-6 months	Kozlik et al. 1959
Pheasant	Malachite Green, Brilliant Green, Rhodamine B extra, Purple Batik: in 33% alcohol--66% water solution	Applied w/spray gun. Wetting agents useful with some dyes	Field obs.: 2+ mo. on ground; 4-6 mo. flushed	Wadkins 1948
Waterfowl; Mourning Dove	"Airplane Dope": white, yellow and red	On tail and outer half of primaries. Apply thin coat and hold feathers spread until dry to avoid sticking. On small species avoid loading wing tips	Field obs.: about 2 months when flushed	Sowls 1955 Swank 1952
Sage Grouse	Aniline dyes in mixture of equal parts water and 95% grain alcohol	Applied with remote-control spray	Not observed	Moffitt 1942
Ruffed Grouse	Rhodamine B, Auramine, Methyl Violet, Victoria Green, in saturation in 95% ethanol	Dipped tails of adults and rolled young in shallow pan, or sprayed w/atomizer	Field obs.: (shed feathers) and Hand: up to 8 months	Gullion et al. 1961
Mourning Dove; Scaup	Aniline dyes in water, grain alcohol, and acetic acid	Birds dipped and held for drying	Over three months	Winston 1954

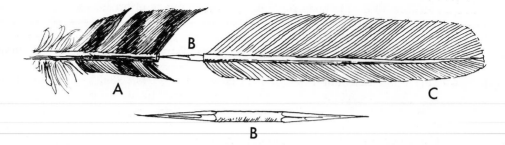

Fig. 18.22. The process of imping (from Wright 1939). The feather of the capture bird A is clipped, and a feather of contrasting color C is attached to it by means of a double-pointed needle B.

lock, affording positive size control and easy application. This band has been used on the legs of grackles, stilts, and herons and the necks of gray squirrels (Downing and Marshall 1959). Rigid plastic (plexiglas) collars up to 3-inches wide have been used for Canada geese; they are visible for up to 1 mile (Ballou and Martin 1964).

Nylon disc bill-markers attached through the nares by noncorrosive silver solder wire have been developed in Minnesota to mark waterfowl and pheasants by Lee and Lindmeir (pers. communication). These markers can also be made of plastic and numbered; their presence does not affect pairing in ducks (Bartonek and Dane 1964).

It should be noted that yellow head-markers have been shown to cause disruption of the pair bond in the mourning dove, although markers of other colors or locations did not (Goforth and Baskett 1965).

Lights have been attached to the legs of mal-lards to follow their flight at night (Bellrose 1958).

Marking Birds Without Capture

Several of the devices listed under the marking of mammals without capture could be adapted to marking birds; the snare-marker (Romanov 1956) has been used on grouse in the U.S.S.R.

Canadian workers have colored ruffed grouse at a short distance by throwing a blown hen's egg, filled with printer's ink dissolved in xylene or carbon tetrachloride. They also placed aluminum and bronze dust in dusting places and found it later in shed feathers (Bendell and Fowle 1950). Birds have also been marked at close range by squirting ink on them with a large syringe (Pearson and Pearson 1955) or by splattering paint (Miller, pers. communication). An automatic spray device was developed for the sage grouse

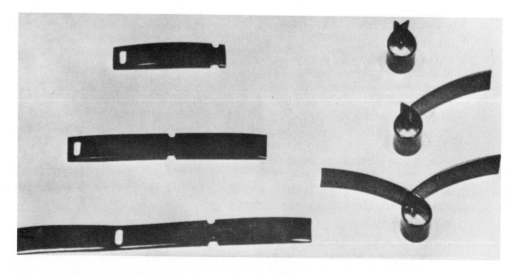

Fig. 18.23. Plastic neck marker developed by Downing and Marshall (1959).

Fig. 18.24. Compressed-air device for spraying dye. It is buried in the ground with only the sprinkler-head and trip valve (right) showing. Air valve is on the left (from Moffitt, 1942).

(Moffitt 1942). This consisted of a cylinder half filled with aniline dye in a 50:50 water and 95% grain alcohol solution. The solution was put under air pressure. A pipe, capped with a spray head, and equipped with a valve, led upward. The valve could be operated manually from a distance. The cylinder was buried on the dancing ground, so that only the pipe protruded (Fig. 18.24).

Mossman (1960) applied 2 to 3 cc of "thief detection powder" to a set of eggs of the glaucous-winged gull and found that the parent birds were brilliantly colored with purple. The eggs, also, were colored but the birds did not desert them.

CHAPTER NINETEEN

USE OF DOGS IN WILDLIFE MANAGEMENT

FRED C. ZWICKEL, PhD

Assistant Professor, Department of Zoology
University of Alberta
Edmonton, Alberta, Canada

Dogs have been used extensively in both wild-life research and management; their use may be considered a technique, or part of a technique. They may be essential to some techniques, or simply add to the effectiveness of others. Dogs often make it possible to reduce costs and human labor, reduce human biases, and increase sample sizes. Many breeds can do things for which man has no ability, or do some things better than man. They often increase the morale of a field crew (and thus its effectiveness) by increasing the total efficiency of a given operation, an advantage which may be overlooked. Conversely, if improperly used, they may have the opposite effect on both morale and biases.

The uses of dogs in wildlife work can be grouped into five broad categories: (1) locating wildlife e.g., for censusing, making brood counts, and searching for dead animals, (2) collecting laboratory and museum specimens or capturing wildlife alive (which may or may not include initial location of the animal), (3) studies of the behavior of birds or mammals when being trailed by dogs, (4) the protection of property from wildlife, and (5) facilitating the proper harvest of certain species where this is not otherwise possible.

TYPES OF DOGS

A dog is not *just a dog*. The American Kennel Club recognizes 115 different breeds and there are some 800 true-breeding types in the world (Hafez 1962). In wildlife work, it is important to choose the proper breed for a given job. Jobs can be classified into the following general types: herding, flushing, pointing, retrieving, and trailing.

Most of the dogs used in wildlife work come from hunting varieties; and within this group, there are many types that have been bred for different reasons. Davis (1962) and Griffen (1964) each gave a good background to hunting breeds and to their abilities and qualities, and Burns (1952) discussed the heritability of some traits of hunting dogs. There are many kinds of dogs from which to choose, as well as a potential for developing new breeds, or crossbreeds, to fulfill specific requirements. Winge (1950) presented a detailed discussion of inheritance and cross-breeding in dogs, with special emphasis on hunting breeds.

USE OF DOGS IN STUDIES OF BIRDS

Dogs have been used extensively for making censuses and brood counts of upland birds and undoubtedly greatly increase the efficiency of these operations. Wight (1930) was an early champion of the use of dogs in wildlife studies and estimated that a Gordon setter increased the efficiency of his census of upland birds by three times. Later, Bennett and Henderickson (1938) reported that a hunting season for bobwhite quail in Iowa was opened principally as the result of censuses made with the aid of bird dogs. Kozicky et al. (1956) described the adaptation of this technique on a statewide basis.

Bennett (1938) used Chesapeake retrievers, Irish water spaniels, and pointers; Sowls (1950), Labrador retrievers; and Keith (1961), both pointing and flushing breeds of dogs for locating waterfowl nests. Sowls pointed out that dogs are very helpful for finding most or all nests on a given area. It is noteworthy that Keith's dogs located a large number of nests that had been terminated.

Pointing breeds can be used successfully for relocating color-marked blue grouse (Bendell and Zwickel, Table 19.1) and spruce grouse (Stoneberg, Table 19.1). They have also been useful for finding nests of red grouse (Jenkins et al. 1963) and blue grouse (Zwickel 1965). Additionally, in both of the latter studies, the dogs pointed nests of a considerable number of ground-nesting birds other than galliformes, nests of microtines, and pointed a variety of different mammals.

Dogs are useful for collecting birds as laboratory or museum specimens; and in the case of game birds, this role certainly needs no documentation. Additionally, Gashwiler (Table 19.1) found beagles to be very useful for retrieving songbirds that he shot. Dogs also may be helpful for removing all birds from a study area (Bendell and Elliot 1966). They are valuable for searching for birds dying from natural causes (Jenkins et al. 1963) or from insecticides (Finley 1965) and have been used to find crippled bobwhite quail (Robel 1965), ring-necked pheasants (Stokes 1954), band-tailed pigeons (Brown, Table 19.1), and waterfowl (Marshall, Table 19.1). Marshall also used a springer spaniel and a Labrador retriever to pick up ducks stricken with botulism. He found that his dogs readily learned that only living ducks were desired and reported that a good dog can pick up three to four ducks to every one picked up by a man in the same amount of time. Dogs have also been used to pick up carcasses of botulism victims so they could be destroyed (Rodgers, Table 19.1).

Waterfowl banding programs are often made easier with the help of dogs. Retrieving breeds have been used extensively for capturing flightless ducks (Gollop 1956 and Addy 1956), but retriever-caught ducks seem to have a higher mortality rate than trap-caught birds (Lensink 1964). Dogs are also useful for herding flightless waterfowl into drive-traps (Addy 1956). Bowhay (Table 19.1) used a crossbred sheepdog to chase, knock down, and hold flightless Canada geese for banding, and Addy (1956) notes that Chesapeake and Labrador retrievers may be used for capturing flightless geese.

A number of breeds of small dogs have been used for "tolling" ducks. The dog is here trained to lure ducks into a "decoy" trap at the command of a handler who is hiding nearby (Anon. 1947 and Eygenraam 1959). In practice, the dog is commanded to appear and disappear from between a series of louvre-like blinds arranged along the shore of a narrow waterway. As many ducks become curious at the disappearance and reappearance of the dog, they are led by him, at the handler's commands, down the waterway into a large curved funnel that eventually leads into a trap. Once the ducks are well into the funnel, the handler appears at its mouth and drives them into the trap.

Dogs also can be used to help capture other game birds for banding. Klimstra (Table 19.1) found them to be an effective aid when night-lighting bobwhite quail. Zwickel and Bendell (1967) used pointers to both find and "pin down" blue grouse prior to capture with a "noosing" pole, and Stoneberg (Table 19.1) adapted this technique to treeing spruce grouse for capture. In like manner, Lehman (1966) described the use of dogs for pointing woodcock so they could be netted for banding. Entire broods were sometimes captured in one netting. Pointing breeds were also used to find and "hold" red grouse for poachers in 19th century Britain (Leslie and Shipley 1912). Once a covey was under point, the poachers would gently drag a net over the covey. This technique could undoubtedly be used by wildlife workers. Capturing young game birds for aviary studies may be made much easier with the use of dogs.

Whereas pointing breeds are usually considered as specialists for working with upland birds, they will locate many other birds and mammals also and, thus, might be used for both finding and capturing species for which they have not been used to date. Breeds other than those

Table 19.1. Names and addresses of persons who have used dogs in wildlife work as described in the text but about which nothing has been published to date. This list is presented so that persons with bona fide interests in the techniques involved can contact the handlers for necessary details.

Name	Address
Bandy, P. J.	Fish and Wildlife Branch, Hut B-6, Univ. of Brit. Col., Vancouver 8, B. C., Canada
Bendell, J. F.	Dept. of Zoology, Univ. of Brit. Col., Vancouver 8, B. C., Canada
Bowhay, E. J.	Wash. State Dept. of Game, 600 No. Capitol Way, Olympia, Wash. 98501
Brown, E. R.	Wash. State Dept. of Game, 600 No. Capitol Way, Olympia, Wash. 98501
Downing, R. L.	U. S. Fish and Wildlife Service, P. O. Box 2570, Ashville, North Carolina
Gashwiler, J.	U. S. Fish and Wildlife Service, Extension Hall, Oregon State Univ., Corvallis, Oregon 97331
Johnson, S.	Alabama Cooperative Wildlife Research Unit, Auburn University, Auburn, Alabama
Klimstra, W. D.	Cooperative Wildlife Research Laboratory, Southern Illinois Univ., Carbondale, Ill. 62901
Marchinton, L.	Alabama Cooperative Wildlife Research Unit, Auburn University, Auburn, Alabama
Marshall, D. B.	U. S. Fish and Wildlife Service, P. O. Box 3737, Portland, Oregon 97208
Pierson, D.	Wash. State Dept. of Game, 600 No. Capitol Way, Olympia, Wash. 98501
Rodgers, R. S.	The Wm. L. Finley National Wildlife Refuge, Corvallis, Oregon 97330
Simard, B. R.	Ministere du Tourisme de la Chasse et de la Péche, Service de la Faune, Hotel du Gouvernment, Québec, Canada
Stoneberg, R.	Dept. of Zoology, Univ. of Alberta, Edmonton, Alberta, Canada
Wight, H. M.	Dept. of Fisheries and Wildlife, Oregon State Univ., Corvallis, Oregon 97331
Yoakum, J. D.	Bureau of Land Management, Nevada State Office, 3000 Booth St., Reno, Nevada 89502
Zwickel, F. C.	Dept. of Zoology, Univ. of Alberta, Edmonton, Alberta, Canada

now in general use might also be of value in wildlife studies. For instance, the Finnish barking dog (the pystikorva) that is used for hunting capercaillie (Koskimies 1957) probably would be ideal for treeing species such as spruce grouse.

Hamerstrom et al. (1965) described some of the reactions of displaying prairie chickens to intrusions by domestic dogs. However, the study of behavior of birds, as determined by using dogs, is an almost untouched field. Much could be learned about game birds by keeping close observations and records of both the actions of dogs and the reactions of birds to dogs.

USE OF DOGS IN STUDIES OF MAMMALS

Dogs have not been used as widely for counting mammals as they have for birds. However, Anderson (1961) used dogs for obtaining marked: unmarked ratios of roe deer in a study to estimate the effectiveness of hunting. Caldwell (1963) used hounds for obtaining an index to the relative abundance of raccoons on different habitat types in Florida. Additionally, Cunningham (1962) used hounds to recover raccoons after trapping and marking to obtain a Petersen-Lincoln estimate of the population size. Goodrum (1940) used dogs as an aid in estimating the relative abundance of squirrels and Babakov (1961) suggested the use of huskies for censusing squirrels. The Finnish barking dog is used for hunting squirrels and it (or similar breeds) might also be useful for censusing squirrels.

Leopold (1933) and Longhurst et al. (1952) pointed out that dogs could be used to herd big game animals from agricultural areas. The herding of big game animals with dogs may be useful in other ways. A common problem in ground censuses of big game, especially in mountainous country, is that there are often areas of "dead ground" which the observer does not have time to cover adequately. Since well-trained sheepdogs will work to hand signals at distances up to one mile (Hafez 1962), such dogs might be used profitably to drive game from these areas so they can be counted. Sheepdogs might also be helpful for keeping game already counted from areas still to be counted. The color of the dog could be an important consideration here, as Darling (1937) points out that light-colored collies do not move sheep as well as dark ones.

Dogs have been used extensively for collecting laboratory or museum specimens of game or fur-bearing mammals; and, as with birds, this use needs no documentation. A few special instances might be noted, however. Small "den" dogs are regularly used for bringing fox pups from their dens in the midwest, and this technique might be useful to biologists who need young foxes or other canids for their studies (T. G. Scott, pers. communication). Additionally, in a population study, Kalela (1961) used dogs for collecting wandering lemmings. He felt that dog-caught animals gave a less-biased picture of the sex and age ratio of the population than trap-caught animals. In a related way, collections of animals with hunting dogs may be the best way of obtaining unbiased food habits data on species such as raccoons. The stomachs of trap-caught raccoons usually contain no food. Those collected with a light and gun, but without dogs, are likely to be taken in areas where they are concentrated at a particular food source. In another population study, Anderson (1953) used dogs to help remove all roe deer from his study area. Dogs also have been used for helping to remove cottontail rabbits from enclosures in Missouri (Wight, Table 19.1) and certainly would be useful in like manner for removing ungulates from large enclosures (or exclosures).

Dogs have been used more often for capturing mammals for marking than for counting them. A redbone hound (Brown, Table 19.1), a Labrador retriever (Bandy, Table 19.1), a Vizsla (Downing, Table 19.1) and sheepdogs (Bowhay and Zwickel, Table 19.1), have all been used to run down and capture black-tailed deer fawns for tagging. The use of dogs in these studies often resulted in the capture of both of a set of twins where only one might have been caught without dogs. Also, fawns up to 1 week older than can be normally captured by man, are readily caught by dogs.

Brown (Table 19.1) used a Labrador retriever and a black and tan hound to capture elk calves for tagging, and Murie (1951) noted that dogs have been used for capturing elk calves for domestication. Ritcey and Edwards (1956) used Labrador retrievers to help capture moose calves for tagging, and Russian biologists have used dogs to capture calves of caribou, but the breed used is unknown to the author. Yoakum (Table 19.1) used a Labrador retriever to capture kids of prong-horned antelope. He reported that the dog tripled his efficiency in this operation.

It is sometimes suggested that young cervids have no scent. However, the author's English pointer has regularly pointed fawns of black-tailed deer that were bedded down (at times out of her sight) and young enough to be captured. Brown (Table 19.1) also noted that his dogs were helpful in locating elk calves by smell.

A rather unusual method of capturing roe deer has been developed in England (Bramley 1966). The deer are run into 5-ft high nets with the aid of trained beagles. About 80% of the population on one study area has now been captured (principally with this technique) and individually marked.

Hornocker et al. (1965), Pierson (Table 19.1), and Cunningham (1962) have used hounds for bringing mountain lions, black bears, and raccoons respectively, to bay for immobilization with drugs. The animals were individually marked and often relocated for identification by running with dogs. Pierson instrumented some of his bears with radios and found dogs valuable for recapturing these animals so they could be re-instrumented. He pointed out, however that only about one in ten good "cat" or "coon" dogs will run black bears successfully.

Simard (Table 19.1) has used a pack of three Norwegian elk hounds to bring moose to bay for immobilization. Simard also used his elk hounds to trail and locate drugged moose that were lost from sight before becoming immobile. In other studies involving immobilization, Merriam (1962), Hill (1966), and Downing (Table 19.1) found dogs valuable for trailing drugged deer that had been lost from sight before the drugs took effect. Downing found that, when using dogs, the speed of immobilization was unimportant. Thus, he could reduce the recommended dosage of the drug, and, consequently, the mortality. He has recently made 60 consecutive captures (using nicotine) without a loss due to the drug. A Vizsla that he now uses for trailing such deer finds the immobilized animal, returns to the handler, and then leads the handler to the deer. Downing estimated that 19 of the last 48 deer that he has immobilized would have been lost without the help of this dog.

Taber and Dasmann (1958) pointed out that a good dog is useful for finding wounded deer. Downing (Table 19.1) used a Weimaraner to trail crippled deer so as to estimate crippling losses. Of 69 wounded deer that were found, 41 left no visible trail, so could not have been trailed by man. Biologists in several southeastern states have used dogs for the purpose of finding wounded deer on game management areas where hunting deer with dogs is otherwise prohibited (Johnson and Marchinton, Table 19.1).

Several workers have studied the behavior of wild lagomorphs being pursued by dogs. Carr (1939) noted the escape reactions of marsh rabbits when running ahead of dogs and Lowe (1958) and Toll et al. (1960) studied the home range of swamp rabbits when being chased by dogs. The latter authors found these determinations of home range to correspond closely to those determined from trapping individually marked rabbits. They suggested that running rabbits with dogs is a rapid and simple technique for studying their home range. Tyson (1959) used dogs to trail deer and determine the extent of their movement during the night. From this information he was able to develop a workable track-count population census method.

In the Southeast, where hunting deer with dogs is a common practice, there is need for a great deal of research on the dog-deer relationship. Marchinton (1964) used dogs to study the movement patterns of deer that were being pursued. Recently at the Alabama Wildlife Research Unit he has used dogs to chase radio-instrumented deer. Some biologists feel that hunting deer with dogs more nearly simulates natural predation and may thus offset some of the deleterious genetic effects that may result from the extermination of natural predators (Marchinton, Table 19.1).

GENERAL ASPECTS ON THE USE OF DOGS

The running of birds and mammals with dogs might be adaptable for studying behavior in many different species. Scott and Fuller (1965) pointed out that man's selective breeding of dogs has modified the dogs' behavior mainly quantitatively, rather than qualitatively. Thus, some breeds of dogs might be used as simulated predators to study the basic hunting patterns of canids. The growing field of biotelemetry adds still greater possibilities to this aspect. Since dogs can be instrumented much easier than wild animals, radio-equipped dogs might be used to secure information on the behavior of both predators and prey. (However, because of individual variability among dogs, large scale tests might be required.)

In general, most uses of dogs in the wildlife field involve their sense of smell. Krushinskii and Floess (cited in Hafez 1962) reported that 10-20 mg injections of amphetamine markedly increased the sense of smell and trailing accuracy in hunting dogs. This technique might be exploited by wildlife biologists. However, amphetamine must be used with some caution and, before use, a veterinarian should be consulted.

The use of dogs as pack animals certainly has not been exploited to its fullest by wildlife biologists. Hafez (1962) pointed out that dogs can carry up to one-half their own body weight. An outstanding example of their potential capability is the use of sled dogs. The encouragement of the use of dogs by sportsmen for increasing their hunting success, for reducing crippling losses, and for adding to the enjoyment of their hunt should not be overlooked by biologists as a management technique.

It is probable that many well-equipped ecological stations and wildlife agencies will, in the future, as some have in the past (e.g. Idaho Cooperative Wildlife Research Unit 1949-50, P.D. Dalke, Table 19.1, include a kennel with various breeds of dogs as a necessary part of their capital equipment. Even now, the Nature Conservancy's Unit of Grouse and Moorland Ecology in Scotland maintains a kennel with pointing breeds for use in their studies of red grouse, and Bendell (Table 19.1) maintains a stock of pointing dogs for his studies of blue grouse. The Alabama Cooperative Wildlife Research Unit also maintains a kennel with raccoon and deer hounds and bird dogs for research purposes.

HANDLING AND TRAINING

The value of dogs to wildlife biologists is dependent on the inherent abilities of the dogs, plus their domesticability. After finding a breed that suits a need, one must *bring the dog under control*. A fine dog, ill-trained, may be more bother than it is worth.

The ability to train and handle a dog is an art that comes easier for some people than for others. However, there are many books available on training, and practically anyone with a little patience and understanding can train dogs adequately for use in most situations. Three useful general references are *Bird Dogs in Sport and Conservation* (Yeatter 1948), the *Sports Illustrated Book of Training Dogs* (Sports Illustrated 1959), and *Modern Dog Encyclopedia* (Davis 1956).

Training often is considered by some wildlifers to be a long and laborious procedure. Others consider it an easy and not very time consuming by-product of the normal course of field work. Workers at the Alabama Cooperative Wildlife Research Unit find it more economical and satisfactory to purchase trained pointers and setters than to train them. Others have found that the type of skill needed, e.g. to capture a deer fawn, is impossible to obtain other than through special training; ie. wildlife needs are often unrelated to hunting, which is the usual professional training available. A trained quail dog will cost between $150 and $200, whereas a puppy, initially acquired for little money but reared and trained by a wildlifer, will cost much more if the wildlifer's time is included. On the other hand, all dogs need not be purchased and pups from personal kennels cost "nothing." The decision to purchase or to self train a dog depends partly on the kind of training required. A few simple commands, well learned, will bring most dogs under adequate control for many types of field work. Basic training includes a response by the dog to its name and the commands "go," "come," "sit," "heel," "no," and "whoa," and, for some types of work, "fetch." With intensive training, the author and co-workers have taught a number of breeds to respond adequately to all these commands within 3 weeks or less, with some of the dogs being only about 6 months of age at the time. It cannot be stressed too strongly that for most effective use, the dog must be under control of the handler.

A wildlife biologist is sometimes dissatisfied with the performance of dogs in his work, often because he is asking a dog of one breed to do something for which it has little or no ability. It is also important to recognize that there are individual differences within breeds, or within litters, and that some individuals are of no value for field work. Some trainers estimate that only about one-half the pups from any given litter will be worth training, and trainability usually cannot be evaluated when the puppy is very small. One must be willing to put useless dogs aside, as they may be more of a liability to a study than an asset.

The proper care, feeding, and handling of dogs while in the field is an important consideration if they are to perform most efficiently. The *Guide to Waterfowl Banding* (Addy 1956) gives an excellent coverage of this subject.

CHAPTER TWENTY

CRITERIA OF SEX AND AGE

RICHARD D. TABER, PhD[1]

Professor; School of Forest Resources
University of Washington
Seattle, Washington

One of the most powerful tools of the wildlife investigator is an understanding of the structure of the population and of the kill. By structure is meant the division of the population into age and sex classes. This division permits a determination of breeding females, their young of the year, and, in long-lived species, of yearling and even older classes. Thus the production and the survival of that production may be found—information of fundamental importance to an understanding of population dynamics. See Chapter 22.

Some animals on favorable range breed and produce young during the season in which they are born. Examples are the cottontail, mice, and rats. Others breed for the first time when a little under 1 year old. Examples are pheasants,

quail, mallard, and coyote. Still others breed for the first time at about 2 years, or even later. It is not possible to give a normal time of first breeding for each species, especially among mammals, because within each species there is a good deal of variation related to such factors as the length of the breeding season and the nutritive plane of the individual animal. Mule deer, for example, rarely have been known to breed as fawns and produce young on their first birthday (Rampont 1926, Shantz 1943, Robinette and Gashwiler 1950). On good range they usually first breed as yearlings, giving birth at 2 years. On over-crowded or unproductive range, however, they may not breed until 2-1/2 years of age, or even older (Taber 1953, Longhurst pers. communication). Thus, a statement that mule deer breed as yearlings would be true for most mule deer but untrue for many others.

[1]Received for publication, August 1966.

DEFINITIONS

Some terms frequently used in population analysis are defined as follows:

immature or juvenile = an individual too young to breed and still distinguishable from breeding adults by external characters

subadult = an individual which has not bred but which externally resembles an adult

yearling = an individual over one but under 2 years

two-year-old = an individual over 2 but under 3 years

adult = an individual which has bred

population turnover = the length of time it takes a given year-class to disappear from the population. This may more precisely be stated as the time required for 100 animals to be reduced to 0.5 animals (Petrides 1949).

Animals which have a high reproductive rate also have a high turnover rate. For pheasants and quail, for example, the turnover rate is usually about 4 or 5 years, less if mortality is high and more if it is low. At any one time the population consists mostly of animals under 1 year old. A 3-year old animal is rare. Because of this rapid turnover and the scarcity of older individuals, population analysis is usually satisfied if, during the fall hunting season, a distinction may be drawn between the animals entering the population during that year and the older animals. For that reason a good deal of attention is given below to criteria for distinguishing between these two classes.

Among longer-lived animals it is highly desirable to define criteria of age for those over 1 year, so that this group, which constitutes the majority of the population, may be broken into age-groups. These criteria are necessary for an analysis of population dynamics. Consequently, more detailed age criteria have been developed for most of our North American species of big-game mammals. These aging techniques are based on the rate of tooth replacement and wear, the rate of skeletal maturation, the periodic growth of horns, etc. These methods, which will be dealt with below, are extremely useful. The investigator should be cautioned, however, that these processes of growth are to some extent controlled by health and nutrition. They may be slower in one individual and more rapid in another. Such factors must be considered if they are to be used with reliability.

In the discussion which follows, birds and mammals are considered separately. The treatment of each of these major groups is introduced by a discussion of the changes which take place generally due to growth and development. These growth changes are illustrated with examples for various species which have been studied adequately. The usefulness of an understanding of maturation, however, goes far beyond what has already been described. It opens the way for development of sex and age criteria in species which have hitherto not been studied from this point of view.

DETERMINING AGE AND SEX IN BIRDS

Stage of Incubation

Candling has long been used as a practical means of determining (1) whether the eggs of domestic birds contain living embryos, and (2) the stage (age) of incubation. Commercial candling devices may be used successfully even with eggs that have opaque shells. Weller (1956) has described a simple field candler for waterfowl eggs.

The appearance of the embryo at various stages of incubation has been described by Hanson (1954) for the mallard, wood duck, and bobwhite. A series of pictures showing the bobwhite quail embryo at various stages of incubation is given by Roseberry and Klimstra (1965), and reproduced in Fig. 20.1. McCabe and Hawkins (1946) show the stages in development of the Hungarian partridge before hatching. Fant (1957) has done the same for the ring-necked pheasant (Fig. 20.1) as have Labisky and Opsahl (1958).

Determining Age of Young Birds

In young birds, there is a rapid succession of molts as the natal down is lost. The juvenal plumage comes in and then is replaced by adult plumage. Thus there is a change in both size and appearance as the chicks mature. Gollop and Marshall (1954) made use of this fact in devising a system for the age classification of artificially-raised wild ducklings. Their "plumage-appearance" classes are shown in Table 20.1. Table 20.2 shows the approximate age in days when each of 11 species of ducks molts through these plumage subclasses.

In gallinaceous birds, a rather accurate method

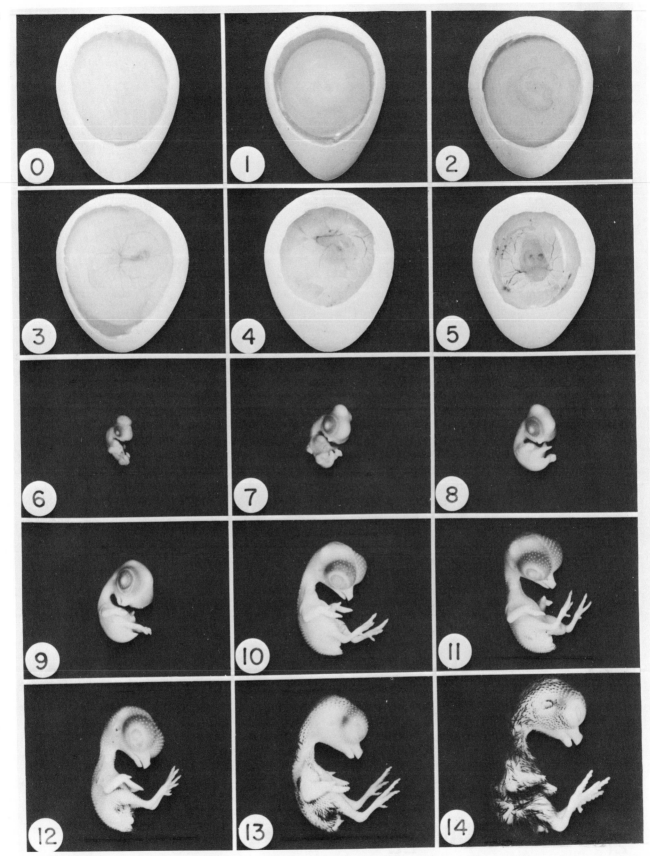

Fig. 20.1. Development of bobwhite quail A and ring-necked pheasant B during incubation (from Roseberry and Klimstra 1965, and Fant 1957, respectively).

B

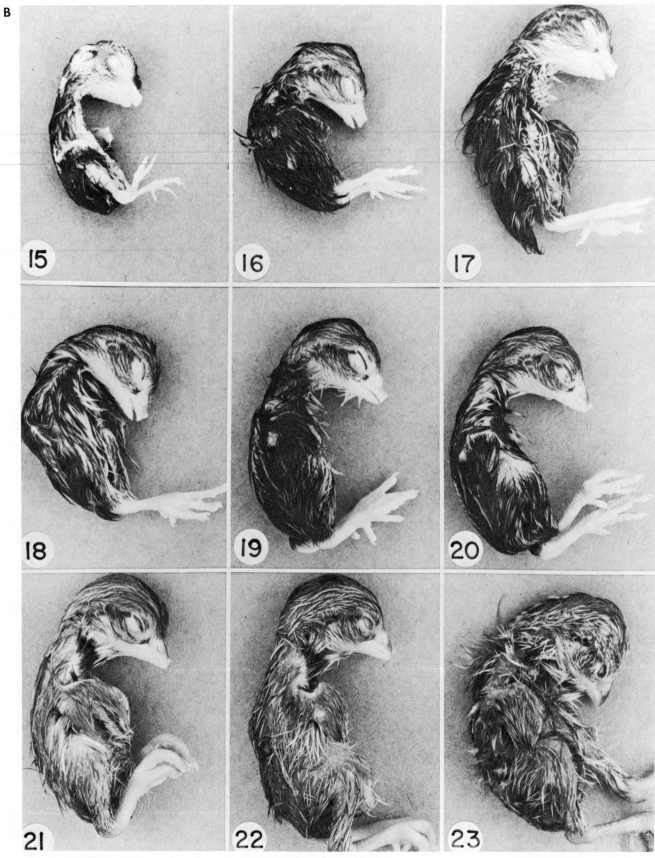

Fig. 20.1. Continued.

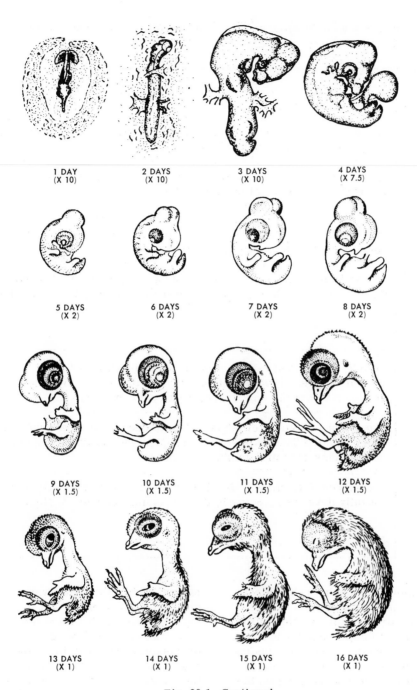

1 DAY
(X 10)

2 DAYS
(X 10)

3 DAYS
(X 10)

4 DAYS
(X 7.5)

5 DAYS
(X 2)

6 DAYS
(X 2)

7 DAYS
(X 2)

8 DAYS
(X 2)

9 DAYS
(X 1.5)

10 DAYS
(X 1.5)

11 DAYS
(X 1.5)

12 DAYS
(X 1.5)

13 DAYS
(X 1)

14 DAYS
(X 1)

15 DAYS
(X 1)

16 DAYS
(X 1)

Fig. 20.1. Continued.

of aging chicks is based on the replacement and growth of primaries and secondaries—the remiges or main flight-feathers of the wing. In ring-necked pheasant, bobwhite, and Hungarian partridge, for example, the post-juvenal molt of the primaries begins at four weeks of age and continues in a regular pattern until about 16 weeks, permitting aging to the nearest week within that span. Table 20.3 gives information on primary

replacement for those species in which it is known.

The primaries are numbered consecutively from one to ten, commencing with the innermost. This numbering follows the sequence in which the primaries are molted, the outer ones being shed and replaced last. The willow ptarmigan, ruffed grouse, Hungarian partridge, and the quails molt only through primary #8 in their

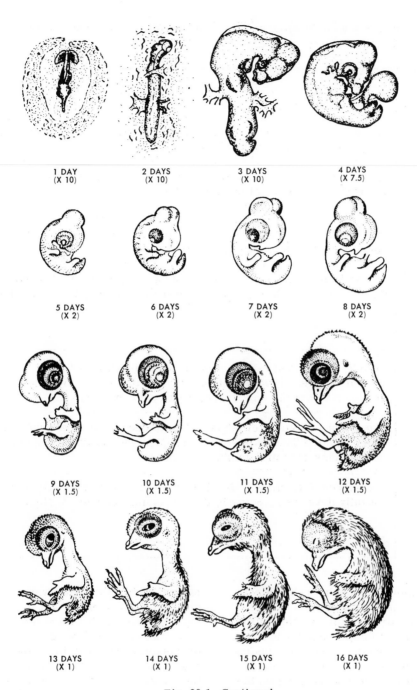

Table 20.1. Development of a wild duckling as viewed under ideal conditions (from Gollop and Marshall 1954). See Table 20.2 for use in aging.

Plumage Class	Sub-class	Description
I	a	*"Bright Ball of Fluff."* Down bright. Patterns distinct (except diving ducks). Body rounded. Neck and tail not prominent.
Downy young; no feathers visible	b	*"Fading Ball of Fluff."* Down color fading, patterns less distinct. Body still rounded. Neck and tail not yet prominent.
	c	*"Gawky-Downy."* Down color and patterns faded. Neck and tail become prominent. Body becomes long and oval.
II Partly feathered as viewed from the side	a	*"First Feathers."* First feathers show on side under ideal conditions, stays in this class until side view shows one-half of side and flank feathered.
	b	*"Mostly Feathered."* Side view shows one-half of side and flank feathered. Primaries break from sheaths. Stays in this class until side view shows down in one or two areas only (nape, back or upper rump).
	c	*"Last Down."* Side view shows down in one or two areas only (nape, back or upper rump). Sheaths visible on erupted primaries through this class. Stays in this class until profile shows no down.
III Fully-feathered as viewed from side	a	*"Feathered-Flightless."* No down visible. Primaries fully out of sheaths but not fully developed. Stays in this class until capable of flight.

first fall. In determining the number of the latest-shed primary, which is indicated by a gap or a growing replacement feather which is blue at the base, it is usually safer to count backwards from ten, the outermost primary, since confusion sometimes arises as to where the secondaries end and the primaries begin. Fig. 20.2 shows the location and numbering of the feathers.

Chessness (1966) provides a visual colored guide for aging young ring-necked pheasants. This is obtainable from Full Color Co., 279 Riverwood Drive, Burnsville, Minnesota 55378.

The Bursa of Fabricius

In most birds which have been studied there is an outpocketing from the dorsal wall of the cloaca. This blind sac, which may open into the cloaca or which may have the opening occluded by a membrane, is called the bursa of Fabricius (Fig. 20.3). The function of this organ is not precisely known but its growth and regression are related to the sexual maturity of the bird; in the young bird it increases in length until the time when the sex cells are just beginning division, then it begins to diminish. In some species it disappears by the time sexual maturity is reached (Gower 1939). In others it regresses to a certain point, where it remains. In many species, sexual maturity is attained before 1 year of age. In these birds the bursa begins regression shortly after the first of the year. During the usual hunting season, the presence of a large bursa in any of these rapidly maturing species definitely identifies a young-of-the-year. The situation with

Table 20.2. Approximate age-span and midpoint (in days) for each plumage subclass for 11 ducks, with supplementary data (after Gollop and Marshall 1954).

Species	Plumage Subclass (see Table 6.1)							Flying	Primaries break from sheaths	Areas of last down visible
	Ia	Ib	Ic	IIa	IIb	IIc	IIIa			
Mallard	1-4-6	7-10-12	13-16-18	19-22-25	26-31-35	36-41-45	46-51-55	52-60	35 days	Rump
Black Duck	1-3-5	6-9-12	13-16-18	19-22-25	26-30-33	34-39-43	44-52-60	58-63		
Gadwall	1-4-6	7-11-14	15-17-18	19-23-27	28-33-38	39-42-44	45-48-50	48-52	31	Nape & back
Bald-pate	1-4-7	8-10-12	13-16-18	19-23-26	27-31-35	36-39-41	42-46-50	47+	30	Nape & rump
Pintail	1-3-5	6-9-12	13-16-18	19-21-23	24-29-33	34-39-43	44-48-51	46-57	31	Back
Blue-winged Teal	1-3-5	6-8-9	10-12-13	14-18-21	22-26-30	31-34-36	37-39-40	35-44	30	Nape & rump
Shoveller	1-4-6	7-10-13	14-16-17	18-23-27	28-32-35	36-40-44	45-48-50	47-54	33	Nape & back
Red-head	1-4-6	7-13-18	19-22-24	25-29-32	33-39-45	46-50-54	55-58-60	60-63	43	Rump & back
Ring-necked Duck	1-3-5	6-8-10	11-14-16	17-21-24	25-28-30	31-35-38	39-44-49	49-53		
Canvas-back*	1-5-9	10-14-18	19-22-25	26-29-32	33-37-42	43-48-53	54-59-65	56-68	40	Rump & back
Lesser Scaup	1-3-6	7-10-13	14-17-20	21-25-28	29-31-33	34-38-42	43-47-50	47+		

*Dzubin (1959) gives a waterline (swim) ratio of length of young: adult hen: 1 day old—1:3; Subclass IIa—2:3; Subclass IIIa—3:3.

regard to involution of the bursa in individuals which are prevented from breeding by dominance relations is not yet known.

In other species, such as geese, sexual maturity is reached after 1 year. In these birds the regression of the bursa is more gradual, and also more irregular, since not all birds come into breeding condition at the same time.

When the bursa is relatively large and opens into the cloaca (as in the ring-necked pheasant) it may be determined and measured in the living bird by probing; a deep bursa in fall or winter indicates a young bird (Kirkpatrick 1944). In many species, however, the bursa either does not open into the cloaca or has a lumen too slender to probe readily. In these species the bird must be dissected if age is to be detected by this means.

The Sex Organs of Birds

Fig. 20.4 shows the generalized sex apparatus of male and female birds. The testes of the male lie on the roof of the body cavity, along the backbone and just forward of the kidneys. In general, the left testis is larger than the right one. Both are functional (Wing 1956). The testes are smooth, compared to the ovary, which is pebbled. The testes may be light or dark in color. Testis size is measured by length and width and by weight or volume.

Table 20.3. Development of primary feathers of the wing with age (in days) in immature gallinaceous birds and the mourning dove.

Species	Primary number (A = begins growth; B = fully grown)																				Authority
	1		2		3		4		5		6		7		8		9		10		
	A	B	A	B	A	B	A	B	A	B	A	B	A	B	A	B	A	B	A	B	
Willow Ptarmigan	18		25		30		35		40		46		53		65	91**	Juvenal not replaced				Westerskov 1956
Ruffed Grouse	14	45	20	49	27	63	35	68	42	77	49	83	61	98	74	119	Juvenal not replaced				Bump et al. 1947
Blue Grouse	21-28	28-35	28-35		28-42		35-49		42-56		49-63		63-70		77-91		Juvenal not replaced				Smith and Buss 1963
Hungarian Partridge	24		32		40		46		52		59		73		87	105	Juvenal not replaced				McCabe and Hawkins 1946
Ring-necked Pheasant	28		35		42		48		56		63		70		82		91		98	112	Buss 1946
Bobwhite	26-30	54-58	33-37	56-60	40-44	60-64	44-50	70-76	52-58	81-89	58-62	99-107	69-77	120-128	97-105	146-154	Juvenal not replaced				Petrides and Nestler 1943
Red-Legged Partridge	29		34		41		49		58		70		86		105	130	Juvenal not replaced				Petrides 1951
Coturnix Quail	22-		23-		27-		34-		34-		40-		49-		Juvenal not replaced						Wetherbee in press
California Quail	29	55	32	62	38	70	46	80	52	90	62	108	72	121	100	141	Juvenal not replaced				Raitt 1961
Mourning* Dove	25 ±4		30 ±4		37 ±5		45 ±6		54 ±8		66 ±10		80 ±14		96 ±16		117 ±18			142 ±20	Swank 1955

*Figures in column A represent age at which the juvenal feather is dropped. The second figure represents one standard deviation.

**Bergerud, Peters, and McGrath (1963) point out that this feather can be identified by its soft quill to 112 days.

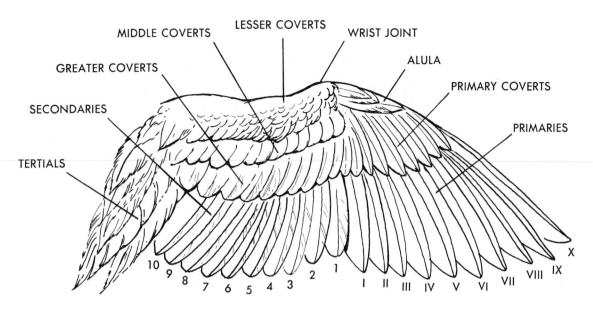

MIDDLE COVERTS

LESSER COVERTS

WRIST JOINT

GREATER COVERTS

ALULA

PRIMARY COVERTS

SECONDARIES

PRIMARIES

TERTIALS

Fig. 20.2. Nomenclature and position of numbered feathers of a typical wing (from Godin 1960).

The sex organs of the female begin in early life as paired ovaries, but the right fails to develop so that only the left ovary becomes functional. In some members of the Falconiformes (perhaps one-half or more of all individuals) the right ovary persists, but it is usually not functional. The same occurs also in some ducks and a few other species, and perhaps 5% of common birds have a vestige of the right ovary. Ordinarily the right oviduct, like the right ovary, is not functional (Wing 1956). White or yellowish in the non-breeding season, the ovary grows larger and more orange as the breeding season approaches, due to the growth of the egg follicles and their protrusion. During the laying season the ovary looks something like a cluster of grapes, the individual follicles far outshadowing the body of the ovary in size.

The shed ovum (and the yolk of the egg) becomes surrounded by the white albumen and encased in a shell as it travels down the oviduct to the cloaca. As the egg passes down the oviduct, the oviduct walls are stretched. The oviduct of a bird which has laid eggs remains larger than the oviduct of one which has not yet laid eggs and in early spring especially this may be a useful criterion for separating young females from old.

In adult females also, the opening of the oviduct may be seen (especially in large birds) as a conspicuous slit in the left cloacal wall. In immature females the oviduct is blocked by a membrane, so the left cloacal wall is unbroken. See Fig. 20.5.

The Cloaca and Related Structures

The cloaca of a bird is the common outlet both for reproduction and for the elimination of waste. In many species, especially large forms like waterfowl, the appearance of the cloaca is an accurate guide in determining both sex and age.

As described by Hochbaum (1942) and illustrated in Fig. 20.5, the penis of the male is located on the wall of the cloaca, on the anterior side in young birds and on the left side in adults. In females, the oviduct opens on the left side of the cloaca but in young birds this opening is usually covered by a membrane. The bursa of Fabricius opens (when it is not covered by a membrane) posterior to the opening of the digestive tract.

The presence and appearance of these structures are indications of sex and age. Their use has been most widespread in waterfowl, where size is large and other criteria are often not reliable.

Since the appearance of the various cloacal organs is closely related to sexual maturity, it is important to know beforehand the age at which sexual maturity is reached in the species in question. Thus waterfowl may be divided into two groups: those which breed at 1 year of age and those which breed later. In the first group are mallard, gadwall, baldpate, teal, shoveller, pintail, redhead, canvasback, lesser scaup, wood duck; while the second group includes geese,

334

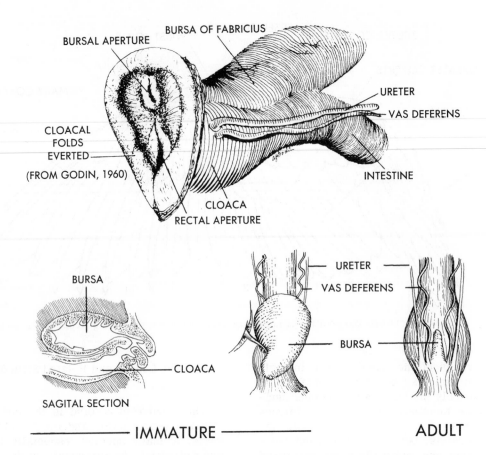

BURSAL APERTURE

BURSA OF FABRICIUS

URETER

VAS DEFERENS

CLOACAL
FOLDS
EVERTED

(FROM GODIN, 1960)

INTESTINE

CLOACA

RECTAL APERTURE

BURSA

CLOACA

SAGITAL SECTION

URETER

VAS DEFERENS

BURSA

IMMATURE

ADULT

Fig. 20.3. Bursa of Fabricius. *Top:* Excised cloaca and related parts of nonbreeding game birds. (A) Bursal aperture; (B) Bursa of Fabricius; (C) Ureter; (D) Vas deferens; (E) Intestine; (F) Cloaca; (G) Rectal aperture; (H) Cloacal folds everted (from Godin, 1960). *Bottom:* Location and appearance of the bursa and related structures in the California quail (redrawn by Godin from Christman, in Lewin 1961).

swans, goldeneye, bufflehead, harlequin duck, scoters, and eiders.

In examining the sex organs of a living duck, the bird is held belly up, tail away, with the outer fingers of each hand holding the wings and legs (Fig. 20.5A). The vent is located with the forefingers. As the vent is located, the tail is pressed backwards with the forefingers and the thumbs are placed on either side of the vent. The thumbs are separated slightly, with a gentle pressure. This opens the vent. As the cloaca is exposed, if the penis is present it will protrude. The penis shows two stages of development. In immature males the penis is a small, unsheathed organ; in adults it is large and enclosed with a conspicuous sheath (Fig. 20.5C).

In the female there is no penis. If the bird is adult, the opening of the oviduct may be seen on the left wall of the cloaca. In immature birds of both sexes the opening of the bursa of Fabricius is present; in mature birds it is absent.

The penis of the immature male duck is merely a short, fleshy appendage (Fig. 20.5C) attached to the forewall of the cloaca just within the cloacal lip. It shows a conspicuous left-hand twist, giving it the appearance of a miniature pigtail. It is never more than 12 mm in length. The penis of the immature bird retains its small, unsheathed form, with little or no change in size or appearance until the young bird is 5 to 10 months old. Then, when the postjuvenal molt has been completed, the adult penis, 50 to 90 mm or more in length, develops. These two growth stages of the penis cannot easily be confused, except during the very short period of transition. The two stages show no important variations in different species of ducks.

As an age criterion in early-maturing waterfowl, the penis is reliable only during the summer, autumn, and early winter. The period of reliability ceases for all individuals of a species when the earliest developing young drakes assume the adult

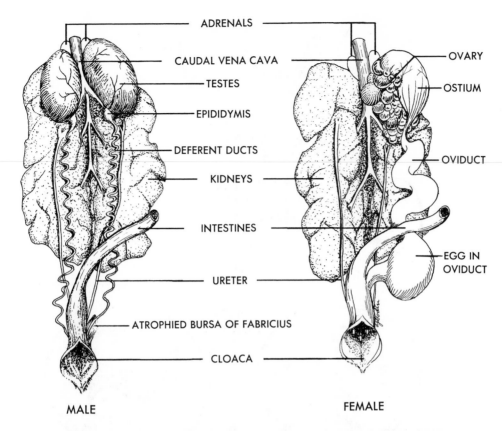

ADRENALS

CAUDAL VENA CAVA — — OVARY

TESTES — — OSTIUM

EPIDIDYMIS

DEFERENT DUCTS

KIDNEYS — — OVIDUCT

INTESTINES

— EGG IN OVIDUCT

URETER

ATROPHIED BURSA OF FABRICIUS

CLOACA

MALE   FEMALE

Fig. 20.4. Excised urogenital system of typical breeding birds. *Left:* Male has paired testes (the left is generally the larger) whereas the female, *Right* has a single irregular shaped ovary and convoluted swollen oviduct on the left side (from Godin 1960).

penis. With respect to this time limit, the species studied at Delta, Manitoba, fall into two groups: Group 1 — Adult penis never assumed by young males before December 31: gadwall, baldpate, green-winged teal, blue-winged teal, shoveller, redhead, canvasback, and lesser scaup. Group 2 — adult penis sometimes assumed by young males before December: mallard and pintail. The species not studied in sufficient numbers to warrant final classification may be tentatively grouped as follows: (1) cinnammon teal, ring-necked duck, greater scaup, ruddy duck; (2) black duck, wood duck.

In wild mallards and pintails, and probably black ducks, the penis is a reliable indicator of age to November 16. After that, until the end of December, the bursa must be used in aging drakes.

The age and sex characters used for hens—the presence or absence of the oviduct opening and the bursa of Fabricius—are difficult to see in the living bird. If the cloaca is swabbed with a 10% solution of cocaine, the sphincter muscle of the

vent may be relaxed sufficiently to permit examination of the cloaca in the living female. In dead birds the lips of the vent are grasped with thumbs and forefingers and stretched to relax the sphincter muscle. With a blunt probe the sites of the openings of the oviduct (left wall of cloaca ventral to large intestine) and the bursa (posterior dorsal wall of cloaca) may be investigated. In adults, a shallow bursal cavity may persist for a time. The bursa appears to be a reliable indicator of age at least through December, according to Hochbaum (1942).

Plumage As a Criterion of Age and Sex

As a general rule, birds assume new feathers in advance of the breeding season. The breeding plumage, especially in adult males, is often brighter than the plumage of the nonbreeding season. In some species, the male is easily distinguished from the female at any season by differences in plumage, the possession of spurs,

336

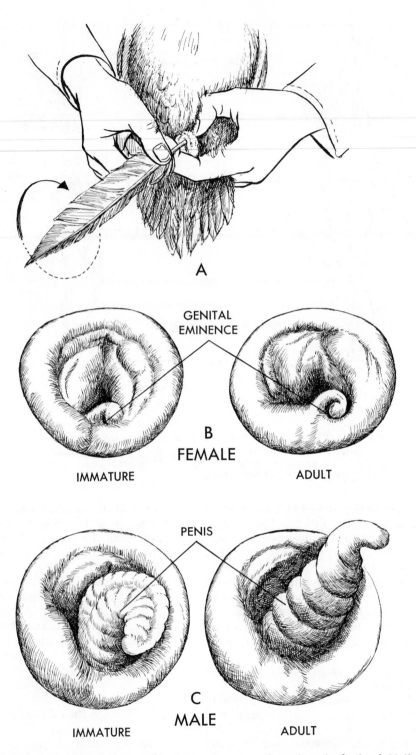

Fig. 20.5. Cloacal characteristics used to determine sex and age in waterfowl. *A* Method of holding and for measuring the bursa of Fabricius. The probe is held in the right hand and rotated into the bursa. *B* Location of oviduct and bursa of Fabricius in female waterfowl *Left:* Immature. *Right:* Adult. *C* Penis stages in Canada Geese. *Left:* Immature unsheathed penis with conspicuous left hand twist. *Right:* Sheathed penis of sexually mature adult. Bursa is present in both immature male and female; after Addy and MacNamara, 1948 (from Godin 1960).

crests, or wattles. In some species, the sexes resemble each other at least during part of the year. Thus, waterfowl may be difficult to sex in the eclipse plumage which follows the breeding season, when all the wing feathers are molted simultaneously and the bird assumes a drab, concealing plumage. In some species, such as geese, the sexes appear alike even during the breeding season.

Generally the feathers of the young bird differ in some respects from those of the old. Very often, when the bird is entering its first breeding season, it retains some juvenal feathers, especially wing coverts, in its new breeding plumage. These feathers are thus an indication of age. Such diagnostic primary coverts are found in bobwhite and other quail. In the Hungarian partridge, the scapulars are diagnostic of age. There is reason to hope that eventually similar plumage differences between young and old will be found for all short-lived birds.

In birds which mature more slowly, such as geese, there is less difficulty in distinguishing young-of-the-year in fall. Areas which are white in the adult tend to be dingy or mottled in the young; areas which are pure black in the adult tend to be dull or brownish black.

CRITERIA OF AGE AND SEX FOR SPECIES OF NORTH AMERICAN GAME BIRDS

In the paragraphs which follow, the principal game birds of North America will be taken up by groups, and the special criteria of age and sex which have been found most useful for each group will be given.

Waterfowl

The cloacal characters which are commonly used to age and sex waterfowl have been described above. Another criterion which may be used to distinguish between young-of-the-year and older birds, during the fall hunting season, is the appearance of the tips of the rectrices, or large tail feathers. In the juvenile tail there is a notch at the tip caused by the breaking-off of a short section of the shaft. This break is caused by the loss of the down, which precedes the regular tail feather in emergence from the feather follicle in the very young bird. The condition in the young is illustrated in Fig. 20.6. This technique must be used with caution, because some individuals

molt the tail feathers before or during the hunting season.

GEESE

Geese mature more slowly than most other birds, so the juveniles are usually readily distinguished by cloacal characters and by their plumage, as may be seen in Tables 20.4 and 20.5. An illustrated table, similar to Table 20.1, for aging Canada goose goslings, has been prepared by Yocom and Harris (1965).

DUCKS

The characters of the cloaca and the tail feathers most useful for determining sex and age have been described (Figs. 20.5 and 20.6).

Kortright (1943) has noted that sex in many ducks may be revealed by bill markings: "Females of most River and Pond Ducks show dusky markings and dark spots on the upper mandible, which markings are lacking in the males." This method of sex determination is applicable to all members of genus Anas. In the adult black duck, the feathers of the sides of the chest show a central buff marking which is U-shaped in males and V-shaped in females, the bottom of the letter being toward the tip of the feather in each case (Kortright 1943).

Additional criteria of age are given in Table 20.6 for dabbling ducks and in Table 20.7 for diving ducks. The feather tracts referred to are shown in Fig. 20.7.

Because of the relative ease with which wings may be obtained from hunters, special efforts have been made to discover age and sex criteria in the wing plumage. Some of these characters of wings of waterfowl are shown in Tables 20.5, 20.6, and 20.7. In addition, more detailed studies on the mallard have permitted the development of keys for determination of sex and age from wing characters. These keys are given in Table 20.8. Many additional species are covered in the handbook prepared by Carney (1964).

Gallinaceous Birds

Before taking up the various species of quail, grouse, partridge, etc. individually, it is well to point out the criteria of age which are common to all or most of them. As a rough rule of thumb, the strength of the lower jaw separates the immatures from the adults in fall. If a dead bird is supported by the lower jaw alone and shaken, and

Fig. 20.6. Tail feathers as age criteria in waterfowl. *Left:* Juvenile tail with down attached at tip of shaft. *Center:* Juvenile tail with characteristic "V" notch. *Right:* Adult tail with pointed tip (from Godin 1960).

the jaw breaks, it is generally a young bird; if the jaw does not break it is generally old.

A similar test is based on the flexibility of the breastbone. In a young bird the tip of the breastbone may be easily bent with one finger; in an old one it is rigid.

As a group, the gallinaceous birds molt their wing and tail feathers in sequence, rather than all at once, as in waterfowl. As it approaches adult size in the fall, the young bird grows wing feathers of adult size during the postjuvenal molt. However, in most species, except the ring-necked pheasant, the two outer primaries of the immature bird are not replaced during this molt. They are replaced 1 year later, during the first postnuptial molt, and annually thereafter. The two outer juvenal primaries differ in shape (Fig. 20.8) from the adult primaries, being more pointed at the tip, and sometimes narrower (Wright and Hiatt 1943).

In gallinaceous birds, the appearance of the cloaca has not been used as extensively to determine sex as it has in waterfowl because plumage and other characters are better sex criteria. However, the bursa of Fabricius is a reliable age character and often can be determined by probing in the living bird.

GROUSE

As a group, the grouse are all alike in that the two sexes resemble each other superficially (although the male is markedly heavier) and the young in their first fall tend to resemble the adult female.

The young do not molt the two outer primaries in their first summer. In fact, if the hunting season is held before the fall molt, there will be yearling birds in the bag which have adopted adult plumage except for the juvenal outer primaries, which have not yet been replaced. If this replacement pattern is understood, it is possible to distinguish the juvenile age-class.

A general criterion of age in the fall, which has been used for white-tailed ptarmigan (Westerskov 1956), and might be useful for other grouse as well, is the "cranium test." The bird's head is held between the index and middle fingers and the thumb is pressed on the forehead. In young birds the cranium will break, whereas it is not possible to press in the brain case of an adult ptarmigan held in this manner.

Criteria of sex and age in grouse are summarized in Table 20.9.

Table 20.4. A key to distinguish between immature, yearling, and adult Canada geese of both sexes (from Hanson 1962).

1. Some or all tail feathers with notched, worn tips and relatively narrow vanes; color blackish brown 6

   All tail feathers with unnotched, unworn tips and relatively broad vanes; color black 2

2. Primaries pointed at tips 6

   Primaries obtuse or rounded at tips 3

3. Penis present 4

   Penis absent 5

4. External portion of sphincter muscle a pale flesh color; penis intermediate in size, usually a pale flesh color, translucent and smooth; bursa open and easily probed, usually to a depth of 15-20 mm; spur of each wing smooth and feathered over at tip. . . *yearling male*

   External portion of sphincter muscle dark red or purple; penis large, dark red or purplish, with wrinkled surface and fairly prominent venation; bursa closed, or, if open, shallow and probed with difficulty; top of each wing spur enlarged and knobby at tip and more or less denuded of feathers . . . . *adult male*

5. External portion of sphincter muscle not much larger than that of immature and light flesh-red; oviduct closed at juncture with cloaca; bursa open and easily probed, usually to a depth of 15-20 mm, as in yearling male . . . . *yearling female*

   External portion of sphincter much larger than that of either immature or yearling female and dark red or blotched with purple; oviduct open and easily probed, bursa closed, or, if open, shallow and probed only with difficulty . . . . *adult female*

6. Penis present . . . . *immature male*

   Penis absent . . . . *immature female*

SAGE GROUSE

See Table 20.10. The male does not acquire full breeding plumage until the second winter.

Eng (1955), in a study of the wings collected on October 4 in Montana, found that sex could be determined in old and young alike by the relative length of the primaries, different primaries being diagnostic for different molt stages, as shown in Table 20.11. Measurements were made from the point of insertion to the top of the feather.

It often happens that during the hunting season the males have passed through their postnuptial molt while in some females this molt is not yet complete. Thus, in males there are only two types of outer primaries—the pointed immature primaries of the immature birds and the rounded primaries of the adults (Eng 1955).

In females, however, there may be three sorts—the two given above and in addition the pointed immature primaries still retained by a yearling hen which has not yet completed her postnuptial molt. The differences resulting from a full year of wear on the juvenile primaries, which should be the basis for distinguishing between immature and yearling hens, have not yet been described.

Where the three or four outer primaries have not yet been molted, one aging character is known in addition to the difference between the shape of juvenal and adult primaries noted above. This character is the difference in measurements (see Table 20.11) between primaries #9 and #8. In adults, #8 is longer than #9; in immatures #8 is shorter than #9 (Eng 1955).

SHARP-TAILED GROUSE

See Table 20.9. The sex criterion based on color pattern in the central tail feathers is illustrated in Fig. 20.9.

340

Table 20.5. Plumage and feet characters for distinguishing age in geese and brant (after Kortright 1943). Immature characters are italicized.

Species	Characters
Canada Goose	HEAD AND NECK: Shiny black; *dull brown-black*. CHEEKS: white; *brownish-white and/or marked with dusky*. UPPER TAIL COVERTS: white; *whitish, brown-gray at tips*. SIDE: brown-gray, barred with white; *indistinctly mottled*.
Snow Goose	HEAD AND NECK: white w/rusty spots; *whitish, mottled w/brown-gray, esp. above*. PRIMARY TIPS: black; *gray-black*. MANTLE AND WING COVERTS: white; *white washed w/grayish*. FEET: Pink; *gray*.
Blue Goose	HEAD AND NECK: White; *bluish-gray*. LESSER WING COVERTS: pure gray; *tipped w/brown*. GREATER WING COVERTS: black centers and white edges; *plain pale gray*.
Ross's Goose	HEAD AND NECK: white; *brown/gray shading through eye to nape and down hind neck*. FOREBACK: white; *brownish gray*. SECONDARIES AND TERTIALS: white; *gray or brown on centers*. PRIMARIES: black; *mottled w/white toward bases*. FEET: dull red; *pink*. BILL: carmine red or pale purple, w/upper mandible corrugated, with warty protuberances near base; *greenish, becoming pinkish through winter, w/o protuberances*.
White-front Goose	HEAD: white band around front of face at base of bill; *no face patch*. BILL: pink, pale bluish at base, yellow-orange at nostrils—nail white or whitish; *dull yellowish or gray w/lilac tinge—nail dusky*.
American Brant	HEAD AND NECK: leaden black w/white collar broken front and back; *brownish-black w/white neck feathers barely discernable*. TAIL: usually tipped w/whitish; *black*. BACK AND SCAPULARS: edged with light brown; *edged with buffy white*.
Black Brant	HEAD AND NECK: leaden black w/white collar at top of neck, broken behind; *brownish-black, no white collar*. SECONDARY COVERTS: brownish-black, slightly paler at tips; *white-tipped*. Mottled appearance on upper underparts. This appearance results from the fact that patches of the unmottled tan-colored juvenile feathers are intermixed with newly replaced dark brown and black adult feathers.

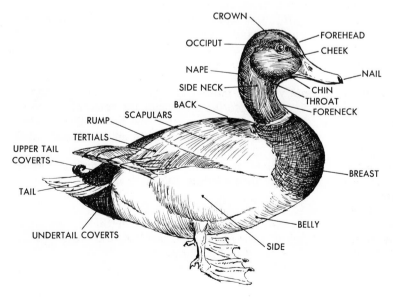

Fig. 20.7. General topography of waterfowl (after Kortright 1943).

Table 20.6. Plumage characters for distinguishing age in dabbling ducks (after Kortright 1943). Note: immature characters are italicized; ♂♂ are treated first.

Species	Characters
Mallard	♂♂: TERTIALS: Longer, brighter, more chestnut brown; *shorter, duller, less suffused w/chestnut brown.* BACK, CHEST, SIDES: No female feathers; *some female-like feathers.* ♀♀: TERTIALS: long, narrowly edged w/buff; *short, browner, broadly edged w/buff.*
Black Duck	♂♂♀♀: GREATER COVERTS: wider and more distinct dusky tips; *narrower and less distinct dusky tips.* TERTIALS: larger, more pointed at tips; *smaller, more rounded at tips, browner and duller.* SECONDARIES: wider, 3 outer iridescent; *narrower, 3 outer less iridescent.*
Gadwall	♂♂♀♀: TERTIALS: pale grayish buff; *shorter and duller.* GREATER COVERTS: black, 3 outer ones grayish white; *black sometimes replaced w/dusky, mottled w/gray.*
Baldpate	♂♂: LESSER AND MIDDLE COVERTS: former brownish gray along forward edge of wing, latter white, grayish brown inwardly; *buffy, clouded w/dusky and w/dark shafts.* TERTIALS: black w/white edges, gray-brown on inner webs; *browner w/very narrow whitish edgings.* ♀♀: LESSER AND MIDDLE COVERTS: brownish-gray tipped w/whitish; *darker, browner, w/narrower edgings.* GREATER COVERTS: tipped w/blackish, then sometimes narrowly w/white; *dusky, w/only a thin bar of whitish near tips.* SECONDARIES ON INNER BORDER OF SPECULUM: black, occasionally glossy green; *dark gray.*
Pintail	♂♂: LESSER AND MIDDLE COVERTS: brownish gray; *browner, less gray, edged w/buff.* TERTIALS: long and gray, w/glossy black stripes; *rounded, shorter, olive-brown.* ♀♀: GREATER COVERTS: edged w/cinnamon buff to white; *white-tipped.* TERTIALS: dull brown, edged w/buffy or whitish; *plainer and w/buff markings.*
Green-winged Teal	♂♂: GREATER COVERTS: Gray w/broad tips of buffy brown; *usually w/narrower cinnamon tips.* TERTIALS: brownish gray, sometimes edged w/white; *olive brown, edged w/buff.* ♀♀: SPECULUM: bright green; *duller, w/green area smaller.*
Blue-winged Teal	♂♂: TERTIALS: greenish black streaked w/buff; *sepia, edged w/buff.* SPECULUM: iridescent green; *duller.* ♀♀: TERTIALS: brown, w/lighter edgings; *duller and browner.* GREATER COVERTS: slaty, tipped w/white; *much less white, often w/dusky spots and bars.*
Cinnamon Teal	As in Blue-winged Teal.
Shoveller	♂♂: TERTIALS: pointed, greenish-black, streaked w/white; *rounded, dull, olive-brown.* LESSER AND MIDDLE COVERTS: Cobalt blue; *duller, grayer, w/little blue.* ♀♀: SPECULUM: metallic green; *olive-brown or dusky, w/little green.* LESSER AND MIDDLE COVERTS: grayish blue; *duller, grayer, w/little blue.*
Wood Duck	♂♂: EYE: bright orange to vermillion; *light brown.* TERTIALS: inner ones black w/white tips, outer ones black, glossed w/metallic blue; *shorter, narrower, dull brown.* ♀♀: The ages cannot be distinguished from plumage after about November. EYE: blackish-brown; *dark brown.*

Table 20.7. Winter plumage characters for distinguishing age in diving ducks and tree ducks (after Kortright 1943). Note: immature characters are italicized; ♂♂ are treated first.

Species	Characters
Redhead[1]	♂♂: COVERTS: gray, slightly flecked w/whitish; *less gray, more brown.* SPECULUM: pearl gray; *almost solid gray.* ♀♀: COVERTS: brownish gray; *more brown.*
Ring-necked Duck[1]	♂♂: NECK: Narrow chestnut collar, incomplete behind; *collar hardly visible.* TERTIALS: outer webs greenish black, inner webs grayish; *brown w/greenish gloss.* ♀♀: no age characters in plumage after December.
Canvasback[1]	♂♂: SPECULUM: pearl gray, shading into white bar behind; *almost solidly gray.* COVERTS: brownish gray; *brown w/gray markings.* ♀♀: COVERTS: dusky, finely spotted and barred w/white, giving grayish appearance; *browner, w/gray markings indistinct or lacking.*
Scaup (Greater and Lesser)[1]	♂♂: TERTIALS: dusky, w/greenish iridescence; *dark brown, faintly glossed w/greenish.* ♀♀: no age characters in plumage after about November.
American Golden-eye[2,3]	♂♂: LESSER COVERTS: forward and inner ones black, rest white; *dusky, edged w/light gray.* GREATER COVERTS: white, though basally black; *black, central ones broadly tipped w/white.* PRIMARIES: slaty black; *dusky.* ♀♀: GREATER COVERTS: central ones white w/black tips; *generally not black tipped.* MIDDLE COVERTS: gray, tipped w/white; *grayish, basally dusky.*
Barrow's Golden-eye[2,3]	♂♂: LESSER AND MIDDLE COVERTS: former black, latter white; *dusky, some of latter tipped w/light gray.* SECONDARIES: mainly white w/outer ones blackish; *three outer ones black.* ♀♀: as in American Goldeneye.
Bufflehead[2,3]	♂♂: HEAD: except for white patch, black glossed w/purple, violet, and green; *few glossy feathers.* GREATER COVERTS: mainly white, w/some dark feathers mostly along forward edge of wing; *dark grayish brown w/white spots.* ♀♀: cannot be distinguished by plumage in autumn.
Old Squaw[2,4]	♂♂: SPECULUM: chestnut brown; *dusky.* TWO MIDDLE TAIL FEATHERS: greatly elongated and pointed; *not long.*
Harlequin Duck[2,3]	♂♂: BILL: bluish gray; *brown.* RUMP: steely blue black; *brown.* ♀♀: BILL: dusky; *brown.*
Steller's Eider[2,3]	♂♂: SPECULUM: blue black; *dull blue.* OUTER SECONDARIES: tipped with white; *dusky.* ♀♀: SPECULUM: dull blue; *dusky.*
American Eider[2,5]	♂♂: CROWN: iridescent glossy black; *(first autumn) brown, (second autumn) black mottled with grayish brown.* BREAST: black; *(first autumn) dull brown, (second autumn) dull brownish black.*
King Eider[6]	♂♂: CROWN: pearl gray; *(first autumn) dark brown, (second autumn) dull gray.* LESSER AND MIDDLE COVERTS: pure white; *(first autumn) dusky, with paler edges, (second autumn) white, margined and shaded with dusky.* ♀♀: BILL: pale greenish or yellowish; *(first autumn) grayish olive.*

Table 20.7. Continued.

Species	Characters
Spectacled Eider[6]	♂♂: HEAD: circle of dense silvery white feathers framed in black around eye; (first autumn) *spectacle only faintly indicated.* ♀♀: BREAST AND BELLY: dusky brown; (first autumn) *brown, spotted with dusky.*
White-winged Scoter[4],[6]	♂♂: HEAD: black, with small crescent-shaped white spot behind and below eye; (first autumn) *brownish black, with white patch in ear region.* FEET: orange vermillion on inner sides, purplish pink on outer; (first autumn) *light brownish red.* ♀♀: FEET: light brownish red, webs blackish; (first autumn) *outer side of tarsus blackish, inner side of tarsus and toes dull purplish brown.*
Surf Scoter[3],[4],[6]	♂♂: HEAD: black except for white patch on forehead and long triangular white patch on nape, pointing backwards; (first autumn) *dusky brown, with only light patches on sides of head,* (second autumn) *black with nape patch but no forehead patch.* ♀♀: BREAST: mottled grayish and dusky; (first autumn) *pale gray or whitish.* HEAD: dusky brown with vague whitish patch on back of head; (first and second autumn) *no whitish patch.*
American Scoter[2],[3],[4]	♂♂: BREAST: black; *whitish, marked with grayish brown.* ♀♀: BREAST: brown; *whitish marked with grayish brown.*
Ruddy Duck[1],[3],[4]	♂♂: CHEST: rich reddish chestnut; *dusky, broadly tipped with buff.* CHEEKS: white; *no clear white area.* ♀♀: BREAST: bright silvery white, some feathers of forebreast often with gilt tips; *mottled with dusky.* CHEST: marked with broken bars of dark brown and buffy brown; *dusky, broadly tipped with buff.*
Black-bellied Tree Duck[1]	UNDERPARTS: brown chest, black breast; *grayish buff.*
Fulvous Tree Duck[1]	UPPERTAIL COVERTS: creamy; *tipped with brown.*

[1] Species in which males assume adult plumage the first spring after hatching.
[2] Species in which males assume adult plumage the second autumn after hatching.
[3] During their first winter the juvenile males resemble adult females.
[4] No eclipse molt occurs in these species.
[5] Males do not attain full adult plumage until the fourth autumn (i.e. when 4.5 years old). In females the adult plumage is assumed to third autumn.
[6] Males and females do not attain full adult plumage until the third autumn.

PRAIRIE CHICKEN

See Table 20.9. The sex criterion based on the tail markings is illustrated in Fig. 20.9.

RUFFED GROUSE

See Table 20.9. Sexing of adult Wisconsin grouse is accomplished by measuring the central tail feathers (Fig. 20.10); males of all ages have (plucked) feathers longer than 15 cm, while females have feathers under 15 cm (Hale, Wendt, and Halazon 1954).

Aging during the fall may be accomplished by use of bursal depth, taking 5 mm as the dividing point between juveniles and adults. Aging of ruffed grouse also may be done by wing characters. The juvenal outer two primaries are pointed, while those of the adult are rounded. In case of doubt, the base of the quill in primary #8 should be examined for scaly remnants of its feather sheath. In the juvenile, #9 and #10 do not show these remnants; in the adult they do (Hale, Wendt, and Halazon 1954). K. E. Hungerford (pers. communication) uses the following criteria for sexing and aging Pacific Northwest grouse: length of center

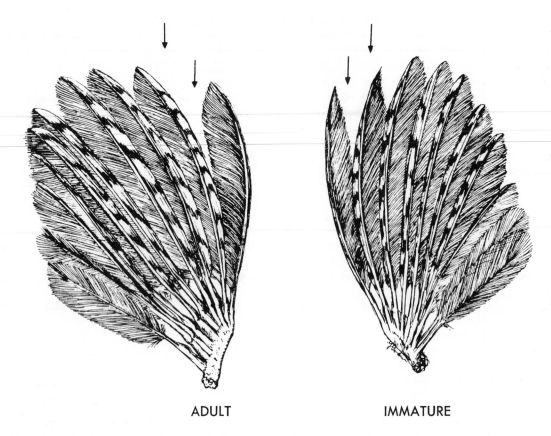

ADULT   IMMATURE

Fig. 20.8. The two outer primaries in immature gallinaceous birds (except the ring-necked pheasant) are retained through the first winter. The immature No. 9 and No. 10 primaries are pointed *(Right)* as compared to the rounded tips of these feathers in adults *(Left)*, as shown in the wings of the ruffed grouse (from Godin 1960). See Fig. 20.13 for illustration of the No. 10 primaries from immature and adult eastern wild turkeys.

unplucked feather (i.e. from tip to skin line). $L \geq 15.2$ cm = adult male; $15.2 > L \geq 14.0$ cm = adult female; $L < 14.0$ cm = juvenile.

Many cocks are mirror-trapped in the spring. At that time young (almost 1 year old) males (in Wisconsin) may be distinguished from older males by the following criteria (Dorney and Holzer 1957):

a. Width of shaft of 9th primary at point where larger proximal barbs begin: Young—0.117 inch or less; old—0.117 inch or more.

b. Length of central tail feather (after 2 months of drying): Young—159 mm or less; old—170 mm or more.

c. Width of shaft of central tail feather (dried): Young—0.087 inches or less; old—0.092 inches or more.

d. Bursa: Only used if bursa is closed, in which case the bird is considered old.

e. Contour of 9th and 10th primary, as above.

f. Sheathing at base of primaries, as above.

These authors found that if all these criteria are used most questionable cases can be reliably aged.

WILLOW PTARMIGAN

Criteria of sex and age in this species have been studied recently by Bergerud, Peters, and McGrath (1963). Age in chicks up to 20 days can be determined by wing length (carpal joint to tip of longest primary). The stage of primary replacement (see Table 20.3) can be used to 112 days, by which time the quill of primary #8 is fully hardened. In October, juvenile birds can be distinguished from adults by the gloss and pigment of the distal primaries: in juveniles the gloss on primary #8 is more pronounced than on 9 and 10, whereas there is little or no difference in gloss among the three outer primaries in adults; in juveniles the area of black pigment on primary #8 is smaller than that on #9, whereas in adults the area of black pigment on primary #8, including

Table 20.8. Keys to age and sex in mallards, based on wing characters (Carney and Geis 1960).

A. AGE DETERMINATION FOR MALES

1. Tertial coverts (one or more of five most proximal coverts)
   a. Any of the following:
      (1) Much frayed.
      (2) Faded.
      (3) Noticeably narrow and dull colored . . . . .Immature
   b. Not as above 2
2. Tertials
   a. Any of the following:
      (1) "Pearly" color lacking.
      (2) Much frayed at tips.
      (3) Much faded.
      (4) Sprouting new tertial after December 1 . . . . .Immature
   b. Not as above 3
3. Primary coverts (tip of inner web on four most distal coverts)
   a. "Conspicuously" to "minutely" edged light. . . . . .Immature
   b. No light edging present 4
4. Middle coverts
   a. Any of the following:
      (1) Edged (usually very finely) with light brown.
      (2) Appear small; narrow to a rounded tip; somewhat trapezoidal.
      (3) Edges much frayed . . . . .Immature
   b. Lack light brown edge; may be "washed" with dark rufous; appear large; tip a
      smoothly rounded arc; edges smooth . . . . .Adult

B. AGE DETERMINATION FOR FEMALES

1. Tertial coverts (one or more of five most proximal coverts)
   a. Any of the following:
      (1) Much frayed.
      (2) Faded.
      (3) Noticeably narrow.
      (4) No white edging on two most posterior coverts . . . . .Immature
   b. Not as above 2
2. Tertials
   a. Any of the following:
      (1) Much frayed tips.
      (2) Much faded . . . . .Immature
   b. Not as above 3
3. Primary coverts (tip of inner web on four most distal coverts)
   a. "Conspicuously" light edged . . . . .Immature
   b. "Minutely" light edged or unedged 4
4. Middle coverts
   a. Any of the following:
      (1) Appear small; narrow to a rounded tip; somewhat trapezoidal.
      (2) Edges much frayed . . . . .Immature
   b. Appear large; tips are smoothly rounded arcs; edges smooth . . . . .Adult

C. SEX DETERMINATION

1. Scapulars (if present)
   a. Vermiculated . . . . Male
   b. Not vermiculated 2

Table 20.8. Continued.

2. Most proximal underwing coverts
   a. Vermiculated . . . . Male
   b. Not vermiculated 3
3. White bar anterior to the speculum
   a. Extends uninterrupted proximally at least partially over tertials . . . . Female
   b. Does not extend uninterrupted over tertials . . . . Male

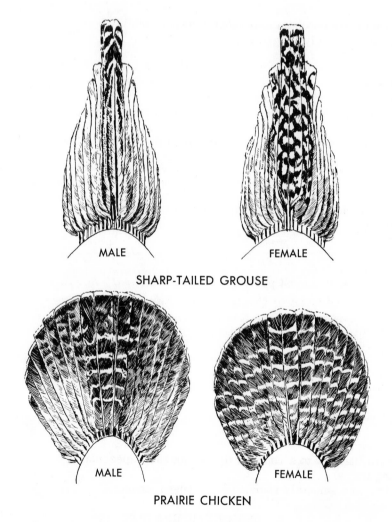

MALE   FEMALE

SHARP-TAILED GROUSE

MALE   FEMALE

PRAIRIE CHICKEN

Fig. 20.9. Tail patterns as criteria of sex in prairie grouse. *Top:* Predominantly longitudinal striping in males and cross-barring in females of sharp-tailed grouse. *Bottom:* Absence of barring in outer tail feathers of male and barring of all tail feathers in female prairie chicken (after Thompson 1958).

Table 20.9. Sex and age characters in the grouse. In column (1) the female characters are italicized; in column (2) the immature characters are italicized.

Species	Criteria for distinguishing sex (1)	Criteria for distinguishing age (2)
Sage Grouse	AVERAGE WT.: 6 lbs.; *3.5 lbs.* THROAT: black band upper throat, scaly white fore-neck feathers; *grayish white upper throat, no scaly feathers.* AVERAGE TAIL LENGTH: 11.5 inches; *7.5 inches.* FLIGHT: even; *body dips from side to side* (P). In juveniles the male has a middle toe one full toe-nail length longer than the female (P).	UPPER BREAST: solid feather pattern; *triangular patch of feathers showing dark spots and light vertical streaks* (through early fall). TOE COLOR: dark green; *light yellowish-green* (P).
Sharp-tailed Grouse	CENTRAL TAIL FEATHERS: longitudinal pattern of light and dark markings; *transverse pattern* (S).	OUTER PRIMARIES: unworn, same color as other primaries; *rough and worn, lighter than other primaries* (A).
Prairie Chicken	HEAD AND NECK: longer pinnae, much larger air sacs, orange flesh colors on neck and "eyebrows"; *shorter pinnae, inconspicuous air sacs, no orange flesh colors* (E). TAIL: less barred; *more barred* (E).	OUTER PRIMARIES: same as Sharp-tailed Grouse.
Ruffed Grouse autumn (see text for spring characters)	CENTRAL PLUCKED TAIL FEATHER LENGTH: 15.0 cm. or more; *14.9 cm. or less* (HW&H). COLOR BARE SPOT OVER UPPER EYELID, 8-14 WK. CHICKS: subdued orange to bright red-orange; *little or no color* (Pa).	PRIMARIES: 8, 9, and 10 rounded with sheathing at base; *8 rounded, 9 and 10 pointed, with sheathing on 8 only* (HW&H).
Blue Grouse	CERVICAL AIR SACS: (from 8 weeks of age) surrounded by white feathers, tipped w/bluish black; *surrounded by grayish brown feathers* (C). HEAD, NAPE, INTERSCAPULARS: no barred feathers; *some barred feathers* (R&F).	Immatures look like ad. ♀ except CONTOUR FEATHERS: shaft streaks dark; *shaft streaks dull white* (GB&S). TAIL: gray bar at end; *no gray bar* (GB&S). BELLY: gray patch; *no gray patch* (GB&S). BREAST: Dark brown; *pale buffy or white* (GB&S). Also see text.
White-tailed Ptarmigan	HEAD: red "eyebrows" prominent; *"eyebrows" not prominent.* COLORED FEATHERS: reddish brown, not heavily barred; *gray-brown or tan, heavily barred* (H).	OUTER PRIMARIES: usually pure white, often with black shafts, 8th primary never shorter than 9th; *usually mottled with brown or black, 8th primary often shorter than 9th* (H).[1]

References: A = Ammann (1944); C = Caswell (1954); E = Edminster (1954); GB&S = Grinnell, Bryant, and Storer (1918); H = Hewitt (*pers. comm.*); HW&H = Hale, Wendt, and Halazon (1954); Pa = Palmer (1959); P = Patterson (1952); R&F = Ridgeway and Friedmann (1946); S = Snyder (1935).
[1]Weeden (1961) found for rock ptarmigan that outer primary shape and pigmentation were not reliable age criteria.

Table 20.10. Key for the determination of age and sex from sage grouse wings (from Crunden 1963).

1. Molting primaries include 10, 9, or 8 3
2. Not as above 8
3a. Total length of wing* greater than 290 mm. . . . . *male*—4
3b. Total length of wing* less than 290 mm. . . . .*female*—6
4a. *Male*, molting primaries 10 and/or 9. . . . . *adult*
4b. *Male*, molting primary 8 5
5a. *Male*, length of wing* to tip of primary 4 greater than 259 mm. *adult*
5b. *Male*, length of wing* to tip of primary 4 less than 259 mm. . . . .*juvenile*
6a. *Female*, molting primaries 10 and/or 9 . . . . *adult*
6b. *Female*, molting primary 8 7
7a. *Female*, length of wing* to tip of primary 4 greater than 215 mm. . . . .*adult*
7b. *Female*, length of wing* to tip of primary 4 less than 215 mm. . . . .*juvenile*
8a. Primary 8 longer than 9 . . . . *adult*—3
8b. Primary 8 shorter than 9 . . . .*juvenile*—9
9a. *Juvenile*, length of wing* to tip of primary 8 greater than 259 mm. . . . . *male*
9b. *Juvenile*, length of wing* to tip of primary 8 less than 259 mm. . . . .*female*

*From "wrist–joint" (see Fig. 20.2) to tip of longest primary.

Table 20.11. Age of sage grouse as shown by differences in length of primaries #8 and #9 and bursal depth of birds collected in October (After Eng 1955).

	Difference in length (mm) between primary #9 and #8		Bursal depth (mm)	
	Adult	Immature	Adult	Immature
Sample size	13	20	13	19
Maximum	24	-27*	7	25
Minimum	11	- 4	0	13
Average	17.3	-12.3	1.6	18.9

*Negative figures indicate #9 is shorter than #8 by mm shown.

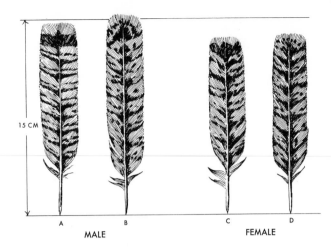

15 CM

A   B   C   D

MALE   FEMALE

Fig. 20.10. Central tail feathers of ruffed grouse may be used in aging. Note greater length of male feathers. *A* Male, complete band; *B* Male, intermediate band; *C* Female, intermediate band; *D* Female incomplete band (from Godin 1960).

flecking, is equal to or greater than the area of black pigment on #9. Since the willow ptarmigan sheds its two outer primaries at 14-15 months of age, it is possible to recognize a yearling class; primaries of the preceding year can be easily recognized by their faded and worn condition.

Determination of sex within any given age-class can be based (in order of increasing accuracy) on tail pigment, wing length, rectrix length, and wing and rectrix length combined. The female often has a browner tail, particularly of the central upper tail coverts, whereas the male has a black tail. Female wings and tails are shorter than those of males.

BLUE GROUSE

See Table 20.9. Sexing is comparatively easy in blue grouse. The aging of young in the fall is best done on the basis of the outer tail feathers. In the juvenile bird these are shorter, more rounded, and narrower, while in the adult they are longer, more square-tipped, and wider (Van Rossem 1925). Petrides (1942) measured these outer tail feathers and found that, at 1/2 inch below the tip, the immature feathers were from 3/4 to 7/8 inch wide, while adult feathers were 1-1/4 to 1-1/2 inches wide. Bendell (1955) reported on the total length of the plucked outer tail feathers as follows: immature/male—13.2 to 15.2 cm; adult male—16.2 to 19.4 cm; immature female—11.1 to 13.4 cm; adult female—13.8 to 16.1 cm. Bendell found the juvenile bursa (in

September) to be 1 to 2 cm deep, while in the adult it was reduced or absent. Further details on the relation of age to plumage in blue grouse, along with photographs of chicks from hatching to 16 weeks of age is given in Smith and Bus (1963).

RING-NECKED PHEASANT

There is no difficulty in distinguishing the sex in adults, except in an occasional intersex. In rare instances, the male plumage is found in females whose ovaries are inactive. A shot occasionally lodges in the ovary of a hen, causing an intersex to be produced. These individuals are readily recognized by their partial male plumage and the absence of spurs.

Sex may be determined in newly-hatched ring-necked pheasants by means of the shape and extent of the eye field (see Fig. 20.11). In the female a comparatively wide strip of longer down extends approximately one-quarter of the circumference of the eye field. In the male, this strip of down is much narrower (Latham 1942).

Immature birds in the fall closely resemble adults. Unlike many other gallinaceous birds they often replace the two outer primaries (#9 and #10) during the postjuvenal molt and so display primaries of adult shape during the fall (Wright and Hiatt 1943).

The use of the bursa of Fabricius is the most reliable tool in aging ring-necked pheasants during the hunting season. Since some adult birds retain a shallow bursa, the question is where to draw the line between young and adult birds. Stokes (1954), working on Pelee Island, Ontario, considered 8 mm and 6 mm as the maximum bursal depths for adult cocks and hens respectively during the hunting season, when the young birds were about 20 weeks old. In California, where the birds are about 27 weeks old during the hunting season, the trough in the bimodal curve of bursal depths of cocks falls at 6 to 8 mm (Harper, Hart, and Schaffer 1951), suggesting a slightly shallower maximum bursal depth for adults. In South Dakota, Nelson (1948) found that the bursa in adult cocks reached a maximum depth of 10 mm. It appears that acceptance of 8 mm as the maximum depth in adult cocks would involve little error in the populations which have been studied.

Dahlgren, Twedt, and Trautman (1965), found that juveniles could be distinguished from adults in the fall by lens weight but the adults could not be broken into year-classes.

The spur is often used as a criterion of age. A spur-gauge was devised to separate young from old on the basis of the distance from the tip of

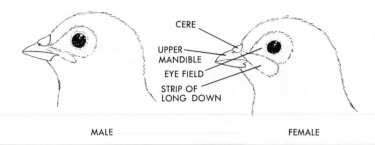

MALE   FEMALE

Fig. 20.11. A sex character for newly-hatched ring-necked pheasants (after Latham 1942).

the spur to the opposite side of the leg (Kimball 1944). However, since the spur of the young bird continues to grow all fall and there is some overlap between the spur length of young and old birds, this criterion has been found inadequate (Stokes 1957). The appearance of the spur during the fall, as shown in Table 20.12, has been used as a supplemental age criterion. In one test, however, it was found that experienced workers mis-aged 20% of adult and 1% of juvenile cock pheasants, apparently because of differences in subjective judgment (Gates 1966).

The "jaw test" already described can be used in questionable cases to provide evidence of age (Linduska 1943) but is not of sufficient accuracy to be used as the sole criterion (Nelson 1948).

WILD TURKEY

This species, the largest North American upland game bird, requires more time to reach adult size than most other birds do. Therefore, weight differences may be used to distinguish between young and older turkeys. McDowell (1956: 18), working with the eastern wild turkey in Virginia, found that first-fall hens weighed less than 8 pounds, first-fall gobblers normally weighed from 8 to less than 14 pounds, older

hens usually weighed from 8 to 12 pounds, and older gobblers weighed 14 or more pounds.

First-year turkeys may be distinguished most easily from older birds by: (1) the unequal contour of the spread tail feathers (caused by the late replacement of the central four to six rectrices), (2) the pointed outer (#10) primary (see Fig. 20.13), and (3) the presence of the bursa of Fabricius in first-fall turkeys (Mosby and Handley 1943: 93-96).

It is difficult to sex the wild turkey with accuracy by external characters until enough of the post-juvenal molt is completed to show adult breast feathers. Usually by the 16th week of age, young hens may be distinguished from gobblers by the shape and tip-coloring of the breast feathers. The breast feathers of the hen are rounded and buff-tipped whereas these feathers in the gobbler are squamate and black-tipped (Fig. 20.14). Experienced observers can sex turkeys by the larger head and longer neck, longer tarsi, and greater height of the gobbler. The presence or absence of a beard is not completely diagnostic of either sex or age. The beard on the breast of the gobbler may reach 1.5 to 2 inches in length the first fall, seldom protruding far beyond the breast feathers. The second fall the beard seldom exceeds 5 inches in length, is

Table 20.12. A comparison of fall spur characteristics in adult and young male ring-necked pheasants (after Linduska 1943).

Character-istic spur	Age	
	Adult	Young
Color	Very dark	Light
Shape	Acutely pointed, sharp often decurved	Usually straight along edges, point more obtuse
Texture	With hard, glossy surface	Soft surface, without luster

spread loosely, and has a burned appearance on the end. Older birds have beards usually 8 inches long, or more, and uniform in diameter and color. However, because of wear, etc., beards are not a reliable criterion of age (Latham 1956). The beard is absent from immature hens (first fall) and seldom exceeds about 3 inches in length when present in older hens (Edminster 1954).

The sex of adult turkeys can be determined by the relative size and shape of their droppings, according to Bailey (1956). Droppings of the adult male are straighter, longer, and greater in diameter than those of the hen. The typical male dropping has a curlicue on the larger end. In the fall, immature (young of the year) males may be separated from older males by a difference in dropping diameter; young males have droppings seldom exceeding 10 mm in diameter, while older males may have droppings as large as 15 mm in diameter. Female droppings differ from those of the male by their smaller diameter (5 to 8 mm) and their looped, spiral, or bulbous shape (see Fig. 20.15).

BOBWHITE

Occasionally difficulty is encountered in determining whether a bobwhite is immature or adult from the characters of the two outer primaries and the tip coloring of the greater upper coverts. For such cases, it has been found that the shape of greater primary covert #7 is useful. This feather is plucked out and compared to specimens from known young and known adults. In the immature bird this covert has a uniform

brownish tint, is usually tipped with buff, and the barbs and vanes separate easily, giving a ragged, mussy appearance. This covert in the adult bird holds together better, giving a sleek appearance, is darker, and without tip markings (see Fig. 20.16 and 20.17). In addition, most adult 7th greater primary coverts have more whitish-downy tipping on the basal 15 to 20 barbs (Haugen 1957).

COTURNIX QUAIL

In addition to the criteria listed in Table 20.13, the adult breeding male has a swollen cloacal protuberance which is red in color. The cloaca exudes a teaspoonful of froth if squeezed. This froth is often found on the droppings of males (Coil and Weatherbee 1959).

HUNGARIAN PARTRIDGE

The sex of an adult partridge can be determined by the scapular and median wing coverts (Fig. 20.18). The male has dark "shoulder" feathers, each with a single median buff stripe; in the female these feathers are lighter and each has a wide median buff stripe and two to four buff crossbars (McCabe and Hawkins 1946).

The immature birds in fall look like adults and may be distinguished from them by the pointedness of the two outer primaries (McCabe and Hawkins 1946), and by their yellow feet. Adults are blue-gray (Edminster 1954).

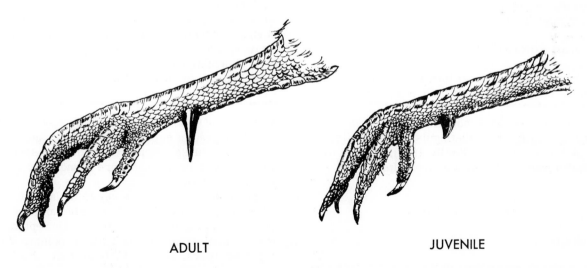

ADULT   JUVENILE

Fig. 20.12. Size of spur as an age criterion of fall-shot cock ring-necked pheasant. *Left:* Adult (over 1 year old). *Right:* Juvenile (from Godin 1960).

IMMATURE　　　　**ADULT**

Fig. 20.13. Primaries No. 10 of adult and immature Eastern wild turkey. Note that the tip of the adult primaries are broadly rounded and barred, with white almost to the extreme tip; the tip of immature primaries are pointed and plain gray in color and lack definite barring (original report by Petrides 1942; sketch by Grace Smyth).

CHUKAR PARTRIDGE

The adults are almost identical, the male being slightly larger. The adult male has spurs but the adult female sometimes also has them. External sex characters have not been found. Immature birds are difficult to distinguish from adults but the pictures and key of Smith (1961), dealing with wing differences due to age, are helpful.

Other Game Birds

WOODCOCK

See Table 20.14. Fig. 20.19 illustrates an age character and Fig. 20.20 a sex character in the wing of the woodcock. Martin (1964) gives a key for determining the age (immature, subadult, and adult) of woodcock from January through March by wing characters.

MOURNING DOVE

See Table 20.14. Swank (see Table 20.3) describes a method for aging young mourning doves by the progression of the postjuvenal molt. He points out that this molt is probably slowed by disease or injury and that even in normal birds it may be completed by October 15 (Swank 1955). Wight (1956) found this method of aging reliable only up to the point where the eighth primary has been shed; doves molting the ninth or tenth primary seldom displayed whitetipped primary coverts. For mourning doves too far advanced to age by the primary coverts, Wight (1956) developed a rapid method of determining whether or not the bursa was present. With heavy shears he made a transverse cut immediately posterior to the vent, without cutting the cloaca. The tail is completely severed. If the bursa is present, it lies immediately dorsal to the vent and is a round yellow structure 10 to 12 mm long and 6 to 8 mm wide, having fine vermiculations. He reports that the bursa may readily be detected by probing.

BAND-TAILED PIGEON

H. M. Wight (pers. communication) reported his findings and those of G. D. Silovsky and others on aging band-tailed pigeons (*Columbia fasciata*). Wing plumage characters and primary molt patterns enabled age identification during September-October. Wing plumage characters were only partially useful in age identification during December since some immatures had attained adult plumage. The presence or absence of a glandular bursa was a valid indicator of age from September through December. Primary molt patterns and wing plumage characters were employed in the construction of a key for September-October. Tests of this key indicated a high degree of accuracy possible in age determination. Bursal depth and the presence or absence of a neck ring were found to be invalid as indicators of age.

Table 20.15 presents a key to the age of band-tailed pigeon wings during September and Ocotber. During trapping in May and June and in September, sex identification poses little problem. Wight reported (pers. communication) that about 95% accuracy is obtained from examining the gonads and cloaca. The plumage differences, though

Table 20.13. Sex and age characters in ring-necked pheasant, wild turkey, and quail. Note: In column (1) female characteristics are italicized; in column (2) immature characters are italicized.

Species	Criteria for distinguishing sex (1)	Criteria for distinguishing age (2)
Ring-necked Pheasant	See text.	See text.
Eastern Wild Turkey	See text.	See text.
Bobwhite	HEAD: forehead, chin and throat and wide line from beak running back just above and behind eye white with blackish edging; *these areas buff.* CROWN: mottled w/blackish brown; *mottled w/rusty brown (E).*	GREATER UPPER PRIMARY COVERTS: uniform gray; *buff-tipped* (Le) (see Fig. 20.17).
California Quail	HEAD: conspicuous club-tipped black topknot; *topknot inconspicuous.* PLUMAGE: fairly bold and colorful; *dull.*	GREATER UPPER PRIMARY COVERTS: uniform gray; *buff-tipped* (Le).
Gambel's Quail	Similar to California Quail.	GREATER UPPER PRIMARY COVERTS: uniform gray; *buff-tipped* (Le).
Scaled Quail	SIDE OF FACE: uniform pearl gray, with exception of brownish ear patch; *streaked dirty gray.* THROAT: normally clear white just behind mandible, blending into yellowish or buffy wash on lower throat; *lighter ground color than face, with dark streaks, without yellowish wash* (W).	GREATER UPPER PRIMARY COVERTS: uniform gray; *buff-tipped* (Le).
Mountain Quail	PLUME: longer; *slightly shorter.* HINDNECK: gray clearer; *duller.* LOWER SURFACE: brighter; *slightly duller* (GB&S).	GREATER UPPER PRIMARY COVERTS: uniform gray; *buff-tipped* (Le).
Corturnix Quail	CHIN AND THROAT FEATHERS: (nuptial) reddish-brown, rounded with black median stripe; (non-breeding) long, lanceolate, whitish, with black median stripe; *long, lanceolate, light cinnamon, margined near tip with rufous or black spots, without black median stripe* (We).	OUTER PRIMARIES: rounded; *sharp.* PRIMARY COVERTS: without white rachises; *with white rachises* (We).

Authority: (E) = Edminster 1954; (GB&S) = Grinnell, Bryant, and Storer 1918; (Le) = Leopold 1939; (W) = Walmo 1956; (We) = Weatherbee, in press.

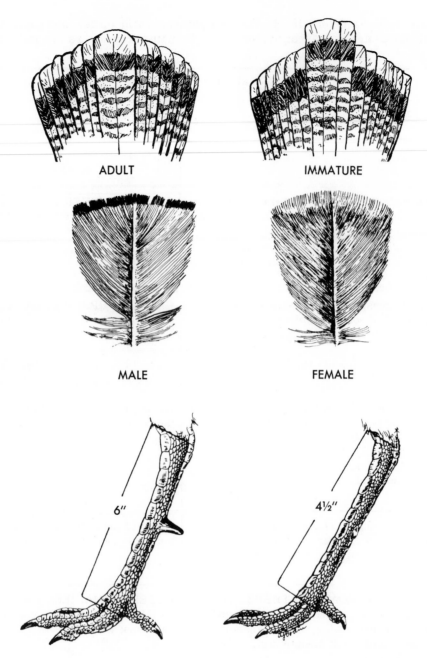

ADULT   IMMATURE

MALE   FEMALE

Fig. 20.14. Sex and age characters in the eastern wild turkey. *Top:* The adult shows an even contour of the spread tail *Left* whereas the immature *Right* has an irregular contour. *Middle:* Breast feather of male *Left* is flattened and black-tipped, whereas that of female *Right* is rounded and buff-tipped. *Bottom:* Foot of male is about 6 inches and bears a spur, while that of the female is only about 4-1/2 inches (from Godin 1960).

subjective, are thought to be accurate enough in a banding program.

The plumage of males is brighter with a more rosy hue to the breast and head; females are duller and have brown or gray breasts and necks.

KING RAIL

The sexes are similar in plumage. During September and October the young progress toward adult plumage. By November they are practically

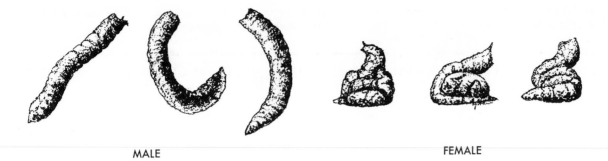

MALE   FEMALE

Fig. 20.15. Dropping configurations as indicators of sex for the eastern wild turkey. *Left:* Typical gobbler configurations. *Right:* Typical configurations of the hen; after Bailey 1956 (from Godin 1960).

in adult plumage, although they do not attain their full brilliancy of color until the next molt (Bent 1926).

CLAPPER RAIL

The adults of both sexes are identical in appearance. The juvenile plumage is similar to that of the adult but the streaking on the back is duller and less strikingly contrasted, the lower surface is very much lighter, more *buffy* in tone, and the barring on the sides and flanks scarcely or not at all in evidence (Grinnell, Bryant, and Storer 1918).

COOT

Adult coots may be sexed in the field by their voice and by the larger erectile neck-ruff of the male. Dead birds may be sexed and aged with

fair accuracy by means of the criteria listed in Table 20.14.

DETERMINING SEX AND AGE IN MAMMALS

Mammals, like birds, tend to become more sexually distinct as they approach breeding age. However, the age at which a mammal first breeds is strongly influenced by its nutritional history. Birds apparently show less variability in this regard, perhaps because their diet tends to fluctuate less in quality. For example, practically all hen ring-necked pheasants breed for the first time the first spring following hatching. Cottontails born late in the season, or toward the edge of their range, will also breed for the first time the year following their birth. But cottontails born early in the year, on a range

ADULT   IMMATURE

Fig. 20.16. Age criteria, based on wing characters, of all quail in Table 20.13 except coturnix quail. *Left:* Primary coverts in adult are of uniform color. *Right:* Primary coverts in immature individuals have tips of light color (from Godin 1960).

Table 20.14. Sex and age characters in shorebirds, pigeons, doves, and rails. Note: In column (1) female characters italicized; in column (2) immature characters italicized.

Species	Criteria for distinguishing sex (1)	Criteria for distinguishing age (2)
Woodcock	BILL: usually under 67 mm; *usually over 69 mm* (E). WEIGHT: under 175 grams; *over 200 grams* (G). OUTERMOST PRIMARY WIDTH (2 cm. from tip): average 2.5 mm; *average 3.9 mm* (G).	OVIDUCT WIDTH: not under 3 mm; *not over 1 mm* (G). BURSA: absent; *present* (G). MIDDLE SECONDARIES: dark-tipped; *light tipped* (M).
Wilson Snipe	Adults identical (GB&S).	STRIPE FROM SIDE OF BILL TO EYE: dark brown; *black* (GB&S). CHEEK AND CHIN: buffy and whitish, flecked w/dusky-diagonal dark stripe on lower cheek beneath ear; *mixed white, black, and cinnamon* (GB&S).
Mourning Dove	BREAST: faint pink; *brown* (GB&S). CROWN: bluish-gray; *brown* (GB&S).	PRIMARY COVERTS: uniform; *white-tipped* (P&M). BURSA: absent; *present* (W).
White-winged Dove	CROWN & BACK OF NECK: purplish; *grayish brown* (E). SIDE OF NECK: iridescent green-gold; *grayish-brown* (E).	GREATER PRIMARY COVERTS: tips plain; *tips light colored* (E). FEET AND LEGS: red; *pink or salmon.*
Virginia Rail	Adults identical (GB&S).	TOP OF HEAD, HIND NECK: blackish, narrowly streaked w/olive brown; *dull black w/traces of buffy feather edgings* (GB&S). LOWER SURFACE: cinnamon brown, fading to lighter on belly; *mixed black and white, latter predominating down middle of breast and on belly* (GB&S). LOWER TAIL COVERTS: mixed blackish, white, and cinnamon; *dull cinnamon* (GB&S).
Coot	CULMEN AND SHIELD LENGTH (yearlings and immatures): 43.2-49.7 mm; *36.7-44.6 mm.* METATARSUS PLUS MIDDLE TOE LENGTH: 128 mm or over; *127 mm or less* (both of these criteria are only fair) (Gu).	LEGS: tarsi red-orange (very old), clear yellow (third year), yellow-green (second year); *tarsi blue or gray-green* (imm.) (Gu).

Authorities: (E) = Edminster 1954; (G) = Greeley 1953; (GB&S) = Grinnell, Bryant, and Storer 1918; (Gu) = Gullion 1952; (M) = Martin 1964; (P&M) = Pearson and Moore 1940; (W) = Wight 1956.

which permits rapid development, will breed during the year of birth. Some of the smaller mammals further complicate matters by having not a single annual production of young as most game birds do (pigeons, doves, and Cotournix quail are exceptions) but several litters during a single breeding season.

Determining Sex in Mammals

THE MAMMALIAN REPRODUCTIVE TRACT

Sexing by the gonads, or internal sex organs, is certain, usually even in very young mammals. The male has two testes, sometimes permanently

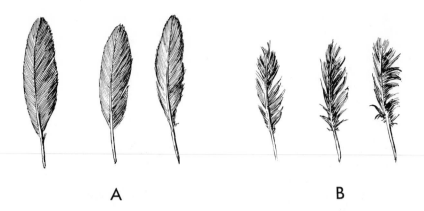

A   B

Fig. 20.17. Seventh greater primary coverts of bobwhite, showing sleek appearance in adult *(A)* and ragged *(B)* appearance in juvenile (after Haugen 1957). See Fig. 20.2 for location of this feather on the wing (from Godin 1960).

outside the body wall in a scrotum, as in human, but in many species capable of being withdrawn into the body cavity. The female mammal has two functional ovaries. These are located on mesentaries on the sides of the body cavity, one on each side. They are much smaller than the testes and sometimes difficult for a beginner to recognize. They may usually be found by tracing back the Fallopian tubes from the uterus. See Fig. 20.21.

The adult female mammal is further identified by the presence of prominent mammae, or nipples. These vary in number from species to species and may be difficult to see in females which have not yet bred.

Mammals, instead of having one common opening, as in birds, usually have separate openings for the digestive tract and the urogenital system. The penis of the male is easily seen in some species but in others it is generally retracted, so that only the opening from which it

can emerge is visible. In species with a retracted penis it is usually possible to feel it under the skin or force it out with pressure. Some species have a penis bone, or baculum, which will be discussed under criteria of age.

In the female the two ovaries are located about one-fourth of the way from the anus to the diaphragm, toward the upper (dorsal) part of the abdominal cavity. They are slightly pebbled and usually white or pale yellow in color. The Fallopian tubes open into the uterus, the two branches, or horns, of which join the vagina. The opening, or vulva, in many species superficially resembles the male urogenital opening. No penis is present but the clitoris of the female may resemble a penis. In any given species the location of the urogenital orifice with respect to the anus, and its external appearance, which are learned after a few dissections, are indicative of sex, but between species the situation is variable.

THE SEXUAL DIFFERENTIATION OF THE PELVIS

In many mammals the young are fairly large at birth. During the process of birth they must pass through the pelvic girdle of the female. In some species, the lower line of fusion of the two halves of the girdle is resorbed before giving birth, so that the walls of the girdle may spread. In others, there is a loosening of the ligaments holding the two sides of the girdle together. These effects are apparently caused by the secretion of female sex hormone in the blood stream. Some species do not have a loosening of the bond between the two halves of the pelvic girdle but the female sex hormones still cause modifications in the

MALE   FEMALE

Fig. 20.18. Scapular feathers from Hungarian partridge. Note center stripe in feather from male and barring on feather from female (sketch by Jens von Sivers *in* Thompson 1958, after McCabe and Hawkins 1946).

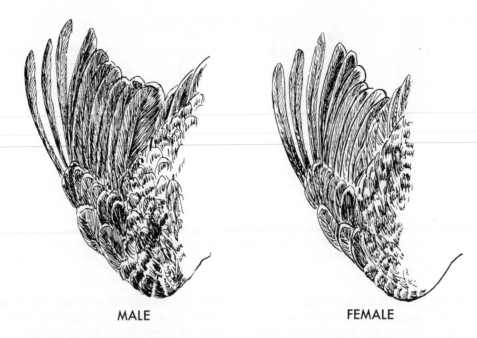

MALE   FEMALE

Fig. 20.19. Woodcock sex determination from outer primaries. Note narrow width of outer primaries, commencing at a point 2 cm below tip, of the male bird as compared with the greater width of the female feather (sketch by Jens von Sivers *in* Thompson 1958, after Greeley 1953).

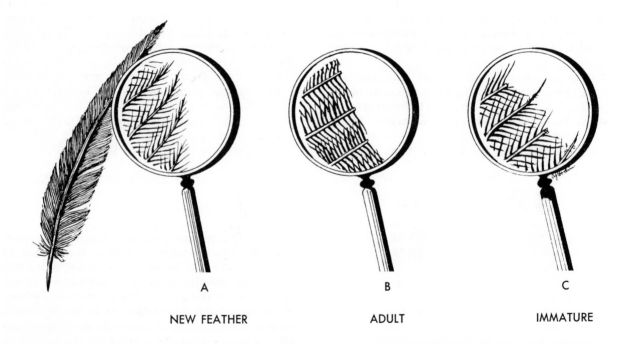

A   B   C

NEW FEATHER   ADULT   IMMATURE

Fig. 20.20. Age criteria of the American woodcock based on wear of primaries No. 8, No. 9, and No. 10 in fall-shot birds. *A* New feather, *B* Tips of adult primaries show even wear, with the ends of the barbs either square in shape, with a very shallow "V"-shaped notch. *C* The tips and distal edges of the immature primaries exhibit more wear and are characterized by "V"-shaped notches on the ends of the barbs. Approximate magnification 5X (after Sheldon et al. 1958, from Godin 1960).

Table 20.15. Key to age of band-tailed pigeon wings, September-October.

I.
1. White and/or pale brown tipping of lesser, middle and greater coverts . . . . Immature.

2. No white or brown tipping . . . . .II.

II.
1. Unmolted primaries fringed with white; tips entire showing little or no wear; unmolted secondaries (if present) not worn . . . . Immature.

2. Primaries not fringed with white tips; often not entire worn and sometimes "V" notched; unmolted secondaries (if present) heavily worn on leading edge and sometimes tips . . . . Adult.

Immatures may have a full set (10) of primaries since they have not yet begun to molt. However, none of the immatures will have completed the primary molt. Immatures will be molting primaries 1 through 7.

Adults may not have begun the primary molt, completed the molt or be molting primaries 1 through 10. In addition, some adults will be molting two non-adjacent primaries simultaneously.

shape of the pelvis. For this reason, there are generally significant differences between the appearance of the pelvis of one sex and the other in most mammalian species, especially in individuals which have passed through one breeding season.

In the male, the pelvis has a special function which sometimes leaves its mark on the posterior border of the ischium and helps in sex identification—that of forming a point of attachment for some of the ligaments which support the penis. The point of attachment of a ligament commonly is marked by a raised, roughened area of bone, growing more pronounced with age (Fig. 20.22).

Determining Age in Mammals

In mammals, as in birds, criteria of age are based on physical maturation. There appears to be more variation between individual mammals in this respect than between individual birds. This means that criteria of age are generally somewhat less precise for mammals than they are for birds.

SCHEDULES OF FETAL DEVELOPMENT

In species with a long gestation period, it is sometimes desirable to determine the period of breeding and implantation of the fertilized ova. This may be done by aging the fetuses and dating back to the time of implantation. Descriptions of fetal development have been worked out for deer

and elk, and will be given in the sections devoted to those species.

TOOTH DEVELOPMENT AS AN INDICATOR OF AGE

Most mammals have a definite number and pattern of teeth as adults. Some of these teeth come in as permanent teeth. Others replace the previous milk (or deciduous) teeth. Often, there is an annual deposit of cementum on the tooth roots, and an annual deposit of secondary dentine in the pulp cavity. The sequence of appearance, replacement, and, to a lesser extent, wear, is fairly regular and is a useful basis for estimates of age.

THE MATURATION OF LONG BONES

As a mammal grows, its long bones lengthen from the tips. Each long bone has, while it is growing, a cartilaginous zone at each end covered by a bony cap, the epiphysis. Bone is deposited at the inner side of the cartilaginous zone, pushing the cap further out as the bone grows. When growth is complete the cartilage is replaced by solid bone, so that the cap and the shaft are fused firmly together. The presence of the cartilaginous zone, a line representing its recent presence, or its complete absence, are criteria of use in aging many mammals.

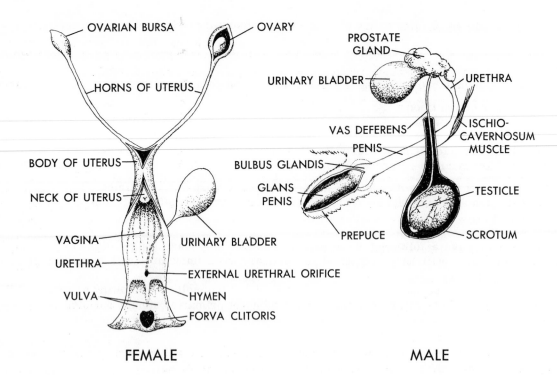

Fig. 20.21. General view of genitalia of female and male animals (Canidae). *Left:* Excised internal female genital organs, dorsal view. *Right:* Lateral view of male genital organs (from Godin 1960).

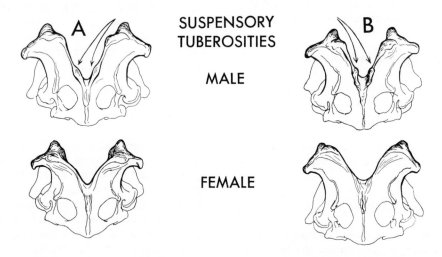

Fig. 20.22. Pelvic girdle of the white-tailed *A* and black-tailed *B* deer, viewed from the rear, showing the suspensory tuberosities for the attachment of the penis ligaments in the male and their absence in the female (after Taber 1956).

THE BACULUM (OR OS PENIS)

In some species, notably the bears and the members of the dog and weasel families, the males have a bone (the baculum) in the penis. The baculum changes with age and so is a good age indicator in some species.

HORN GROWTH AS AN INDICATOR OF AGE

Animals with permanent horns, such as sheep and goats, commonly show the effects of periods of good (summer) and poor (winter) food conditions. When forage is good the horns grow rapidly, emerging as fairly smooth structures. During the period of poor forage (except in young of the year) the horn essentially stops growth, and this stoppage is marked by a ridge.

WEIGHTS AND MEASUREMENTS

When any given animal population has been thoroughly investigated it is usually possible to establish criteria of weight or measurement which will serve to indicate age, up to the point when rapid growth is finished. Different populations, however, often require different criteria.

THE WEIGHT OF THE LENS OF THE EYE

The lens of the eye in man, the cottontail, and probably most other mammals, grows continuously through life, and so provides a potential indicator of age. Lord (1959) has described its use for the cottontail; the results are summarized in the section on that mammal.

CRITERIA OF AGE AND SEX FOR SELECTED MAMMALS

Fur-bearing and Miscellaneous Mammals

BATS

A vespertilionid bat (*Myotis myotis*) has been studied by Sluiter (1961), who found that the young were born in June and can be distinguished from adults until October by smaller size, darker fur, and relatively longer ears. Sexual maturity is reached during the second year of life. Females which have not yet given birth can be recognized by examination of the reproductive tract during the first and second winters of life. Juvenile males can be recognized by the reproductive tract

during the first winter only. Tooth abrasion continues through life but overlap between age-classes precludes use of the results of tooth wear as a reliable criterion of age.

BLACK BEAR

In this species age and sex have been correlated with weight, tooth eruption, the completion of skeletal growth and the size of the baculum. The most reliable criterion of age apparently consists of the alternate layers of light and dark cementum on the roots of the teeth. The number of dark layers seen on the root of the canine in longitudinal section indicates the age less 1 year (Marks and Erickson 1966, Stoneberg and Jonkel 1966).

Some other age characters are summarized in Table 20.16 and Fig. 20.23.

EUROPEAN BROWN AND GRIZZLY BEARS (URSUS ARCTOS)

The European brown bear is closely related to the grizzly and big brown bears of North America. The sexes differ in size, the female being some 20 to 25% lighter than the male (Coutourier 1954: 20) and in life the female is often accompanied by cubs.

The young may be aged by inspection if undisturbed in the field as cubs or yearlings, since young are born only during the winter and family groups often stay together so that sizes may be compared.

Dead individuals may be aged by tooth succession as shown in Table 20.17.

The grizzly bear has been accurately aged by the number of annuli in the third lower molar; the number of dark annuli equals the age less one. Further, the age is positively correlated with zygomatic width (Mundy and Fuller 1964).

OPOSSUM

See Table 20.18. Young animals may be aged (McGrady 1938) by the dental formula:

$$3 \text{ months} = \frac{5120}{4120}; \quad 4 \text{ months} = \frac{5131}{4132};$$

$$5 - 8\text{-}1/2 \text{ months} = \frac{5132}{4133};$$

$$7 - 11 \text{ months} = \frac{5133}{4134};$$

$$10 \text{ months} = \frac{5134}{4134}$$

Table 20.16. Age characters in the black bear (from Marks and Erickson 1966).

0-1	Weight <60 lb; skull length + width <288 mm; skull round posteriorly and all sutures open; on leaving natal den (3 mo.) most deciduous teeth present; usually all permanent teeth erupt during first year; canine begins eruption about 9 mo. and completes about 15 mo.; baculum rod-shaped, 85 mm long and 1.5 grams in weight; all forelimb epiphyses widely separated from their diaphyses.
1-2	Weight 60-110 lb; skull longer, dorsally flattened with rudimentary sagittal and lamboidal crests; coalescence of occipital sutures beginning; apex of root of third incisor closes and dentino-enamel junction of upper canines emerges beyond alveolar margin; teeth mostly unworn; baculum mean length about 100 mm and mean weight about 2.3 g; metacarpals of forelimbs fuse.
2-4	Interparietal sutures close, as do external apexes of canine root canals; the two mesial incisors and lower second molar may show slight wear; baculum mean length 133 mm and mean weight 5.8 g.
4-6 (females)	Basioccipital-basisphenoid, maxilla-premaxillary, interfrontals, and lamboidal sutures usually closed by end of fifth year; wear shows on all incisors and frequently on molar cusps; ephiphyres of ulna and radius fuse.
(males)	Basioccipital-basisphenoid suture coalesces by end of sixth year and lamboidal suture between 5 and 7; teeth as in female; mesial closure of epiphyses of radius and ulna begins; baculum mean length 149 mm and mean weight 9.3 g.
6-8 (females)	Internasal and interpremaxillary sutures close; fusion complete in all forelimb bones.
(males)	Interfrontal suture coalesces between 6 and 7, the maxilla-premaxillary at 7, and the internasal between 6 and 8; fusion complete in all forelimb bones; baculum mean length 172 mm and mean weight 12.9 g.
Over 8	Progressive wear on all teeth, many worn down to the dentine, periodontal disease and broken teeth common; baculum mean length 177 mm and mean weight 15.1 g.

RACCOON

See Table 20.18. Young raccoons are weaned about 16-20 weeks of age. During this period their age may be determined by tooth eruption, following the data in Table 20.19.

Dried weight of the eye is a reliable indicator of age up to one year of age only (Sanderson 1961). However, Montgomery (1963) reports that both freezing and decomposition tend to reduce lens weight and lead to an under-estimate of age. Live males may be aged by weight in the fall and winter (Sanderson 1950) but since weights vary from one area to another, the line of overlap should be determined locally. Means of breaking the adult segment of the population into age-groups have not yet been developed.

During the winter, juveniles may be identified by means of X-rays of the distal ends of the radius and ulna and the epiphyses are distinct and not fused with the shafts (Petrides 1959). However, thin epiphyseal lines (Fig. 20.24) often persist through the following year (Sanderson 1961). In carcasses of males taken during the winter, the penis of a juvenile cannot be extended over one-half its length, while that of an adult can be extended more than one-half its length (Sanderson 1961).

DELAYED IMPLANTATION IN MUSTELIDAE IN RELATION TO AGING

Because most members of the weasel family show a delay between the time that the ovum is

Table 20.17. Tooth eruption in the European brown bear (Coutourier 1954:145).

Age	Stage of tooth eruption
3 mo.	All milk teeth and also first true molar are in place before this time.
4 mo.	The first lower incisor appears.
5 mo.	The first upper incisor appears.
7 mo.	The second lower molar appears.
8 mo.	The second upper and lower incisors and the second upper molar appear.
12 mo.	The third lower incisor appears.
13 mo.	The third upper incisor and the third and fourth lower premolars appear.
16 mo.	The fourth upper premolar appears.
Between 16 and 24 mo.	The third lower molar appears and then the canines.

fertilized and the time that it is implanted, there is often confusion concerning the length of the gestation period and the age at first breeding. In management, the principal question concerning age-classes is: during the harvest period, should a distinction be made between three classes (juveniles, subadults which have not yet produced young, and adults) or merely two (juveniles and adults)? Data on this question are presented in Table 20.20 for the principal members of the weasel family. In connection with this table it should be noted that the period between the implantation of the fertilized ovum and the production of young is probably not over 2 months for any of the animals listed.

MINK

See Tables 20.18, 20.20, 20.21, and 20.22. Baculum weight of Missouri ranch mink in the winter may be used to separate juveniles (80 - 235 mg) from adults (180 - 420 mg) with 85 - 90% accuracy

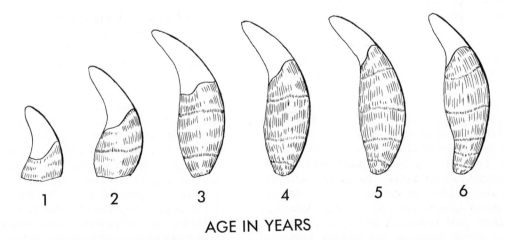

AGE IN YEARS

Fig. 20.23. Tooth development of the black bear in Alaska, showing correlation of annulations on the root of the right upper canine with age. All individuals taken in November (drawn by Godin, after Rausch 1961).

Table 20.18. Sex and age characters in opossum, raccoon, mink, badger, striped skunk, and long-tailed weasel. Note: In column (1), female characters italicized; in column (2), immature characters italicized.

Species	Criteria for distinguishing sex (1)	Criteria for distinguishing age (2)
Opossum	SECONDARY SEX CHARACTERS (reliable from 17 days): scrotum; *pouch outline and nipple rudiments* (R)	FEMALE POUCH (distinguishes those which have bred from those which have not): rusty inside and border, teats (dried winter) 3 mm diam. On pelts, pouch flabby, fatty, dark, and prone to tear; *pouch white, shallow or practically absent; on pelts, pouch not flabby, fatty, dark or prone to tear* (P)
Raccoon	DISTANCE FROM EXTERNAL URINARY OPENING TO ANUS: several inches; *not over one inch* (St.). URINARY PAPILLA: penis bone felt by palpation; *no penis bone* (S). CASED SKIN (if not too fat): roughened area near middle of belly (site of preputial orifice), small teats may show through skin; *no rough area, teats large* (S)	BACULUM: plate or knob at distal end (S), bone of basal end not porous (D); *distal end cartilaginous, basal end porous.* UTERINE HORNS (distinguishes those which have had litters from those which have not): opaque, 4-7 mm diam., w/placental scars; *translucent, 1-3 mm diam., w/o placental scars* (S)
Mink	CASED SKINS: penis scar present; *penis scar absent* (P-50a)	TEATS (of female): dark, raised, over 1 mm diam.; *unpigmented, scarcely raised, under 1 mm diam.* (P-50a)
Badger	Same as mink	TEATS (of female): 4-6 mm diam., 4-10 mm long even in dried skins; *1.5 mm diam. and 1 mm long in dried skins* (P-50a)
Striped Skunk	Same as mink	TEATS (of female): at least 2 mm diam. and 2.5 mm long, usually dark; *under 1 mm, usually flesh-covered* (P-50a)
Long-tailed Weasel	Same as mink	TEATS (of female July-October): enlarged; *not visible* (W)

Authorities: (D) = Dellinger 1954; (P) = Petrides 1949; (P-50a) = Petrides 1950; (R) = Reynolds 1945; (S) = Sanderson 1950; (St) = Stuewer 1943; (W) = Wright 1948.

(Elder 1951). Montana ranch mink had juvenile bacula 203 ± (1 st. dev.) 25.4 mg and adult 395 ± 90.0 mg (Lechleitner 1954).

Other osteological characters of age in mink are: (1) Lateral supra-sesamoid tubercle of femur. This tubercle increases in size with age and is more evident in males than in females. It is a small lateral tubercle on the distal end of the femur just proximal to the large lateral condyle and the facet of the lateral sesamoid bone (Fig. 20.25). It is small or missing in juveniles, which also show a porous bone surface in the region of the caudal epiphysis. Adult animals have a medium or large tubercle. (2) The jugal-squamosal suture on the zygomatic arch of the skull is commonly present in immature animals and absent in adults. These findings are for mink in Montana. See Tables 20.21 and 20.22 (Lechleitner 1954, Greer 1957).

Dellinger (unpublished), testing the reliability of the lateral supra-sesamoid tubercle as an age criterion in Missouri, found among 222 wild mink aged by the baculum that aging by the femur gave 13.5% overlap. In 60 known-age ranch mink the overlap was 18.3%. This observation suggests that there may well be marked differences

Table 20.19. Mean ages of raccoons at eruption of deciduous and permanent teeth (Montgomery 1964).

Tooth	Upper		Lower	
	Mean Age (days)	Sex	Mean Age (days)	Sex
Deciduous				
First incisor	34.0	2.8*	28.5	2.2*
Second incisor	25.4	2.2*	37.3	2.1*
Third incisor	26.2	1.2	33.0	2.4*
Canine	29.3	0.9	29.3	0.8
First premolar	64.5	1.9	60.7	1.8
Second premolar	46.2	1.0	43.4	1.6
Third premolar	49.2	1.2	48.4	1.2
Fourth premolar	48.7	1.0	48.7	1.0
Permanent				
First incisor	65.6	1.4	65.9	1.0
Second incisor	73.3	1.3	72.6	1.2
Third incisor	96.6	1.7	85.5	1.9
Canine	111.7	3.9	105.6	3.6
First molar	81.0	1.2	78.1	1.5

*The following percentages of these teeth either did not erupt or erupted and were shed before examination of the animals; upper first incisor and lower second incisor, 66.7; lower first incisor, 16.7; upper second incisor, 5.5; lower third incisor, 33.3.

between populations in different areas because of differences in the length of the growing season, food supply, soil fertility, and perhaps other factors influencing nutrition and growth.

PINE MARTEN

See Tables 20.20 and 20.22. Clear-cut criteria for distinguishing the yearling class have not been worked out.

Nasal sutures are probably unfused in juveniles and fused in adults. The sagittal crest is more pronounced in males than females and also more pronounced in old than in young. In the female the presence of a sagittal crest indicates probable adulthood; however, some adult females apparently have no crest. In males a sagittal crest under 20.0 mm indicates that the individual is immature. In addition, it seems probable that males with sagittal crests over 30.0 mm and females with crests of over 20.0 mm may be termed "very old" (Marshall 1951).

Newby and Hawley (1954), working with live pine marten, distinguished sex on the basis of the presence or absence of the baculum (determined by palpation), through observation of the vulva, or on the basis of the larger over-all size and broader head of the male. These same authors estimated age on: the basis of weight (juvenile females reached adult weight at three months, juvenile males at about four months); the softer appearance of the juvenile pelage (until late September); development of the sagittal crest; development of the head of the male baculum (enlarged in adults—see Fig. 20.26); and mammae of females (large and conspicuous in adults, inconspicuous in juveniles). Criteria for distinguishing the yearling and 2-year-old classes are not yet reported.

RIVER OTTER

Adults may be sexed by the relative positions of the anus and urogenital opening (see Fig. 20.27). Friley (1949) sets up four age-groups on the basis of baculum characters; the values for each class are derived from the sum of the products of length (mm) x weight (mg) plus length x volume (cc). The classes are: *very young*—below 225; *immature*—225-249; *young adult*—650-845; and *old adult*—over 845. Whether these correspond to the age-classes juvenile, yearling, two-year-old, and adult is not yet known. See Table 20.22 for further information.

Table 20.20. Some aspects of reproduction in members of the Mustelidae which determine whether there are classes in the harvest in addition to juvenile and adult.

Species	Breeding season	Season of birth	Gestation period*	Delayed implantation?	Age of ♀ at first breeding	Age of ♀ at first parturition	What classes in addition to immature and adult in winter population?	Authority
Mink	Winter	Early May	39-75 days	Yes	10 months	12 months	None	Hanssen 1947, Enders 1952
Pine Marten	July-Aug.	April	220-265 days	Yes	27 months	36 months	Yearling and two-year old	Asdell 1964
Long-tailed Weasel	July	Spring	205-337 days	Yes	3 or 4 months	12 months	None	Wright 1948
Fisher	March	April	338-358 days	Yes	12 months	24 months	Yearling (females only)	Hall 1942, Eadie and Hamilton 1958
Badger	July-Aug.?	Spring	Probably about 9 months	Yes	15 months?	24 months?	Yearling	Hamlett 1932
Wolverine	July-Aug.?	Spring	Probably about 9 months	Yes	15 months?	24 months?	Yearling	Wright and Rausch 1955
Striped Skunk	Feb.-March	Spring	62 days	No	10 months	12 months	None	Wight 1931
River Otter	Dec.-March	Nov.-Jan.	288-380 days	Yes	36 months?	48 months	Yearling, two and three-year-old	Friley 1949, Liers 1951

*The period between copulation and parturition.

WOLVERINE

See Tables 20.20 and 20.22. In adult males the sagittal crest seems to extend posteriorly further than in the immatures. A measurement of this character can be obtained indirectly by subtracting the condylobasal length from the greatest length of the skull. In 7 adult males this averaged 14.9 mm and in 12 immature males it averaged 11.6 mm. The difference was found significant at the 5% level. The same situation is probably true in females but has not been adequately tested (Wright and Rausch 1955).

All adults have all usual skull sutures closed;

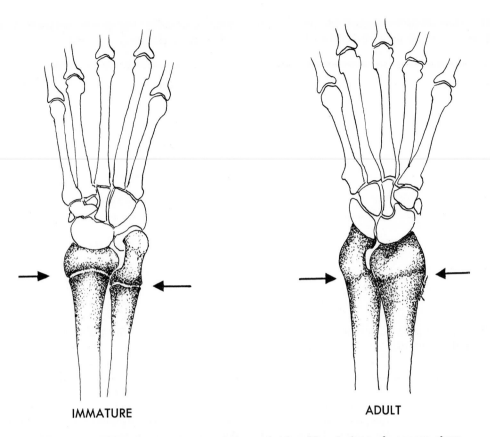

IMMATURE

ADULT

Fig. 20.24. Drawing made from X-ray photograph of radii and ulnae of raccoon showing open (immature) and closed (adult) epiphyses (after Sanderson 1961, from Godin 1960).

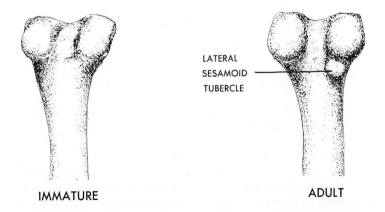

LATERAL
SESAMOID
TUBERCLE

IMMATURE

ADULT

Fig. 20.25. Femurs of mink showing lateral supre-sesamoid tubercle of adult and its absence in the immature (from Lechleitner 1954, by Godin).

Table 20.21. Use of femur tubercle (present on at least one side) and jugal-squamosal suture (absent on at least one side) as aging criteria in combination for mink (after Greer 1957).

Age classes	Total number	Number	Per cent
Femur tubercle absent and jugal-squamosal suture present			
Juveniles	495	468	95
Femur tubercle present and jugal-squamosal suture absent			
Adults	388	375	97

Table 20.22. Criteria of age based on the baculum of some mustelids (the term "head" means the basal, or proximal, enlargement).

Species	Characteristics of baculum in young*	Characteristics of baculum in old*	Authority
Mink	No ridge. Head not always morphologically distinct. Wt. 172 (1 S.D.) 34.2 mg	Distinct ridge on baculum at head, which is distinct. Wt. 398 (1 S.D.) 97.0 mg	Lechleitner 1954
Long-tailed Weasel	Heads scarcely larger than shafts. Wt. 14-29 mg	Heads greatly expanded. Wt. 53-101 mg	Wright 1947
Striped Skunk	Head not enlarged. Shaft irregularly curved.	Head enlarged. Shaft more straight.	Petrides 1950
Badger	Short light-weight, with only shallow grooves, w/o protuberances and with head only slightly enlarged and never ridged.	Long, heavy, with prominent grooves and protuberances and with head much enlarged and often sharply ridged.	Petrides 1950
Pine Marten	Wt. under 100 mg	Wt. over 100 mg	Marshall 1951
River Otter	649 or under**	650 or over**	Friley 1949
Wolverine	Wt. 653-1458 mg (avg 1134 mg)	Wt. 1780-2940 mg (avg 2338 mg)	Wright and Rausch 1955

*Young means young of the year in the winter; old means older.
**Sum of products of length (mm) x weight (mg plus x volume (cc)).

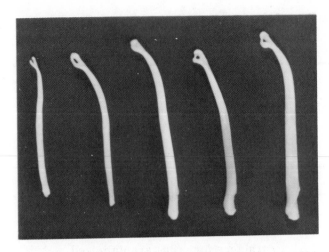

Fig. 20.26. Bacula of known-age pine marten arranged with proximal end to bottom. Ages from left to right: 5 months, 9 months, 3 years, 8 years, and 14 years.[2]

immatures in winter have malar-temporal, internasal and naso-maxillary sutures open (Wright and Rausch 1955).

FISHER

There are only two fall age-classes, juvenile and adult (see Table 20.18). They may be recognized by skull characters and baculum development (Wright and Coulter 1967).

Canidae

RED AND GRAY FOX

Lens weights can be used to separate juvenile from adult specimens, but there are differences between local populations, presumably caused by differences in nutrition (Friend and Linhart 1964).

Pelts are readily sexed by the presence or absence of "scar" marking the site of the penis. Age criteria, as given in Tables 20.23 and 20.24, are found in the size and shape of the baculum, for males, and the appearance and size of the teats for females.

Table 20.23 indicates that gray, but not red foxes may be aged by means of baculum weight and probably length.

In the red fox, the proximal epiphysis of the humerus closes at 9-9 1/2 months of age in New York (Reilly and Curren 1961).

COYOTE

Since coyotes commonly breed in the year following birth (Young and Jackson 1951) the

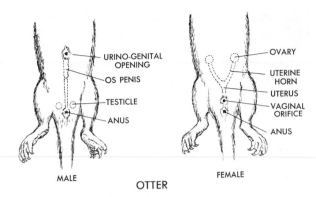

Fig. 20.27. Normal position of genitalia in male and female river otter. The presence of penis is readily determined in the male river otter by palpation in the live and dead animal (sketch adapted from Thompson 1958).

criteria used for foxes should apply. In addition, Gier (1957) has given a reconstruction of tooth-wear from 1 through 8 years of age (Fig. 20.28).

WOLF

Wolves do not breed until 3 years for males and 2 years for females but are "fully grown" at 18 months (Young and Goldman 1944). No specific age characters have been recorded.

PINNIPEDIA

Lens weight for the fur seal has been found to increase to at least 14 (male) and 21 (female) years of age, whereas body weight does not increase appreciably after 10 years. Lens weight, however, showed too much overlap between age-classes above 2-year-old to be useful as an age criterion.

On the other hand, pinnipeds seem generally to display annuli in the dentine deposits within the pulp cavity of canines, and cementum deposits on the apex of the root. Both of these may be examined in longitudinal sections of the teeth (Kenyon and Fiscus 1963). In some genera (*Callorhinus, Eumetopias, Zalophus, Odobenus,* and *Mirounga,* at least) there are annuli visible as ridges on the outer surface of the canines (Scheffer 1950, Mansfield 1958, Laws 1953, Kenyon and Fiscus 1963).

Lagomorphs and Rodents

COTTONTAIL

Sex is determined in the live animal as follows: When the cottontail is relaxed, the penis

Table 20.23. Measurements (early winter) of red and gray fox bacula in Central Ohio (after Petrides 1950).

Age class (according to baculum shape)	Red Fox			Gray Fox		
	Number	Length (mm)	Weight (mg)	Number	Length (mm)	Weight (mg)
Subadult	18	54.4 ± 4.8*	342 ± 70	5	51 ± 1.7	280 ± 62
Adult	5	54.5 ± 1.5	492 ± 103	5	57 ± 2.6	528 ± 100

*1 standard deviation.

Table 20.24. Age characters for red and gray fox. Characters for young are italicized.

Anatomical structure	Characters
BACULUM:	(♂♂) Larger, heavier, with enlarged and roughened basal area; *smaller, lighter, w/o large, rough basal area* (P)
TEATS:	(♀♀) Over 2 mm diam, dark, obvious to touch in dry pelts; *under 1 mm diam, light colored, scarcely raised* (separates those which have bred from others) (P)
EPIPHYSES OF RADIUS AND ULNA (by X-ray):	No cartilage plage at distal end of radius and ulna; *cartilage plate at distal end of radius and ulna (cartilage plate at distal epiphyseal gap)* (separates young up to 8-9 months from adults) (S & H)

(S & H) = Sullivan and Haugen 1956; (P) = Petrides 1950.

of the male and the clitoris of the female (which somewhat resembles the penis) are withdrawn into the body. For examination, these organs can be erected by applying downward pressure with a thumb and forefinger placed in front of and behind the genital region, respectively.

The penis is a cylindrical organ whose basal sheaths unfold on erection in the manner of a small telescope. A tiny terminal opening is apparent on close inspection.

The clitoris of the female is nearly as large as the penis of a young male and might be mistaken for it. However, it differs in being flattened posteriorly, and in having no terminal opening. The vaginal opening is located between the base of the clitoris and the anus, but is not always visible. In young females it is covered by the vaginal membrane.

Small rabbits are hardest to sex. In a young male the distal portion of the penis may "open up" along the mid-ventral line to somewhat resemble the clitoris. This flattening of the termi-

nal region of the penis does not extend, however, to the base of the organ, as it does in the clitoris.

When about half relaxed, the tip of the immature penis will be seen to be rather blunt, with sheaths visible at its base. The immature clitoris is sharp pointed, with no basal sheath. When fully erected the tip of the penis points *posteriorly*, while the fully erected clitoris has a tip bent *anteriorly* (Petrides 1951).

Age in nestlings is best determined (Beule and Studholme 1942) by the length of the tarsus, or hind foot, as follows, where the first number is the age in days and the second is the length of the tarsus in millimeters: 2-22.5; 4-26.7; 6-30.0; 8-34.2; 10-38.0; 12-42.3.

During the hunting season, cottontails are commonly classed as juveniles or adults on the basis of the presence or absence of the epiphyseal groove or line on the humerus or femur (Hale 1949) as shown in Fig. 20.29. Wight and Conaway (1962) report that in Missouri the detection of this epiphyseal line in X-rays becomes progressively

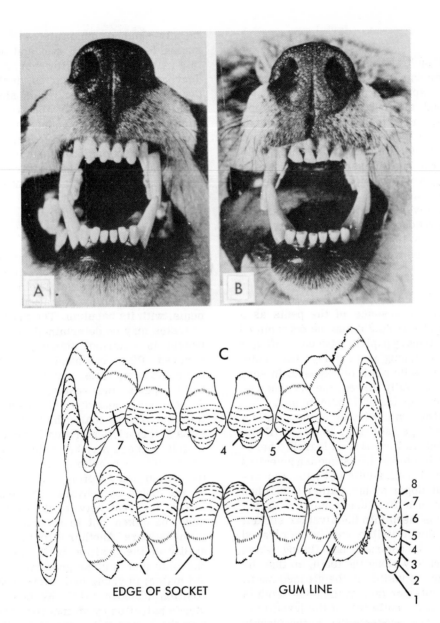

Fig. 20.28. Determination of age of coyotes by tooth wear. Frontal view of the teeth of coyotes aged as follows: *A* 2 years; *B* 5 years; *C* composite drawing made by superimposing pictures like A and B to show extent of annual wear.

less reliable as an indicator of age from late November. Lord (1959) has reported on the weight of the lens of the eye in known-age rabbits up to 30-months old. His procedure was: When the rabbit was killed, the eyes were removed immediately and placed in 10% formalin for 1 week. The lens were then dried, usually for 24-36 hr in an oven at 80° C, with circulating air, until no further moisture was being lost. It was then weighed immediately on a precision balance with a relatively small weighing chamber. Speed in weighing is important because the lenses are hygroscopic, gaining moisture while they are being weighed. Some of his results are: 1 month— 18.6-20.3 mg; 2 months—54.0-79.3 mg; 3 months— 91.2-105.7 mg; 4 months—126-132 mg; 6 months—159.8-163.5 mg; 12 months—209.1 mg; 18 months—228.2-234.5 mg; 24 months—248 mg; 30 months—257.4 mg (Lord 1959). This method was recommended over use of the epiphyseal X-ray by Wight and Conaway (1962) for Missouri cottontails.

JACKRABBIT

Black-tailed jackrabbits can be aged by lens weight. Tiemeier and Plenert (1964) give a curve that shows lens weight increase to at least 680 days, but beyond about 200 days their sample size is not sufficient to assess the amount of variability to be expected among individuals of the same age. These authors divide their jackrabbits into three age classes on the basis of condition of the proximal epiphyseal groove of the humerus: I-0-5 mo., definite groove; II-5-14 mo., definite line; III-over 14 mo., no line. Ear and hind foot length reached full size within age class I, but age classes II and III could probably be distinguished by lens weight.

MUSKRAT

The presence or absence of the penis as a criterion of sex (Table 20.25) may be determined by grasping the urinary papilla between forefinger and thumb and stripping posteriorly. The penis, if present, will be either felt or exposed. In very young rats, not yet fully furred, the presence or absence of visible nipples will indicate sex.

The molt pattern on the inside of the skin is a good indicator of age (see Fig. 20.30) until the molt is completed, in February or March. Thereafter the most reliable way to distinguish juveniles (almost 1 year old) from adults is by the appearance of the first upper molar. Sather (1954) has described the juvenile first upper molar as having fluting which runs deep into the alveolar socket, so that the end is not visible even in the cleaned skull. The adult, in contrast, has fluting which extends only part way along the tooth, so that the end of the fluting is visible in the cleaned skull. In addition, the anterior face of the adult tooth is discernably humped, while that of the juvenile is straight. The author suggests that in the freshly killed animal it may be necessary to cut the gum away to see these characters clearly.

Olsen (1959) has further refined this technique by distinguishing (in muskrats trapped in March and April) between three age-classes, as follows (all description applies to the upper right molar): (1) highly developed roots, and end of fluting extruded well below the bone line—adults; (2) moderate root development and end of the fluting just barely or not quite emerged from the bone line—subadults of about 10 months of age; (3) little or no root development and fluting ending deep in the alveolar socket—juveniles averaging about 7 months of age.

The zygomatic breadth was used to separate freshly-skinned muskrats, with subadults measuring less than 40.6 mm and adults more than this (Alexander 1951). However, this measurement decreases as the skull dries, declining by 0.5 mm over the first 5 days. This shrinkage totalled 0.7 mm by the end of the first year. Summer humidity (70 to 80%) caused an increase of 0.3 mm in this measurement (Alexander 1960).

The ossification of the baculum has been shown to be a reliable age criterion for Missouri muskrats (see Elder and Shanks 1962, and Fig. 20.31).

BEAVER

See Tables 20.25, 20.26, and 20.27. It is difficult to determine the sex of a live beaver, unless it is a lactating female. The most reliable technique is a search, by palpation, for the testes and penis, with its baculum. The presence or absence of testes may be determined as follows: place the beaver in a normal standing position, with head covered. Place one hand so that it lies lateral to the pubic symphysis, with the finger tips anterior to the pubis and resting on the soft abdomen. Press lightly and draw the hand posteriorly. If the animal is a male, the testis can be felt as it slips anteriorly under the finger tips. If no testis is felt, a check may be made by palpation for the *os penis,* or baculum. This is done by placing the thumb and forefinger immediately posterior to the pubic symphysis and passing them back toward the vent between the castor glands. Care must be taken not to misinterpret concretions in the castors. Another difficulty lies in the variability of the position of the penis. It may be at one side and in close proximity to the castors in old males; in young males it is always in a median position (Osborn 1955). Kennedy (1952) recommends palpation by an insertion of the index finger into the cloaca and urogenital orifice. The finger is passed anteriorly into the vestibule or cavity that exists between the castor glands. About one inch from the external opening the finger, moved from side to side in the male, will contact the penis. This method was first described by Bradt (1938). Fig. 20.32 illustrates the appearance and location of beaver genitalia.

If beaver skulls are available, they may be aged on the following grounds: kits—skull small, with no sagittal crest and temporal ridges poorly developed and widely separated (15 mm or more at the anterior end of the interparietal bone), the sagittal crest begins to appear on some specimens; 2-year-olds—sagittal crest starting development, temporal ridges converge toward rear and are

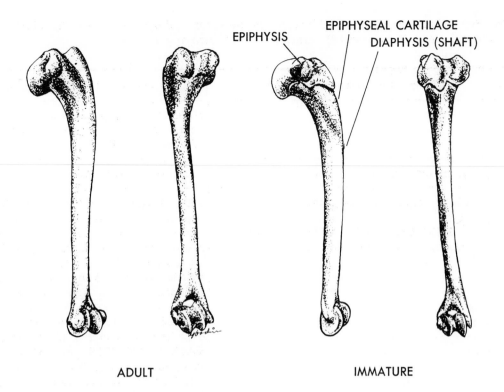

EPIPHYSIS   EPIPHYSEAL CARTILAGE   DIAPHYSIS (SHAFT)

ADULT   IMMATURE

Fig. 20.29. Lateral and posterior view of humerus of cottontail. Note epiphyseal cartilage between epiphysis and diaphysis in immature and its absence in the adult (from
Hale 1949, after Godin 1960).

about 5 mm apart at anterior end of interparietal
bone; adult—temporal ridges meet, or nearly
meet, on anterior process of interparietal bone,
or anterior to it, and the sagittal crest is very
pronounced. These findings refer to Alaskan
beaver taken in winter (Buckley and Libby 1955).

Stretched skins (blankets) increase in size
with age (see Table 20.26). The increase in size
with age (as reflected in live weight, tail area, and
zygomatic breadth) has been used to divide beaver
into four age-groups, as shown in Table 20.27.
The dorsal view of beaver bacula for four age-
classes are shown in Fig. 20.33.

For more detailed studies, the age of beaver
can be determined from annuli in the cementum
on the root of the first mandibular molar. The
first layer of cementum is deposited during the
animal's third summer; a contrasting (lighter)
layer is deposited during the winter (van Nostrand
and Stephenson 1964).

SQUIRRELS (GRAY AND FOX)[2]

Squirrels are born with the eyes closed and
hairless; thereafter, their post-natal development, to six weeks, is as shown in Table 20.28.
Squirrels are sexed by examination of the external genitalia.

Several aging techniques have been developed
which enable the aging of squirrels as to immatures and adults. Body weights have been used
as presented in Table 20.29 under the reservation
that weights are dependent on many external conditions independent of age.

The degree of development of the external
genitalia (Table 20.29) has also been used, but
this also has its limitations in that fully adult

[2]The assistance of Mr. R. B. Hamilton, Graduate
Fellow, Virginia Cooperative Wildlife Research Unit
with writing this section is gratefully acknowledged.

Table 20.25. Sex and age criteria for rabbits, hares, muskrat, and beaver. Note: In column (1) female characters are italicized; in column (2) immature characters are italicized.

Species	Criteria for distinguishing sex (1)	Criteria for distinguishing age (2)
Cottontail Rabbit	See text	HUMERUS: Epiphyseal line or groove absent; *epiphyseal line or groove present* (up to 9 months) (H)
Hares	Like Cottontail Rabbit (L)	Like Cottontail Rabbit (L)
Muskrat	PELT: nipples absent; *nipples present* (Sch) URETHERAL PAPILLA (fresh or live animals): penis present; *penis absent* (B & B)	PELT PRIMENESS PATTERN: Irregular, spotted or mottled; *regular longitudinal arrangement* (subadult); *lyre-shaped unprime area on dorsal side* (juveniles) (A & P) (see Fig. 20.30) PENIS: Over 5.15 mm diam., dark, w/blunt rounded tip; *under 5.15 mm diam, lighter red, w/knob-shaped tip* (Sch) (B & B) TESTIS LENGTH (fall & early winter): over 11.65 mm; *under 11.65 mm* (Sch) VAGINAL ORIFICE: membrane thin or missing; *closed by thick membrane* (Sch) PLACENTAL SCARS (where there are no barren adults): present; *absent* (Sch)
Beaver	VENTRAL OPENINGS (from tail forward): 1 (rectum), 2 (paried vestibular pouches), 1 (penis recess), a total of 4; *1 (rectum), 1 (vagina), 1 (urethra), 2 (vestibular pouches), a total of 5.*	LIVE WT. (Alaska, winter-trapped): 41 lb and over (adults); *32-40 lb (2 yr olds); 22-31 lb (yearlings); 10-21 lbs (kits)* (B & L)

References: (A & P) = Applegate and Predmore 1947; (B & B) = Baumgartner and Bellrose 1943; (B & L) = Buckley and Libby 1955; (H) = Hale 1949; (L) = Lechleitner 1957; (Sch) = Schofield 1955.

males may be mistaken for immature males during the sexually quiescent period. Under favorable conditions immature females may breed and appear to be over one year old.

To be able to age the fall harvest of this popular game and species and construct an age structure to assess productivity and "population health" is the most important need and use of a good aging criterion for squirrels. A normal November sample will contain spring-born juveniles (8 to 9 months of age), summer-born juveniles (3 to 4 months), and adults (over one year). The three classes can be separated by the characters of the tail pelage, as viewed from below: *young juvenile*—two, sometimes three, dark lines running through the reddish-brown primary hairs of the tail, lower or proximal one-third of tail naked beneath; *older juvenile (subadult)*—dark lines as in juvenile, lower one-third of tail covered with short appressed hairs; *adult*—tail bone obscured by appressed secondary hairs that radiate out over and partially cover the long primary hairs of the tail. As shown in Figure 20.34, the lines or bars so prominent in young of the year have become weakened in color intensity and are diffuse in the tails of adults (Sharpe 1958). Pelage characteristics which reveal age are particularly attractive in that live animals can be aged and then released to give known age individuals in the population.

Another readily applied, field aging technique for the gray squirrel which is based upon pelage characteristics is the method developed by Barrier and Barkalow (1967). In winter pelage the late fall harvest can be separated into: *summer juvenile*—pelage in rump region when separated and laid flat by the thumbs will reveal no yellow prebasal band in the black underfur and the majority of banded guard hairs will be black tipped; *spring-juvenile*—using same technique the yellow prebasal band in the black underfur will be absent

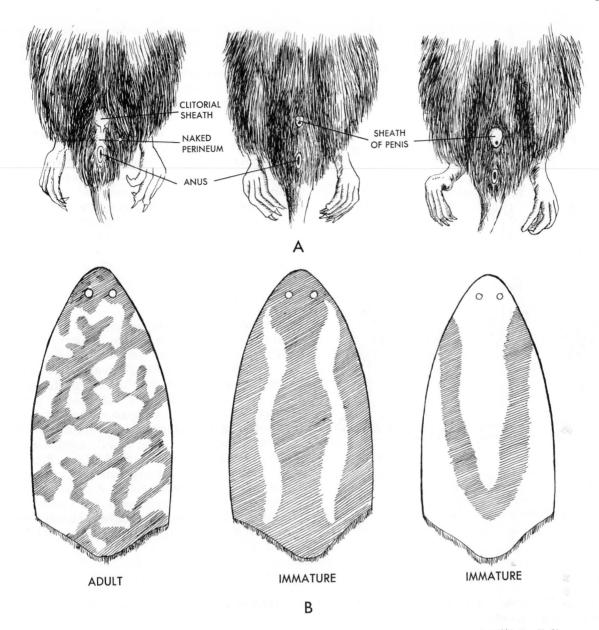

Fig. 20.30. Sex and age criteria as shown in genitalia and hide primeness in muskrats. *(A)* Genitalia: *Left*—immature female with naked perineum; *Center*—immature male, note size difference of penis sheath; *Right*—adult male. *(B)* Pelt primeness; *Left*—adult with irregular mottled dark-colored areas; *Center-Right*—immatures showing classes of patterns. White areas denote primed sections of hide; shaded areas are unprime (after Dozier 1942, from Godin 1960).

or indistinct and all banded guard hairs will be white tipped; *adult*—there is a distinct, yellow prebasal band in the black underfur and all banded guard hairs will be white tipped.

One skeletal method to separate juvenile from adult squirrels is the degree of closure of the distal epiphyses of the radius and ulna, which are responsible for growth of these long bones. X-ray reveals that the epiphyses described remain open through the 18th week of life and that an epiphyseal line may still be detected until the 12th month. Thereafter, the epiphyseal line is absent (Petrides 1951, Carson 1961).

The weight of the lens of the eye increases with age and has been used to distinguish age classes in fox squirrels shot in October and November in Michigan. The age classes and their lens weights found are: *summer born*—to about 28 mg; *spring*

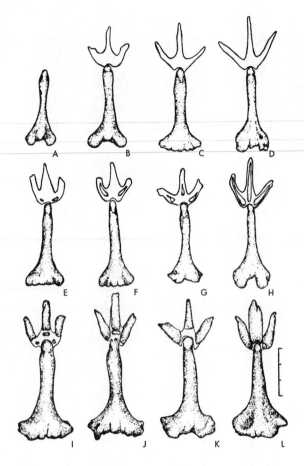

Fig. 20.31. Age changes in the bacula of muskrat. A-D: about 4-8 months old; E-H: about 8-15 months old; I-L: adult—over 15 months old. Scale in mm (from Elder and Shanks 1962).

born—from 29 to 39 mg; *older*—with some evidence of different year-classes but with considerable overlap among them (Beale 1962). The lens weight technique can be utilized without known age weights or curves by plotting lens weight by frequency and noting natural breaks in the frequency distribution, provided a substantial sample is processed. This method would allow separation of summer young, spring young and adults.

While there are several aging techniques which are applicable to squirrels, it is realized that they are subject to external factors not related to age, such as range condition and health, and also to be experience and ability of the investigator. With this in mind, it is always desirable to employ as many of the techniques as possible and arrive at a conclusion based on all the information available.

WOODCHUCK

Woodchucks in spring may be divided into young, yearlings, and adults, using the following criteria (Davis 1964):

Young: weigh 300-450 g about May 15 and gain about 19 g/day from June through September; do not begin molt until early July, pelage remains short and fine later in season than that of older animals—up to September; incisors narrow, long, pointed, unstained; head small; muzzle narrow and pointed; lens weight mean 12.32 mg (S.D. 2.8).

Yearling (young of previous year): in March and April size, head shape and incisors like young; from February through April testes white (although some yearlings have pigmented testes in March and April); lens weight mean 21.78 mg (S.D. 1.7).

Table 20.26. Aging beaver by measurements of round-stretched (blanket) pelts. Measurement is length plus width, in inches.

Area	Pelt measurement in inches				Authority
	Kits	Yearlings	Two-year olds	Adults	
Alaska	40-52	53-59	60-64	65+	Buckley and Libby 1955
Montana*	38-52	53-61	62+ (2-year-olds and above)		Townsend 1953 and pers. communication

*Recent Montana studies indicate that while pelt size is a useful criterion of age, the limits for each age group may vary with the locality.

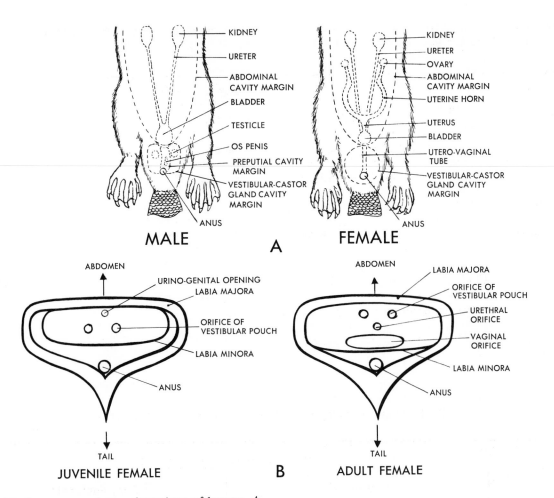

MALE · A · FEMALE

JUVENILE FEMALE · B · ADULT FEMALE

Fig. 20.32. Some age and sex characters of beaver. *A* Schematic representation of penis and testes in the vestibularcastor cavity of male *(Left)* and normal position of the uterus of the female *(Right)*. Dissection is required to identify these organs. *B* Diagramatic representation of the anal-uriogenital opening when stretched laterally as by the forefingers. This procedure can be performed on live or dead beaver (sketches by G. J. Knudson *in* Thompson 1958).

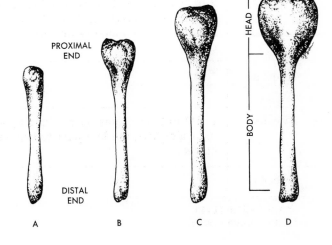

Fig. 20.33. Age determination of summer-trapped beaver. The tail of the baculum reaches its definitive shape and size in the yearling class, the body in the larger forms of the two and three-year olds, and the head continues to develop even in the four-year old and over class. *A* Immature (kit); *B* Yearling; *C* 2- and 3-year old; *D* 4-year old and over (after Friley 1949, from Godin 1960).

Table 20.27. Weights, tail dimensions, and zygomatic breadths of four age-groups of beaver caught in March or April (after Patric and Webb 1960).

Age-class	Age in months	Age Characters					
		Weight (Pounds)		Tail dimensions* (Inches)		Zygomatic breadth (Inches)	
		Average	Range	Average	Range	Average	Range
Kits	10-21	14	12-17	24	16-28	2.70	2.50-3.00
Yearlings	22-23	22	20-26	38	34-42	3.30	3.20-3.40
Two-year Olds	34-35	30	28-34	44	43-45	3.55	3.50-3.60
Adults	46 plus	—	35-up	—	46-up	—	3.65-up

*Length times width, in inches, of scaled portion of tail.

Table 20.28. Development of young fox and gray squirrels.

Age	Developmental characters of	
	Fox Squirrel*	Gray Squirrel**
New born	1/2 oz	
1 week	1 oz, first hair appears on back of head and shoulders.	
2 weeks		Emerging hair darkens dorsal surface.
3 weeks	2 oz, covered with dark hair beginning to turn brown on tail and around eyes and mouth. Lower incisors appear and ears open.	Hair about 1 mm long. Ears open. Lower incisors erupted.
4 weeks		Silver hair on tail about 2 mm long. Upper incisors erupting.
5 weeks	2-1/2 to 3 oz. Eyes open. Hair appearing under tail, the last part to become furred.	At least one eye open.
6 weeks		Underside of tail covered with hair.

*After Allen (1943).
**After Uhlig (1955).

Table 20.29. Characteristics for distinguishing between adult and juvenile fox and gray squirrels in October and November (from Uhlig 1956).

Adult	Juvenile
MALE	
Ventral and posterior end of scrotum darkened and generally free of hair.	Posterior end of scrotum with smooth skin, brown to black, and possibly free of hair. Summer juveniles with scrotum covered with hair, small testes, may be difficult to detect. Spring males may sometimes be mistaken for adults.
FEMALE	
Mammary glands large and noticeable, not hidden by hair; teats are black-tipped in fox squirrels. On gray squirrels the black spots may be absent, or about the size of a pin point.	Teats inconspicuous, more or less hidden by the hair. Spring females occasionally have young before the hunting season and are classified as adults.
MALES AND FEMALES	
Tails rectangular, block-shaped, sides parallel or nearly so. Unless in an emaciated condition, the weight of adults is over 14 oz.	Tails pointed, triangular, sides not parallel. Spring juveniles will weigh over 14 oz. Summer juveniles will be under 14 oz. A rough index to age of summer juveniles is: 8 weeks—5 oz; 10 weeks—7 oz; 14 weeks—11 oz; 16 weeks—13 oz; and 18 weeks—14 oz.

Adult: incisors broader, with worn points and darkly stained; testes light to dark brown; lens weight mean 28.53 mg (S.D. 4.5).

SMALL RODENTS

For determining sex in small rodent (voles, lemmings, deer mice) skeletons found in raptor pellets, etc., use is made of the proportions of the pelvic girdle (the three bones—illium, ischium, and pubis together constitute the innominate; the two innominates constitute the pelvic girdle). Use is made of the fact that the pubic arm of the pelvis tends to be narrower and longer in proportion to the ischial arm in the male (Dunmire 1955).

Big-game Mammals

DEER

Deer, both mule and white-tailed, may be easily sexed in the flesh, but it is occasionally necessary to determine sex from the skeleton. This is possible, in animals over 2 years of age, by the presence of tuberosities where the ligaments which support the penis attach in the male and their absence in the female (Taber 1956) (see Fig. 20.22).

It is sometimes desirable to age the unborn deer, or fetus, for the purpose of determining the date of conception. Often this is done on the basis of crown-rump length, but since both mule deer and white-tailed deer vary in size from race to race, it is better to determine fetal age by developmental characters. The stages of fetal development are shown in Table 20.30, based on the work of Armstrong (1950) and Hudson and Browman (1959). Determination of sex in very small fetal white-tailed deer has been accomplished by examining the extra-embryonic membranes microscopically for the presence of sex chromatin particles next to nuclear membranes; the presence of such particles indicated female sex and their absence indicated male sex (Segelquist 1966).

Aging is routinely based on the sequence of tooth eruption and wear. Both species attain a full set of permanent teeth by about thirty months of age. There are, however, some differences in the schedule of eruption, which are apparent in the tables below. The location and nomenclature of deer teeth are shown in Fig. 20.35.

Ordinarily, the lower jaw is used for aging studies, since it can be detached readily in the field and saved. To facilitate examination of the teeth of live-trapped ungulates, Barnes and Longhurst (1960) describe a technique for obtaining dental-impression tray. The device shown below called a "jaw breaker" has been used to easily open jaws of deer with rigor mortis. Thus, the hide of trophy animals need not be cut.

Nellis (1966) provides evidence that lens weight is highly correlated with stage of gestation in mule deer.

MULE DEER

The eruption of the teeth of the lower jaw has been used as an aging technique for mule deer up to 30 months of age as shown in Table 20.31.

It should be recognized that the schedules of eruption and replacement may deviate under conditions of severe debilitation due to disease or malnutrition, or under exceptionally good conditions for growth and development.

After the adult dentition is attained, deer may be aged by the relative amount of wear on the cheek-teeth. This is less accurate than the system based on replacement, and the older ages especially can be estimated only approximately. For this reason many workers do not attempt to age adult deer to the year but lump them into two categories, *prime* and *old*. Robinette et al. (1957), with known-aged mule deer, have proposed an aging system based on the relative amount of wear on the molars. They use a ratio between the sum of the widths of the seven occlusal surfaces on the baccal (cheek) side and the sum of the heights above the gum line of the corresponding lingual (tongue-side) crests. The former is divided by the latter, so that the ratio increases with the age of the animal. The method of taking these measurements is shown in Fig. 20.36 and the ratios as used in aging are presented in Table 20.32.

These same authors (Robinette et al. 1957) have presented a series of photographs (Fig. 20.37) of the lower jaws of deer of known age, which are useful for comparison with jaws for which the investigator desires to estimate the approximate age.

Low and Cowan (1963) have shown that microscopic examination of the annuli in the cementum of the root of the first incisor can give highly accurate determinations at all ages.

In the black-tailed race of the mule deer, Longhurst (1964) found lens weight to be a satisfactory criterion of age at least through 5 years.

WHITE-TAILED DEER

Aging white-tailed deer is similar to the techniques used for the mule deer but the schedule of eruption and wear differs slightly, as shown in Table 20.33 and Fig. 20.38.

Haugen and Speake (1958) give a method of determining the age of white-tailed fawns in Alabama up to 30 days, based on the growth of the front hoof. New growth on the hoof proceeds from a ringed groove. Proximal to this groove there are longitudinal striations on the hoof, while distal to it the striations are radial. A measurement is taken (in mm) from the bases of the distal hairs on the outside half of a front hoof to the ring described above, along the front edge of the hoof. This measurement is multiplied by 2.2, and 0.66 is added to this product to give the age of the fawn, in days.

The system of aging white-tailed deer in New York, described above, proved not entirely satisfactory in Michigan, so Ryel, Fay, and Van Etten (1961) worked out a key for Michigan white-tailed deer of known age (Table 20.34).

Annuli in the cementum on the roots of the first incisor (Gilbert 1966) and the first molar (Ransom 1966) are accurate indicators of all ages.

The weight of the lens as a criterion of age

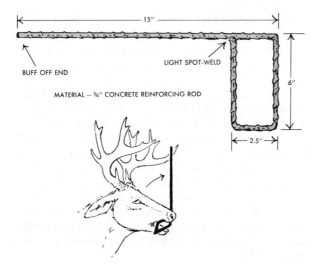

15"

LIGHT SPOT-WELD

BUFF OFF END

MATERIAL — ⅜" CONCRETE REINFORCING ROD

6"

2.5"

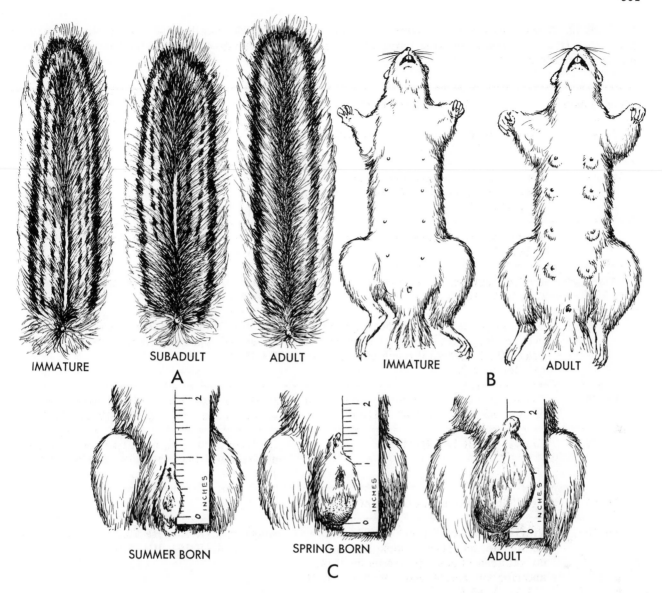

Fig. 20.34. Sex and age criteria for squirrels *A* Age may be determined by examination of the ventral surface of the tail. *Left:* Juvenile, the shorter secondary hairs are absent on the lower side of the tail bone. *Center:* Subadults, short appressed hairs are present on lower third of the tail bone. *Right:* The appressed hairs obscure the outline of the tail bone in the adult (after Sharp 1958). *B* Mastology of the female squirrel. *Left:* Juvenile, with nipples minute and barely discernable. *Right:* Lactating adult, nipples black pigmented with most of hair worn off. *C* Scrotal measurements of male squirrels. *Left:* Summer born, the testes are abdominal and the skin is just beginning to pigment. *Center:* Spring born, the testes are large and the scrotum is pigmented but it is heavily furred. *Right:* Adult has shed most of the fur from the scrotum (after Allen 1943; from Godin 1960).

has been studied by Lord (1962). He found that lens weight increases rapidly to 2.5 years and slowly thereafter. Furthermore, pen-raised deer, presumably because of their higher nutrient plane, had heavier lenses than wild deer.

ELK

The fetal, or unborn, elk may be placed in its proper stage of gestation by measurements, as shown in Table 20.35.

Table 20.30. Stages in fetal development (days of gestation) in white-tailed deer (from New York) and mule deer (from Montana), showing physical characteristics, crown-rump* and hind-foot** measurements (in millimeters).

Age in days	White-tailed Deer[#]	Mule Deer[##]
37-40	Eyelids absent; no vibrissae follicles noticeable. C-R 17.1-27.0	
41-44	Vibrissae follicles present above eye, under eye, on muzzle, on cheeks. C-R 27.7-29.6	
45-52	Eyelids absent; mouth open. *48 days:* C-R 37.8	*48 days:* Vibrissae follicles just present above eye. C-R 32.4
53-60	Eyelids formed; mouth closed. *60 days:* C-R 62.7; HL 20.7	*57 days:* Eyelids cover eye. C-R 59.2; HF 20.5
61-65	Fetus loses fish-hook shape; angle formed between long axis of body and straight line drawn from muzzle through ear equal to or greater than 90.	*61 days:* Vibrissae follicles visible on chest and upper forelimbs. C-R 74.3; HF 29.0
66-68	Pre-orbital fold at anterior median side of eye. *66 days:* C-R 83; HL 30.5	*68 days:* Vibrissae follicles appear on abdomen and trunk. C-R 94.7; HF 37.2
73-75	*75 days:* C-R 113; HL 43.6	*73 days:* Brown pigment on nose between nostrils and down to lip. C-R 110.7; HF 45.7
76-85	Gray pigment appears on top of nose.	
86-90	Vibrissae broken through skin over eye, on muzzle, on cheeks; black pigment on dorsal area of nose; brown pigment on anterior surface of nose. *90 days:* C-R 167.3; HL 69.8	*86 days:* C-R 155; HF 73.9 *89 days:* C-R 164; HF 77.0
91-95	Brown pigment on surface of lower lip; black pigment along closing surface of eyelids; metatarsal gland appears as oblong white spot on tarsus.	
96-105	Hooves black-pigmented. *98 days:* C-R 197.2; HL 98.8	
106-110	Nostrils open. *107 days:* C-R 224.2; HF 114.5. *110 days:* C-R 233.2; HL 124	
111-120	Incomplete hair covering; light pigment spots on trunk; eyelashes grown; dark spots (both sexes) at position of antler-bud. *115 days:* C-R 252; HL 127	*111 days:* Nostrils open; legs and hooves brownish black; hair on muzzle. C-R 232; HF 127. *117 days:* Hair appears on legs. C-R 252; HF 143

Table 20.30. Continued.

Age in days	White-tailed Deer[#]	Mule Deer[##]
121-132	Hair present on anterior and posterior surfaces of skin covering proximal ends of femur and humerus; tarsal glands present.	
133-150	Appearance of hair on legs; row of stiff bristles around top of hoof. *135 days:* C-R 318.5; HL 192	*137 days:* Hair margins metatarsal and covers tarsal gland. C-R 311; HF 185. *144 days:* Short hair present just above hooves; teeth still covered with membrane. C-R 327; HF 193
151-180	Hair covering as in adult; incisors still covered by membrane; black pigment covers nose; metatarsal gland with complete hair covering. *159 days:* C-R 396; HL 251	*161 days:* Tips of incisors and canines exposed. C-R 397; HF 262 *174 days:* Hair covering as in newborn fawn. C-R 443; HF 278
181-200	Incisors erupted; tarsal gland with complete hair covering. *181 days:* C-R 445; HL 304 *192 days:* C-R 459; HL 314	

*C-R is the crown-rump or forehead-rump measurement.
**HF is the measurement of hind feet from the tip of the hoof to the angle of hock.
***HL is the measurement of the hind leg from the tip of the hoof to the tubercle of the tibio-fibula.
#From Armstrong 1950.
##From Hudson and Browman 1959.

The aging of elk is based on the rate of tooth replacement and wear as in deer. Table 20.36 gives the pattern of replacement and eruption.

Aging of older classes is based on relative wear. Quimby and Gaab (1957) listed five specific characters commonly found in 3-year old and five characters commonly found in 4-year-old elk jaws (Table 20.37). They concluded, however, that visual comparisons provided a better basis for aging (see Fig. 20.39 and 20.40).

Knight (1966) made a study of age changes in the radius and ulna of Montana elk, and provides a key for the determination of age up to 4 years.

MOOSE

Simkin (1967) compared tooth wear, eye lens weight, and incisor cementum ring counts as methods for aging moose. He concluded that counting the cementum rings was the most reliable method now available to age moose. The eye-lens weight method he thought promising and perhaps a better technique than tooth wear. He noted that lens weight age classification depends on arbitrary selection of the division point between weight classes and objective application of the age criteria. Tooth wear classification, however, depends on arbitrary criteria and arbitrary application.

He noted that neither the lens weight nor cementum ring count methods were field techniques and did not provide hunters with on-the-spot aging of their animals. He suspected that hunter cooperation would decline unless the hunters could be convinced that they would be sent the results of laboratory aging of their kill. Collecting teeth or eyes is much more convenient than collecting lower jaws.

The replacement of milk with adult teeth is more rapid in the moose than in the deer or elk, being complete by about 19 months of age. The schedule of eruption and replacement is summarized in Table 20.38.

Studies of aging by tooth wear as a means of aging older moose have been made by Passmore, Peterson, and Cringan (Peterson 1955). They

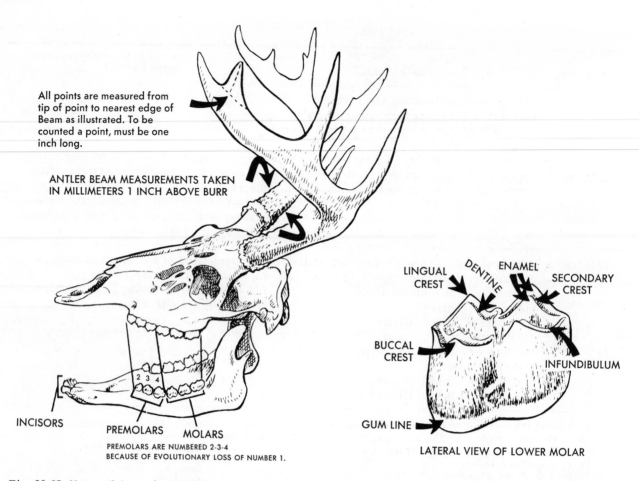

All points are measured from tip of point to nearest edge of Beam as illustrated. To be counted a point, must be one inch long.

ANTLER BEAM MEASUREMENTS TAKEN IN MILLIMETERS 1 INCH ABOVE BURR

INCISORS

PREMOLARS   MOLARS

PREMOLARS ARE NUMBERED 2-3-4 BECAUSE OF EVOLUTIONARY LOSS OF NUMBER 1.

LINGUAL CREST   DENTINE   ENAMEL   SECONDARY CREST

BUCCAL CREST   INFUNDIBULUM

GUM LINE

LATERAL VIEW OF LOWER MOLAR

Fig. 20.35. Nomenclature of ungulate teeth. *A* Nomenclature and location of teeth of white-tailed deer. *B* Temporary and permanent pincers. *C* Anatomy of lower-jaw molars (from Riney 1951, by Godin 1960).

Table 20.31. Tooth eruption in the lower jaw of the mule deer (from Cowan, 1936 and Dasmann, 1958). Milk or deciduous tooth—D; adult or permanent tooth—P. Parentheses indicate that the tooth is in the process of eruption at that particular time.

Age	Incisors			Canine	Premolars			Molars		
	1	2	3	1	2	3	4	1	2	3
1 to 3 weeks	D	D	D	D	D	D	D	–	–	–
2 to 3 months	D	D	D	D	D	D	D	(P)	–	–
6 months	D	D	D	D	D	D	D	(P)	(P)	–
12 months	P*	D P	D	D	D	D	D	P	(P)	–
18 months	P	P	P	D	D	D	D	P	P	(P)
24 months	P	P	P	P	(P)	(P)	(P)	P	P	(P)
30 months	P	P	P	P	P	P	P	P	P	P

*Replacement and eruption are taking place at this time.

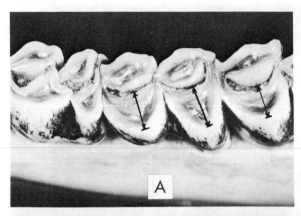

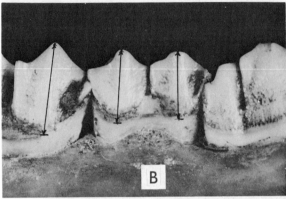

Fig. 20.36. Method of taking measurement of width of the occlusal surface and height above gum line to define age-classes in mule deer. *A* The width of the occlusal surface. *B* Height above gum line (from Robinette et al. 1957).

found that as the teeth of the lower jaw became more worn with age, the results could be expressed by two measurements of the posterior buccal (cheek-side) crest of the second molar:

1. *Width*—greatest width measured across the occlusal surface of the crest and recorded as the average of measurements from the left and right sides of the jaw.

2. *Height*—height from the base of the crown, which is well defined by a line of constriction at the point of union with the roots, to the occlusal surface; recorded as an average height for the left and right teeth.

Other useful measurements reflecting age were:

3. *Length of lower jaw*—measured from the anterior-most point of the jaw (excluding teeth) to the posterior rim of the angle, on one side only.

4. *Length of diastema*—the distance between the alveoli of the canine and the first premolar (technically premolar No. 2) measured on one side only.

5. *Length of toothrow*—greatest length of toothrow crowns of the lower cheek-teeth, measured on one side only.

6. *Width of first incisor*—greatest width across the tooth measured on one tooth only.

The results of these measurements are summarized in Table 20.38.

From the data in Table 20.39 it may be seen that as the animals grow older the width of the buccal crest grows greater, while its height grows smaller. Therefore an index obtained by dividing

Table 20.32. Molar tooth ratios for different age-classes for the Rocky Mountain mule deer (after Robinette et al. 1957). See text and Fig. 20.36 for the method of taking measurements to determine the ratio.

Age in years	Molar ratio	Age in years	Molar ratio
2.5	0.33	10.5	0.73
3.5	0.40	11.5	0.80
4.5	0.45	12.5	0.88
5.5	0.50	13.5	0.97
6.5	0.54	14.5	1.10
7.5	0.58	15.5	1.25
8.5	0.62	16.5	1.46
9.5	0.67		

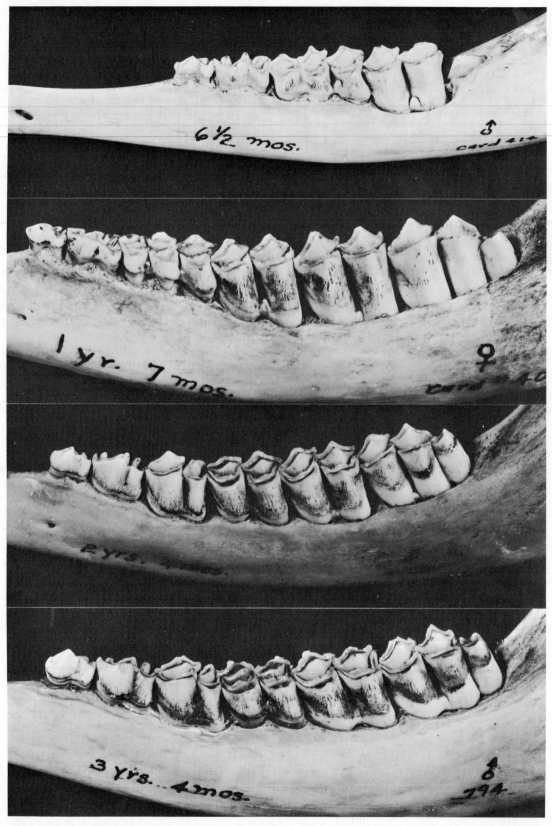

Fig. 20.37A. Lower jaw of Rocky Mountain mule deer showing progressive tooth replacement and wear from 6-1/2 months through 3 years, 4 months (Robinette et al. 1957).

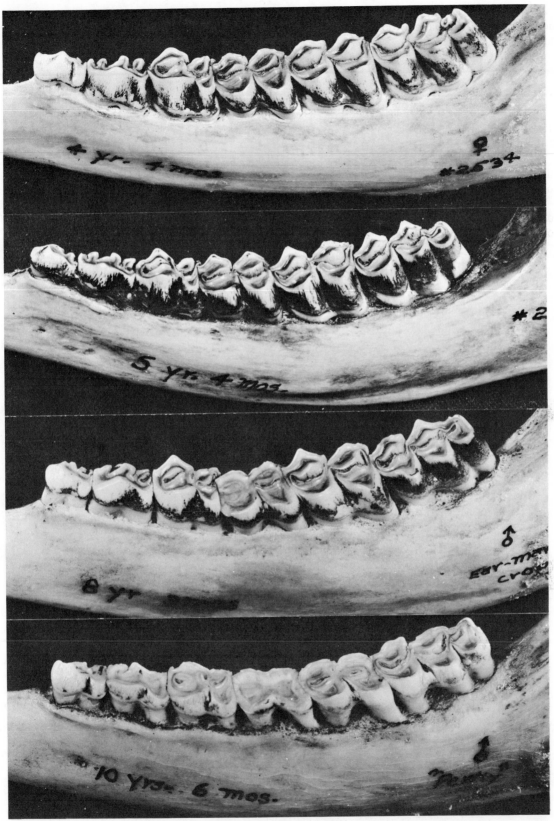

Fig. 20.37B. Lower jaw of Rocky Mountain mule deer showing progressive tooth wear from ages of 4 years, 4 months through 10 years, 6 months (Robinette et al. 1957).

Table 20.33. Tooth eruption in the New York white-tailed deer (after Severinghaus 1949). Milk or deciduous tooth—D; permanent tooth—P; parentheses indicate that tooth is in process of erupting at that particular time.

Age	Incisors			Canine	Premolars			Molars		
	1	2	3	1	2	3	4	1	2	3
1 to 3 weeks	(D)	(D)	(D)	(D)	(D)	(D)	(D)			
2 to 3 months	D	D	D	D	D	D	D	(P)		
6 months	P	D	D	D	D	D	D	(P)		
12 months	P	P	P	P	D	D	P	P	(P)	
18 months	P	P	P	P	P	(P)	(P)	P	P	P
24 months	P	P	P	P	P	P	P	P	P	P

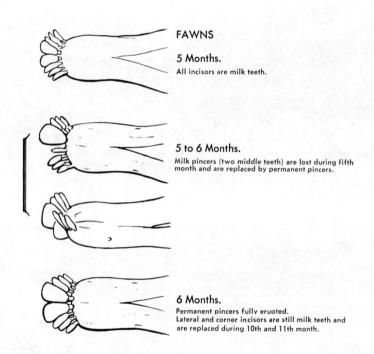

FAWNS

5 Months.
All incisors are milk teeth.

5 to 6 Months.
Milk pincers (two middle teeth) are lost during fifth month and are replaced by permanent pincers.

6 Months.
Permanent pincers fully erupted.
Lateral and corner incisors are still milk teeth and are replaced during 10th and 11th month.

Fig. 20.38. Sequence of eruption and wear for white-tailed deer of New York.

YEARLINGS: 1 Yr. 4-5 Mos.

Milk premolars moderate to heavily worn.

FOURTH MILK PREMOLAR IS THREE CUSPED.

Permanent premolars.
PREMOLARS ARE NUMBERED 2-3-4
BECAUSE OF EVOLUTIONARY LOSS OF NUMBER 1.

Third molar
not fully erupted.

YEARLINGS: 1 Yr. 6 Mos.

LOSS OF MILK PREMOLARS AND PARTIALLY ERUPTED PERMANENT PREMOLARS.
FOURTH PERMANENT PREMOLAR TWO CUSPED.

Molars sharp.

Third molar
not fully erupted.

YEARLINGS: 1 Yr. 7 Mos.

PERMANENT PREMOLARS usually fully erupted slight wear occasionally showing on
grinding surfaces. Slight wear but no dentine line showing on crests of last (third molar).

CHECK UPPER THIRD
MOLAR to verify for 1 yr.
7 mos. or 2½ yr. class.
(Third molar partially
erupted.)

LOWER THIRD MOLAR
fully erupted 1 yr. 8 to 10 mos.

Upper third
molar fully erupted
1 yr. 10 mos. to 2 yrs.

2½ YEARS:
Permanent Premolars and Molars

UPPER THIRD MOLAR fully erupted, slight wear.

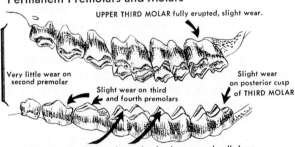

Very little wear on
second premolar

Slight wear on third
and fourth premolars

Slight wear
on posterior cusp
of THIRD MOLAR

Lingual crests of first and second molar sharp, enamel well above
narrow dentine of the crest.

3½ YEARS: Molars

LINGUAL CRESTS OF FIRST MOLAR blunt,
SECONDARY CRESTS prominent and blunt.

Dentine line in crests of
first and second molar
wider than enamel.

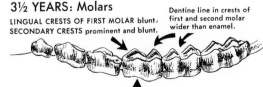

FIRST MOLAR worn to within 6-7 mm.
of gum on buccal side.

4½ YEARS: Molars

LINGUAL CRESTS ON FIRST MOLAR
ALMOST WORN AWAY.
Secondary crests visible.

First molar worn
to within 5-6 mm.
of gum on buccal side.

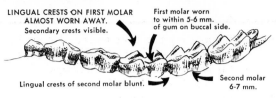

Lingual crests of second molar blunt.

Second molar
6-7 mm.

5½ YEARS: Molars

Original lingual crests of first molar worn away,
SIMULATED LINGUAL CRESTS APPEAR.
Secondary crests worn away.
First molar worn to within 4-5 mm. of gum on buccal side.

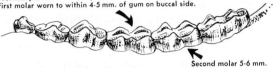

Second molar 5-6 mm.

Dentine crests on all molars much broader than enamel.

6½ YEARS: Molars

NO LINGUAL CRESTS ON FIRST MOLAR and worn to within
3-4 mm. of gum on buccal side.

Second molar 4-5 mm.

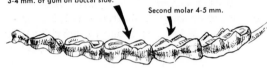

7½ YEARS: Molars

FIRST MOLAR WORN TO WITHIN 2-3 MM. ON BUCCAL SIDE.

Second molar 3-4 mm.

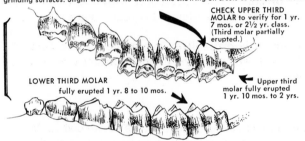

8½-9½ YEARS: Molars

ALL MOLARS WORN TO WITHIN 2-3 MM. OF GUM ON BUCCAL SIDE.

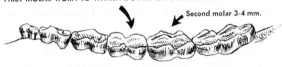

10½ YEARS AND OLDER: Molars

FIRST MOLAR at or below gum line.

SECOND AND THIRD within 1-2 mm. of
gum line on buccal side.

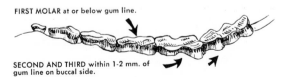

mm SCALE

0
5

Fig. 20.38. Continued.

390

Table 20.34. Key to age of Michigan white-tailed deer collected in November (from Ryel et al. 1961).

1. a) Temporary incisors entire or possibly center ones replaced by larger permanent teeth. First molar present, but rarely the second.—Fawns, 5-6 months old.
   b) All permanent incisors present. Third molar erupted, although posterior cusp may not be visible.—1-1/2 years old or older.—2.
2. a) Temporary premolars present (fourth premolar 3-parted), or permanent premolars replacing temporary ones.—1-1/2 years old.
   b) All permanent premolars in position and fully erupted (fourth premolar 2-parted).—1-1/2 years old or older.—3.
3. a) No wear on permanent premolars. Posterior cusp of third molar generally not erupted. Little or no wear on crests of third molar and dentine, if showing, in a narrow line.—1-1/2 years old.
   b) Greater wear indicated, last crest of third molar erupted.—2-1/2 years old or older.—4.
4. a) Wear absent or very slight on third premolar; slight on fourth, usually with only slight amounts of dentine showing on anterior surface. Lingual crests of all molars usually sharp, dentine line very narrow on third molar. Slight wear on last cusp of third molar.—2-1/2 years old.
   b) Wear further advanced.—3-1/2 years old or older.—5.
5. a) Last cusp of third molar flattened, hollowed-out or both. Third premolar with thin to moderate dentine line on anterior surface. Lingual crest of first molar blunt. Lingual crests of other molars sharp.—3-1/2 years old.
   b) Further wear indicated.—4-1/2 years old or older. It is difficult to determine the age accurately above 3-1/2 years due to individual variation in tooth wear. However, certain wear characteristics are found in most jaws of each age group.

Characteristics are listed below:

4-1/2—5-1/2 years old: Lingual crests of first molar present but flat. Crests of second molar rounded as first molar in 3-1/2 year group. Posterior cusp of third molar may be worn so it slopes laterally downward. Third and fourth premolars further worn. Second premolar may or may not show wear.

6-1/2—8-1/2 years old: Fourth premolar and first molar usually flat, lingual crests of second molar sometimes missing, especially at upper age limits. Third molar retains lingual crests at all stages.

9-1/2—12-1/2 years old: Wear on mandibular cheek teeth greater than above, but in no instance are all teeth flat. Usually there is evidence of lingual crests remaining, at least on the third molar. Extreme variation in wear may occur, especially in the fourth premolar and first molar. Presence or absence of incisors not a valid criterion of this age group, since known-age specimens and several deer known to be older all retained incisor teeth in good condition.

Old age: No lingual crests present. Molar teeth frequently hollowed-out or entirely flat. Teeth may be missing or show extremely uneven wear, and some shrinking away of bone around roots of teeth may have occurred.

Table 20.35. Fetal development of the Rocky Mountain elk of Montana (from Morrison, Trainer, and Wright 1959). Birth occurs at about 247 days.

Age in days from conception	Development characters and measurements
25	Body not yet C-shaped. C-R* 6.2
30	Body C-shaped; mandible well formed; 4th branchial cleft apparent. C-R 8.2; HL** 0.7
37	Body C-shaped; snout becoming formed; olfactory pits well developed; external ear beginning to differentiate; branchial clefts becoming obliterated. C-R 14.4; HL 3.0
43	Body less C-shaped; head, neck, and body regions well differentiated; mouth open; vibrissae follicles visible around eye. C-R 24.0; HL 5.0
59	Body fish-hook-shaped; hooves and dew claws formed; vibrissae follicles on muzzle and lower jaw; eyelids complete and closed. C-R 65.0; HL 19.5
90	Lachrymal sinuses have a prominent fold of skin around them. C-R 167.5; HL 75.0
123	Body no longer fish-hook-shaped; hooves pinkish with black pigmentation forming on anterodorsal edges; muzzle brown-tipped; vibrissae protrude 1-2 mm from follicles around eyes, muzzle, and lower jaw. C-R 305.0; HL 178.5
182	Entire body well haired except axillae and inner ear surfaces; nose black and reticulated with deep wrinkles. C-R 540.0; HL 378
247	(Full term) C-R 925.0; HL 406

*C-R = the distance in millimeters from the anterior-most to the posterior-most points of the body (early stages) or anterior-most point of the crown to the tuberosity of the ischium (later stages).
**HL = the distance in millimeters between the tubercle of the tibio-fibula and the point of the hoof.

Table 20.36. Tooth eruption in the Rocky Mountain elk (from Quimby and Gaab 1952). Milk or deciduous tooth—D; permanent tooth—P; parentheses indicate that the tooth is in process of erupting at that particular time.

Age	Incisors 1	2	3	Canine 1	Premolars 2	3	4	Molars 1	2	3
1/2 year	D	D	D	D	D	D	D	P		
1-1/2 years	P	D P	D	D	D	D	D	P	P	
2-1/2 years	P	P	P	P	D (P) P	D (P) P	D (P) P	P	P	P
3-1/2 years	P	P	P	P	P	P	P	P	P	P

Table 20.37. Characters for describing and distinguishing between the lower jaws of 3- and 4-year-old elk (Quimby and Gaab 1957).

Character No.	Three-Year-Old Characters	Four-Year-Old Characters
I	Cond. of PM_2-occlusal surface sharp with dentine not exposed continuously in either right or left tooth.	Cond. of PM_3-no circle of enamel on occlusal surface about two thirds of the distance back from anterior edge of tooth in either the right or left tooth.
II	Cond. of PM_3-dentine not exposed continuously across occlusal surface of buccal crest of either right or left tooth.	Cond. of PM_4-infundibulum of the anterior cone *not* completely surrounded by dentine (interrupted by enamel) in both the right and the left tooth.
III	Cond. of PM_4-at least one-half circle of enamel on anterior occlusal surface of both right and left teeth.	Cond. of M_1-same as character II, but different tooth.
IV	Cond. of M_3-posterior end (edge) of anterior lingual crest completely covered with enamel on both right and left teeth.	Cond. of M_2-same as character II, but different tooth.
V	Cond. of M_3-crest of buccal side of posterior cone not below crest of lingual side in either right or left tooth.	Cond. of M_3-the infundibulum of the posterior cone *not* completely surrounded by dentine (interrupted by enamel) on both the right and the left tooth.

Table 20.38. Tooth eruption and replacement in the lower jaw of Ontario moose (after Peterson 1955). Milk or deciduous tooth—D; permanent tooth—P; parentheses indicate that tooth is in process of erupting at that particular time.

Age	Incisors			Canine		Premolars			Molars		
	1	2	3	1	2	3	4	1	2	3
Birth	D	D	D	D	(D)	(D)	(D)			
1 month	D	D	D	D	(D)	D	D			
3 months	D	D	D	D	D	D	D	(P)		
5 months	D	D	D	D	D	D	D	P		
9 months	P	D	D	D	D	D	D	P	(P)	
12 months	P	D	D	D	D	D	D	P	P	
14 months	P	D	D	D	D	D	D	P	P	(P)
17 months	P	P	P	(P)	(P)	(P)	(P)	P	P	(P)
19 months	P	P	P	P	P	P	P	P	P	P

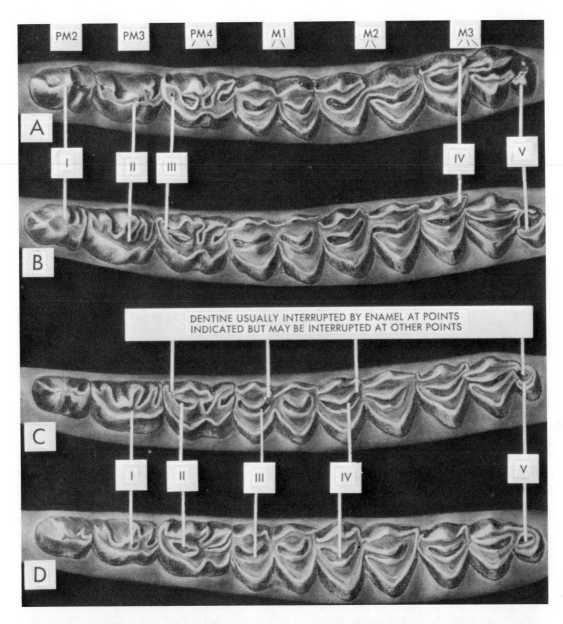

Fig. 20.39. Occlusal surface of the left mandibular cheek teeth of elk illustrating "3-" and "4-year old" characters. *A* 3-year old showing all "3-year old characters" positive. *B* 4-year old showing all "3-year old characters" negative. *C* 4-year old showing all "4-year old characters" positive. *D* 5-year old showing all "4-year old characters" negative (from Quimby and Gaab 1957).

the height into the width is useful as an expression of age. Also, the length of the lower jaw and the length of the diastema both grow longer with age, whereas the length of the tooth-row becomes shorter. Here again there is opportunity to derive relationships useful in expressing age, although these authors have not done so.

Antlers are of some use in determining age, expecially in yearlings. Yearling (1-1/2-years-old) bulls usually have an antler spread of

14-1/8 to 28 inches, a total of from 2 to 8 points (counting both antlers), a greatest-palm width of 5-1/2 inches or less, a greatest palm length of 7-1/2 inches or less, and a minimum antler beam circumference of 5-3/8 inches or less (Cringan *in* Peterson 1955).

Sergeant and Pimlott (1959) have studied the pattern of cement deposition in the pulp cavity of the first incisor of the moose as an indicator of age. They found that in thin longitudinal (sagittal)

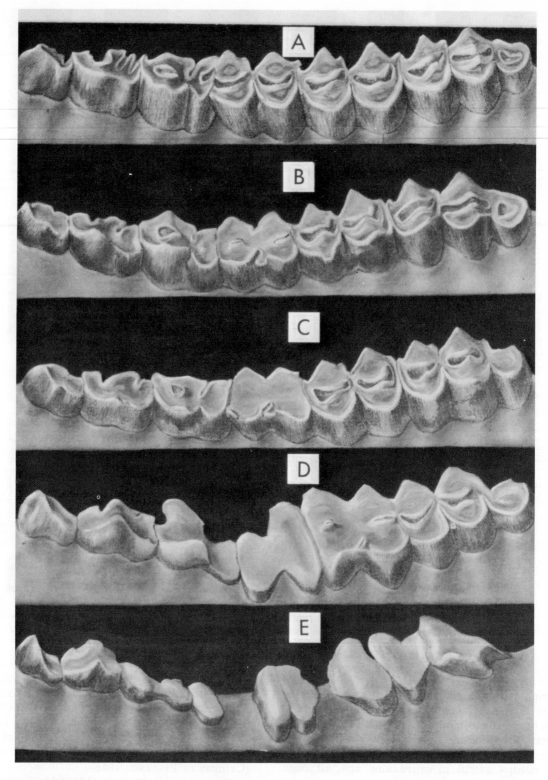

Fig. 20.40. Side occlusal view of mandibular cheek teeth of the elk. *A* 7-year old. *B* 8-year old. *C* 9-year old. *D* 15-year old. *E* 21-year old (from Quimby and Gaab 1957).

Table 20.39. Changes in the teeth and jaws of moose with age (after Passmore, Peterson, and Cringan *in* Peterson 1955).

Character		Age in Years							
		2.5	3.5	4.5	5.5-6.5	7.5-8.5	9.5-10.5	11.5-13.5	14.5-16.5
Width of posterior buccal crest of M$_2$ (mm)	Mean	6.1	7.0	7.9	8.6	9.1	9.5	10.6	
	S.D.	0.378	0.361	0.348	0.368	0.409	0.395	0.929	
Height of posterior buccal crest of M$_2$ (mm)	Mean	19.0	17.6	16.0	14.1	12.7	11.3	8.4	6.6
	S.D.	0.810	0.960	0.721	0.688	0.574	0.925	1.93	1.28
Ratio of the width to the ht. of post-buccal crest of M$_2$ (%)	Mean	32.1	40.0	49.5	60.1	71.5	85.3	121.0	
	S.D.	2.40	3.16	3.54	3.95	4.61	8.72	27.0	
Width of first incisor (mm)	Mean	12.3	12.3	12.1	12.1	12.0	11.8	11.6	11.5
	Range	11.2-13.0	11.3-13.5	10.3-13.1	11.0-13.5	11.5-12.6	11.1-12.9	11.0-12.5	9.3-12.6
Length of lower jaw (mm)	Mean	451	462	464	467.5	467.6	464.1	466.1	470.0
	Range	435-470	444-478	446-486	444-489	443-448	437-482	451-483	455-481
Length of diastemma (mm)	Mean	160.5	166.0	169.5	172.2	173.7	173.1	176.4	177.5
	Range	148-181	154-188	148-185	157-190	159-189	150-189	163-196	166-192
Length of tooth-row (mm)	Mean	166.0	168.0	167.8	167.1	165.8	162.3	163.8	161.4
	Range	158-175	157-181	160-175	159-177	158-172	158-170	158-173	154-171

sections, there were alternating opaque and translucent layers visible (under magnification) in this cement. They proposed that the opaque cement was deposited in summer and fall and the translucent cement in winter and spring—one pair of zones thus indicating 1 year. They thought that the first opaque zone was deposited about the time of birth. This method has not yet been checked against a large series of known-age jaws, but so far it seems promising. It is of interest to note that the red deer or Europe (*Cervus elaphus*) has long been aged by the seasonal deposition of "secondary dentine," which begins in the third year. European workers regret that this system cannot be applied to *Alces* (Von Marienfrid 1939).

CARIBOU AND REINDEER

Determination of sex in caribou, where both sexes are antlered, can be made from the length of the dentary bone (incisor base to angle of jawbone) providing that the age is correctly estimated (Bergerud 1964).

Table 20.40. The sequence of tooth eruption and replacement in the barren-ground caribou (after Banfield 1954). Milk or deciduous tooth—D; permanent tooth—P; parentheses indicate that tooth is in process of erupting at that particular time.

Age	Incisors 1	2	3	Canine 1	Premolars 2	3	4	Molars 1	2	3
Birth	D	D	D	D						
1 week	D	D	D	D	D	D	D			
10 weeks	D	D	D	D	D	D	D	(P)		
6 months	D	D	D	D	D	D	D	(P)		
10 months	D (P)	D (P)	D (P)	D	D	D	D	P	(P)	
16 months	P	P	P	P	D (P)	D (P)	D (P)	P	P	(P)
18 months	P	P	P	P	P	P	P	P	P	(P)
22 months	P	P	P	P	P	P	P	P	P	P

Table 20.41. Tooth eruption and replacement in the lower jaw of the bison (after Hogben, ms.). Milk or diciduous tooth—D; permanent tooth—P; parentheses indicate that the tooth is in process of erupting at that particular time.

Age	Incisors 1	2	3	Canine 1	Premolars 2	3	4	Molars 1	2	3
1 year	D	D	D	D	D	D	D	P	(P)	
2 years	P	D P	D	D	D P	D	D	P	P	(P)
3 years	P	P	D	D	(P) P	(P) P	D (P)	P	P	(P)
4 years	P	P	P	D	P	P	P	P	P	P
5 years	P	P	P	(P)	P	P	P	P	P	P

Visual determination of sex may be made in caribou calves. The calves tend to lift their tails when alarmed; then the female can be recognized by the tuft of long hairs around the vulva (Bergerud 1961).

Aging of caribou and reindeer is by replacement, eruption, and wear of the teeth of the lower jaw. The schedule of eruption and replacement is shown in Table 20.40.

Older animals are aged by means of the relative wear on the cheek teeth. The posterior cusp of the M_3 first shows wear at 26 months.

The ratio of the width of the dentine (D) to that of the enamel (E) on the lingual crest of the anterior cusp of the first molar, expressed as D/E, was found to be: 1-1/2 years—1.0; 3 years—1.5; 3-1/2 years—2.5; 4-1/2 years—3.0; 7 years—4.0; 7-1/2 and 8-1/2 years—5.0 (Banfield 1954).

Caribou can also be aged by means of transverse sections of the pedicles. These sections show dark, vacuolated bone (summer growth) and light, fine-grained bone (fall and winter growth). The pattern is most clear in young animals; increasing obscurity with age limits its usefulness as an aging technique to about the fifth year (Banfield 1960).

MUSK-OX

Sex and age in the musk-ox are best determined by the appearance of the horns, since most animals must be classified while alive. Calves are readily identified by their size. Yearlings are small and have small, straight, horn projections: in males the length of the horn sheath is probably about 100 mm and in females about 66 mm.

Immature animals include bulls of 2-1/2 to 5-1/2 years and cows of 2-1/2 and 3-1/2 years. Sex is difficult to determine in 2-1/2 year old animals, although the horns of bulls are whiter and project more nearly straight from the head than those of females. During the fourth year the horns of the females have developed to the point where their basal depression reaches the maximum, almost touching the jaw, and the apical portions turn upward and out. They are then considered adults. Bulls are considered adults from their sixth year, which is marked by the growth of their horns completely over the forehead (Tener 1954).

BISON

Bison may be aged by the eruption, replacement, and wear of the teeth of the lower jaw. They have a full mouth by their fifth or sixth year (see Table 20.41).

Beyond the fifth year, bison may be tentatively assigned to age-classes as defined by Fuller (1959). He considered three adult-classes as follows: *young adult*—about 5 and 6 years of age; *adults*—from 7 to 11 years of age; and *aged*—over 12 years of age. His criteria are: *young adults*: wear on C_1 not exceeding 2 mm; M_2 style circle or loop; M_3 style not worn or tip only worn; horns of bulls not stepped at tip. *Adults*: wear on C_1 2 to 4 mm; M_3 style rarely a loop; horns of bulls stepped at tip (tips blunted and shredded by new horn piercing through the old sheath). *Aged*: wear on C_1 more than 4 mm; M_3 style usually a loop; horns of bulls stepped at tip.

SHEEP

The most intensively studied wild sheep form has been the bighorn sheep but most sex and age criteria probably apply equally well to the Dall sheep of the North. At a distance it is possible to distinguish lambs but not to sex them. Yearlings, especially rams, unless closely examined for the scrotum, cannot be clearly distinguished from adult ewes. Two-year-old and older rams are easily distinguished by their large horns. The younger-adult rams (less than 3/4 curl) may be separated from the older ones (3/4 curl or over) according to Jones, Flittner, and Gard (1954).

Sheep in the hand may be readily aged by the

Table 20.42. Tooth eruption and replacement in the lower jaw of the bighorn sheep (based on Cowan 1940, Deming 1952, and upon specimens at Montana State University). Milk or deciduous tooth—D; permanent teeth—P; parentheses indicate that the tooth is in process of replacement at that particular time.

Age	Incisors			Canine	Premolars			Molars		
	1	2	3	1	2	3	4	1	2	3
Birth	D	D	D	D	D	D	(D)			
1 month	D	D	D	D	D	D	D			
6 months	D	D	D	D	D	D	D	(P)		
12 months	(P)	D	D	D	D	D	D	P	(P)	
16 months	P	D	D	D	D	D	D	P	P	
24 months	P	D	D	D	D	D	D	P	P	
30 months	P	D	D	D	(P)	(P)	D	P	P	(P)
36 months	P	(P)	D	D	(P)	(P)	(P)	P	P	(P)
42 months	P	P	D	D	P	P	P	P	P	P
48 months	P	P	P	P	P	P	P	P	P	P

Table 20.43. Tooth eruption and replacement in the lower jaw of the Dall sheep (from Hemming, 1968). Milk or deciduous tooth--D; permanent tooth—P; brackets indicate that the tooth is in process of replacement at that particular time.

Age	Incisors			Canine	Premolars			Molars		
	1	2	3	1	2	3	4	1	2	3
5 Days	D	D	D	D	(D)	D	D			
1-1/2 months	D	D	D	D	D	D	D	(P)		
4 months	D	D	D	D	D	D	D	P		
5 months										
8 months										
10 months	D	D	D	D	D	D	D	P	(P)	
11-1/2 months										
13 months	(P)	D	D	D	D	D	D	P	P	
16 months	P	D	D	D	D	D	D	P	P	
17 months										
18 months										
19 months										
20 months										
21 months										
22 months	P	D	D	D	D	D	D	P	P	(P)
23 months										
25 months	P	(P)	D	D	D	(P)	(P)	P	P	P
28 months	P	P	D	D	(P)	(P)	(P)	P	P	(P)
30 months	P	P	D	D	(P)	P	P	P	P	(P)
32 months	P	P	D	D	P	P	P	P	P	(P)
33 months	P	P	(P)	D	P	P	P	P	P	(P)
35 months	P	P	P	D	P	P	P	P	P	(P)
40 months	P	P	P	D	P	P	P	P	P	P
45 months	P	P	P	(P)	P	P	P	P	P	P
47 months	P	P	P	P	P	P	P	P	P	P

evidence of alternating slow and rapid growth in the horns. Smooth areas represent periods of rapid horn growth, while ridges, or checks, represent periods of slower growth. Some authors believe that rapid and slow growth occur in response to better and poorer periods of nutrition but Cowan (1940) suggests that the checks represent the cessation of growth during the breeding season. Whatever the cause, there is an inconspicuous check which marks the first winter. Often it is a slight swelling. The first obvious check is formed at about 1-1/2 years, and one is formed each year thereafter. Cowan (1940) reports that the bighorn growth rate slows after 5 years of age, and that after 8 or 10 years (in the bighorn ram) the annual increment is so slight that it is often impossible to distinguish growth rings. In bighorns, too, the horn-tips are often worn and splintered. He found in male thin-horned sheep that growth persisted for a longer period, so that

heads with 12 or 13 and even as many as 15 well-defined checks occurred. In thin-horned rams the splintering of horn-tips is rare. In ewes, the same author found that the growth of the horns slows in the fifth and sixth year and is negligible thereafter in northern races of the bighorn; the horns of the southern races grow faster and for a greater number of years (Cowan 1940).

"Dall sheep may also be aged by annuli in the cementum of the root of the first permanent incisor. Cementum deposition begins about the time the tooth begins to erupt. Light cementum is deposited during summer and fall (up to the rut); dark cementum is deposited from the rut to the lamb drop. The age equals the count of dark zones plus one. These zones show up well when a thin saggital section of the untreated tooth is examined with an ultra-violet microscope (150X), since the light zones fluoresce but the dark zones do not."

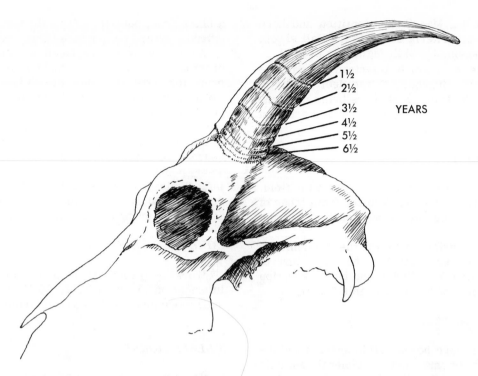

Fig. 20.41. Annual rings on the horn of the mountain goat (after Brandborg 1955).

Table 20.44. Tooth eruption and replacement in the lower jaw of the mountain goat (after Brandborg 1955). Milk or deciduous tooth—D; permanent tooth—P; parentheses indicate that the tooth is in process of replacement at that particular time.

| Age | Incisors | | | Canine | Premolars | | | Molars | | |
	1	2	3	1	2	3	4	1	2	3
1 week	(D)	(D)	(D)		(D)	(D)	(D)			
6 months	D	D	D	D	D	D	D	(P)		
10 months	D	D	D	D	D	D	D	(P)	(P)	
15-16 months	(P) P	D	D	D	D	D	D	P	(P)	(P)
23 months	P	D	D	D	D	D (P)	D (P)	P	P	(P)
26-29 months	P	(P)	D	D	(P)	(P)	(P)	P	P	(P)
38-40 months	P	P	(P)	D	P	P	P	P	P	P
48 months	P	P	P	(P)	P	P	P	P	P	P

(Hemming, J. E., Mandibular dentition and horn development as criteria of age in the Dall sheep, *Oris dalli* Nelson. J. Wildl. Mgmt., in press.)

Sheep, like other North American bovidae, are slower than the members of the deer family in achieving adult dentition, 4 years being required for completion of tooth replacement and eruption (Table 20.42 and 20.43).

MOUNTAIN GOAT

Goats are difficult to sex visually in the field, since the horns of the males differ from those of the females mainly by being heavier, but not longer.

Aging is possible both by the intermittent growth of the horn, causing the formation of annual rings (see Fig. 20.41), and by the eruption and replacement of the teeth (Table 20.44).

PRONGHORN ANTELOPE

The males have horns in this species and the females may or may not. In general, animals with horns longer than the ears are adult males. The adult male is marked with a black mask covering the face up to the horns; the female has a black nose, but only a faint shadow of dark hair extends upward on her face (Einarsen 1948).

Aging by tooth replacement and wear is practicable. Because the molars and premolars erupt for most the adult life as fast as they are worn down, the height of the tooth above the gumline is not a good index of age. However, in the course of wear the infundibula, or recesses in the grinding surfaces of the teeth, are gradually reduced in depth and ultimately disappear. This wear permits aging on the basis of how many infundibula are present. Table 20.45 shows the normal sequence of tooth eruption and replacement in the pronghorn antelope.

COLLARED PECCARY

Work on peccaries is in its infancy but the information given in Table 20.46 will be useful until more precise data are available.

RHESUS MONKEY

The rhesus monkey *(Macaca mulatta)* has become a more common laboratory animal in recent years; as a result, many wildlife biologists

Table 20.45. Tooth eruption and replacement in the lower jaw of the pronghorn antelope (after Dow 1952, and Dow and Wright 1962). Milk or deciduous tooth—D; permanent tooth—P; parentheses indicate that the tooth is in process of eruption at that particular time.

Age	Incisors			Canine	Premolars			Molars		
	1	2	3	1	2	3	4	1	2	3
Birth	D						D			
6 weeks	D	D	D	D	D	D	D	P		
15-17 months	P	D	D	D	D	D	D	P	P	P
27-29 months	P	P	D	D	P	P	P	P	P	P
39-41 months	P	P	P?	(P) P	P*	P*	P*	P	P	P
4-1/2 years	P	P	P?	(P) P	18 to 20 infundibula[#]					
5-1/2 years	P	P	P?	(P) P	13 to 16 infundibula					
6-1/2 years	P	P	P		10 infundibula					

*Total of 24 infundibula.
#See text for explanation; infundibula on both sides are totaled.

Table 20.46. Tooth eruption in the lower jaw of the collared peccary (after Sowls 1961). Milk or deciduous tooth—D; permanent tooth—P; parentheses indicate that the tooth is in the process of eruption at that particular time.

Age	Incisors 1	2	3	Canine 1	Premolars 1	2	3	Molars 1	2	3
2-6 months	D	D	D	D	D	D	D	D	D	D
7-10 months	D	D	D	D	D	D	D	P	D	D
11-12 months	D	D	D	P	D	D	D	P	D	D
13-18 months	D	D	D	P	D	D	D	P	P	D
19-21-1/2 months	D	D	D	P	D	D	D	P	P	(P)
Over 21-1/2 months	D	P	P	P	P	P	P	P	P	P

are having closer contact with this animal. A rough separation of the rhesus monkey into age-classes may be made on the following basis (from Barbehenn and Wilber 1958) shown in Table 20.47.

Most of the animals covered in this section are economically important animals of North America. If no information is given for such a North American animal it is because no information has been found. Age and sex criteria have been worked out for many other birds and mammals of the world but space considerations have precluded their coverage here.

Table 20.47. Age criteria for the rhesus monkey (from Barbehenn and Wilber 1958). Milk or deciduous tooth—D; permanent tooth—P.

Age	Incisors 1	2	3	Canine 1	Premolars 1	2	3	Molars 1	2	3
Infant	D	D		D	D	D				
				or less						
Juvenile	D	D		D	D	D		P		
				or						
	P	P		D	D	D		P	P	
Subadult	P	P		D	P	D		P	P	
				to						
	P	P		P	P	P		P	P	
Adult	P	P		P	P	P		P	P	P
Old adult	Teeth are severely worn or missing									

CHAPTER TWENTY-ONE

ESTIMATING THE NUMBERS OF ANIMALS IN WILDLIFE POPULATIONS

W. SCOTT OVERTON, PhD

Professor, Department of Statistics
Oregon State University
Corvallis, Oregon

and

DAVID E. DAVIS, PhD

Head, Department of Zoology
University of North Carolina
Raleigh, North Carolina

The many and diverse schemes for estimation of population numbers and density fill a voluminous literature that cannot possibly be completely treated in a single chapter in this manual. The writers have attempted to assemble these methods into a coherent and orderly treatment and the papers referenced have been chosen to illustrate the development. The reader should be aware that the references represent only a part of the literature and that the cited passages and results represent only a small part of the material in the references cited.

The primary purpose of this chapter is to catalog standard *techniques* of population estimation, with instructions regarding their use and limitation. In addition, an attempt is made to elaborate the development of the *technique* of constructing population estimators to fit special circumstances. This approach requires emphasis on the construction of a *sampling model*. It is suggested that the user of the techniques in this chapter consider the estimation of population numbers and density to be just one objective in a more general study of the population, so that validation of assumptions and the general process of model building is viewed as part of the study, per se, rather than as merely a means to the end of estimation of numbers.

Several expository papers deal generally with the subject of this chapter. The book by Ricker (1958) is still perhaps the best general reference for estimation methods used by fishery workers. Watt (1968:189-225) gave a lucid and penetrating analysis of problems in systems measurement, including population estimation, and Southwood (1966) presented a detailed and extensive treatment of estimation methods for insects. Recent papers by Regier and Robson (1967) and Robson and Regier (1968) covered several general methods, and Isakov (1961) presented many applications of census methods to studies of a large variety of birds and mammals.

Dice (1952) briefly discussed censuses for animals in a community; Kendeigh (1944) reviewed estimates of bird populations. Scattergood (1954) classified methods very simply and Dorn (1954) described the problems of sampling in "natural experiments." Hickey (1955) summarized the principal census technique used in estimating gallinaceous birds, usually on a statewide basis. Davis (1956) compiled and illustrated a number of census methods.

The methods employed in collecting the data and the form of the calculating formulae will depend on the species, the season of the year, the habitat, the purpose of the study, and on any other feature of the problem that might conceivably influence the observations and the validity of the method. It is assumed here that the worker is familiar with the ecology of the species and with the relevant behaviorial patterns and environmental features. It is hoped that he will be able to learn from this chapter some techniques of assessing the validity of a method and of modifying a method to conform to the peculiar circumstances of his problem.

In general the goal of population estimation should be two-fold. It is desired to obtain the best possible estimates commensurate with the objectives of the study and the time, resources, and personnel available. One also wishes to be able to make a statement regarding the accuracy of the estimate—how well the assumptions are met and the effect of sampling error. To this end, considerable attention is given in this chapter to the problems of collecting concomitant information to be used in validating assumptions, modifying the estimator if assumptions are ill-founded, and evaluating variances and confidence limits.

Many of the methods included here are complex, particularly in the more recent versions based on realistic models of real situations. This complexity has been introduced reluctantly, but, it is felt, necessarily. Complexity is the price of realism and the present degree of realism is none too great. In fact, the degree of complexity here is far below that of most contemporary literature on the subjects covered, as a quick literature review will show.

Computers will soon prove of very great value in the routine processing of census and survey data. When they become generally available, it will be desirable to advance to even more realistic and complex solutions to the problems; there will be no premium on simplicity, so long as the users understand the principles and are able to comprehend the constraints and limitations of the models on which the computer solutions are based.

DEFINITIONS

The following definitions are established for use in the chapter. These are made more or less explicit, depending on the needs of the subsequent material, and the ideas involved are developed more fully in the text. See Fig. 21.1.

● Census

A complete count or tally of animals *over* (a) a specified area at a specified point in time, or (b) a specified interval of time at a specified point in space (area).

● Sample Census

A complete count or tally of animals over (a) a *sample* of a specified area at a specified point in time, or (b) a *sample interval of time* from a specified interval of time at a specified point in space.

● Census Index

A count or ratio which is relative in some sense to the total number of animals in a specified population. A sample census is a special case of a census index.

●Census Estimate

An estimate of the total number of animals in a specified population, obtained from a census index.

●Accuracy (of an estimator)

A measure of how close one might reasonably expect an estimate to approximate the quantity being estimated.

●Precision (of an estimator)

A measure of how close one might reasonably expect an estimate to approximate its *expected value*.

●Bias (of an estimator)

The difference between the expected value of an estimator and the quantity being estimated.

●Consistency (of an estimator)

Consistency is a very important property that is difficult to define simply *and* accurately, particularly with regard to sample estimates from finite populations. (For a formal definition, see Fisher 1956:146 and Chapman and Junge 1956:379). An intuitive explanation is: an estimator which approaches the parameter as the sampling in-

tensity increases is called consistent. An unbiased estimator with a variance which decreases with increasing sample size will be consistent. However, many biased estimators are also consistent, and such a one will have a bias that *decreases* as the sampling intensity *increases*. The symbol → is used to denote consistency so that the expression $\hat{T} \rightarrow T$ is read as, "T-hat is consistent for T." (Meaning also that $\hat{T}$ approaches T in probability as sampling intensity increases.)

●Model

An *abstraction* of the true experimental situation, representing all relevant features of reality. When used in estimation, the model will be constructed in such a way that the unknown quantities are expressed in terms of the known (or observed) quantities.

●Parameter

A constant characterizing the model. Some parameters are known and others are unknown. In this chapter, the unknown parameters, population size and density, are of particular interest.

●Statistic

A number characterizing a sample or experi-

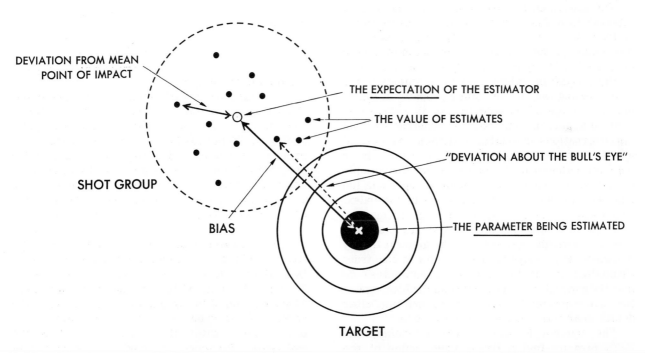

Fig. 21.1. Illustration (a graphic model) of the analogy between estimation and firing a rifle. Variance is the mean squared deviation about the mean point of impact, MSE is the mean squared deviation about the center of the bullseye. A rifle with a tight shot group has high "precision." A few turns for elevation and windage will change "bias" and "accuracy" but not "precision." The accuracy of a gunner is a measure of the distance of his shots from the center bull. If he has adjusted properly for elevation and windage his "bias" will be zero.

406

ment. In this chapter, the statistics of interest are usually estimators of parameters or measures of accuracy of those estimators.

THE STATISTICS OF ESTIMATING POPULATION NUMBERS

The General Statistical Background

If the quantity T is a defined population total, then a general formula can be written for an estimate of T,

$$\hat{T} = At,$$

where the symbol (^), read "hat," denotes an estimating rule (estimator) for the quantity on which the hat is placed, where t is (in some sense) a sample total, and where A is an expansion factor. This form of the estimator is chosen to conform with the general probability estimator of scientific sampling (Formula 1), and the special problems of estimation of population numbers fit within this general theory. The reader who wishes to study this subject is referred to Stuart (1962), Edwards (1964), Cochran (1963), and Sampford (1962).

The fundamental idea is that the population of interest is defined over a *Universe* of sampling units which may have either spatial or temporal dimension, or both, or whose dimension may even be abstract. The parameter, T, is usually the sum of the population values over the elements of the Universe, but may be any other property of interest. A sample of these elements is selected in some manner and the index, t, constructed from the observations or population elements associated with the sample. In general, t will be a formula or rule for calculating a number from the sample observations; we use the symbol to represent the rule as well as a particular value of the index. The form of the rule, t, depends on the manner in which the sample is selected and on the sample size, as does the value of A. The general theory of probability sampling teaches how to construct estimators (rules for calculating estimates) so that the estimators have certain desirable properties. These properties will be discussed in greater detail so an introduction is needed here.

The symbol E means *expected value,* and $E(\hat{T})$ means simply, the *average* value of the number $\hat{T}$ which would be obtained if the entire experiment were repeated over and over under exactly the same conditions. That is, $E(\hat{T})$ is the average value of $\hat{T}$ over all possible samples.

If $E(\hat{T}) = T$, then it is said that $\hat{T}$ is *unbiased.* However, it is important to note that bias cannot usually be estimated. Ordinarily, bias is evaluated theoretically in terms of the sampling model, but it often can be said only that an estimator is biased or unbiased, and nothing be said about the magnitude of the bias if it exists. This is why the property, *consistency,* is of interest, because bias is known to be under control if the estimator is consistent.

Then $V(\hat{T})$, the variance of $\hat{T}$, is defined as the average value of $(\hat{T} - E(\hat{T}))^2$ over all possible samples. $MSE(\hat{T})$, the mean square error of $\hat{T}$, is defined as the average value of $(\hat{T} - T)^2$ over all possible samples. That is, translating word definitions into mathematical ones,

$$V(\hat{T}) = E\{(\hat{T} - E(\hat{T}))^2\}$$

and

$$MSE(\hat{T}) = E\{(\hat{T} - T)^2\}.$$

It follows after brief consideration that

$$MSE(\hat{T}) = V(\hat{T}) + B^2,$$

where

$$B = \{E(\hat{T}) - T\},$$

the bias of the estimator.

An illustration will help to make the point. Consider the analogy, estimating a parameter is like firing a rifle at a target. The bull's eye is analogous to the parameter being estimated. The process of aiming and firing under a particular set of conditions is analogous to the process of collecting data and calculating an estimate under a particular set of circumstances. The location of the bullet strike is analogous to the value of an estimate.

Now, imagine a *very* large number of shots fired at this target. Then the mean point of impact is analogous to the *expectation* of the estimator. This is where the rifle is firing, *on the average.* The precision of the estimator is analogous to the spread of the group about the *mean point* of impact. The greater the spread, the less the *precision. Variance* is used to measure this property. The *accuracy* of the estimator is analogous to the spread of the group about the *bull's-eye. MSE* is used to measure this property, and the greater the value of MSE, the less the *accuracy* of the estimator. Last, the distance from the mean point of impact to the bull's-eye is analogous to the *bias* of the estimator. (The rifle is not correctly sighted for the conditions of firing.)

"Point" estimates are generally obtained through application of a formula of the type indicated previously,

$$\hat{T} = At,$$

where t is a statistic calculated from the data, and A is a function of known parameters in the model. An "interval" estimate, in the form of confidence limits, will usually be of value in imparting some information as to the *precision* of $\hat{T}$. This interval estimate will be expressed as a probability statement,

$$P\{T_L \leq T \leq T_U\} = 1-\alpha$$

which is read: "The probability (measure of confidence) that T lies between a lower value, T_L, and an upper value, T_U, is calculated to be $1-\alpha$." Frequently, $1-\alpha = 0.95$ is chosen, but occasionally use will be found for other levels of confidence.

In the following sections, the various estimators will be put into the framework of both the point estimator and the interval estimator. The theory behind the derivation will change, but the *form* of the finished result will be invariant.

Models and Their Role in Population Estimation

A model is an abstraction of reality. When a model is to be used for a specific purpose, it should account for all relevant features of the experimental situation lest an error be made in the form of an unrecognized complexity. It should exclude all irrelevant features lest the experimental procedure be made too complex. Such an admonition is easy to make but difficult to execute; the modeler should try to conform to this ideal.

The above statement can also be interpreted in reverse. If an experiment or estimating formula is to be criticized as being too complex or too simple, then it can legitimately be done only on the basis that the *model* behind the experiment or formula is too complex or too simple. This being the case, there is no excuse for general criticism; a criticism should be explicit for the features of the model. Of course, this requires that the model

be explicitly identified, a practice which is also endorsed.

Now it is an operational axiom of science that in order to use a model, one must verify its applicability. That is, a correspondence must be established and accepted between the elements of the model and the elements of the experimental situation. This is usually done implicitly, but it sometimes is helpful to make the correspondence explicit, for the rules of correspondence are really part of the model and sometimes influence later model development.

Some model features are structural, such as species, sex, age, social classes, phenotypic classes, or geographic limitations, and some are relational or functional. In its simplest form, the model will consist of a set of statements defining the structural aspects of the experimental situation (defining, for example, the population of interest and its relevant structure) and another set of statements defining the relevant relations. As an example, see the later Section in this chapter entitled "The Petersen or Lincoln Index."

It is often said that a model is constructed from assumptions, although the status of many of the model statements is higher than the lay usage of "assumption" would permit. However, some of them may actually be assumptions in the sense that they are open to question, and a "good" experiment will provide data for validation of the questionable assumptions and perhaps an alternate solution if some of the assumptions prove untenable.

It is important to note that in the models of population estimation the relational statements often relate behavorial characteristics of the species, so that it is important to recognize potential relevant behavorial patterns. If these patterns are known, they can be modeled. If they are suspected, then they can be studied by definition of appropriate supplementary data.

It is also important to note that relational elements of the models are dependent on the conduct of the experiment. If a model for a particular experiment is unacceptable, it is often possible to reconstruct the experiment so that the resultant model *is* acceptable.

In the final analysis, it is the perogative of the individual researcher to choose his model according to his dictates. It is his responsibility to disclose it to his fellow workers for their criticism, but he alone has to make the choice. It will be to his advantage to develop his capacity as a modeler and to explicitly verify the applicability of his models, or, alternatively, to point out their weaknesses.

The Basic Sampling Schemes

The following sampling schemes are the ones most commonly used in field sampling. Each is briefly described and general formulae are given for estimation of the population total and for confidence limits of the simpler ones. For elaboration of this treatment, reference is made to Cochran (1963) and Sampford (1962).

A notational dilemma must be recognized since there is need to develop sampling notation for discrete sampling units in terms of the conventional theory, and also need to develop notation for plotless sampling (as in the mark-recapture methods). This can be accomplished in a consistent manner by using notation according to the structure of the *sampling model,* so that in some cases the symbol T will be used for the total number of animals and in others the symbol N denotes the same quantity.

The sampling model is as follows. There is a set $\mathcal{U} = \{u_1, u_2, \ldots, u_N\}$ of sampling units, each unit of which has a defined number of animals. That is, u_1, is a sampling unit containing y_1 animals, u_2 is a sampling unit containing y_2 animals, etc., there being N sampling units in the Universe. Conventional sampling techniques provide means of selecting units from $\mathcal{U}$ in such a manner that it is possible to estimate the quantity $T = \Sigma y$, summation over $\mathcal{U}$. In methods like tag-recapture, the elements of the Universe are usually the animals themselves, so that $T = N$.

In general, then, the elements of the Universe may be units of space, units of time, time by area units, abstract units or the animals of interest. Given this structural model for the typical sampling situation, the general theory of sampling may be applied.

SIMPLE RANDOM SAMPLING

Select a number, n, of the sampling units in such a way that each unit in the Universe has an equal probability of being selected. (This is sometimes called random sampling without replacement.) Then

$$\hat{T} = \left(\frac{N}{n}\right) t$$

where

$$t = \Sigma y,$$

summation over the sample, and the lower and upper confidence limits of T are calculated by,

$$(T_L, T_U) = \hat{T} \pm 2\sqrt{\hat{V}}$$

where

$$\hat{V} = N\left(\frac{N-n}{n}\right) s^2$$

where the sample variance, s^2, is calculated in the usual manner,

$$s^2 = \frac{1}{n-1}\left[\Sigma y^2 - \frac{t^2}{n}\right].$$

STRATIFIED RANDOM SAMPLING

The sampling units are grouped into strata, or sub-universes, such that the hth stratum contains N_h sampling units. Then a sample of n_h units is selected from the hth stratum, perhaps in the manner of a simple random sample, and the process repeated for each stratum. Then, the estimate and variance for the hth stratum is constructed in the manner dictated by the sampling method used in that stratum and,

$$\hat{T}_y = \Sigma \hat{T}_{yh}$$

and

$$\hat{V} = \Sigma \hat{V}_h,$$

with summation over strata in each case.

SYSTEMATIC SAMPLING

The sampling units are *ordered* according to some criterion (e.g., spatial location or temporal order) and samples are taken at regular intervals along this ordering. Several estimators of T and of confidence limits are available, depending on the assumptions made about the nature of variability along the ordering. Unless a pronounced trend is present, it is usually adequate to treat this as a simple random sample and use the formula for that method. Other available techniques are beyond the scope of this chapter.

TWO-STAGE AND DOUBLE SAMPLING

These two techniques are very valuable in field surveys, but the technical details are again too involved for this chapter. However, it will be useful to state the essential features.

In two-stage sampling, a sample of units is selected, perhaps by simple random sampling. Then, for *each* of these selected sampling units, the quantity of interest is *estimated* by some sampling procedure (rather than being *measured* directly). An example of application of a two-stage sample is as follows. Suppose the objective to estimate the number of quail in a state having, say, 100 counties. Twenty counties are selected at random for the first stage sample. The job now is to estimate the number of quail in each selected county. To accomplish this, consider the problem for a single county and construct a frame of land units, perhaps farms, such that the entire county is contained in these non-overlapping and recognizable (on the ground) land units. Let there be 1,000 land units in a selected county, and suppose 50 of them are selected at random. Now, on each of the selected units the quail are counted. (Further stages may be employed, but the pattern should now be clear). Then the number of quail is estimated according to the sampling method used in this particular county. This procedure is repeated for each selected county, and then the county estimates are plugged into the estimating formula appropriate to the sampling method used in the first stage.

In a *double sample,* certain properties are measured on the set of units selected at the first phase (as for example by a simple random sample) and then a sub-sample of these units is selected for measurement of other properties. This technique is very valuable in many field sampling situations, and is used in two general classes of problems. First, let the measurement of primary interest be observed on the units in the first stage sample, and a sub-sample of units selected for observation of some measurement of secondary interest. This, the quantity of secondary interest, is estimated with reduced cost and reduced precision. An example of this use of double sampling: Let a sample of farms be selected for quail census and a sub-sample of these sample farms be selected for determination of covey composition.

Second, suppose the observation of primary interest, y, is very costly, and that an approximation to this measurement may be made through another less costly measurement, x. Then x is observed over the first phase sample and the ob-servation of y on the second phase sample used to *calibrate* the results of the first phase. An example of this use of double sampling: Let x be the number of doves heard calling at a call station and y be the density of dove nests within a certain radius of the station (c.f., Lowe 1956).

The technique of *ratio estimation* is frequently used with double samples and the method is potentially quite valuable for use with index methods.

Methods of Statistical Estimation

Given a statistical *model* for an experimental situation (e.g., estimation of population numbers) an estimator can be constructed by one of several recognized methods, or one may be chosen that has some other general appeal. To recapitulate, the model (or at least the part of interest here) is a set of statements which relates the observations (data) to the unknown parameters of interest. An *estimator* is a rule for calculating *estimates* of the parameter(s) from the data. It is obvious that the form of the estimator should in some sense be dictated by the model.

If the probability distribution of the data is completely specified by the model then one of the conventional statistical techniques can be used; least squares, maximum likelihood, method of moments, to mention the most common. For example, maximum likelihood estimators are frequently used in tag-recapture studies (c.f., Schnabel 1938). Given an appropriate model, any statistician can assist in use of these methods. He can also assist in building the model!

A technique which is more useful to the field man than the common conventional techniques is called *the method of expectation.* In this method, the model is written in the form of *expectation statements.* An expectation statement equates the expectation of each datum and the set of parameters. The number of data should be reduced by some suitable means (e.g., summation or averaging) so as to reduce the number of statements to the number of parameters. This is a very critical process, and the validity of the procedure depends on the manner in which the data reduction is made. Unfortunately, the theoretical considerations are quite beyond the level of this paper. Fortunately, intuitive reductions are usually adequate.

The second and last step is made by substituting the observed data into the equations for the expectations and solving for the parameters of interest. Complications: if there are fewer equations than parameters, the system cannot be

410

solved and more statements must be developed. If there are more equations (statements) than parameters, more "data reduction" must be done. Examples of use of this method will be given.

The above methods (maximum likelihood, least squares, method of expectation, etc.) are oriented to sampling situations in which the statistical distribution of the observations is specified (perhaps incompletely in the case of the expectation method). These methods are appropriate to plotless samples and sometimes even to samples taken by sampling units from a finite universe. Another general method which is used in the theory of finite sampling is related to the method of expectation and can be stated as follows.

If the ith element in the universe has probability p_i of being included in the sample, where p_i can vary among the elements, where $p_i > 0$ for all i, and a sample S of units has been taken, then

$$\hat{T} = \sum_S (y/p) \qquad (1)$$

is unbiased for T.

This will be referred to as the *general theorem of probability sampling,* Formula 1 as the *general probability estimator,* and the theorem will be used in several places throughout the chapter. The reader is reminded that $\hat{T}$ is the estimator of T and that y_i is the observation made on the ith sampling unit. Further $\sum_S (y/p)$ denotes summation of the quantity y/p over all sampling units in the sample.

Variances, Confidence Limits, and Replicated Sampling

There is probably no need at this point to convince the reader that it is highly desirable that a statement of estimated numbers of animals be accompanied by a statement of accuracy of that statement. Such a statement of accuracy involves consideration of the sampling error of the estimation procedure as well as consideration of biases due to various causes such as model failure. These points have been emphasized over and over in several chapters of this manual.

Several points are made in this section. First, specification of variance and an estimator of variance usually requires a more complete specification of the model than is required for specification of the estimator of population numbers. See for example, the section entitled "The Petersen of Lincoln Index" for a discussion of this point.

Second, even if the variance and variance estimator are well modeled, it is not always reasonable to use the usual normal approximation confidence limits defined by $\pm 2\sqrt{V}$. In fact, distributions of many population estimators are asymmetrical (e.g., "skewed"), so that asymmetrical confidence limits are desirable. Thirdly, it is often possible to construct the sampling procedure in such a manner that several independent estimates of the population are obtained, and such that the variation among these estimates provides a valid measure of the variance of the pooled or mean estimate. When this can be done, the confidence limits are valid if the estimator is valid, and are not dependent on additional model constraints. This procedure is called replicated sub-sampling or inter-penetrating sampling depending on the exact form it takes.

The most common procedure for normal approximation confidence limits is as follows. The investigator has an estimate $\hat{T}$ and an estimate of the variance of $\hat{T}$, which is designated $\hat{V}$. Then

$$(T_L, T_U) = \hat{T} \pm 2\sqrt{\hat{V}} \qquad (2)$$

gives approximate 95% confidence limits on T. That is, one can make the statement,

$$P\{T_L < T < T_U\} \doteq 0.95. \qquad (3)$$

This is read "The probability that T lies between T_L and T_U is approximately 0.95." Some writers use C (for confidence) instead of P and the two usages should be interpreted as equivalent.

A second common procedure for normal approximation of confidence limits is actually more desirable when applicable (though identical in some cases). In this procedure the random variable, say X, is identified. A probability statement on X is made and this statement solved for the confidence statement on T. That is, let $E(X) = G(T)$ and the probability function of X be specified. Then write

$$P\{X_L < X < X_U\} = 0.95$$

where X_L and X_U are functions of T. Then solve for T, obtaining

$$P\{T_L < T < T_U\} = 0.95.$$

This is illustrated by derivation of the confidence limits for the Lincoln Index estimator of N under the assumption that X is distributed as Poisson with expectation Mn/N. (See the section entitled "The Petersen or Lincoln Index.") By the normal approximation to the Poisson, we can write

$$X_L = \frac{Mn}{N} - 2\sqrt{\frac{Mn}{N}} = E(X) - 2\sqrt{V}$$

$$X_U = \frac{Mn}{N} + 2\sqrt{\frac{Mn}{N}} = E(X) + 2\sqrt{V}$$

so that the confidence statement may be written

$$P\left\{\left(X - \frac{Mn}{N}\right)^2 < 4\left(\frac{Mn}{N}\right)\right\} = 0.95,$$

the solution of which is the solution to the quadratic equation,

$$X^2 - 2\frac{XMn}{N} + \left(\frac{Mn}{N}\right)^2 - 4\frac{Mn}{N} = 0.$$

This solution turns out to be

$$N = \hat{N}\left[\frac{(X+2) \pm 2\sqrt{X+1}}{X}\right], \qquad (4)$$

which incidentally is a good approximation to the confidence limits for the Lincoln Index for $X > 50$. (This formula is given again in the later section on that method.)

A third method is related to the second, but oriented toward tables and graphs (e.g., Adams 1951; Fig. 21.2). For example, Table 21.1 gives 95% confidence limits on N/λ, where λ (read "lambda") $= Mn$ if the Lincoln Index is used. The limits for a particular value of X are looked up and the following statements written:

$$P\{\text{tabular value} < N/\lambda < \text{tabular value}\}$$

$$= 0.95 \qquad (5)$$

$$P\{(\text{tabular value})\lambda < N < (\text{tabular value})\lambda\}$$

$$= 0.95.$$

To use the Clopper and Pearson graphs (Fig. 21.2) one uses the same approach. Look up confidence limits for p given X/n, and write these

$$P\{p_L < p < p_U\} = 0.95.$$

Then substitute, $p = M/N$, obtained from $E(X) = Mn/N$ so that $E(X/n) = M/N$, with the result

$$P\left\{p_L < \frac{M}{N} < p_U\right\} = 0.95,$$

and solve for N,

$$P\left\{\frac{M}{p_U} < N < \frac{M}{p_L}\right\} = 0.95.$$

This same procedure can also be used with normal approximation formulae for the values p_L and p_U but sometimes a negative value of p_L is obtained in this way or a value of p_U greater than 1. When this occurs, one should recognize that 0 is a lower bound for p_L and 1 is an upper bound for p_U and treat them accordingly. The attempt, say, to solve the equation

$$P\left\{-.1 < \frac{M}{N} < .3\right\} \doteq 0.95$$

for N leads to a nonsense set of confidence limits, while the modified statement,

$$P\left\{0 < \frac{M}{N} < .3\right\} \doteq 0.95$$

has a satisfactory solution,

$$P\left\{\frac{M}{.3} < N < +\infty\right\} \doteq 0.95.$$

Examples of the use of these tables and graphs are given in the sections dealing with specific estimating procedures, so that a quick numerical example will suffice here. Suppose that one has a Lincoln Index experiment in which ($M = 100$) animals are marked and ($n = 100$) are recaptured of which ($X = 20$) are marked. Then to use Table 21.1, calculate $\lambda = nM = 10000$ and look up $X_L = .03004$ and $X_U = .0773$. Then write

$$P\{.03004 < N/\lambda < .0773\} \doteq 0.95$$

and solve, letting $\lambda = 10000$,

$$P\{300.4 < N < 773\} \doteq 0.95.$$

To use the Clopper-Pearson graph (Fig. 21.2), calculate $X/n = 20/100 = .2$ and locate .2 along the horizontal axis of the graph. From this point, follow the vertical line and locate the intersection with the two curves marked 100 (for $n = 100$). Project these two intersections onto the vertical axis, reading $p_L = .125$ and $p_U = .295$. Then, write

Table 21.1. A table for use in setting confidence limits on N when estimated by the Lincoln Index or Schnabel Method. The tabular values are 95% confidence limits on $1/E(x) = N/\lambda$. Adapted from Chapman (1948).

x	Lower Limit	Upper Limit	x	Lower Limit	Upper Limit
0	0.0885	—			
1	0.0720	19.489	26	0.02478	0.0563
2	0.0767	2.821	27	0.02408	0.0539
3	0.0736	1.230	28	0.02342	0.0516
4	0.0690	0.738	29	0.02279	0.0495
5	0.0644	0.513	30	0.02221	0.0475
6	0.0600	0.388	31	0.02165	0.0457
7	0.0561	0.309	32	0.02112	0.0440
8	0.0526	0.256	33	0.02061	0.0425
9	0.0495	0.217	34	0.02014	0.0410
10	0.0468	0.188	35	0.01968	0.0396
11	0.0443	0.165	36	0.01925	0.0384
12	0.0420	0.147	37	0.01883	0.0372
13	0.0400	0.133	38	0.01843	0.0360
14	0.0382	0.121	39	0.01805	0.0350
15	0.0365	0.111	40	0.01769	0.03396
16	0.0350	0.1020	41	0.01733	0.03300
17	0.03362	0.0945	42	0.01700	0.03210
18	0.03233	0.0880	43	0.01668	0.03124
19	0.03114	0.0823	44	0.01636	0.03043
20	0.03004	0.0773	45	0.01606	0.02966
21	0.02901	0.0729	46	0.01578	0.02892
22	0.02806	0.0689	47	0.01550	0.02822
23	0.02716	0.0653	48	0.01523	0.02755
24	0.02632	0.0620	49	0.01498	0.02691
25	0.02552	0.0591	50	0.01475	0.02625

$$P\{.125 < p < .295\} \doteq 0.95 \,,$$

substitute p = M/N and solve for N,

$$P\left\{\frac{100}{.295} < N < \frac{100}{.125}\right\} = 0.95$$

$$P\{339 < N < 800\} = 0.95 \,.$$

Adams (1951) gives more detailed instructions for use of the Clopper-Pearson graphs.

Some simple methods are useful in making tests and comparisons. When many comparisons are being made, the "overlapping confidence limits" method is very convenient. That is, failure of confidence limits to overlap constitutes rejection of the hypothesis that the two estimates are of the same population number. (Note again that it cannot be said that the numbers *are* the same if the limits *do* overlap, it just cannot be said that they are different!)

Chapman and Overton (1964) discussed several aspects of the testing question and suggested several approximate procedures as useful in field studies. The usual statistical tests (t, χ^2, F) are sometimes appropriate, as are some of the non-parametric methods (sign test, rank sum test).

The *replicated sample* has been little used in population studies, but has a very great potential in those studies in which the variances cannot be modeled. For example, Chapman (1962) and Chapman and Johnson (1968) have applied this technique to the estimation of fur seal populations. The concept is very simple, although it may sometimes be difficult to execute a valid application. The experiment is replicated in such a way that each replication reflects all of the possible sampling and observational error. In the simplest form, suppose that a simple random sample has been taken of elements from some Universe. Then a random partitioning of the sample will provide appropriate "replicated samples." If the sampling

CONFIDENCE BELTS FOR p (CONFIDENCE COEFFICIENT .95)

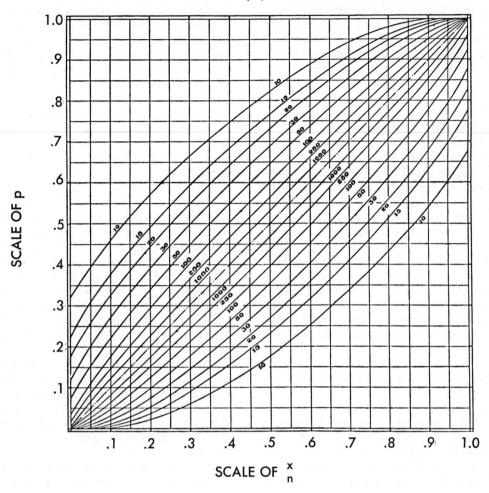

Fig. 21.2. Confidence limits for the binomial distribution at the 95 per cent level. From Adams (1951) with permission.

situation is more complex, replication is more complex.

Then, an estimate is constructed from each sub-sample and also a *best estimate*, either by averaging the sub-sample estimates or by pooling the sub-samples. Confidence limits can be obtained in two ways:

1. Let there be k sub-samples and let

$$s^2 = \frac{1}{k-1} \sum_{i=1}^{k} (\hat{N}_i - \bar{\hat{N}})^2$$

where $\bar{\hat{N}}$ is the average of the $\hat{N}_i$.

Then $P\left\{\bar{\hat{N}} - 2\sqrt{\frac{s^2}{k}} < N < \bar{\hat{N}} + 2\sqrt{\frac{s^2}{k}}\right\} \doteq 0.95$.

2. Let there be k sub-samples and let $\hat{N}_{(1)}$ be the least of these and $\hat{N}_{(k)}$ the greatest. Then

$$P\{\hat{N}_{(1)} < N < \hat{N}_{(k)}\} = 1 - \left(\frac{1}{2}\right)^{k-1} \quad (6)$$

provides *exact* confidence limits for the *median* of the distribution of $\hat{N}$, which are quite acceptable as confidence limits for N. As a special case, let k = 5. Then

$$P\{\hat{N}_{(1)} < N < \hat{N}_{(5)}\} = 1 - \left(\frac{1}{2}\right)^4 = \frac{15}{16} .$$

That is, one has confidence $\left(\frac{15}{16}\right)$ or 0.94 that N lies between the smallest and largest estimates of five replicated sub-samples.

A method has been proposed (Boguslavsky 1956) for use in estimation of a small population. Obviously, if all individuals have been marked, subsequent samples cannot contain unmarked individuals. A table can be prepared from probability considerations, showing the number of successive collections (in which all animals are marked) necessary to permit the conclusion that, at a level of 90% confidence, the population is less than the specified total. This method has not been tried and obviously is suitable only for very small populations. It is possible, however, to extend the idea to large populations if the result is expressed in terms of density instead of absolute numbers.

On reflection, this idea has considerable merit, not only as a technique, but in calling attention to the fact that for many real situations it is more important to know that a population is "at least as great as _____" or "no greater than _____" than it is to know the absolute level. A clever investigator can construct experiments and analyses to yield good statements of this type in many situations in which "good" estimates of actual numbers are not obtainable.

The Statistical Properties of Indices

Although most of this chapter is devoted to the problem of estimating an absolute number of animals in some defined population, or equivalently, the density of some population, the great majority of management surveys provide only indices to population levels. The index t has been earlier defined as a function of the observations (not to be confused with Student's t), such that (At) provides an estimate of the population level (or density) and such that A may be (1) specified by the sampling design, (2) estimated from additional sample data, or (3) modeled in some other way.

Now consider the use of the statistic t as an index to trend in a particular region or as a comparative index from one region to another. The most elementary consideration dictates that if A is not constant from one region to another or from year to year, then the comparisons and trends are faulty. Thus, it must be assumed that the expansion factor A is a constant over the conditions involved in the comparison in order that the index comparisons be meaningful. See Table 21.2.

At the same time, it should be pointed out that the assumption of constant A is less restrictive than the constraint necessary for calculation of A for each instance, so that there is a definite need for indices per se. In fact, a good case can be made for treating the population estimates as indices, particularly in cases in which some of the assumptions are suspect and, inversely, a justification can be made for attempting to calibrate any index into a population estimate on the grounds that it is improved as an index in the process.

The various indices can be described as two distinct types. One is a count of animals made in a manner which does not allow direct population estimation by application of sampling theory. This is a sample census without known sampling probabilities. Examples are roadside counts and time-area counts.

When the attempt is made to *estimate* the sampling probabilities and construct the index t and the scaling parameter A so as to estimate the population total, the method is here called a *pseudo sample census*. When the sampling probabilities are known, the method is called a *sample*

Table 21.2. Comparison of ground and aerial counts of deer, Cedar Ridge Area, Colorado, 1955 (Gilbert and Grieb 1957).

Condition and Type of Count	January 15	February 12	March 5
Snow conditions	Poor to fair	Excellent	Good
Ground count of deer	695	690	601
Aerial count (both crews)			
Average number	237.6	338.2	357.2
95% confidence limits	±16.9	±19.3	±25.8
Average per cent of "total" animals counted	34.2	49.0	44.6

census. (See "Sample Censuses" in the next section.)

The other major kind of index is one based on counts of some associated population. The method yields at the one extreme a virtual tally of a game population (track counts of quail in snow) and, on the other, indices which are very difficult to calibrate (e.g., call counts). This technique can be considered (in its best light) as a *double sample* . . . extensive counts made of the associated variables (tracks or pellets) with intensive analysis of the associated variable-animal relationship. These methods are considered in the section entitled, "Methods Involving Animal Signs and Related Objects."

The problem of calibrating a count of either of these two types to yield a more useful index to population density and number has received a great deal of attention in the literature. One approach was illustrated by McClure (1939), who made an intensive study of dove calling activity and constructed correction factors to adjust the number of calling doves heard to the total number of doves in the audible radius (or fixed plot). He used a factor to adjust for time of day, temperature, weather and wind speed, and each count was multiplied by the average of the four factors appropriate to the conditions under which the count was made. Then each count was corrected to a measure of density by dividing by the acres in the audible radius.

Although McClure's numerical technique was primitive, the approach is sound. Today, an investigator is more likely to use a multiple regression approach to adjustment for the influence of weather or time of day as it is well established that multiple regression is better adapted to this than is multiple ratio analysis, but this is just a refinement of method.

Duke (1966), in a study of the effects of environmental factors on the singing counts of woodcock, presented his data in a manner useful for simple calibration. However, he seemed not to have been aware of the calibration potential. Again it would be desirable if these data were analyzed so that correlated effects were accounted for—perhaps by a multiple regression technique.

By "calibration," then, we mean adjustment to account for the recognized effect of some exogenous variable as weather or time of day. Typically, a count at, say, 9 a.m. will be adjusted to the equivalent value at, perhaps, sunrise. Similarly, a count adjustment will be made at a wind velocity of Beaufort 3 to the equivalent value at zero-wind. The net effect of these adjustments is reduction in variance of the index. Except for the error introduced by the inaccuracy of adjustment, the resultant index is equivalent to one made under very carefully controlled and constant environmental conditions, and, hence, the comparison of two values of the index is enhanced.

An alternative to statistical calibration is often practiced, this being the simple restriction of the index to "standard conditions." For example, the standardized dove call counts are restricted seasonally to a short period that is optimal for at least part of the country and a route is run at an exactly specified time of day. This gains freedom from development and application of the calibration formulae, at the expense of inflexibility in field operation. It is obvious that the idea cannot be extended to weather factors, except to rule out weather extremes, as too many aborted routes would result from specification of very narrow limits.

Calibration of the index to density of animals per unit of area has also been done in several ways. The attempt by McClure to determine the audible radius (or to count the calling doves within 100 yards) was typical of early censuses. Lowe's (1956) attempt to measure density of nests in the vicinity of the call station is also worth reference. These calibrations may refine the index, but they do not convert it to a measure of population density. The terrain represented by roadside counts (either of calls or of animals) must be considered atypical of the countryside in general, so that density of animals along the roads would itself be only an index to the overall density.

Prediction of some more concrete quantity such as hunting success or other index to hunting season abundance over a region or within a study area is another matter, particularly if the prediction is sufficiently advanced in time for regulatory considerations. There are clear cut advantages to such predictions and the technique of multiple regression lends itself nicely to simultaneous consideration of indices, weather variables and other factors of interest (Smith and Gallizioli 1965, Norton et al. 1962, Bennitt 1951, Critcher and Overton 1960).

Another variable that causes some concern in comparison of indices is the observer. Carney and Petrides (1957) show an increased variance accountable to observer inexperience. Further, anyone who has any experience in road counts or call counts recognizes that an experienced observer will see many more animals than will an inexperienced one and that the ability to hear calls varies greatly from one observer to another.

If it is reasonable to assume an additive observer effect, then it is possible to design census experiments such that observer effects are removed from the analysis in the same way that block effects are removed in analysis of variance. This approach will suffice if one is making comparisons among several areas and can properly plan the observations. Heath (1961) has pointed out that under a realistic model it is necessary to take logs of auditory counts in order to obtain additive observer effects.

The calibration of observer effect in a more general study is another matter, and a good "standard" does not seem available. In the case of the auditory index, a measurement of audible radius would definitely bear on the question and it is certain that if one could measure audible radius for each observation one could construct a greatly improved index. This would seem worthy of investigation. On the other hand, no supplementary observation would seem to bear on the question of incomplete sight counts except comparative counts for two observers. This is of the same nature as the bird dog problem discussed in the section devoted to Frye's method of quail census.

Most of the published studies of relationship of indices to population abundance and exogenous variables have been of the nature of definition and evaluation of a general relationship, the results of which would then be applied to the index wherever run. Although this application has obvious utility, it would seem likely that use of the double sampling technique would be far more satisfactory. For example, Lowe's (1956) techniques could be applied in a double sample as follows. (See Table 21.3.) Conduct a call count of doves in the usual manner. Then select one of the stations in some probability sampling manner (perhaps with probability proportional to the sunrise equivalent count for the station). Then survey the 150 acres defined in a circle about the selected station for nests. Then let

$$t = (\Sigma x_i) \left(\frac{y_s}{x_s}\right)$$

where t = the index for the route,
Σx_i = sum of sunrise equivalent calls over the stations in the route,
y_s = number of nests in the 150 acres around the selected station,
x_s = the sunrise equivalent calls for the selected station.

Table 21.3. Relationship between breeding density and call-index (average number of doves calling per station) on a call-count route (Lowe 1956).

| Year | Breeding pairs per 150 acres | May-June call index | | Pairs per calling dove |
		Number of counts	Av. calls per station	
1951	4	17	2.60	1.54
1952	3	8	1.28	2.19
	2	8	1.47	1.36
	3	8	2.00	1.50
	2	8	0.50	4.00
	0	8	0.50	0.00
Mean - 1952	2.0		1.15	1.81
1954	4	6	1.67	2.39
	2.5	6	1.33	1.88
	3	8	2.67	1.12
	4	8	2.00	2.00
	5.5	8	2.33	2.36
	1.5	8	1.00	1.50
	2.5	8	0.33	0.76
Mean - 1954	3.3		1.62	1.72
Average of all data	2.85		2.28	1.74

This is a form of the conventional double sample with ratio estimation, and other forms could easily be chosen. The point is that calibration can be made in terms of measurements that are made under the identical conditions of those of the index, so that the observer is freed of assumptions regarding applicability of, say, Lowe's data to call counts in Florida in 1960.

METHODS INVOLVING DIRECT COUNTS OF ANIMALS

The most direct way to determine the number of animals in a population is to count them all. Such a complete count is called a census, and censuses are used rather more widely than one might suspect at first thought. For convenience, two types of census are recognized, (1) *spatial* censuses and (2) *temporal censuses*. The essential statistical features of these are identical.

A *spatial census* is one in which a count is made of all the animals in a *specified area* at a specified "point" in time. If the population is closed—if there is no recruitment or loss to the population over a period of time—then this period is to all practical purposes a "point" in time, at least so far as the *census* is concerned. The count is "instantaneous" in its properties if not in its execution.

The Territory-Mapping Method

A common spatial census is the territory-mapping method. This method is commonly used for fall census of bobwhite quail in habitats such that coveys exhibit well defined territories (c.f., Rosene 1957, Mosby and Overton 1950). The general method requires that the area of interest be surveyed repeatedly until the distinct coveys are identified and counted. Judgment decisions are required, particularly in the case of coveys appearing or disappearing suddenly in the middle of the census period and in the case of coveys which have part of their territory on and part off the area. Coveys may be located and counted in many ways: by location with trained dogs, by tracks in snow, or by listening for morning or noon calls.

As used here, "territory" might be considered virtually synonymous with "home range," in that no implication is made of territory defense in the sense of belligerent behavior. However, the method requires that an individual, or group of individuals, exhibit a spatial identifiability which may be considered an ecological territoriality, if not a behavorial one. The concept is quite definitely not that of "home range," though it is not quite that of "territory," either, in some cases.

The territory-mapping technique has also been used on a number of other species, many during breeding season when one or the other sex may have a well-defined territory. Examples are given by Lack (1954) and Mayfield (1953) for song birds and Odum and Kuenzler (1955) have treated the problems of estimating size of territory in birds. Graham (1940) suggested an intersection method for locating drumming grouse. Mosby and Handley (1943) used the territory-mapping method to census turkeys over the entire state of Virginia. Radio-telemetry studies have advanced the precision of such mapping studies. (See Chapter 9.)

Drive Counts

Drive-counts are frequently possible for populations such as deer (Morse 1943). The technique is variable, usually has modification dictated by the particular area, but will be something as follows. Two crews of observers are required, one crew to drive the area, the other to be stationed around the area to monitor deer leaving or entering the area. A suitable area is one that can be monitored on the boundaries. Well defined and cleared boundaries are desirable, and it is essential that it be possible for the monitors to observe *clearly* the boundary at least as far as the next observer. All monitors will look in the same direction (e.g., clockwise) around the boundary, and each will count all deer leaving the area, and all entering the area between his post and the next observer. The monitor counts are discontinued as soon as the drive crew has passed. This ensures one and only one observer tallying each animal crossing the line. A common variant: if the drive area is surrounded by a dirt road, one can substitute a track count for the monitors (Tyson 1959).

The drive crew, spaced at most a few yards apart, lines up along one side of the area. The drivers then move through the area, keeping in line and in close spacing. Each individual tallies the animals passing through the line only to his right (or left) between himself and the next person in line.

The total number of animals is then calculated as the sum of the animals leaving the area ahead of the drive crew plus the sum of the animals passing back through the drive line. The sum of animals entering the area ahead of the drive crew and the sum of animals passing forward through the drive line are then subtracted from the total count to yield the net count of deer.

Tyson (1952) presented data from drive counts on Eglin field in which a strong positive relationship existed between the number of drivers and the density of deer seen. The implication is that many deer were missed when the drive lines were thin, although details of the drives are not sufficiently complete for the relation to be properly evaluated.

In a number of other situations, total counts may be made, such that no essential difference exists between the counts and a drive census, except that the structuring of the observation is less complex. These methods may be called *"sweep"* methods. In essence, the observer passes through the area, carrying an imaginary *drive line, "sweeping"* the area for animals of the specified

418

population. Ideally, this constitutes an instantaneous count, though it may sometimes be necessary to adjust counts for animals moving ahead of or behind the observer. Examples of this method are: airplane counts of waterfowl (Chattin 1952, Stewart et al. 1958), airplane counts of big game (Evans et al. 1966, Siniff and Skoog 1964). "Drive" counts of pheasants with one to three men (Trippensee 1948) are of this type, as are "complete" counts of prairie chickens on booming grounds (Lehman 1941) and elk in concentration areas (Cahalane 1938), to name a very few of a multitude of applications and references. A variation is to photograph a concentration of animals for later counting (Fig. 21.3).

Temporal Censuses

A *temporal* census is one in which the spatial dimension is a "point" and the count is made of all animals passing the point during some interval of time. This technique is adapted to certain cases in which migrating animals use a well-defined route, as for example, the Interstate deer herd (Interstate Deer Herd Committee 1950:29) which summers in Oregon and winters in California. This herd is censused by a track count conducted on roads crossing the migration route, the "census" figures being the difference between northbound and southbound tracks. The data in Table 21.4 illustrate the difference in migration times among years. As the census roads do not completely cover the migration route, this count is somewhat less complete than it might appear.

Other common examples of temporal censuses are, counts of crows and herons entering roosts and of wood ducks entering roost ponds. Anadromous fish are regularly counted as they pass through fish ladders on many west coast dams.

Extermination or Total Capture

Probably the first and most accurate deer census for a large area in America was obtained in the removal of 22,362 deer from 1,142 square miles of the Stanislaus National Forest in California during the hoof-and-mouth disease control program of 1921-23 (A. Leopold 1933). In Europe, the total extermination of deer herds on shooting preserves to eliminate old stock before introducing "fresh" deer is sometimes practiced. In such programs a rather complete census of the herd is obtained. It is obvious that the total extermination of wild animals is both costly and time

Fig. 21.3. Flock of greater snow geese off Atlantic Coast near Back Bay, Virginia. A total of 24,263 geese were counted from this aerial photograph. Each dot was marked with a pin hole while tallying with an automatic counter (photo courtesy of Ernest Atkinson).

consuming. Furthermore, this method of obtaining a census would have a rather restricted use, mainly in detailed research programs.

Even where the population can be trapped rather easily only the catchable part of the population can be dealt with. For example, it is usually possible to capture a high proportion of woodland deer mice (Stickel 1946) yet this catch does not include young mice still in the nest. In other cases particular individuals may avoid traps, as Geis (1955) found for rabbits. Hence these counts refer to the "trapable" part of the population and any population study should indicate what is known, if anything, about the "non-trapable" individuals. Species may differ greatly in trapability. For example, Beer et al. (1954) found that most of the deer mice were caught in 2 days, but that some meadow voles avoided traps for 15 days. Stickel

Table 21.4. Track count of Interstate Deer Herd on northward migration in 1947 and 1948 (Interstate Deer Herd Committee 1950).

Date of track count	Number of deer migrating north	
	1947	1948
April 10	2,152	
15	588	36
20	403	53
25	172	162
30		21
May 5		369
10		392
15		878
25		653
Totals	3,315	2,564

(1946) caught, marked, and released deer mice in an area and then set snap-traps. All of the mice captured in the snap-traps were marked, indicating that she had captured all individuals except: (1) those not old enough to be caught and (2) those that avoided both live- and snap-traps. Normally these exceptions are immaterial to the problem under investigation.

Comments on Reliability of Censuses

If a count is purported to be a total census, then there is no question of variance or confidence limits in the sampling sense. However, it is apparent that with few exceptions such a census will have errors of one sort or another. Therefore, a census datum should be accompanied by a critical evaluation of its accuracy and by an explicit statement of the constraints and definitions under which it was collected.

Sample Censuses

A sample census is defined to be a census conducted on a part (sample) of the spatial dimension or temporal dimension over which the census is defined, and such that a statistical estimate of the complete census counts may be made from the sample. The material of the section devoted to the basic sampling methods applies directly. Suppose the Universe is the area over which a census is desired. Then divide this into sampling units of smaller areas. Now, if each of the smaller areas were censused, and the census datum on the ith area were y_i, then the total over all sampling units is equal to the total over the Universe,

$$T = \Sigma y_i \ .$$

If a sample of the sampling units is taken in some way, and census made in each of the *sampled* units, T can be *estimated* from the sample values in a manner according to the method of selecting the sample. For example, if a simple random sample is taken, then the most common estimator of T is,

$$\hat{T} = N\bar{y},$$

and confidence limits for $\hat{T}$ are obtained as in the previous section.

Siniff and Skoog (1964) gave an excellent example of application of random sampling methodology to a stratified sample census of caribou, including the use of the technique of optimum allocation of effort among strata, and Tyson (1952) presented an estimate of total deer from drive counts on a sample of plots. Kozicky et al. (1956) present a stratified random sample census for quail in Iowa.

Jumber et al. (1957) reported a sample census of mourning doves. The number of dove nests and the number of young produced were estimated by expansion of the census of sample areas.

Sample strip aerial counts of nesting waterfowl provide the standard aerial nesting inventory data for North America (Anon. 1956, Stewart et al. 1958) and strip aerial censuses are used for a number of other species. Typically, the strip counts are made so as to count the animals in a strip of fixed width. The strips are selected in some systematic manner and the estimate is usually of the form

$$\hat{T} = At$$

where A = area of interest/area of sample.

The annual waterfowl breeding ground survey is worthy of some elaboration. A description of survey procedures can be found in Stewart, et al. (1958). Aerial transects are conducted at 100 to 200 feet and waterfowl are counted, by species, within a 1/8th mile strip on each side of the plane. Transects are broken into 18-mile segments to provide an estimate of variability.

Two major sources of error are recognized. The strip width must be visually estimated and this is difficult to do accurately. Second, many waterfowl will not be seen due to vegetation and other causes. The latter problem has been studied (c.f., Diem and Lu 1960 and Martinson and Kaczynski 1967) and a method of calibration for unobserved birds devised. Air-ground calibration counts are now a standard feature of the inventories. See Table 21.2 and Table 21.5.

In summary, it should be apparent that the sample census is a direct application of a total census to sample areas, and that the wildlifer needs only to know census techniques and sampling principles in order to successfully use a sample census. Several precautions are in order. In dividing the Universe into sampling units, the population is partitioned into sub-populations. It is important to recognize that this accentuates any difficulty of definition at the edges of the plots. It must also be kept in mind that all of the requirements of censuses are still relevant.

Pseudo Sample Censuses

A number of techniques (e.g., the King grouse census) have been developed which are really sample censuses over portions of the Universe, which portions have not been delinated. These techniques are directly comparable to the variable plot vegetation sampling techniques which have come into widespread use over the past 20 years, but have one important difference. It is possible in the vegetation sampling to deduce the selection probability from the sampling scheme, and so obtain probability estimators. In animal populations, this has not successfully been done, except in terms of simplifying assumptions.

Nevertheless, the pseudo sample census is an important class of estimation techniques, which is capable of producing useful estimates, even though the statistical properties have not been properly evaluated.

It must be emphasized that the distinction between these methods and the true sample censuses is only that appropriate expansion factors are not specified by the sampling procedure, but rather must be estimated from the field data, or modeled. All considerations of representativeness of the population by the sample are still in effect.

THE KING METHOD, WITH VARIATIONS

The classical pseudo sample census is the *King strip census.* The appeal of the method is the direct simplicity of application. One walks along a "census line," (usually a blazed permanent trail through the area of interest) and measures the distance to each animal (or group of animals) observed. Then the "effective width" of the strip (i.e., the sample size) is calculated as some function of the observed distances. Principal variants involve differences in the definition of the distance (from observer to the observation, e.g., the grouse, or perpendicularly from the observation to the line) and differences in the method of calculation of the effective width of strip from the measurements. The reader will find the paper by Hayne (1949) of particular interest. The present treatment essentially follows his.

An idealized model can be constructed as follows. Let the observer's path be *representative* according to whatever criteria apply. That is, observations along the route can be expanded to inferences about an area of interest. Suppose then that the path leads through some spatial distribution of animals that do not avoid the observer, but rather remain hidden until some instant at which they flush or otherwise can be observed. Further, suppose that their subsequent movements do not confuse subsequent observations. Fig. 21.4 will illustrate this situation, and provide an experiment which will verify the formulae.

An experiment: In the above figure, mark off vertical transects at, say, 1/20th of an inch in-

Table 21.5. Example of index calibration. Adjusted waterfowl breeding population counts derived from a species-visibility index and an aerial-ground index, Parklands, Alberta, Canada (from Diem and Lu 1960).

Time periods[1]	Species	No. of ducks observed	Species-visibility index[2]	Corrected total	Aerial-ground index[3]	Corrected total
Year with trees bare						
6 a.m.	Mallard	2,790			1.79	4,833
to	Bw. teal	960			2.00	1,920
9 a.m.	Scaup	1,300			2.27	2,951
9 a.m.	Mallard	2,400			1.85	4,440
to	Bw. teal	380			5.88	2,234
12 p.m.	Scaup	1,000			1.78	1,780
	Mallard	5,100	1.78	9,078		9,273
Total	Bw. teal	1,340	3.75	5,025		4,154
	Scaup	2,300	1.95	4,485		4,731
Year with leaved trees						
6 a.m.	Mallard	1,600			1.64	2,624
to	Bw. teal	300			13.18	3,954
9 a.m.	Scaup	800			1.96	1,568
9 a.m.	Mallard	1,100			3.45	3,795
to	Bw. teal	500			5.55	2,775
12 p.m.	Scaup	900			1.82	1,638
	Mallard	2,700	1.78	4,806		6,419
Total	Bw. teal	800	3.75	3,000		6,729
	Scaup	1,700	1.95	3,315		3,206

[1] Aerial-ground index is based on aerial flights at 8 a.m. and 11 a.m.
[2] Taken from Smith (1956).
[3] Derived by dividing the number of ducks counted on the ground by the number of ducks counted in the aerial census.

tervals, and apply the formula to the results of each transect. An animal is seen when the transect intersects its circle. Average all of the estimates. The "true" population density is 1.5 animals per square inch. The average of all estimates should be close to this number. (All units must be inches in the example.)

Derivation of the formula: It is assumed that the jth animal, when in its *present* position, will flush whenever the observer approaches within d_j feet. That is, the probability of observing the jth animal is proprotional to d_j. (To see this, consider Fig. 21.4.) Project a circle onto one side of the rectangle. Then, the jth circle projects into a line segment of length $2d_j$. The probability that the starting point, selected at random along the side, will lie in any line segment is proportional to the length of the segment. This is the probability of starting at a point such that the animal will be seen.) If sampling is from a convenient rectangle, as in the figure, it is possible to calculate the probability, $p_j = 2d_j/D$, where D is the distance of the side. Then, a general statistical estimation formula is evoked (see the section, "Methods of Statistical Estimation").

$$\hat{N} = \sum_{obs} 1/p_j = (D/2) \sum_{obs} 1/d_j \ ,$$

yielding an estimate of total number of animals on the plot. If this is divided by the *area* of the study plot, an estimate of density is obtained,

$$\frac{\hat{N}}{A} = \frac{Dc}{2A} \sum_{obs} 1/d_j = \frac{c}{2L} \sum_{obs} 1/d_j \ , \quad (7)$$

422

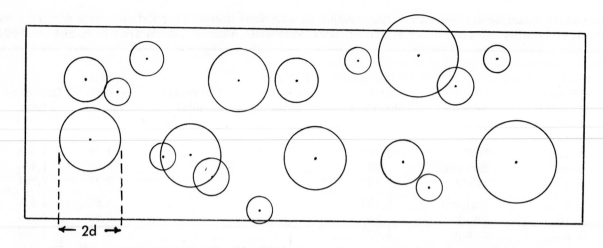

Fig. 21.4. A sampling experiment to illustrate Hayne's modification of the King method. Conduct a random sample of this population by selecting a point at random along the horizontal axis. Then, project a vertical "transect" from this point. The animals "seen" are those whose circle intersects the transect. Then apply the formula (7) either to a single transect or to the pooled observation from several transects. (Note: an animal should be counted each time observed!)

which is identical to Hayne's formula for density (A = DL, c is a conversion factor for units, and L is the length of the plot. In general, L is the length of the transect).

Formulae exist for direct estimates of the variance of this estimator, but these are not likely to be of value. The following approach is recommended. If a number, say n, of random transects are chosen, then the appropriate variance is obtained by estimating the density (or total population) from *each transect,* and then calculating the variance among these estimates. The overall estimate of density can best be made as a simple mean of the several estimates. This *replicated sample* approach is recommended a number of times in this chapter and treated in general in the section with that title.

Some complications are apparent. In many cases the assumption will be questioned that an animal will flush at the same distance if it is approached (1) directly or (2) along a path that will by-pass it. That is, wildlifers would be happier with a flush model like:

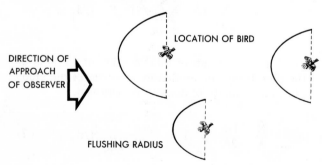

Flush radius

The solid lines denote the position of the observer at which time the animal is observed. Since this model is direction specific, the flush radius is defined only towards the direction of approach. Here, the probabilities of observing the animals are proportional to the widest part of the pattern (generally proportional to the length of the projection of the pattern on the perpendicular to the line of travel). However, the length of this projection cannot be inferred from the observations without explicitly specifying the form of the flush pattern. Logically, an explicit non-circular flush pattern is no less defensible than a circular one, but there is a natural reluctance to make assumptions of this kind and no examples are known to the writers in which such a pattern is modeled. (As this chapter goes to press, Gates et al. 1968, proposed a statistical distribution for flush distances in a paper dealing with modification of the King method. This amounts to another way of solving the modeling problem, and their results also relate to the later discussion of Frye's modification of the King method.) See Table 21.6.

In any event, if some non-circular pattern is assumed, it will be necessary to measure not only distance, d_j, from observer to flush point, but also the angle, θ_j, of the observation from the line (or distance, d_j, plus perpendicular distance, h_j, from flush point to the line). Then $p_j = g(d_j, \theta_j)$ or $p_j = g(d_j, h_j)$ will be calculated, where the form of the function g is determined by the assumed form of the flush pattern. Then plug p_j into the formula for $\hat{N}$ (Formula 1).

Further, if θ or h is measured, it is possible to test the assumption that the pattern is circular. Hayne (1949) suggests a simple test using $\sin \theta$ (or h/d), and points out that this statistic has an expected average of 0.5 if the assumption of circularity holds.

Some further complications will appear if an experiment is conducted as suggested with Fig. 21.4, particularly with regard to edge effect. The animal whose circle extends over the edge does not project into a full 2d length segment on the vertical axis, but poses no problem on the horizontal axis. Again, it is apparent that one must make special assumptions or (alternatively) rules must be made to properly account for such effects. Several other apparent difficulties are discussed in the literature cited.

FRYE'S STRIP CENSUS

O. E. Frye devised a method of quail censusing which is superficially quite similar to King's method, but which on examination proves to have very different properties. The method is not well documented in the literature so that the present treatment is derived from discussion with Frye and from Overton's personal experience with the method between 1950 and 1955 (Overton 1953).

Quail are censused along permanent transects using trained dogs. The perpendicular distance h between point of location and the transect is recorded, as well as number of birds in the covey. Frye's formula was simple. He calculated the average distance $\bar{h}$, and the number t of quail found *within* this average distance and estimated the total population as

$$\hat{T} = \frac{CA}{2L\bar{h}} t \qquad (8)$$

where again C is a correction factor for units of measurement,

A is the acreage of the study area, and L is the length of transect.

Frye recognized that this formula underestimated the population, but used it as an indicator of trend as well as a minimal estimate. During this same period, Overton (1953) used the same formula with t defined as the total number of birds observed, within and outside the strip, in an attempt to more closely estimate the actual population level. Empirical evaluation indicated that the general level was approximately correct, but that abberations in the collection (for example, performance of the dogs) had an effect on the estimates that was not accounted for.

An attempt to derive a theory for this method is informative. An assumption is made that a covey h yards from the transect has probability $p = p(h)$ of being located. Then, by the general theorem of probability sampling,

$$t = \Sigma y_i / p_i \ ,$$

summation over all observed coveys, where y is the number of birds in the ith covey, is an unbiased estimate of the total number of birds in those coveys such that $p > 0$. Given any particular rule, $p(h)$, it is possible to calculate t as well as

Table 21.6. Testing of Hayne's and King's census methods using 200 burlap sacks and a theoretical sight distance (Robinette et al. 1956).

Survey number	Population Estimated by	
	Hayne's method	King's method
1	292	156
2	252	150
3	210	152
4	231	147
Mean	246	154
Departure from 200 in percent	+23	-23
Confidence limits	191-302	145-157

424

the area in the "sample." For example, hypothesize that

p = 1 if h is between 0 and 10,

p = (200-h)/190 if h is between 10 and 200,

p = 0 if h is greater than 200.

Then t can be calculated by the formula and $\hat{T}$ by the general theorem,

$$\hat{T} = \frac{CAt}{2L(200)} \ ,$$

since the "width" of strip represented by t is the total width such that p > 0, i.e., 2(200). Overton (1954) attempted to construct estimates of p from the field data with the disappointing result that the estimates of T were based *only* on the density of birds in a narrow strip upon which it was *assumed* that all birds were found. That is, he estimated the probability of observing a covey in, say, the 50-60 yard strip as the number of coveys found at that distance divided by the number of coveys found within 10 yards of the line. This works, but the resultant estimator is based only on observations within 10 yards of the line.

Further, the p-curve is obviously a function of dog activity and hence varies from dog to dog, which fact prevents the use of "standard" curves. It is necessary to calculate the appropriate curves for each set of data. The conclusion is inescapable. If one wishes to use this technique to obtain a good estimate of quail density (or total numbers), it is necessary to use only those observations lying within a strip on which one is "sure" that all of the quail have been located. It follows that the optimum field strategy is to attempt to hold the dogs on the widest strip narrow enough so that one is sure all birds are found.

In field application several complications exist. It is difficult to get dogs to work properly in the corner of a strip when the transect corners. More importantly, it is very difficult to devise an objective determination of the exact spot "occupied" by a covey. Many coveys will flush over a wide range or will run for a considerable distance before holding or flushing. Ideally, the "location" should be determined at that point at which the covey's activity was first disturbed by dogs or handler, but this is impractical and some compromise is indicated.

Eberhardt (1968) admonishes *against* a solution such as suggested above, regarding restriction of the strip. It is agreed that whenever possible the observational operations should be modeled to allow use of all obtainable data. The above example is considered an exception, caused by the difficulty in standardizing the bird dogs.

TIME-AREA COUNTS

Goodrum (1940) appears to have been the first to use squirrel time-area counts. The method is clearly related to the King method and is a variant of the squirrel time count index. Although it has the formal structure of a pseudo sample census, it should be treated as an index.

The observer selects a point in squirrel woods, sits down and counts squirrels for 30 min. The distance to the farthest squirrel seen defines the "area" of the sample. Then squirrels seen per 100 acres is calculated on a cumulative daily basis and the census is stopped when the index ceases to fluctuate (Uhlig 1956). Uhlig advises that counts should be made between 6 and 9 a.m.; other observers sometimes utilize afternoon counts as well.

This technique yields a good index to squirrel populations, but requires some additional standardization. For example, an objective method must be chosen by which to determine the "location" of a squirrel, and to decide whether a "new" squirrel should be tallied or identified with one already tallied. Uhlig advises that four or five men working for a month can obtain reliable estimates for a 10,000 acre area.

Roadside Counts

Roadside counts have long been a standard procedure for obtaining trend indices in upland game. In this method, country roads are traveled for the specific purpose of counting the numbers of individuals of the species being censused which are then related to the number of miles traveled. Thus, in the case of rabbits, if a 20-mile census-route was driven, and 10 rabbits seen, the census-index would be given as 0.5 rabbits per mile. Roadside censuses are used widely in the midwestern states to census both rabbits and pheasants. Some states secure the cooperation of rural mail carriers to obtain estimates of the abundance of their principal game species (Greeley et al. 1962).

The advantages of this method are obvious. Large areas are quickly and easily traversed in the comfort of an automobile. Unfortunately, the factors affecting the roadside census are so many and important (Newman 1959) that investigators who ignore them are obtaining useless information. Factors other than abundance that determine the numbers of animals seen during a census are: (1) activity of the animals as affected by hour of day, food supply, and weather, or (2) condition of roadside cover. Rabbits regulate their activity according to standard time, having an evening and an early morning peak of activity which is almost completely unrelated to sunrise or sunset (Lord 1959). Pheasants on the other hand are regulated by the time of sunrise and have an early morning peak in their activity. There are likewise seasonal changes in the amount of activity by rabbits (and presumably other species) which has an important effect on the roadside-census results. In addition there are seasons when roadsides are used as cover by animals. During the winter in the midwestern states, pheasants, rabbits, and quail frequently take advantage of the vegetative cover associated with the roads in this intensively cultivated region.

Daily weather changes have an effect on animal activity which is not yet clearly known. It is apparent that periods of intense cold will inhibit the activity of animals. Also, rain or snow storms interfere with the vision of the observer; therefore, investigators must avoid such unusual weather conditions. The condition of the roadside vegetative cover has an important effect on the visibility of game. The tall vegetation of late summer seriously impedes observations while the snow cover of late winter enhances them.

It would appear that the strong influence of so many factors on the roadside census would reduce its value. However, ways are available to circumvent most of these factors, although it should be mentioned that use of these ways increases the work required to perform the census. The confusing effects of seasonal changes in activity may readily be avoided by comparing only those censuses made during some given month. A census made in March should never be compared with one made in August because the change in activity may have a greater effect on the census results than the shift in the abundance of the animals. The effects of weather on the roadside-census results may be reduced by avoiding unusual weather conditions and by performing the total census over a period of many days during the month. The technique of calibration (as discussed in the section, "Statistical Properties of Indices") can also be employed to make indices more comparable and reduce the effect of environmental changes.

Dasmann and Taber (1956) present a detailed discussion of seasonal variation in habits and visibility of sex and age classes of black-tailed deer. Such information is very valuable in planning and interpreting index counts.

Howell (1951) combined features of several methods to develop a roadside estimate of considerable promise for birds. He determined the absolute number of birds in small areas and compared these numbers with the number seen on a routine roadside trip through the area. He calculated a measure of conspicuousness of each species by determining the ratio of those seen on the roadside count to the absolute number along the road. For example, if he saw 3 robins along a road where he knew from territorial counts that there were 10 robins, then he calculated the index of conspicuousness as 0.3. If this number is interpreted as the estimated probability of observing a robin, then the general theorem can be applied in obtaining an estimate from a count of robins on another route. Thus, if 6 robins are counted, under similar conditions, the estimate would be

$$\hat{N} = 6/0.3 = 20 \ .$$

Hewitt (1967) reported a roadside count of redwing blackbirds in which he recorded the location of singing males. On a subsequent count he recorded the proportion of these males again seen, by which proportion he estimated the probability of observing a male on the second count. The resultant estimate,

$$\hat{N} = n/\hat{p}$$

is identical in structure to a Lincoln Index. He extended the idea to several successive counts along the transect, obtaining a Schnabel estimate of N.

It is readily recognized that spotlight counts and horseback or foot counts of big game or upland game are closely related to roadside counts. Therefore, it is not unreasonable to treat them all (along with the King census method) as strip transects. The status of a particular count in the general category actually relates to the interpretive value, or inferential value, of the index. It is frequently a poor assumption that roadsides are typical (and hence representative) of the area in general, so that the index cannot usually be expanded to a population estimate. However, many exceptions to this will be found, as in much of the Florida deer country, or in the cut over Coast Range of Oregon.

Many state game departments (e.g., Oregon) use indices such as horseback counts of deer and elk and spotlight counts of deer as regular trend indices. The severe limitations of these indices are generally recognized. In the Douglas fir country, for example, population level and visibility both vary with time elapsed since logging, so that the characteristics of the index routes change from year to year. Nevertheless, useful management data are obtained (c.f., Annual Game Report, Oregon State Game Commission, Portland). An attempt is currently being made to classify the spotlight routes by relevant habitat features so as to adjust the annual index for route changes. (Pers. communication, Francis Ives, Corvallis, Oregon.)

The roadside count was a standard feature of the Southeastern Dove Study (Southeastern Assoc. 1957), both as uncontrolled counts (total tally of doves against total miles driven by biologists and game wardens) and as controlled counts during which specific routes were driven at specified times for the express purpose of counting doves.

Miscellaneous Methods

THE METHOD OF BOUNDED COUNTS

Robson and Whitlock (1964) have devised an estimation procedure which utilizes a non-parametric statistical model. The sampling situation is as follows. One makes a series of counts, $n_1, n_2, \ldots, n_k$ of animals from a population, such that at any one counting instance, there is a positive probability that all animals might be seen. (This occurrence might be *extremely* unlikely, but nevertheless *could* happen.) Then the maximum likelihood estimator for the total number, N, is given by the highest count of all counts made,

$$\hat{N}_0 = \max n_i \; .$$

It is obvious that $\hat{N}_0$ is biased, as max n_i will always be equal to or below N, but it is also obvious that $\hat{N}_0$ is consistent. Here use is made of a theorem by Quenouilli (1956) which defines an estimator constructed by a process called (by others) *jackknifing* which has a substantially reduced bias. Applying this theorem to the present problem, let

n_k be the largest value of n_i and

n_{k-1} be the next largest value.

Then

$$\hat{N}_1 = 2n_k - n_{k-1} \qquad (9)$$

is unbiased to order $1/k^2$. Further, an approximate upper confidence limit at $100(1-\alpha)\%$ is given by,

$$N_U = n_k + \left(\frac{1-\alpha}{\alpha}\right)(n_k - n_{k-1}) \; . \qquad (10)$$

So far as is known, this method has not been applied to numbers of game species, but it would seem to apply to several published instances. Consider for example the brown bear survey reported by Erickson and Siniff (1963). The problem is an aerial survey of brown bears along a series of streams during a salmon run. Counts were made three times on each of 9 days between July 31 and August 16, inclusive. To fit the model, it is necessary to hypothesize that it is possible, even if very unlikely, that one *could* count all of the bears in the population being sampled on some lucky day. The observed counts are (94, 67, *118*, 81, 16, 34, 62, 40, 91, 81, 43, 95, 65, 44, *113*, 86, 48, 70, 54, 29, 76, 54, 30, 72, 61, 18, 76). Then

$$\hat{N} = 236 - 113 = 123$$

and

$$N_U = 118 + \left(\frac{0.95}{0.05}\right)(5) = 118 + 19(5) = 213$$

$$N_L = 118 \; .$$

It is apparent from Erickson and Siniff's discussion of the counting technique that modification could be made in the counts to better conform to the bounded count method. However, it would appear that this would be an ideal sampling situation for fulfillment of the assumptions of the method, unless there is some behavioral trait which affects presence. For example, if some animals are kept away from the salmon streams while others are feeding, then the assumption can be questioned that it is possible for all to be seen on the same count.

HANSON'S METHOD

Hanson and Chapman (unpub. ms) have suggested a method of population estimation based on incomplete counts in which they assume that the observations (counts) are binomially distributed. A derivation of their method follows.

Given that a "count" of animals has been made in a certain population, then N can be estimated (see Formula (1), the general probability estimator),

$$\hat{N} = \Sigma \, 1/p_i$$

where p_i is the probability of observing (counting) the ith animal and where summation is over all observed animals. If $p_i = p$ for all i, then this can be written as

$$\hat{N} = \frac{x}{p} \, ,$$

where x is the number of animals counted. Now, given n counts of animals in this population, an average of all the possible estimates can be written as

$$\hat{N} = \frac{1}{p} \frac{1}{n} \, \Sigma x = \frac{\overline{x}}{p} \, ,$$

all of which follows conventional sampling theory.

The essence of Hanson and Chapman's idea is that if the assumption is made that the x_j are binomially distributed, then p can be estimated as

$$\hat{p} = \frac{\overline{x} - s^2}{\overline{x}} \, ,$$

where s^2 is the usual sample variance among the x_i, so that

$$\hat{N} = \frac{\overline{x}^2}{\overline{x} - s^2} \qquad (11)$$

Although the model derivation is a bit vague, this idea has considerable intuitive appeal. It would appear likely that many situations exist in which one can *model* the counts so that one can estimate p.

METHODS INVOLVING ANIMAL SIGNS AND RELATED OBJECTS

A great many instances are reported in the literature in which some sign or evidence of presence of animals is measured. A cursory review of state game agency programs indicates that these are perhaps the most widely used means of keeping tabs on game populations. The variety

of methods is overwhelming. Consider call counts of doves, quail, pheasants, and other upland game birds; track counts of deer; nest counts of squirrels; pellet counts of deer, rabbits, and other mammals; dropping counts of grouse; counts of excavations, lodges, or dens; or any other physical or auditory evidence of presence of animals.

The way in which these methods are utilized is also highly variable. On the one extreme, signs or lack of signs can be used to indicate presence or absence of a species in an area. On the other, an attempt may be made to calibrate the index so as to yield an estimate of numbers of the species. However, by far the greatest use of these counts is intermediate: as an indication of trend; as an index to relative abundance. In this respect, counts of signs are identical to index counts of animals, so far as their limitations and statistical properties.

The Auditory Index

Counts of auditory signs of animal presence have a long history. Stoddard (1931) reported the use of counts of whistling cocks as a technique for measuring abundance of quail and a statewide standardized quail call index was started in Missouri in 1939 (Bennitt 1951). McClure (1939) described in detail a census method for mourning doves based on counts of calling doves and (1944 and 1945) a crowing cock census for pheasants. Kimball (1949) also reported a roadside pheasant crowing census. In 1951 standardized dove call count routes were established under the Southeastern Cooperative Dove Study (Southeastern Assoc. 1957). Drumming counts of ruffed grouse were reported by Petraborg et al. (1953) and Hungerford (1953). Auditory counts have also been reported for woodcock (Kozicky et al. 1954), Gambel quail (Smith and Gallizioli 1965) chukar partridge (Williams 1961) and other species as turkeys and squirrels.

Foote et al. (1958) described a randomized dove call count census featuring randomly selected routes within ecological strata of seven southeastern states. This design forms the basis for the current management routes (Wight and Baysinger 1963) and culminates several years of investigation of the call index (Southeastern Assoc. 1957). The standardized route consists of 20 stations at 1 mile intervals, with counts beginning 30 min. before sunrise. Calling doves are counted for 3 min. at each of the 20 stations with 3 min. allowed for travel between stations. Thus, the total elapsed time for the census is 2 hours, standardizing the

"hour" effect. All counts are run between May 20 and June 10.

Approximately 650 comparable dove call routes are run annually in the 48 states and parts of Canada. Results of these indices are published in the Annual Mourning Dove Status Report, Bureau of Sport Fisheries and Wildlife (See Table 21.7.)

It is generally recognized that auditory activity, like other animal activity, is influenced by time of day, weather conditions, season of the year, and a great many other factors which may or may not be apparent to the investigator. For example, McClure (1939) constructed correction factors for wind, cloud cover, temperature, and time of day in describing a call census for doves and later (1945) presented differences in pheasant crow count indices under variation in time of day, temperature and relative humidity. Bennitt (1951) reported an attempt to calibrate quail call indices for regional effects and for the effects of temperature. He advocated that counts be discontinued if wind rose above Beaufort 3.5 or if rain began, and presented evidence that type of road and cloudiness had no appreciable effect. Kozicky (1952) analyzed the effect of several weather variables on pheasant crowing counts and found significant effects of wind and dew but none for temperature or cloud cover.

The influence of time of day is apparent from all studies and several methods have been proposed to adjust for it. Generally, the most popular solution has been to standardize the counts with respect to the period of the day during which the counts are made. Heath (1961) advocated uniform spacing of stations over the prescribed time even if the number of stations is somewhat smaller than the number accommodated by the allowed time. An alternative solution (equivalent to Heath's if the temporal function is linear) is to adjust each count to the equivalent count at, perhaps, sunrise.

A number of studies have been made of the variability of counts, with evaluation of the contribution of stations, days, observers, and hour of day, in addition to that of weather factors, to variance among observations (McGowen 1953, Carney and Petrides 1957, Kozicky 1952). Several studies have also been made of the behavorial aspects of calling. Cohen et al. (1960) reported statistical evidence that calling activity of individual doves is serially correlated—that calling activity is intermittent and not random. Frankel and Baskett (1961) and Jackson and Baskett (1964) showed that calling activity is related to the formation of the pair bond and to stages of the

Table 21.7. Trends in the Breeding Population Index (mourning doves). This table typifies the routine management data collected on a national basis. The first figure is the adjusted average number of doves heard per route, the second, an index to total population (from Wight and Baysinger 1963. Table 2, in part, Mourning Dove Status Report).

State	1957	1958	1959	1960	1961	1962	1963
Alabama	21.1	23.8	18.7	22.7	20.1	19.5	16.0
	1,078	1,216	955	1,159	1,027	996	817
Arizona	33.1	31.0	33.6	26.3	47.1	32.8	31.2
	3,759	3,521	3,816	2,987	5,350	3,725	3,539
Arkansas	32.6	33.7	30.0	28.0	30.5	16.9	25.8
	1,719	1,777	1,582	1,476	1,608	891	1,360
California	36.7	41.2	55.1	59.5	42.7	48.0	48.0
	5,179	5,814	7,776	8,397	6,026	6,774	6,774
Colorado	57.6	46.4	23.8	34.9	16.8	16.8	12.5
	4,192	3,377	1,732	2,540	1,223	1,223	910
Connecticut	9.0	7.0	6.0	9.6	5.2	5.2	4.5
	35	27	24	38	20	20	17
Delaware	31.0	30.0	54.0	49.0	36.0	44.0	40.0
	61	59	107	97	71	87	79
Florida	13.8	11.0	11.0	12.9	12.0	14.5	12.4
	749	597	597	700	651	787	673
Georgia	21.4	15.9	18.9	24.0	20.4	23.8	20.4
	1,252	930	1,106	1,404	1,194	1,393	1,194

nesting cycle. Also, it is generally accepted that for several species calls are contagious, that the calling of one cock pheasant or one male bobwhite will stimulate another to call. Kimball (1949) recognized that this phenomenon in pheasants may cause the calling index t to increase disproportionately to N.

Underlying all of the studies of variability, effect of weather, and behaviorial aspects of the auditory index is a general awareness that the index must be calibrated to account for these factors. Bennitt (1951) used linear regression to calibrate t with the hunting success of the following season. The relationship was significant but the value of R^2 too small to justify a very great expenditure of money in making the index. Norton et al. (1961) have since shown some errors in Bennitt's calculations, but the conclusions are unchanged. Rosene (1957) also used a linear regression technique to relate number of calling cocks to the number of coveys the following fall. His analysis was also shown by Norton et al. (1961) to be faulty, in that the predictive value of the index was not temporal. That is, Rosene's data do not show that the index can be used to accurately predict temporal changes in the populations. However, they do show that the call index is a good estimator of the population level on an area; spatial predictability is good, so that one can infer that the call index reflects general population level.

Smith and Gallizioli (1965) take advantage of the lessons learned from reappraisal of Bennitt's and Rosene's data and present good evidence (Fig. 21.5) that the spring call index is a useful predictor of temporal variation in hunting success of Gambel quail in Arizona. They point out that the index appears to reflect both spring population level and breeding success, so that it is of greater management value than is a simple index to the spring population level.

The above studies relate to predictability of the fall population. The question of how well the call index relates to the level of the breeding population has been studied by Lowe (1956) and Dorney et al. (1958). In the latter study, for ruffed grouse, one area, 3 years, there was insufficient variability for a meaningful analysis

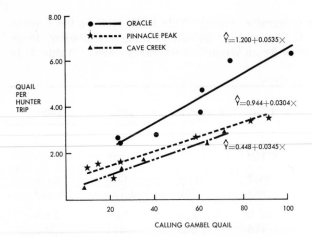

Fig. 21.5. Relationship between calling cock Gambel quail and hunter success (from Smith and Gallizioli 1965 with permission).

(N = 25, 25, 30; t = 58, 71, 66; A = 0.43, 0.35, 0.45). Lowe's data, average density of pairs of doves for several areas on 3 years (N = 4, 2.0, 2.85; t = 2.60, 1.15, 2.28; A = 1.54, 1.74, 1.25), are a little more convincing.

The current status, then, of the auditory index is that it is a widely used management index for quail, doves, pheasants, and woodcock. In general, the index is standardized as to selection of route, starting and stopping time, number of stations per route and season of the year at which the index is determined. Some procedures attempt to adjust the index for effect of weather. Some are used as indices of spring population levels and others have been studied as predictors of fall populations or hunting success. With a few exceptions, it is judged that the potential value of this index has not been realized, that the call index is potentially much more valuable than one would infer from the general literature. Further development along the line of Heath (1961) will likely prove rewarding, as will additional development of calibration techniques.

Track Counts

Track counts of a number of species have been used extensively as indices, but the development of an estimator of population numbers requires specific modeling of the relationship between animal numbers and the spatial distribution and abundance of tracks. Tyson (1952, 1959) presented an attempt to model the counts of tracks as a function of numbers of deer and so obtain an estimator of numbers. The following is essentially as reported by him. Assume that:

1. Deer bed in essentially the same place on successive days.
2. Nightly activity is confined to a "range" of travel, D.

Now, imagine a circle of diameter D, measured in miles, say, defined in the middle of homogeneous deer habitat. Let there be N deer bedding in the circle, each of which has produced two tracks on the perimeter of the circle during the preceding night (activity period). This restriction further clarifies the definition of D. The activity of each deer has been idealized and the activity path has been modified into a straight line extending in some arbitrary direction from his bedding spot. Thus, D is half the average linear distance traveled by a deer during the activity period. Note that in this interpretation the assumption that the deer returns to the previous bedding spot is a convenience but is not necessary to the model. For each such track on the circle, there will be a track produced by a deer bedded outside the circle. Therefore, the following quantities can be written:

1. Total tracks = 4N
2. Total deer = N
3. Area of circle = $\pi D^2 / 4$
4. Circumference of circle = πD.

Thus, *tracks per mile* = t = $4N/\pi D$

Deer per square mile = Y = $4N/\pi D^2$ = t/D.   (12)

Now this derivation is not very sophisticated, but the formula seems to have at least approximate validity. Tyson used this formula with D = 1 for the Eglin Field (Florida) deer herd and found reasonably good agreement with drive counts. The method was used fairly widely in Florida, being well adapted to much of the deer habitat there, but satisfactory methods of calculation to account for varying values of D were not devised. Therefore, the net effect of Tyson's efforts was to allow a density interpretation of the index. The idea would seem worthy of further development. Wright (1951) independently developed a similar method, and Sittler (1965) developed a complex model for essentially the same problem.

Pellet Counts

Counts of pellets, droppings and other fecal material have been made for a number of species, including deer and other large ungulates, rabbits (Cochran and Stains 1961), small mammals (Emlen et al. 1957) and in certain cases gallinaceous birds (Dorney 1958, McClure 1945). Many of these applications are related to "presence or absence" interpretation, but there are a number of exceptions in which the counts are used as indices to population level or even calibrated to an estimate of population number.

The most widespread pellet count, and the best documented, is of deer (Bennett, English, and McCain 1940). Generally, the method appears best adapted to areas in which the deer spend the winter in an environment such that preservation of pellet groups is optimal. Attempts to use the pellet index in the Southeast have been notably unsuccessful, primarily due to problems of differential decomposition and disappearance of pellet groups. The variation in dung beetle activity appears to be important in some cases.

The influence of rain on the count of deer pellet groups was studied by Wallmo et al. (1962) who found a correlation between -0.552 and -0.825 for four areas. The writers concluded that, although the idea of a correction factor to account for the influence of weather was attractive, such a correction factor was impractical (impossible) due to the complexity of the process. This conclusion should be viewed skeptically, although their suggestion that pellet indices be made during dry periods is not without merit.

Smith (1964) reported an average of 13.2 groups per day in Utah for deer on a variety of diets, and Rogers et al. (1958) found an average of 15.2 groups per day. The latter authors discuss the apparent reasons for the higher defecation rate in their studies. The value obtained by Rasmussen and Doman (1943) was 12.7 and Eberhardt and Van Etten (1956) reported an identical average, with significant variation due to diet and age of animals. Neff et al. (1965) reported a defecation rate for elk of 12.5 pellet groups per day.

Smith (1964), on several theoretical and practical considerations, recommended a plot size of 100 sq. ft. Eberhardt and Van Etten (1956) reported use of a circular plot of 1/50th acre size. Their evaluation of the errors made in counting groups apparently led to the more detailed study reported by Van Etten and Bennett (1965) which in turn led to a modified plot design, a rectangular 1/50th acre plot, 12 by 72.6 ft., divided in half longitudinally. This appears to have many advantages, and subsequent development of formulae and theory is oriented to this design.

Application of the method is then as follows.

A number, n, of plots are located in such a manner that the study area is adequately represented. Any of the sampling designs might be employed here. Then the number of pellet groups is counted in each plot. Then, let

$$t = \left(\frac{1}{na'}\right) \Sigma y = \frac{1}{a} \Sigma y$$

be the index, where Σy is the sum of groups counted over all n plots, a' is the area of one plot and $a = na'$ is the area of the entire sample. Then t is expressed as pellet groups per unit area.

Typically, t is related to total deer days of use, or to total deer, by a process somewhat as follows (Eberhardt and Van Etten 1956):

1. Assume a defecation rate.
2. Assume a period (e.g., number of days) over which the groups have been deposited.
3. Assume that the observers can correctly locate and identify the groups relevant to the population and study period.

Then, t, divided by the defecation rate, yields deer days utilization per acre for the study period. If the population is assumed constant, division of the latter index by number of days in the period yields the number of deer per acre. It will be apparent that if, for example, the study area is a wintering ground, then deer days utilization is an important parameter and the observer may not even be interested in total number of deer. In other circumstances the total number is of interest.

The question of necessary sample size is also considered by several authors. For convenience, the problem will be considered in the idealized situation in which pellet groups are distributed at random. In this case, the number of groups in a sample of fixed size is a poisson random variable with expectation and variance, am, where a is the area of the sample and m is the density of groups per unit area. Now, if it is specified that a is the area of the combined sample (e.g., for 100, 1/50th acre plots, a = 2) the sample size question can be given one answer for all sized plots as follows.

Let Σy be the number of groups in the combined sample, and

$$t = \frac{1}{a} \Sigma y$$

be the estimated number of pellet groups per

acre, as before. Then,

$$V(t) = \left(\frac{A-a}{A}\right)\frac{m}{a},$$

where the term in parentheses is the finite population correction factor, and where A is the total acreage of the study area. The f.p.c. will usually be close to 1 and can thus be ignored. Then by a series of manipulations like that reported in the sample size discussion of the mark-recapture methods, the following equation can be obtained for the necessary sample size, in total area of sample,

$$a = \frac{\chi^2}{p^2 m}$$

where χ^2 is tabular chi square with 1 degree of freedom and the desired level of probability and where p is the desired precision. For example, specify that it is wished to estimate group density within ±10% with probability 0.95 in a situation in which approximately 70 deer days of use per acre is expected at 13 pellet groups per day. Then p = 0.1, χ^2 = 3.84, m = 70(13) = 910, and the solution is

$$a = \frac{3.84}{(910)(0.01)} = 0.422 \text{ acres.}$$

If the sampling units are 1/50th acre, then (0.422)50 = 21 plots would be required in order to have a total sample of 0.422 acres.

It should be noted that this model specifying random groups has less variance than will be realized under non-random distribution of groups, so that the sample sizes obtained by this method will yield somewhat less precision than desired. It should also be pointed out that problems of adequately representing the study area are not considered and that adequate representation may require far greater sample sizes. However, this would appear to be a reasonably valid rule of thumb, to be modified according to circumstances.

The divided plot reported by Van Etten and Bennett (1965) is very attractive in that it provides a number of ways in which to study and correct the various sources of error reported by those authors and others. Details on the manner in which this plot is used in Michigan are not given; the statement is made that each observer "crosses over and double checks his partner's half-plot." However, a number of techniques could be employed. Robson's method of bounded counts might apply, or a Lincoln Index, if the investigator is concerned with the problem of missed groups. Other techniques can be applied to observations of misclassification.

Miscellaneous Indices

Uhlig (1956) described an index to squirrel abundance based on counts of leaf nests during late summer and early fall. His procedure is interesting in that he constructed an index to the rate at which nests are being built throughout the season in terms of nests built per day. He then presented comparisons of leaf nests in November and December and time area counts in September made on a total of 1,510 1/5th acre plots over 3 years, during which he found ratios of 1.09, 1.09, and 1.10 nests per squirrel. He did not specify how his index rate of nest construction was converted to an index comparable to the November-December total nests, but it is supposed that a simple integration over the period of construction would suffice. It is clear that an index made in November or December is appropriate if the investigator is satisfied with counts that late. The advantage of the leaf nest count is obvious when a comparison is made in the time required for it and the time-area count method.

Uhlig (1956) theorized that (on his study area) the majority of nests are built by juveniles approximately 18-weeks old. It appears from examination of his data that this conclusion is valid only because there are more juveniles than adults. The number of leaf nests is a much better index of total population than of either adults *or* juveniles.

Hay (1958), Table 21.8, presented a number of counts of evidences of presence of beaver, none of which appear to be even fair indicators of the number of beavers per colony. However, he did show exactly one food cache per colony, so that he recommended a census technique based on a count of food caches, this count to be multiplied by the average number of beavers per colony to obtain an estimate of total beaver. As the greatest variation is likely to be in number of colonies, this suggestion appears to have merit.

METHODS INVOLVING MARKED ANIMALS

Perhaps the most important of the family of pseudo-sample methods are the mark-recapture methods. An extremely large number of variants on this basic technique exist, and the literature is

Table 21.8. Number of beavers per colony, size of main lodge, and number of observable constructions, Colorado. From Hay (1958).

Area	Colony number	Number of beavers[1]	Size of main lodge[2]	Number of active lodges[3]	Number of food caches[4]	Number of scent mounds
North Platte	1	10	857.6	2	1	6
	2	7	2618.0	1	1	3
	3	8	390.0	2	1	14
	4	3	354.3	1	1	2
	5	11	906.7	1	1	11
	6	7	2436.0	3	1	6
Lost Creek	1	4	851.0	1	1	0[5]
	2	7	472.5	1	1	0
	3	6	928.0	1	1	0
	4	2	1398.6	1	1	0
Nutras Creek	1	3	249.9	3	1	29
	2	5	252.0	3	1	12
	3	9	1143.8	3	1	34

[1] From dead-trapping, verified observations, and tagging returns.
[2] Maximum length × width × height in feet, expressed as a multiple.
[3] Lodges known to be occupied during the summer.
[4] From ground observations.
[5] Data not available on these colonies.

further complicated by the fact that the mark-recapture technique is usually used simultaneously to measure mortality or movement, so that a good argument can be made for combining this section of Chapter 21 and sections of Chapter 22 dealing with this field technique. In any event, it sometimes will be necessary to utilize estimates of mortality and movement, at least implicitly, in some of the variants of the mark-recapture methods considered.

Methods of capturing and marking animals are discussed in Chapter 18. Although these topics are seldom referred to in this section, it should always be kept in mind that the estimation formula *must* be consistent with the properties of the capturing and marking procedures used. Some methods will require individual sight identification in the field, others identification in hand. Some methods are very sensitive to capture probabilities, others less so. In general, it will be considered that explicit recognition of the assumptions on which the method is based will suffice to call attention to the specific requirements of marking and capture.

In addition, there is a great deal of widely known tag-recapture lore that just cannot be fitted neatly into the present treatment without greatly expanding it. For example, it is well known that so-called trap-happy animals are often encountered, (Young et al. 1952, Geis 1955, Huber 1962, Yates 1965, Swinebroad 1964). This phenomenon is characterized here as a failure of animals to be equally subject to capture, and it is recognized that it may be either a behavioral trait of the animal, a peculiarity of the trap, or simply a result of spatial proximity to the trap. An excellent way to circumvent this problem, widely known, is to use a different "capture" device for the second phase such that one feels that the response to the second device is independent of the existence of marks. The ultimate in this ploy is Southern's (c.f. Southern and Lowe 1968) use of owls as capturing devices. He recorded the ratio of tags to number of mouse remains in owl pellets.

Brotzman and Giles (1966) discuss computer analysis of capture and recapture data, with suggestions as to data collection and coding. The reader should refer to Chapter 6 and 8 for discussion of this topic.

The Petersen or Lincoln Index

The ratio estimator called the Petersen Estimator or Lincoln Index is basic to most of the tag-recapture methods. A great deal of misinformation has gotten into the literature regarding this method, and an attempt will be made to correct some of this.

First, it is important to note that *the formula,* like many others, can be derived and interpreted in several different ways. The most important is introduced in many elementary courses in statistics as the *urn model,* in which an urn contains N balls, M of which are black. Then n "samples" of the balls are taken and the number, x, which are black is recorded. The problem has several variants. An investigator may be given N, n, and x and asked to estimate M or he may be given M, n, and x and asked to estimate N. The latter leads to a Lincoln Index estimator. Further variants involve the method of sampling. If samples are taken randomly *with replacement*, then the variable x has a binomial distribution and if one samples randomly *without* replacement, x is distributed according to the hypergeometric distribution. The form of the estimator of N is essentially the same in the two cases, but the variances are different. Some restricted form of non-random sampling may even be assumed and the same estimator be retained, but the variance may be greatly different.

Further, as Rupp (1966) has pointed out, the Lincoln Index can be interpreted in terms of a structural relationship among elements of the population with no defined sampling properties. Perhaps even more ways can be found to get the formula. In any event, it is useful (and perhaps even best) to consider a *cannonical* model . . . a model which includes as special cases all of the others.

In terms of a "generalized urn model," the mathematical model may be described as the following set of postulates:

Postulate 1. There exists a set $\mathcal{U}$ containing N elements.
Postulate 2. M of these elements have a particular characteristic, say Y, where $0 < M \leq N$.
Postulate 3. There exists a "sample" of n ob-observations of the elements of $\mathcal{U}$, containing x observations of the characteristic Y.
Postulate 4. $E(x) = nM/N$.

Given these four postulates, the estimator of N is obtained by the method of expectation; equate x to E(x),

$$x = nM/\hat{N},$$

$$\hat{N} = nM/x. \tag{13}$$

The *correspondence* of the usual population estimation problem and the model postulates is apparent when the problem is described in four statements or assumptions:

Assumption 1. There exists a well defined collection (population) of animals containing N individuals.
Assumption 2. M of these individuals are marked, say with a tag.
Assumption 3. There exists a sample of n "observations" of animals from the population, containing x observations of marked animals.
Assumption 4. The *average* probability $\bar{p}_m$ of observing a marked animal is equal to the average probability $\bar{p}_u$ of observing an unmarked animal. That is, $\bar{p}_m = \bar{p}_u$.

Since $E(x) = \bar{p}_m M$ and $E(n - x) = \bar{p}_u(N - M)$, it follows that

$$\frac{E(x)}{M} = \frac{E(n - x)}{N - M} = \frac{E(n)}{N},$$

and for n *fixed*, we can write

$$E(x) = \frac{nM}{N},$$

as a consequence of the assumption that $\bar{p}_m = \bar{p}_u$.

The exact nature of these assumptions will vary slightly from application to application, and it is necessary to be very careful in establishing the exact correspondence with the model. However, given the appropriate assumptions, the Lincoln Index formula (13) can be applied. An example of the calculation of $\hat{N}$ will be shown later.

It should be noted that (13) is also the method of moments estimator and that the same formula is obtained by maximum likelihood under the assumption that x is distributed either binomially or hypergeometrically. However, it is *not necessary* to assume the mathematical form of the distribution in order to obtain the Lincoln Index, as we have indicated in the development of the estimator from the model which did not specify the distribution.

It *is* necessary to assume the form of the distribution in order to write down the variance of $\hat{N}$ as a function of the parameters. For example, Bailey (1952) gives the variance formula under the assumption that x is binomial and Chapman

(1951) gives the variance formula under the assumption that x is hypergeometric. These assumptions are rarely justified in practice, except as *approximations* to reality, so that it is generally recommended that simple approximate confidence limits be constructed (c.f. Chapman and Overton 1966). Table 21.1, from Chapman (1948), is useful for confidence limits when $x \leq 50$ and the Poisson approximation is reasonably accurate for larger x. The following example will illustrate the procedure. Let

$$M = 100$$

$$n = 150$$

$$x = 40 .$$

Then $\hat{N} = \dfrac{\lambda}{x} = \dfrac{100(150)}{40} = 375$ is the point estimator, and confidence limits are obtained from Table 21.1 as

$$N_L = \lambda(0.01769) = 15000(0.01769) = 265$$

$$N_U = \lambda(0.03396) = 15000(0.3396) = 510$$

or from the Poisson approximation as (note that Formula 14 is identical to Formula 4),

$$N_L, N_U = \lambda \frac{(x + 2) \pm 2\sqrt{x + 1}}{x^2} \tag{14}$$

$$= \lambda \frac{42 \pm 2\sqrt{41}}{1600}$$

$$= 9.38(29.2, 54.8) = (274, 514).$$

(This formula is not recommended for values of x less than 50, but this answer compares favorably with the tabular results.) It will be noted that for *very* large x the following formula is equivalent,

$$N_L, N_U = \frac{\lambda}{x^2}(x \pm 2\sqrt{x}) = \frac{\lambda}{x}\left(1 \pm \frac{2}{\sqrt{x}}\right)$$

or,

$$N_L, N_U = \hat{N}\left(1 \pm \frac{2}{\sqrt{x}}\right). \tag{15}$$

The reader may also find the paper by Davis (1964) of interest in respect to setting confidence limits.

Validation of the Lincoln Index Model

In the previous section it was pointed out that Postulate 4 of the Lincoln Index Model is met if the condition A is true:

A. The average probability, $\overline{p}_m$, of observing a marked animal is equal to the average probability, $\overline{p}_u$, of observing an unmarked one.

Now, if A does not hold, Postulate 4 can be satisfied by the restriction B (Overton et al. in press):

B. Given any recognizable population structure which divides the population into sub-populations, *within* each of which the restriction A holds, one or both of the following restrictions holds (both are to be interpreted in the expectation sense):

1. The ratio of marked to unmarked animals is the same for each sub-population. (This implies that the marking rate is uniform over sub-populations.)
2. The sub-populations are represented in the sample in proportion to their numbers. (This implies that the sampling rate is uniform over sub-populations.)

Thus, it can be stated that if either A, B-1, or B-2 can reasonably be assumed to hold, the conventional Lincoln Index can reasonably be utilized. Further, when a recognizable population structure exists, it is possible to examine internal evidence regarding assumptions B-1 and B-2, and so detect serious departure from the conditions necessary to insure good properties of the Lincoln Index. Lastly, if such departures exist, it is possible to construct a stratified Lincoln Index (see next section) which will be free of the biases caused by gross model violations.

These considerations dictate a design strategy for problems in which the Lincoln Index is to be used. The field operation and data recording should be so designed that assumptions B-1 and B-2 may be tested over all recognizable sub-populations. If either B-1 or B-2 prove reasonably well validated, then the conventional Lincoln Index can justifiably be utilized for the population as a whole. If *both* B-1 and B-2 are suspect, either *a priori* or by evidence, then stratified estimates can be constructed *if* the design has been chosen so that the necessary additional data are available. It is important to note that a study design which will provide data for validation will not necessarily provide the additional data needed for stratified estimation. Since such additional data entail additional effort and/or expense, it is conceivable that, in practice, the decision regarding design will be dependent on the strength of the *a priori* degree of belief in the various assumptions.

The kinds of sub-populations usually recognized are those defined by sex and age structure of the population and by location or spatial distribution. In general, it is necessary to be able to determine the category of all animals marked and of all marked animals observed in order to collect empirical data regarding the assumptions. To construct a stratified estimate, it is usually necessary, in addition, to record the category (sub-population) of *all* animals observed, both marked and unmarked. Sometimes it is possible to substitute an acceptable assumption for the latter design constraint.

To illustrate the way in which assumptions can be evaluated, reference is made to Overton et al. (in press). Data collected by Eastman in connection with a population study of the Bryant Mountain wintering ground (mule deer) are presented in Table 21.9. The sub-populations are defined by spatial strata, or subdivisions of the wintering ground. Estimates are first made of the number of marked animals, M, in each stratum at the time of making the observation, assuming that $\bar{p}_m = \bar{p}_u$ and constant for all strata. (Details of these calculations are given in the next section.) Then calculation of $x_h/\hat{M}_h$ yields evidence regarding assumption B-2 and calculation of x_h/n_h yields evidence regarding B-1.

Several comments should be made regarding the data in Table 21.9. It was necessary to construct the first index from *estimates* of M_h, due to the observed movement of deer between strata. That is, M_h is not *known*, but must be estimated. In a survey such as that reported by Strandgaard (1967), in which the strata are sex and age classes, M_h and x_h will be apparent if this use has been anticipated. Determination of x_h requires either individual identification of all observed marked animals or at least identification by stratum of origin. Determination of n_h is more difficult if the strata are sex and age classes, as it requires accurate identification of sex and age for all observed animals. Strandgaard found that he could make such accurate identification only during a part of the year, so that many of his collected data were unusable for the stratified analysis.

Further, a comment should be made about interpretation of the data in Table 21.9 with regard to the assumptions B-1 and B-2. If it is assumed that marked and unmarked animals are equally observable *within strata*, then B-1 implies that the proportion of marked animals observed, x_h/n_h, should be the same for all strata and B-2 implies that $\bar{p}_m$ should be constant over strata. A glance at the table reveals the strong evidence that both of these assumptions are untenable.

Statistical tests of the above assumptions are sometimes difficult to construct. In the present case, the nature of the data and collection procedure is such that χ^2 tests appear reasonably valid.

Table 21.9. Sampling data and estimates of the Bryant Mountain wintering-ground mule deer herd based on data modified from Eastman (1968). Derivation of these data is given in the next section.

Estimated number of marked animals in stratum	Number of marked observed	Estimated relative sampling rate	Total observed	Observed marked ratio
$\hat{M}_h$	x_h	$c\hat{p}_m$	n_h	x_h/n_h
63.0	55	0.873	551	0.10
70.4	50	0.710	871	0.06
149.0	83	0.557	535	0.16
25.6	13	0.508	654	0.02
308.0	201		2611	

Table 21.10. Calculations for χ^2 test of assumption B-2.

Stratum	Observed	Expected	$\frac{(O - E)^2}{E}$
1	55	41.1	4.70
2	50	45.9	0.37
3	83	97.3	2.10
4	13	16.7	0.82
Total	201	201.0	$\chi^2 = 7.99$

In Table 21.10, the expected number in the first stratum is calculated by,

$$E(x_1) = \frac{\hat{M}_1 \, \Sigma x_h}{\Sigma \hat{M}_h} = \frac{(63.0)(201)}{308} = 41.1. \quad (16)$$

Then, χ^2 is compared to the tabular χ^2 for 3 degrees of freedom (95% level) which is 7.81, so that the hypothesis is rejected that assumption B-2 is true. Of course, the investigator still would have been quite suspicious of that assumption even if the calculated χ^2 had not exceeded the tabular χ^2.

The calculation of expected values in this table is illustrated for the expected number of marked animals in Stratum 1, given that B-1 is true and the total of 201 marked animals, 2611 total animals and 551 animals observed in Stratum 1,

$$E(x_1 \mid 201, 2611, 551) = \frac{(201)(551)}{2611} = 42.42.$$

Then, by the formula,

$$\chi^2 = \Sigma \frac{(O - E)^2}{E} = \Sigma \frac{d^2}{E},$$

we find,

$$\chi^2 = \sum_{h=1}^{4} d_h^2 \left(\frac{1}{E(x_{1h})} + \frac{1}{n_h - E(x_{1h})} \right),$$

where the term in brackets is the "multiplier" in the table. For Stratum 1, the multiplier is

$$\left(\frac{1}{42.4} + \frac{1}{508.6} \right) = 0.02555.$$

$$\chi^2 = (12.6)^2(0.02555) + \ldots + (37.3)^2(0.02154)$$

$$= 84.59.$$

Again, the χ^2 statistic has 3 degrees of freedom, so that the critical level at 0.95 is 7.81, and the hypothesis that "B-1 is true" is rejected.

As a consequence of the failure of *both* assumptions, it can be concluded that it is necessary to construct a stratified Lincoln Index. Here a fine philosophical point arises. If either of the tests had been inconclusive (i.e., the differences nonsignificant) the problem would arise of deciding whether or not the assumption holds. Simple failure to reject the null hypothesis is not adequate proof that the null hypothesis is true, so that some subjective judgment would have to be exercised on the matter. The writers' inclination is to use the stratified estimate, if possible, whenever *any* doubt exists regarding the assumptions.

Construction of a Stratified Lincoln Index

This section is devoted to the description of how to construct a stratified Lincoln Index and how to insure that the data are consistent with the assumptions made. The question of validation of assumptions was considered in the preceding section. Reference is made to Overton et. al., (in press), Schaefer (1951), and Chapman and Junge (1956) for a general treatment of a stratified Lincoln Index.

Matrix notation must be used to simplify the algebra of the stratified Lincoln Index. A *matrix* is a rectangular array of numbers; and when a matrix is defined, its dimensions ($r \times c$) are specified, where r and c denote rows and columns. The convention adopted here is that a matrix will be represented by a capital letter, as X, below. An underlined letter, either capital or lower case, indicates a column vector, or a ($r \times 1$) matrix, as $\underline{M}_1$ and $\underline{n}$, below. A prime (') will be used to denote the transpose of a matrix (interchange of rows and columns) and the symbol (-1) the common inverse of a matrix ($X^{-1}X = XX^{-1} = I$), and where it is mentioned that many matrices have no common inverse. A recommended reference for matrix algebra and methods is Searle (1966).

The data available for the k sub-populations, or strata follow:

Table 21.11. Calculations for χ^2 test of assumption B-1.

Stratum	Observed			Expected if B-1 is true		Difference	Multiplier
	Marked	Unmarked	Total	Marked	Unmarked		
1	55	496	551	42.4	508.6	12.6	0.02555
2	50	821	871	67.0	804.0	−17.0	0.01617
3	83	452	535	41.2	493.8	41.8	0.02630
4	13	641	654	50.3	603.7	−37.3	0.02154
Total	201	2410	2611	201	2410	0	

$$\underline{M}_1 = \begin{bmatrix} M_{.1} \\ M_{.2} \\ \vdots \\ M_{.k} \end{bmatrix}, \quad \underline{n} = \begin{bmatrix} n_1 \\ n_2 \\ \vdots \\ n_k \end{bmatrix}, \quad X = \begin{bmatrix} x_{11} & x_{12} & \cdots & x_{1k} \\ x_{21} & x_{22} & \cdots & x_{2k} \\ \vdots & & & \\ x_{k1} & x_{k2} & \cdots & x_{kk} \end{bmatrix}$$

$$\underline{M}_2 = \begin{bmatrix} M_{1.} \\ M_{2.} \\ \vdots \\ M_{k.} \end{bmatrix}$$

where[1] $M_{.j}$ = number of animals originally marked in the jth stratum = $\sum_i M_{ij}$

n_i = number of animals observed in the ith stratum

x_{ij} = number of marked animals observed in the ith stratum that were originally marked in the jth stratum

where $x_{i.} = \sum_j x_{ij}$ = the total number of marked animals observed in the ith stratum

and where further,

M_{ij} = number of marked animals in the ith stratum on the second occasion which were originally in the jth stratum

N_{ij} = total number of animals in the ith stratum on the second occasion which were originally in the jth stratum

and

where $M_{i.} = \sum_j M_{ij}$.

The Chapman-Junge (1956) solution to the stratified Lincoln Index can be developed as follows. Assume that

$$E(x_{ij}) = \frac{x_{i.} M_{ij}}{M_{i.}}, \quad \text{for all } i, j,$$

so that

$$E \left\{ \sum_{i=1}^{k} \frac{M_{i.} x_{ij}}{x_{i.}} \right\} = M_{.j}$$

and by the method of expectation,

$$\sum_{i=1}^{k} \hat{M}_{i.} \left(\frac{x_{ij}}{x_{i.}} \right) = M_{.j}. \tag{17}$$

Now (17) represents a system of k linear equations in k unknowns, the $\hat{M}_{i.}$, which can be written in matrix notation,

$$X' W_1 \hat{\underline{M}}_2 = \underline{M}_1$$

[1]The "dot" notation (e.g., $M_{.j}$ or $M_{i.}$) follows that used commonly in analysis of variance, the dot indicating the summation over the subscript in whose place the dot appears. For example, $x_{.1}$ is the sum of the first column of X and $x_{1.}$ the sum of the first row.

where

$$W_1^{-1} = \begin{bmatrix} x_{1.} & & & \\ & x_{2.} & & \\ & & \ddots & \\ & & & x_{k.} \end{bmatrix}.$$

Then, if X^{-1} exists, it is possible to solve for $\hat{\underline{M}}_2$,

$$\hat{\underline{M}}_2 = W_1^{-1} (X')^{-1} \underline{M}_1, \qquad (18)$$

where $\hat{\underline{M}}_2$ is consistent for

$$\underline{M}_2 = \begin{bmatrix} M_{1.} \\ M_{2.} \\ \vdots \\ M_{k.} \end{bmatrix}.$$

Now if the usual Lincoln Index assumption (c.f., postulate 4) is made that

$$E(x_{i.}) = \frac{n_{i.} M_{i.}}{N_{i.}}, \quad \text{all } i,$$

then by the usual procedure, and substituting $\hat{M}_{i.}$ for $M_{i.}$,

$$\hat{N}_{i.} = \frac{n_{i.} \hat{M}_{i.}}{x_{i.}},$$

and again the system of equations can be expressed in matrix notation,

$$\hat{\underline{N}}_2 = W_2 W_1 \hat{\underline{M}}_2,$$

where

$$W_2 = \begin{bmatrix} n_{1.} & & & \\ & n_{2.} & & \\ & & \ddots & \\ & & & n_{k.} \end{bmatrix}.$$

Now, by substitution, the following can be obtained

$$\hat{\underline{N}}_2 = W_2 W_1 W_1^{-1} (X')^{-1} \underline{M}_1$$

$$= W_2 (X')^{-1} \underline{M}_1. \qquad (19)$$

It should be noted that Chapman and Junge derive this result directly from the assumption,

$$E(x_{ij}) = \frac{n_{i.} M_{ij}}{N_{i.}}$$

in exactly the manner in which $\hat{\underline{M}}_2$ was obtained here.

This solution is illustrated with two examples, one from Eastman (1968) and the other from Strandgaard (1967). Eastman's data, slightly modified to simplify the calculations, are given below. Animals are mule deer and strata are subdivisions of the winter range.

$$\underline{M}_1 = \begin{bmatrix} 71 \\ 62 \\ 153 \\ 22 \end{bmatrix}, \qquad X' = \begin{bmatrix} 55 & 5 & 2 & 0 \\ 0 & 42 & 2 & 0 \\ 0 & 3 & 79 & 2 \\ 0 & 0 & 0 & 11 \end{bmatrix}$$

$$W_1^{-1} = \begin{bmatrix} 55 & & & \\ & 50 & & \\ & & 83 & \\ & & & 13 \end{bmatrix}, \qquad W_2 = \begin{bmatrix} 551 & & & \\ & 871 & & \\ & & 535 & \\ & & & 654 \end{bmatrix}$$

Then $(X')^{-1} \underline{M}_1$

$$= \begin{bmatrix} 0.018182 & -0.002135 & -0.000406 & 0.000074 \\ 0 & 0.023853 & -0.000604 & 0.000110 \\ 0 & -0.000906 & 0.012681 & -0.002306 \\ 0 & 0 & 0 & 0.090909 \end{bmatrix} \begin{bmatrix} 71 \\ 62 \\ 153 \\ 22 \end{bmatrix}$$

$$= \begin{bmatrix} 1.098062 \\ 1.388894 \\ 1.833289 \\ 1.999998 \end{bmatrix},$$

and $\hat{\underline{M}}_2 = \begin{bmatrix} 55 & & & \\ & 50 & & \\ & & 83 & \\ & & & 13 \end{bmatrix} \begin{bmatrix} 1.098062 \\ 1.388894 \\ 1.833289 \\ 1.999998 \end{bmatrix} = \begin{bmatrix} 60.39 \\ 69.44 \\ 152.16 \\ 26.00 \end{bmatrix}$,

and $\hat{\underline{N}}_2 = \begin{bmatrix} 551 & & & \\ & 871 & & \\ & & 535 & \\ & & & 654 \end{bmatrix} \begin{bmatrix} 1.098062 \\ 1.388894 \\ 1.833289 \\ 1.999998 \end{bmatrix} = \begin{bmatrix} 605 \\ 1210 \\ 981 \\ 1308 \end{bmatrix}.$

Then, $\hat{\underline{N}}$ = 4104.

It should be pointed out that the process of obtaining $(X')^{-1}$ from X', the process of inversion of X', may require some assistance from someone familiar with matrix manipulations. For large matrices, a computer is indicated, unless, as in the following example, X is a diagonal matrix.

Strandgaard's example, in which strata are sex and age classes and animals are roe deer as follows:

$$\underline{M}_1 = \begin{bmatrix} 10 \text{ (adult bucks)} \\ 23 \text{ (adult does)} \\ 20 \text{ (buck fawns)} \\ 17 \text{ (doe fawns)} \end{bmatrix}, \quad X = \begin{bmatrix} 59 & 0 & 0 & 0 \\ 0 & 185 & 0 & 0 \\ 0 & 0 & 229 & 0 \\ 0 & 0 & 0 & 173 \end{bmatrix}$$

$$W_1^{-1} = X, \quad W_2 = \begin{bmatrix} 141 & & & \\ & 290 & & \\ & & 229 & \\ & & & 192 \end{bmatrix}, \quad \hat{\underline{M}}_2 = \underline{M}_1,$$

$$\text{and } \hat{\underline{N}}_2 = \begin{bmatrix} 141/59 & & & \\ & 290/185 & & \\ & & 229/229 & \\ & & & 192/173 \end{bmatrix}\begin{bmatrix} 10 \\ 23 \\ 20 \\ 17 \end{bmatrix}$$

$$= \begin{bmatrix} 23.9 \\ 36.1 \\ 20.0 \\ 18.9 \end{bmatrix}$$

Then $\hat{N}$ = 98.9.

This solution will be recognized as the sum of four simple Lincoln Index estimates. The problem is put into the general solution (Formula 19) just for illustration.

The following example will illustrate the use of an alternative estimation scheme (Overton et al. in press), which does not require inversion of the matrix X'. Again the data are from Eastman and have been slightly modified to simplify the calculations.

$$\underline{M}_1 = \begin{bmatrix} 71 \\ 62 \\ 153 \\ 22 \end{bmatrix}, \quad \underline{n} = \begin{bmatrix} 551 \\ 871 \\ 535 \\ 654 \end{bmatrix}, \quad X = \begin{bmatrix} 55 & 0 & 0 & 0 \\ 5 & 42 & 3 & 0 \\ 2 & 2 & 79 & 0 \\ 0 & 0 & 2 & 11 \end{bmatrix}$$

That is, 71 deer were marked in stratum 1, 62 in stratum 2, etc. A total of 551 were observed in stratum 1, of which 55 were marked, and all marked observed in stratum 1 were originally in stratum 1. In stratum 2, 871 were seen, 50 (the sum of the second row of X) of which were marked, of this 50, 5 originally came from stratum 1, 42 from stratum 2, and 3 from stratum 3. First calculate column totals of X, obtaining,

$$[62, \ 44, \ 84, \ 11]$$

and divide the columns of X by the column totals, obtaining Z,

$$Z = \begin{bmatrix} 0.8871 & 0 & 0 & 0 \\ 0.0806 & 0.9545 & 0.0357 & 0 \\ 0.0323 & 0.0455 & 0.9405 & 0 \\ 0 & 0 & 0.0238 & 1 \end{bmatrix}$$

and check that the columns of Z add to 1.000. These columns are to be interpreted as the estimated proportions of animals originating in the various strata (columns) and now located in the other strata (rows). That is, it is estimated that 0.8871 of the animals marked in stratum 1 are still in stratum 1, 0.0806 in stratum 2, 0.0323 in stratum 3 and none in stratum 4. This estimated proportion involves the implicit assumption that animals are observed (sampled) at the same rate in all strata on the second occasion. The estimates will be modified, in the iterative process, to account for observed deviation from this condition.

Now, $\hat{\underline{M}}_2^{(1)} = Z\underline{M}_1$, in matrix notation, this being the first estimate of the number of marked animals in the strata on the second occasion. Numerically then, it is found that

$$\hat{\underline{M}}_2^{(1)} = \begin{bmatrix} 62.98 \\ 70.36 \\ 149.01 \\ 25.64 \end{bmatrix}$$

where
$$62.98 = 71(0.8871),$$

$$70.36 = 71(0.0806) + 62(0.9545) + 153(0.0357),$$

etc.

Next, $\underline{p}^*$ is calculated,

$$\underline{p}^* = \begin{bmatrix} 62.98/55 \\ 70.30/50 \\ 149.01/83 \\ 25.64/13 \end{bmatrix} = \begin{bmatrix} 1.1451 \\ 1.4060 \\ 1.7953 \\ 1.9723 \end{bmatrix}$$

where the elements of $\underline{p}^*$ are inverses of the elements which have been called $c\hat{p}_{mj}$ (Table 21.9), where p_{mj} is the probability of observing a particular marked animal in stratum j. Since nearly a two-fold difference (i.e., 1.1451 to 1.9723) exists between the elements of $\underline{p}^*$, the observer is justified in questioning the assumption of equal probability of observing a marked deer regardless of stratum. Therefore, the estimate $\hat{M}_2$ is modified by expanding each element of $\overline{X}$ by the inverse of the estimated sampling probability for that stratum.

Numerically,

$X^{(2)}$

$$= \begin{bmatrix} 55(1.1451) & 0 & 0 & 0 \\ 5(1.4060) & 42(1.4060) & 3(1.4060) & 0 \\ 2(1.7953) & 2(1.7953) & 79(1.7953) & 0 \\ 0 & 0 & 2(1.9723) & 11(1.9723) \end{bmatrix}$$

$$= \begin{bmatrix} 62.98 & 0 & 0 & 0 \\ 7.03 & 59.05 & 4.22 & 0 \\ 3.59 & 3.59 & 141.83 & 0 \\ 0 & 0 & 3.94 & 21.70 \end{bmatrix}.$$

Again, the elements of $X^{(2)}$ are divided by the column sums (73.60, 62.64, 149.99, and 21.70) to obtain,

$$Z^{(2)} = \begin{bmatrix} 0.8557 & 0 & 0 & 0 \\ 0.0955 & 0.9427 & 0.0281 & 0 \\ 0.0488 & 0.0573 & 0.9456 & 0 \\ 0 & 0 & 0.0263 & 1 \end{bmatrix}$$

and again the columns add to 1.0000. This is the modified estimate of the proportion of animals having moved from stratum j to stratum i, taking into account the evidence of unequal sampling rates in the various strata. The next step is to calculate $\hat{\underline{M}}_2^{(2)} = Z^{(2)}\underline{M}_1$

$$\hat{\underline{M}}_2^{(2)} = \begin{bmatrix} 60.75 \\ 69.53 \\ 151.69 \\ 26.02 \end{bmatrix}, \text{ where } 60.75 = 71(0.8557), \text{etc.}$$

A second iteration would make little change in these figures, as can be quickly verified. Now, the calculation can be made of $\hat{\underline{N}}_2 = W_2 W_1 \hat{\underline{M}}_2^{(2)}$

$$\hat{\underline{N}}_2 = \begin{bmatrix} 609 \\ 1211 \\ 978 \\ 1309 \end{bmatrix} \qquad \text{where } \hat{N}_i = \frac{\hat{M}_{2i}^{(2)} n_i}{x_{i.}}$$

and for example, $\hat{N}_1 = \dfrac{(60.75)(551)}{55}$

$$= 609.$$

Then $\hat{N} = 4107$,

and $N_L, N_U \doteq (4107)(201) \left\{ \dfrac{203 \pm 2\sqrt{202}}{(201)^2} \right\}$

$$= \frac{4107}{201} \left\{ 203 \pm 2(14.21) \right\}$$

$$= \frac{4107(174.58)}{201}, \; \frac{4107(231.42)}{201}$$

$$= 3567, \; 4729.$$

It should be pointed out that these confidence limits are pretty wide under the circumstances, and that they undoubtedly reflect greater sampling error than actually exists in this example. (See the discussion of the effect of sampling without replacement in an earlier section).

The Schnabel Method

The Schnabel Method is a variant of the Lincoln Index. As published by Schnabel (1938) the estimator (20) was derived as an approximation to the maximum likelihood estimator (mle) of N, under a fully specified statistical model (poisson). De-Lury (1951) gave an iterative solution for the exact mle under this model.

However, as has been discussed in earlier sections, the assumptions necessary for a fully specified statistical model are seldom tenable, and wildlifers are usually more interested in the adequate model with the fewest assumptions. The estimator can be derived from a "cannonical" model, which in effect is a generalization of all models leading to the estimator, and the model is found to be closely related to the model developed for the Lincoln Index.

The problem is as follows: observations are made on a series of occasions, each observation corresponding to the observation used in a Lincoln Index. Typically, the number of marked animals is different on each occasion, but this number is assumed to be known, so that on each occasion it is possible to calculate a Lincoln Index estimate of N. An additional feature usually found in application of the Schnabel Method is the marking and release of all unmarked animals captured on the successive observational occasions. This is not essential, but the structural framework of the model was designed for this situation. The question remains, what is the best way to average the different estimates?

The model is as follows: on the ith occasion, n_i animals are observed, x_i of which are marked. It is specified that M_i marked animals are in the population on this occasion. Then, if it is assumed that

$$E(x_i) = \frac{M_i n_i}{N_i} ,$$

it is possible to solve (as in the Lincoln Index) for $\hat{N}_i$,

$$\hat{N}_i = \frac{M_i n_i}{x_i} .$$

Further, if it is now assumed that $N_i = N$ for all i (i.e., the population level is constant over all occasions) then it is possible to write,

$$E(\Sigma x_i) = \Sigma \frac{M_i n_i}{N_i} = \frac{1}{N} \Sigma M_i n_i.$$

Again, by the method of expectation,

$$\hat{N} = \frac{\Sigma M_i n_i}{\Sigma x_i} , \qquad (20)$$

the Schnabel estimating formula.

Chapman and Overton (1966) have noted that approximate confidence limits can be obtained in the manner of limits for the Lincoln Index by letting $x = \Sigma x_i$ and $\lambda = \Sigma M_i n_i$ and then using Chapman's table (Table 21.1) for $x \leq 50$ and the poisson approximation (Formula 4) for $x > 50$.

Overton (1965) gave a modification of the Schnabel Method to account for known removal of animals from the population. This is a simple extension of the above development, as follows. Given the assumption that

$$E(x_i) = \frac{M_i n_i}{N_i} \text{ for all } i,$$

it follows that the estimating equation is given by

$$(\Sigma x_i) = \Sigma \frac{M_i n_i}{\hat{N}_i} , \qquad (21)$$

but if the N_i are unequal, it is impossible to obtain a solution to this expression. However, if it is assumed that

$$N_i = N - Z_i ,$$

where Z_i is the *known* number of animals removed from the population prior to the ith occasion, then it is possible to estimate N by an iterative method. Rewrite (21) as follows,

$$\hat{N} = \frac{\Sigma n_i M_i}{\Sigma x_i} + \left(\frac{1}{\Sigma x_i}\right) \Sigma \left(\frac{Z_i n_i M_i}{\hat{N} - Z_i}\right),$$

$$\hat{N} = \hat{N}^{(0)} + A \qquad .$$

where $\hat{N}^{(0)}$ is the usual Schnabel estimator and A = 0 if all $Z_i = 0$. Now a first approximation to A is given by

$$A^{(1)} = \frac{\Sigma Z_i n_i M_i}{\Sigma n_i M_i}$$

and the first approximation to $\hat{N}$ is given by

$$\hat{N}^{(1)} = \hat{N}^{(0)} + A^{(1)}, \qquad (22)$$

which is apparently very close in most examples. A closer approximation may be obtained by defining

$$\overset{*}{N}{}^{(j)} = \frac{1}{2}\left(\hat{N}^{(j-1)} + \overset{*}{N}{}^{(j-1)}\right),$$

with

$$\overset{*}{N}{}^{(1)} = \hat{N}^{(0)}.$$

Then let,

$$A^{(j)} = \frac{1}{\Sigma x_i} \Sigma \left(\frac{Z_i\, n_i\, M_i}{\overset{*}{N}{}^{(j)} - Z_i}\right)$$

and

$$\hat{N}^{(j)} = \hat{N}^{(0)} + A^{(j)}. \qquad (23)$$

The process is illustrated in Table 21.12. The suggested confidence limits are obtained by defining

$$\lambda = \Sigma n_i M_i + \Sigma \frac{Z_i\, n_i\, M_i}{(\hat{N} - Z_i)}$$

which quantity is available from the solution in the Table.

Jolly's Method For Multiple Recapture Experiments

A large number of papers on multiple recapture experiments have been published within the last 20 years, but little impact has been made on the wildlife literature. The reason is simple. Few wildlifers have the background to understand the sophisticated modeling and analysis of Darroch (1958, 1959), Leslie and Chitty (1951), Leslie (1952), Leslie, Chitty and Chitty (1953), Jolly (1963, 1965) and Seber (1962, 1965), not to mention a host of others. Despite the complexity, however, the results of these studies are useful in commonly conducted tag-recapture studies, so that some synthesis here is indicated.

The method chosen for treatment owes much to earlier papers, particularly to the series of papers by Leslie et al., (1951-53). No attempt is here made to assign credit to the various features. Jolly's version is used because it lends itself nicely to a hueristic development of the principles involved and because it is up-to-date. His notation is used to facilitate the reader's transition to his more detailed results.

A tag-recapture experiment is conducted during which, on successive occasions, animals are captured from the population. The identity of marked individuals (or at least their recapture history) is recorded, unmarked animals are marked and all (or some) animals are returned to the population. It is assumed that there are losses *and* additions to the population between occasions, so that there are three parameters of interest on each occasion: N_i, the total number of animals in the population; Φ_i, the rate of "survival" from occasion i to i + 1; and B_i, the number of animals in the population at occasion i + 1 that were not present at occasion i. It is further assumed that presence of marks is unrelated to survival or capture probability.

The data are entered into a table in the manner of Table 21.13, where

x_{tj} = the number of marked animals observed at time t which were last observed at time j (the marking occasion is considered an observation for this purpose),

$a_{tj} = \sum\limits_{i=1}^{j} x_{ti}$, partial sums of the rows of x_{tj}'s,

A_j = sum of the jth column of x_{tj}'s

C_j = sum of the jth column of a_j's, *leaving out the top element,*

s_t = total number of marked animals released into the population at occasion t, including those previously marked and new marks, and

n_t = total number of animals examined on the tth occasion

Then, calculations are made as follows:

$$\hat{M}_t = \frac{s_t C_{t-1}}{A_t} + a_{t,t-1},$$

and

$$\hat{N}_t = \frac{\hat{M}_t n_t}{a_{t,t-1}}. \qquad (24)$$

A hueristic development of the above estimators is helpful in utilizing them, even though the table as presented makes the calculations routine. Let t = 4 and consider the factor $C_{t-1} = C_3$. The elements of the x_{tj} table which sum together to yield C_3 are outlined by a solid line. These are the animals marked prior to time t = 4, not seen in 4 but seen subsequently. Next, consider A_4, the sum of elements outlined in the x_{tj} table by a dotted line; a_{43}, circled in the a_{ij} table; and s_4, circled in the s_t table.

Table 21.12. Numerical example of application of modified Schnabel Estimator, allowing for known daily reduction in population size (after Overton 1965).

Day	n_i	m_i	z_i	x_i	X_i	Z_i	M_i	n_iM_i	$A_i =$ $n_iM_iZ_i$	Second Iteration $\overset{*}{N}{}^{(2)} = 448$		Third Iteration $\overset{*}{N}{}^{(3)} = 448.5$	
										$\overset{*}{N}{}_i^{(2)}$	$A_i/\overset{*}{N}{}_i^{(2)}$	$\overset{*}{N}{}_i^{(3)}$	$A_i/\overset{*}{N}{}_i^{(3)}$
1	20	10	10	0	0	0	0	0	0	448	0	448.5	0
2	22	10	11	1	1	10	10	220	2,200	438	5	438.5	5.02
3	18	8	10	0	1	21	20	360	7,560	427	18	427.5	17.68
4	21	9	11	1	2	31	28	588	18,228	417	44	417.5	43.66
5	16	7	7	2	4	42	37	592	24,864	406	61	406.5	61.17
6	18	6	11	1	5	49	44	792	38,808	399	97	399.5	97.14
7	17	5	9	3	8	60	50	850	51,000	388	131	388.5	131.27
8	14	4	8	2	10	69	55	770	53,130	379	140	379.5	140.00
9	17	7	8	2	12	77	59	1,003	77,231	371	208	371.5	207.89
10	16	5	7	4	16	85	66	1,056	89,760	363	247	363.5	246.93
						92	71			356		356.5	
Sum		71	92	16				6,231	362,781		951		950.76

Step 1. $\hat{N}^{(1)} = \hat{N}^{(0)} + A^{(1)} = \dfrac{6,231}{16} + \dfrac{362,781}{6,231} = 389.4 + 58.2 = 447.6;$

2. $\hat{N}^{(2)} = \hat{N}^{(0)} + A^{(2)} = 389.4 + \dfrac{951}{16} = 389.4 + 59.4 = 448.8 = \dfrac{6,231 + 951}{16} = 448.875;$

3. $\hat{N}^{(3)} = \dfrac{6,231 + 950.76}{16} = 448.86 \rightarrow 449;$

4. $\hat{N} = 449$, to the nearest integral value.

Then $\lambda = 6231 + 950.76$

Now a_{43} is the total number of marked animals caught on occasion $t = 4$. It remains to estimate how many more marked animals were in the population at the time of that trapping. Call this number M_4^*, and observe that s_4 is the number of marked animals seen (captured plus new marks) and *released* into the population on this occasion and that A_4 is the number of *these* animals subsequently seen. Then assume

$$E\left(\frac{A_4}{s_4}\right) = E\left(\frac{C_3}{M_4^*}\right),$$

equate expectations and solve for

$$\hat{M}_4^* = \frac{C_3 s_4}{A_4}$$

or in general

$$\hat{M}_t^* = \frac{C_{t-1} s_t}{A_t}$$

and

$$\hat{M}_t = \hat{M}_t^* + a_{t,t-1} \quad .$$

The validity of the assumption on which $\hat{M}_t$ is based is apparent when A_t is considered as a fraction of s_t and C_{t-1} as a fraction of M_t^* and it is recognized that these two fractions are observed under identical survival and observational schedules.

It is seen, then, that Jolly uses a Lincoln Index estimator of M_t^* and it is obvious that $\hat{N}_t$ is again a Lincoln Index with $\hat{M}$ substituted for the usual M,

$$\hat{N}_t = \frac{\hat{M}_t n_t}{a_{t,t-1}} \quad . \tag{24}$$

Table 21.13. Symbolic table for construction of Jolly estimates.

n_t	s_t	j 1	2	3	4	5		t
n_1	s_1						1	
n_2	s_2	x_{21}					2	
n_3	s_3	x_{31}	x_{32}				3	
n_4	(s_4)	x_{41}	x_{42}	x_{43}			4	t
n_5	s_5	x_{51}	x_{52}	x_{53}	x_{54}		5	
n_6	s_6	x_{61}	x_{62}	x_{63}	x_{64}	x_{65}	6	
		A_2	A_3	(A_4)	A_5		Sum	
		a_{21}					2	
		a_{31}	a_{32}				3	
		a_{41}	a_{42}	(a_{43})			4	t
		a_{51}	a_{52}	a_{53}	a_{54}		5	
		a_{61}	a_{62}	a_{63}	a_{64}	a_{65}	6	
		C_1	C_2	(C_3)	C_4		Partial sum (Excluding top element)	

This procedure gives an estimate of N_i for each occasion after the first and prior to the last, and Jolly (1963, 1965) also gives estimators for recruitment, B_i, to the population and for survival rates (Φ_i), as well as for variances and confidence limits.

The Frequency of Capture Method

Another approach has been used to estimate total population from multiple recapture data which utilizes the frequency of recapture of the animals marked. This approach is statistically identical to the approach of estimating total number of species in a community from the frequency of numbers of observed individuals per species, (c.f. Corbett, Williams, and Fisher 1943) and has the same problems of definition and specification. Nevertheless, it has a strong intuitive appeal, and is worthy of some attention here. Principal references are Eberhardt et al., (1963) and Edwards and Eberhardt (1967).

Consider a trapping operation which continues over a period of time (say k occasions) and in which each individual captured is individually identified and records kept of all captures. Then the datum to be analyzed is

$$\underline{n} = \begin{bmatrix} n_1 \\ n_2 \\ \vdots \\ n_k \end{bmatrix}$$

where n_i = number of animals captured i times, and

$\sum\limits_{i=1}^{k} n_i$ = n, the total number of animals captured.

Now define n_0 = the number of animals in the population which have been captured 0 times.

Since $N = n + n_0$, it is apparent that $\hat{N} = n + \hat{n}_0$ so that the problem reduces to estimation of n_0. Intuitively, one feels that the nature of the relationship among the n_i contains some evidence regarding the number of uncaptured individuals. The problem remaining is to model the frequency of capture so that the evidence is utilizable. Two approaches are considered. By specifying the form of the function "explaining" the frequency distribution, a "parametric" estimate of N is obtained. Alternatively, some non-parametric model may be constructed.

As an example of a parametric estimate, Eberhardt et al. (1963), Edwards and Eberhardt (1967), and Nixon et al. (1967) used a geometric model for frequency, yielding the following estimator,

$$\hat{N} = \frac{n}{1 - (n/t)} \tag{25}$$

where n = total number of individuals captured and t = total number of captures.

These authors present evidence that the geometric distribution at least roughly approximates the observed data for several surveys, although they conclude that estimates of n_0 are too high. However, elementary sampling considerations dictate that the geometric distribution cannot pos-

Table 21.14. An artificial example illustrating the use of Jolly's estimates. The table is structured identically to Table 21.13 to facilitate interpretation of the formulae.

n_t	s_t	1	2	3	4	5		
				j				
10	10						1	
12	10	3					2	
15	15	1	2				3	t
10	10	2	2	4			4	
12	12	2	1	2	4		5	
15	12	1	2	3	2	3	6	
$\hat{N}_t$	$\hat{M}_t$	9	7	9	6	3	Sum	
46.28	11.57	3					2	
98.35	19.67	1	3				3	
32.92	26.33	2	4	8			4	t
54.67	41.00	2	3	5	9		5	
		1	3	6	8	11	6	
		6	10	11	8		Partial sum	

where π_i is the probability of capturing the ith animal at least once during the experiment. Now p_i may be estimated, $\hat{p}_i = \dfrac{x_i}{k}$, where x_i = number of times the ith animal is captured. Then

$$\hat{\pi}_i = 1 - (1 - \hat{p}_i)^k = 1 - \left(1 - \frac{x_i}{k}\right)^k,$$

or

$$(1 - \hat{\pi}_i) = \left(1 - \frac{x_i}{k}\right)^k$$

$$= \text{antilog}\left\{ k\left[\log (k - x_i) - \log k\right]\right\}.$$

Then, by the theorem,

$$\hat{N} = \sum_{x=1}^{k} \frac{n_x}{\pi_x},$$

which is in turn estimated by

$$\hat{N}_1 = \sum_{x=1}^{k} \frac{n_x}{\hat{\pi}_x}. \tag{26}$$

sibly hold, except as a "transient" distribution. Therefore, it must be concluded that the published agreement with the geometric distribution must be in some degree fortuitous. The possibility is raised, however, of the existence of a stopping rule such that the sampling is ended when the desired distribution of capture frequency is achieved. This appears worthy of some further thought. It should also be noted that Formula 25 is consistent for the total number of animals having positive probability of capture, so that it is possible that the estimator is not as restrictive as one might think.

Consider, now, derivation of a non-parametric estimator of N, given the frequency of capture data. This is based on the fundamental theorem of probability sampling with inclusion probabilities estimated from rate of capture. Model: Let animal u_i have probability p_i, $0 < p_i \leq 1$, of capture on a given occasion, where p_i is constant over all k occasions, but variable among animals. Then, for a given experiment, $\pi_i = 1 - (1 - p_i)^k$,

Examination of comparative data from Edwards and Eberhardt's (1967) Table 3 (see Table 21.15 above) reveals a pattern of interest. These data are collected from a population of known size, and several different estimators are used, with the following results. (Example 4 has been added to their results)

Total captures	76
Known population size	135

Estimates constructed on distribution of capture frequency.
1. Poisson model for frequency (mle)   100.2
2. Geometric model for frequency (mle)   163.5
3. Geometric model for frequency (regression)   135.7
4. Non-parametric frequency (Overton)   102.5

Table 21.15. Numerical example of Formula 26. Using Edward's data (Edwards and Eberhardt 1967: Table 3) the following calculations are made: (k = 18, log k = 1.255).

x	n_x	$k-x$	$\log(k-x)$	$k[\log(k-x) - \log k]$	$(1-\hat{\pi}_x)$	$n_x/\hat{\pi}_x$
1	43	17	1.230	$-18(0.025) = -0.450$	0.3575	66.9
2	16	16	1.204	$-18(0.051) = -0.918$	0.1200	18.2
3	8	15	1.176	$-18(0.079) = -1.422$	0.0376	8.3
4	6	14	1.146	$-18(0.109) = -1.962$	0.0198	6.1
5	0	13	1.114	$-18(0.141) = -2.538$	0.0029	0.0
6	2	12	1.079	$-18(0.176) = -3.168$	0.00068	2.0
7	1	11	1.041	$-18(0.214) = -3.852$	0.00014	1.0

$$\hat{N} = 102.5$$

Estimates constructed from tag-recapture models
(5) Schnabel   96.0
(6) Schumacher-Eschmeyer   97.3

In order to interpret these results, the following points should be considered. First, estimates 1, 2, 4, 5, and 6 are consistent for the total number, N*, of animals which have probability of capture strictly greater than zero. Further, 1, 4, 5, and 6 approach N* from below (as k increases) if there are some animals in the population with low capture probabilities. Of all considered, only 2 and 3 attempt to account for the uncatchable animals and the difference in these is strictly statistical--they are based on the same model.

This evaluation points up the greatest appeal of this approach. *All* other models considered in this chapter, including the catch-effort models, the recapture models, the direct estimation models, and all the rest, involve the assumption that all animals in the population are subject to capture or observation. The geometric model of Eberhardt is justified on the empirical evidence that at least some kinds of recapture data under some intensities and conditions of sampling satisfy this model reasonably well. Within the limits of validation, this amounts to discovery of a law modeling the relative abundance of uncatchable animals in the population and leading to an estimation procedure which accounts for those animals at least at moderate sampling intensities. Need for further investigation of this point is indicated.

One further comment should be made. In most multiple recapture experiments the researcher will have much more information regarding the population numbers than is contained in the frequency of capture datum. Thus, it is likely that other methods (e.g., Jolly's) will prove more efficient in most cases, so far as estimation of catchable animals is concerned.

Miscellaneous Methods

Hayne (1949) has pointed out (for a multiple recapture experiment) that if the proportion marked in the sample, x/n, is plotted against cumulative removal, M, then x/n approaches 1 as M approaches N, and that one can solve for N graphically, or by some mathematical model relating the two variables. Now, once it is recognized that n_t is a measure of sampling effort at time t and that $1 - \frac{x}{n} = \frac{n-x}{n}$, the proportion of unmarked animals in the population, it is seen that this method is a special case of the Leslie Method to be described later. It is worthy of note that this special case does not require reduction in the population—only reduction in the uncaptured segment of the population. That is, one can pretend that previously caught individuals have been removed and so use the "removal method."

The Schumacher-Eschmeyer Method (1943) was developed for the marking experiment generally appropriate to the Schnabel Formula, but in which unequal probabilities of capture cause violation of the Schnabel Model. The method prescribes the formula,

$$\hat{N} = \frac{\Sigma M^2 n}{\Sigma Mx}, \qquad (27)$$

where summation is over all occasions.

Planning the Mark-Recapture Experiment

Several aspects of planning the mark-recapture experiment should be treated. The importance of assumption validation has already been emphasized as has the importance of making sure that the model fits the experimental situation. Now, it is necessary to address more mundane questions like the sample size needed for a certain level of accuracy or "when can we stop sampling?"

Robson and Regier (1964) give a good development of the sample size question with useful graphs for determination of sample size under

448

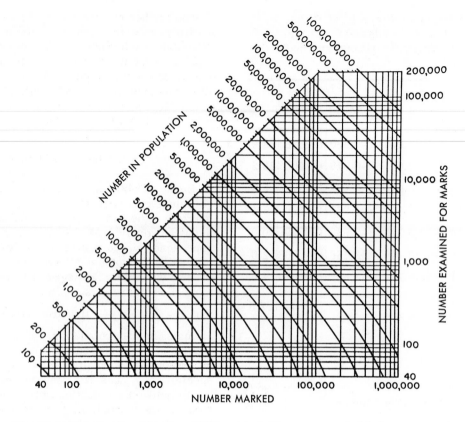

Fig. 21.6. Sample size when $1-\alpha = 0.95$ and $p = 0.25$; recommended for management studies. Data based on normal approximation to the hypergeometric distribution (from Robson and Regier 1964).

various situations. The graph recommended for use in management studies is reproduced here (Fig. 21.6).

A formula is useful in using these graphs, and it can be shown that the following is a good approximation to the calculating formulae used by Robson and Regier.

$$Mn = \frac{z^2 N (1 - p_1)(1 - p_2)}{p^2} \qquad (28)$$

where M = total marked animals
　　　N = total number of animals
　　　n = number of animals observed in the second phase
　　　p_1 = n/N
　　　p_2 = M/N
and　　p = the desired relative precision: i.e., estimates will be within 100p% of the true value 100(1 - α)% of the time.
　　　z = the standard normal deviate for (1 - α). (α = 0.05 in the R-R graphs

so that z = 1.96.) α is discussed further in most statistics books.
Further, if p_1 and p_2 are small, then

$$Mn = z^2 N/p^2 \text{ is a good approximation.} \quad (29)$$

Example: Given z = 2, p = 0.25, and N $\doteq$ 5,000, we find by Formula 29,

$$Mn = (4)(5,000)/0.0625 = 320,000.$$

Therefore, if M = 250, then the sample size must be n = $\frac{320000}{250}$ = 1280, and if M = 500, then the number needed is n = 640.

To use the graph, note that M and n are interchangable, so that either n or M may be treated as the ordinate. For the above example, find M = 250 on the ordinate, locate the intersection with N = 5,000, and drop to the value of n $\doteq$ 1100. For M = 500 on the abscissa, project up to N = 5000, and across to n $\doteq$ 550.

Note that in both cases Formula 29 gives slightly larger values of required n than does the graph. This is due to the correction for finite population in the graph, which correction is not made in the formula.

A stopping rule for comparison of population density on two areas by the Schnabel Method is given by Chapman and Overton (1966).

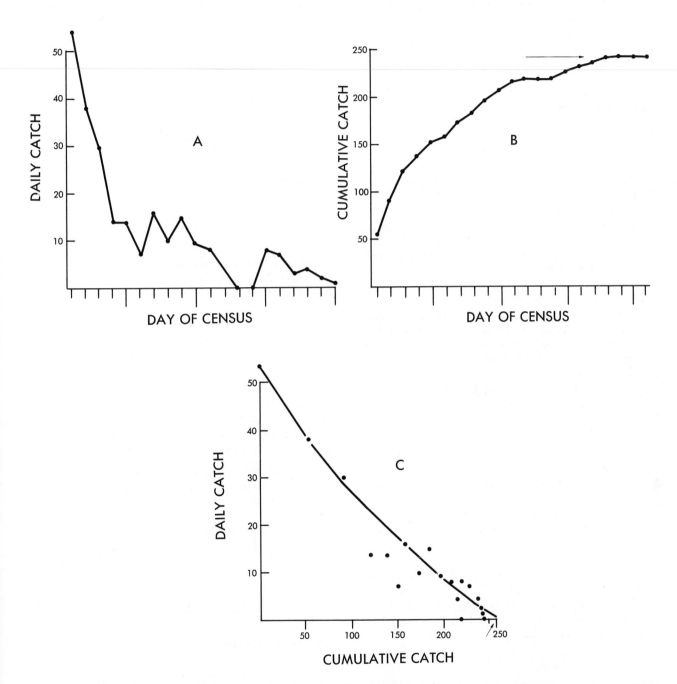

Fig. 21.7. Three graphical representations of the same data (from Emlen 1943). *A*. A direct record of catch. *B*. A Davis graph. If cumulative catch is plotted against cumulative effort, the curve will approach an asymptote as all catchable animals are caught. An estimate of the asymptote is equivalent to an estimate of N. . A Leslie graph. If catch rate is plotted against cumulative catch, the curve will approach the horizontal axis. An estimate of the intercept is equivalent to an estimate of N.

METHODS INVOLVING "REDUCTION" OF THE POPULATION SIZE AND RATE OF "CAPTURE"

This group of methods is based on the principle that rate of capture or observation decreases as the population decreases. In order to utilize this principle, it is necessary to model capture rate as a function of population size, and a number of models have been proposed. For additional reading, reference is made to Ricker (1958), Hayne (1949), Moran (1951), Zippin (1956, 1958), and DeLury (1947, 1951, and 1954).

The Graphical Solution

The simplest form of the method is graphical. Plot *rate of capture* (ordinate) against *cumulative removal* to obtain a "Leslie Graph," (Fig. 21.7 C). Extrapolate to the point at which rate of capture becomes zero, at which point all animals that are subject to capture will have been removed. The variations in the method involve variations in specification of the form of relationship between capture rate and cumulative removal. Effectively, the mathematical solutions are nothing more than objective extrapolation procedures. Note, however, that the Leslie graph may be allowed to curve and generally to yield the "best" extrapolation, which flexibility is also provided by the graphical method illustrated in parts A and B of Fig. 21.7. In the example presented, it appears that curve B yields the best result.

The Leslie Method

Assume that one unit of capture effort (e.g., a trap night) has the probability p of capturing any particular animal, and assume that additional units of effort at time t are noninterfering. Then the expected number n_t of animals taken by one unit of effort at time t is pN_t and the expected number by the total effort is pf_tN_t, where f_t is the total effort at time t. Symbolically, these assumptions can be written,

$$E(n_t) = pf_tN_t$$

or

$$E(n_t/f_t) = pN_t.$$

Now

$$N_t = N_0 - M_t,$$

where M_t, the cumulative number "removed" from the population prior to time t, is also known, and a linear structural equation can be written for (n_t/f_t) as a function of M_t,

$$E(n_t/f_t) = pN_0 - pM_t. \tag{30}$$

Given, then, a series of observations (n_t, f_t, M_t), it is possible to estimate p and N_0 by linear regression. Rewrite (30) in the form of a simple linear regression equation by substituting as follows: $x = M_t$, $\beta = p$, $\alpha = pN_0$, $y = n_t/f_t$. Thus

$$E(y) = \alpha + \beta x.$$

Then,

$$\left. \begin{array}{l} \hat{\beta} = \dfrac{\Sigma(x - \bar{x})(y - \bar{y})}{\Sigma(x - \bar{x})^2} \\[2em] \hat{\alpha} = \bar{y} - \hat{\beta}\bar{x} \end{array} \right\} \text{, the usual linear regression estimates,}$$

and by the above correspondence these estimates are translated into estimates of the parameters of interest,

$$\hat{p} = -\hat{\beta},$$

$$\hat{N}_0 = -\hat{\alpha}/\hat{\beta}.$$

A word of caution is in order. If $\hat{\beta}$ turns out to be positive, then the appropriate N_t intercept does not exist and the *estimator $\hat{N}_0$ is undefined*! To say this another way, as $\hat{\beta}$ approaches zero from below, $\hat{N}_0$ approaches infinity. As $\hat{\beta}$ equals and exceeds 0, $\hat{N}_0$ is undefined. Negative estimates by this method are *always* of this form, and should be interpreted as indeterminate, or very large.

A special case can be recognized when f_t is constant in t (i.e., if effort is equal on all occasions). Multiply equation (30) through by f_t, obtaining

$$E(n_t) = f_t pN_0 - (f_t p) M_t \tag{31}$$

which can be written

$$E(y) = \alpha + \beta x$$

where

$$\alpha = f_t pN_0 = -\beta N_0$$

$$\beta = -f_t p$$

That is, in this case it is possible to regress daily capture n_t on cumulative capture M_t and obtain the same answers.

Another special case of interest is given by Zippin (1956), where only two occasions are involved. Assuming equal effort on the two occasions,

$$\hat{N} = \frac{n_1^2}{n_1 - n_2} \qquad (32)$$

For example, suppose 100 traps are operated on each of two nights with 25 animals taken on the first night and 10 on the second. Then Formula (32) yields,

$$\hat{N} = \frac{(25)^2}{25 - 10} = \frac{125}{3} = 42.$$

The restriction noted above for the general Leslie Method is quite apparent here. If $n_1 = n_2$, Formula 32 is obviously undefined. More generally, the method requires $n_2 < n_1$.

DeLury's Method

Consider a sampling situation conforming to the catch-effort method, in which the total cumulative effort, F_t, is known for each occasion, and there exists a consistent estimate y of (n_t/f_t) for each occasion (this includes the special case in which n_t/f_t is known exactly). An example might occur on a public hunting area on which a total tally of hunters is available but hunting success must be estimated from a sample of hunters. The problem is to model y, the estimate of (n_t/f_t), as a function of F_t. Recall the model (Equation 30),

$$(n_t/f_t) = pN_0 - pM_t = pN_t.$$

Now N_t, the total number of animals present at time t, is a decreasing function of F_t, and may be modeled,

$$N_t = N_0 (1 - p)^{F_t}, \qquad (33)$$

the geometric model for population decrease under a constant attrition rate, p, per unit of pressure. Here, write the model (substituting y for (n_t/f_t)),

$$y = pN_0 (1 - p)^{F_t} \epsilon \qquad (34)$$

$$= pN_0 \left(e^{-p'F_t} \right) \epsilon$$

and

$$\ln y = \ln(pN_0) - p' F_t + \ln \epsilon$$

where ϵ is a multiplicative error.

Now if p is very small, as it usually is, then $p = p'$, so that the model becomes

$$\ln y = \ln(pN_0) - pF_t + \ln \epsilon, \qquad (35)$$

which model is due to DeLury (1951). Note that (35) requires natural logarithms ($\log_e$). This may be modified for common logs (to base 10) by writing

$$\log y = \log (pN_0) - 0.4343pF_t + \log \epsilon . \qquad (35a)$$

It should be pointed out that an estimator can be obtained from this model which does not require p to be very small. Recall (34) and write

$$\log y = \log (pN_0) + \left[\log (1 - p) \right] F_t + \log \epsilon \cdot \qquad (36)$$

Now, solve by least squares (regress $\log y_t$ on F_t) and equate the parameters as follows

$$\hat{p} = 1 - \text{antilog } \hat{\beta},$$

$$\hat{N}_0 = \frac{\text{antilog } \hat{\alpha}}{1 - \text{antilog } \hat{\beta}} \cdot$$

A comment on the DeLury model is appropriate. The model for N_t as a function of F_t (e.g., Equation 33) is not consistent with the fundamental assumption of the Leslie Method--that units of effort on a single occasion are non-interfering. Rather, Equation (33) implies that the occasion structure is unimportant. A consistent model for N_t (given the Leslie model assumption) would be

$$N_t = N_0 \prod_{i=1}^{t-1} (1 - pf_i),$$

$$= N_0 (1 - pf_1)(1 - pf_2) \cdots (1 - pf_{t-1}),$$

but this does not seem to lead to a simple estimator of N_0. (The symbol Π is to a multiple product as the symbol Σ is to a multiple sum.)

Alternate DeLury Method Solution

An alternative solution to the sampling situation for which the DeLury Method is appropriate may be more satisfactory in many terrestrial sampling problems. Recall the Leslie Model, (30)

$$(n_t/f_t) = pN_t = pN_0 - pM_t.$$

If $y_t \rightarrow n_t/f_t$, it follows that consistent estimators of n_t and M_t are given by the equations,

$$\hat{n}_t = f_t y_t,$$

and

$$\hat{M}_t = \sum_{t=1}^{t-1} \hat{n}_t.$$

That is, if $y_t \rightarrow n_t/f_t$, then $\hat{n}_t \rightarrow n_t$ and $\hat{M}_t \rightarrow M_t$.

Therefore, by regressing y_t on $\hat{M}_t$, estimates can be obtained that are comparable to the regression solution of the Leslie method. The objection may be raised that the independent variables of this regression analysis are measured with error. It is true that this causes some statistical difficulty (particularly for small samples) but it is considered likely that these difficulties are lesser than those caused by model inconsistencies and approximation.

Application of the Method in a Multiple Recapture Experiment

DeLury (1951 and 1954) makes a strong appeal for consideration of the information contained in capture-recapture experiments regarding the reduction in rate of capture of unmarked animals as the number of marked (removed) animals increases. That is, let the number of captures, n_t, be the number of *unmarked* animals captured, and f_t the units of effort on the tth occasion. Then

$M_t = \sum_{i=1}^{t-1} n_i$, the total number of animals in the

population previously captured, where n_i is now defined as the number of animals captured for the first time on the ith occasion. Now, the Leslie and DeLury methods can be applied directly.

General Discussion

The application of these methods requires acceptance of the assumptions on which they are based . . . a comment which has been made about all methods. Thus, it behooves the researcher to critically appraise his sampling situation with regard to the assumptions.

First, the regression equations, 30, 31, 34, 35, 35a, 36, *all* require the assumption that $N_t = N_0 - M_t$, i.e., that the only change in the population is through known removal. This assumption can be modified if one can estimate other components of change in N. That is, if q is the number of animals lost through natural mortality during the sampling period, then $N_t = N_0 - q - M_t$.

Second, the equations require the assumption that p is constant in time, that a unit of effort has the same average probability of removing a particular individual, given that the individual is still present, regardless of the time or how many individuals have been removed previously. This is probably the greatest source of model violation in terrestrial applications. Many species have seasonally changing susceptibility or vulnerability to capturing devices. If the change with season is known, or if it can be estimated, the model can also be modified to account for this.

The assumption of constant p can also be violated if individuals within the population have different vulnerabilities, as those with largest p are caught (on the average) early in the program and the average p is then a decreasing function of number removed. This results in a concave curve of n_t/f_t on M_t, with the consequence that linear extrapolation will underestimate N_0. It is easier to modify the procedure to account for this effect than it is for the preceding one of seasonally changing vulnerabilities.

It should be noted that this condition of unequal probability of capture can be imposed by the field design. For example, if traps are left at the same location throughout the study, certain animals will be more or less vulnerable due to spatial proximity to the trap. Daily relocation of traps will solve the trap configuration problem, but poses other problems. A reasonable compromise is to move the traps several times during a study.

The third assumption of the Leslie model is that each unit of effort expended at time t exerts the same "force" on the population, with no interference among the units (without compensating effects). Expressed another way, this requires that the expected catch by the first unit (say by the first trap or hunter) without competition, is equal to the expected catch by the 100th unit (trap or hunter) given that the first 99 are operating. This is fairly restrictive, but will be seen to hold in many circumstances. When it does not hold, the generally recommended approach is to adjust daily effort to some standard units of effort, which approach can account for variation among devices as well as for interference, but which obviously requires additional information.

THE METHOD OF SELECTIVE REDUCTION OR INCREASE

The method of selective reduction or increase is also called the dichotomy method or the change in composition method. Kelker (1940) appears to have been the first to use this general group of methods. Numerous examples have since been published of their use, and important expository papers have been written by Petrides (1949), Chapman (1955), Hanson (1963), Chapman and Murphy (1965), and Rupp (1965). The present treatment essentially follows the approach of the latter two references.

The General Model

First, a population structure is recognized and modeled in (1) recognizable classes of animals and (2) time. In the simplest form there are two classes of animals and two occasions (e.g., sampling dates), so that a complete structural model is given by $(N_{11}, N_{12}, N_{21}, N_{22})$ where N_{ij} is the number of animals in the ith population class on the jth occasion.

Now, given the datum $(X_1, X_2, X_3, \ldots)$, the next step is to equate the datum to the population elements, either by identity or by model assumption, and so construct the *structural* equations. To illustrate, suppose that X_1 is the number of animals of class 1 removed between times 1 and 2, X_2 is the number removed from class 2 between times 1 and 2, X_3 is the ratio of numbers in the two classes at time 1 and X_4 is the ratio of numbers at time 2. Now, from these definitions, four structural equations can be written in terms of the structural components of the population,

$$X_1 = N_{11} - N_{12},$$

$$X_2 = N_{21} - N_{22},$$

$$X_3 = N_{11}/N_{21},$$

$$X_4 = N_{12}/N_{22}.$$

These, being four equations in four unknowns, can be solved for the unknowns, $N_{11}, N_{12}, N_{21}, N_{22}$. This solution can take many forms, but they must all yield the same answers; and generally the solution is much simpler if numbers are inserted directly into the structural equations. To illustrate the symbolic solution, consider the following steps:

1) $X_1 = N_{21}X_3 - N_{22}X_4$

   $X_2 = N_{21} - N_{22}$

2) $X_1/X_3 = N_{21} - N_{22}X_4/X_3$

   $X_2 = N_{21} - N_{22}$

3) $\dfrac{X_1}{X_3} - X_2 = N_{22} - N_{22}\dfrac{X_4}{X_3} = N_{22}\left(1 - \dfrac{X_4}{X_5}\right)$

4) $N_{22} = \left(\dfrac{X_1 - X_2X_3}{X_3}\right)\left(\dfrac{X_3}{X_3 - X_4}\right) = \left(\dfrac{X_1 - X_2X_3}{X_3 - X_4}\right)$

and then,

$$N_{12} = X_4N_{22}$$

$$N_{11} = X_1 + N_{12}$$

$$N_{21} = X_2 + N_{22} \quad .$$

Now,[2]

---

[2]Recall the (·) notation used earlier. Given a double subscripted variable, a (·) in the position of one subscript indicates summation over that subscript. Thus $N_{.1} = N_{11} + N_{21}$ and $N_{2.} = N_{21} + N_{22}$.

$$N_{.1} = N_{11} + N_{21}$$

$$= X_1 + X_2 + \left(\frac{X_1 - X_2 X_3}{X_3 - X_4}\right) + X_4 \left(\frac{X_1 - X_2 X_3}{X_3 - X_4}\right)$$

$$= \frac{(X_1 + X_2)(X_3 - X_4) + (X_1 - X_2 X_3) + X_4 X_1 - X_2 X_3 X_4}{X_3 - X_4}$$

$$= (X_3 + 1)(X_1 - X_2 X_4)/(X_3 - X_4). \qquad (37)$$

By inspection the fundamental limitation of this method can be discovered: if $X_3 = X_4$, it is improper to solve for N_{22}, for division by $X_3 - X_4$ is necessary and division by zero is not allowed. That is, there must be differential rates of removal before the method will work.

Rupp's Formula

Consider Rupp's (1966) formula, changed to the present notation by the following correspondences,

$$M = -X_1 = N_{12} - N_{11}$$

$$F = -X_2 = N_{22} - N_{21}$$

$$p_1 = (X_3 + 1)/X_3 = N_{11}/(N_{11} + N_{21})$$

$$p_2 = (X_4 + 1)/X_4 = N_{12}/(N_{21} + N_{22})$$

Then

$$N_{.1} = \frac{M - p_2(M + F)}{p_2 - p_1} , \text{ after Rupp,} \qquad (38)$$

$$= \frac{-X_1(X_4 + 1)(X_3 + 1) + X_4(X_3 + 1)(X_2 + X_1)}{(X_4 - X_3)}$$

$$= (X_1 - X_2 X_4)(X_3 + 1)/(X_3 - X_4), \text{ as above.}$$

The Case of Estimated X's

Now the most convenient form of the formula will depend on the manner in which the data are available, but so long as 4 distinct pieces of information are available, 4 structural equations can be written equating the known values to the population values and a solution determined for the population values.

As presented above, X_1 is exactly the number of animals of type 1 removed from the population between times 1 and 2, X_3 is exactly the ratio of animals of type 1 to animals to type 2 and time 1, etc. It is obvious that these quantities will not usually be known exactly, or at least, the wildlifer does not expect always to know all four exactly. For example, he might know exactly the number of buck deer and doe deer taken by hunting and have sight records before and after the season yielding estimates of the ratio of bucks to does on the two occasions. In this case he will have

$$X_1 = N_{11} - N_{12}$$

$$X_2 = N_{21} - N_{22}$$

$$(n_{11}/n_{21}) = X_3 = (N_{11}/N_{21}) + \epsilon_1$$

$$(n_{12}/n_{22}) = X_4 = (N_{12}/N_{22}) + \epsilon_2,$$

and it is appropriate to use the same formula (37) if an assumption is made of the consistency of X_3 for (N_{11}/N_{21}) and X_4 for (N_{12}/N_{22}), as then the estimator $\hat{N}_{.1}$ will be consistent for $N_{.1}$. That is, to use the same formula, it is assumed that X_3 approaches (N_{11}/N_{21}) as the number of animals observed becomes large, and similarily that X_4 approaches (N_{12}/N_{22}).

If any of the X's are random variables (as opposed to population constants), it is appropriate to put a "hat" on the quantity given by Equations (37) and (38). That is, write $\hat{N}_{.1}$ in place of $N_{.1}$. It is also appropriate in this case to consider the variance of $\hat{N}_{.1}$. Several persons (Kelker 1964, Chapman and Murphy 1965) have suggested that the delta method (or propagation of error method, Deming 1964) is useful.

This yields fairly messy formulae which vary with all of the special cases, and there seems little to be gained by including special cases in this treatment. In general, if there are k uncorrelated variables, $X_1, X_2, \ldots, X_k$, then the variance is approximated by,

$$V(\hat{N}) \doteq \sum_{i=1}^{k} \left(\frac{\partial \hat{N}}{\partial X_i}\right)_E^2 V(X_i), \qquad (39)$$

where the E indicates that the term in brackets is

to be evaluated at the *mean value,* or *expectation,* of the variables involved. An estimate of $V(\hat{N})$ involves substitution of observed values into the elements of this expression. Note that if one of the X's is a known constant, then $V(X) = 0$ and that term drops out of the variance expression. If the X's are correlated, one must add terms to $V(\hat{N})$,

$$2\left(\frac{\partial \hat{N}}{\partial X_i}\right)_E \left(\frac{\partial \hat{N}}{\partial X_j}\right)_E \text{cov}(X_i, X_j),$$

for each correlated pair (X_i, X_j).

An Example

Dasmann (1952:227) gives a good example of the use of this technique in estimating a deer population. The prehunting value (X_3) was 74 bucks to 139 does and the post-hunting value (X_4) was 50 bucks to 139 does. From a check of hunters it was known that $246 = X_1$ bucks were killed, and $X_2 = 0$. To illustrate substitution directly into the structural equations:

(1) $246 = \hat{N}_{11} - \hat{N}_{12}$

$0 = \hat{N}_{21} - \hat{N}_{22}$

$74/139 = \hat{N}_{11}/\hat{N}_{21}$

$50/139 = \hat{N}_{12}/\hat{N}_{22}$

(2) $\hat{N}_{11} = 246 + \hat{N}_{12}$

$\hat{N}_{21} = \hat{N}_{11} (139/74)$

$\hat{N}_{22} = \hat{N}_{12} (139/50)$

(3) $\hat{N}_{11} = 246 + \hat{N}_{12}$

$\hat{N}_{11} = \hat{N}_{12} (74/50)$

(4) $0 = 246 + \hat{N}_{12} (1 - 74/50)$

(5) $\hat{N}_{12} = 50(246)/24 = 512.5$

$\hat{N}_{11} = 512.5 + 246 = 758.5$

$\hat{N}_{21} = 1424.75$

(6) $\hat{N}_{.1} = \hat{N}_{11} + \hat{N}_{21} = 2183.25.$

The same answer is obtained by substitution into Equation (37), writing $\hat{N}_{.1}$ for $N_{.1}$ since some of the data are estimates,

$$\hat{N}_{.1} = \left(\frac{74}{139} + 1\right)(246 - 0)/\left(\frac{74}{139} - \frac{50}{139}\right)$$

$$= (213)(246)/24$$

$$= 2183.25.$$

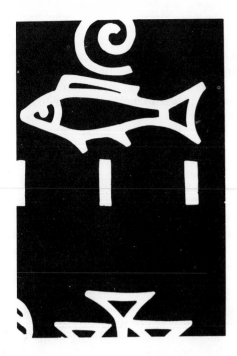

CHAPTER TWENTY-TWO

POPULATION ANALYSIS[1]

L. L. EBERHARDT, PhD

Battelle-Northwest
Richland, Washington

"Animal population analysis" means the process of attempting to determine the structure (i.e., the age and sex composition) of a population and the forces controlling the past and future composition of that population. Populations of wild animals rarely are static—hence the term "population dynamics." Fluctuations of numbers almost invariably are accompanied by changes in structure. In fact, knowledge of the internal workings of a population will ordinarily provide a good notion as to probable future changes in the numerical abundance of that population. Such predictions are the wildlife manager's principal goal in population analysis.

The basic ingredients for a study of any population are birth and death rates, age and sex composition, and numerical abundance. Given good estimates of these essentials, few complications of mathematics, logic, or terminology are in-

[1]This chapter is based in part on work performed under United States Atomic Energy Commission Contract AT(45-1)-1830.

volved in understanding population behavior in general terms. Unfortunately, a complete array of the needed data is never available, and all sorts of difficulties arise in trying to get along with the observations that can be obtained.

Most of the problems have to do with sampling the population of interest. Virtually all methods for sampling wild animal populations are susceptible to biases of various kinds. The several age and sex groups react differently to hunting or trapping (the methods by which most sufficiently large samples are obtained). For these, and other reasons, one has always to be suspicious about the validity of data and to try to cross-check against other sources of information. Thus the actual process of analyzing a wild population depends on knowing a good deal about the species, local conditions, and the people involved in collecting records, as well as the more scientific aspects of the problems.

Essential measurements may be divided into three general classes: (1) estimates of actual numbers, as of the total legal harvest on some particular area, (2) indices, or measures of relative abundance—e.g., the number seen per hour of observation, and, (3) rates and proportions, as, for example, births per female or proportion of males in a sample. It usually happens that all three kinds of measurements must be used in a given study, and unfortunately they are not always compatible. One can seldom apply a rate to an index and come up with a usable product. As a result, a given population cannot be adequately analyzed without estimating the actual numbers present.

To sum up, uncertainties about validity or adequacy of the basic records and the necessity for employing different kinds of measurements (numbers, indices, and rates) pretty well prohibit half-way measures. One either gets the whole story, in terms of numbers of individuals, or winds up floundering in the dark. The rest of this chapter will be devoted to specific topics having to do with such a synthesis.

Basic Mathematics and Statistics

No very complex mathematics need be involved for a majority of practical studies. The student of populations does need to know how to handle logarithms and exponents in simple algebraic statements. In these days, most people are familiar with compound interest, and it is usually desirable to be able to also employ the "exponential function" or "exponential curve" which approximates very closely the usual interest formula compounded at very short time intervals. Any modern high school mathematics text will provide these essential tools.

Probably it ought to be mentioned that population mathematics can get very much more involved, yet still be inadequate for a complete understanding of the subject. The mathematical theory of probability, in its advanced forms, is indeed complex, yet is inadequate to encompass the full details of the famous *Tribolium* populations—small beetles capable of living out normal life spans in the uncomplicated habitat of a vial of flour. But the present text is designed for applied problems and a working knowledge thereof, rather than the intricacies of present population research, so mathematical complexity will be avoided as much as possible.

There is one very important pitfall for every practicing wildlife biologist, and it seems that virtually everyone fails to avoid it completely. That is the matter of expecting a few observations to provide an unreasonable amount of information about a population. With skulduggery excluded, few people expect to predict accurately the results of a half-dozen tosses of a coin or a few rolls of dice. Much of statistical methodology has to do with what happens in such "chance" operations, and the unhappy facts of life include one which says that variability of an average depends on the square root of the number of observations. Thus, quadrupling a sample can, at best, only double the amount of information provided.

There is hardly space here for a short course in statistics, but the reader is warned that attention to variability is essential. Everyone interested in population studies probably ought to try a series of very simple sampling exercises by way of getting a "feel" for the fluctuations encountered in small samples. The only tools needed are a table of random numbers (almost all elementary statistics books have them), pencil and paper, and some patience. The following table provides an example, using "age-classes" constructed by assuming a 50% annual mortality and exact replacement of losses, so that in an "average" hundred animals there should be 50 one-year olds, 25 two-year olds, and so on. One then just goes down any two-digit column in the table of random numbers and checks off each pair of digits according to its "age" as follows:

Ages	Corre- sponding serial numbers in a popu- lation of 100	Obser- vations	Total	Per- cent
"One-year olds"	00-49	₸₦ ₸₦L₸₦ ₸₦₦|||	24	48
"Two-year olds"	50-74	₸₦L ₸₦\/	10	20
3	75-87	₸₦||	7	14
4	88-93	||	2	4
5	94-96	||||	4	8
6 and older	97-99	|||	3 / 50	6 / 100

The example here comes out not too badly; 48% was obtained where 50 was expected, 20% for 25, and so on, in a sample of 50. But this is where some patience is essential—one ought to draw a dozen or more samples of from 10 to 100 observations each and to try applying various calculations of rates and ratios to the results. The usual statistical technique used in intercomparing such samplings is the chi-square test. The application of this simple criterion would save much laborious study of data as well as some later embarassment.

For the above example, the chi-square test is calculated as follows:

Age Class	Observed Sample	Expected Number	Observed Minus Expected
1	24	25.0	-1.0
2	10	12.5	-2.5
3	7	6.2	0.8
4	2 }		
5	4 }	6.3	2.7
6 and older	3 }		
	50	50.0	0.0

Chi-square is then calculated as:

$$\sum \frac{(\text{observed}-\text{expected})^2}{\text{expected}} = 1.80$$

Here the last 3 classes were grouped to avoid a bias caused by calculating chi-square with small expected numbers. The tabulated value for 3 degrees of freedom is 7.81 at the 5% level of significance, indicating what one would expect in this case, i.e., no evidence of a difference.

A tabulation of 10 such samples of 50 observations follows:

Age Class	1	2	3	4	5	6	7	8	9	10
1	24	19	25	23	22	24	27	25	26	17
2	10	18	9	10	15	12	10	10	16	17
3	7	5	6	7	6	6	7	10	3	10
4	2	5	7	5	3	3	2	2	4	3
5	4		1	2	3	4	2	3	1	
6+	3	3	2	3	1	1	2			3
	50	50	50	50	50	50	50	50	50	50
Chi-square	1.80	4.48	3.15	2.84	0.94	0.53	0.77	3.10	2.94	6.52

Just 1 sample in the 10 gave a chi-square value greater than that tabulated for the 10% level (6.25), and this is exactly what would be expected.

A rather famous example of the complete removal of a roe deer herd (Anderson 1953) can be examined in the same way as above to give an approximate test for changes in age structure as the shooting proceeded. If the removals are grouped in successive lots of about 50 (using the tabulation of Quick 1958) we can show the first "sampling" of the herd as follows:

FIRST GROUP

Age	Available population	Number shot (O)	Expected number (E)	$\frac{(O-E)^2}{E}$
1	91	13	21.4	3.3
2	41	14	9.6	2.0
3	34	8	8.0	0.0
4	17	2	4.0	1.0
5	13	6		
6	8	3		
7	4	1	7.0	5.1
8	3	3		
9	2	0		
Total	213	50	50.0	$\chi^2 = 11.4$

The "expected number" is calculated on the basis of $^{50}/213$ times the number initially alive in each age group (i.e., on the assumption that all age-groups are equally vulnerable).

The same calculations are then applied to the succeeding two samples (where the "available population" is naturally the survivors of the previous hunting):

SECOND GROUP

Age	Available population	Number shot (O)	Expected number (E)	$\frac{(O-E)^2}{E}$
1	78	31	26.8	0.6
2	27	5	9.3	2.0
3	26	6	8.9	0.9
4	15	7	5.2	0.6
5	7	4		
6	5	1		
7	3	1	5.8	0.2
8	0	0		
9	2	1		
Total	163	56	56.0	$\chi^2 = 4.3$

THIRD GROUP

Age	Available population	Number shot (O)	Expected number (E)	$\frac{(O-E)^2}{E}$
1	47	23	23.8	0.0
2	22	13	11.1	0.3
3	20	9	10.1	0.1
4	8	4	4.0	0.0
5	3	1		
6	4	3		
7	2	0	5.0	0.0
8	0	0		
9	1	1		
Total	107	54	54.0	$\chi^2 = 0.4$

The chi-square value for the first group exceeds that expected in 5 samples out of 100 (9.5), while the values in the next two groups are much smaller than would be expected as a matter of chance. Adding up the chi-squares from all three groups gives a value of 16.1 with 12 degrees of freedom, as compared to the 5% level of 21.0. While it should be emphasized that the use of chi-square here is only an approximation, the statistical evidence for real differences between age-classes in removal rates seems rather shaky. Note, too, that the different age-groups do not seem to show any consistent pattern of differences from expected numbers. The uncomfortable conclusion of any moderately careful study is that samples of even several hundred animals don't really yield a lot of information, and assertions of changes in, say, proportion of yearlings from place to place or year to year based on such samples are likely to be extremely misleading. Yet a sample of even 100 game animals is not easily or quickly obtained, nor are there any known substitutes. The investigator must proceed cautiously and pay serious attention to results of statistical tests of significance.

Span of Time For Analysis

Several kinds of troubles have been and are yet to be mentioned here. Some of these are partially alleviated by the passage of time. As a series of years of records build up, so do the opportunities for cross-checking and spotting anomalies. With a deer population, one can "follow" a given age-class for several years and eventually get a fair notion of the overall annual survival. Small game populations "turn over" much more rapidly, but even so, only a series of records permits one to decide whether various rates jibe or make sense relative to other measures. A hard and fast rule is not available, but experience shows that one can scarcely expect to do much analysis without data from at least 3 or 4 successive years.

Bias

As has already been mentioned, behavioral differences between sex and age groups are to be expected in most species. Since samples large enough for practical use so often depend on examining the hunter's bag, any sort of differential vulnerability to hunting or selectivity by the hunter will result in the sample not truly representing the population. Trapping, too, is subject to the prospect that, e.g., young animals may be less wary (or, conversely, may be less active and infrequently caught). Such biases are likely to be due to differences in rates and thus not be constant in time or with accumulating sampling effort. An example for pheasants (Eberhardt and Blouch 1955) can be described with a little algebra.

The example is over-simplified in several respects, one of which is that hunting effort is assumed to be applied to the population in successive units. For illustration, n successive "units of hunting effort" are assumed to be expended on an area containing N_a adult cock pheasants (over 1 year old) and N_j juvenile cocks (hatched in the current season). If the adults are taken at a rate r_a and juveniles at the higher rate r_j, then the harvest of one class may be described by compound interest rules as:

$$\text{Kill} = rN \qquad \text{for } 1^{\text{st}} \text{ unit of effort} \\ \text{(which leaves } N - rN \\ = N(1-r) \text{ survivors)}$$

$$= rN(1-r) \qquad \text{for } 2^{\text{nd}} \text{ unit of effort} \\ \text{(leaving } N - rN - rN(1-r) \\ = N(1-r)^2 \text{ survivors)}$$

$$= rN(1-r)^{n-1} \text{ for the } n^{\text{th}} \text{ unit of effort}$$

Thus the age ratio (juveniles/adult) in the bag is the ratio of the two kills:

$$\frac{K_j}{K_a} = \frac{r_j}{r_a} \frac{N_j}{N_a} \left(\frac{1-r_j}{1-r_a}\right)^{n-1} \qquad (1)$$

which decreases as n increases. Taking logarithms:

$$\log \frac{K_j}{K_a} = \log\left(\frac{r_j}{r_a} \frac{N_j}{N_a}\right) + (n-1) \log\left(\frac{1-r_j}{1-r_a}\right) \qquad (2)$$

and representing the quantities which can be measured by checking hunter's bags as:

$$Y = \log\left(\frac{K_j}{K_a}\right) = \log \text{ of age ratio}$$

$$X = n-1 = \text{cumulated hunting effort}$$

and the other quantities as A and B we get:

$$Y = A + BX$$

which is the equation of a straight line. An example is shown in Fig. 22.1 with the hunting effort scale in percentage units due to uncertainty about the actual hours expended in the two years. The reader should note that the left scale of Fig. 22.1 is in logarithms (base 10), and that the average age ratios dropped from about 20 to less than 10, a substantial change. Further, unless the actual rates are estimated, (not just their ratio) one cannot determine the "true" age ratio from the above equations.

Not very much progress seems to have been made in dealing with this problem, perhaps because it is often just not recognized. A complete analysis of a population age structure often depends on some sort of solution. Some further examples are given for deer by Maguire and Severinghaus (1954) and Eberhardt (1960). Eberhardt et al. (1963) describe the situation for cottontail rabbits (see especially p. 22 and 26). Fig. 22.2 shows an effect of different methods of measuring age ratios.

Historical Aspects

Many biologists have forgotten that "population" comes from the Latin "populus," meaning people. But people nowadays speak freely of populations of all kinds, ranging from people to galaxies. A word with Greek origin, "demography," largely has been reserved to cover the study of human populations. Since the biology and mathematics of animals and people are much the same, it does not seem unreasonable to speak of "animal demography" as have a few writers.

462

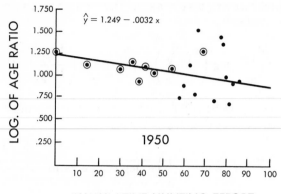

$$\hat{y} = 1.249 - .0032 x$$

LOG. OF AGE RATIO

1950

CUMULATIVE HUNTING EFFORT

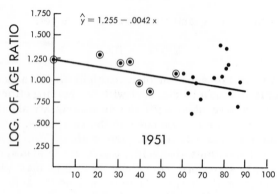

$$\hat{y} = 1.255 - .0042 x$$

LOG. OF AGE RATIO

1951

CUMULATIVE HUNTING EFFORT

Fig. 22.1. Changes in logarithm of Michigan pheasant age ratios with cumulative hunting effort (Eberhardt and Blouch 1955). Encircled points are those based on at least 100 pheasants.

Cole (1957) said that Plato "had a definite concept of optimum population size and an understanding of factors regulating population size." In a detailed and very readable review, Cole traced the history of population study, noting that an Italian (Botero) preceded by some 200 years the 1798 essay of Malthus in recognizing the potential for geometric growth of populations. It was not until about the 17th century that mathematical aspects of population study received notable study, with the names of Buffon, Malthus, and DeMoivre perhaps being best-remembered. The modern aspects began to be developed as early as the 1830's, and animal studies are often dated by reference to Darwin's study of evolution in mid-century. However, Skellam (1955) noted that Linnaeus described potential population increase in plants by a geometric growth scheme in 1740.

Early in the 20th century, Lotka, Volterra, and Pearl began work which is essentially the core of modern knowledge and theory about populations.

The student should refer to the book by Allee et al. (1949) for additional perspective on the origins of ecological population studies.

SURVIVAL

Success or failure of any population is necessarily expressed as the balance between births and deaths. A host of factors affect birth and death rates, both directly and through chains of coaction and reaction. Single factors may be predominate in affecting mortality (and, less often, reproduction) and one of the goals of wildlife management is to regulate such factors.

Excepting mankind, no single species shows any evidence of taking over the earth, so a long-term balance between births and deaths obviously holds for a majority of species. Consequently, any form with a high birth rate must have a high death rate, and vice versa. There are some interesting arguments about the evolutionary status of mortality vs. reproduction, which run somewhat along the chicken and egg line—which came first? That is, is there a selective advantage (in terms of evolution) to an increased reproductive rate, which is later compensated by an increase in mortality?

The game manager is necessarily concerned with the year to year status of populations, and on this scale reproduction and mortality seldom balance out exactly. Thus the convenient argument available to those who take the long view cannot be used and estimates of birth and death rates must be attempted each and every year.

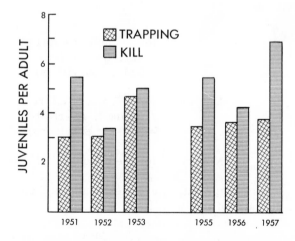

Fig. 22.2. Cottontail rabbit age ratios obtained by two methods on the same Michigan area (Eberhardt et al. 1963).

This is why the present section is headed "survival" rather than "mortality"—simply because it is often easier to estimate a survival rate. The distinction is almost but not quite as trivial as it seems. It is true that annual mortality and survival rates for any specified group of animals have to add up to unity, since an animal either survives or dies. But when the manager considers a population he often will want to avoid getting the very high mortality just after birth entangled with that occurring later in life, and thus may estimate only survival (or mortality) beyond a certain age. Also, managers dealing with populations outside the hunting season will be concerned primarily with survivors, rather than losses.

The Annual Cycle

Almost anyone interested in wildlife is aware of the annual rhythms of a majority of populations. Births are often concentrated in a relatively short season at the beginning of a period of generally favorable conditions, during which the young reach a stage of maturity sufficient to contend with the approaching season of food scarcity and more severe weather conditions. A completely general description is not possible (i.e., consider the arctic microtines whose "easy times" appear to occur when most other northern species are contending with the rigors of winter), but we can visualize a somewhat hypothetical annual cycle of population abundance (e.g. Fig. 22.3).

While a knowledge of life history features will suffice to determine the general shape of a cycle of annual abundance, measuring it poses tremendous problems. With many species it seems, too, that the critical period is that of the most severe environmental conditions (usually winter) so that the future course of a population may not depend primarily on the reproductive period. At any rate, the difficulties of measuring population size, age structure, reproductive rates, etc., are such that managers normally have to settle for an effort to obtain a reliable measure of population status at one time during the year, and to relate indices of conditions in other seasons to that one "good fix."

Presumably some period just prior to the hunting season might be selected as being most desirable for an accurate estimate of population parameters, but it usually turns out that the availability and quality of the data determine the calendar date of the "best" estimate. Also, to the wildlife administrator's dismay, he almost always has to wait until "all of the numbers are in," and

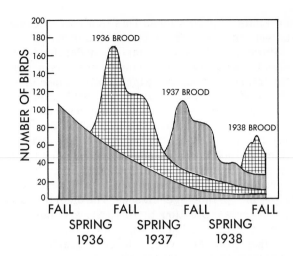

Fig. 22.3. Changes in a population of valley quail during a period of three years (Emlen 1940).

may not be able to estimate population behavior until a year after it occurred.

It is apparent then, that an annual cycle may exist and be very important, but a graph of the available data is likely to show a series of points (one for each year) rather than the sinusoidal curve of Fig. 22.3.

Population Density and Survival

Like so many ecological principles, it is fairly evident that the current density (numbers per unit area) of a population must influence its future behavior, but it is extremely difficult to prove such an assertion for specific cases. Part of the problem is a lack of knowledge of many details of population processes, making any "proof" of general assertions thus dubious, or at least subject to criticism. This all results in a controversy about "density-dependence" and "density-independence" of various features of natural populations.

Without going into the arguments pro and con, the point of view is taken here that population density does have a great deal to do with both the survival of individuals and the future size of the population. Thus a carrying-capacity exists and may fluctuate annually with weather conditions, as well as with longer term habitat changes. Population numbers tend to adjust towards this capacity. Many of the ungulates seem to be notable exceptions to such a principle, though, and attempts to explain or allow for particular cases lead to trying to decide what factors control various kinds of populations. This is a controversial subject, and out of the scope of this book.

However, it is important to understand that animal populations do evidently possess a certain internal elasticity which pulls either up or down, depending on circumstances of the moment. An example of one mechanism for "compensation" is observable in many, if not most, of the more long-lived vertebrates. The younger age-classes either do not breed at all, or produce relatively few young per female, with a steady increase in reproductive rate with age to what are sometimes called the "prime" age-classes. The older animals may show a reduction in fertility, and possibly even no reproduction at all (few game animals live that long, however). Hence a graph of reproductive rate plotted against age (Fig. 22.4) may look like an inverted "U." Unusually unfavorable environmental conditions tend to affect the very young and the very old most severely, leaving the survivors concentrated in the ages when reproduction is greatest, and thus facilitating a "bounce back" or "rebound" when conditions improve.

An example of a density-dependent relationship is that reported by Chapman (1961) for fur seals. Data for a number of years indicate that survival of male seals depends on an optimal size of pup population (Fig. 22.5). As the pup population increases, there is initially a fairly consistent increase in number of males ultimately available (as 3 year olds) for harvest. But beyond some "optimal" point, harvests actually decrease if there are too many pups. Chapman fitted two mathematical relationships to the data (Fig. 22.5) in an attempt to estimate what harvest of females ought to be permitted to keep the population at a level of maximum sustained yield.

Competing Risks

A reasonably good population estimate will probably be available at one particular time each year. However, there will be occasions when it is desirable to calculate numbers at some other time working either forwards or backwards from the selected time. The manager thus wants to apply a survival rate over varying lengths of time. For many purposes the compound interest formula already described will do the job. Sometimes, though, there may be two or more sources of mortality to contend with, and these forces may operate simultaneously, thus "competing."

Perhaps the most frequent use of the concept of competing risks has been in fisheries manage-

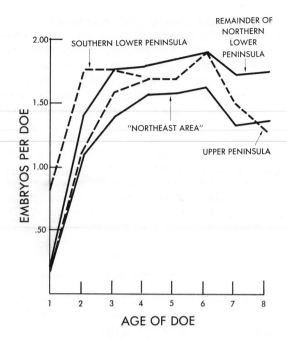

Fig. 22.4. White-tailed deer reproductive rates plotted against age for several different Michigan areas (Eberhardt 1960).

ment, where long harvesting periods make it essential to work with mortality due to both fishing and to other causes—usually lumped as "natural" mortality. An exposition of the basic formulae is given by Ricker (1958:24-26), and an application to small game (cottontail rabbit) populations is to be found in the report by Eberhardt et al. (1963).

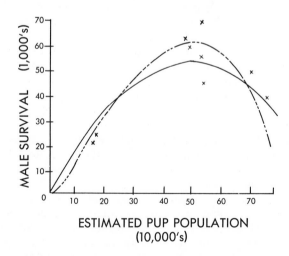

Fig. 22.5. Survival (to age 3) of male fur seals plotted against estimated pup population. Curves are two theoretical relationships fitted to the data (Chapman 1961).

Estimating Survival and Mortality

So far as estimation goes, a primary distinction between survival and mortality is: (1) an annual *survival rate* for a given age-class is estimated from measures of the numerical abundance at the same calendar date in two successive years, and (2) mortality is often measured by the number of animals killed by legal harvest or found dead in surveys. Some aspects of estimating harvest are discussed by Eberhardt and Murray (1960), and mortality surveys have been described by Robinette et al. (1954, 1956) and Whitlock and Eberhardt (1956).

The difficulties in estimating survival are those of estimating population size and age composition. That is, the concept is deceptively simple—if there are N_i animals of age i alive today, and N_{i+1} (of age i+1) one year later, then the annual survival rate is:

$$\frac{N_{i+1}}{N_i} = s$$

The troubles arise primarily in measuring population size, and secondarily in allowing for movements in and out of the area being studied. Presence of some tagged animals helps greatly in assessing the possible importance of these movements.

If the population size is measured at some time other than the hunting season, but age composition data come from bag checks, there may be questions as to the applicability of the composition data at the time of population measurement. Sometimes only an index to population size is available, so there is the chance that weather conditions, etc., may vary the relation of index to true population density between measurements. Further problems include the prospect of differential vulnerability to hunting, as already discussed. No easy or broadly applicable solutions are available for these problems. Most of them have to be dealt with as they come up, but at least half of the battle is won if the investigator is anticipating particular sources of trouble.

Longevity is sometimes discussed in population studies, and may be given two meanings. One, sometimes called "ecological longevity," is essentially the average length of life observed under natural conditions. Most wild animals die violent deaths, and thus fail to live to any sort of "old age," but under satisfactory conditions in captivity, one may hope to observe what has been called "physiological longevity." Thus the average age of a deer in a fairly heavily hunted herd may be 3 or 4 years or less, while an animal of the same species may survive in a park to beyond 20 years. When very large samples (many thousands) of wild deer are examined, a few such old-timers do turn up, so the two notions are not really respectively "wild" and "tame" in nature.

Life Tables

Life tables are a well-known means for presenting population survival and mortality data. Their use for demographic (study of human populations) and actuarial (life insurance) purposes is of considerable importance and has a long history. Many such tables have been prepared for animal populations, so anyone concerned with such studies should be familiar with their construction and use. Shortcomings of life tables are importantly two: (1) only half the story is told, i.e., that of losses, since the usual table contains no reproductive data, as such, and (2) the table applies either only at a given point in time, or to what are called "stationary" populations, which means that births exactly balance deaths and all rates are constant over the history of the population tabled. It has already been pointed out that this is a dangerous assumption for most wild animals.

A very good discussion of the life table is available in the book by Allee et al. (1949:294-301), which should be consulted for further details and examples, as may a well-known paper by Deevey (1947).

Life tables are usually classified in two categories, depending on how the data from which they are constructed were obtained. One of these is the so-called "cohort" (or "dynamic") table, obtained from records of the fate of a group of animals (the "cohort") all born at the same time. Such tables are obviously difficult to prepare for wildlife studies, since one must be able to keep track of a given group of newborn animals, and do so until all, or virtually all, die. The second category constitutes the "current" (or "time-specific") table, wherein the mortality of each age-class in a given population is recorded over a year's time, thus describing the current status of the population.

The two kinds of tables are thus identical only if mortality rates for each age-class ("age-specific" mortality) are the same from year to year. Since this is a rather unlikely state of affairs for game animals (as well as for most other species) we usually would like to have a series of "current" life tables—one for each year. Unfortunately, really adequate data for life tables on wild animals are almost non-existent. But since the wildlife worker will find both kinds of tables described in the literature, it is important to discuss some of the problems and shortcomings.

We start out by describing a "cohort" table. For convenience, most tables begin with an arbitrary number of newborn animals (usually 1,000 or 10,000). The first line of such a table might appear as follows:

x	l_x	d_x	q_x
0	1,000	620	0.620

Here, the entry under x corresponds to the age at the beginning of the year, i.e., newborn animals. That under l_x is the number alive at the beginning of the year, under d_x the number of deaths during the year, and q_x is the fraction dying in the year, i.e., 62%.

Moving on to the next line:

x	l_x	d_x	q_x
0	1000	620	0.620
1	380	167	0.439

we see the survivors (380) listed at the beginning of the next full year of life ($x=1$) and that 167 die during that year for a mortality rate of 44%, substantially less than that in the first year of life. Filling out the rest of this hypothetical table gives:

x	ℓ_x	d_x	q_x
0	1000	620	0.620
1	380	167	0.439
2	213	85	0.399
3	128	51	0.398
4	77	32	0.416
5	45	19	0.422
6	26	14	0.538
7	12	6	0.500
8	6	4	0.667
9	2	2	1.000

The reader will perceive that, since the table begins with an arbitrary number of animals, the information in the table is really summarized by the entries in the q_x or mortality rate column. A "current" table will have exactly the same appearance, but a different basis for construction since it reflects only one year of observation.

Many life tables have been prepared from band returns, with the most extensive such tables in wildlife studies being those prepared for waterfowl. Unfortunately the returns down through the years for birds banded in a particular year are seldom sufficient to prepare a life table, so the results of a number of years of banding are usually combined. The following discussion illustrates some of the problems in preparing such tables by showing the basic data symbolically, and assuming that only the results of one year of banding are used (which would correspond to a "cohort" or "dynamic" life table).

The number of birds banded is represented by N. Then some fraction (p_0) of these are shot and reported in the first hunting season following banding. Note that p_0 is the product of two fractions, one being the proportion of all banded birds shot and the second the proportion of such bands actually reported (some birds will be "crippling losses" not recovered while a sizeable fraction of hunters who shoot banded birds simply don't send in the bands). The fraction of banded birds surviving a full year after banding is represented by s_0 (so that $1-s_0$ represents the total mortality for that year, including hunting and all other causes). For simplicity it is assumed here that banding takes place just before hunting season. The annual survival rate is s as previously defined.

A table may now be constructed to represent a sequence of years:

Year	Number Alive at Beginning	Number Shot and Reported
0	N	$p_0 N$
1	$s_0 N$	$p_1 s_0 N$
2	$s_0 s_1 N$	$p_2 s_0 s_1 N$
3	$s_0 s_1 s_2 N$	$p_3 s_0 s_1 s_2 N$
4	$s_0 s_1 s_2 s_3 N$	$p_4 s_0 s_1 s_2 s_3 N$

A different survival rate (s_i) has been shown for each year, as well as a different proportion (p_i) of bands returned each year. The situation begins to look rather complicated and some simplifying assumptions need to be made for any progress. The most reasonable one seems to be that the p_i for two successive years might be approximately the same. In that case, dividing the number shot and reported in the second year of a pair by the same quantity for the first year of the pair, an estimate is obtained of the survival rate for that year. That is, consider years 2 and 3:

$$\frac{\text{number shot and reported in year 3}}{\text{number shot and reported in year 2}} = \frac{p_3 s_0 s_1 s_2 N}{p_2 s_0 s_1 N}$$

$$= s_2$$

if $p_2 = p_3$.

This seems to be about the best that can be done, in the sense that we have used the least complicated assumption in sight. A serious difficulty is that the actual numbers involved are usually small, and the estimates thus formed will be quite variable.

Simplifying matters as much as possible (and thus making some much less plausible assumptions) it is assumed that all of the p_i are the same (and equal to p) and all the $s_i = s$. Then the basic table of data becomes:

Year	Number alive at beginning	Number shot and reported
0	N	pN
1	sN	psN
2	$s^2 N$	$ps^2 N$
.	.	.
.	.	.
.	.	.
x	$s^x N$	$ps^x N$
.	.	..
.	.	.
.	.	.
n	$s^n N$	$ps^n N$

A common practice in making a "cohort" or "dynamic" life-table from banding returns involves adding up the "number shot and reported" and using that number as the first entry in the l_x column. Values of d_x are taken as the individual year-group entry from the same column (e.g., $d_2 = ps^2 N$) and the table completed in the

usual manner (i.e., $l_{x+1} = l_x - d_x$). The terms involved can be summed (using a geometric series) as follows:

$$\text{Sum} = pN \left\{ 1 + s + s^2 + \ldots + s^n \right\} = pN \left\{ \frac{1-s^{n+1}}{1-s} \right\}$$

and, following the procedure above, the life table becomes:

x	l_x	d_x	q_x
0	$pN \left\{ \dfrac{1-s^{n+1}}{1-s} \right\}$	pN	$\dfrac{1-s}{1-s^{n+1}}$
1	$psN \left\{ \dfrac{1-s^{n}}{1-s} \right\}$	psN	$\dfrac{1-s}{1-s^{n}}$
.	.	.	.
.	.	.	.
.	.	.	.
x	$ps^x N \left\{ \dfrac{1-s^{n-x+1}}{1-s} \right\}$	$ps^x N$	$\dfrac{1-s}{1-s^{n-x+1}}$
.	.	.	.
.	.	.	.
.	.	.	.
n	$ps^n N$	$ps^n N$	1

A striking feature of the results is that the q_x values are biased estimates of $1-s$. In most circumstances, the bias will be small for the first entries in the table, but it certainly is not negligible for the higher values of n, reaching the ultimate by making the last mortality value always 100 percent! Such an effect is quite noticeable in many of the published "survivorship curves" based on life table data. One cannot, of course, neglect the fact that mortality rates no doubt do increase in the very oldest age-groups.

Some investigators also produce, from exactly the same data, a "current" or "time-specific" life table, but they, in this case, enter the basic data in the l_x column, and compute the balance of the table from:

$$d_x = l_x - l_{x+1}$$

The end result is:

x	l_x	d_x	q_x
0	pN	$pN(1-s)$	$(1-s)$
1	psN	$psN(1-s)$	$(1-s)$
.	.	.	.
.	.	.	.
.	.	.	.
x	ps^xN	$ps^xN(1-s)$	$(1-s)$
.	.	.	.
.	.	.	.
.	.	.	.
n	ps^nN	$ps^nN(1-s)$	$(1-s)$

The analysis given above has been simplified by neglecting some features considered in many studies of band returns. One of these features is that first year returns are often not used or corrected for differential return rates. Also, as has been mentioned above, it is usually necessary to use the returns from several years of banding, thus making "composite" tables. But the important consideration is *not* the life table itself—what really counts is to get valid estimates of the survival (or mortality) rates. Each attempt to do this is a special case, and the investigator must *always* try to check the assumptions, using whatever supplementary information he can get.

In the situation described here, one logical thing to do is to plot the number shot and reported against the year of recovery. If that number is represented by y, then the general term is:

$$y = ps^xN = pNs^x \qquad (3)$$

and taking logarithms:

$$\log y = \log (pN) + (\log s)\, x \qquad (4)$$

and this is the equation for a straight line:

$$Y = \log y = A + Bx$$

Consequently if p and s are truly constant, plotting the logarithm of the number of returns against the year of recovery should yield approximately a straight line, and ordinary regression calculations might be used to provide an estimate of pN (from the Y-intercept, A) and log s (as the slope, B). Since the algebraic model used here does not include any mortality in the first returns (i.e., the first value in the "number shot and returned" column is pN), these will not enter in regression calculations. But it will usually be the case that the first returns should be treated differently than all others. Also, if all the assumptions hold, the regression intercept is an estimate of log (pN) so this estimate could be compared with the actual number of first returns as a partial check on the assumptions.

Two sets of data will be examined briefly to illustrate the point. The first has been used to illustrate calculation of "dynamic" (cohort) and "time-specific" (current) life-tables by Hickey (1952). The data came from returns of adult mallards banded in 1926-34 on the Pacific coast. First-year returns were not included. Since age at banding was not known, and a number of years are combined, the x column of the life table cannot be interpreted as age. This means that one really has to assume mortality does not change with age to use the data.

Year of return (dated from banding)	Number shot and reported	"Dynamic" life table			"Time-specific" life table		
		l_x	d_x	q_x	l_x	d_x	q_x
1-2	845	1411	845	0.60	845	561	0.66
2-3	284	566	284	0.50	284	160	0.56
3-4	124	282	124	0.44	124	52	0.42
4-5	72	158	72	0.46	72	43	0.60
5-6	29	86	29	0.34	29	0	0.00
6-7	29	57	29	0.51	29	17	0.59
7-8	12	28	12		12	5	
8-9	7	16	7		7	2	
9-10	5	9	5		5	2	
10-11	3	4	3		3	2	
11-12	1	1	1		1	1	
Totals	1411		1411		1411	845	

While the two sets of mortality estimates are not greatly discrepant, the author strongly recommends against use of the "dynamic" calculations, on the grounds that the "time-specific" calculations are likely to be freer of biases. Plotting the number shot and reported on semi-logarithmic graph paper (Fig. 22.6) suggests a definite curvature, rather than the straight line expected if survival remains constant.

Geis (1959) prepared a composite table for canvasbacks banded as flightless young in Manitoba and Saskatchewan in the years 1953 to 1957. His table makes use of a correction for "banded birds available," a concept which needs to be explained before discussing estimation of survival. The need for such a correction arises because returns for the more recently banded ducks are available for only the first few years of life. To secure nearly complete data, it is necessary to wait 5 or more years after the last banding.

Since Geis utilized data on young ducks shot in the hunting season following summer banding, it will be necessary to consider the survival rate (s_0) for these young from banding to the following hunting season, and also the higher vulnerability to hunting exhibited by young birds.

As before, an assumption is made that survival beyond the first year is at a constant rate (s), and the proportion of banded ducks shot and returned (p) also is constant beyond the first year, with a higher rate (p_0) in the first year. First a table is constructed showing number of surviving banded ducks through the year. The number of ducks banded each year appears in the left hand column (as N_0, N_1, etc.), and the entries in the corresponding row show symbolically the number of survivors. Thus N_0 young-of-the-year are banded in the first year and $s_0 N_0$ of these survive to the first hunting season (in the column headed by a zero). Survival up to the next hunting season is assumed to be at the adult rate (s), so $s(s_0 N_0)$ are alive at the beginning of that season, and so on. Ducks born and banded the next year (N_1) are not subjected to hunting until that fall, so the entries simply appear shifted over one column to the right. The complete table is:

Year banded	Number banded	Number alive at the beginning of hunting season				
		0	1	2	3	4
0	$N_0 = 316$	$s_0 N_0$	$s(s_0 N_0)$	$s^2(s_0 N_0)$	$s^3(s_0 N_0)$	$s^4(s_0 N_0)$
1	$N_1 = 179$		$s_0 N_1$	$s(s_0 N_1)$	$s^2(s_0 N_1)$	$s^3(s_0 N_1)$
2	$N_2 = 127$			$s_0 N_2$	$s(s_0 N_2)$	$s^2(s_0 N_2)$
3	$N_3 = 129$				$s_0 N_3$	$s(s_0 N_3)$
4	$N_4 = 199$					$s_0 N_4$
	950					

If the table entries are converted to number of ducks shot and reported (multiplying by p_0 or p as appropriate) and then added by age at hunting season, the first few columns of Geis' Table 2 are as follows:

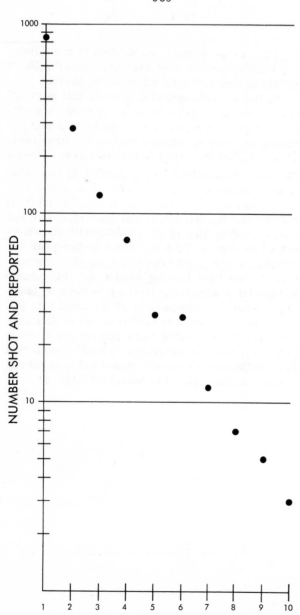

Fig. 22.6. Mallard band returns (Hickey 1952).

Age-group	Number shot and reported	Number "available"	"d_x"
0	$p_0 s_0 (N_0 + N_1 + N_2 + N_3 + N_4) = 210$	$N_0 + N_1 + N_2 + N_3 + N_4 = 950$	$p_0 s_0 = 0.2210$
1	$p s_0 s (N_0 + N_1 + N_2 + N_3) = 25$	$N_0 + N_1 + N_2 + N_3 = 751$	$p s_0 s = 0.0333$
2	$p s_0 s^2 (N_0 + N_1 + N_2) = 11$	$N_0 + N_1 + N_2 = 622$	$p s_0 s^2 = 0.0177$
3	$p s_0 s^3 (N_0 + N_1) = 5$	$N_0 + N_1 = 495$	$p s_0 s^3 = 0.0101$
4	$p s_0 s^4 (N_0) = 2$	$N_0 = 316$	$p s_0 s^4 = 0.0063$
Totals	253		

The last column is the number shot and reported divided by the number available, expressed here as a decimal fraction rather than converted to a per 1000 basis as Geis gave it. In symbols, entries in the last column are (excepting the first entry):

$$d_x = p s_0 s^x \qquad (5)$$

and taking logarithms:

$$\log d_x = \log (p s_0) + (\log s) x \qquad (6)$$

It would thus be possible to make a regression calculation to estimate the value of log s (as the "slope" of the regression line) and hence to estimate s. Since the first entry in the "d_x" column is $p_0 s_0$, and the y-intercept is log ($p s_0$), there would be no way to estimate first-year mortality. One could calculate the ratio

$$\frac{p_0 s_0}{p s_0}$$

as a measure of relative size of p_0 and p, however.

A plot of the data (Fig. 22.7) suggests no strong evidence against the assumption that the quantities

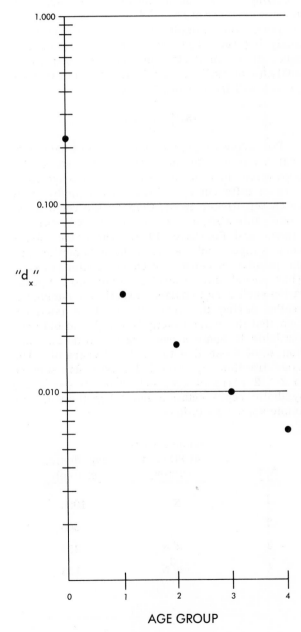

Fig. 22.7. Plot of d_x by age group (Geis 1959).

p and s remain constant after the first year of life. However, the wildlifer can hardly expect to make any very strong statements on the basis of such small numbers of returns and in view of the necessity for estimating two rates (p and s) from data from five different hunting seasons.

There are some statistical difficulties in applying ordinary regression calculations to survival data, in part due to the very small numbers in the older age groups exerting too much influence on the estimate of survival. Probably a more important consideration in the above examples is that the returns from individual "banding-years" should be examined separately for any evidence of changes in survival from year to year. Some simple methods are available for analyzing such data and will be described below. Since these methods can also be used in the analysis of "kill-curves," the basics of that approach will first be described.

Kill-curves

For many years, fisheries workers have used "catch-curves" to study the past history of a population through analysis of the relative numbers of different ages found in a sample of the catch (cf. Ricker 1958). Comparable records for game animals have been called "kill-curves" (Hayne and Eberhardt 1952). The basic idea is very simple, but requires the assumption that the population being studied is constant in size. Thus enough new "recruits" come into the population each year to balance exactly the number of deaths during the year. It might be assumed, then, that there are exactly N 1-1/2 year old deer available to hunters every fall, and that a fraction, s, of these live to be 2-1/2 years old. The same fraction (s) of the 2-1/2 year olds survive to 3-1/2 years of age, and so on. If s=1/2, the symbolic representation and a hypothetical example appear as follows:

Age	Number alive at start of hunting	Hypothetical example
1	N	1000
2	sN	500
3	s^2N	250
4	s^3N	125
.	.	.
.	.	.
.	.	.

Thus we have very much the same kind of situation as with band returns.

Estimating Survival From Band Returns or Kill Curves

It is now possible to reconsider band return analysis to establish a set of symbols for some of the factors involved, then to show how the same set can be applied to "kill-curves," and how to estimate survival and to make certain simple statistical tests. Examples of data under study are waterfowl band returns and deer age composition samples.

Supposing young ducks are banded in the summer, the subsequent course of events is as follows:

N = number of young banded

s_oN = number surviving from banding to hunting season

a_os_oN = number shot in the first hunting season—a_o is thus proportion of young ducks shot by hunters

$(1-c)a_os_oN$ = number of young ducks shot and recovered by hunters—thus c represents the proportion which are shot and lost ("cripples" that do not recover).

$d(1-c)a_os_oN$ = number of bands (from young ducks shot in hunting) that are actually reported

let $p_o = d(1-c)a_o$

then p_os_oN = number of bands reported from young ducks, and, if survival rate for the year beginning at the start of hunting is s_1, then:

s_os_1N = number alive at the next hunting season, and now classified as adults

ps_os_1N = number of bands reported in the next hunting season, where $p=d(1-c)a$, that is, the fraction reported (d) and crippling loss (c) are considered to be the same as for first-year ducks, but that the fraction shot (a) may be different (it usually is considerably smaller for adults).

If, as required for the analyses described here, p and s remain constant for adult ducks, a summary can be made as follows:

$p_o s_o N$ = number of bands reported in first year

$p s_o s_1 N$ = number of bands reported in second year

$p s_o s_1 s N$ = number of bands reported in third year

.
.
.

$p s_o s_1 s^{x-1} N$ = number of bands reported in x^{th} year

For kill-curves, exactly the same table can be made, but a slight change in the definitions is needed (and the analysis must be restricted to one sex):

N = initial population (say new-born male fawns)

$s_o N$ = survive to first hunting season (6 months old)

$a_o s_o N$ = number killed in first hunting season (if fawns are not legal game, or hunted under special regulations, a_o may be very small)

$(1-c) a_o s_o N$ = number recovered by hunters (c=crippling loss, as before)

$d(1-c) a_o s_o N$ = number examined at checking stations (i.e., d is proportion of total kill examined)

Again let $p_o = d(1-c) a_o$ and that a different fraction (a) of adults are killed so that:

$p = d(1-c)a$ In this case, a will usually be considerably larger than a_o (just the reverse of the waterfowl example).

The complete table is identical to the previous one, but there is a very important difference in the process leading up to it. For the band-return example, it was assumed that N young ducks were banded in the same year, and the table represents band returns for a series of years all coming from the same "banding-class," and having a constant survival rate (etc.) as adults. A kill-curve, on the other hand, is based on a sample of deer of different ages, *all shot in the same year*. Hence, to get the table shown, it must be assumed that there are exactly N new-born fawns every year for a series of years, and that the survival rates (sq, s_1, and s) do not change during that series of years. Since the sample is taken in one hunting season,

d only applies once. Since a_o, a, and c contribute importantly to mortality (and thus influence survival) as well as make up the constants p_o and p_1 they too must hold constant over the years considered.

In the remainder of this section, estimates of survival and so on were taken from the literature on fisheries research. The mathematical bases are described in papers by Chapman and Robson (1960), Paulik (1963), and Chapman (1965). Applications to fisheries studies are given in expository papers by Robson and Chapman (1961) and Paulik (1962) and the interested student should read these two papers.

In virtually all big-game studies, estimation of survival will begin in the second hunting season, due to the markedly higher vulnerability of young animals to shooting, and lower total survival in at least the first 6 months of life. Since a test of significance is given below for difference between the first age-class included and all other classes, the investigator can begin with the youngest age class he judges it reasonable to include, conduct the test, and exclude that class in subsequent calculations if necessary.

The calculations require that the youngest class considered be coded as zero, the next as 1 and so on, as shown in the following table. The calculations will be illustrated by examining a kill-curve. The data are ages of buck white-tailed deer checked in the Upper Peninsula of Michigan in 1959 (Ryel and Fay 1960).

Age	Coded Age	Number examined
1-1/2	0	N_o = 425
2-1/2	1	N_1 = 274
3-1/2	2	N_2 = 149
4-1/2	3	N_3 = 53
5-1/2	4	N_4 = 17
6-1/2	5	N_5 = 8
7-1/2	6	N_6 = 6
8-1/2	7	N_7 = 3
9-1/2	8	N_8 = 1
10-1/2	9	N_9 = 1
		n = 937

The Chapman-Robson equation for estimating survival is:

$$\hat{s} = \frac{T}{n + T - 1} \qquad (7)$$

where n = total number examined (937) and:

$$T = N_1 + 2N_2 + 3N_3 + \ldots + KN_K \qquad (8)$$

$$= 274 + 2(149) + 3(53) + 4(17) + 5(8) + 6(6)$$

$$+ 7(3) + 8(1) + 9(1) = 913$$

and

$$\hat{s} = \frac{913}{1849} = 0.4937$$

The equation for variance of the estimate is:

$$V(\hat{s}) = \frac{T}{n+T-1} \left[\frac{T}{n+T-1} - \frac{T-1}{n+T-2} \right] \qquad (9)$$

$$= \frac{913}{1849} \left[\frac{913}{1849} - \frac{912}{1848} \right] = 0.0001353$$

so the standard error is:

$$\sqrt{0.000135} = 0.0116$$

and approximate 95% confidence limits are set by adding and subtracting 2 standard errors. The survival estimate is thus:

$$\hat{s} = 0.494 \pm 0.023$$

However, some other aspects of the data should be investigated before accepting this quite precise estimate as representative of survival rates. An approximate test of the compatibility of numbers in the first age-class with the rest of the data is given by the quantity

$$Q = \frac{(s-s'_o)^2}{\dfrac{T(T-1)(n-1)}{n(n+T-1)^2(n+T-2)}} \qquad (10)$$

where s is the survival rate already estimated (0.4937) and

$$s'_o = \frac{n-N_o}{n} = \frac{937 - 425}{937} = 0.5465,$$

Thus

$$Q = \frac{(0.4937 - 0.5465)^2}{\dfrac{913(912)(936)}{937(1849)^2 1848}} = \frac{0.002788}{0.0001316} = 21.2$$

Q is a chi-square variate with one degree of freedom, so a test of significance at the 5% level of significance depends on comparing Q with 3.841. Obviously the number of 1-1/2 year olds is not compatible with the assumption of constant survival rates, although this does not necessarily prove survival for 1-1/2 year olds is not the same as that for older bucks. It only demonstrates a lack of agreement with the postulated model. Now if the first year-class is excluded, the ages recorded, and the values of T, s, and Q calculated:

Age	Coded Age	Number examined
2-1/2	0	$N_o = 274$
3-1/2	1	$N_1 = 149$
4-1/2	2	$N_2 = 53$
5-1/2	3	$N_3 = 17$
6-1/2	4	$N_4 = 8$
7-1/2	5	$N_5 = 6$
8-1/2	6	$N_6 = 3$
9-1/2	7	$N_7 = 1$
10-1/2	8	$N_8 = 1$
		$n = 512$

$$T = 149 + 2(53) + 3(17) + 4(8) + 5(6) + 6(3)$$
$$+ 7(1) + 8(1) = 401$$

$$s = \frac{T}{n+T-1} = \frac{401}{912} = 0.4397$$

The result is a good deal lower than the previous estimate. To check how well the 2-1/2 year olds match the older classes, Q is again computed:

$$s'_o = \frac{n-N_o}{n} = \frac{512 - 274}{512} = 0.4649$$

$$Q = \frac{(0.4397 - 0.4649)^2}{\dfrac{(401)(400)(511)}{512(912)^2(911)}} = \frac{0.000635}{0.000211} = 3.00$$

The result is now less than the chi-square value for the 5% level of significance but still above the value at the 10% level, which is 2.71. At this point the reader should be reminded that blind adherence to simple statistical tests is just about as unsatisfactory a procedure as paying no attention to variability at all. To make any real "sense" out of the data, one must know the past history of the herd, reproductive rates, weather and range conditions, etc. About all that can be done here is to look at one more feature of the data. This is accomplished by comparing the observations with the expected relative frequencies on the assumption that the calculated survival rate is correct. The symbolic representation for number in each age class can easily be summed (using a geometric series) to get the relative proportion in each age class. Multiplying this relative frequency by total sample size (n) gives the number to be expected in each age-class, if survival were exactly as estimated. The following table shows the calculations:

There will often be some doubt about the accuracy of aging older animals. The wildlifer might believe that there are very few errors in aging the 2-1/2 through 4-1/2 year olds, but that the 5-1/2 year olds and all older deer ought to be classed just as "5-1/2 and older." (For comments on white-tail aging see Ryel et al. 1961.) The Chapman-Robson methods provide a means for calculating survival on the basis of grouped ages and are illustrated as follows, using the previous data:

Age	Coded Age	Number of deer
2-1/2	0	$N_0 = 274$
3-1/2	1	$N_1 = 149$
4-1/2	2	$N_2 = 53$
5-1/2+		$m = 36$
		$n = 512$

Age	Coded Age	Relative frequency	Expected number (E)	Observed number (O)	(E-O)
2-1/2	0	$(1-s) = 0.5603$	286.9	274	12.9
3-1/2	1	$(1-s)s = 0.2464$	126.2	149	-22.8
4-1/2	2	$(1-s)s^2 = 0.1083$	55.4	53	2.4
5-1/2	3	$(1-s)s^3 = 0.0476$	24.4	17	7.4
6-1/2	4	$(1-s)s^4 = 0.0209$	10.7	8	2.7
7-1/2 and older	5+	(difference) 0.0165	8.4	11	-2.6
		1.0 1.0000	512.0	512	0.0

Comparing the expected and observed numbers, it can be seen that there still seems to be a suggestion of a trend, something which may be observed by plotting the logarithms of numbers in each age class against the age classes (or using semi-logarithmic graph paper as shown in Fig. 22.8).

A chi-square calculation gives the value 8.52 with 4 degrees of freedom. Since the corresponding value for the 5% level of significance is 9.49, there is no evidence of a difference in rates from this test either. It should be noted that the history of the herd studied suggests a decline in "recruitment" and thus invalidates one of the necessary assumptions for the survival estimates.

$$T = N_1 + 2N_2 + \ldots + KN_K + (K+1)m \quad (11)$$

$$= 149 + 2(53) + 3(36) = 363$$

where K is the coded age of the oldest class believed reliable (here K=2) and m is the total number of animals in the age-classes lumped together (here m=36). The estimate of s is:

476

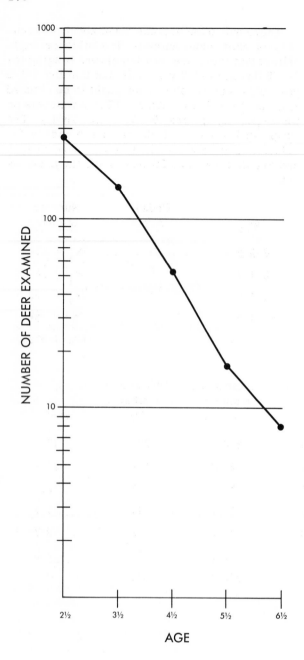

Fig. 22.8. Kill-curve for male white-tailed deer.

$$\hat{s} = \frac{T}{n-m+T} = \frac{363}{839} = 0.433$$

and its variance is approximately

$$V(\hat{s}) = \frac{s(1-s)^2}{n(1-s^{K+1})} \qquad (12)$$

$$= 0.000296$$

giving confidence limits: s = 0.433 ± 0.034

So far as estimating survival goes, lumping the older age classes does not lose much information. The formula for relative efficiency of "lumping" versus "complete" samples is:

$$\text{Relative efficiency} = 1-s^{K+1} \qquad (13)$$

$$= 1-0.081 = 0.919$$

So in this example, 1/0.919 = 1.08, and it would be necessary to obtain 8% more records to get the same precision for grouped as for ungrouped data.

In some cases the investigator's knowledge of the history of the population being studied will suggest that the assumptions required for analysis can be accepted only for a part of the curve. A severe winter or unusually liberal hunting season may have changed the number of "recruits" or survival rate. In this situation, only a segment of the curve can be analyzed and the rest must be discarded. A procedure much like the above is available for such calculations in the paper by Robson and Chapman (1961), which also gives a table to simplify calculating s in this particular case. The estimating equations must otherwise be solved by iteration.

The reader is reminded that calculations for all of the above are exactly the same for analyzing band-return data. But he should never lose sight of the fact that the *assumptions* necessary for using the formulae *are* different, and only a good knowledge of the population being studied can supply a basis for judging validity of those assumptions.

Fig. 22.9 shows a comparison of estimates of survival rates for buck deer obtained in two ways. One (plotted on the vertical axis) depended on combining a population index and age-structure data. The second (horizontal axis) used age-structure data on annual harvests over a span of years. Fig. 22.10 shows the same general comparison for does. Details of the methods, and of differences between years and areas (which contribute to the "scatter" of points) are too lengthy for discussion here, but there is evidence of general agreement in survival estimates, and these are supported by other information (cf. Eberhardt 1960). However, the survival rates estimated from age data alone did not correlate with the other two methods (Fig. 22.11).

So far as the objective of this chapter is concerned, one can show the essential life table in-

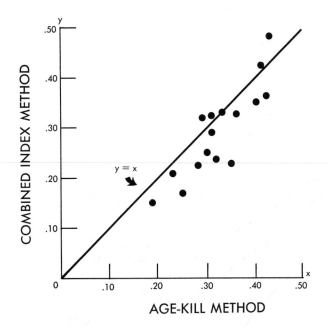

Fig. 22.9. Estimates of annual survival for buck white-tailed deer made by two methods, for a number of Michigan areas and years (Eberhardt 1960).

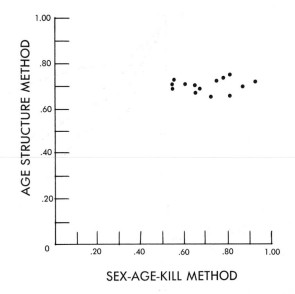

Fig. 22.11. Estimates of annual survival for doe white-tailed deer, showing the failure of estimates based on age data alone to agree with other sources (Eberhardt 1960).

formation in the form of a survival curve, in which the fraction of animals born (or reaching some other age more suitable for the data at hand) that live to a given age is plotted against age. What results, of course, is a curve which begins at unity (at the initial age considered) and drops off,

never-increasing, to zero at the last age considered. Some examples are available in Fig. 22.12.

RECRUITMENT

The biologist faced with the job of population analysis soon comes to realize that "reproduction" is indeed difficult to measure. Although it may be possible to determine egg or embryo production rates, mortality immediately after birth is almost invariably high, but virtually impossible to measure directly. One may thus be forced to begin calculations at some later stage in life in order to get satisfactory data (or any at all, in some cases). Fisheries workers use the term "recruits" to describe fish just reaching "catchable" size (which of course depends on the method of capture). One may thus speak conveniently of "recruits" to the particular population being considered. Usually such recruits will, for game animals, be of about the same age. This is not necessarily the case for fish.

Various terms with special meanings are in use in population studies. These include fecundity, or egg production, fertility—production of living young, and natality. Allee et al. (1949:272) define natality as the "population-increase factor," and sub-classify it first as "potential" and "realized" natality, then as "absolute" and "partial" potential,

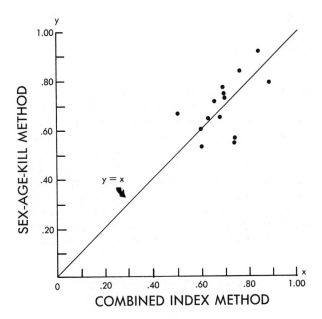

Fig. 22.10. Estimates of annual survival of doe white-tailed deer made by two methods (Eberhardt 1960).

478

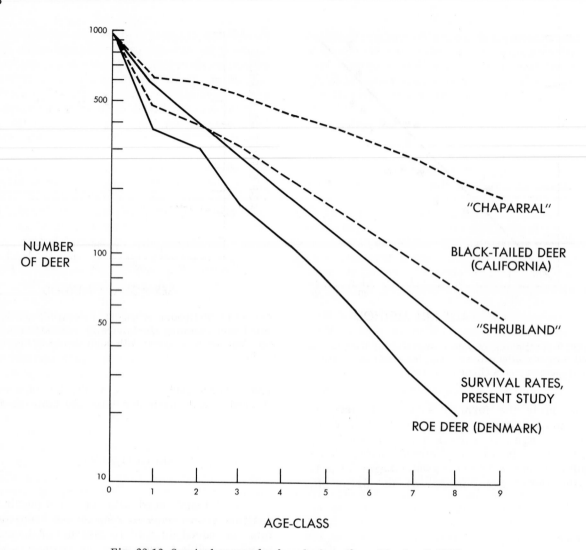

Fig. 22.12. Survival curves for female deer (from Eberhardt 1960).

plus some further definitions. Largely, this all means that animals are capable of producing a great many more young than circumstances ever permit, and the various subclassifications are efforts to categorize what happens in practice. The greatest difficulty is that success depends on both reproduction and mortality, so that descriptions in terms of one factor alone are not sufficient. Much of the concern of the wildlifer is with those animals that are recruited either to a hunted population or to the population which he can best measure. One may well need to try to work back to birth or hatching times, but the circumstances will usually dictate what measurements are available and these conditions should be carefully described. Any single term is usually inadequate.

It has already been mentioned that those species having a high rate of production of young must also exhibit high mortality, else they would quickly inherit the earth. Rules of thumb are thus possible, in which an average production of young is converted to the mortality necessary to keep the population at the same size. Calculations of this kind may be useful occasionally, but they neglect the fact that few populations do hold nearly constant in size, thus tend to give a false impression of mortality rates. This is because, as noted above, mortality just after birth is normally very high, then may decrease steadily until very old age.

POPULATION STRUCTURE

Thorough analysis of an animal population requires not only knowledge of gains (reproduction or recruitment) and losses (mortality) but also an understanding of the underlying structure of the population. The age composition or (age distribution) is especially important (at least in big game), since it usually affects the overall reproductive and mortality rates.

Most populations exhibit what are called age-specific birth and death rates. In nearly all cases it is convenient to consider only females in analyzing age structure since males can conveniently be "tacked on" at later stages of a study. Thus age-specific reproduction is defined as the number of additional females produced per year by each female alive at the beginning of the year. The meaning of "produced" depends on the data available and needed. Often counts of late-term embryos are readily obtained while in other circumstances a rate derived from fairly well-grown young may be used. Age-specific mortality rates are defined as the fraction of new-born animals which die during a given year of their lives, i.e., the proportion that dies between one "birthday" and the next. Shorter periods can, of course, be used.

An example of age-specific reproductive rates has already been given for white-tailed deer. Such data are unfortunately not available for many animals, but various lines of evidence (e.g. reproductive physiology) suggest that the same general pattern holds quite universally for those species whose physiological longevity exceeds a few years. One difficulty is that very large samples are needed in order to obtain a satisfactory assessment of the range of reproduction. It goes without saying, too, that aging techniques need to be reliable for this purpose.

Age-specific mortality also undoubtedly exists in virtually all animals, but is even harder to assess than age-specific reproduction. Usually the pattern is roughly "U" shaped, with a very high rate just at birth, decreasing to the prime of life, and slowly increasing thereafter. At best only the first part of the curve is ordinarily seen though, because there are just too many hazards attendant on the life of wild animals. Thus, after the "young-and-foolish" stage, the effects of changing physiology, etc., are pretty well swamped by violent "accidental" deaths. Further, these rates are very difficult to measure, so both biases and limited samples add ups and downs to the actual curve. For most game population work, it seems likely that no more than two or three values of mortality rate might be used. One rate might apply to the first few months (or less) of life, a second to the period up to early sexual maturity, and a third thereafter. In fact, most practical

experience suggests that the investigator is fortunate if he can obtain reliable estimates of one overall mortality rate appliable from, say, 3 to 6 months of age onwards, and a very crude measure of "juvenile" mortality.

If the age-specific rates do not change markedly from year to year, they then determine the age-structure of the population. Some mathematics are involved in demonstrating the situation and the various complexities are described by Lotka (1939) who originally worked out the details and coined the term "stable age-distribution" ("normal" age-distribution has also been used). It is important to remember that the notion, like most such concepts, is only an approximation. Some people go further, and say the stable age-distribution is a physical impossibility, except for a static or "stationary" population. The source of difficulty is that, if the age-specific reproductive and mortality rates hold constant, and are not exactly balanced, then the population is either increasing or decreasing. Neither such condition can go on indefinitely, but the mathematical definition of a stable age-distribution implies just that.

On the other hand, neglecting population structure, or supposing population size to be essentially constant usually constitutes an admission of inadequate knowledge or understanding. Predictions of the future course of a population can only be made if the age structure is known relative to its "stable" condition. If the age structure is much different from the stable situation, then it will tend to shift towards stability and will cause the rate of population increase (or decrease) to also change. In some cases, oscillations may be set up, further compounding the matter.

In practice, most wildlife populations seem to show a sequence of years of increase or decrease. The population in one year is almost always closely correlated with that of the year before. There may often be an approach to the stable age-distribution, but even if there is not, the concept is extremely useful in appraising the future trend of the population.

One more complexity is involved here. It constitutes another "impossibility" or paradox. This is the mathematical fact that if age-specific birth and death rates hold constant from year to year, then when the stable age-distribution is reached, the rate of population change will become constant and remain so. This has been called the "intrinsic rate of increase" (or decrease) by Lotka, and has possibly led to more obscure definitions in textbooks and papers than any other concept in population ecology. Again, the notion cannot be simply disposed of by describing it as an impossibility since it can be shown that a constant rate of population change cannot be defined otherwise, unless a ridiculously complex set of changes is taking place.

The practical approach to the quandry described above is to realize that conditions may indeed hold fairly constant over a span of years so that the stable age-distribution is approximately established, ultimately something changes, and a new process of stabilization may take place, followed by another change or series of changes, and so on, endlessly. These principles have been used by demographers for 50 years and seem to do nicely for more and more animal populations as better data are obtained.

A full appraisal of the details and mathematics of the stable age distribution cannot be given here, but it is important that the basic formulae and an approximate justification be available to the wildlife investigator. Therefore, an algebraic derivation is given below for somewhat simplified conditions. In particular, it is assumed that all reproduction occurs at one time each year. For a great many animals, this is not a bad approximation. The actual season of births is often relatively short, and young may not enter the calculations until they are some months old when differences in birth-dates may have become more or less evened-out physiologically.

However, the scheme described here may not work very well for a species like the cottontail where several litters may be produced over a number of months. Going entirely to the other extreme, species such as some parasites may produce young continuously and one must then use mathematics on a continuous time scale (where here discrete units of time are used). It turns out, though, that even the continuous equations are most easily solved by approximating the resulting integrals by summations of the kind given below.

Age Structure of a Female Population

The derivation is started by assuming the end result, so what follows does not prove anything, but merely shows how the equations work. Time units of 1 year are used and the assumption made that the population is growing geometrically, which

means that a constant fraction, r, is added to the total each year. Of course there are losses, but gains are assumed to exceed losses so as to give an increase each year:

N_0 = number of animals present initially

rN_0 = number added in first year

$N_1 = N_0 + rN_0 = N_0(1+r)$ = population at end of 1st year

$N_2 = N_1 + rN_1 = N_0(1+r)^2$ = population at end of 2nd year

$$N_t = N_0(1+r)^t \qquad (14)$$

= population at end of the tth year

The above equation neglects the prospect that results will include fractions of animals, and this is quite justifiable if the populations are of moderate size (if one birth more or less makes any appreciable difference probabilistic methods must be used anyhow).

Now if the reader is willing to go along with equations which use fractional animals he perhaps will not mind also considering the initial population size as unity. Anyone made uncomfortable thereby is invited to start out with, say, 10,000 (or even 1,000) animals, whereupon he can discard any fractional animals that come up (but being careful to round to the nearest whole animal). The price paid is extremely tedious arithmetic, unless a computer is used.

The description is begun with a population represented by unity at an initial time conveniently labelled as zero. The observer must keep track both of what happens to the initial population as time goes on, and of its progeny and of subsequent generations. Consequently, the calculations are exhibited in a table, with time on the left margin and generations across the top. Further, there is need to consider death rates, which are represented as a constant fraction, q, so that 1−q=p is the annual survival rate. In order for the population to increase as initially postulated here, a fraction, r, must be added each year.

Thus the first entry, at time zero, is generation 1. A fraction (p) of these "pioneers" survive the first year, appearing just below the original entry:

Time	Generation			Total population size
	$\underline{1}$	$\underline{2}$	$\underline{3}$	
0	1			1
1	p	q+r		1+r

.
.
.

However, the population is supposed to increase in the first year by a fraction (r), becoming 1+r. Consequently the losses (q) must be made up along with the fraction gained, so the entry corresponding to time 1 and generation 2 is shown as q+r.

Carrying the table forward another year results in:

Time	Generation			Total population size
	$\underline{1}$	$\underline{2}$	$\underline{3}$	
0	1			1
1	p	q+r		1+r
2	p^2	p(q+r)	(q+r)(1+r)	$(1+r)^2$

Here it can be seen that the "pioneers" have declined to p^2, and the second generation (column 2, time 2) has also been reduced by mortality, becoming p(q+r). Continuing the postulated increase again requires enough births to replace losses and add a fraction r, so the losses in the two generations are added (remembering p+q=1) and the results obtained are:

$$p-p^2 + (q+r) - p(q+r) = q(1+r)$$

Then the postulated fraction (r) times the previous year's total is added (which is r(1+r)) and the number which has to be "recruited" as the third generation is obtained:

$$q(1+r) + r(1+r) = (q+r)(1+r)$$

giving the required population total as $(1+r)^2$.

The third-year population can be constructed in exactly the same way, and the pattern becomes clear:

Time	Generation				Total
	$\underline{1}$	$\underline{2}$	$\underline{3}$	$\underline{4}$	
0	1				1
1	p	q+r			1+r
2	p^2	p(q+r)	(q+r)(1+r)		$(1+r)^2$
3	p^3	$p^2(q+r)$	p(q+r)(1+r)	$(q+r)(1+r)^2$	$(1+r)^3$

Now the ith year can easily be written and generations added to get the general form after a sizable number of years have elapsed:

$$\text{Total} = p^i + p^{i-1}(q+r) + p^{i-2}(q+r)(1+r)$$

$$+ p^{i-3}(q+r)(1+r)^2 + \ldots + p^{i-k}(q+r)(1+r)^{k-1}$$

$$+ \ldots + p(q+r)(1+r)^{i-2} + (q+r)(1+r)^{i-1}$$

$$= (1+r)^i$$

Where the dots (. . .) represent terms omitted and represented by the kth generation.

Dividing through by the total, $(1+r)^i$, gives the generations as proportions:

$$\left(\frac{p}{1+r}\right)^i + \frac{q+r}{1+r}\left[\left(\frac{p}{1+r}\right)^{i-1} + \left(\frac{p}{1+r}\right)^{i-2} + \ldots\right.$$

$$\left. + \left(\frac{p}{1+r}\right)^{i-k} + \ldots + \left(\frac{p}{1+r}\right) + 1\right] = 1 \quad (15)$$

Since $\frac{p}{1+r}$ is less than unity, large powers of this quantity will tend to become very small yielding the obvious result that the "pioneer" generation tends to become a vanishingly small proportion of the total as we consider some much later year (i.e., as i becomes large). Also, the quantity in brackets becomes nearly equivalent to an infinite geometric series, and the above equation becomes approximately:

$$\left(\frac{q+r}{1+r}\right)\left(1 - \frac{p}{1+r}\right)^{-1} = \left(\frac{q+r}{1+r}\right)\left(\frac{1+r}{1+r-p}\right)$$

$$= \left(\frac{q+r}{1+r}\right)\left(\frac{1+r}{q+r}\right) = 1 \quad (16)$$

Then the proportion corresponding to any one generation, say the xth is:

$$C_x = \left(\frac{q+r}{1+r}\right)\left(\frac{p}{1+r}\right)^x \quad (17)$$

Looking back to the tables above, it can be seen that the newest generation in any year (the "recruits") divided by the total for that year (right-hand column) is always equal to:

$$\frac{q+r}{1+r} = b \quad (18)$$

which is a measure of reproduction and will be denoted by the symbol, b. Further, survival is considered constant (p), so that survival for x years is represented by p^x. Then the above equation can be rewritten as

$$C_x = b(1+r)^{-x} p^x \quad (19)$$

and this gives the expected proportion in age-class x.

Reproduction

For a discussion of population reproduction the same assumed growth rate is maintained and an age-specific reproductive rate (m_x) is defined as the number of female young produced per female of age x. Of course "produced" has to be defined in units appropriate to the age the newest generation is introduced into the table above. That is, for deer some degree of realism might be obtained if the assumption is made that survival rates are constant after about 6 months. But if reproductive rates are measured as embryo per doe of age x, a survival factor has to be inserted from late gestation to 6 months of age.

For present purposes the assumption is made that m_x measures reproduction at entry into the tables. Thus, summing over all age classes gives:

$$\text{total reproduction} = b = \sum_{x=0}^{\infty} C_x m_x \quad (20)$$

That is, the overall average reproductive rate is the number of new recruits (q+r) divided by the total number of females (1+r) at the time a new generation enters the tables, giving b on the left side of the equation. On the right side, an average reproductive rate is obtained by weighting the rate (m_x) for each age class by its relative abundance (C_x). The limits $(0,\infty)$ of summation need a little interpretation. The zero class is naturally the new recruits (or new-born, if that is the case) and this age-class and perhaps 1 or at most 2 more will not breed, hence $m_0 = 0$ (etc.). The upper limit is shown as infinity but can of course be represented as the oldest class present.

If C_x is replaced by its definition from equation (19), and b is canceled out, then the result is:

$$1 = \sum_0^{\infty} (1+r)^{-x} p^x m_x \quad (21)$$

which now includes all the quantities primarily involved in population analysis—reproduction, survival, and population growth rate.

If survival is not constant over the classes considered, p^x can be replaced with a product of appropriate rates, or p_x can be written as meaning survival from birth to age x.

A rearrangement of equation (19) is sometimes useful. It is obtained by dividing both sides by b and summing (remembering that C_x is a proportion and its sum adds to unity):

$$\frac{1}{b} = \sum_{0}^{\infty} (1+r)^{-x} p^x \qquad (22)$$

Stable Age Distribution

Some rather more complicated mathematics is needed for rigorous proof that the above leads to the stable age-distribution. Several proofs are given in Lotka's papers, and by P. H. Leslie (1945, 1948). The reader should note that equation (20) can be used to estimate the value of r if survival and age-specific reproductive rates are available. The solution is by "trial and error" but goes very rapidly. Once r is determined, equations (19) and (22) permit construction of the corresponding age distribution, which can then be compared with that of the population actually studied. Some examples are given in the next section.

Age Structure of Male Population

It was previously mentioned that, since the recruitment to the male segment of a population is proportional to that in the female segment, a separate calculation for males could be "tacked on" to the tables for females. Using p_1 and $1 - p_1 = q_1$ as survival and mortality rates for males, it is possible to go through essentially the same process of constructing tables as for females, getting the eventual result for male age structure:

$$C_x = \left[\frac{q_1 + r}{1+r}\right] (1+r)^{-x} p_1^x \qquad (23)$$

Total Population Size

Combining males and females, with the initial ("pioneer") female population still represented by unity:

Total population at time x

$$= (1+r)^x \left[1 + \frac{q+r}{q_1 + r}\right] \qquad (24)$$

where the term on the right inside the brackets represents the number of males, and equal numbers of males and females are "recruited" each year.

Sex Ratio

Using the relation above, sex ratio becomes

$$\text{females/males} = \frac{q_1 + r}{q + r} \qquad (25)$$

hence, as to be expected, high male mortality rates (q_1) make for a large sex ratio.

An Example of Age Structure Analysis

An analysis of some data on white-tailed deer in Michigan (Eberhardt 1960) will serve to illustrate the use of the above formulae. Location of the areas discussed below is shown in Fig. 22.13. The calculations apply only to female deer, and assume constant age-specific reproductive and mortality rates.

The most serious difficulty encountered in the analysis was in obtaining satisfactory estimates of survival rates. There was clear evidence of long-term trends in population size, so estimates based on age structure alone would be biased due to the violation of the assumption of constant population size. Although extensive mortality surveys were conducted, these only covered the overwinter period and were known to underestimate losses. Estimates of actual population size were available, but subject to several uncertainties.

The principal method actually used had the following elements:

(1) Age and sex composition data from examination of deer killed in hunting seasons were used to estimate age and sex structure for each year. Because antlerless deer were not harvested nearly as heavily as bucks, it was necessary to find a "common denominator" between the two classes of data. The most reasonable such link seemed to be to assume there were equal numbers of bucks and does in the 1-1/2 year age class. Plausibility of this assumption depends mainly on the fact that the same hunting regulations apply to both sexes up to that time. While the sex ratio at birth is about 113:100, the force of mortality seems to act a little more heavily on males and tends to even this ratio out fairly rapidly.

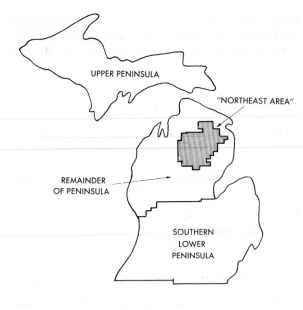

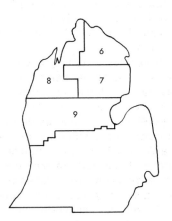

MAJOR STUDY AREAS

Fig. 22.13. Michigan areas referred to in the example of age structure analysis.

(2) An annual index to population size, based on a number of sources, was then applied to the age and sex structure data to obtain such an index for eight classes: adult does, 1-1/2-year old does, 2-1/2 year old and older does, adult bucks, 1-1/2 year-old bucks, 2-1/2 year-old and older bucks, buck fawns, and doe fawns. The population index was derived from several sources, through procedures too complex to describe briefly, but its validity was supported by comparisons with two other methods, as shown in Fig. 22.14.

The survival estimates were then obtained by dividing the index value for a particular class in 1 year by the value for that class 1 year earlier. Thus the 2-1/2 year-old and older doe group in 1 year is composed of the survivors of the adult doe class of the year before ("adult" includes 1-1/2 year-old and older animals for this purpose). The ensuing estimates were sufficiently variable and uncertain so that it did not seem reasonable to use more than two age-specific rates: (a) 0.58 for survival from late embryonic life to 1 year of age and (b) 0.70 per year thereafter.

Reproductive rates were secured by embryo-counts on does accidently killed on highways or shot in damage control, etc. Such records for 9 years are exhibited in Fig. 22.15. Averages of these data were applied as age-specific reproductive rates.

The actual calculations were based on a solution of equation (21) of the preceding section, using the quantities shown in Table 22.1. Since reproductive rate in the first age group (at birth) is zero, the equation becomes:

$$1 = \sum_{x=1}^{\infty} (1+r)^{-x} p_x m_x \qquad (26)$$

Solutions were obtained by guessing a value for r, summing the products of $(1+r)^{-x}$ times $p_x m_x$, comparing the sum with unity, and selecting a new value of r for the next trial. Only a few trials are needed to obtain two-digit accuracy. Beyond age class 1, $p_x = 0.58 (0.70)^{x-1}$ since only the two survival rates (0.58 and 0.70) were used.

Once estimates of r were obtained (Table 22.1), equation (22) could be used to estimate the "birth rate" coefficient, b, and this in turn served to compute the stable age composition of equation (19). The estimates of stable age composition (Table 22.2) could then be compared with recorded ages (Table 22.3). The "northeast area" data check very closely indeed with expectation, while the adjoining areas "remainder of Peninsula" show somewhat poorer agreement, and the Southern Lower Peninsula data show a rather unsatisfactory "fit."

In the southern area, the available data did not permit satisfactory estimates of survival rate, so the results are somewhat suspect on that score. History of the northeast area populations was such as to best meet the assumptions required, in the sense that these dense deer populations had been gradually decreasing for a long time period, and were probably not much influenced by a liberal

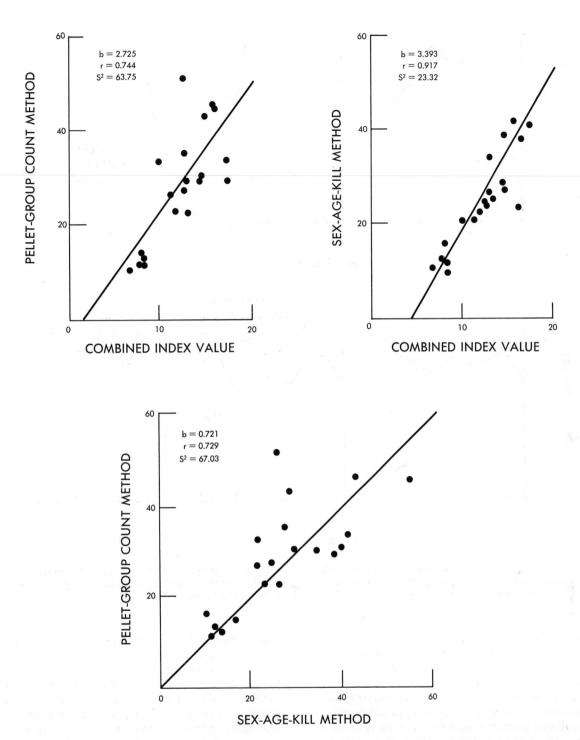

Fig. 22.14. A comparison of measures of deer population levels obtained by three methods on six areas. b = regression slope, r = correlation coefficient, s2 = variance about regression. (Eberhardt 1960).

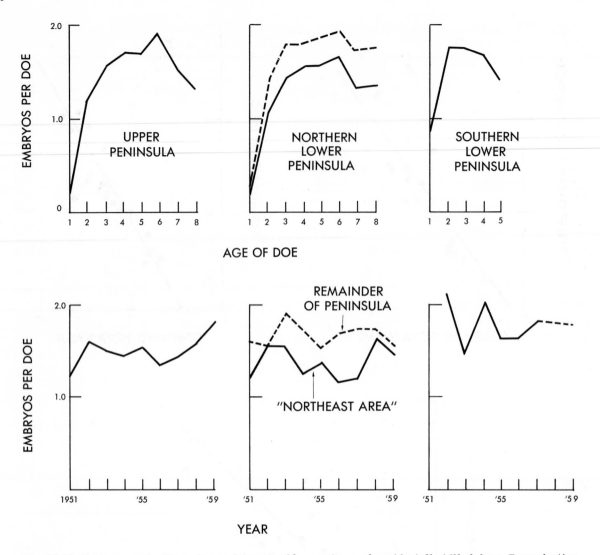

Fig. 22.15. Embryo production rates as determined from autopsy of accidentally killed deer. Reproductive rates by age of doe (upper figure) are based on averages of records from 1951 to 1959. Lower figures are annual averages of records from two-year-old and older does (Eberhardt 1960).

antlerless harvest in 1952, while the less dense herds in the remainder of the northern Lower Peninsula may well have been sufficiently reduced in number to prevent reestablishment of conditions leading to the stable age-distribution by the time of the study. The "farmland" herds of the southern Lower Peninsula were increasing at a very rapid rate (possibly as much as 15% per year).

Records of about 200 does found in mortality surveys are compared with the expected losses from the stable age structure in Table 22.4. Since the records were obtained by a sampling scheme (stratified sampling) and choice of years directed towards measuring over-winter losses (princi-

pally starvation), the observations are biased in that direction. Thus there is an excess of losses in the youngest group (fawns) and less than expected in the youngest of the adult classes. One rather striking feature of this and the preceding table is that there seems to be little evidence of markedly higher mortality in the older age classes. However, whitetails are known to live upwards of 20 years, so relatively few wild deer seem likely to reach a point where "old age" may sharply increase mortality rates.

A comparison of calculated stable age distributions with the relative frequency of age-classes actually recorded (Fig. 22.16) suggests that no 1 year is likely to be "typical." Most importantly

Table 22.1. Estimates of rate of population change (r) from reproductive and mortality data.

Age x	Survival to Given Age p_x	Northeast Area Reproductive Rate m_x	Remainder of Peninsula m_x	x	Southern Lower Peninsula p_x	m_x^{**}
0	1.0000	0	0	0	1.000	
1	0.5800	0.047	0.085	1	0.700	0.390
2	0.4060	0.503	0.658	2	0.490	0.832
3	0.2842	0.663	0.832	3	0.343	0.832
4	0.1989	0.733	0.846	4	0.240	0.799
5	0.1392	0.743	0.870	over 4*	0.70^x	0.799
6	0.0974	0.771	0.898			
over 6*	$0.58(0.70^x)$	0.644	0.827			
Estimate of r		-0.035	+0.023			+0.141

*Constant reproductive and mortality rates are assumed beyond those shown (sum of products computed from geometric series $m_x(0.70^x)$.
**Lower Peninsula value of m_x has been used as 0.799 beyond 4 years of age due to lack of sufficient records.

Table 22.2. Stable age distributions as computed from reproductive and survival data.

x	p_x	Northeast Area C_x	Remainder of Peninsula C_x	x	Southern Lower Peninsula p_x	C_x
0	1.0000	0.3136	0.3577	0	1.0000	0.3865
1	0.5800	0.1885	0.2028	1	0.7000	0.2371
2	0.4060	0.1367	0.1388	2	0.4900	0.1455
3	0.2842	0.0992	0.0950	3	0.3430	0.0892
4	0.1989	0.0719	0.0650	4	0.2401	0.0548
5	0.1392	0.0522	0.0444	5	0.1681	0.0336
6	0.0974	0.0378	0.0304	6	0.1176	0.0206
7	0.0682	0.0274	0.0208	7	0.0824	0.0126
8	0.0478	0.0199	0.0142	8	0.0576	0.0077
9	0.0334	0.0144	0.0097	9	0.0404	0.0048
10+	$0.58(0.70^x)$	0.0382	0.0211	10+	0.70^x	0.0076
		0.9998	0.9999			1.0000
r		-0.035	+0.023			+0.141

Table 22.3. Ages of "shot or accidentally killed" female deer.

| Age | Northeast Area | | Remainder of Peninsula | | Age | Southern Lower Peninsula | |
	Observed	Expected*	Observed	Expected*		Observed	Expected*
0	155	151	268	251	0	116	134
1	83	90	110	143	1	90	82
2	63	65	114	98	2	73	51
3	64	48	98	67	3	43	31
4	33	34	43	46	4	17	19
5	25	25	26	31	5+	9	31
6	14	18	21	21			
7	10	13	12	15			
8	13	10	6	10			
9	4	7	0	7			
10+	15	18	6	15			
	479	479	704	704		348	348

*Based on a stable age distribution.

this diagram reveals the hazards of attempting to estimate survival rates of female deer from age data alone.

One final feature of the age data may be mentioned. By setting $r=0$ in equation (21), the game manager can estimate the maximum mortality which a population might withstand and make

Table 22.4. Ages of female deer found dead in extensive mortality surveys.

Age	Observed	Expected*
0–1	106	77
1–2	18	33
2–3	14	24
3–4	18	17
4–5	9	13
5–6	5	9
6–7	6	7
7–8	8	5
8–9	4	3
9–10	2	3
10+	8	7
	198	198

*Based on a stable age distribution.

some predictions about the effect of increased or decreased hunting harvest. Such calculations for some Michigan areas (Fig. 22.17) demonstrate that both herd density and habitat also have an important influence, so that analysis of population structure must be accompanied by other kinds of information for effective management.

POPULATION SIZE AND TRENDS

In this chapter, some of the many difficulties and uncertainties associated with studies of unconfined animal populations have been outlined. In every population study there are weaknesses or outright gaps in the data, so there may be little direct assurance that the estimates do in fact represent what actually happened in the populations.

In the face of so much uncertainty, only cross-checks can provide reassurance. One important such check is to be able to compare predictions of population trend based on the "vital characteristics" (i.e., survival and reproduction) with independent measures of population behavior. Such a comparison may be made without estimates of absolute population size; that is, by using an index or relative measure of population trend.

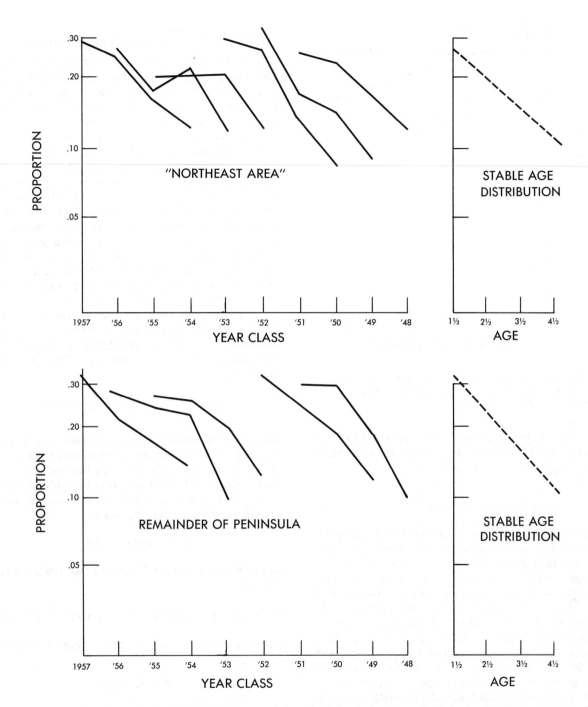

Fig. 22.16. Adult doe age distributions as determined from deer examined during hunting season (Eberhardt 1960).

However, one of the usual goals in wildlife work is to secure an optimal game harvest. "Kill figures" are estimates of absolute numbers, so working usefully with indices also requires an estimate of absolute population size. Estimating population size is treated in another chapter. Its

importance must be emphasized as well as the fact that estimating absolute size can rarely if ever be successfully avoided.

Growth curves are important facets of population analysis, but only the very simplest of such curves, the geometric, has been discussed here.

490

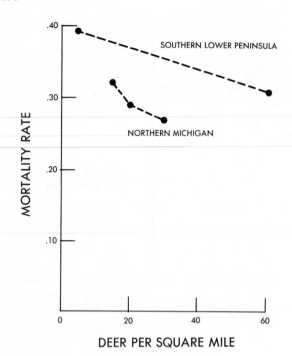

MORTALITY RATE

SOUTHERN LOWER PENINSULA

NORTHERN MICHIGAN

DEER PER SQUARE MILE

Fig. 22.17. Calculated mortality rates for some stationary populations based on the assumption $r = 0$ (Eberhardt 1960).

Behavior of populations was expressed in terms of equation (14), which is essentially equivalent to the exponential curve given by

$$N(t) = N(o)e^{rt} \qquad (27)$$

when time is measured as a continuous variable.

As noted before, growth or decline of a population cannot go on indefinitely. Circumstances in which animals have been introduced into new habitats, or in which populations otherwise start at a low level, usually show an initial growth period which is virtually identical with the simple geometric (or exponential) curve. As "limiting factors" come into play, growth slows down, and reaches an ultimate plateau (or the population may fluctuate about such an upper asymptote).

The simplest mathematical description of such an S-shaped curve is one which postulates that the rate of increase per unit of time is proportional to population size (as has already been considered) minus a term proportional to the square of population size already attained. This yields the logistic curve, for which the underlying differential equation is:

$$\frac{dN}{dt} = rN - aN^2 \qquad (28)$$

Interpreting $\frac{dN}{dt}$ as rate of change per unit time yields the description above. As population size increases, it is evident that the right-hand negative term will ultimately "catch up" to rN since it involves the square of population size, so that the rate of increase becomes zero.

Although the logistic curve has been very widely applied, about all that can be said in its favor is that it is relatively simple, and the fact that leveling off of the curve is associated with N^2 lets one interpret it as "interactions" between members of a population. Smith (1952) describes some of the shortcomings of previous uses of the logistic. Anyone working with populations ought to be familiar with the logistic curve, if for no other reason than because references to it are common, often in terms which imply more than any real data have yet demonstrated.

The Michigan deer data described in the previous section provide an example of the use of estimates of rates of population change. Taking logarithms of the "geometric" formula given above gives:

$$\log N_t = \log N_o + [\log(1+r)]t \qquad (29)$$

which is the equation of a straight line and can thus be fitted by simple regression methods. In the Michigan example, an index to population size was used. If it is assumed that the index value at time t bears a constant proportional relation to actual population size, N_t, then:

$$\text{Index value} = kN_t$$

where k is a constant. Then the regression equation is:

$$\log[k N(t)] = \log[k N(o)] + [\log(1+r)] t \qquad (30)$$

and the slope (B) of the linear regression equation

$$Y = A + Bx$$

where $Y = \log$ of index value at time t

$$x = t = \text{time units}$$

$$B = \log(1+r) = \text{regression "slope"}$$

provides an estimate of $\log(1+r)$.

Results for some northern Lower Peninsula areas (Fig. 22.18) suggest the assumption of a constant rate of change from year to year may be realistic. The necessary information for a composite index of the kind used above was not available in the southern Lower Peninsula, but two sources (Fig. 22.19) give estimates of r between 0.13 and 0.18. Although the higher estimate might be preferred on the basis of statistical "precision" (much smaller scatter of points around the regression line—see Fig. 22.19), there is a possibility that the buck kill might have been increasing somewhat more rapidly than the population, as a result of increasing hunter awareness of good hunting in that area.

For several reasons, rates of change from index data were estimated for areas somewhat different (see Fig. 22.13) from those used in estimating rates of change from population dynamics data (summarized in Table 22.1). The areas are sufficiently similar in boundaries for comparison, however, so the estimated annual rates of change are shown in Table 22.5.

Thus estimates of r from population index data support those obtained from population analysis. The reader is reminded that, in the presence of so many uncertainties about the validity of the assumptions needed for estimating the vital characteristics of wildlife populations, this kind of cross-check is extremely important.

METHODS OF DATA COLLECTION

It is hardly necessary to say that a successful population study depends primarily on collection of data on the population. Both methods and opportunities vary greatly from species to species, and from place to place. Some general and a few special features will be brought out here, but the investigator concerned with a particular species and place can hardly expect to proceed without carefully reviewing the literature and local knowledge pertinent to that species.

The available money and manpower resources almost always determine what kind of details can be secured. Nature of the study also depends heavily on the land area involved. Small-area studies normally are designed for some special research purpose, and require—or can afford—fairly intensive efforts. Live-trapping and marking may be feasible or necessary on a small area, but virtually impossible on large areas. Most of the discussion here is concerned with projects which must deal with areas measured in hundreds or thousands of square miles. The methods generally are applicable on a smaller scale, but require attention to details of locale and species not feasible here.

Table 22.5. A comparison of rates of annual population increase in three areas of Michigan as obtained by two methods.

	Northeast Area	Remainder of Peninsula	Southern Lower Peninsula
Estimates from "population dynamics"	-0.035	+0.023	+0.141
Estimates from index data			
Area 7	-0.031		
Area 8		+0.040	
Area 9		+0.043	
Southern Lower Peninsula			+0.133, +0.184

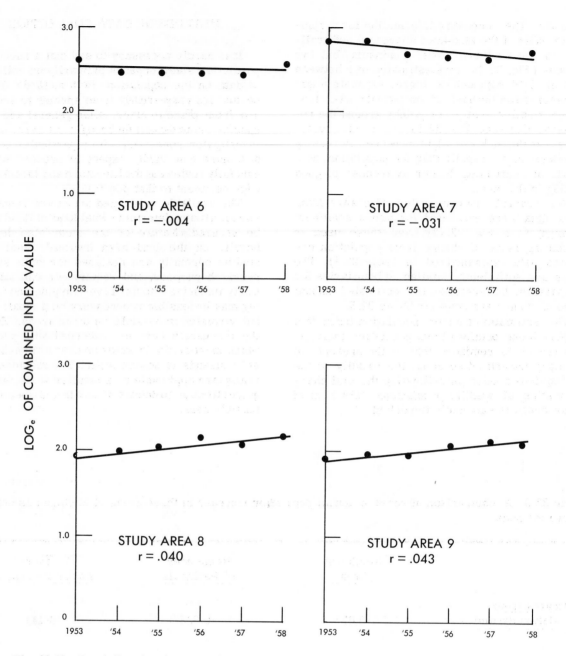

Fig. 22.18. Population trends on study areas (as shown in Fig. 22.13). (Eberhardt 1960.) In this figure, r indicates estimated rate of increase.

One of the most difficult questions concerning field studies is that of getting a sufficient volume of observations without sacrificing quality. Taking large samples may require the help of a sizeable number of untrained people who often do not understand or care about the problems involved. There is a crucial need in wildlife management for improved methods for getting sufficiently large sample sizes at a reasonable cost, but

wholly satisfactory ways to fulfill that need are not yet available.

Estimates of population density have been mentioned earlier as being of great importance in population analysis, but are dealt with in another chapter. The reader should be reminded, though, that an important share of the costs of field work will need to be devoted to measurement of population size. Consequently, it is crucial that

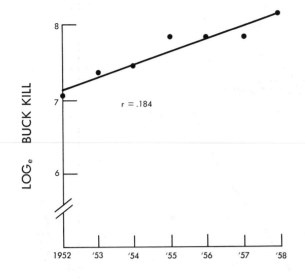

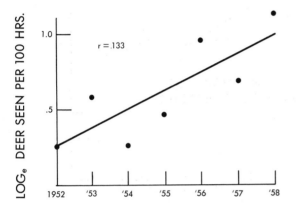

Fig. 22.19. Trend of two deer population indices for the southern Lower Peninsula (Eberhardt 1960).

usually needs to be controlled or "weighted" to be satisfactory.

Estimates of game harvest from checking stations are rarely reliable. This is a matter of sampling biases in where and when the stations operate, versus behavior of hunters and their success. Furthermore, costs of operating such stations dictate that the emphasis be on that data which must be taken by trained personnel. Useful game kill surveys depend more and more on contacting hunters by mail. Sportsmen seem to be almost a unique group in their willingness to reply to such mail inquiries, in which response rates of over 90% may be obtained by reminder cards and letters, whereas the usual kind of survey by mail may yield responses from 10 to 15% of the people contacted. Under special circumstances, surveys by telephone or personal interview may be required, or used to supplement contact by mail. Some details are given by Eberhardt and Murray (1960).

The use of "hunter report cards" (provided with the hunting license) has fortunately been on the decline across the country. Estimates based on such methods can be expected to be seriously biased, as a consequence of the tendency for a higher proportion of successful hunters to report their take. This bias necessarily changes with changes in the proportion of all hunters reporting, (see, for example, Hayne and Eberhardt 1954 and Fig. 22.20).

Direct surveys of game mortality from causes other than legal hunting have largely been confined to assessment of starvation losses in deer and elk. In some special circumstances (epidemics or large-scale poisoning by pesticides) it may be feasible to conduct such surveys for smaller animals. If usable estimates of numbers lost are to be obtained, the surveys must be based on scientific sampling methods. Nearly always stratified random sampling will be employed, since this combines the biologist's knowledge of regional intensity of the problem with trustworthy methods of sampling. A good job of stratification can keep the costs within tolerable limits. An example of one such study was given by Whitlock and Eberhardt (1956), and the stratification used is shown in Fig. 22.21.

Surveys concerned with reproduction may include such things as embryo or corpora lutea counts, and nesting studies. The importance of local differences needs to be emphasized again and considered in designing and analyzing the surveys. Visual counts of adults and progeny may be used (e.g. "brood" surveys) and enjoy quite varied reputations depending on locale and cir-

the needs of both facets be combined as far as possible in any field operations.

Data on age and sex composition usually depend on bag checks during the hunting season. The techniques of aging, sexing and so on are described elsewhere in this book, and the actual operation of "checking stations" depends very much on local conditions and regulations. A feature of great importance is the determination of the location where the animals examined were actually killed. This requires good maps, an interviewer who "knows the country," and much patience. Analysis of detailed data on large areas almost always shows marked local differences, and it is anything but safe to assume such differences will be averaged out overall. It is true, of course, that data almost always do have to be averaged over sizable areas, but such averaging

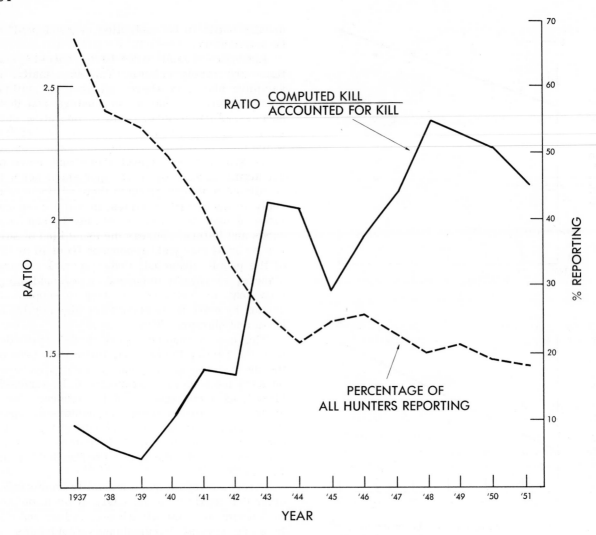

Fig. 22.20. Change of bias in "hunter report card" system with changing response rate (Hayne and Eberhardt 1954).

cumstances. For example, doe-fawn ratios may be usefully obtained in some western states, but are regarded with grave doubts in other places with heavy vegetative cover.

Sampling natural populations is both a very difficult and too-often neglected subject. Some of the problems are described by Eberhardt (1963). An accounting of the techniques of sampling requires a sizable book and can hardly be described here. Of several such books available, perhaps the most frequently used (from the wildlife standpoint) is that by Cochran (1963). Some uses of stratified random sampling were reported by Eberhardt (1957).

In concluding this section, the reader ought to be warned that a good deal is lacking, both here and in general knowledge of methods for gather-

ing data out-of-doors. Wildlifers often have not taken the strict point of view necessarily adopted by sampling experts, simply because that could virtually put them out of business! That is, validity of sampling methods can only be demonstrated formally by requiring that the samples be selected by the technique of randomization. When the wildlife investigator deals with sampling over a land area, it is feasible and essential to draw samples by actual reference to tables of random numbers. But trying to design such a scheme for a population of mobile and secretive animals, or for sampling hunters during their return home from hunting is quite another matter, and one (of many) for which no satisfactory solutions are yet known.

Where randomized sampling *is* possible, the only safe course is to take full advantage of the

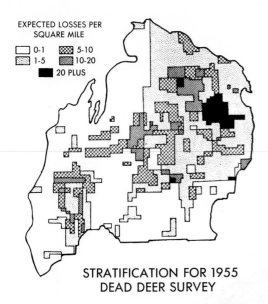

EXPECTED LOSSES PER
SQUARE MILE

☐ 0-1   ▦ 5-10
▨ 1-5   ▧ 10-20
■ 20 PLUS

STRATIFICATION FOR 1955
DEAD DEER SURVEY

Fig. 22.21. Example of stratification used for a large-scale sample survey (Whitlock and Eberhardt 1956).

opportunity. Such evidence as is available points to a strong tendency for individual selections of supposedly representative samples to be consistently biased. For example, Hayne (1952) conducted an experimental study of ability to select a representative sample of the lengths of small fish, with the "population" conveniently laid out in a pan. Virtually all of the samples drawn were appreciably biased towards longer fish (Fig. 22.22).

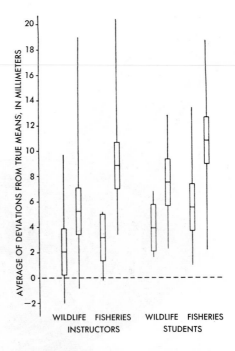

Fig. 22.22. Biases in a "judgment" sampling experiment (Hayne 1952).

CHAPTER TWENTY-THREE

IDENTIFYING, EVALUATING, AND CONTROLLING WILDLIFE DAMAGE

TERRY E. ANDERSON[1]

Staff Specialist
Division of Wildlife Services
Bureau of Sport Fisheries and Wildlife
Washington, D.C.

A PERSPECTIVE

Statements and policies on controlling animal damage have been issued by Howard (1965), Spear (1967), the U.S. Department of the Interior (1967), and The Wildlife Society (1963, 1968). A separate chapter would be needed to properly discuss the perspective, the philosophy, or the principles of controlling or managing wild animals which are damaging or about to cause damage adversely affecting one or more of man's interests. A void would be created in this chapter,

however, if the issues involved in wild animal damage control were not at least briefly discussed.

Although wild animals have long been a source of food and pleasure, they are also at times a problem for mankind. Birds in orchards, rice fields, corn fields, and livestock feedlots; rodents in forests, orchards, grasslands, and fields; carnivores in western livestock areas; birds sharing airspace with jet airplane traffic; rats in ghettoes; and wild animals transmitting diseases to man, his pets, and livestock are all examples of problems which wild animals sometimes pose for man. It is logical to assume that, as the human population increases, the number and scope of these problems will also increase, because the increase in human population will result in greater competition between man and other animals which must share the same envi-

[1]The author wishes to express his appreciation to various members of the Division of Wildlife Services, Bureau of Sport Fisheries and Wildlife, for providing a critical review of this chapter.

ronment. The need for controlling animal damage will also increase as land managers work to re-establish and maintain forests and grasslands, and when agriculturalist's profit margins decrease.

Animal damage control is one of the many tools available to and used by natural resource managers. In addition to a relatively "pure" control function with genera such as *Mus*, and *Rattus*, animal damage control is a tool that may be compared with harvest regulation, habitat acquisition and manipulation, protection of rare species, conservation education, and enforcement of regulations. Like all resource management tools, animal damage control must be applied intelligently and responsibly to achieve the desired results.

Because the ultimate objective of animal damage control must be to *control the damage*, animals should not be categorized as nuisance species, as good or bad, or as beneficial or detrimental. Each species, each population, and sometimes each individual must be considered within and judgements made for each particular situation. Control of animal numbers should be limited to offending individuals or particular groups—not the species as a whole.

The attitude of society is another important aspect to be considered when applying animal damage control. Keeping in tune with the "personality of society" is as important as knowing the latest developments in wildlife management. Aesthetic values of wildlife are as important to many segments of our society as economic and sporting values are to others.

Control of damage through cultural practices would of course be an ideal solution; however, too few of these techniques have been developed that are both effective and practical or that provide the total solution to the problem. Meanwhile, resource managers must face the inevitable. Certain situations require the removal of individual animals or the reduction of local populations. It is desirable that those who must make the ultimate decision—to remove or not to remove—will come from the ranks of the professional wildlife biologists and ecologically intelligent commercial pest control operators who are best able to make objective judgements.

DAMAGE AND ITS IDENTIFICATION

If resource losses are great enough that control of a species may be considered, it must be ascertained which species is responsible for the mortality or damage before deciding whether to initiate control or before selecting the control tool. Complete accuracy in evaluating the cause of mortality or damage to a resource may be difficult, but errors can be minimized by intensive investigation and by carefully evaluating observations.

Predation and its Identification

When the carcass of an animal or the remains of a nest are found, the exact cause of the loss should be ascertained. Predation cannot be assumed. Tracks and droppings at the carcass provide clues to the cause of death and an effort should be made to locate and identify these, but these clues alone are not conclusive evidence of the cause of death. Toxic plants and water, senility, wounds, starvation, disease, and in the case of suspected nest predation, destruction by farm machinery or by livestock trampling are possibilities that should not be overlooked.

CARCASS EXAMINATION

Whether or not predation caused the death of a species of livestock, game, or poultry may be determined by a careful external check of a fresh carcass for tooth and claw marks and tears. Determining the cause of death becomes more difficult, however, as the carcass becomes older. Techniques for determining time since death are suggested by Gill and O'Meara (1965). Lacking conclusive external evidence, the carcass should be skinned and the muscle tissue examined for tooth or claw-puncture marks and for bruises and blood clots that may have been made by a predator. When it is known that a predator fed on a carcass, but not whether it actually made the kill, finding bruises or clots may clarify the issue, since bruises and clots are not formed after an animal is dead. This evidence proves that the animal did not die passively from natural causes.

AREA EXAMINATION

The area around the carcass should be examined for signs of a struggle. These signs may appear as tug-of-war drag marks made by the combatants' feet. When the prey species is large, one or more of its body impressions may also be found in the earth or snow where it was thrown by the predator during the chase. Bits of wool, hair, or feathers extracted by the predator during the struggle may also be found in the area. These signs should not be confused with similar materials sometimes spread from the carcass by wind, or by carrion-feeding birds and mammals. Tracks and droppings found in the area can be used to identify animals which have visited the carcass, and droppings may also be used to determine the foods of the visiting animals.

Blood stains are also useful in determining whether predation has occurred. Blood near the wound, elsewhere on the carcass, and on the earth, snow, rocks, vegetation, or other objects in the area of the struggle may also be evidence of predation.

NEST PREDATION

Losses of game-bird or poultry eggs are often difficult to pinpoint since nest predators include animals as varied as shrews, ground squirrels, raccoons, dogs, magpies, skunks, and snakes. As stated before, losses are also caused by farm machinery and trampling of livestock. Tracks in the immediate area, and egg shells in scats may be the only clues to indicate the damaging species. Several animals, however, have characteristic ways of feeding on eggs. These are discussed in the following section.

Identifying Predator Species

Most predator species have characteristic behavioral patterns of attacking and feeding on prey. The feeding characteristics and representative prey species found on several predators' menus are given as aids for identifying specific predator species. Predators of similar size and appearance or those whose killing and feeding behavior is similar have been grouped accordingly.[2]

COYOTES, DOGS, WOLVES

These three canids prey on rodents, rabbits, deer, antelope, sheep, calves, poultry, swine, and birds. Wolves sometimes prey on such large wild ungulates as caribou, moose, and elk.

Livestock and big game animals attacked by

[2]Jerry Davis' unpublished manuscript, "Identification of Predators By Their Feeding Habits," University of Idaho, January, 1964, was very helpful in preparing the section on feeding characteristics of predators.

wolves are nearly always "hamstrung" or seized by the flank. Slash marks made by the canine teeth may be found on the rear legs and flanks. The downed animals are usually disemboweled and unborn young may be eaten first, although the eyes and udder were first eaten on an elk-kill (Young and Goldman 1944).

Young and Goldman (1944) and Stenlund (1955) observed that wolves fed first on the hams, brisket, and entrails of deer; however, the flank and hamstrings were still the points of attack.

Adult deer are usually the largest prey of coyotes. The coyote typically kills by attacking the thoracic region; however, the hind legs and flanks may also be attacked on large deer and calves. Calves bobtailed by coyotes are evidence of this behavior. Ozoga and Harger (1966) reported that autopsies of white-tailed deer killed by coyotes revealed tooth marks and hemorrhage in the upper neck and head region, but almost no injury to other parts of the body. The focal point of the attack was the throat. Once down, the deer were frequently dispatched by bites to the head; some fang marks penetrated the skull.

Adult sheep and large lambs are most often attacked in the head and throat. The throat of an adult sheep attacked by a coyote may resemble a throat that has been slit with a knife. Preferred parts are the hindquarters, unborn young, and udder. The paunch and intestines may be removed and dragged a short distance from the carcass. Smaller animals, such as lambs and fawns, are often seized by the head and killed by crushing some facial bones. This is also true with elk calves (Robinson 1952).

Coyotes and dogs occasionally cause severe losses to penned sheep or turkeys without touching an animal. Harassment by the predator from outside the pen can cause the enclosed animals to stampede and pile-up in a corner resulting in deaths by suffocation. Tracks outside the pen will aid in identifying the predator.

Dogs most often attack the hindquarters and flanks of calves, deer, and sheep. Several areas of the body of these prey may be torn after an attack by dogs; however, the victim may not be killed. Stiles (1967) observed the initial points of attack by dogs on deer in Massachusetts were the hindleg muscles and tendons; very little feeding followed the kills.

BEARS

Grizzly and black bears often kill sheep, and occasionally cattle and horses.

Bears usually kill by biting the head or neck or by slapping the prey. Torn and mutilated carcasses characterize victims of bear attacks. In eating, black bears will peel back the hide in a manner that resembles case-skinning. They may remove the carcass to a more secluded spot to eat, if the kill is made in the open.

Davenport (1953) and Cahalane (1961) reported that black bears may eat the udders of females before opening the animal. The victim is usually opened ventrally and the heart and liver are consumed. The intestines are usually strewn about and the animal may be partly skinned in an attempt to locate the firm fleshy parts. Fecal deposits are generally found within 100 ft of the carcass and a bed is often nearby.

A study by Murie (1948) indicated grizzly bears have a well-defined feeding pattern on cattle. Cattle are killed by a bite through the dorsal part of the neck. The stomach and intestines are removed and the bear begins feeding on the brisket, ribs, and proximal end of the forelegs. The heart and liver are sometimes eaten, and the hindquarters are taken last.

The presence of a bear has been known to stampede range sheep, causing damage as the herd piles up in a timber blow-down or stampedes over a steep embankment.

BOBCAT, LYNX, COUGAR

These felines prey on deer, sheep, rabbits, and porcupine. Bobcats and lynx also prey on poultry, and cougars are known to prey on cattle and horses. Bobcats also kill domestic house cats.

Cougars usually dispatch a large prey by leaping on its shoulders and biting its neck (Young and Goldman 1946). The shoulders, sides, or back of the cougar's victim will bear obvious claw marks. Cahalane (1961) reported that cougars usually disembowel their prey, but feed first on the ribs or loin.

Bobcats almost invariably kill adult deer by leaping on their backs or shoulders, often when they are lying down, and biting them on the ventral part of the neck. The wind pipe is pinched and the jugular vein may be punctured. Very young fawns, lambs, and smaller prey are usually killed by a bite through the dorsal part of the neck or head (Young 1958). Stiles (1967) identified deer killed by bobcats by the sheared clumps of hair along the back, the needle like punctures of the claws along the back and neck, and deep open wounds caused by biting near the throat or lower jaw. Saunders (1963) described a caribou bleeding from the neck and shoulder which had been attacked by a lynx, and Seton (1937) stated that lynx and bobcat often attacked deer at the throat.

Bobcats prefer the hindquarters of deer or sheep in most cases; however, the shoulder and neck region or the flank are sometimes eaten first. The stomach is generally untouched. In most cases the carcass is partly covered with litter or snow—especially the parts that have been fed upon. Observations by Smith (1946) and Pollack (1951) indicate bobcats consume all but a portion of the intestines of rabbits. Stiles (1967) observed one rabbit kill where a bobcat partially buried the stomach, intestines, and hind feet; on another, only the hind feet and intestines were buried. Poultry are usually killed by biting the head and upper vertebrae (Young 1958); the heads are usually eaten. Bobcats and lynx will also prey on bird eggs.

It is probably impossible to distinguish between the bobcat and the lynx by their droppings (Murie 1954) and feeding habits. In areas occupied by both, the tracks near the carcass help determine which was responsible. The lynx has more widespreading toes and hairy feet, distinguishing it from the bobcat.

Cougars, bobcats, and lynx almost always attempt to cover their kills with litter. Bobcats reach out 12-14 inches in scratching litter whereas cougars reach approximately 36 inches (Young 1958). The distance between the canine teeth and the diameter of the tooth marks will also help distinguish a cougar kill from that of the bobcat and lynx.

FOX

The largest prey of the fox are young lambs and pigs, adult jack rabbits, and turkeys, although mice and rabbits are staples for the fox. Fox will attack adult sheep and though they may injure them they usually do not kill them. Fox will, however, feed upon larger animals as carrion.

The prey is usually carried some distance from the kill location, often to a den. The remains are often hidden in debris or partly buried in a hole scratched in the soil. Einarsen (1956) observed that foxes often urinate on uneaten remains and that the odor is an identifying sign. Many dead weasels were observed around fox dens in a study by Latham (1946); none, however, were eaten. The fox can climb over a fairly high chicken-wire fence while removing poultry (Burkholder 1955).

Einarsen (1956) noted that the breast and legs of birds killed by fox are eaten first and the other appendages are scattered about. The toes of the victim are usually drawn up in an unnatural position because of tendens pulled when the fox strips meat from the leg bone. Smaller bones are likely to be sheared off. Foxes often kill more young birds than they can eat when they find a nest. The young birds are left where killed, with tooth marks under the wing on each side of the body, and the head is often missing (Anon. 1936).

Eggs are usually opened enough to be licked out; the shells are left beside the nest and are rarely removed to the den although fox dens are noted for containing the remains of their prey, particularly the wings of birds.

BADGER

Badgers sometimes prey on rabbits, but their diet consists mainly of prairie dogs, pocket gophers and ground squirrels. They may also destroy the nests of ground-nesting birds and occasionally kill small lambs, and half-grown domestic turkeys, parts of which they may bury in a hole resembling their den.

Badgers usually consume all of a prairie dog except the head and fur along the back. This characteristic probably holds true for much of their prey; however, signs of digging near prey-remains are the best evidence for the work of a badger.

RACCOON

There is little evidence that raccoons prey heavily on mammals. They do, however, occasionally kill poultry, small lambs and kid goats; they usually feed on only the eyes and tongue of lambs and goats. They also prey on birds and their eggs. The heads of adult birds are usually bitten off and left some distance from the body (Anon. 1936). The breast and crop may be torn and chewed, the entrails are sometimes eaten, and there may be bits of flesh near water. In a poultry house, the heads of many birds may be taken in one night.

One or more of the eggs may be removed from poultry or game-bird nests and may be eaten away from the nest. The shells are heavily cracked with the line of fracture being along the long axis of the egg (Davis 1959). There is often some disturbance of nest materials.

SKUNK

Skunks, although often accused of killing poultry and small game species, kill few adult birds as compared to the nests they rob (Einarsen 1956). Most rabbits, chickens, and pheasants are eaten as carrion, even though they are dragged to the skunk's den (Crabb 1948). When skunks do kill poultry, they generally will kill only one or two birds and maul them considerably. Crabb (1941) observed that spotted skunks are quite effective in controlling rats and mice in grain and corn storage buildings. They kill these rodents by biting and chewing the head and foreparts; the carcasses are not eaten.

Skunks are notorious egg robbers and the signs of their work are quite obvious. Eggs are usually opened at one end and the edges are crushed as the skunk punches its nose into the hole to lick out the contents (Einarsen 1956, Davis 1959). The eggs may appear as hatched, except for the edges. They are sometimes removed from the nest, though rarely more than 3 ft. Canine tooth marks on the egg will be at least 1/2 inch apart. When in a more advanced stage of incubation, the eggs are likely to be chewed into small pieces.

DOMESTIC CATS

Domestic cats rarely prey on anything larger than a duck, pheasant, or rabbit. Einarsen (1956) noted their messy feeding behavior. Portions of their prey are often strewn over several hundred square feet in open areas. The meaty portions of large birds are almost entirely consumed leaving loose skin with feathers attached. Small birds are generally consumed, with only the wings, and scattered feathers remaining. Cats usually leave teeth marks on every exposed bone of their prey.

WEASELS AND MINK

Weasels and mink have similar feeding techniques. They kill their prey by biting them through the skull, upper neck, or jugular vein (Hamilton 1933, Cahalane 1961). The victims show characteristic single or double sets of tooth punctures on the neck or head. Weasels will attack animals as large as snowshoe hares. Hamilton (1933) observed that weasels may consume an entire chipmunk or partly grown rat, including bones and fur. Mink rarely attack anything larger than a muskrat or duck.

Errington (1943) noted that mink, while eating large muskrats, make an opening at the back or side of the neck. As it eats away flesh, ribs, and pieces of the adjacent hide, it skins the animal by pulling the head and hindquarters out through the same hole. McCracken and Van Cleve (1947) noted the same feeding behavior in weasels eating small rodents. Both predators often kill more poultry than is needed for food. Burkholder (1955) noted that weasels may place many dead chickens neatly in a pile. The head and breast is usually eaten by both animals.

Teer (1964) observed that blue-winged teal eggs destroyed by weasels were broken at the ends, with openings 15-20 mm in diameter. Small punctures, often in pairs, were found in the sides or ends of all broken eggs, and embryos were missing.

OPOSSUM

The most noted predation by the opossum is on birds and their eggs. Chickens killed by opossum are mauled considerably (Burkholder 1955). Opossum usually commence feeding on poultry at the anal opening. Young poultry or game birds are entirely consumed with only a few wet feathers remaining; egg shells are chewed into small pieces and left in the nest.

RATS

Norway rats kill adult chickens by biting their throats and they often kill more than needed for food. They usually feed on more of the carcasses than weasels, and usually take them to a more secluded area to do so. Their victims may be found piled in a corner or in burrows (Burkholder 1955). Rats have also been known to kill new-born lambs, the point of attack being the navel.

CROWS, RAVENS, MAGPIES, GULLS

Crows, ravens, magpies and gulls are well known robbers of other birds' nests. Crows usually remove the egg from the nest before breaking a hole in it. The raven and magpie break a hole up to an inch in diameter. The raven leaves a clean edge along the break, never crushed, whereas the magpie often leaves dented, broken edges. Ravens eat young birds (Anon. 1936), as do gulls.

In certain areas crows, ravens, and magpies kill new-born lambs by pecking their eyes. At times they may also damage cattle by picking on fresh brands or sores which may cause infection of the area, loss of weight, or even severe wounds.

Crop, Forest, and Range Damage & its Identification

Determining if wildlife is damaging standing or stored crops, forage, or trees is not usually as difficult as determining if predation has occurred. Damage to crops is usually caused by birds, members of the deer family, and rodents; exceptions occur, however, such as coyotes eating watermelons and cantaloupes, raccoons or skunks damaging field or sweet corn, or bears damaging apiaries and trees in orchards and forests.

An investigator will often be able to observe a wild animal doing the damage, e.g., antelope eating unharvested wheat, elk feeding from a haystack, blackbirds eating field corn, or rats feeding in a granary.

Tracks, droppings, tooth marks, dens, feathers, burrows, and trails cut through vegetation by small rodents will help determine if the damage was caused by wildlife and if so by what species.

Once an area's fauna is determined, the cause of damage is easier to establish because each species has individual behavioral characteristics. For example, by using snap traps, a rodent population may be found to consist of *Peromyscus* and *Microtus*. Which one of these rodents could be responsible for a loss of vegetation reproduction from seeds? It undoubtedly would be the *Peromyscus*, since *Microtus* forage chiefly on grass and the cambium layers of plants, and the seed-eating preference of *Peromyscus* has been well documented. Therefore, if the damage justified control, *Peromyscus* would be the target species.

An extensive study and literature review by Lawrence, Kverno, and Hartwell (1961) on identifying wildlife damage to conifers in the Northwest points out several characteristics which are of value to orchard, forest and range managers in many other areas. Parts of this and other studies are presented here to assist in identification of damage caused by certain species.

RED SQUIRRELS

Conspicuous field signs indicating red squirrel damage are green, unopened cones scattered on the ground under mature conifers and accumulations of cone scales which mark favorite squirrel feeding stations. The oblique-cut, characteristic of rodent feeding, though not present on the base of individually cut cones, is evident when branchlets bearing several cones are cut. Although squirrel-cached cones are an important source of conifer seed, cone cutting may have an adverse effect on future seed crops.

DEER MICE, SHREWS, GROUND SQUIRRELS, AND CHIPMUNKS

In controlled feeding experiments, small mammals have consumed large numbers of seeds during an evening's feeding. Deer mice and shrews each consumed over 200 Douglas fir seeds (Garman and Orr-Ewing 1949, Kangur 1954); ground squirrels consumed 340; and chipmunks consumed 237 ponderosa pine seeds (Siggins 1934). Such seed-eating activities are not readily apparent to the casual observer; but a careful search in sheltered situations, near rotten logs or stumps, for example, should reveal accumulated hulls from rodent-opened seeds.

Many rodents collect and cache more seeds than they use. Frequently, seeds left in these caches germinate to produce small clusters of seedlings commonly observed in the ponderosa pine, white pine, and Douglas fir regions.

POCKET GOPHERS

Gophers develop extensive burrow systems among roots for feeding purposes. Scattered flat fan-shaped mounds of soil are evidence of their presence. These mounds contrast with the volcano-shaped mounds that moles push up when burrowing deeply. The pocket gopher can be a problem on cultivated, forest, range, and orchard lands.

Gophers may seriously damage a crop such as alfalfa by feeding on the leaves, stems and roots. Many plants may be killed when their roots are cut. Another problem attributed to gophers is water-loss caused by their burrowing in fields and canals. Roads have been washed out by escaping irrigation water. Gopher mounds in hay fields cause excessive breakdown and wearing of "sickle-mowers." These mounds may also provide good seed beds for noxious weeds.

Orchards offer suitable habitat for pocket gophers in areas where alfalfa and weeds become established between the trees. Gophers then may cause severe damage and may even kill some trees by feeding on the tree roots.

Pocket gophers can cause serious losses in ponderosa pine (Dingle 1956) and Douglas fir plantations and their root-cutting and burrowing activities can prevent pine reproduction in forest clearings (Moore 1943).

Root-cutting by gophers in plantations is frequently not noticed until crowns turn brown from summer drought or seemingly healthy green trees are tipped at odd angles by the wind. These young trees can be easily pulled from the ground to reveal root-cutting and barking around the root collar. Beneath snow, pocket gophers forage above ground and tunnel through snow to gnaw the bark of young trees. Lodgepole pines have been found barked to the height of 5 ft by pocket gophers working under the cover of deep snow (Moore 1940). Above-ground stem barking injuries caused by the pocket gopher show small tooth marks 1/16 inch-wide that are distinct from the broader grooves left by porcupines and the fine gnawed surface left by meadow voles. When the roots of small seedlings are cut off, the entire sapling may be pulled down into the burrow and eaten.

VOLES

Voles (pine mice, prairie voles, meadow mice, *etc.*) are responsible for damage to forest environments, orchards, ornamentals, and hay fields. Basal barking (gnawing on bark at the base of a tree) on young seedlings by voles has a finely gnawed appearance with tooth marks at various angles. Gnawing injuries on large seedlings and saplings may extend from the root collar upward on the bole for a foot or more. Small trees up to 1/4-inch in diameter are frequently gnawed through, leaving stumps which look like minature beaver work. Voles may also girdle the roots of 15-20 year old trees. Meadow voles, active during daytime, can frequently be seen scurrying along their well-traveled runways. Deep subterranean trails and gnawed roots indicate damage by pine mice.

DEER

Browsing by deer often results in economic losses to orchardists and tree farmers. Damage to trees is most serious to younger newly planted trees. Damage to these trees not only occurs by browsing, but also by antler rubbing during summer months.

Browsing injuries by deer are easily distinguished from clipping injuries of rodents. Deer, possessing lower incisors only, leave a splintered break on dormant woody stems. When browsing occurs in early spring, bark may slip, leaving a stripped stem for some distance below the break. During the growing season when the soft, turgid new shoots are browsed, a blunt break occurs. Supplementary signs include well-defined trails, distinctive tracks, and droppings.

RABBITS

Rabbits are responsible for damage to tree seedlings, truck crops, grain fields, gardens, and ornamentals. They can also strip the bark from established orchard trees.

All rabbits produce similar clipping injuries to tree seedlings. When clipping a tree, rabbits leave a clean, knife-like, oblique cut on the stem. They usually clip stems of 1/4-inch diameter or less up to heights of 20 inches. Repeated clipping can suppress the height or deform seedlings, small grains, and other crops.

In many instances, rabbits can be observed doing the damage. Additional field sign includes their tracks in the damage area, their trails leading to and from the damage area, and their droppings which often occur in clusters at the base of the damaged plants.

PORCUPINES

Porcupines leave broad, prominent incisor marks in the exposed sapwood of larger trees. Feeding on older trees is confined to the unplated bark of the upper trunk. Top girdling in pine produces a characteristically bushy crown. On seedlings and the thinner-barked Douglas fir, basal girdling on young, pole-sized trees may occur. Branch cutting to feed young animals may occur on trees in the vicinity of breeding dens.

BEAVERS

Beaver damage usually consists of felling valuable timber, plugging culverts, or constructing dams which cause flooding of valuable crops or timber. The stumps of beaver-cut trees are characteristically cone shaped with chips at the base and are 1-2 ft in height. The broad chisel-like tooth marks on the stump are distinctive. Beavers may strip and eat the bark from felled trees or cut billets from the branches and trunk to be carried to water. Supplemental field signs of beaver activity are freshly peeled sticks floating in water or along the shore, well-traveled trails to cutting areas, and their tracks.

MUSKRATS

Feeding habits of muskrats may result in some damage to grain or garden crops growing near water; however, the major cause for concern is extensive burrowing which may result in the collapse of dams or dikes.

Muskrat activity is indicated by presence of their houses, underwater dens visible during low water, slides, cave-ins along the bank as a result of undermining by the muskrat burrows, visual sightings of individual muskrats, tracks, and droppings.

NUTRIA

Grazing by nutria may cause extensive damage to rice, sugarcane, and alfalfa fields. Their burrows may also seriously damage dikes, bayou banks, drainage canals, and irrigation ditches. Their activities may also destroy levees used to control water levels in rice fields.

They are easily observed in the damaged area or swimming in adjacent waterways. Their tracks, droppings, and trails to and from the damage area give evidence of their presence.

BEARS

A feature of bear-girdling is an array of long, vertical grooves on exposed sapwood and large strips of bark at the base of the tree. Although barking may occur higher up, basal girdling is more common. Barking by bears differs markedly from that caused by rodents, which eat the bark and leave horizontal or diagonal tooth marks. Supplemental field signs are stumps and logs which have been ripped apart by bears in search of insects, "sign trees" which bears have repeatedly rubbed and clawed, and tracks and droppings.

MARMOTS

Marmots (woodchucks, rock chucks, etc.) can cause damage to many crops. Damage to legumes and truck gardens is often severe. The majority of the damage is caused by the animals consuming the plants. Earthen mounds from their burrows and the burrows themselves may also damage haying and other farm equipment. Their burrows may also cause a loss of irrigation water when dug along water conveying ditches.

Marmot damage is usually evidenced by areas where plant production has been terminated or reduced by grazing by these rodents. Supplemental signs include droppings, burrows, and trails leading to and from the damaged area to dens or loafing areas. In the spring, occupied woodchuck burrows are easily recognized because in clearing them, they leave dirt pellets ranging from marble size to fist size at the burrow entrance.

BIRDS

Red-winged blackbirds, grackles, starlings, robins, crows, house finch and many other species of birds cause extensive damage to many forms of agricultural production including sprouted corn, ears of growing corn, cherries, grapes, holly, blueberries, feed in livestock feed lots, rice, etc. The easiest and most obvious method of determining the species responsible for the damage is by observation.

Damage to Urban and Industrial Facilities

Another area demanding the attention of wildlife resource managers is animal-man conflicts in suburbia, "uptown," industrial, and ghetto situations. Rats in homes and warehouses, bats and squirrels in attics of homes, starlings and pigeons roosting on business buildings, woodpeckers pecking at homes, squirrel and bird nests in telephone and electric wires, and pocket gophers gnawing underground cables are examples of these problems which cannot be ignored. If there is doubt that wildlife is causing the damage, check for tracks, droppings, feathers, trails, dens, toothmarks and burrows.

Rabies and Its Identification

Rabies is an acute contagious disease of mammals caused by a virus and characterized by symptoms of mental disturbance, excitability, paralysis, and death (Richards 1961). It is a problem which may necessitate animal control when wild animals are transmitting rabies to man,

his pets, or livestock. The rabies virus, which is found in the saliva of contagious animals, is usually passed on by a bite, but may also be picked up through cuts or scratches when rabid animals are handled carelessly. Impermeable gloves should always be worn when handling a suspected rabid animal or a specimen.

A change in an animal's normal behavior is usually the first symptom. A rabid animal may appear sick; it may appear underweight because it has stopped eating and drinking; it may be very vocal or very silent; it may be overly friendly or aggressive; and it may be paralyzed in some of its limbs.

If a rabies suspect can be captured, it should be isolated and quarantined for 10 days. When symptoms develop prior to the tenth day, allow the disease to run its full course. If symptoms of rabies are noted on the tenth day, continue the quarantine period.

To determine if an animal has died of rabies, the brain must be submitted to a diagnostic laboratory. The head of the animal must be removed and placed in a sealed plastic bag. Care must be taken not to damage the brain. If the brain is damaged, a portion of the spinal column should be included. The specimen should be refrigerated for shipment to a laboratory.

DAMAGE ASSESSMENT

It may be necessary to conduct a control program based on anticipated damage. In such cases, the probability that significant damage is highly likely to occur is sufficient to justify control. Coyotes present on a lambing range and kangaroo rats on rangeland to be reseeded are examples where control may be needed before actual damage occurs. Once it has been determined which wildlife species is causing damage, or may cause damage, it must then be determined whether there is a *need* for controlling that species.

If damage is probable or has already occurred, the decision to initiate control must be determined by evaluating: (1) the amount of damage that has occurred; (2) the additional damage or anticipated damage that may occur without control; (3) the cost versus the benefits of the control program; (4) the aesthetic value of the species involved; and (5) the impact the control program might have on non-target organisms and on the ecosystem in general.

MECHANICAL AND CHEMICAL
CONTROL TECHNIQUES

General Considerations

REGULATIONS

Before initiating an animal damage control program, check local, State, and Federal regulations that may apply to the target species or the control tools that may be considered.

TECHNICAL ASSISTANCE

Resource managers can obtain guidance and advice from several sources when confronted with an animal damage problem. These include the Department of the Interior's Bureau of Sport Fisheries and Wildlife, Division of Wildlife Services; State Agricultural Extension Services; State Conservation Departments; and private pest control operators. Manufactures of various animal damage control tools are listed later in this chapter.

In any animal damage control program, environmental manipulation may also be employed with mechanical and chemical control tools. Control tool(s) selected should be practical, selective, and humane. The following section lists the more common mechanical and chemical control tools that are used to alleviate or control wildlife damage.

Mechanical Control—For Birds

CAGE OR LIVE TRAPS

These traps (Fig. 23.1) have been used successfully in reducing English sparrow, pigeon, starling, and grackle populations. They are most commonly used to remove nuisance pigeon populations from urban areas and in alleviating bird damage to orchards.

There are several variations of these traps, but basically all consist of a rectangularly shaped frame covered with wire mesh (chicken wire). The birds enter through small openings but cannot escape. Traps are baited with food and water and live decoy birds may be used as an attraction for luring other birds into the trap. Care of decoys used in a trap is very important. Decoy birds must have an ample supply of food and water. For best results, traps should be placed near the area where damage is occurring. Plans for this type of trap are available from the Bureau of Sport Fisheries and Wildlife, Division of Wildlife Services, Washington, D.C. 20240. Some traps can be purchased from private sources.

Fig. 23.1. A decoy enclosure trap used near a severely damaged corn field in Maryland. Biologist to right of door herds birds to gathering cages within trap. Other uses of the trap are for collecting specimens for study and banding. (Photo by F. C. Schmid, Bureau of Sport Fisheries.)

GAS EXPLODERS

Gas exploders (Fig. 23.2) have been used to alleviate bird depredations in grain fields and orchards for several years. Gas exploders produce loud explosions at automatically timed intervals. In some exploders, the explosion is produced when water drips onto carbide powder producing acetylene gas. In others, tanks of butane or propane gas are used. The explosion is produced when a spark or pilot flame ignites the gas (Mitchell and Linehan 1967). There are several different exploders on the market with numerous refinements, such as a battery-operated firing mechanism and photo-electric cells which activate the apparatus at daylight and shut it off at dark.

The location of the exploders should be changed frequently to increase effectiveness. They can be mounted on cars or trucks and driven around and through areas where depredations are occurring.

Use of gas exploders has been restricted in some States because of annoyance to neighbors, and in these areas a permit is necessary before the exploder can be operated.

PROTECTIVE NETS

Nets have been successfully used to cover trees and shrubs to prevent bird depredations. Small-mesh nets are effective in protecting individual fruit trees, ornamental shrubs and to a lesser extent, low-growing berry plants, such as blueberries and strawberries. The netting is made of plastic, nylon, spun paper, or string, and with some degree of care can be used for several seasons. Installation of the netting is frequently a problem since it is difficult to get the material draped over a tree in a manner that will protect the fruit. A frame may be needed to prevent the birds from feeding through the mesh.

Fig. 23.2. Types of acetylene exploders available to protect crops. Carbide (left and right) and acetylene tank (center) models are shown. Exploders should be placed on posts or platforms above the crop to be protected and their location changed every other day. These or similar models will protect 5–30 acres depending on local conditions and bird pressure. Regular preventive maintenance of units is essential.

508

SHOOTING

Shooting, whether to frighten or kill depredating birds has limited application. Discharging firearms is usually prohibited by law in urban areas. In cases of agricultural depredations, the use of firearms has more application and success. Firing a .22 cal. rifle over a field has been effective, though dangerous, in frightening birds from grain crops. One rifleman from a high position (rooftop, silo, tall platform), using a .22 cal. rifle, can protect a solid block of corn as large as 100 acres by firing a bullet earthward into the midst of the depredating birds (Mitchell and Linehan 1967).

A shotgun firing either regular ammunition or shell crackers is an effective bird-scaring tool. Shellcrackers are special shotgun shells that discharge a projectile which explodes after traveling about 200 yards. A single gunner on foot with regular shotgun shells cannot adequately protect more than about 5 acres of standing corn suffering severe depredation from birds. Shellcrackers greatly extend the effective range of shotgun shooting, but they should not be fired over or into dry vegetation, such as grass, grain, or brush, since the exploding projectile may be a fire hazard (Mitchell and Linehan 1967).

FLOODLIGHT TRAPS

Floodlight traps (Fig. 23.3) have been effective at times in capturing large numbers of birds at night at roost sites. The trap consists of several huge metal frames which support a funnel-shaped net. The large end of the funnel is positioned to open toward the roosting birds. The rear of the net opens into a long, low tent. Floodlights are located at the front of the trap. The birds are driven toward the trap by men walking through the roost. As the birds are flushed, they fly toward the light, enter the trap, and are captured in the tent. Cost of manpower and materials necessary to set up this trap make it impractical in most instances.

OTHER DEVICES

Miscellaneous devices such as scarecrows, ribbons, pie pans, revolving lights, roman can-

Fig. 23.3. A floodlight trap (photo by Bureau of Sport Fisheries and Wildlife).

Fig. 23.4. The steel leg-hold trap in a blind set.

dles, etc., have limited success in bird control. Scarecrows, to be effective, must be moved frequently. If used, ribbons and pie pans should be suspended in a manner so they are moved by the wind. Revolving lights have been used in buildings to frighten birds, but with little success. Wind action on gas-filled balloons located in fields has some effect in scaring birds.

Grids of twine strung over a field will deter gulls from damaging a crop in some cases. This technique has been used successfully in protecting tomato crops.

Mechanical Control—For
Predators and Rodents

STEEL LEG-HOLD TRAPS

Steel traps (Fig. 23.4) are manufactured to capture animals ranging in size from rats to bears. They are placed underground or in shallow water to capture such animals as coyotes, bobcats, fox, mink, beaver, raccoon, skunks, muskrats, nutria, and cougars. These traps may or may not be baited. If placed without bait, usually in the travel lane of the animal, the set is called a "blind set." A "baited set" uses the animal's food, or some other lure such as fetid meat, urine, or musk to attract the animal to the trap.

The location of the trap is the key to success. It should be placed only in areas where the offending animal naturally and regularly frequents. Dirt sets are made by digging a hole the size of the trap and deep enough so the trap will be approximately 1/2 inch below the surface when placed in the excavation. The trap is attached to a firm anchor, usually a stake, or attached to a "drag." A canvas cloth is placed over the pan and under the jaws to prevent clogging of the trigger mechanism. Then dirt, sand, or other material that is natural to the environment is used to cover the trap. If bait is used, it is placed above or behind the trap.

Traps placed underwater for beaver, muskrats, or mink are usually placed at the animal's entrance and exit points from the water. The stake or anchor material should be placed in the water in such a way that the trapped animal can reach deep water and drown.

With the exception of the bear trap, the steel trap has the advantage of being relatively safe to humans and livestock. Steel traps are the most effective method known for controlling bobcats.

Traps have the disadvantage of not being selective, and may catch several species of animals including domestic dogs and cats before the desired individual or species is captured. Placed near a carcass, steel traps may capture non-target carrion-feeding birds and mammals such as eagles, skunks, buzzards, and badgers. Because steel traps for bears are large and powerful, they are dangerous to humans and livestock. Extreme care must be taken when using this device. If a steel bear trap is used, it should be placed in a pen accessible to bear but not to livestock, warning signs posted, and two clamps suspended nearby for opening the trap. The use of bear traps is illegal in some States.

Weather can adversely affect steel traps and prevent them from springing when stepped on by an animal. They can become frozen in the ground or water, buried under snow or high water, or "mudded-in" after a rain. If buried in sand or a very dry soil, wind can blow the covering material away leaving the trap exposed.

Steel traps must be checked often so captured animals will not suffer needlessly. Strychnine or a tranquilizer tab can be attached to the trap jaw to reduce suffering (Balser 1965). After capture, an animal will usually gnaw at the trap and ingest this material. Obviously, the strychnine tabs should only be used in areas where there is no danger of capturing a non-target species. Tranquilizer tabs are valuable when animals are to be captured, then tagged or fitted with transmitters and released, or held for other purposes.

BOX TRAPS

Box traps are usually rectangular-shaped traps made from wood or heavy-gauge mesh wire.

510

Fig. 23.5. Suitcase traps such as the Bailey beaver trap are effective for live trapping and moving nuisance animals.

They are used to capture animals alive and un-injured, and are excellent to use in areas where more dangerous control tools could not be used, such as in residential areas to remove skunks or opossums from under houses. A trap is usually placed in an animal's travel lane or at the en-trance of its den and it is most successful when baited. When the animal enters the trap, it trips a device which closes the entrance door. These traps often are more efficient when covered with burlap or some other material which blends with the environment. Box traps can be used to capture animals ranging in size from mice to dogs, but they are usually impractical in capturing large wild animals or large numbers of a species living in the wild.

BAILEY AND HANCOCK LIVE TRAPS

These traps, used to capture beaver alive, (Fig. 23.5) are made of flexible mesh wire. When set, the Bailey trap resembles an open suitcase and the Hancock trap resembles a suitcase only half open. When the triggering device is tripped

the trap closes with the animal uninjured between the two halves. These traps are best suited for use in fairly shallow water at the beavers en-trance and exit routes or in water travel lanes. Both traps can be baited with an ear of corn, or a fresh piece of aspen, cottonwood, willow, or other edible woody plant.

SNAP TRAPS

These are the common rat or mouse traps that are usually placed in buildings. Traps baited with peanut butter and/or uncooked oatmeal work well. These traps can be used outdoors to capture small field rodents for research purposes when live animals are not needed.

SNARES

Snares, made of wire or cable are among the oldest control tools known to man. They can be used effectively to catch several species, but are

Fig. 23.6. The body snare is here set in a trail under a wire fence. A light wire supports the snare in a proper position.

Fig. 23.7. The Aldrich spring-activated animal snare (Box 253, Castle Rock, Washington) is effective in trails or when placed near a bait "cubby" as shown here.

most frequently used to capture rabbits, coyotes, and bears. They have limited application, but are effective when the proper conditions exist. They are much lighter and more convenient to use than steel traps in several respects, but unlawful in some States.

Body snares (Fig. 23.6) are set where they are likely to catch the animal's head. This could be at a "crawl" under a fence, a trail under some brush, a den entrance, or some other narrow passageway. As the animal enters the loop formed

by the cable, his body thrust or movement tightens the noose, and the animal is held.

The foot snare (Fig. 23.7) is tripped with a device which is activated when an animal places its foot on the trigger. When sprung, the noose is drawn securely around the animal's foot. This snare has been used effectively to capture depredating grizzly and black bears. It has also been used effectively for black, grizzly, and polar bear research; these animals were snared, tranquilized, tagged and released. It is most effective

512

COYOTE GETTER
Natural Size

A

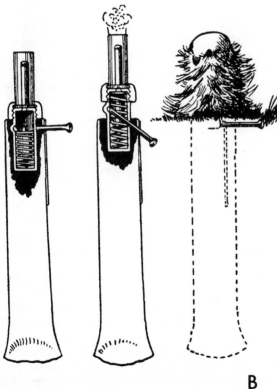

B

Fig. 23.8. The coyote-getter discharges sodium cyanide into the mouth and nose of an animal when it pulls the "fur" bait projecting from the ground.

on bears because a pen can be built and they can be "led," so to speak, into the snare. A foot snare, when used for bear control, is very safe—much more so than the steel bear trap. A human can step into the bear snare and not be injured.

HUMANE COYOTE-GETTER

The humane coyote-getter, or cyanide gun, (Fig. 23.8 A and B) was developed specifically for the control of coyotes and foxes. It is a mechanical device which expels sodium cyanide and consists of a shell holder wrapped with fur, cloth, wool, or steel wool; a firing unit; a .38 cal. shell containing the sodium cyanide; and a 5-7 inch hollow stake. The stake is driven into the ground, the firing unit is cocked and placed in the stake, and the shell holder containing the cyanide shell is screwed onto the firing unit. A fetid bait, usually made from fish, brains, or blood, is carefully spread on the shell holder. An animal attracted by the bait will try to pick up the baited shell holder. The cartridge fires when the animal pulls up on the shell holder and the cyanide is blown into the animal's mouth. The noise (similar to a .22 cal. discharging), and the wad hitting the roof of the animal's mouth frightens the animal, causing it to run from the device. A study by Robinson (1943) indicated coyotes traveled an average of 73 yards from the getter before expiring. Some individuals traveled as far as 600 yards. In this study, 584 coyote-getters were discharged by coyotes and 419 of the animals were found. Of the 165 not recovered it is probable some escaped and others were killed but not found.

The coyote-getter is not specific for coyotes; dogs, skunks, raccoons, foxes, bears, and opossums are also attracted, however, the coyote-getter is more efficient and more selective than steel traps (Robinson 1943), and weather does not seriously affect its operation. Coyotes have been known to dig through 15 inches of snow to discharge one of these devices. This tool does not have to be checked as often as steel traps, because it kills quickly.

Coyote-getters can injure the user or an innocent party if accidentally discharged. The main danger to people is the wad from the cartridge, which has enough force to break the skin or

Fig.23.9. The coyote-getter shown in place with a marker to reduce hazards to humans.

damage an eye. Warning signs should be posted when using this device. Research is presently underway to develop a coyote-getter in which a spring is used to eject the cyanide. This would eliminate the danger the wad presents in the current device. See Fig. 23.9.

CONIBEAR TRAPS

Conibear traps are used chiefly in shallow water for muskrat and beaver control. They are manufactured in three sizes and have the humane feature of killing quickly. These traps have a pair of rectangular wires that close like scissors when released, killing the animal with a quick body blow. Conibear traps have the added features of being lightweight and easily set. The principal disadvantage of a Conibear trap is that non-target animals will also be killed if captured. Human safety must be considered when using these traps, for larger models could be hazardous to pets and children. Consequently, these models should be used only in areas free of human habitation. Care by the user must also be practiced when setting larger models of this trap.

CALLING

Calling predators, mainly coyotes, bobcats, and fox, is a sport as well as a control tool in organized animal damage control programs. Oral or recorded calls are used to imitate the sound of a rabbit in distress. The curious or hungry predators are lured by the call into shooting range. Calling has proved effective in controlling trap-wise coyotes. This method is selective and relatively safe. Most effective results for foxes and coyotes are obtained by calling in the early morning or late afternoon. Fox calling is also effective at night (Morse and Balser 1961). Camouflage and a clear view should be considered when the caller is selecting his stand.

DENNING

Den hunting is used to locate coyote and fox pups. When coyote or fox depredations are occurring in the spring, chances are the adults are killing to provide food for their pups. If the pups are found and destroyed, predation should cease. If predation persists, animals from additional

514

Fig. 23.10. The burrow builder constructs an underground burrow and places in it a gopher poison.

dens or pups that have escaped from dens previously located may be the cause.

Dens are found by tracking the adults. "Den sign" will resemble a wheel; the hub being the den and the spokes the adult trails to and from the den. When leaving the den, the parents may wander as they hunt for food, but after food has been obtained, they will return to the den in a straight line. The den hunter should follow the straight-line trail.

Den hunting usually takes a lot of time and work. High winds and hard ground can make tracking very difficult. If a den is found, the hunter should be careful of cave-ins while digging it out.

Den sites are good locations for taking with traps or calls adult coyotes and fox that have successfully evaded previous control efforts. Den hunting to locate pups has been used in research to determine coyote movements (Robinson and Cummings 1951). Dens were located, pups captured, tagged, released, and tag returns used to plot the distance traveled from their birthplace.

BURROW BUILDER

The burrow builder (Fig. 23.10) is a tractor-drawn mechanical tool which dispenses a toxic bait for controlling pocket gophers. The burrow builder constructs an underground artificial burrow and places Gophacide, 1080, or strychnine-treated grain baits in the simulated gopher burrow. The artificial burrows are constructed 20-30 ft apart, usually at a depth of 8 to 12 inches. The proper depth to set the machine can be de-

Fig. 23.11. Special traps such as the gopher trap are useful for eliminating individual animals from gardens and yards.

termined by locating the gopher burrows by probing with a pointed instrument and measuring the depth of the burrow. The machine can then be set accordingly. Eighty to 100 acres of gopher-infested land can be treated in a day with this tool. During their underground travels, the gophers intersect the artificial burrows, consume the toxic bait, and die underground.

The trail builder is a variation of the burrow builder. The burrow is shallower and its diameter less than that constructed by the burrow builder. Trail builders construct artificial burrows to control vole damage in orchards or tree plantings. Zinc phosphide treated grain is the bait most commonly used in this machine.

OTHER TRAPS

Special traps (Fig. 23.11) are available for capturing moles and pocket gophers. These traps are placed in underground burrows used by these animals and effectively rid yards or gardens of individual animals.

Chemical Controls

Several chemicals have been developed to control wildlife damage. The most effective ones used for this purpose are discussed here. All of these toxicants can present a hazard to the ecosystem, but when used with care, this danger is minimal.

COMPOUND 1080 OR SODIUM MONOFLUOROACETATE

Compound 1080 is a highly stable, water soluable, organic salt. It is used to control coyote and field rodent damage in western animal damage control programs. It is a very effective and selective canid control tool. It is also used by private pest control operators to control *Rattus* populations. Compound 1080 is sold by manufacturers only to government agencies and bonded pest control operators. Because this material is very toxic, it should be used only by professionals trained in its use. Technical assistance for using this material is available through field offices of the Bureau of Sport Fisheries and Wildlife, Division of Wildlife Services.

STRYCHNINE

Strychnine is a white, bitter toxicant used as an avicide, predacide, and rodenticide. Strychnine sulfate is more soluable in water than strychnine alkaloid; however, the alkaloid form is the most commonly used form for animal control because the taste of strychnine sulfate is more noticeable. Strychnine is very toxic to most mammals and birds, with the exception of gallinaceous birds which are relatively resistant. When used as a predacide, warning signs should be prominently posted and baits should not be placed in areas where they would be accessible to domestic pets or other non-target species.

Strychnine is an effective toxicant for coyotes, fox, raccoons, badgers, skunks and opossums when placed in the center of a bait made from hamburger, lard, or tallow. The baits should be small, 1/2 to 1 inch in diameter. This will allow the target species to gulp the bait. If a large bait is used, the animal may chew it and reject it after tasting the bitterness of the strychnine. The bait can be rolled or mixed with sugar to offset the bitter taste. These baits, often called "tallow-baits," are placed on the ground by the target animal's travel lanes, near their kill, or in other frequented areas. To hide them from birds, the baits can be placed under cow chips or in clumps of grass. Stychnine should not be placed in a carcass, because it presents a greater hazard to non-target species and the possibility of a target animal tasting and then rejecting the strychnine is greater.

To control predation on game-birds or poultry, strychnine can be dissolved in water, mixed with honey or syrup, combined with food coloring, and injected into eggs with a syringe after withdrawing about 10 cc of the egg's content. Removing this small portion from the egg prevents the shell from cracking when the strychnine solution is injected. The word "POISON" should be printed on the egg shell. This written warning, along with the food coloring on the inside of the egg are safety factors. These eggs are placed in clusters of two or three along travel lanes used by the depredating animals. All uneaten eggs and the remains of eaten eggs should be gathered at the end of the control program and destroyed by deep burial.

Strychnine-treated grain is used to control a variety of field rodents. When used as a field rodenticide, strychnine treated oats are thinly scattered near the rodent's den, burrow, or in the area where damage is occurring. Strychnine-treated milo or wheat is effective on house mice, but strychnine baits are not taken by rats of the genus *Rattus*. In controlling kangaroo rats, and other desert rodents, Compound 1080 oats proved to be more effective and more economical than strychnine-treated oats (Wood 1965).

Strychnine-treated baits can also be used effectively to control some species of birds. Strychnine corn is a very effective feral pigeon control tool. Whole kernal recleaned corn should be used in pigeon control. Recleaned corn helps eliminate small particles such as weed seeds, cracked corn, or smaller grains which could be easily ingested by smaller birds.

As a general rule, when using lethal grain baits for bird control, control should only be conducted when snow has covered the birds' normal food supply and when non-target species do not predominate. Knowledge of migration routes and times of migration are needed to plan bird damage control programs.

Strychnine-treated wheat, milo, or cracked corn may be used for English sparrow control, but results have been erratic. Lethal grain is most readily accepted after a term of lengthy prebaiting with untreated grain.

Magpies can be effectively controlled by using coarsely ground tallow mixed with strychnine.

516

They can usually be drawn to a fresh carcass or entrails and the treated baits can be placed around these "draw stations." All remaining baits should be destroyed by deep burial after the desired degree of control has been achieved. Caution must be used when tallow baits are placed for magpie control because they may attract and kill dogs, cats, eagles, hawks, or other non-target species.

GOPHACIDE

Gophacide is a recently developed toxicant for pocket gopher control. Eventually it may replace strychnine and Compound 1080 for this purpose. When properly distributed with a mechanical burrow-builder or by hand, Gophacide kills 90% or more of the pocket gophers in a treated area (Ward et al. 1967). It also presents only a slight hazard to other animals because the bait is placed in sub-surface burrows where the gophers die.

DRC-1339 (STARLICIDE)

The Bureau of Sport Fisheries and Wildlife conducted extensive tests on an avicide given the code name DRC-1339. This chemical is commercially available under the trade name "Starlicide" for use in controlling starlings in cattle and hog feedlots and poultry yards. Decino, et al. (1966) report DRC-1339 is highly toxic to starlings, well accepted, relatively non-toxic to rats, and generally less toxic to most other birds. Hawks are particularly resistant and there appears to be little danger to them or to mammalian carnivores that might eat DRC-1339 poisoned starlings. Poultry pellets are treated with this avicide and broadcast outside feed bunkers. After ingesting the pellets, the majority of the birds die in their roost. This material is most effective in northern areas when snow covers the starling's normal food supply causing the birds to congregate in feedlots. Because this material is commercially available only in pellet form, best results are achieved when pellets are being fed in the problem area.

ANTICOAGULANTS

Several anticoagulants have been developed as rodenticides. They are commonly called anticoagulants because they cause capillary fracture or platelette malfunction. Some of these toxicants are Warfarin, Pival, Fumarin, and Diphacinone.

Anticoagulants are effective, relatively safe compared to other toxicants, but can cause secondary poisoning. Most are often used for rat (*Rattus*) and house mouse (*Mus*) control. Anticoagulants are classified as multiple-dose toxicants, i.e., for them to be effective the animals must feed on the bait more than once. As a rule of thumb, bait for rats and mice must be available for from 2 to 3 weeks for effective population control. The toxic material can be mixed with water or with dry bait such as rolled oats, corn meal, cracked grains, or a combination of these materials. Because of the necessity of multiple feedings, large quantities of the bait should be placed and replaced as necessary—a factor which increases the cost of this control tool.

An anticoagulant has been tested as a possible tool in controlling orchard mouse damage (Libbey et al. 1966 and Marsh et al. 1967). A treated-grain bait was attached by an edible glue to the inside of a water-repellent paper tube. This method may have future use as a means to control vole damage in orchards.

ZINC PHOSPHIDE

Zinc phosphide is a metallic toxicant used as a rodenticide. It is effective and most often used in rat (*Rattus*), vole, muskrat, and nutria damage control programs. Zinc phosphide baits are prepared from sweet potatoes, carrots and apples for nutria and muskrat control; apples, cracked corn and oats for vole control; and dog and cat food are used for *Rattus* control.

Zinc phosphide has an odor attractive to rodents, but repulsive to most other animals. It is coated (using vegetable oil) or dusted on the bait, then the baits are tumbled to assure even distribution. Tartar emetic is sometimes added to baits used in controlling the species *Rattus*. This safety feature will cause most other species to regurgitate any baits they pick up, but rats cannot regurgitate.

Treated baits for muskrat control can be placed in their burrows during periods of low water, or if burrow openings cannot be found, baits may be dropped into the tunnel through a hole made by probing with a pointed instrument. The hole is then covered with sod.

Treated baits for muskrat and nutria control can be placed on rafts (4' x 4' or 4' x 8') anchored in the vicinity of the damage or activity. The rafts can be made from plywood and styrofoam. Prebaiting is necessary to assure success in nutria control. Ten pounds of bait material should be used per raft in each pre-bait operation. The amount of treated bait to be used per raft can be determined by the amount of pre-bait consumed.

Application of zinc phosphide baits for vole control will vary according to each situation and species involved; baits are either broadcast on the surface or placed in underground runways. Trail builders may be used to place bait in artificial runways.

Zinc phosphide is also a valuable tool in controlling rats (*Rattus*) in situations where the hazard to non-target species, including man, and contamination of the environment, including human and livestock feed, is minimal.

GAS CARTRIDGES

Gas cartridges are cardboard cylinders (3-1/2'' long and 1-1/2'' in diameter) used in marmot, fox, prairie dog, badger, and coyote control. After the fuse is lit, the cartridge is placed in the burrow or den. The entrance is then tightly sealed with earth. The burning cartridge causes death by suffocation.

These are not bombs and will not explode if properly used. Cartridges are available from the field offices of the Bureau of Sport Fisheries and Wildlife, Division of Wildlife Services.

DDT

Bats can be eliminated from buildings by spraying the roosting area with 50% wettable DDT. Bats get the chemical on their feet and body and ingest it during grooming. A 50% microfine DDT dust is also commercially available for use in mouse (*Mus*) control efforts. This material can be placed in the travel lanes and burrows used by mice. As with bats, control is achieved when mice ingest the DDT during grooming.

THIRAM AND ZAC

These are taste repellants which can be applied by spraying or brushing to protect the bark of trees and shrubs during the winter or vegetable and flower crops during the spring growing season from deer and rabbit damage (U.S. Department of the Interior 1960, 1962, Dietz and Tigner 1968). Flowers and garden crops should be retreated at 10 day intervals to cover new growth and retreatment may be necessary after hard rains. These materials should be applied following directions found on the label. These repellants are not recommended for application to leaves, stems, or fruits of plants to be harvested for table use.

Chemical repellants cost less than mechanical barriers such as hardware cloth or aluminum foil and are usually easier to apply. However, as trees must be retreated at least one per year and herbaceous plants and shrubs more often, the total cost is often more than the original cost of mechanical protectors. Another factor to be considered is that some damage will occur because the animals must feed on the plants before they are repelled.

REPRODUCTIVE INHIBITORS

Research is now being conducted to develop reproductive inhibitors for species of wildlife such as coyotes and pigeons. In the future, it may be possible to control certain nuisance-animal populations without using mechanical control tools or lethal chemicals. This would not eliminate the need for present methods, but would provide another tool to combat animal damage.

Bird Control Devices—Sources of Supply

The following devices and materials are sold for preventing bird damage to crops and/or discouraging unwanted roosts. This list is not necessarily complete. Listing implies no endorsement of either a product or the technique it represents.

Bird control chemicals shipped in interstate commerce should be registered with the U.S. Department of Agriculture. Registration is not required for mechanical devices such as exploders, traps, etc.

AUTOMATIC EXPLODERS

Alexander-Tagg Ind., Inc., 395 Jacksonville Rd., Warminster, Pa. 18974

Fisher Manufacturing Co., 308 Bradford St., Seaford, Del. 19973

B. M. Lawrence & Co., 24 California St., San Francisco, Cal. 94111

Reed-Joseph Co., P.O. Drawer 479, Greenville, Mississippi, 38701

Salt Lake Stamp Co., 389 West-2nd South, Salt Lake City, Utah 84101

Smith Roles, Inc., Office and Warehouse at Kenmore, N. Dakota 58746

518

Plant located at Box 967, Saskatoon, Saskatchewan, Canada.

STICKY BIRD-REPELLENTS

These are "sticky" materials (available in various forms) to keep birds from roosting on ledges, sills, trees and other places. A-Aerosol; C-Cartridge for caulking gun; P-Paste; S-Spray (for trees, etc.); T-Tube.

Aegis Laboratories, Inc., 6817 Stony Island Ave., Chicago, Ill. 60649 (C,P,S,T)

Animal Repellents, Inc., P.O. Box 168, Griffin, Ga. 30223 (T)

Archem Corp., 1514 Eleventh St., Portsmouth, Ohio 45662 (P)

Baum's Castorine Co., Inc., 200 Matthew St., Rome, N.Y. 13441 (P)

A. Z. Bogert Co., 1000 E. Mermaid Lane, Philadelphia, Pa. 19118 (C,P)

Chem-O-Craft Specialties, Box 185, Argo, Ill. 60501 (C,P)

Hub States Chem. & Equip. Co., 2002 N. Illinois St., Indianapolis, Ind. 46202 (A,C)

Huge Company, Inc., 884 Hodiamont Ave., St. Louis, Missouri 63112 (C,P)

National B.C. Sales, Inc., P.O. Box 1, Skokie, Ill. 60076 (A,C,P,S)

Tanglefoot Co., 314 Straight Ave., S.W., Grand Rapids, Mich. 49502 (A,C,P)

EXPLODING SHOTGUN SHELLS (SHELL CRACKERS)

This is a 12-gauge shotgun shell, (except as noted) containing, instead of pellets, a king-sized firecracker, which is projected a distance of 150 yards or more.

W. V. Clow Seed Co., 1107 Abbott St., Salinas, Cal. 93901 (Bomb in special pistol)

Colt's Inc., Firearms Division, 150 Huyshope Ave., Hartford, Conn. 06102

Penguin Associates, Inc., Box 97, Parkesburg, Pa. 19365

Stoneco, Inc., 5403 N. Federal Blvd., Denver, Colo. 80221

Western Fireworks Company, Route 1, Box 308, Canby, Oregon 97013

METAL PROJECTORS OR WIRES

These are sharp wire devices that are installed along building ledges, window sills etc., to discourage birds from roosting.

Nixalite Company of America, 2509 Fifth Ave., Rock Island, Ill. 61201

Stan-Gard Pigeon & Bird Repellent Co., Inc., 523 W. 184th St., N.Y., N.Y. 10033

LIVE TRAPS

The following companies or individuals manufacture live traps or parts designed for the capture of small birds:

Bob-N-Jack Trap, 110 Eighth St., Farmington, Minnesota, 55024 (pigeons)

Russell S. Davis, Clayton, Illinois, 62324 (small land birds 2 & 4 cells, sparrows)

Havahart, P.O. Box 551, Ossining, New York, 10562 (pigeons, sparrows)

Johnson's, Box 33, Waverly, Kentucky, 42462 (pigeons, sparrows, starlings)

Richwood Box Mill, RFD 2, Box 307, Detroit Lakes, Minn., 56501 (sparrows, starlings)

Sensitronix, 2225 Lou Ellen, Houston, Texas, 77018 (pigeons, sparrows, starlings)

Charles Siegel & Son, 5535 Lynch Ave., Chicago, Ill., 60630 (bobs, bobs in frame, and completed traps for pigeons)

Twin City Pigeon Eliminating Co., 315 Fourth St., Downers Grove, Ill., 60515 (None sold-services pigeon traps-branches in various parts of the U.S.)

Roy Vail Co., 103 Wentworth Road, Antwerp, Ohio, 45813 (sparrows)

MOVING AND WHIRLING DEVICES

Whirling, bright-colored or shiny objects act as scare devices; move or change them frequently except Flomar Company device.

Gilbert H. Bostock, Franconia, N.H. 03580. "Glitterband Bird Scarers" imported from England. Aluminum strips for seedlings, crops, bushes or trees.

Flomar Company, 315 Fifth Ave., North, Minneapolis, Minnesota 55401 (series of aluminum badges on strand of wire installed on ledges, sills, etc.)

Germain's Inc., 4820 E. 50th Street, Los Angeles, California 90058 (10 flying disks to a package)

HAWKS AND OWLS

As a natural enemy of most birds, it has been reported that these simulated models have repelled some birds.

General Fibre Co., 217 Cedar St., St. Louis, Mo. 63102 (Great horned owls and S & S2-faced owls)

Pitcher Plastics, P.O. Box 547, Bath, N.Y. 14840 (A plastic hawk to be suspended above fruit crops)

PROTECTIVE NETTING

Animal Repellents, Inc., P.O. Box 168, Griffin, Ga. 30223 (Acrylic fiber webbing)

Apex Mills, Inc., 49 W. 37th St., N.Y., N.Y. 10018 (Semi-rigid nylon, 1'' mesh, widths 4-1/2, 9, 18 ft., lengths 21 to 1000 ft).

E. I. DuPont de Nemours & Co. Inc., "Vexar" sales, River Road, Buffalo, N.Y. 14207 (Polyethylene, green. 7/8'' mesh, 9 ft. width. In 6, 18, and 100 ft. rolls)

Gilbert H. Bostock, Franconia, N.H. 03580. "Scaraweb" imported from England. Cord of fine rayon fibers to cover seedlings, berries, shrubs, and trees.

J. A. Cissel Co., Inc., 120 East 34th St., N.Y., N.Y. 10016 (Polypropylene; meshes 5/8, 7/8, and 1'' in widths 13, 25, and 23 ft. respectively, 100 ft. rolls. Also 7/8'' mesh, 50 ft. wide in 200 ft. rolls).

Moodus Net & Twine, Inc., Moodus, Conn. 06469 (Nylon, black 1'' mesh, 18 ft. wide only, long lengths)

Nichols Net & Twine Co., R.R. 3, Bend Road, East St. Louis, Ill. 62201 (Various types of cotton or nylon netting, cannon nets, custommade nets)

Union Carbide Corp., Plastic Products Div., 270 Park Ave., N.Y., N.Y. 10017 (Polyethylene. Recommends type #5, 1/2'' mesh, 7 ft. x 100 ft. Inquire as to other meshes, widths, and lengths).

PYROTECHNICS: FIREWORKS

Alpha Enterprises, Inc., P.O. Box 12242, Houston, Texas 77017

Clipper Pyrotechnic Corp., Red Devil Fireworks Co., P.O. Box 63, Lynwood, Cal. 90262

The J. E. Fricke Co., 40 N. Front St., Philadelphia, Pa. 19106 (fuse rope only)

REVOLVING LIGHTS

The lights revolve automatically, flashing alternate color beams. They may repel birds from both inside and outside of buildings.

R. E. Dietz Company, 225 Wilkinson St., Syracuse, N.Y. 13201

The Huge Company, Inc., 884-6 Hodiamont Ave., St. Louis, Mo. 63112

SOUND DEVICES

These devices produce sounds (sonic and ultrasonic) to repel or attract birds.

Bio-Sonics Control Co., 23045 Altamead, Mountain View, Cal. 94040 (Tape player, will sell or rent units for starling control only)

Bird-X Inc., 325 W. Huron St., Chicago, Ill. 60610 (UHF ultrasonic bird siren to repel birds)

Electronic Game Calls, Inc., 210 W. Grand Ave., Wisconsin Rapids, Wis. 54494 (A portable unit, records to call in crows, can use other records)

B. M. Lawrence & Co., 24 California St., San Francisco, Cal. 94111 (A portable unit of Klaxon horns with batteries)

Wightman Electronics, Inc., P.O. Box 989, Easton, Maryland 21601 (A portable record player, has starling distress call and other animal records)

Animal Traps and Snares—Sources of Supply

This list of manufacturers of animal traps is prepared only for information and is not necessarily complete. The inclusion of names does not imply endorsement as to quality or prices.

LIVE ANIMAL TRAPS (For birds, refer to Bird Control Devices—Sources of Supply)

Campbell Cage Co., Inc., P.O. Box 545, Campbell, California, 95008

Hancock Trap Co., 110 S. 19th St., Hot Springs, South Dakota, 57747 (beavers)

Havahart, P.O. Box 551, Ossining, N.Y. 10562

Johnson's, P.O. Box 33, Waverly, Kentucky 42462

King Products, Inc., 4 East Main St., Gosport, Indiana, 47433 (mice)

Kness Manufacturing Co., Inc., Albia, Iowa, 52531 (mice)

National Live Trap Corp., P.O. Box 302, Tomahawk, Wisconsin 54487

E. E. Nupp & Sons, Starford (Indiana County), Pennsylvania 15777 (rabbits)

Sensitronix, 2225 Lou Ellen, Houston, Texas 77018

Shawnee, 3934-A Buena Vista, Dallas, Texas, 75204 (Primarily a fish trap but will catch mink, muskrats, etc.)

H. B. Sherman, P.O. Box 683, De Land, Florida, 32720 (Primarily for gophers, mice & rats but will custom make other traps)

H. J. Spencer and Sons, P.O. Box 131, Gainesville, Florida, 32601 (Primarily for mice and rats but will custom make other traps)

Sullivan's Sure Catch Traps, P.O. Box 1241, Valdosta, Georgia 31602

Traps, Route 4, Owensboro, Kentucky 42301 (collapsible turtle trap)

Worcester Wire Novelty Co., Inc., Timonium Road, Timonium, Md., 21093 (rats)

MOLE TRAPS

Nash Mole Traps, R.F.D. 1, Scotts, Michigan 49088 (choker-loop)

Tyler Products, 4525 Fifth St., N.E., Puyallup, Wash., 98371 (diamond-jaw)

Woodstream Corp., Animal Trap Div., P.O. Box 327, Lititz, Pa. 17543 (prong and scissors-jaw types)

POCKET GOPHER TRAPS

Z. A. Macabee Gopher Trap Co., 110 Loma Alta Ave., Los Gatos, Calif. 95030

Tyler Products, 4525 Fifth St., N.E., Puyallup, Wash., 98371

Woodstream Corp., Animal Trap Div., P.O. Box 327, Lititz, Pa. 17543

RAT AND MOUSE TRAPS (Deadfalls)

Boyer-Winona Corp., P.O. Box 278, Winona Lake, Ind., 46590 (mice)

McGill Metal Products Co., 110 Prairie St., Marengo, Ill. 60152

J. R. Schuyler and Co., 152 W. Fourth St., Bloomsburg, Pa. 17815

Woodstream Corp., Animal Trap Div., P.O. Box 327, Lititz, Pa. 17543

SNARES

Aldrich Animal Trap Co., P.O. Box 244, Challam Bay, Washington 98326

Raymond Thompson Co., 15815 Second Place, W., Alderwood Manor, Wash. 98036

Woodstream Corp., Animal Trap Div., P. O. Box 327, Lititz, Pa. 17543

STEEL TRAPS

The Hawkins Co., (Blake & Lamb, Inc.) Box 175, South Britain, Conn., 06487

Oberto Trap Co., P.O. Box 88, Iron Belt, Wisconsin 54536

Woodstream Corp., Animal Trap Div., P.O. Box 327, Lititz, Pa. 17543 (Victor and Newhouse Traps)

CHAPTER TWENTY FOUR

POPULATION MANIPULATION

ROBERT H. GILES, JR., PhD

Associate Professor, Wildlife Management
Virginia Polytechnic Institute
Blacksburg, Virginia

MANIPULATING THE POPULATION ITSELF, P_1

MANIPULATING BEHAVIORAL IMPACT, P_2

MANIPULATING THE POPULATION POTENTIAL, BP

MANIPULATING INTRINSIC RESISTANCE, IR

MANIPULATING MIGRATION, E AND I

MANIPULATING ENVIRONMENTAL RESISTANCE, ER

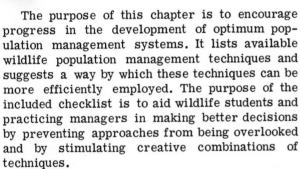

The purpose of this chapter is to encourage progress in the development of optimum population management systems. It lists available wildlife population management techniques and suggests a way by which these techniques can be more efficiently employed. The purpose of the included checklist is to aid wildlife students and practicing managers in making better decisions by preventing approaches from being overlooked and by stimulating creative combinations of techniques.

The equation which is presented provides a simple approach for organizing the major factors influencing population density. It has been found helpful in developing rational population management methods and encouraging wildlifers to consider and evaluate techniques more carefully and completely before employing them.

Neither a chapter nor a book can be written that will tell each wildlife manager what techniques will achieve each of his possible management objectives for all wildlife species, in all environments, and with all of the peculiarities and constraints of technology in each area. Guides are therefore needed for the rational manager to make decisions between and among many alternatives to achieve the successful management act.

Selection of an individual practice is not a major task. There is, however, great difficulty in selecting a combination of techniques, a managerial system, that is right for the present and future and into which the individual practices fit. Figure 24.1 illustrates one technique for describing such a system and for handling the ideas involved. The figure suggests the complex interactions of the decision process and the need for objective consideration of all alternatives in a well-described system. By weighting or ranking the desirability or probability of each branch, the relative desirability of each pathway through the tree can be estimated. (See Luce and Raiffa 1957.) The tree shows the relation of each decision to past and subsequent decisions and thus provides for the formulation of an effective wildlife method.

Wildlife management deals essentially with habitat, wildlife populations, and man. A convenient tool for mentally handling and subsequently manipulating the population component of the managerial process is the equation:

$$P_1 + P_2 = IR(BP) - (I-E) - ER.$$

Common units of density or rate of increase should be used throughout the equation where

P_1 is the population, its density or rate of increase.

P_2 is the behavioral impact of a population, e.g. the difference between the real and the ap-

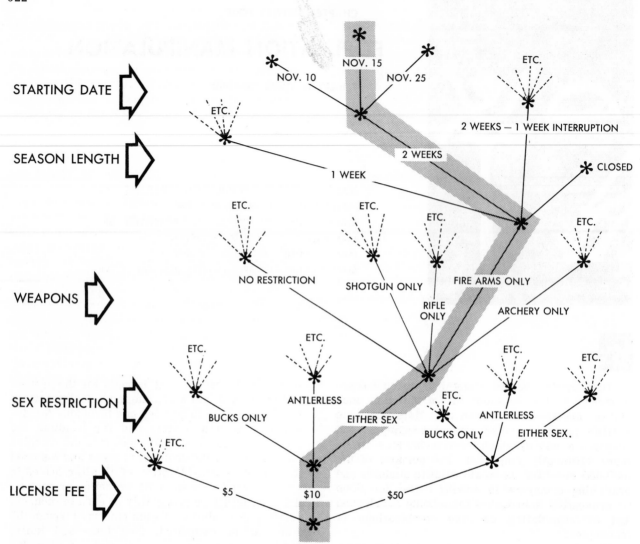

STARTING DATE

NOV. 10   NOV. 15   NOV. 25   ETC.

SEASON LENGTH

ETC.

2 WEEKS – 1 WEEK INTERRUPTION

2 WEEKS

1 WEEK

✱ CLOSED

WEAPONS

ETC.   ETC.   ETC.   ETC.

NO RESTRICTION   SHOTGUN ONLY   FIRE ARMS ONLY

RIFLE ONLY   ARCHERY ONLY

SEX RESTRICTION

ETC.   ETC.   ETC.   ETC.

BUCKS ONLY   ANTLERLESS   EITHER SEX   ANTLERLESS   BUCKS ONLY   EITHER SEX.

LICENSE FEE

ETC.

$5 $10 $50

Fig. 24.1. Diagram of a stem of a decision tree. Only one of all possible stems is shaded. By quantifying the desirability or probability of each "branch," an optimum pathway through the tree can be selected (or the probability calculated) to formulate a set of regulations and laws that will accomplish a desired population and harvest.

parent population size in a migration corridor, within a fenced area, or on a fertilized tract where food quality is increased. As far as known, this factor has not been measured in the field.

IR is intrinsic resistance or the restriction on the population potential to reproduce, including, e.g., ovulation failure, male infertility, and other basic physiological phenomena.

BP is the theoretical potential population density; or it may be considered to be the ability of a population to increase. It is the inherent maximum population size or reproductive rate under optimum field conditions.

E is emigration or movement from an area, whether natural or not.

I is immigration or movement into an area, whether natural or not.

ER is the environmental resistance to the achievement of the population potential; it has three major components, abiotic, floral, and faunal, (including man). The faunal components are inter-specific resistance, e.g., predators; and intraspecific resistance, e.g., the destruction of a population's food supply by the population itself.

The equation rarely has any utility for calculations; its greatest usefulness is in identifying the major factors regulating population size and considering the relationship of these factors. The equation is primarily a conceptual tool. When the variables are quantified with real or hypothetical numbers of animals or rates of increase, the values of unknowns can be derived algebraically and general evaluations made. Examples are:

Variables as Numbers of Animals

$$P_1 + P_2 = IR(BP) - (I-E) - ER$$

$$1000 + 100 = 0.95(1500) - (50-50) - 325$$

On Management Unit A, there are 1000 animals with an additional behavioral impact of 100 animals, due to impeded movement caused by road construction. These animals are the residual of a potential population of 1500, modified by density-stress phenomena activity of 0.95, and reduced by 325 animals due to the total effects of disease, limited food supply, and predation. About 5% emigration and immigration balance out.

Variables as Rates

$$P_1 + P_2 = IR(BP) - (I-E) - ER$$

$$0.25 + 0.0 = 0.95(0.30) - (0.05 - 0.05) - 0.035$$

On Management Unit B, a population with a potential rate of production of 0.30 and no more than a 5% population-stress phenomena activity, and no migration, must have an environmental resistance of 0.035 to achieve a measured population rate of increase of 0.25.

A population can respond in only three ways to management action; it can increase, stabilize, or decrease. Depending on how each of the techniques listed in this chapter is used for manipulating populations, it can draw one of these responses. Wildlife management will reach a new level of sophistication when it precisely defines its objectives in quantities of the above three types of change desired from each management practice for each target species on a specific area. The time is past for "we want more game"; the objective must be specified as, "we want a grouse population increase on area C of 0.05 for 3 years and then to maintain stability at that population for 10 years."

MANIPULATING THE POPULATION ITSELF, P_1

Techniques for influencing P_1 are listed under each variable of the equation. The two previous examples suggest, in part, how these techniques should be considered. Two other examples, although incomplete, may be of aid.

The well-read, well-educated manager is given the objective of increasing a grouse population. He goes through the list asking, first, can this practice increase, stabilize, or decrease my population? Many of the practices in the list can do all three, depending on how they are employed. For example "Access Trails" can be built to *increase* harvest, they can be closed to *reduce* harvest, or certain strategic trails can be closed and others opened to *stabilize* harvest.

Every entry in the checklist should trigger recall or suggest new possible entries. The more well-read and creative the reader, the more valuable will be the list. The manager next asks, "Since the technique can be employed to increase the population, will it fit the budgetary, topographic, personnel, and other constraints or restrictions of my area?" He then checks the possible techniques and, on re-inspection, examines each critically to see which will exactly achieve his objective at the least total managerial cost.

The manager may start with another objective. That is, having reduced a population in a control program, he finds the reduction not adequate and he then seeks new methods to employ. He asks the above same questions: (1) Will the technique (broadly taken) reduce animals taken (in any way known to the manager); (2) Is it practical to use; and (3) Is it economically feasible? Other considerations (see Chapter 1) should also be given. He then adopts that set (see Fig. 24.1) which is optimum for his purposes. There are other related uses of this technique for research, systems design, planning, law and regulation setting, loss amelioration, and enhancement.

MANIPULATING BEHAVIORAL IMPACT, P_2

-----Use repellents
-----Use scare devices
-----Use attractants
-----Do buffer feeding, e.g. providing an additional, less valuable food supply to take feeding pressure off a desirable food
-----Do vanguard feeding, e.g. pre-stocking release of predator-susceptible birds
-----De-value or increase the "value" of the individual animal, e.g. rewards for numbered bear ear tags
-----Re-evaluate losses or benefits
-----Alter behavior by diversions, travel lanes, fences, etc.

-----Use exclosures
-----Fences
-----Rodent proofing
-----Protective containers

MANIPULATING THE POPULATION POTENTIAL, BP

-----Sterilize animals
-----Vasectomy
-----Castration
-----Chemo-sterilants
-----Mechanical contraceptive devices
-----Irradiation
-----Hormones
-----Control primary sex ratios
-----Virus
-----Nutrition
-----Chemical
-----Modify ovulation rates
-----Hybridization
-----Artificial genetic selection
-----Modify the age of puberty, e.g. earlier puberty by higher nutrition
-----Modify weaning age
-----Modify proportion of population copulating, e.g. hunting season dates

MANIPULATING INTRINSIC RESISTANCE, IR

-----Regulate the population around the threshold of the population-stress phenomena
-----Increase or decrease visual, audial, and olfactory contacts between individuals of a population
-----Change line-of-sight between antagonists, e.g. nesting birds
-----Change pheasant nest density to influence nest abandonment due to premature hen response to newly-hatched chick calls from adjoining nests
-----Use chemicals

MANIPULATING MIGRATION, E AND I

-----Control release, e.g. shooting preserve releases before the gun
-----Stocking from semi-wild populations
-----Transplant from wild-trapped populations
-----Introduce species new to an area

-----Use horseback herding
-----Use helicopter or aircraft herding or hazing
-----Build barrier fences
-----Build cattle guards
-----Build fence baffles and breaks (big game crossing units)
-----Encourage or build wire-fences with appropriate spacing for antelope
-----Use trained dogs
-----Build and plant drift fences and vegetation barriers
-----Restrict human harassment during migrations
-----Employ encirclement and drives

MANIPULATING ENVIRONMENTAL RESISTANCE, ER

-----Manipulate habitat (Chapter 14)
-----Manage predator populations
-----Manage buffer species populations
-----Regulate diseases and parasites
-----Regulate intermediate hosts of pathogens, e.g. molluscicides
-----Trapping (Chapter 18)
-----Live
-----Dead
-----Use entanglement techniques, e.g. adhesives on bird roosts
-----Use soporifics
-----Use detergents, e.g. surfactant solutions
-----Use poison
-----Employ gasses e.g. for bats, woodchucks
-----Pre-season or inter-season population harassment
-----To reduce hunting kill
-----To increase hunting kill
-----Conduct shoots, e.g. ranger elk-harvests
-----Regulate hunting
-----Regulate the type of hunter
-----Sex
-----Age
-----Resident, non-resident
-----Skill (past success)
-----Skill (marksmanship)
-----Interest and knowledge (tests)
-----Regulate the species to be hunted
-----Number of each species to be harvested
-----Quota/unit/season
-----Daily limit
-----Season limit
-----Possession limit
-----Life-time limits, e.g. big horn sheep

-----Regulate the sex, e.g. male, female, either sex, antlerless, bearded turkeys
-----Restrict age, e.g. as correlated to body size or horn growth
     -----Longevity, e.g. old-age harvest of elk
     -----Adult, sub-adult categories in live trapping removal
-----Appearance restrictions
     -----Size (or weight)
     -----Antlers or horns
     -----Color
     -----Pelage quality
-----Location restrictions
     -----Refuges and sanctuaries
     -----Rest areas
     -----Open areas
     -----Hunt units, e.g. county, topographic, artificial
     -----Restrict blind, hunting or trapping units, hunting points
-----Access
     -----Restrict by fences, gates, road barriers, signs
     -----Create by
          -----Airports and helioports
          -----Trails
          -----Roads
          -----Bridges, foot and road
          -----Carrying services
          -----Providing motorized travel
          -----Guide or packer requirements
-----Licenses and Permits
     -----Resident
          -----Number
          -----Cost
          -----Availability
          -----Land owner requirement
          -----Age requirement
     -----Non-resident
          -----Number
          -----Cost of permits
          -----Availability
          -----Age requirements
     -----Lotteries for permits
-----Method of take (Similar considerations apply to trapping)
     -----Hunting practices
          -----Drives
          -----Stalks
          -----Blinds
          -----Towers and shooting platforms
          -----Safety clothing and camouflage
          -----Use of calls or attractants
          -----Use of baits and salt
          -----Use of dogs
     -----Weapon

     -----Shotguns
     -----Rifles
     -----Pioneer weapons
     -----Limit caliber and muzzle velocity
     -----Limit shot size and bullet weights
     -----Archery
     -----Limit pull or arrow cast
     -----Limit arrow point specifications
     -----Limit to non-lead shell shot
     -----Crossbow
     -----Sling shot, etc.
     -----Survival methods, e.g. snares and deadfalls
-----Number of shots, e.g. shell restrictions for waterfowl blinds
-----Time restrictions
     -----Starting time during day
     -----Daily closing time
     -----Weekend hunting
     -----Sunday hunting
     -----Starting date
     -----Length of season
     -----Interrupted season
     -----Variable-length seasons (closing when desired number is taken)
     -----Presence or absence of snow
-----Influence hunting or trapping desire and efficiency
     -----Education
     -----Signs, signals, announcements
     -----Hunting maps
     -----Weapon sighting-in grounds
     -----Provide firing lanes free of cover
-----Conduct enforcement
     -----Checking stations
     -----Violation-deterrent activity
-----Control accidents
     -----Animal scare reflectors
     -----Warning signs for autos
     -----Fencing
     -----Road closure
     -----Vehicle speed barriers
     -----Cover removal along roads

The wildlifer on a management area has a relatively small assortment of proven manipulation techniques. He has relatively little information on techniques and a heterogeneous and sketchy literature from which to get it. His major sources are state and federal reports which are often mimographed, poorly indexed, and given only limited circulation. There is neither the medium nor the inclination of many field men to report actively the results of their population manipulation practices.

526

Wildlifers do not yet have completely suitable expressions for population density stress activities, for modifications in biotic potential, for behavioral impact, or for migration rates. Effectiveness at manipulating populations hinges upon the wildlifer's ability to measure populations and their changes. The difficulties of making estimates and the confidence limits on estimates that are made are amply elaborated in Chapter 21. Wildlifers do have indicators, trends, and opinions formulated from years of experience. It often seems that populations survive and do well, not *because* of scientific managerial skills, but *in spite* of management and due to the hardiness of the ecosystem and the artistry of a few managers.

Nevertheless, wildlifers can and do manipulate populations. When the manipulation process is studied more closely, the results reported to the wildlife management community, and the consequences examined more carefully, then the predictability of the consequences of managerial action will increase. Then wildlife management will advance as a science for the benefit of man and the wildlife resource.

APPENDIX TABLE I.

Hatching success of game birds, compiled by D. E. Davis. Only studies that record at least 50 nests are included and the reference cited gives only the senior author's name. Investigators are urged to refer to the original publication for additional data. Since data on nesting success vary greatly with time and place, the following list may be considered only approximation of true values. The data listed below have been checked but errors creep into tabulations of this type; the editor will be pleased to be notified of any errors. Asterisk (*) indicates data not given.

Species	Place	Reference	Hatching		Success	
			No. of eggs	Percent of eggs hatching	No. of nests	Percent of successful nests
Canada Goose	Montana	Atwater, '59	72	29.9	*	*
Canada Goose	Illinois	Kossack, '50	927	56.6	96	*
Canada Goose	Wyoming	Craighead, '49	*	*	88	23.9
Canada Goose	Utah	Williams, '37	410	80.6	95	*
Canada Goose	Calif.	Dow, '43	*	*	170	52.5
Canada Goose	Calif.	Dow, '43	*	*	248	60.0
Canada Goose	Calif.	Naylor, '53	1904	82.6	360	68.5
Canada Goose	Calif.	Miller, '53	810	87.0	201	78.6
Canada Goose	Calif.	Naylor, '54	432	85.2	117	71.0
Canada Goose	Calif.	Collins, '54	*	*	201	17.8
Canada Goose	Montana	Geis, '56	1221	88.4	383	57.5
Mallard	Utah	Williams, '37	1582	60.0	185	59.0
Mallard	Calif.	Earl, '50	417	49.4	60	52.0
Mallard	Mont.	Girard, '41	1793	71.2	*	*
Mallard	U.S.A.	Kalmbach, '37	*	*	188	55.7
Mallard	Calif.	Miller, '54	1622	91.4	209	85.2
Mallard	Calif.	Hunt, '55	*	*	206	51.5
Mallard	Calif.	Anderson, '56	*	*	510	12.7
Mallard	Calif.	Anderson, '57	616	83.4	161	38.5
Gadwall	Calif.	Miller, '54	3834	94.2	381	90.3
Gadwall	Utah	Williams, '37	6000	85.0	660	71.0
Pintail	Calif.	Hunt, '55	*	*	98	39.8
Pintail	Utah	Williams, '37	969	82.0	135	65.0
Pintail	U.S.A.	Kalmbach, '37	*	*	52	48.0
Blue-winged Teal	Iowa	Bennett, '38	*	*	223	57.0
Blue-winged Teal	U.S.A.	Kalmbach, '37	*	*	76	22.4
Blue-winged Teal	Mont.	Girard, '41	888	71.8	107	*
Cinnamon Teal	Utah	Williams, '37	2655	84.0	326	62.0

APPENDIX TABLE I.   Continued.

Species	Place	Reference	Hatching		Success	
			No. of eggs	Percent of eggs hatching	No. of nests	Percent of successful nests
Ring-necked Pheasant	Iowa	Klonglan, '55	*	*	162	17.3
Ring-necked Pheasant	Iowa	Hammer-strom, '36	723	82.3	64	*
Ring-necked Pheasant	Iowa	Hammer-strom, '36	*	*	232	19.0
Ring-necked Pheasant	Iowa	Hammer-strom, '36	*	*	445	23.1
Ring-necked Pheasant	Iowa	Hammer-strom, '36	*	*	139	37.4
Ring-necked Pheasant	Colo.	Yeager, '51	*	*	333	65.0
Ring-necked Pheasant	Minn.	Erickson, '51	*	*	241	28.6
Ring-necked Pheasant	Mich.	English, '41	*	*	193	35.0
Ring-necked Pheasant	Wisc.	Errington, '37	1000	78.9	126	71.3
Ring-necked Pheasant	Minn.	Carlson, '43	*	*	90	30.0
Ring-necked Pheasant	Ohio	Strode, '41	*	*	358	72.0
Ring-necked Pheasant	Wisc.	Buss, '46	*	*	350	29.9
Ring-necked Pheasant	Ont.	Ball, '52	777	73.5	230	32.1
Ring-necked Pheasant	Iowa	Weston, '53	*	*	72	18.0
Sage Hen	Wyoming	Patterson, '52	*	*	216	38.4
Sage Hen	Utah	Rasmussen, '38	*	*	98	62.2
Clapper Rail	N. Jersey	Kozicky, '49	513	87.3	56	89.3
Coot	Manitoba	Kiel, '55	1394	99.0	380	97
Coot	Calif.	Hunt, '55	*	*	163	96.5
Mourning Dove	Georgia	Hopkins, '53	*	*	66	49.0
White-winged Dove	Texas	Kiel and Harris, '56	10295	40.2	*	*

APPENDIX TABLE I. Continued.

Species	Place	Reference	Hatching		Success	
			No. of eggs	Percent of eggs hatching	No. of nests	Percent of successful nests
Cinnamon Teal	Calif.	Hunt, '55	*	*	147	55.8
Shoveller	Mont.	Girard, '39	1135	69.7	107	*
Wood Duck	Iowa	Leopold, '51	868	80.0	63	*
Wood Duck	Mass.	McLaughlin, '52	12180	83.5	1427	64.3
Redhead	Utah	Williams, '37	2651	26.0	212	62.0
Redhead	Iowa	Low, '45	*	*	160	56.2
Redhead	Iowa	Low, '45	827	80.7	122	*
Redhead	Calif.	Miller, '54	*	*	60	45.0
Ring-necked Duck	Maine	Mendall, '58	*	*	189	68.3
Lesser Scaup Duck	U.S.A.	Kalmbach, '37	*	*	94	47.8
American Eider	Maine	Paynter, '51	462	27.6	134	29.1
Ruddy Duck	Iowa	Low, '41	546	69.4	71	73.2
Marsh Hawk	N. Dak.	Hammond, '49	303	57.8	60	71.6
European Partridge	England	Lack, '47	57202	90.4	*	*
European Partridge	England	Middleton, '35	*	*	7251	78.0
European Partridge	England	Middleton, '35	59825	93.0	4090	*
European Partridge	Wisc.	McCabe, '46	*	*	435	32.0
European Partridge	Wash.	Yocum, '43	*	*	68	32.5
European Partridge	Wash.	Knott, '43	*	*	113	37.1
Bobwhite	Wisc.	Errington, '33	*	*	53	50.9
Bobwhite	Texas	Parmalee, '55	*	*	59	62.9
California Quail	Calif.	Glading, '38	*	*	83	24.8
Ring-necked Pheasant	Penn.	Randall, '40	*	*	310	20.3
Ring-necked Pheasant	Wash.	Buss, '50	*	*	63	27.0
Ring-necked Pheasant	Oregon	Eklund, '42	*	*	145	44.8
Ring-necked Pheasant	Iowa	Baskett, '47	*	*	75	36.0
Ring-necked Pheasant	Iowa	Baskett, '47	*	*	140	25.0
Ring-necked Pheasant	Iowa	Baskett, '47	689	82.4	318	23.2
Ring-necked Pheasant	Iowa	Baskett, '47	1319	83.0	533	25.5

APPENDIX TABLE II.

Clutch size of game and predatory birds, compiled by D. E. Davis. Only data from investigations including at least 25 complete clutches are included. Reference cites only the senior author. These data have been checked but the editor would be pleased to know of any errors. Refer to the original paper for more details. Asterisk (*) indicates standard deviation not given by author.

Species	Place	Reference	Number of clutches	Mean	Standard deviation
Canada Goose	Calif.	Miller, '53	158	5.13	1.35
Canada Goose	Montana	Geis, '56	358	5.34	1.31
Canada Goose	Idaho	Steel, '57	189	5.2	*
Brant	N. W. Terr.	Barry, '56	203	3.97	1.00
Mallard	Calif.	Hunt, '55	108	8.5	*
Mallard	Calif.	Miller, '54	178	9.2	*
Pintail	Calif.	Hunt, '55	40	7.2	*
Pintail	Calif.	Miller, '54	41	9.2	*
Blue-winged Teal	Iowa	Glover, '56	87	8.0	*
Cinnamon Teal	Calif.	Miller, '54	32	10.7	*
Cinnamon Teal	Calif.	Hunt, '55	76	9.3	*
Gadwall	Calif.	Miller, '54	344	11.1	*
Shoveller	Calif.	Miller, '54	35	11.1	*
Redhead	Calif.	Miller, '54	27	13.8	*
Wood Duck	Mass.	McLaughlin, '52	664	13.60	4.82
Ring-necked Duck	Maine	Mendall, '58	423	9.04	1.45
American Eider	Maine	Gross, '38	110	3.25	1.05
American Eider	Quebec	Lewis, '39	1131	4.04	1.01
Marsh Hawk	U.S.A.	Hammond, '49	60	5.05	0.76
Sparrow Hawk	Oregon	Roest, '57	60	4.73	0.63
Ring-necked Pheasant	Penn.	Randall, '41	157	10.60	3.18
Ring-necked Pheasant	Iowa	Kozicky, '56	60	8.7	*
Gray Partridge	England	Lack, '47	4051	14.60	2.38
Clapper Rail	New Jer.	Kozicky, '49	104	9.97	2.10
Clapper Rail	Virginia	Stewart, '51	71	8.38	1.56
Clapper Rail	Calif.	Zucca, '54	27	7.92	*
Virginia Rail	Iowa	Tanner, '54	28	8.10	4.5
Sora Rail	Minnesota	Pospichal, '54	29	9.9	*
American Coot	Iowa	Provost, '47	37	8.84	1.27
American Coot	Manitoba	Kiel, '55	169	9.9	1.3
American Coot	Calif.	Hunt, '55	256	8.7	*
American Woodcock	Maine	Mendall, '43	122	3.96	0.20

APPENDIX TABLE III.

Gestation periods (copulation to birth) of selected North American mammals. Common and scientific names, except for domestic animals, are from Miller and Kellog.

Common Name	Scientific Name	Gestation Period	Authority
Badger	*Taxidea taxus*	90 days	Asdell, '46
		9 mo.	Hamlett, '32
Bat, Big Brown	*Eptesicus fuscus*	90 days	Asdell, '46
Bat, Big-eared, Western	*Corynorhinus rafinesquii*	73 days	Asdell, '64
Bat, Hoary	*Lasiurus cinereus*	90 days	Asdell, '46
Bat, Little Brown	*Myotis lucifugus*	50-60 days*	Asdell, '64
Bat, Northern Red	*Lasiurus borealis*	30 days	Asdell, '46
Bat, Pygmy	*Pipistrellus subflavus*	44 days	Asdell, '46
Bear, Black	*Ursus americanus*	210 days	Asdell, '64
Bear, Grizzley	*Ursus horribilis*	195-210 days	Asdell, '64
Beaver	*Castor canadensis*	128 days	Asdell, '64
Bison	*Bison bison*	Approx. 270 days	Asdell, '64
Bobcat	*Lynx rufus*	50 days	Asdell, '64
Caribou	*Rangifer tarandus*	210-240 days	Asdell, '64
Cat, Domestic	*Felis catus*	63 days	Asdell, '64
Chipmunk, Eastern	*Tamias striatus*	31 days	Asdell, '64
Cottontail, Eastern	*Sylvilagus floridanus*	30 days	Asdell, '64
Cow	*Bos taurus*	280 days	Asdell, '64
Coyote	*Canis latrans*	60-65 days	Asdell, '64
Deer, Mule	*Odocoileus hemionus*	199-207 days	Asdell, '64
Deer, White-tailed	*Odocoileus virginianus*	187-198 days	Haugen, '59
		197-222 days	Asdell, '64
Dog, Domestic	*Canis familiaris*	63 days	Asdell, '64
Dog, Prairie, Black-tailed	*Cynomys ludovicianus*	30-35 days	Asdell, '64
Dog, Prairie, White-tailed	*Cynomys gunnisoni*	90 days	Asdell, '46
Dolphin, Common	*Delphinus delphis*	276 days	Asdell, '64
Elk	*Cervus canadensis*	249-262 days	Asdell, '64
Fisher	*Martes pennanti*	338-358 days	Asdell, '64
Fox, Arctic	*Alopex lagopus*	60 days	Asdell, '64
Fox, Gray	*Urocyon cineroargenteus*	63 days	Asdell, '64
Fox, Red	*Vulpes fulva*	49-55 days	Asdell, '64
Goat, Domestic	*Capra hircus*	150 days	Asdell, '64
Goat, Rocky Mountain	*Oreamnos americanus*	147 days	Asdell, '64
Gopher, Pocket	*Thomomys talpoides*	40 days	Asdell, '64
Ground Squirrels	*Citellus* spp.	(See squirrels, ground)	
Hare, Snowshoe	*Lepus americanus*	38 days	Asdell, '64
Horse	*Equus caballus*	329-345 days	Asdell, '64
Jack Rabbit, White-tailed	*Lepus townsendi*	33 days	Asdell, '64
Lynx	*Lynx canadensis*	63-70 days	Asdell, '64
Man	*Homo sapiens*	267 days	Asdell, '64
Marten	*Martes americana*	220-265 days	Asdell, '64
		220-276 days	Asdell, '46

APPENDIX TABLE III. Continued.

Common Name	Scientific Name	Gestation Period	Authority
Mink	*Mustela vison*	45-70 days	Asdell, '64
Mole, Eastern	*Scalopus aquaticus*	Approx. 42 days	Asdell, '46
Mole, Hairytail	*Parascalops breweri*	28-42 days	Asdell, '64
Mole, Star-nosed	*Condylura cristata*	Approx. 180 days	Asdell, '46
Moose	*Alces alces*	240-250 days	Asdell, '64
Mouse, Deer	*Peromyscus maniculatus*	24 days	Asdell, '64
Mouse, Grasshopper	*Onychomys leucogaster*	33 days	Asdell, '64
Mouse, Harvest	*Reithrodontomys megalotis*	23 days	Asdell, '64
Mouse, Harvest, San Luis Valley	*Reithrodontomys montanus*	21 days	Asdell, '64
Mouse, Meadow	*Microtus pennsylvanicus*	21 days	Asdell, '64
Mouse, House	*Mus musculus*	19 days	Asdell, '46
Mouse, Wood	*Peromyscus leucopus*	23 days	Asdell, '64
Mouse, Woodland Jumping	*Napaeozapus insignis*	21 days	Asdell, '46
Muskrat	*Ondatra zibethica*	28 days	Asdell, '64
Opossum	*Didelphis virginianus*	12-1/2 days	Asdell, '64
Otter, River	*Lutra canadensis*	288-380 days	Asdell, '64
Otter, Sea	*Enhydra lutris*	240-270 days	Asdell, '64
Pig, Domestic	*Sus scrofa*	112-115 days	Asdell, '64
Porcupine	*Erethrizon dorsatum*	112 days	Asdell, '64
Porpoise, Harbor	*Phocoena phocoena*	300-330 days	Asdell, '64
Pronghorn	*Antilocapra americana*	240 days	Asdell, '64
Rabbit	*Sylvilagus* and *Lepus*	(See cottontail, hare, and jack rabbit)	
Rat, Black	*Rattus rattus*	21 days	Asdell, '64
Rat, Cotton	*Sigmodon hispidus*	27 days	Asdell, '64
Rat, Rice	*Oryzomys palustris*	25 days	Asdell, '64
Rat, Northeastern Wood	*Neotoma magister*	30-36 days	Asdell, '46
Rat, Whitethroat Wood	*Neotoma albigula*	30 days	Asdell, '64
Raccoon	*Procyon lotor*	63 days	Asdell, '64
Sea Lion, California	*Zalophus californianus*	Approx. 345 days	Asdell, '64
Seal, Elephant	*Mirounga angustirostris*	340 days	Asdell, '64
Seal, Harbor	*Phoca vitulina*	240-250 days	Fisher, '54
Sheep, Bighorn	*Ovis canadensis*	180 days	Asdell, '64
Sheep, Domestic	*Ovis aries*	150 days	Asdell, '64
Shrew, Short-tailed	*Blarina brevicauda*	17-20 days	Asdell, '64
Shrew, Smokey	*Sorex fumeus*	21 days	Asdell, '64
Squirrel, Flying	*Glaucomys volans*	40 days	Asdell, '64
Squirrel, Fox	*Sciurus niger*	45 days	Asdell, '64
Squirrel, Gray	*Sciurus carolinensis*	44 days	Asdell, '64
Squirrel, Ground, Calif.	*Citellus beecheyi*	30 days	Asdell, '64
Squirrel, Ground, Richardson	*Citellus richardsonii*	28-32 days	Asdell, '64
Squirrel, Ground, 13-lined	*Citellus tridecemlineatus*	28 days	Asdell, '64
Squirrel, Red	*Tamiasciurus hudsonicus*	40 days	Asdell, '64
Skunk, Striped	*Mephitis mephitis*	62 days	Asdell, '64

APPENDIX TABLE III. Continued.

Common Name	Scientific Name	Gestation Period	Authority
Walrus, Pacific	*Odobenus divergens*	330 days	Asdell, '46
Weasel, New York	*Mustela noveboracensis*	205-337 days	Wright, '48
Whale, Sperm	*Physeter catadon*	480 days	Asdell, '64
Wolf, Gray	*Canis lupus*	60-63 days	Asdell, '64
Wolverine	*Gulo luscus*	270(?) days	Wright and Rausch, '55
Woodchuck	*Marmota monax*	31-32 days	Asdell, '64

*Probably delayed implantation.

APPENDIX TABLE IV.

American Ornithologist Union (1957) numbers and recommended band sizes of North American birds. Adapted from Form BBM-D-1400 of the Migratory Bird Population Station, Bureau of Sport Fisheries and Wildlife (U. S. Fish and Wildlife Service), Patuxent Wildlife Research Center, Laurel, Maryland. Full numbers represent A.O.U. numbers as listed in the 5th edition of the A.O.U. Check-list (1957). Decimals have been added by the Banding Office to identify hybrids, extra-limital species, and readily identified subspecies.

A.O.U. No.	Species	Band Size	A.O.U. No.	Species	Band Size
007	Common Loon	8	095	Sooty Shearwater	7A
008	Yellow-billed Loon	9	096	Slender-billed Shearwater	4
010	Arctic Loon	7B	090	Manx Shearwater	5
011	Red-throated Loon	7B	093	Black-vented Shearwater	-
002	Red-necked Grebe	7A	093.1	Townsend's Shearwater	-
003	Horned Grebe	6	092.1	Little Shearwater	-
004	Eared Grebe	5	092	Audubon's Shearwater	-
005	Least Grebe	4	198.1	Black-capped Petrel	-
001	Western Grebe	7A	098.1	Bermuda Petrel	-
006	Pied-billed Grebe	5	099	Scaled Petrel	-
082	Short-tailed Albatross	-	111	White-faced Petrel	-
081	Black-footed Albatross	7B	099.1	Bonin Island Petrel	3
082.1	Laysan Albatross	7B	105	Fork-tailed Petrel	1A
081.1	Blackfooted x Laysan	7B	106	Leach's Petrel	1A
082.2	Black-browed Albatross	-	108	Ashy Petrel	1B
102	Cape Petrel	-	106.2	Harcourt's Petrel	-
086	Fulmar	6	107	Black Petrel	1A
097	Black-tailed Shearwater	-	103	Least Petrel	1B
088	Cory's Shearwater	-	109	Wilson's Petrel	1B
091	Pink-footed Shearwater	-	110	Black-bellied Petrel	-
095.1	Pale-footed Shearwater	-	113	Red-billed Tropic-bird	-
089	Greater Shearwater	-	112	White-tailed Tropic-bird	-
096.1	Wedge-tailed Shearwater	5	113.1	Red-tailed Tropic-bird	5
096.2	New Zealand Shearwater	-	125	White Pelican	9
096.4	Christmas Is. Shearwater	4	126	Eastern Brown Pelican	9

APPENDIX TABLE IV. Continued.

A.O.U. No.	Species	Band Size	A.O.U. No.	Species	Band Size
126.9	W. Indian Brown Pelican	-	178.2	Mute Swan	9
127	California Brown Pelican	-	179	Whooper Swan	9
126.1	Chilean Brown Pelican	-	180	Whistling Swan	9
114	Blue-faced Booby	7B-8	181	Trumpeter Swan	9
114.1	Blue-footed Booby	-	145.9	Unidentified Swan	9
115	Brown Booby	7A	172	Canada Goose	8
116	Red-footed Booby	7B	172	Lesser Canada Goose	8
117	Gannet	9	172.9	Hutchins' Goose	7B
119	Great Cormorant	8	172.7	Cackling Goose	7A
120	Double-crested Cormorant	8	173	Brant	7B
120.9	Florida Cormorant	-	174	Black Brant	7B
120.8	White-crested Cormorant	-	175	Barnacle Goose	-
120.7	Farallon Cormorant	-	176	Emperor Goose	7B
120.1	Guanay Cormorant	-	171	White-fronted Goose	7B-8
121	Olivaceous Cormorant	7A	169	Lesser Snow Goose	7B
122	Brandt's Cormorant	8	169.9	Greater Snow Goose	-
123	Pelagic Cormorant	7B-8	169.5	Snow x Blue Goose	7B
124	Red-faced Cormorant	-	169.6	Snow x Canada Goose hybrid	7B
118	Anhinga	8	169.1	Blue Goose	7B
128	Magnificent Frigate-bird	7A	170	Ross' Goose	7B
128.1	Great Frigate-bird	7B	177	Black-bellied Tree Duck	7A
192	Great White Heron	8	178	Fulvous Tree Duck	7A-6
194	Great Blue Heron	7B	132	Mallard	7A
195	Gray Heron	-	132.3	Mallard, hand reared	7B
201	Eastern Green Heron	5-6	132.3	Mallard x Black Duck hybrid	-
201.7	Anthony's Green Heron	5	132.4	Laysan Teal	5
200	Little Blue Heron	6	133.1	Mexican Duck	7A
200.1	Cattle Egret	6	133	Black Duck	7A
198	Reddish Egret	6			
196	Common Egret	7B	133	Black Duck, hand reared	7B
			134	Mottled Duck	7A
197	Snowy Egret	6-5	135	Gadwall	6
197.9	Brewster's Egret	6	143	Pintail	6
199	Louisiana Heron	6	138	Common Teal	4
202	Black-crowned Night Heron	7A	139	Green-winged Teal	4
203	Yellow-crowned Night Heron	7A	140	Blue-winged Teal	5
			141	Cinnamon Teal	5
191	Eastern Least Bittern	4	136	European Widgeon	6
191.9	Western Least Bittern	4			
190	American Bittern	6	137	American Widgeon	6
188	Wood Ibis	-	142	Shoveler	6
186	Glossy Ibis	6	144	Wood Duck	5-6
			146	Redhead	6
187	White-faced Ibis	6	150	Ring-necked Duck	6
184	White Ibis	6			
185	Scarlet Ibis	-	147	Canvasback	7A
183	Roseate Spoonbill	-	148	Greater Scaup	6-5
182	American Flamingo	9	149	Lesser Scaup	6-5
			151	Common Goldeneye	6

APPENDIX TABLE IV. Continued.

A.O.U. No.	Species	Band Size	A.O.U. No.	Species	Band Size
152	Barrow's Goldeneye	6-7A	352	Bald Eagle	9
153	Bufflehead	5-6	352.1	Steller's Sea Eagle	-
154	Oldsquaw	5-6	331	Marsh Hawk	5
155	Harlequin Duck	-	364	Osprey	8
157	Steller's Eider	-	362	Caracara	7B
160	Common Eider	7A	354.7	Gyrfalcon	7B
162	King Eider	-	355	Prairie Falcon	6
158	Spectacled Eider	6			
164	Velvet Scoter	-	356	Peregrine Falcon	7B-7A
			359	Aplomado Falcon	5
165	White-winged Scoter	7A	357	Pigeon Hawk	4
166	Surf Scoter	7A	360	Sparrow Hawk, eastern male	3
163	Common Scoter	7A	360	Sparrow Hawk, eastern female	3A
167	Ruddy Duck	7A			
168	Masked Duck	5	360	Sparrow Hawk, western m & f	3A
			311	Chachalaca	5
131	Hooded Merganser	5	297	Blue Grouse	5
129	Common Merganser	7A	298	Spruce Grouse	5
130	Red-breasted Merganser	5-6	299	Franklin's Grouse	-
156	Hybrid ducks, except Mallard x Black	-	390	Ruffed Grouse	6-5
325	Turkey Vulture	7B	301	Willow Ptarmigan	5
326	Black Vulture	8	302	Rock Ptarmigan	5
324	California Condor	9	304	White-tailed Ptarmigan	-
326.1	King Vulture	9	305	Greater Prairie Chicken	6
328	White-tailed Kite	6-5	305.9	Attwater's Prairie Chicken	-
327	Swallow-tailed Kite	5	307	Lesser Prairie Chicken	-
329	Mississippi Kite	5	308	Sharp-tailed Grouse	6
330	Everglade Kite	5	309	Sage Grouse, female 6, male	7A
334	Goshawk	7A-7B	289	Bobwhite	3A
332	Sharp-shinned Hawk, male	3-2	290	Coturnix Quail	3
332	Sharp-shinned Hawk, female	4-3	291.1	Crested Quail	-
333	Cooper's Hawk	5	293	Scaled Quail	3A
337	Red-tailed Hawk	7B	294	California Quail	3A
337.6	Harlan's Hawk	7B	295	Gambel's Quail	3A
339	Red-shouldered Hawk	7A	292	Mountain Quail	4
343	Broad-winged Hawk	5	296	Harlequin Quail	3A
342	Swainson's Hawk	7A	309.1	Ring-neck. Pheasant, f. 6, m.	7A
340	Zone-tailed Hawk	7A	309.2	Reeves Pheasant	-
341	White-tailed Hawk	-	288.2	Chukar	-
			288.1	Gray Partridge	3A
344	Short-tailed Hawk	-	310	Turkey	9
347	Rough-legged Hawk	7B	204	Whooping Crane	9
348	Ferruginous Hawk	7B	206	Sandhill Crane	9
346	Gray Hawk	5	207	Limpkin	-
335	Harris' Hawk	7A			
			208	King Rail	5
345	Black Hawk	-	209	Belding's Clapper Rail	6
349	Golden Eagle	9	210	California Clapper Rail	6
351	Gray Sea Eagle	-			

APPENDIX TABLE IV. Continued.

A.O.U. No.	Species	Band Size	A.O.U. No.	Species	Band Size
211	Clapper Rail	5	238	Sharp-tailed Sandpiper	1A-1B
212	Virginia Rail	3	239	Pectoral Sandpiper	1A-1B
213	Spotted Crake	-	240	White-rumped Sandpiper	1A
214	Sora	3	241	Baird's Sandpiper	1A
215	Yellow Rail	2	242	Least Sandpiper	1
216	Black Rail	-	244	Curlew Sandpiper	-
217	Corn Crake	-	243	Dunlin	1A
218	Purple Gallinule	$\underline{4}$	231	Short-billed Dowitcher	2
219	Common Gallinule	5-$\overline{6}$	232	Long-billed Dowitcher	2
220	European Coot	-	233	Stilt Sandpiper	1A
221	American Coot	6-5	246	Semipalmated Sandpiper	$\overline{1}$
288	Jacana	3A	246.7	Semi. or Western Sandpiper	1
285	European Oystercatcher	-	247	Western Sandpiper	1
286	American Oystercatcher	5	262	Buff-breasted Sandpiper	1A
287	Black Oystercatcher	5	249	Marbled Godwit	4
269	Lapwing	5	250	Bar-tailed Godwit, male 3A, f.	4
274	Semipalmated Plover	1A-1B	251	Hudsonian Godwit	3A
277	Piping Plover	1A	252	Black-tailed Godwit	-
278	Snowy Plover	1B	260	Ruff	3A
279	Mongolian Plover	-	248	Sanderling	1A
280	Wilson's Plover	2	245	Spoon-bill Sandpiper	-
273	Killdeer	$\underline{2}$	225	American Avocet	4
281	Mountain Plover	3-2	226	Black-necked Stilt	3A
271	Eurasian Golden Plover	-	222	Red Phalarope	1A
272	American Golden Plover	2-3	224	Wilson's Phalarope	$\overline{2}$
270	Black-bellied Plover	$\underline{3}$	223	Northern Phalarope	1A
282	Surfbird	$\overline{2}$	036	Pomarine Jaeger	$\overline{4}$
283	Ruddy Turnstone	2	037	Parasitic Jaeger	3A
284	Black Turnstone	2	038	Long-tailed Jaeger	$\underline{3A}$
228	American Woodcock	3	035	Skua	$\overline{7A}$
227	European Woodcock	-	042	Glaucous Gull	$\overline{7B}$
230	Common Snipe	3	043	Iceland Gull	7B
264	Long-billed Curlew	4-5	044	Glaucous-winged Gull	7B
265	Whimbrel	4	047	Great Black-backed Gull	7B
268	Bristle-thighed Curlew	5-4	048	Slaty-backed Gull	7B
261	Upland Plover	3	049	Western Gull	6
263	Spotted Sandpiper	1B	050	Lesser Black-backed Gull	-
256	Solitary Sandpiper	$\underline{1A}$	051	Herring Gull	6
259	Wandering Tattler	$\overline{3}$	053	California Gull	5
258	Willet	4	054	Ring-billed Gull	5
254	Greater Yellowlegs	3-3A	055	Mew Gull	5-4
255	Lesser Yellowlegs	2	055.1	Black-headed Gull	5
234	Knot	3-3A	058	Laughing Gull	5
235	Purple Sandpiper	-	059	Franklin's Gull	4
235.6	Rock Sandpiper	-	060	Bonaparte's Gull	4-3
			060.1	Little Gull	-

APPENDIX TABLE IV. Continued.

A.O.U. No.	Species	Band Size	A.O.U. No.	Species	Band Size
057	Heermann's Gull	5	013	Common Puffin	6-5
039	Ivory Gull	4	014	Horned Puffin	5
040	Black-legged Kittiwake	4	012	Tufted Puffin	6-5
041	Red-legged Kittiwake	4	314	White-crowned Pigeon	4-5
061	Ross' Gull	3	314.1	Scaly-naped Pigeon	-
062	Sabine's Gull	3	312	Band-tailed Pigeon	5
063	Gull-billed Tern	3A	313	Red-billed Pigeon	5
068	Trudeau's Tern	-	313.1	Rock Dove	-
069	Forster's Tern	3	317	Zenaida Dove	-
070	Common Tern	3	317.1	Mountain Dove	-
071	Arctic Tern	3	319	White-winged Dove	3A
072	Roseate Tern	3	316	Mourning Dove	3A
073	Aleutian Tern	1B	315.1	Spotted Dove	3A
075	Sooty Tern	3	315.2	Ringed Turtle Dove	3
076	Bridled Tern	2	315.3	Philippine Turtle Dove	-
			315.4	White-thr. Ground Dove	-
074	Least Tern	1A	315.5	Marianas Fruit Dove	-
065	Royal Tern	5	315.6	Barred Dove	2
065.1	Cayenne Tern	-	320	Ground Dove	2
066	Elegant Tern	3			
067	Sandwich Tern	3A	321	Inca Dove	2
064	Caspian Tern	5	321.1	Scaled Dove	3
077	Black Tern	2	318	White-fronted Dove	3A
078	White-winged Black Tern	-	318.1	White-bellied Dove	-
079	Noddy Tern	3	322	Key West Quail Dove	-
079.1	Hawaiian Noddy Tern	2	322.1	Ruddy Quail Dove	4
079.2	Fairy Tern	2	386	Mangrove Cuckoo	3
080	Black Skimmer	4	387	Yellow-billed Cuckoo	2
032	Razorbill	6	388	Black-billed Cuckoo	2
030	Common Murre	6	385	Roadrunner	5
031	Thick-billed Murre	6	383	Smooth-billed Ani	3
034	Dovekie	3/4	384	Groove-billed Ani	3
027	Black Guillemot	4	365	Barn Owl	6
028	Mandt's Guillemot	-	373	Screech Owl	5
029	Pigeon Guillemot	4	373.1	Whiskered Owl	5
023	Marbled Murrelet	-	374	Flammulated Owl	3A
024	Kittlitz's Murrelet	-	375	Great Horned Owl	9-8
025	Xantus' Murrelet	-	376	Snowy Owl	8
026	Craveri's Murrelet	-	377	Hawk-Owl	5
021	Ancient Murrelet	-	379	Pygmy Owl	2
016	Cassin's Auklet	3	380	Ferruginous Owl	2
017	Parakeet Auklet	-	381	Elf Owl	2
018	Crested Auklet	-	378	Burrowing Owl	4-3A
020	Least Auklet	-	368	Barred Owl	7B
019	Whiskered Auklet	-	369	Spotted Owl	7A
015	Rhinoceros Auklet	-			

538

APPENDIX TABLE IV. Continued.

A.O.U. No.	Species	Band Size	A.O.U. No.	Species	Band Size
370	Great Gray Owl	7B	408	Lewis' Woodpecker	3
366	Long-eared Owl	6	402	Yellow-bellied Sapsucker	1B-1A
367	Short-eared Owl	6	402.9	Red-naped Sapsucker	1A
371	Boreal Owl	4	403	Red-breasted Sapsucker	1A
372	Saw-whet Owl	3A	404	Williamson's Sapsucker	1A
416	Chuck-will's-widow	3	393	Hairy Woodpecker	2
417	Whip-poor-will	1A-3	394	Downy Woodpecker	1B
417.1	Buff-collared Nightjar	-	396	Ladder-backed Woodpecker	1B
418	Poor-will	1B	397	Nuttall's Woodpecker	1B
419	Pauraque	2	398	Arizona Woodpecker	-
420	Common Nighthawk	1A	395	Red-cockaded Woodpecker	-
421	Lesser Nighthawk	1B	399	White-headed Woodpecker	1A
422	Black Swift	1A	400	Blk-back 3-toed Woodpecker	-
423	Chimney Swift	1B	401	Northern 3-toed Woodpecker	-
424	Vaux's Swift	1	392	Ivory-billed Woodpecker	3A
425	White-throated Swift	2	441.1	Rose-throated Becard	-
437	Lucifer Hummingbird	XB	444	Eastern Kingbird	1B
428	Ruby-throated Hummingbird	XB	445	Gray Kingbird	-
429	Black-chinned Hummingbird	XB	446	Tropical Kingbird	1A
430	Costa's Hummingbird	XB	447	Western Kingbird	1A
431	Anna's Hummingbird	XA	448	Cassin's Kingbird	1A
432	Broad-tailed Hummingbird	XA	442	Fork-tailed Flycatcher	-
433	Rufous Hummingbird	XB	443	Scissor-tailed Flycatcher	1A
434	Allen's Hummingbird	XB	449	Kiskadee Flycatcher	2
435	Heloise's Hummingbird	XB	451	Sulphur-bellied Flycatcher	-
436	Calliope Hummingbird	XB	452	Great Crested Flycatcher	1A
426	Rivoli's Hummingbird	X	453	Wied's Crested Flycatcher	1A
427	Blue-throated Hummingbird	X	454	Ash-throated Flycatcher	1A
438	Rieffer's Hummingbird	-	455	Olivaceous Flycatcher	1
439	Buff-bellied Hummingbird	XB	456	Eastern Phoebe	1-0
440	Xantus' Hummingbird	-	458	Black Phoebe	1
441	Broad-billed Hummingbird	XB	457	Say's Phoebe	1
389	Coppery-tailed Trogon	-	463	Yellow-bellied Flycatcher	0
390	Belted Kingfisher	3A	465	Acadian Flycatcher	0
390.1	Ringed Kingfisher	-	466	Traill's Flycatcher	0
391	Green Kingfisher	2	467	Least Flycatcher	0
412	Yellow-shafted Flicker	3	468	Hammond's Flycatcher	0
412.3	Hybrid Flicker	3	469	Dusky Flycatcher	0
413	Red-shafted Flicker	3	469.1	Gray Flycatcher	0
414	Gilded Flicker	3	464	Western Flycatcher	0
405	Pileated Woodpecker	4-3	470	Buff-breasted Flycatcher	0
409	Red-bellied Woodpecker	2	460	Coues' Flycatcher	1
410	Golden-fronted Woodpecker	2	461	Eastern Wood Pewee	0
411	Gila Woodpecker	2-3	462	Western Wood Pewee	0
406	Red-headed Woodpecker	2	459	Olive-sided Flycatcher	1
407	Acorn Woodpecker	1A			

APPENDIX TABLE IV.   Continued.

A.O.U. No.	Species	Band Size	A.O.U. No.	Species	Band Size
471	Vermilion Flycatcher	0	745	Black-eared Bushtit	X-0
472	Beardless Flycatcher	X̲	727	White-breasted Nuthatch	1-1B
473	Skylark	1B	728	Red-breasted Nuthatch	0-1
474	Horned Lark	1B	729	Brown-headed Nuthatch	0-1
615	Violet-green Swallow	1̲	730	Pigmy Nuthatch	0-1
614	Tree Swallow	1	726	Brown Creeper	X-0
616	Bank Swallow	0̲	742	Wrentit	1
617	Rough-winged Swallow	0	701	Dipper	1A
613	Barn Swallow	1̲	721	House Wren	0
612.3	Cliff x Barn Swallow	-	722	Winter Wren	0
612	Cliff Swallow	1	719	Bewick's Wren	0
612.1	Cave Swallow	1	718	Carolina Wren	1
611	Purple Martin	1A	713	Cactus Wren	1A
484	Gray Jay	2̲	725	Long-billed Marsh Wren	0
485	Oregon Jay obscurus (only)	3̲	724	Short-billed Marsh Wren	0
485.9	Gray Jay griseus (only)	3	717	Cañon Wren	0̲
477	Blue Jay	3	715	Rock Wren	0̲
478	Steller's Jay	3	703	Mockingbird	2
479	Florida Scrub Jay	2-3	703.1	Chuchubi, Mimus gilvus	-
481	Scrub Jay	2̲	704	Catbird	1A
480	Formerly Woodhouse's Jay	-	705	Brown Thrasher	2
482	Mexican Jay	3	706	Long-billed Thrasher	2
483	Green Jay	2	709	Gray Thrasher	-
475	Black-billed Magpie	4	708	Bendire's Thrasher	2
476	Yellow-billed Magpie	3A̲	707	Curve-billed Thrasher	2
486	Common Raven	6̲	710	California Thrasher	2
487	White-necked Raven	5	711	Le Conte's Thrasher	2
488	Common Crow	5	712	Crissal Thrasher	2
489	Northwestern Crow	4	702	Sage Thrasher	1B
490	Fish Crow	4̲	761	Robin	2
492	Piñon Jay	3̲	762	San Lucas Robin	-
491	Clark's Nutcracker	3	764.2	English Robin	-
735	Black-capped Chickadee	0	763	Varied Thrush	2
736	Carolina Chickadee	0	755	Wood Thrush	1A
737	Mexican Chickadee	0	759	Hermit Thrush	1B
738	Mountain Chickadee	0	759.8	Dwarf Hermit Thrush	1
739	Gray-headed Chickadee	0	758	Swainson's Thrush	1B
740	Boreal Chickadee	0	757	Gray-cheeked Thrush	1B
741	Chestnut-backed Chickadee	0	756	Veery	1B
731	Tufted Titmouse	1B	766	Eastern Bluebird	1-1B
732	Black-crested Titmouse	1B	767	Western Bluebird	1B̲
733	Plain Titmouse	1B̲	768	Mountain Bluebird	1B̲
734	Bridled Titmouse	0	765	Wheatear	1
746	Verdin	X-0	764	Bluethroat	0
743	Common Bushtit	X-0	754	Townsend's Solitaire	1B̲

APPENDIX TABLE IV. Continued.

A.O.U. No.	Species	Band Size	A.O.U. No.	Species	Band Size
747	Arctic Warbler	0	649	Olive-backed Warbler	0
751	Blue-gray Gnatcatcher	X-0	651	Olive Warbler	0
752	Black-tailed Gnatcatcher	X-0	652	Yellow Warbler	0
748	Golden-crowned Kinglet	X-0	657	Magnolia Warbler	0
749	Ruby-crowned Kinglet	X-0	650	Cape May Warbler	0
694	White Wagtail	-	654	Black-throated Blue Warbler	0
696	Yellow Wagtail	0	655	Myrtle Warbler	0
697	Water Pipit	1	656	Audubon's Warbler	0
700	Sprague's Pipit	1	665	Black-throated Gray Warbler	0
618	Bohemian Waxwing	1A	668	Townsend's Warbler	0
619	Cedar Waxwing	1B	667	Black-throated Green Warbler	0
620	Phainopepla	1B	666	Golden-cheeked Warbler	0
621	Northern Shrike	2	669	Hermit Warbler	0
622	Loggerhead Shrike	2	658	Cerulean Warbler	0
493	Starling	2	662	Blackburnian Warbler	0
493.1	Crested Mynah	-	663	Yellow-throated Warbler	0
630	Black-capped Vireo	1	664	Grace's Warbler	0
631	White-eyed Vireo	0	659	Chestnut-sided Warbler	0
632	Hutton's Vireo	1	660	Bay-breasted Warbler	0
633	Bell's Vireo	0	661	Blackpoll Warbler	0
634	Gray Vireo	1	671	Pine Warbler	0
628	Yellow-throated Vireo	1	670	Kirtland's Warbler	0
629	Solitary Vireo	1	673	Prairie Warbler	0
623	Black-whiskered Vireo	1	672	Western Palm Warbler	0
625	Yellow-green Vireo	1	672.9	Yellow Palm Warbler	0
624	Red-eyed Vireo	1	674	Ovenbird	1
626	Philadelphia Vireo	1	675	Northern Waterthrush	1-0
627	Warbling Vireo	1	676	Louisiana Waterthrush	1
635	Bahama Honeycreeper	0	677	Kentucky Warbler	1
636	Black-and-white Warbler	0	678	Connecticut Warbler	1
637	Prothonotary Warbler	0	679	Mourning Warbler	1
638	Swainson's Warbler	0-1	680	Macgillivray's Warbler	0-1
639	Worm-eating Warbler	0-1	681	Yellowthroat	0
642	Golden-winged Warbler	0	682	Belding's Yellowthroat	-
641	Blue-winged Warbler	0	682.1	Ground Chat	-
641.2	Brewster's Warbler	0	683	Yellow-breasted Chat	1B
641.3	Lawrence's Warbler	0	690	Red-faced Warbler	0
640	Bachman's Warbler	0	684	Hooded Warbler	0
647	Tennessee Warbler	0	685	Wilson's Warbler	0
646	Orange-crowned Warbler	0	686	Canada Warbler	0
645	Nashville Warbler	0	687	American Redstart	0
644	Virginia's Warbler	0	688	Painted Redstart	0
647.1	Colima Warbler	0	688.2	House Sparrow formerly 533.1	1-1B
643	Lucy's Warbler	0			
648	Parula Warbler	0	688.3	European Tree Sparrow	1B

APPENDIX TABLE IV. Continued.

A.O.U. No.	Species	Band Size	A.O.U. No.	Species	Band Size
494	Bobolink	1B-1A	602	White-collared Seedeater	X-0
501	Eastern Meadowlark	3-2	515	Pine Grosbeak	1A
501.1	Weatern Meadowlark	3	524	Gray-crowned Rosy Finch	1B
497	Yellow-head. Blackbird, male	2	525	Black Rosy Finch	1B
497	Yellow-head. Blackbird, fem.	1A	526	Brown-capped Rosy Finch	1B
498	Redwinged Blackbird, male	2	526.1	European Goldfinch	0
498	Redwinged Blackbird, female	1A	527	Hoary Redpoll	0
500	Tricolored Blackbird	2	528	Common Redpoll	0
506	Orchard Oriole	1B	533	Pine Siskin	0
503	Black-headed Oriole	-	529	American Goldfinch	0
503.2	Spotted-breasted Oriole	-	530	Lesser Goldfinch	0
505	Hooded Oriole	1B	531	Lawrence's Goldfinch	0
503.1	Lichtenstein's Oriole	-	521	Red Crossbill	1B
504	Scott's Oriole	1B	522	White-winged Crossbill	1B
507	Baltimore Oriole	1A	586	Olive Sparrow	1
508	Bullock's Oriole	1A	592.1	Green-tailed Towhee	1A
509	Rusty Blackbird	2	587	Rufous-sided Towhee, eastern	1A
510	Brewer's Blackbird	2	587	Eastern Towhee	1A
513	Boat-tailed Grackle, male	4	588	Rufous-sided Towhee, western	1A
513	Boat-tailed Grackle, female	3	588	Spotted Towhee	1A
511	Com. Grackle, Purple & Fla.	3	591	Brown Towhee	1A
511.8	Bronzed Grackle	3	592	Abert's Towhee	1A
511.9	Formerly Bronzed Grackle	-	605	Lark Bunting	1A
495	Brn-headed Cowbird-1A,	Dwarf-1B	541	Ipswich Sparrow	1B
496	Bronzed Cowbird	1A	542	Savannah Sparrow	1
607	Western Tanager	1B	543	Belding's Savannah Sparrow	-
608	Scarlet Tanager	1B	544	Formerly Large-bill Sparrow	-
609	Hepatic Tanager	2	546	Grasshopper Sparrow	0
610	Summer Tanager	1B	545	Baird's Sparrow	1
593	Cardinal	1A	548	Le Conte's Sparrow	1
594	Pyrrhuloxia	1A	547	Henslow's Sparrow	0
595	Rose-breasted Grosbeak	1A	549	Sharp-tailed Sparrow	1
596	Black-headed Grosbeak	1A	550	Seaside Sparrow	1B
597	Blue Grosbeak	1B	551	Dusky Seaside Sparrow	1B
598	Indigo Bunting	1	551	Cape Sable Sparrow	-
599	Lazuli Bunting	0	540	Vesper Sparrow	1B
600	Varied Bunting	0	552	Lark Sparrow	1B
601	Painted Bunting	0	579	Rufous-winged Sparrow	0
603	Black-faced Grassquit	0	580	Rufous-crowned Sparrow	1
603.1	Melodious Grassquit	-	575	Bachman's Sparrow	1
604	Dickcissel	1B	576	Botteri's Sparrow	1
514	Evening Grosbeak	1A	578	Cassin's Sparrow	1
517	Purple Finch	1	573	Black-throated Sparrow	0
518	Cassin's Finch	1B	574	Sage Sparrow	1
519	House Finch	1			

APPENDIX TABLE IV. Continued.

A.O.U. No.	Species	Band Size	A.O.U. No.	Species	Band Size
566	White-winged Junco	1	554.7	Puget Sound Sparrow	1B
567	Slate-colored Junco	0	554.8	Nuttall's Sparrow	1B
567.8	Slate-colored x Oregon	0	557	Golden-crowned Sparrow	1B
567.9	Oregon Junco	0	558	White-throated Sparrow	1B
572	Guadalupe Junco	-	558.7	White-thr. Sparrow x Junco	-
570.8	Gray-headed Junco	$\frac{0}{1}$	558.1	Curaçao Sparrow	-
570.8	Red-backed Junco		585	Fox Sparrow	1A
570	Mexican Junco	1	583	Lincoln's Sparrow	1
571	Baird's Junco	-	584	Swamp Sparrow	1
559	Tree Sparrow	1	581	Song Sparrow	1-1B
560	Chipping Sparrow	0	539	McCown's Longspur	1
561	Clay-colored Sparrow	0	536	Lapland Longspur	$\frac{1B}{1}$
562	Brewer's Sparrow	0	537	Smith's Longspur	
563	Field Sparrow	0	538	Chestnut-collared Longspur	1
569	Worthen's Sparrow	-	534	Snow Bunting	1B
565	Black-chinned Sparrow	0	535	McKay's Bunting	1B
553	Harris' Sparrow	1A			
554	White-crowned Sparrow	1B			
554.9	Gambel's Sparrow	1B			

APPENDIX TABLE V.

Common and technical (binomial only) names (A.O.U. Committee 1957) of the principal game birds of North America.

Common Name	Technical Name	Order	Family	Number of Races
Bobwhite	*Colinus virginianus*	Galliformes	Phasianidae	3
Brant, American	*Branta bernicla*	Anseriformes	Anatidae	1
Black	*Branta nigricans*	Anseriformes	Anatidae	1
Bufflehead	*Bucephala albeola*	Anseriformes	Anatidae	1
Canvasback	*Aythya valisineria*	Anseriformes	Anatidae	1
Chicken, Greater Prairie	*Tympanuchus cupido*	Galliformes	Tetraonidae	3
Coot, American	*Fulica americana*	Gruiformes	Rallidae	1
Dove, Ground	*Columbigallina passerina*	Columbiformes	Columbidae	3
Mourning	*Zenaidura macroura*	Columbiformes	Columbidae	2
White-winged	*Zenaida asiatica*	Columbiformes	Columbidae	3
Duck, Black	*Anas rubripes*	Anseriformes	Anatidae	1
Fulvous Tree	*Dendrocygna bicolor*	Anseriformes	Anatidae	1
Ring-necked	*Aythya collaris*	Anseriformes	Anatidae	1
Ruddy	*Oxyura jamaicensis*	Anseriformes	Anatidae	1
Wood	*Aix sponsa*	Anseriformes	Anatidae	1

APPENDIX TABLE V. Continued.

Common Name	Technical Name	Order	Family	Number of Races
Eider, Common	*Somateria mollissima*	Anseriformes	Anatidae	4
King	*Somateria spectabilis*	Anseriformes	Anatidae	10
Gadwall	*Anas strepera*	Anseriformes	Anatidae	1
Goldeneye,				
Barrow's	*Bucephala islandica*	Anseriformes	Anatidae	1
Common	*Bucephala clangula*	Anseriformes	Anatidae	2
Goose, Blue	*Chen caerulencens*	Anseriformes	Anatidae	1
Canada	*Branta canadensis*	Anseriformes	Anatidae	10
Ross'	*Chen rossii*	Anseriformes	Anatidae	1
Snow	*Chen hyperborea*	Anseriformes	Anatidae	2
White-fronted	*Anser albifrons*	Anseriformes	Anatidae	3
Grouse, Blue	*Dendragapus obscurus*	Galliformes	Tetraonidae	8
Ruffed	*Bonasa umbellus*	Galliformes	Tetraonidae	10
Sage	*Centrocercus urophasianus*	Galliformes	Tetraonidae	2
Sharp-tailed	*Pedioecetes phasianellus*	Galliformes	Tetraonidae	6
Spruce	*Canachites canadensis*	Galliformes	Tetraonidae	5
Mallard	*Anas platyrhynchos*	Anseriformes	Anatidae	2
Merganser,				
Common	*Mergus merganser*	Anseriformes	Anatidae	1
Hooded	*Lophodytes cucullatus*	Anseriformes	Anatidae	1
Red-breasted	*Mergus serrator*	Anseriformes	Anatidae	2
Oldsquaw	*Clangula hyemalis*	Anseriformes	Anatidae	1
Partridge, Gray (Hungarian)	*Perdix perdix*	Galliformes	Phasianidae	1
Pheasant, Ring-necked	*Phasianus colchicus*	Galliformes	Phasianidae	1
Pigeon, Band-tailed	*Columba fasciata*	Columbiformes	Columbidae	3
Pintail	*Anas acuta*	Anseriformes	Anatidae	1
Ptarmigan, Rock	*Lagopus mutus*	Galliformes	Tetraonidae	13
White-tailed	*Lagopus leucurus*	Galliformes	Tetraonidae	3
Willow	*Lagopus lagopus*	Galliformes	Tetraonidae	7
Quail, California	*Lophortyx californicus*	Galliformes	Phasianidae	7
Gambel's	*Lophortyx gambelii*	Galliformes	Phasianidae	3
Harlequin	*Cyrtonyx montezumae*	Galliformes	Phasianidae	1
Mountain	*Oreortyx pictus*	Galliformes	Phasianidae	5
Scaled	*Callipepla squamata*	Galliformes	Phasianidae	2
Rail, Clapper	*Rallus longirostris*	Gruiformes	Rallidae	10
King	*Rallus elegans*	Gruiformes	Rallidae	1
Rail, Sora	*Porzana carolina*	Gruiformes	Rallidae	1
Virginia	*Rallus limicola*	Gruiformes	Rallidae	1

APPENDIX TABLE V. Continued.

Common Name	Technical Name	Order	Family	Number of Races
Redhead	*Aythya americana*	Anseriformes	Anatidae	1
Scaup, Greater	*Aythya marila*	Anseriformes	Anatidae	2
Lesser	*Aythya affinis*	Anseriformes	Anatidae	1
Scoter, Common	*Oidemia nigra*	Anseriformes	Anatidae	2
Surf	*Melanitta perspicillata*	Anseriformes	Anatidae	1
White-winged	*Melanitta deglandi*	Anseriformes	Anatidae	2
Shoveler	*Spatula ciypeata*	Anseriformes	Anatidae	1
Snipe, Wilson's	*Capella gallinago*	Charadriiformes	Scolopacidae	3
Swan, Mute	*Cygnus olor*	Anseriformes	Anatidae	1
Trumpeter	*Olor buccinator*	Anseriformes	Anatidae	1
Whistling	*Olor columbianus*	Anseriformes	Anatidae	1
Teal, Blue-winged	*Anas discors*	Anseriformes	Anatidae	2
Cinnamon	*Anas cyanoptera*	Anseriformes	Anatidae	1
Green-winged	*Anas carolinensis*	Anseriformes	Anatidae	1
Turkey, Wild	*Meleagris gallopavo*	Galliformes	Meleagrididae	4
Widgeon, American	*Mareca americana*	Anseriformes	Anatidae	1
Woodcock, American	*Philohela minor*	Charadriiformes	Scolopacidae	1

APPENDIX TABLE VI.

Common and technical (binomial only) names (Miller and Kellogg 1955) of the principal game and fur-bearing mammals of North America.

Common Name	Technical Name	Order	Family	Number of Races
Antelope, Pronghorn	*Antilocapra americana*	Artiodactyla	Antilocapridae	5
Badger	*Taxidea taxus*	Carnivora	Mustelidae	15
Bear, Big Brown	*Ursus middendorffi*	Carnivora	Ursidae	1
Bear, Black	*Euarctos americanus*	Carnivora	Ursidae	15
Grizzly	*Ursus horribilis*	Carnivora	Ursidae	4
Polar	*Thalarctos maritimus*	Carnivora	Ursidae	3
Beaver	*Castor canadensis*	Rodentia	Castoridae	25
Bison (Buffalo)	*Bison bison*	Artiodactyla	Bovidae	2
Bobcat	*Lynx rufus*	Carnivora	Felidae	12
Caribou, Barren Ground	*Rangifer arcticus*	Artiodactyla	Cervidae	9
Greenland	*Rangifer tarandus*	Artiodactyla	Cervidae	2
Woodland	*Rangifer caribou*	Artiodactyla	Cervidae	3
Cat, Margay	*Felis wiedii*	Carnivora	Felidae	7
Cat, Ringtail (Cacomistle)	*Bassariscus astutus*	Carnivora	Procyonidae	13

APPENDIX TABLE VI. Continued.

Common Name	Technical Name	Order	Family	Number of Races
Cottontail, Desert	*Sylvilagus audubonii*	Lagomorpha	Leporidae	12
Eastern	*Sylvilagus floridanus*	Lagomorpha	Leporidae	22
Mountain	*Sylvilagus nuttallii*	Lagomorpha	Leporidae	3
New England	*Sylvilagus transitionalis*	Lagomorpha	Leporidae	1
Cougar (See Mt. Lion)				
Coyote	*Canis latrans*	Carnivora	Canidae	19
Deer, Black-tailed	*Odocoileus hemionus*	Artiodactyla	Cervidae	11
Whitetail	*Odocoileus virginianus*	Artiodactyla	Cervidae	30
Elk (Wapiti)	*Cervus canadensis*	Artiodactyla	Cervidae	4
Ferret, Black-footed	*Mustela nigripes*	Carnivora	Mustelidae	1
Fisher	*Martes pennanti*	Carnivora	Mustelidae	3
Fox, Arctic	*Alopex lagopus*	Carnivora	Canidae	3
Gray	*Urocyon cinereoargenteus*	Carnivora	Canidae	15
Kit	*Vulpes velox*	Carnivora	Canidae	2
Red	*Vulpes fulva*	Carnivora	Canidae	12
Swift (See Kit Fox)				
Goat, Mountain	*Oreamnos americanus*	Artiodactyla	Bovidae	3
Ground Hog (See Woodchuck)				
Hare, Arctic	*Lepus arcticus*	Lagomorpha	Leporidae	8
European	*Lepus europaeus*	Lagomorpha	Leporidae	2
Little Chief (Pika)	*Ochotona princeps*	Lagomorpha	Ochotonidae	31
Snowshoe (American Varying)	*Lepus americanus*	Lagomorpha	Leporidae	16
Tundra	*Lepus othus*	Lagomorpha	Leporidae	2
Jaguar	*Felis onca*	Carnivora	Felidae	5
Lion, Mountain	*Felis concolor*	Carnivora	Felidae	15
Lynx	*Lynx canadensis*	Carnivora	Felidae	3
Marten	*Martes americana*	Carnivora	Mustelidae	6
Mink	*Mustela vison*	Carnivora	Mustelidae	14
Moose	*Alces alces*	Artiodactyla	Cervidae	4
Muskox	*Ovibos moschatus*	Artiodactyla	Bovidae	3
Muskrat	*Ondatra zibethicus*	Rodentia	Cricetidae	15
Nutria	*Myocastor coypus*	Rodentia	Capromyidae	1
Ocelot	*Felis pardalis*	Carnivora	Felidae	5
Opossum	*Didelphis marsupialis*	Marsupialia	Didelphiidae	12
Otter, River	*Lutra canadensis*	Carnivora	Mustelidae	19
Sea	*Enhydra lutris*	Carnivora	Mustelidae	2
Peccary	*Pecari tajacu*	Artiodactyla	Tayassuidae	10

546

Common Name	Technical Name	Other	Family	Number of Races
Polecat (See Skunk)				
Pronghorn (See Antelope)				
Puma (See Mt. Lion)				
Rabbit, Brush	*Sylvilagus bachmani*	Lagomorpha	Leporidae	13
Marsh	*Sylvilagus palustris*	Lagomorpha	Leporidae	2
Pigmy	*Sylvilagus idahoensis*	Lagomorpha	Leporidae	1
Swamp	*Sylvilagus aquaticus*	Lagomorpha	Leporidae	2
Raccoon	*Procyon lotor*	Carnivora	Procyonidae	28
Seal, Bearded	*Erignathus barbatus*	Pinnipedia	Phocidae	2
Gray	*Halichoerus grypus*	Pinnipedia	Phocidae	1
Harbor	*Phoca vitulina*	Pinnipedia	Phocidae	4
Harp	*Phoca groenlandica*	Pinnipedia	Phocidae	1
Hooded	*Cystophora cristata*	Pinnipedia	Phocidae	1
Ribbon	*Phoca fasciata*	Pinnipedia	Phocidae	1
Ringed	*Phoca hispida*	Pinnipedia	Phocidae	3
Sheep, Bighorn (Mountain)	*Ovis canadensis*	Artiodactyla	Bovidae	7
White (Thin-horn)	*Ovis dalli*	Artiodactyla	Bovidae	3
Skunk, Hognose	*Conepatus leuconotus*	Carnivora	Mustelidae	2
Hooded	*Mephitis macroura*	Carnivora	Mustelidae	4
Spotted	*Spilogale putorius*	Carnivora	Mustelidae	1
Stripped	*Mephitis mephitis*	Carnivora	Mustelidae	13
Squirrel, Albert	*Sciurus alberti*	Rodentia	Sciuridae	8
Apache Fox	*Sciurus apache*	Rodentia	Sciuridae	1
Arizona Gray	*Sciurus arizonensis*	Rodentia	Sciuridae	3
Eastern Fox	*Sciurus niger*	Rodentia	Sciuridae	9
Eastern Gray	*Sciurus carolinensis*	Rodentia	Sciuridae	6
Red	*Tamiasciurus hudsonicus*	Rodentia	Sciuridae	26
Tassel-eared (See Albert Squirrel)				
Western Gray	*Sciurus griseus*	Rodentia	Sciuridae	3
Wapiti (See Elk)				
Weasel, Least	*Mustela rixosa*	Carnivora	Mustelidae	4
Longtail	*Mustela frenata*	Carnivora	Mustelidae	35
Shorttail	*Mustela erminea*	Carnivora	Mustelidae	20
Wolf, Gray	*Canis lupus*	Carnivora	Canidae	24
Red	*Canis niger*	Carnivora	Canidae	3
Wolverine	*Gulo luscus*	Carnivora	Mustelidae	3
Woodchuck	*Marmota monax*	Rodentia	Sciuridae	9

Appendix VII. A bird management technique guide presented by John R. Beck at the 4th National Bird Control Seminar, Columbus, Ohio, Sept. 16-19, 1968. Numbers are those of the techniques listed below. Underlined numbers represent techniques in common usage; numbers in parentheses represent better methods.

Species / Control Situation	Pigeons			Blackbird - Winter			Starlings			Mixed Flocks Starlings, Grackles, Others			Protected Species (4)			Blackbirds - Summer			English Sparrows			Gulls	Water Fowl	Crows *[4]
	Urban	Agri-cultural	Indus-trial	Urban	Agri-cultural	Indus-trial	Urban	Agri-cultural	Indus-trial	Urban	Agri-cultural	Indus-trial	Urban	Agri-cultural	Indus-trial	Urban	Agri-cultural	Indus-trial	Urban	Agri-cultural	Indus-trial			
Low Hazard	(1-4, 11)	5, 8, 11	1-4, 6, 10, 11	(5-7) 11	2, 5-7, 11, 13	5-7, 11	(1-11)	5, 7, 10, 11, 13	(1-7) (9-11)	(5-7, 11)	5-7, 12, 13	(5-7, 11)	(1,5) (6,8) 12	(1,2,5) (7,8) (10,11,13)	(5-7, 11)	(5,7) 8, 10, 11	(5,7) 8, (10-13)	(5-7)	4, 9, 10, 11	10, 11	2-4, 8-11	5, (11)	5, 7, 12, 13	2, 5, 11, 23
Medium Hazard	14, (16)	(14) 16, 19	14, 16	14, 18	14, 16, 18, 19, 20	(14, 18, 19) 23	17, 18	14, 18, 19, 21	17, 18	14, 23	(14-16) (19-23)	14, 18	14-16, 23	14-16, 19, 20, 23	14, 15	14, 17, 23	(14-16) (19-23)	14, 17, 18, 23	(14-16)	(14-16)	15-17	(14) 17	(23)	14-16, 19-21
High Hazard	(24), 27, 19	24	(24, 27) 19, 29		(24-26)		19, 26	(24-26)	26	26	18, 25, 26			26	18		24-26	26	24	24	(24)	24, (25)		(24) (25)
Restricted	28-30		28, 30		28, 29	28	28, 30	28, 30	19, 28, 30		28, 29			24			28, 29		30		28, 30			

Legal, Chemical, and Public Relations Hazards

— LOW —

1. Entanglents
2. Chemical Repellents
3. Mechanical Barriers (Repellents)
4. Electrical Repellents
5. Audible Repellents
6. Pyrotechnics
7. Shell Crackers

8. Imitations—Visual Repellents
9. Light Devices
10. Netting
11. Habitat Alteration and Sanitation
12. Herding by Vehicle
13. Warning System

— MEDIUM —

14. Shot Guns
15. Rifles and Air Rifles
16. Traps (General)
17. Ultrasonics - Electronics
18. Surfactants[2]
19. Lethal Repellents*[2]
20. Seed Protectants*
21. Cultural Practices[2]
22. Resistant Varieties[2]
23. Legal Hunting System[4]

— HIGH —

24. Toxic Baits*[2]
25. Psycho - Chemicals*[2]
26. Traps (Specific)
27. Soporifics*

RESTRICTED

28. Toxic Sprays or Paints[2,3]
29. Reproductive Inhibitors[3]
30. Fumigation[1,2]

Footnotes:

*Where Registered
[1]Where Essential
[2]Requires Services of Experienced Professional
[3]Experimental Only
[4]Consult Game Laws

LITERATURE CITED

A

Abbott, H. G. and A. W. Coombs. 1964. A photoelectric 35mm camera device for recording animal behavior. J. Mammal. 45(2):327-330.

Abelson, P. H. 1965. Translation of scientific literature. Science 149(3687): 929.

Abercrombie, M., C. J. Hickman, and M. L. Johnson. 1962. A dictionary of biology. Aldine, Chicago, Ill. 254 p.

Abramson, N., and J. Tolladay. 1959. The use of probability sampling for estimating annual number of angler days. Calif. Fish and Game 45(4): 303-312.

Acad. of Sci. of the USSR. 1962. Conservation of natural resources and the establishment of reserves in the USSR. Bul. no. 4. [transl. from Russian]. Israel Program for Scientific Translations, Jerusalem. 108 p.

Ackoff, R. L. 1962. Scientific method: optimizing applied research decisions. John Wiley and Sons, Inc., New York. 464 p.

Adams, L. 1950. A punch-card system suitable for use with small samples in wildlife management and research. U.S. Fish and Wildl. Spec. Sci. Rept. (Wildl.) no. 3, Washington, D.C. 7 p.

Adams, L. 1951. Confidence limits for the Petersen or Lincoln Index used in animal population studies. J. Wildl. Mgmt. 15:13-19.

Adams, L. 1955. A punch-card bibliographic file for vertebrate ecologists. J. Wildl. Mgmt. 19(4):472-476.

Adams, L. 1957. An anlaysis of a population of snowshoe hares. Ph.D. Thesis. Johns Hopkins Univ., Baltimore, Md.

Adams, L. 1957. A way to analyze herbivore food habits by fecal examination. Trans. N. Amer. Wildl. Conf. 22:152-159.

Adams, L. 1959. An analysis of a population of snowshoe hares in northwestern Montana. Ecol. Monogr. 29: 141-170.

Adams, L. 1965. Progress in ecological biotelemetry. BioScience 15(2):83-86.

Adams, L. 1965. Biotelemetry. BioScience 15(2):155-157.

Adams, L. 1965. The use of exploratory surgery to measure productivity in a population of animals. Trans. N. Amer. Wildl. and Nat. Resources Conf. 30:205-211.

Adams, L., and W. C. Smith. 1964. Wildlife telemetry. Proc. Natl. Telemetering Conf., Sec. 2-3, p. 1-7.

Addy, C. E. (comp.). 1956. Guide to waterfowl banding. U.S. Fish and Wildl. Ser., Laurel, Md. 164 p.

Addy, C. E., and L. G. MacNamara. 1948. Waterfowl management on small areas. Wildl. Mgmt. Inst., Washington, D.C. 84 p.

Adomaitis, V. A., H. K. Nelson and F. B. Lee. 1967. The chemical and related technical literature of wildlife conservation. J. Chem. Documentation 7(4):247-249.

Albritton, E. C. 1954. Standard values in nutrition and metabolism. W. B. Saunders Co., Philadelphia, Pa. 380 p.

Aldous, J. G. 1947. Simple method for cross-indexing a reference file. Science 106(2744):109.

Aldous, M. C., and F. C. Craighead, Jr. 1958. A marking technique for bighorn sheep. J. Wildl. Mgmt. 22:445-446.

Aldous, S. E. 1936. A cage trap useful in the control of white-necked ravens. U.S.D.A. Bur. Biol. Surv. Wildl. Res. and Mgmt. Leaflet BS-27. Washington, D.C. 5 p.

Aldous, S. E. 1940. A method of marking beavers. J. Wildl. Mgmt. 4:145-148.

Aldous, S. E. 1944. A deer browse survey method. J. Mammal. 25:130-136.

Alexander, M. M. 1951. The aging of muskrats on Montezuma National Wildlife Refuge. J. Wildl. Mgmt. 15: 175-186.

Alexander, M. M. 1958. The place of aging in wildlife management. Amer. Sci. 46(2):123-137.

Alexander, M. M. 1960. Shrinkage of muskrat skulls in relation to aging. J. Wildl. Mgmt. 24:326-329.

Allee, W. C., O. Park, A. E. Emerson, T. Park, and K. P. Schmidt. 1949. Principles of animal ecology. W. B. Saunders Co., Philadelphia, Pa. vii + 837.

Allen, D. L. 1942. A pheasant inventory method based upon kill records and sex ratios. Trans. N. Amer. Wildl. Conf. 7:329-333.

Allen, D. L. 1943. Michigan fox squirrel management. Michigan Dept. of Conserv., Div. of Game, Pub. 100. Lansing. 404 p.

Allen, D. L. 1956. Pheasants in North America. Stackpole Co., Harrisburg, Pa. 490 p.

Allen, D. L. 1962. Our wildlife legacy. (rev. ed.) Funk & Wagnalls, New York. 422 p.

Allen, G. M. 1939. A checklist of African mammals. Bull. Mus. Comp. Zool. Harvard. 83:1-763.

Allen, J. A. 1909. Biographical memoir of Elliott Coues, 1842-1899, p. 397-446. In Biographical Memoir. Nat. Acad. of Sci., Washington, D.C. (Vol. VI.)

Allen, J. M. 1952. Gray and fox squirrel management in Indiana. Cons. Dept., Indianapolis. P. R. Bull. No. 1. 112 p.

550

Allan, P.F. and W.W. Steiner. 1959. Autumn olive - for wildlife and other conservation uses. U.S.D.A., Washington, D.C. Leaflet No. 458, 8 p.

Alt, F. (Ed.) 1966. Advances in bioengineering and instrumentation. Plenum Press, N.Y. 360 p.

Altman, P.L. and Dorothy S. Dittmer. 1961. Blood and other body fluids. Fed. Am. Soc. for Experimental Biology, Washington, D.C. 540 p.

Altman, P.L. and Dorothy S. Dittmer. 1962. Growth including reproduction and morphological development. Fed. Am. Soc. for Experimental Biology, Washington, D.C. 608 p.

Altman, P.L. and Dorothy S. Dittmer (Eds.). 1964. Biology data book. Fed. Am. Soc. for Experimental Biology, Washington, D.C. 633 p.

Altmann, M., and J. Simon. 1952. Experimental marking of elk for behavior research. Unpub. paper presented at the Western Wildlife Conference. Seattle, Wash. May.

Altsheler, B. 1940. Natural history index—guide. 2nd ed. H.W. Wilson Co., New York. 583 p.

Amer. Assoc. of Museums. 1965. Museums directory of the United States and Canada. 2nd ed. Amer. Assoc. of Mus. and the Smithsonian Institution, Washington, D.C. 1039 p.

Amer. Ornithologists' Union. 1957. Check-list of North American birds. 5th ed. A.O.U., Baltimore, Md. 691 p.

Amer. Soc. of Photogrametry. 1962. A manual of photogrametry (2nd ed.) Amer. Soc. of Photogrametry, Washington, D.C.

American Standards Assoc. 1964. American standard for periodical title abbreviations. The Association, New York. 19 p. [A revision was issued in 1966 which is to be kept current with quarterly supplements.]

Ammann, G.A. 1944. Determining the age of pinnated and sharp-tailed grouse. J. Wildl. Mgmt. 8:170-171.

Amos, T.G. 1965. Time lapse photography with synchronized electronic flash for recording insect behavior. Animal Behavior 13:558-560.

Anderson, C.F. 1966. Anesthetizing deer by arrow. J. Wildl. Mgmt. 25:202-203.

Anderson, H.W. 1966. A simple library filing system for forestry references. Washington Dept. of Nat. Resources. Reprint 1, Olympia, 27 pp.

Anderson, J. 1953. Analysis of a Danish roe-deer population. Den. Rev. Game Biol. 2:127-155.

Anderson, J. 1961. Biology and management of roe-deer in Denmark. La Terre et la Vie, No. 1:41-53.

Anderson, P.K. 1966. The periodical literature of ecology. BioScience 16:794-795.

Anderson, R.M. 1946. Catalogue of Canadian recent mammals. Natl. Mus. of Canada Bull. no. 102 (Biol. Ser. no. 31), Ottawa. 238 p.

Anderson, R.M. 1948. Methods of collecting and preserving vertebrate animals. Natl. Mus. of Canada Bull. 69. Ottawa. 162 p.

Anderson, R.M. 1965. Methods of collecting and preserving vertebrate animals. 4th ed. rev. Nat. Mus. of Canada Bull. no. 69 (Biol. Ser. no. 18). Ottawa, 199 p.

Anderson, S., J.K. Doutt, and J.S. Findley. 1963. Collections of mammals in North America. J. Mammal. 44(4):471-500.

Anderson, W. 1956. A waterfowl nesting study on the grasslands, Merced County, California. Calif. Fish and Game 42:117-130.

Anderson, W. 1957. A waterfowl nesting study in the Sacramento Valley, California. 1955. Calif. Fish and Game 43:71-90.

Andrewartha, H.G. 1961. Introduction to the study of animal populations.

Univ. Chicago Press, Chicago, Ill. 281 p.

Anon. 1936. More game birds by controlling their enemies. More Game Birds In America - A Foundation, New York. 63 pp.

Anon. 1946. Squeaking animals. Nature Mag. 39(8):430-32.

Anon. 1947. The decoy. Severn Wildfowl Trust 1:52-56.

Anon. 1952. The Merck index of chemicals and drugs. 6th ed. Merck & Co., Rahway, N.J. 1167 p.

Anon. 1955. Evaluating and mapping mountain land features for forest management purposes. Wash. Agr. Expt. Sta. Circ. No. 271, 22 p.

Anon. 1956. Standard operating procedures. Section I, Waterfowl Air Survey Instructions. U.S. Fish and Wildl. Serv. 9, Washington, D.C. p. mimeo.

Anon. 1957. Extension of BA's program of cooperative abstracting. Biol. Abstr. 31(8):xii.

Anon. 1958. Scientific and learned societies of Great Britain. 59th ed. George Allen & Unwin, London. 215 p.

Anon. 1959. List of research workers. Executive Council of the Commonwealth Agr. Bureaux, Farnham Royal, Bucks, England. 434 p.

Anon. 1960. Acronyms dictionary. Gale Research Co., Detroit, Mich. 211 p.

Anon. 1960. Directory of university research bureau and institutions. Gale Research Co., Detroit, Mich. 199 p.

Anon. 1961-1966. Checklist of conservation organizations and information. IUCN Bull. Supplement nos. 1. Tanganyika, 2. Sweden, 3. German Federal Republic, 4. Canada, 5. France, 6. Venezuela, 7. Kenya, 8. Uganda, 9. Great Britain, 10. Netherlands, 11. Poland, 12. New Zealand, 13. Finland, 14. Transvall Province,

15. Natal Province, 16. Sudan, and 17. Ethiopia.

Anon. 1961. Report clarifies acquisition of Soviet doctoral dissertations. Scientific Inf. Notes. 3(1):5-6.

Anon. 1963. Directory of British scientists. Ernest Benn Ltd., London. 1289 p.

Anon. 1964. Report: Your views on the conference literature - what BA will do about it. Biol. Abstr. 45(22):xiv.

Anon. 1966. Why Biological Abstracts? Biol. Abstr. 47(17):x.

Anon. 1966. VINITI - current activities. Bibliography, Documentation, Terminology 6(2):71.

Anon. 1966. Information on your personal reference files - a brief summary. Biol. Abstr. 47(8):n.p.

Ansell, W. F. H. 1965. Standardisation of field data on mammals. Zoologica Africana 1(1):97-113.

Anthony, H. E. 1928. Field book of North American mammals. G. P. Putnam's Sons, New York. 674 p.

Anthony, H. E. 1950. The capture and preservation of small mammals for study. Amer. Mus. of Nat. Hist. Sci. Guide No. 61, New York.

Applegate, V. C., and A. E. Predmore, Jr. 1947. Age classes and patterns of primeness in a fall collection of muskrat pelts. J. Wildl. Mgmt. 11: 324-330.

Arata, A. A. 1959. A quick method of gross analysis of muskrat stomach contents. J. Wildl. Mgmt. 23:116-117.

Arlton, A. V. 1936. An ecological study of the mole. J. Mammal. 17:349-371.

Armstrong, R. A. 1950. Fetal development of the northern white-tailed deer (Odocoileus virginianus borealis Miller). Amer. Midland Naturalist 43:650-666.

Arnold, F., and H. G. Reynolds. 1943. Droppings of Arizona and antelope jack rabbits and the "pellet census." J. Wildl. Mgmt. 7:322-327.

Aronson, M. H. 1960. Electronic circuitry for instruments and equipment. Rimbach Pub. Co.

Arvey, M. D. and W. J. Riemer. 1966. Inland biological field stations of the United States. BioScience 16(4):249-254.

Asdell, S. A. 1946. Patterns and mammalian reproduction. Comstock Publishing Co., Ithaca, N. Y.

Ashbrook, R. G., and E. N. Sater. 1945. Cooking wild game. Orange Judd Pub. Co., New York.

Ashcraft, G., and D. Reese. 1957. An improved device for capturing deer. Calif. Fish and Game 43:193-199.

Atkins, H. J. B. (Ed.) 1960. Tools of biological research. Blackwell Scientific Publications, Oxford. 175 p.

Atkinson-Willes, G. L. (Ed.) 1963. Wildfowl in Great Britain: a survey of the winter distribution of the Anatidae and their conservation in England, Scotland and Wales, prepared by the Wildfowl Trust. Monographs of the Nature Conservancy, no. 3. Her Majesty's Stationary Office, London.

Atlantic Waterfowl Council. 1963. Waterfowl habitat developments and management techniques handbook. Habitat Management & Development Committee, Atlantic Waterfowl Council, n.p. 164 p.

Atomic Energy of Canada Ltd. 1960. The AECL radioisotope handbook. Tech. Bull. RP 3. AECL, Ottawa. 64 p.

Atomic Energy of Canada Ltd. 1961. The AECL radioisotope applications handbook. Tech. Bull. RAP-1. AECL, Ottawa. 54 p.

Atwater, M. M. 1959. A study of renesting in Canada geese in Montana. J. Wildl. Mgmt. 23(1):91-97.

Atwood, E. L. 1956. Validity of mail survey data on bagged waterfowl. J. Wildl. Mgmt. 20:1-16.

Awad, F. I. 1954. Nembutal in sheep. Vet. Record 66:226.

B

Babakov, G. A. 1961. Estimation of squirrel stocks over large areas. In Y. A. Isakov, (Ed.), Organization and methods of censusing terrestrial vertebrate faunal resources. Moscow Naturalists Soc., Insti. Geogr. Acad. Sci. USSR. 63 p.

Bailey, A. M. and R. J. Niedrach. 1965. Birds of Colorado. Denver Mus. of Nat. History, Denver, Colo. 2 vols.

Bailey, N. T. J. 1951. On estimating the size of mobile populations from recapture data. Biometrika 38:293-306.

Bailey, N. T. J. 1952. Improvements in the interpretation of recapture data. J. Animal Ecol. 21:120-127.

Bailey, R. E. 1953. Surgery for sexing and observing gonad conditions in birds. Auk 70:497-499.

Bailey, R. W. 1956. Sex determination of adult wild turkeys by means of dropping configuration. J. Wildl. Mgmt. 20:220.

Baines, H. 1958. The science of photography. John Wiley and Sons, New York. 319 p.

Baldwin, S. P. and S. C. Kendeigh. 1927. Attentiveness and inattentiveness in the nesting behavior of the house wren. Auk 44:206-216.

Baldwin, W. P. 1947. Trapping wild turkeys in South Carolina. J. Wildl. Mgmt. 11:24-36.

Balfour-Jones, S. E. 1936. . Proc. Royal Soc. of Medicine. 29:709.

Balham, R. W., and W. H. Elder. 1953. Colored leg bands for waterfowl. J. Wildl. Mgmt. 17:446-449.

552

Ball, K.E. 1952. Nesting of the ring-necked pheasant on Pelee Island, Ontario. Canadian Field Nat. 66:71-81.

Ballou, H.W. (Ed.) 1962. Guide to microreproduction equipment. 2nd ed. National Microfilm Association, Annapolis, Md. 519 p. [Supplements have been issued by the NMA listing new equipment.]

Ballou, R.M., and F.W. Martin. 1964. Rigid plastic collars for marking geese. J. Wildl. Mgmt. 28(4):846-847.

Balser, D.S. 1965. Tranquilizer tab for capturing wild carnivores. J. Wildl. Mgmt. 29:438-442.

Bandy, P.J., I. McT. Cowan, W.D. Kitts, and A.J. Wood. 1956. A method for the assessment of the nutritional status of wild ungulates. Canadian J. Zool. 34(1):48-52.

Banfield, A.W.F. 1954. Preliminary investigation of the barren ground caribou, Part II. Canadian Wildl. Ser., Nat. Pks., Br., Wildl. Mgmt. Bull. Ser. 1, No. 10B. 112 p.

Banfield, A.W.F. 1960. The use of caribou antler pedicels for age determination. J. Wildl. Mgmt. 24:99-102.

Banfield, A.W.F., D.R. Flook, J.P. Kelsall, and A.G. Loughrey. 1955. An aerial survey technique for northern big game. Trans. N. Amer. Wildl. Conf. 20:519-532.

Barbehenn, K.R., and C.G. Wilber. 1958. Age and physical characteristics of laboratory rhesus monkeys (Macaca mulatta) U. Directorate of Medical Research, Physiology Division. Chemical Warfare Laboratories Special Pub. 2-9. 17 p.

Barnes, R.D. and W.M. Longhurst. 1960. Techniques for dental impressions, restraining and embeding markers in live deer. J. Wildl. Mgmt. 24:224-226.

Barrier, M.J. and F.S. Barkalow, Jr. 1967. A rapid technique for aging gray squirrels in winter pelage. J. Wildl. Mgmt. 31:831-835.

Barry, F.W. 1956. Observations of a nesting colony of American brant. Auk 73:193-202.

Bartholomew, J.G., W.E. Clarke, and P.H. Grimshaw. 1911. Atlas of zoogeography. Published at the Edinburgh Geographical Institute by John Bartholomew & Co., Edinburgh. (various paging).

Bartlett, L.M. 1954. A technique for recording rapid consecutive field observations. Auk 73:193-202.

Bartonek, J.C., and C.W. Dane. 1964. Numbered nasal discs for waterfowl. J. Wildl. Mgmt. 28(4):688-692.

Baskett, F.S. 1947. Nesting and production of the ring-necked pheasant in north-central Iowa. Ecol. Monogr. 17:1-30.

Bauer, O. 1963. Improving land for California valley quail. Calif. Dept. Fish and Game, Sacramento, Calif. Game Mgmt. Leaflet No. 8. 11 p.

Baumgartner, L.L. 1940. Trapping, handling and marking fox squirrels. J. Wildl. Mgmt. 4:444-450.

Baumgartner, L.L., and F.C. Bellrose, Jr. 1943. Determination of sex and age in muskrats. J. Wildl. Mgmt. 7:77-81.

Baumgartner, L.L., and A.C. Martin. 1939. Plant histology as an aid in squirrel food-habits studies. J. Wildl. Mgmt. 3:266-268.

Beal, F.E.L. 1895. The crow blackbirds and their food. Yearbook Separate, USDA, Washington, D.C. p. 233-248.

Beal, F.E.L. 1897. Some common birds in their relation to agriculture. USDA Farmers Bull. No. 54. 40 p.

Beal, F.E.L. 1911. Food of the woodpeckers of the United States. Biol. Survey Bull. No. 37. 64 p.

Beal, F.E.L., and S.D. Judd. 1898. Cuckoos and shrikes in their relation to agriculture. Biol. Survey Bull. No. 9. 26 p.

Beal, R.O. 1967. Radio transmitter-collars for squirrels. J. Wildl. Mgmt. 31(2):373-374.

Beale, D.M. 1962. Growth of the eye lens in relation to age in fox squirrels. J. Wildl. Mgmt. 26(3):208-211.

Beale, D.M. 1966. A self-collaring device for pronghorn antelope. J. Wildl. Mgmt. 30(1):209-211.

Beck, J.R. 1952. A suggested food rank index. J. Wildl. Mgmt. 16:398.

Beck, J.R., and Doris O. Beck. 1955. A method for nutritional evaluation of wildlife foods. J. Wildl. Mgmt. 19:198-205.

Becker, E.R., and R.L. Roundabush. 1945. Brief directions in histological technique. Collegiate Press, Ames, Iowa, 80 p.

Bednarik, K. 1961. Waterfowl hunting on a controlled public area. Tech. Report, Pub. No. W-127, Ohio Dept. Nat. Resources, Columbus, Ohio. 16 p. (mimeo.).

Beebe, W. 1926. Pheasants: their lives and homes. New York Zoological Society and Doubleday, Doran, New York. 309 p.

Beer, J.R., P. Lukens, and D. Olson. 1954. Small mammal populations on the islands of Basswood Lake, Minnesota. Ecology 35:437-445.

Beer, J.V. and H. Boyd. 1962. Weights of pink-footed geese in autumn. Bird Study (92):91-99.

Behney, W.H. 1936. Nocturnal explorations of the forest deermouse. J. Mammal. 17:225-230.

Bellrose, F.C. 1955. A comparison of recoveries from reward and standard bands. J. Wildl. Mgmt. 19:71-75.

Bellrose, F.C. 1958. Celestial orientation by wild mallards. Bird-Banding 29:75-90.

Bellrose, F.C. 1964. Radar studies of waterfowl migration. Trans. N. Amer. Wildl. and Nat. Resources Conf. 29:128-143.

Bellrose, F.C. 1964. Report on bird migration surveillance during 1963 at U.S. Weather Bureau WSR-57 stations. Unpubl. Rep. 5 p.

Bellrose, F.C. 1967. Radar in orientation research *In* Proc. XIV International Ornithological Congress, Oxford, p. 281-309.

Bellrose, F.C., and H.G. Anderson. 1943. Preferential rating of duck food plants. Ill. Nat. Hist. Survey. Bull. 22:417-433.

Bellrose, F.C., and R.R. Graber. 1963. A radar study of the flight directions of nocturnal migrants. Proc. 13th Int. Ornithological Congr. Vol. 1 (Abstract).

Bellrose, F.C., K.L. Johnson, and T.U. Meyers. 1964. Relative values of natural cavities and nesting houses for wood ducks. J. Wildl. Mgmt. 28(4):661-676.

Bendell, J.F.S. 1955. Age, molt and weight characteristics of blue grouse. Condor 57:354-361.

Bendell, J.F.S. and P.W. Elliott. 1966. Habitat selection in blue grouse. Condor 68(5):431-446.

Bendell, J.F.S., and C.D. Fowle. 1950. Some methods for trapping and marking ruffed grouse. J. Wildl. Mgmt. 14:480-482.

Bennet, E.V. 1961. Aspects of vocalization in the redwinged blackbird, *Agelaius phoeniceus* (Linnaeus), as determined by audiospectrographic analysis. Ph.D. Diss., Cornell Univ., Ithaca. 176 p.

Bennett, L.J. 1938. The blue-winged teal, its ecology and management. Collegiate Press, Menasha, Wis. 144 p.

Bennett, L.J., P.F. English, and R. McCain. 1940. A study of deer populations by use of pellet-group counts. J. Wildl. Mgmt. 4:398-403.

Bennett, L.J., and G.O. Hendrickson. 1938. Censuring *(sic)* the ringneck pheasant in Iowa. Trans. N. Am. Wildl. Conf. 3:719-723.

Bennett, L.J., and G.O. Hendrickson. 1938. Censusing quail in early fall. J. Wildl. Mgmt. 2(4):169-171.

Bennitt, R. 1951. Some aspects of Missouri quail and quail hunting, 1938-48. Mo. Cons. Comm. Tech. Bull. No. 2, 51 p.

Bent, A.C. 1926. Life histories of North American marsh birds. U.S. Natl. Mus. Bull. 135. Washington, D.C.

Benton, A.H. and W.E. Werner, Jr. 1966. Field biology and ecology. McGraw-Hill, New York. 499 p.

Benton, Mildred. 1964. The biological serial record center. Coll. and Res. Libr. 25:111-112.

Bergerud, A.T. 1961. Sex determination of caribou calves. J. Wildl. Mgmt. 25(2):205.

Bergerud, A.T. 1964. Relationship of mandible length to sex in Newfoundland caribou. J. Wildl. Mgmt. 28(1):54-56.

Bergerud, A.T., A. Butt, H.L. Russell, and H. Uhalen. 1964. Immobilization of Newfoundland caribou and moose with succinylcholine chloride and Cap-Chur equipment. J. Wildl. Mgmt. 28(1):49-53.

Bergerud, A.T., and W.E. Mercer. 1966. Census of the willow ptarmigan in Newfoundland. J. Wildl. Mgmt. 30(1):101-113.

Bergerud, A.T., S.S. Peters, and R. McGrath. 1963. Determining sex and age of willow ptarmigan in Newfoundland. J. Wildl. Mgmt. 27(4):700-711.

Bergman, G. 1961. Allin ja mustalinnun muuttokannat Keväällä 1960. [The migrating populations of the long-tailed duck *(Clangula hyemalis)* and the common scoter *(Melanitta nigra)* in the spring, 1960]. Suomen Riista 14:69-74.

Bergman, G., and K.O. Donner. 1960. Die jetzige Grösse des Früjahrs-bestandes von *Clangula hyemalis* (L.) und *Melanitta nigra* (L.) am Finnischen Meerbusen. Ornis Fennica 37:117-122.

Bergman, G., and K.O. Donner. 1964. An analysis of the spring migration of the common scoter and the long-tailed duck in Southern Finland. Acta Zoologica Fennica 105:1-59.

Berkeley, E.C. 1949. Giant brains or machines that think. John Wiley and Sons, New York, xvi+270 p.

Bernice P. Bishop Museum. 1964. Dictionary catalog of the library: Bernice P. Bishop Museum, Honolulu, Hawaii. G.K. Hall, Boston, Mass. 9 vols.

Best, G.A. (Ed.) 1962. Rowland Ward's records of big game. 11th ed. Rowland Ward Ltd., London. 374 p.

Besterman, T. 1955. A world bibliography of bibliographies. 3rd ed. Societas Bibliographica, Geneva. 4 vol. [A new edition is in preparation, 1967].

Bethune, J.E. 1967. Mathematical programming approach to the allocation of resources to publically supported timber management research. Ph.D. Diss., Univ. of Georgia, Athens.

Betts, Monica M. 1954. Experiments with an artificial nestling. Brit. Birds 47:229-231.

Betts, Monica M. 1956. Further experiments with an artificial nestling gape. Brit. Birds 49:213-215.

Beule, J.D., and A.T. Studholme. 1942. Cottontail rabbit nests and nestlings. J. Wildl. Mgmt. 6:133-140.

Beveridge, W.I.B. 1957. The art of

554

scientific investigation. W. W. Norton, New York. 178 p.

BIAC. 1967. Biotelemetry equipment source directory. AIBS Information Module M12. 19 p.

Bigler, W. J. 1966. A marking harness for the collared peccary. J. Wildl. Mgmt. 30(1):213-214.

Bischoff, A. I. 1958. Productivity in some California deer herds. Cal. Fish and Game. 44(3):153-259.

Bishop, D. 1959. Science thesis control in Europe and America. Am. Doc. 10(1):51-58.

Bishop, S. C. 1947. Handbook of salamanders. Comstock Publishing Co., Ithaca, N.Y.

Biswell, H. H. and J. H. Gilman. 1961. Brush management in relation to fire and other environmental factors on the Tehama deer winter range. Calif. Fish and Game 47(4):357-389.

Biswell, H. H., R. D. Taber, D. W. Hedrick, and A. M. Schultz. 1952. Management of chamise brushlands for game in the north coast region of California. Calif. Fish and Game 38(4):453-484.

Black, Dorothy M. (Comp.). 1965. Guide to lists of master's theses. Amer. Library Assoc., Chicago, Ill. 144 p.

Black, H. C. 1958. Black bear research in New York. Trans. N. Amer. Wildl. Conf. 23:443-461.

Blacklith, R. E. 1958. Nearest-neighbor distance measurements for the estimation of animal populations. Ecology 39:147-150.

Blackwelder, R. E. 1963. Books on zoology (including natural history, physiology, genetics, parasitology, ecology, paleontology, entomology, etc.). Society of Systematic Zoology, Carbondale, Ill. 110 p. [A supplement was issued in 1965.]

Blackwelder, R. E. and Ruth M. 1961. Directory of zoological taxonomists

of the world. Southern Illinois University Press, Carbondale, Ill. 404 p.

Blair, W. F. 1941. Techniques for the study of mammal populations. J. Mammal. 22:148-157.

Blair, W. F., A. P. Blair, P. Brodkorb, F. R. Cagle, and G. A. Moore. 1957. Vertebrates of the United States. McGraw-Hill, N.Y. 819 p.

Blake, S. F. and Alice C. Atwood. 1942 and 1961. Geographic guide to the floras of the world: An annotated list, with special reference to useful plants and common plant names. USDA Misc. Pub. 401 and 797.

Blaker, A. A. 1965. Photography for scientific publication: a handbook. Freeman Co., San Francisco, Calif. xii+158 p.

Blank, T. H., and J. S. Ash. 1956. Marker for game birds. J. Wildl. Mgmt. 20:328-330.

Bledsoe, B. 1954. Master's theses in science, 1952. Biblio Press, Washington, D.C. 252 p.

Blood, D. A. and A. L. Lovaas. 1966. Measurements and weight relationships in Manitoba elk. J. Wildl. Mgmt. 30(1):135-140.

Boguslavsky, G. W. 1956. Statistical estimation of the size of a small population. Science 124 (3216):317-318.

Bohl, W. H. 1956. Experiments in locating wild chukar partridges by use of recorded calls. J. Wildl. Mgmt. 20: 83-85.

Bole, B. P., Jr. 1939. The quadrat method of studying small mammal populations. Scientific Publications of the Cleveland Museum of Natural History 5(4):15-77.

Bookhout, T. A. and E. M. Harger. 1964. An accurate, inexpensive scale for laboratory use. J. Mammal. 45(2): 313.

Boone and Crockett Club Committee on

Records of North American Big Game. 1964. Records of North American big game. Holt, Rinehart and Winston, New York. 398 p.

Booth, E. S. 1950. How to know the mammals. William C. Brown, Dubuque, Iowa. 206 p.

Borell, A. E. 1962. Russian-olive for wildlife and other conservation uses. U. S. D. A., Washington, D. C. Leaflet No. 517. 8 p.

Borhegyi, S. F. and E. A. Dodson (Comp.). 1961. A bibliography of museums and museum work, 1900-1960. Milwaukee Public Museum Publications in Museology no. 1. 102 p. [A supplement was published in 1961.]

Borror, D. J. and C. R. Reese. 1953. The analysis of bird songs by means of a vibralyzer. Wilson Bul. 65(4): 271-276.

Bottle, R. T. and H. V. Wyatt. 1967. The use of biological literature. Butterworths, London. 286 p.

Bourlière, F. 1964. The natural history of mammals. 3rd ed. [transl. from French]. Alfred A. Knopf, New York. 387 p.

Box, T. W. and J. Powell. 1965. Brush management techniques for improved forage values in south Texas. Trans. N. Amer. Wildl. and Natural Res. Conf. 30:285-295.

Box, T. W. 1966. Range management theses, 1961-1965. J. Range Mgmt. 19(5):310-313. [Earlier compilations appeared in volumes 14:51-54 for 1961 and 15:57-58 for 1962 of the Journal. The Range Management Council voted in February 1966 to continue preparing an annual listing.]

Boyd, R., and M. C. Coghill. 1964. Trampoline elk. Colo. Outdoors 13(2):16-19.

Bradt, G. W. 1938. A study of beaver colonies in Michigan. J. Mammal. 19:139-162.

Brainerd, G. W. 1939. An illustrated

field key for the identification of mammal bones. Ohio State Archaeol. Hist. Quart. 48:324-328.

Bramley, P. 1966. Roe deer. Nat. Conserv. Unit of Grouse and Moorland Ecol., Prog. Rep. 12:70-72.

Brand, A.R. 1935. A method for intensive study of bird song. Auk 52:40-52.

Brandborg, S.M. 1955. Life history and management of the mountain goat in Idaho. Idaho Dept. Fish and Game, Wildl. Bull. 2. 142 p.

Brander, R.B. 1965. Factors affecting dispersion of ruffed grouse during late winter and spring on the Cloquet Forest Research Center, Minnesota. Ph.D. Diss., Univ. Minnesota.

Brazenor, C.W., and K. Geoffrey. 1953. Anaesthesia for reptiles. Copeia 3:165-170.

Breckenridge. W.J. and J.R. Tester. 1961. Growth local movements and hibernation of the Manitoba Toad, *Bufo nemiophrys*. Ecology 42(4):637-646.

Breed, R.S., E.G.D. Murray and N.R. Smith. 1957. Bergey's manual of determinative bacteriology. 7th ed. Williams & Wilkins, Baltimore, Md. 1094 p.

Brinker, R.C. and W.C. Taylor. 1955. Elementary surveying (3rd ed.) International Textbook Co., Scranton, Pa.

British Museum. 1903-1940. Catalogue of the books, manuscripts, maps and drawings in the British Museum (Natural History). Longmans & Co., London. 5 vol. 3 suppl.

British Ornithologists' Union. 1952. Check-list of the birds of Great Britain and Ireland. Prepared by the List Sub-Committee, London. 106 p.

Brock, T.D. 1966. Principles of microbial ecology. Prentice-Hall, Inc., Englewood Cliffs, N.J. 306 p.

Brody, S. 1945. Bioenergetics and growth. Reinhold Publ. Corp., New York. 1023 p.

Brohn, A., and L.J. Korschgen. 1950. The precipitin test—a useful tool in game law enforcement. Trans. N. Amer. Wildl. Conf. 15:467-478.

Broley, Jeanne. 1950. Identifying nests of the Anatidae of the Canadian prairies. J. Wildl. Mgmt. 14:452-456.

Brotzman, R.L., and R.H. Giles, Jr. 1966. Electronic data processing of capture-recapture and related ecological data. J. Wildl. Mgmt. 30(2):286-292.

Brown, C.H. 1956. Scientific serials. ACRL Monograph 16. Amer. Library Assoc., Chicago, Ill. 189 p.

Brown, E.R. and C.F. Martinsen. 1959. Browse planting for big game. Washington Game Dept., Olympia, Biol. Bull. No. 12, 63 p.

Brown, G.H. 1952. Illustrated skull key to the recent land mammals of Virginia. Va. Coop. Wildl. Res. Unit Release No. 52-2, Blackburg. 75 p. (multilithed).

Brown, L.N. 1961. Excreted dyes used to determine movement of cottontail rabbits. J. Wildl. Mgmt. 23:199-202.

Brown, L.N. and C.H. Conaway. 1961. Dye excretion as a method for determination of small mammal home range. Amer. Midland Nat. 66:128-137.

Brown, P., and G.B. Stratton (Eds.). 1963. World list of scientific periodicals published in the years 1900-1960. 4th ed. Butterworths, London. 3 vol. [Kept up to date by annual supplements which are taken from the British Union Catalogue of Periodicals.]

Brunetti, O.A. 1965. The use of paper chromatography in wildlife law enforcement. Proc. 45th Ann. Conf. West. Assoc. of State Game and Fish Commissioners, 6 p.

Bryan, J.H.D. 1966. A multi-purpose information retrieval system based on edge-notched cards. BioScience 16(6):402-407.

Bryant, M.M. 1943. Area determination with modified acreage grid. J. Forestry 41:764-765.

Bryant, Margaret M. 1962. Current American usage. Funk and Wagnalls Co., New York. 290 p.

Buchanan, D.C., A. Nakao, and G. Edwards. 1953. Carbon isotope effects in biological systems. Science 117:541-545.

Buckley, J.L., and W.L. Libby. 1955. Growth rates and age determination in Alaskan beaver. Trans. N. Amer. Wildl. Conf. 20:495-507.

Buckner, C.H. 1964. Preliminary trials of a camera recording device for the study of small mammals. Canad. Field Naturalist 78(2):77-79.

Buckner, C.H. 1964. Metabolism, food capacity, and feeding behavior in four species of shrews. Canad. J. Zool. 42:259-279.

Buechner, H.K. 1950. Life history, ecology, and range use of the pronghorned antelope in Trans-Pecos, Texas. Amer. Midland Naturalist 43:257-354.

Buechner, H.K. 1950. Use of the helicopter in wildlife work. J. Wildl. Mgmt. 14(4):472-473.

Buechner, H.K., A.M. Harthoorn, and J.A. Lock. 1960. Recent advances in field immobilization of large mammals with drugs. Trans. N. Amer. Wildl. and Nat. Resources Conf. 25:415-422.

Bump, G. 1950. Wildlife habitat changes in the Connecticut Hill Game Management Area. Cornell Univ. Agri. Exp. Sta. Memoir 289, Ithaca, N.Y. 75 p.

Bump, G., R.W. Darrow, F.C. Edminister, and W.F. Crissey. 1947. The ruffed grouse: life history, propagation, management. N.Y. State Cons. Dept., Albany. 915 p.

Bureau of Navy Personnel. 1964. Fundamentals of electronics, Vol.1, Basic electricity. NAVPERS 93400 - 1/July. U.S. Supt. Doc., Washington, D.C.

Burkholder, B.L. 1955. Control of small predators. U.S. Fish and Wildl. Ser. Circ. 33, Washington, D.C. 8 p.

Burleigh, T.D. 1958. Georgia birds. Univ. Oklahoma Press, Norman. 746 pp.

Burns, M. 1952. The genetics of the dog. Commonwealth Bureau of Animal Breeding and Genetics, Tech. Commun. No.9. Cummingham and Sons, Edinburg. 122 p.

Burt, W.H. 1948. The mammals of Michigan. rev. ed. Univ. Michigan Press, Ann Arbor. 288 p.

Burt, W.H. 1957. Mammals of the Great Lakes region. Univ. Michigan Press, Ann Arbor, 246 p.

Burt, W.H. and R.P. Grossenheider. 1964. A field guide to the mammals. 2nd ed. Houghton Mifflin, Boston, Mass. 284 p.

Burton, M. 1962. Systematic dictionary of mammals of the world. Thomas Y. Crowell, New York. 307 p.

Buss, I.O. 1946. Wisconsin pheasant populations. Wisc. Cons. Dept. Pub. 326, Madison. 184 p.

Buss, I.O. and C.V. Swanson. 1950. Some effects of weather on pheasant reproduction in southeastern Washington. Trans. N. Amer. Wildl. Conf. 15:364-378.

Bussman, J. 1933. Experiments with the terragraph on the activities of nesting birds. Bird-banding 4:33-40.

Buttress, F.A. 1966. World list of abbreviations. 3rd ed. Leonard Hill Ltd., London. 186 p.

C

Caceres, C.A. (Ed.). 1965. Biomedical telemetry. Academic Press, New York. 382 p.

Caceres, C.A., and J.K. Cooper. 1965. Radiotelemetry: A clinical perspective, p. 85-105. In C.A. Caceres, (Ed.), Biomedical telemetry. Academic Press, N.Y.

Cagle, F.R. 1960. Increase of biological serials—a destructive trend? AIBS Bull. 10(1):13-14.

Cahalane, V.H. 1938. The annual northern Yellowstone elk herd count. Trans. N. Amer. Wildl. Conf. 3:388-389.

Cahalane, V.H. 1947. Mammals of North America. Macmillan Co., New York. 682 p.

Caillouet, C.W., Jr. 1960. Nutrient content of some seeds and fruits utilized as food by wildlife in Louisiana. M.S. Thesis, La. State Univ. 72 p.

Caldwell, J.A. 1963. An investigation of raccoons in north central Florida. M.S. Thesis. Univ. of Fla., Gainesville.

Calhoun, J.B. (Ed.) 1956. 1951 annual report—North American census of small mammals; Population dynamics of vertebrates, Compilations of research data. Administrative pub. Release No. 5, U.S. Dept. H.E. and W., Inst. Mental Health, Bethesda 4, Md.

Calkins, H.A., and J.B. Yule. 1935. The Abney level handbook. U.S. Forest Service, Washington. 44 p.

Camp, R.R. (Ed.) 1949. The hunter's encyclopedia. The Stackpole and Heck Co., Harrisburg. 52 p.

Campbell, D.L. 1960. A colored leg strip for marking birds. J. Wildl. Mgmt. 24:431.

Campbell, W.G. 1954. Form and style in thesis writing. Houghton Mifflin, Boston, Mass. 114 p.

Carlson, E.C. 1943. Unusual pheasants nests from Minnesota. Flicker 15: 29-31.

Carney, S.M. 1964. Preliminary keys to waterfowl age and age and sex identification by means of wing plumage. U.S. Fish and Wildl. Ser. Spec. Rep. (Wildl.) No. 82, vi + 47 p.

Carney, S.M., and A.D. Geis. 1960. Mallard age and sex determination from wings. J. Wildl. Mgmt. 24: 372-381.

Carney, S.M., and G.A. Petrides. 1957. Analysis of variation among participants in pheasant cockcrowing censuses. J. Wildl. Mgmt. 21:392-397.

Carney, S.M. and G. Smart. 1964. Comparisons between hunters' reports and spy-blind observations during the 1961-62, 1962-63, and 1963-64 hunting seasons. USDI, Bureau of Sport Fisheries and Wildlife, Migratory Bird Population Station, Laurel, Md. Admst. Rpt. No. 44. 10 p.

Carpenter, J.R. 1938. An ecological glossary. Univ. Oklahoma Press, Norman. 306 p.

Carpovich, E.A. 1960. Russian-English biological and medical dictionary. 2nd ed. Technical Dictionaries, New York. 400 p.

Carr, A.F., Jr. 1939. Notes on escape behavior in the Florida marsh rabbit. J. Mammal. 20(3):322-325.

Carson, J.D. 1961. Epiphyseal cartilage as an age indicator in fox and gray squirrels. J. Wildl. Mgmt. 25: 90-93.

Casey, R.S. et al. 1958. Punched cards: their applications to science and industry. 2nd ed. Reinhold, New York. 697 p.

Casteel, D.A. 1967. Timing of ovulation and implantation in the cottontail rabbit. J. Wildl. Mgmt. 31(1):194-197.

Casto, W., and C.C. Presnall. 1944. Comparison of coyote trapping methods. J. Wildl. Mgmt. 8:65-70.

Caswell, E.B. 1954. A method for sexing blue grouse. J. Wildl. Mgmt. 18: 139.

Caws, S.H., F.W. Coultas, J. Hewitt, and E.W. Houghton. 1958. Geometrical cross-section polar diagrams of birds. Ministry of Aviation (U.K.). Unpubl. MS.

Chambers, R.E., and P.F. English. 1958. Modifications of ruffed grouse traps. J. Wildl. Mgmt. 22:200-202.

Chamrad, A.D. and T.W. Box. 1964. A point frame for sampling rumen contents. J. Wildl. Mgmt. 28(3):473-477.

Chandler, A.C. 1916. A study of the structure of feathers, with reference to their taxonomic significance. Univ. Calif. Publ. Zool., Univ. Calif. Press, Berkeley. 13:243-446.

Chapin, J.P. 1946. The preparation of birds for study. Amer. Mus. of Nat. Hist. Sci. Guide No. 58. N.Y. 48 p.

Chapman, D.G. 1948. A mathematical study of confidence limits of salmon populations calculated from sample tag ratios. Internatl. Pacific Salmon Fish. Comm. Bull. 2:69-85.

Chapman, D.G. 1951. Some properties of the hypergeometric distribution with application to zoological sample censuses. Univ. Calif. Pub. Stat. 1: 131-160.

Chapman, D.G. 1954. The estimation of biological populations. Ann. Math. Stat. 25(1):1-15.

Chapman, D.G. 1955. Population estimation based on change of composition caused by a selective removal. Biometrika 42:279-290.

Chapman, D.G. 1961. Population dynamics of the Alaska fur seal herd. Trans. N. Amer. Wildl. Conf. 26: 356-369.

Chapman, D.G. 1962. Problems in the analysis of tagging experiments, with particular reference to fur seal experiments. Paper presented to the session "Sampling for Zoologists,"

AAAS Meeting, Philadelphia, Pa., Dec. 30.

Chapman, D.G. 1965. The estimation of mortality and recruitment from a single-tagging experiment. Biometrics 21(3):529-542.

Chapman, D.G., and A.M. Johnson. 1968. Estimation of fur seal pup populations by randomized sampling. J. Wildl. Mgmt.

Chapman, D.G., and C.O. Junge, Jr. 1956. The estimation of the size of a stratified animal population. Ann. Math. Stat. 27:375-389.

Chapman, D.G., and G.I. Murphy. 1965. Estimates of mortality and population from survey-removal records. Biometric Soc. 21(4):921-935.

Chapman, D.G., and W.S. Overton. 1966. Estimating and testing differences between population levels by the Schnabel estimation method. J. Wildl. Mgmt. 30(1):173-180.

Chapman, D.G., and D.S. Robson. 1960. The analysis of a catch curve. Biometrics 16(3):354-368.

Chapman, F.M. 1912. Color key to North American birds with bibliographical appendix. D. Appleton and Co., New York. 356 p.

Chattin, J.E. 1952. Appraisal of California waterfowl concentrations by aerial photography. Trans. N. Amer. Wildl. Conf. 17:421-426.

Cheatum, E.L. 1949. Bone marrow as an index of malnutrition in deer. N.Y. Conservationist 3:19-22.

Chesness, R.A. 1966. Pheasant aging guide. Wildl. Soc. News. No. 103: 30.

Chitty, D. 1937. A ringing technique for small mammals. J. Animal Ecol. 6: 36-53.

Chitty, D., and M. Shorten. 1946. Techniques for the study of the Norway rat (Rattus norvegicus). J. Mammal. 27:63-78.

Clapp, Jane. 1962. Museum publications: a classified list and index of books, pamphlets and other monographs, and of special reprints. Part II. Publications in biological and earth sciences. Scarecrow Press, New York. 610 p.

Clark, G.L. 1961. The encyclopedia of microscopy. Reinhold, New York. 693 p.

Clark, W. 1946. Photography by infrared; its principles and applications. John Wiley and Sons. New York. 472 p.

Clark, W.K. 1957. Seasonal foods of the Kodiak bear. Trans. N. Amer. Wildl. Conf. 22:145-151.

Clover, M.R. 1954. A portable deer trap and catch-net. Calif. Fish and Game 40:367-373.

Clover, M.R. 1956. Single-gate deer trap. Calif. Fish and Game 42:199-201.

Cochran, G.A., and H.J. Stains. 1961. Deposition and decomposition of fecal pellets by cottontails. J. Wildl. Mgmt. 25:432-435.

Cochran, W.G. 1963. Sampling techniques. (2nd ed.) John Wiley and Sons, Inc., N.Y. xvii + 413 p.

Cochran, W.W. 1966. Some notes on the design of a directional loop antenna for radio-tracking wildlife. AIBS Information Module. 4 p.

Cochran, W.W. 1967. 145-160 mc wildlife beacon transmitter. AIBS Information Module M15. (mimeo).

Cochran, W.W., R.R. Graber, and G.G. Montgomery. 1967. Migratory flights of Hylocichla thrushes in spring: a radio telemetry study. The Living Bird (In press).

Cochran, W.W., and R.D. Lord, Jr. 1963. A radio-tracking system for wild animals. J. Wildl. Mgmt. 27(1): 9-24.

Cochran, W.W., D.W. Warner, J.R.

558

Tester, and V.B. Kuechle. 1965. Automatic radio-tracking system for monitoring animal movements. BioScience 15(2):98-100.

Cockrum, E.L. 1952. Mammals of Kansas. Univ. Kans. Mus. Nat. Hist. Pubs. 7(1):1-303.

Cockrum, E.L. 1960. Recent mammals of Arizona. Univ. Arizona Press, Tucson. 284 p.

Cockrum, E.L. 1962. Introduction to mammalogy. Ronald Press, New York. 455 p.

Coffin, D.L. 1953. Manual of veterinary clinical pathology. 3rd ed. Comstock. Ithaca, N.Y. 322 p.

Cohen, A., H.S. Peters, and L.E. Foote. 1960. Calling behavior of mourning doves in two Midwest life zones. J. Wildl. Mgmt. 24:203-212.

Coil, W.H., and D.V. Weatherbee. 1959. Observations on the cloacal gland of the Eurasian quail *Coturnix coturnix*, Ohio J. Sci. 59:268-270.

Cole, G.F. 1960. Key browse survey method. Proc. Ann. Conf. Western Assoc. State Game and Fish Comm. 39:181-186.

Cole, L.C. 1957. Sketches of general and comparative demography. *In* Population Studies: Animal ecology and demography. Cold Spring Harbor Symposia in Quantitative Biology, Vol. 30, The Biol. Laboratory, Cold Spring Harbor, Long Island, N.Y.

Collias, N.E. 1963. A spectrographic analysis of the vocal repertoire of the African village weaverbird. Condor 65(6):517-527.

Collias, N. and M. Joos. 1953. The spectrographic analysis of sound signals of the domestic fowl. Behavior 5:175-188.

Collier, E. 1957. Revolutionary new trap. Outdoor Life, Sept. 1957, p. 38-41, 68, 80 and Oct. 1957, p. 70-73, 80, 82.

Collins, B.D. 1954. A nesting study of the Canada goose at Tule Lake and Lower Klamath National Wildlife Refuges. Proc. Ann. Conf. Western Assn. State Game and Fish Comm. 33:172-176.

Collins, H.H., Jr. 1959. Complete field guide to American wildlife: east, central and north. Harper, New York. 683 p.

Colwell, R.N. 1964. Aerial photograph - A valuable sensor for the scientist. Amer. Scientist 52(1):17-49.

Conference of Biological Editors. Committee on Form and Style. 1964. Style manual for biological journals. 2nd ed. Amer. Inst. Biol. Sci., Washington, D.C. 20016. 117 p.

Committee on Wildlife Terminology. 1957. Glossary of wildlife terms. J. Wildl. Mgmt. 21(3):375.

Conn, H.J. 1961. Biological stains. 7th ed. Williams and Wilkins Co., Baltimore, Md. 335 p.

Considine, D.M. and S.D. Ross. 1964. Handbook of applied instrumentation. McGraw-Hill Book Co. N.Y. 17 Chapters, (various paging).

Cooch, G. 1953. Techniques for mass capture of flightless blue and lesser snow geese. J. Wildl. Mgmt. 17:460-465.

Cook, A.H. 1943. A technique for marking mammals. J. Mammal. 24:45-47.

Cooley, M.E. 1948. Improved toe-tag for marking fox squirrels. J. Wildl. Mgmt. 12:213.

Cooperative State Research Service, USDA. 1965. Professional workers in state agricultural experiment stations and other cooperating state institutions. 1965-66. U.S. Dep. Agr. Handbook no. 305. 276 p.

Corbet, G.B. 1966. The terrestrial mammals of western Europe. Dufour Editions. Philadelphia, Pa. 264 p.

Corbett, A.S., C.B. Williams, and R.A. Fisher. 1943. The relation between the number of species and the number of individuals in a random sample of an animal population. J. Animal Ecol. 12:42-58.

Corbin, J.B. 1965. An index of state geological survey publications. Scarecrow Press, New York. 667 p.

Cornsweet, T.N. 1963. The design of electric circuits in the behavioral sciences. John Wiley and Sons. New York. xii + 329 p.

Cottam, C. 1936. Economic ornithology and the correlation of laboratory and field methods. USDA. Wildl. Res. and Mgmt. Leaf. B-30, Washington, D.C. 13 p.

Couey, F.M. 1949. Review and evaluation of big game trapping techniques. Proc. Ann. Conf. Western Assoc. State Game and Fish Comm. 29:110-116.

Coulombre, A.J. 1966. Embryology. BioScience 16(5):368-370.

Coultas, F.W., and E.W. Houghton. 1959. The complex dielectric constant of a feather sample at X and S-bands. Ministry of Aviation (U.K.). Unpubl. MS.

Coulter, M.W. 1958. A new waterfowl nest trap. Bird-Banding 29:236-241.

Coutourier, M.A.J. 1954. L'ours Brun, *Ursus aretos* L. Dr. M. Coutourier. 45, Rue Thiers, Grenoble, France. 904 p.

Cowan, I. McT. 1936. Distribution and variation in deer (genus *Odocoileus*) of the Pacific coastal region of North America. Calif. Fish and Game 22: 155-246.

Cowan, I. McT. 1940. Distribution and variation in the native sheep of North America. Amer. Midland Naturalist 24:505-580.

Cowan, I. McT., A.J. Wood, and H.C. Nordan. 1962. Studies in the tranquilization and immobilization of deer *(Odocoileus)*. Can. J. Compar. Med., Vet. Sci. 26(3):57-61.

Cowan, J. 1959. 'Pre-fab' wire mesh cones gives doves better nest than they can build themselves. Outdoor Calif. 20(1):10-11.

Cowardin, L.M. and J.E. Ashe. 1965. An automatic camera device for measuring waterfowl use. J. Wildl. Mgmt. 29(3):636-640.

Cowdry, E.V. 1952. Laboratory technique in biology and medicine. 3rd ed. Williams and Wilkins Co., Baltimore, Md. 382 p.

Cox, E.L. 1949. Mathematical bases of experimental sampling for estimation of size of certain biological populations. Va. Agr. Exp. Sta., Blacksburg. 42 p.

Crabb, W.D. 1941. A technique for trapping and tagging spotted skunks. J. Wildl. Mgmt. 5:371-374.

Crabb, W.D. 1941. Civits and rat killers. Farm Sci. Reporter. (Iowa Farm Sci.) 2:12-13.

Crabb, W.D. 1948. The ecology and management of the prairie spotted skunk in Iowa. Ecol. Monogr. 18: 202-232.

Craighead, F.C., Jr., and J.J. Craighead. 1949. Nesting Canada geese on the Upper Snake River. J. Wildl. Mgmt. 13:51-64.

Craighead, F.C., Jr., and J.J. Craighead. 1965. Tracking grizzly bears. BioScience 15(2):88-92.

Craighead, J.J., M. Hornocker, W. Woodgerd, and F.C. Craighead, Jr. 1960. Trapping, immobilizing, and color-marking grizzly bears. Trans. N. Amer. Wildl. Conf. 25:347-363.

Craighead, J.J., and D.S. Stockstad. 1956. A colored neckband for marking birds. J. Wildl. Mgmt. 20:331-332.

Craighead, J.J., and D.S. Stockstad.

1960. Color marker for big game. J. Wildl. Mgmt. 24:435-438.

Crispens, C.G., Jr. 1960. Quails and partridges of North America; a bibliography. Univ. Washington Publications in Biology. 20:1-125.

Critcher, T.S. and W.S. Overton. 1960. Preliminary evaluation of the controlled road sight count as an index to mourning dove population levels. Proc. 14 Ann. Conf. Southeastern Assn. Game and Fish Commissioners, Biloxi, Miss. October.

Crissey, W.F. 1953. The use of a dictating machine to record aerial observations. J. Wildl. Mgmt. 17:539-540.

Crockford, J.A., F.A. Hayes, J.H. Jenkins, and S.D. Feurt. 1957. Field application of nicotine salicylate for capturing deer. Trans. N. Amer. Wildl. Conf. 22:579-583.

Crockford, J.A., F.A. Hayes, J.H. Jenkins, and S.D. Feurt. 1957. Nicotine salicylate for capturing deer. J. Wildl. Mgmt. 21:213-220.

Cronemiller, F.P., and S.A. Fisher. 1946. Censusing a deer herd by sampling methods. Trans. N. Amer. Wildl. Conf. 11:349-356.

Crow, A.B. 1965. Theses and dissertations in forestry, game management, fisheries, and related subjects at Louisiana State University. LSU Forestry Notes no. 64. [This list covers the period January 1964 to August 1965. It was preceded by three earlier lists (nos. 22, 45 and 54) covering the period 1926 to August 1963.]

Crunden, C.W. 1963. Age and sex of sage grouse from wings. J. Wildl. Mgmt. 27(4):846-849.

Cummings, G.E., and O.H. Hewitt. 1964. Capturing waterfowl and marsh birds at night with light and sound. J. Wildl. Mgmt. 28(1):120-126.

Cunningham, E.R. 1962. A study of the eastern raccoon. *Procyon lotor* L. on the Atomic Energy Commission

Savannah River Plant. M.S. Thesis. Univ. of Ga., Athens.

Cushwa, C.T. 1968. Fire: a summary of literature in the United States from the mid-1920's to 1966. USDA, U.S. Forest Service, Southeastern Forest Experiment Sta., Ashville, N.C. ii+ 117.

D

Dahlgren, R.B., C.M. Twedt, and C.G. Trautman. 1965. Lens weights of ring-necked pheasants. J. Wildl. Mgmt. 29(1):212-214.

Dahm, P.A. 1957. Uses of radioisotopes in pesticide research. *In* R.L. Metcalf (Ed.), Advances in pest control research. Intersci. Pub. Inc., New York. 1:1-514.

Dalke, P.D. 1935. Droppings analysis as an indication of pheasant food habits. Proc. Am. Game Conf. 22: 387-391.

Dalke, P.D. 1937. The cover map in wildlife management. J. Wildl. Mgmt. 1:100-106.

Dalke, P.D. 1941. The use and availability of the more common winter deer browse plants in the Missouri Ozarks. Trans. N. Amer. Wildl. Conf. 6:155-160.

Dalke, P.D. 1942. The cottontail rabbits in Connecticut. Conn. Geol. and Nat. Hist. Survey Bull. 65:47.

Dalke, P.D., W.K. Clark, Jr., and L.J. Korschgen. 1942. Food habit trends of the wild turkey in Missouri as determined by dropping analysis. J. Wildl. Mgmt. 6:237-243.

Darroch, J.N. 1958. The multiple-recapture census. I. Estimation of a closed population. Biometrika 45: 343-359.

Darroch, J.N. 1959. The multiple-recapture census. II. Estimation when there is immigration or death. Biometrika 46:336-351.

Dane, B., C. Walcott and W.H. Drury.

560

1959. The form and duration of the display actions of the goldeneye *(Bucephala clangula)*. Behavior 14: 265-281.

Darling, F. F. 1937. A herd of red deer. Oxford University Press, London. 215 p.

Darlington, P. J. 1957. Zoogeography: the geographical distribution of animals. Wiley, New York. 675 p.

Dasmann, R. F. 1952. Methods for estimating deer populations from kill data. Calif. Fish and Game 38:225-233.

Dasmann, R. F. 1964. Wildlife biology. Wiley, New York. 231 p.

Dasmann, R. F., and R. D. Taber. 1955. A comparison of four deer census methods. Calif. Fish and Game 41: 225-228.

Dasmann, R. F. and R. D. Taber. 1956. Determining structure in Columbian black-tailed deer populations. J. Wildl. Mgmt. 20:78-83.

Daubenmire, R. 1952. Forest vegetation of northern Idaho and adjacent Washington, and its bearing on concepts of vegetation classification. Ecol. Monogr. 22:301-330.

Davenport, L. B., Jr. 1953. Agricultural depredation by the black bear in Virginia. J. Wildl. Mgmt. 17:331-340.

Davenport, L. A., W. Shapton, and W. C. Gower. 1944. A study of the carrying capacity of deer yards as determined by browse plots. Trans. N. Amer. Wildl. Conf. 9:144-149.

Davis, D. E. 1942. A new census method applied to Cuban birds. Ecology 23: 370-376.

Davis, D. E. 1954. A simple method for obtaining attentive data. Auk 71(3): 331-332.

Davis, D. E. 1956. Manual for analysis of rodent populations. Edwards Bros., Ann Arbor, Mich. 82 p.

Davis, D. E. 1964. Evaluation of characters for determining age in woodchucks. J. Wildl. Mgmt. 28(1):9-14.

Davis, D. E., and W. T. Fales. 1949. The distribution of rats in Baltimore, Maryland. Am. J. Hyg. 49:247-254.

Davis, D. E. and C. Zippin. 1954. Planning wildlife experiments involving percentages. J. Wildl. Mgmt. 18(2): 70-78.

Davis, H. P. (Ed.) 1956. Modern dog encyclopedia. Stockpole Co., Harrisburg, Pa. 638 p.

Davis, H. P. (Ed.). 1962. Hunting dogs and their uses. Collier Books, New York. 125 p.

Davis, J. 1965. The "singing male" method of censusing birds: a warning. Condor 67(1):86-87.

Davis, J. M. 1966. Uses of airphotos for rural and urban planning. USDA Agric. Handbook No. 315. iv+39 p.

Davis, J. R. 1959. A preliminary progress report on nest predation as a limiting factor in wild turkey populations. Proc. 1st Nat. Wild Turkey Mgmt. Symp., Memphis, Tenn. S. E. Sect. of the Wildl. Soc. 200 p.

Davis, L. I. 1964. Biological acoustics and the use of the sound spectrograph. Southwestern Nat. 9(3):118-145.

Davis, W. S. 1964. Graphic representation of confidence intervals for Petersen population estimates. Trans. Amer. Fish. Soc. 93:227-232.

Davison, V. E. 1940. A field method of analyzing game bird foods. J. Wildl. Mgmt. 4:105-116.

Davison, V. E. 1962. Taste, not color, draws birds to berries and seeds. Audubon Mag., 64(6):346-350.

Davison, V. E. 1963. Mourning doves' selection of foods. J. Wildl. Mgmt. 27(3):373-383.

Davison, V. E. 1964. Selection of foods by gray squirrels. J. Wildl. Mgmt. 28(2):346-352.

Davison, V. E., L. M. Dickerson, K. Graetz, W. W. Neely, and L. Roof. 1955. Measuring the yield and availability of game bird foods. J. Wildl. Mgmt. 19:302-308.

Davison, V. E., and K. E. Graetz. 1957. Managing habitat for white-tailed deer and wild turkeys. Trans. N. Amer. Wildl. Conf. 22:412-424.

Davison, V. E., and R. A. Grizzell. 1961. Choice foods that attract birds in winter in the southeast. Audubon Mag. 63:48-54.

Davison, V. E., and R. A. Grizzell. 1961. Choice food of birds—summer and fall. Audubon Mag. 63:162-167, 180.

Davison, V. E., and W. H. Hamor. 1960. A system for classifying plant food of birds. J. Wildl. Mgmt. 24:307-313.

Dawson, W. L. 1923. The birds of California. South Moulton Co. San Diego, Calif. 4 vol.

Dayton, W. A. 1950. Glossary of botanical terms commonly used in range research. Rev. USDA. Misc. Pub. 110. 40 p.

Dean, F. C., and G. A. Galloway. 1965. A Fortran program for population study with minimal computer training. J. Wildl. Mgmt. 29:892-894.

Dearborn, N. 1939. Sections aid in identifying hair. J. Mammal. 20: 346-348.

Decino, T. J., D. J. Cunningham, and E. W. Schafer. 1966. Toxicity of DRC-1339 to starlings. J. Wildl. Mgmt. 30:249-253.

Deevey, E. S., Jr. 1947. Life tables for natural populations of animals. The Quarterly Review of Biology 22:283-314. Reprinted *In* W. E. Hazen 1964. Readings in population and community ecology. E. B. Saunders Co., Philadelphia and London.

Deignan, H.G. 1961. Type specimens of birds in the United States National Museum. U.S. Nat. Mus. Bull. no. 221. 718 p.

Delacour, J. 1951. The pheasants of the world. Charles Scribner's Sons, New York. 347 p.

Dell, J. 1957. Toe clipping varying hares for track identification. N.Y. Fish and Game J. 4:61-68.

Dellinger, G. P. 1954. Breeding season, productivity and population trends of raccoon in Missouri. M. A. Thesis, Univ. of Missouri, Columbia.

DeLury, D.B. 1947. On the estimation of biological populations. Biometrics 3:145-167.

DeLury, D.B. 1951. On the planning of experiments for the estimation of fish populations. J. Fish. Res. Board 8:281-307.

DeLury, D. B. 1954. On the assumptions underlying estimates of mobile populations, p. 287-299. In O. Kempthorne (Ed.), Statistics and mathematics in biology. Iowa State College Press, Ames.

Deming, O. V. 1952. Tooth development of the Nelson bighorn sheep. Calif. Fish and Game 28:523-529.

Deming, W.E. 1964. Statistical adjustment of data. Dover Pub. Inc., New York. 261 p.

DeMoisy, R.G. 1949. Forest surveying. Pt. 1. The use of steel tape, compass, Abney level, and aneroid barometer in forest surveying and mapping. O.S.C. Cooperative Assoc., Corvallis, Oregon. 123 p.

Department of Northern Affairs and National Resources. 1957-59. Translations of Russian game reports. Ottawa, Canada, Queen's Printer. vol. 1-6.

De Roon, A.C. (Comp.). 1958. International directory of specialists in plant taxonomy with a census of their current interests. Regnum Vegetabile vol. 13. Utrecht. 266 p.

DeVos, A., and F.W. Anderka. 1964. A transmitter-receiver unit for microclimatic data. Ecology 45(1):171-172.

Devred, R. F.E. 1963. Index of agricultural research institutions in Europe. Food and Agricultural Organisations of the United Nations, Rome, Italy. v.p.

DeVries, L. 1959. German-English science dictionary for students in chemistry, physics, biology, agriculture, and related sciences. 3rd ed. McGraw-Hill, New York. 592 p.

DeVries, L. 1962. French-English science dictionary for students in agricultural, biological and physical sciences. 3rd ed. McGraw-Hill, New York. 655 p.

Dewhurst, D. J. 1966. Physical instrumentation in medicine and biology. Pergamon Press, Oxford. 205 p.

Dewolfe, Barbara B. 1967. Sound spectrographic analysis of song patterns in Gambel's sparrows (Zonotrichia leucophrys gambelii) Arctic Inst. of N. Amer. Grant-in-aid M49. Progress Report.

Dice, L.R. 1932. Preparation of scientific specimens of mammals in the field. Univ. of Mich. Mus. Zool. Circ. 1, Ann Arbor.

Dice, L.R. 1948. Relationship between frequency index and population density. Ecology 29:389-391.

Dice, L.R. 1952. Natural communities. Univ. Mich. Press, Ann Arbor, 547 p.

Dice, L.R. 1961. Laboratory instruments for measuring the behavior of shy or nocturnal small mammals. J. Mammal. 42(2):159-166.

Diem, K.L. 1954. Use of a deer call as a means of locating deer fawns. J. Wildl. Mgmt. 18(4):537-538.

Diem, K. L. and K. H. Lu. 1960. Factors influencing waterfowl censuses in the parklands, Alberta, Canada. J. Wildl. Mgmt. 24:113-133.

Dietz, D.R. 1965. Deer nutrition research and its application to game-range management. Trans. N. Amer. Wildl. and Nat. Res. Conf. 30:274-285.

Dietz, D.R., and J.R. Tigner. 1968. Evaluation of two mammal repellents applied to browse species in the Black Hills. J. Wildl. Mgmt. 32: 109-114.

Dietz, D.R., R.H. Udall and L.E. Yeager. 1962. Chemical composition and digestibility by mule deer of selected forage species, Cache la Poudre range, Colorado. Colo. Dep. Game and Fish Tech. Publ. 14, 89 p.

Dietz, D.R., R.H. Udall and L.E. Yeager. 1962. Differential digestibility of nutrients in bitterbrush, mountain mahogany, and sagebrush by deer. Proc. Nat. White-tailed Deer Disease Symp. 1:29-36, 39-50.

Dill, H.H., and W.H. Thornsberry. 1950. A cannon-projected net trap for capturing waterfowl. J. Wildl. Mgmt. 14:132-137.

Dingle, R.W. 1956. Pocket gophers as a cause of mortality in eastern Washington pine plantations. J. For. 54:832-835.

Dirschl, H.J. 1962. Sieve mesh size related to analysis of antelope rumen contents. J. Wildl. Mgmt. 26:327-328.

Dixon, J.S. 1934. A study of the life history and food habits of mule deer in California. Calif. Fish and Game 20:181-282, 315-354.

Dodge, W.E., and M.B. Church. 1965. Construction of transmitters for radio-tracking hares and mountain beavers. Northwest Sci. 39(3):118-122.

Dodge, W.E. and D.P. Snyder. 1960. An automatic camera device for recording wildlife activity. J. Wildl. Mgmt. 24(3):341-344.

562

Domay, F. 1964. Handbuch der Deutschen wissenschaftlichen gesellschaften. Franz Steiner Verlag, Wiesbaden. 751 p.

Doremus, H. M. 1964. Livetrapping the short-tailed shrew, *Blarina brevicauda*. J. Mammal. 45(1):144-146.

Dorn, H. F. 1954. Some problems in sampling human populations. p. 241-250. *In* O. Kempthorne (Ed.), Statistics and mathematics in biology, Iowa State College Press, Ames.

Dorney, R. S., and F. V. Holzer. 1957. Spring aging methods for ruffed grouse cocks. J. Wildl. Mgmt. 21:268-274.

Dorney, R. S., D. R. Thompson, J. B. Hale, and R. F. Wendt. 1958. An evaluation of ruffed grouse drumming counts. J. Wildl. Mgmt. 22:35-40.

Doutt, J. K. 1940. Weighing large mammals in the field. J. Mammal. 21(1):63-65.

Dow, J. S. 1943. A study of nesting Canada geese in Honey Lake Valley, California. Calif. Fish and Game 29:3-18.

Dow, S. A. 1952. Antelope aging studies in Montana. Proc. Ann. Conf. Western Assoc. State Game and Fish Comm. 32:220-224.

Dow, S. A., and P. L. Wright. 1962. Changes in mandibular dentition associated with age in pronghorn antelope. J. Wildl. Mgmt. 26:1-18.

Dowden, P. B., H. A. Jaynes, and V. M. Carolin. 1953. The role of birds in a spruce budworm outbreak in Maine. J. Econ. Entomol. 46:307-312.

Dowdeswell, W. H. 1959. Practical animal-ecology. Methnen and Co., London. 316 p.

Downey, J. C. 1966. Insects. BioScience 16(2):134-135.

Downing, R. L., and C. M. Marshall.

1959. A new plastic tape marker for birds and mammals. J. Wildl. Mgmt. 23:223-224.

Dozier, H. L. 1942. Identification of sex in live muskrats. J. Wildl. Mgmt. 6:292-293.

Driscoll, R. S. 1963. Sprouting bitterbrush in central Oregon. Ecology 44(4):820-821.

Driver, E. C. 1949. Mammal remains in owl pellets. Amer. Midland Naturalist 41:139-142.

Dubinin, V. B. 1960. Conservation of natural resources and the establishment of reserves in the USSR. Bulletin no. 2. [Transl. from Russian]. Israel Program for Scientific Translations, Jerusalem. 143 p.

Dumbleton, C. W. 1964. Russian-English biological dictionary. Oliver and Boyd, Edinburgh. 512 p.

Dunmire, W. W. 1955. Sex dimorphism in the pelvis of rodents. J. Mammal. 36:356-361.

Dunnet, G. M. 1957. A test of the recapture method of estimating the number of rabbits, *Oryctolagus cuniculus* (L.), in a warren. CSIRO Wildl. Res. 2:90-100.

Durant, A. J. 1953. Removing the vocal cords of fowl. J. Am. Vet. Med. Assoc. 122:14-17.

Dusi, J. L. 1949. Methods for the determination of food habits by plant microtechniques and histology and their application to cottontail rabbit food habits. J. Wildl. Mgmt. 13:295-298.

Dyer, M. I. 1964. Radar and morphometric studies on transient red-winged blackbird populations. Ph.D. Thesis, Univ. Minn. 156 p.

Dyer, M. I. 1966. Photo-electric cell technique for analyzing radar film. J. Wildl. Mgmt. 31:484-491.

Dziuk, H. E., B. A. Fashingbauer and

J. M. Idstrom. 1963. Ruminoreticular pressure patterns in fistulated white-tailed deer. Amer. J. Veterinary Res. 24:772-783.

Dzubin, A. 1959. Growth and plumage development of wild-trapped juvenile canvasback. J. Wildl. Mgmt. 23:279-290.

E

Eadie, W. R., and W. J. Hamilton, Jr. 1958. Reproduction in the fisher in New York. N. Y. Fish and Game J. 5:77-83.

Eakin, Mary L. 1958. Checklist of forestry items in a working library, 1958. J. For. 56(8):586-591. [A supplement was prepared by E. S. Johnson in the same journal for 1962 as 60(2):91-93.]

Ealey, E. H. M., and G. M. Dunnett. 1956. Plastic collars with patterns of reflective tape for marking nocturnal mammals. CSIRO Wildl. Res. 1:59-62.

Earl, J. P. 1950. Production of mallards on irrigated land in the Sacramento Valley, California. J. Wildl. Mgmt. 20:70-74.

Eastman, D. L. 1968. Special panel, application of the stratified Lincoln index for population estimate of mule deer: Bryant Mountain herd. Ann. Meeting, Oregon Chapt. Wildl. Soc., Newport, Oreg. Feb. 2.

Eastwood, E. 1967. Radar ornithology. Methuen, London.

Eastwood, E., J. D. Bell, and N. R. Phelp. 1959. "Ring angels" over South-East England. Nature 183(4677):1759-1760.

Eastwood, E., G. A. Isted, and G. C. Rider. 1960. Radar "ring angels" and the roosting movements of starlings. Nature 186:112-114.

Eastwood, E., G. A. Isted, and G. C. Rider. 1962. Radar "ring angels" and the roosting behavior of starlings. Proc. Roy. Soc. (London) 156:242-267.

Eastwood, E. and G.C. Rider. 1964. The influence of radio waves upon birds. British Birds 57:445-458.

Eastwood, E., and G.C. Rider. 1965. Some radar measurements of the altitude of bird flight. British Birds 58(10):393-426.

Eastwood, E. and G.C. Rider. 1966. Grouping of nocturnal migrants. Nature 211(5054):1143-1146.

Eberhardt, L. 1957. Some uses of stratified sampling in wildlife investigations. 19th Midwest Wildl. Conf. Rep. No. 2158, (mimeo) Game Div., Mich. Dep. Conser., Lansing, Mich.

Eberhardt, L. 1960. Estimation of vital characteristics of Michigan deer herds. Report 2282 (mimeo), Game Div., Mich. Dep. Conser., Lansing. xiv + 192 p.

Eberhardt, L. 1963. Problems in ecological sampling. Northwest Sci. 37(4):144-154.

Eberhardt, L. 1968. A preliminary appraisal of line transects. J. Wildl. Mgmt. 32:82-88.

Eberhardt, L., and R.I. Blouch. 1955. Analysis of pheasant age ratios. Trans. N. Amer. Wildl. Conf. 20: 357-367.

Eberhardt, L., and R.M. Murray. 1960. Estimating the kill of game animals by licensed hunters. Proc. Social Stat. Sect., Amer. Stat. Assoc. Ann. Meeting.

Eberhardt, L., T.J. Peterle, and R. Schofield. 1963. Problems in a rabbit population study. Wildl. Monogr. No. 10.

Eberhardt, L., and R.C. Van Etten. 1956. Evaluation of the pellet group count as a deer census method. J. Wildl. Mgmt. 20:70-74.

Eddy, S., and A.C. Hodson. 1961. Taxonomic keys to the common animals of the north central states. Burgess Pub. Co., Minneapolis, Minn. 162 p.

Edgar, R.L. 1962. A compact live trap for small mammals. J. Mammal. 43(4):547-550.

Edminster, F.C. 1954. American game birds of field and forest. Charles Scribner's Sons, New York. 490 p.

Edmondson, W.T., (Ed.) 1959. Freshwater biology. 2nd ed. John Wiley, New York. 1248 p.

Edmunson, G.C., Jr., and D.R. Cornelius. 1961. Promising grasses for southern California fuel-breaks. Pacific Southwest Forest and Range Exp. Sta., Berkeley. Misc. Paper No. 58, 13 p.

Edwards, A.L. 1964. Expected values of discrete random variables and elementary statistics. John Wiley and Sons. 146 p.

Edwards, D.K. 1962. Recording animal activity. Science 136:198-199.

Edwards, J., and E.W. Houghton. 1959. Radar echoing area polar diagrams of birds. Nature 184(4692):1059.

Edwards, M.G. 1961. New use of funnel trap for ruffed grouse broods. J. Wildl. Mgmt. 25:89.

Edwards, R.Y. and R.W. Ritcey. 1958. Reproduction in a moose population. J. Wildl. Mgmt. 22(3):261-268.

Edwards, W.R. and L.Eberhardt. 1967. Estimating cottontail abundance from livetrapping data. J. Wildl. Mgmt. 31:87-96.

Einarsen, A.S. 1948. The pronghorn antelope and its management. Wildl. Mgmt. Inst. Washington, D.C. 238 p.

Einarsen, A.S. 1956. Determination of some predatory species by field signs. Oregon State Univ. Monogr. Studies in Zoology no. 10, 24 p.

Eklund, C.R. 1942. Ecological and mortality factors affecting the nesting of the Chinese pheasant in the Willamette Valley, Oregon. J. Wildl. Mgmt. 6:225-230.

Elder, F.C. 1957. Some persistent "ring angels" on high-powered radar. Proc. Weather Radar Conf. 6: 281-290.

Elder, W.H. 1951. The baculum as an age criterion in mink. J. Mammal. 32:43-50.

Elder, W.H., and C.E. Shanks. 1962. Age changes in tooth wear and morphology of the baculum in muskrats. J. Mammal. 43:144-150.

Ellerman, J.R., and T.C.S. Morrison-Scott. 1951. Checklist of palaearctic and Indian mammals, 1758-1946. Trustees of the British Museum, London. 810 p.

Elliot, D.G. 1897. The gallinaceous game birds of North America. Francis P. Harper, New York. 220 p.

Ellis, R.J. 1964. Tracking raccoons by radio. J. Wildl. Mgmt. 28(2):363-368.

Emlen, J.T. 1940. Sex and age ratios in survival of the California quail. J. Wildl. Mgmt. 4:92-99.

Emlen, J.T., Ruth Hine, W.A. Fuller, and P. Alfonso. 1957. Dropping boards for population studies of small mammals. J. Wildl. Mgmt. 21:300-314.

Enders, R.K. 1952. Reproduction in the mink (Mustela vision). Proc. Amer. Phil. Soc. 96:691-755.

Eng, R.L. 1955. A method for obtaining sage grouse age and sex ratios from wings. J. Wildl. Mgmt. 19:267-272.

English, P.F. 1941. Hatchability of pheasant eggs in relation to some known temperatures. J. Wildl. Mgmt. 5:213-215.

Erickson, A.B. 1947. A multiple type rat and mouse holder. J. Wildl. Mgmt. 11:351.

Erickson, A.W. 1957. Techniques for live-trapping and handling black bears. Trans. N. Amer. Wildl. Conf. 22:520-543.

564

Erickson, A.W., D.B. Vessal, C. Carlson, and C.T. Rollings. 1951. Minnesota's most important game bird—the pheasant. Flicker 23:23-49.

Erickson, A.W., and D.B. Siniff. 1963. A statistical evaluation of factors influencing aerial survey results on brown bears. Trans. N. Amer. Wildl. Conf. 28:391-408.

Errington, P.L. 1930. The pellet analysis method of raptor food study. Condor 32:292-296.

Errington, P.L. 1932. Techniques of raptor food habits study. Condor 34: 75-86.

Errington, P.L. 1933. The nesting and life equation of the Wisconsin bobwhite. Wilson Bull. 45:122-132.

Errington, P.L. 1937. Food habits of the red fox in Iowa. Amer. Wildl. 26:5, 6, 13.

Errington, P.L. 1943. An analysis of mink predation upon muskrats in north-central United States. Iowa State A. and M. College Agr. Exp. Sta. Res. Bull. 320:797-924.

Errington, P.L. 1944. Additional studies on tagged young muskrats. J. Wildl. Mgmt. 8:300-306.

Errington, P.L. 1963. Muskrat populations. Iowa State Univ. Press, Ames, Iowa. 665 p.

Errington, P.L., and C.S. Errington. 1937. Experimental tagging of young muskrats for purposes of study. J. Wildl. Mgmt. 1:49-61.

Errington, P.L. and F.N. Hamerstrom, Jr. 1937. The evaluation of nesting losses and juvenile mortality on the ring necked pheasant. J. Wildl. Mgmt. 1:3-20.

Evans, C.D. 1951. A method of color marking young waterfowl. J. Wildl. Mgmt. 15:101-103.

Evans, D.C. 1966. Computer logic and memory. Amer. Sci. 215:75-85.

Evans, F.C., and R. Holdenried. 1943. A population study of the Beechey ground squirrel in central California. J. Mammal. 24:231-260.

Evans, C.D., W.A. Troyer, and C.J. Lensink. 1966. Aerial census of moose by quadrat sampling units. J. Wildl. Mgmt. 30:767-776.

Eygenraam, J.A. On 'the lead' in duck decoys. Trans. Int. Union Game Biol. 4:68-77.

F

Fallon, D. 1965. Eatometer: a device for continuous recording of free-feeding behavior. Science 148:977-978.

Fant, R.J. 1953. A nest recording device. J. Ecol. 22:323-327.

Fant, R.J. 1957. Criteria for aging pheasant embryos. J. Wildl. Mgmt. 21:324-328.

Farmer, D.S. and L.R. Mewaldt. 1953. The recording of diurnal activity patterns in caged birds. Bird-Banding 24(2):55-65.

Fay, F.H. 1960. Technique for trapping small tundra mammals in winter. J. Mammal. 41(1):141-142.

Ferguson, R.B. and J.V. Basile. 1966. Topping stimulates bitterbrush twig growth. J. Wildl. Mgmt. 30(4):839-841.

Fernald, M.L. 1950. Gray's manual of botany. 8th ed. American Book Co., New York. 1632 p.

Fessenden, G.R. 1949. Preservations of agricultural specimens in plastics. USDA. Misc. Pub. 679. 78 p.

Ficken, R.W. and Millicent S. Ficken. 1966. A review of some aspects of avian field ethology. Auk 83(4):637-661.

Finley, R.B., Jr. 1965. Adverse effects on birds of phosphamidon applied to a Montana forest. J. Wildl. Mgmt. 29(3):580-591.

Fisher, A.K. 1894. Hawks and owls from the standpoint of the farmer, p. 215-232. In 1894 Yearbook of Agriculture. U.S. Gov. printing office, Washington, D.C. 608 p.

Fisher, H.I., R.W. Hiatt, and W. Bergeson. 1947. The validity of the roadside census as applied to pheasants. J. Wildl. Mgmt. 11:205-226.

Fisher, R.A. 1956. Statistical methods and scientific inference. Oliver and Boyd, London and Edinburgh. 178 p.

Fisher, R.A., and F. Yates. 1963. Statistical tables for biological, agricultural and medical research. 6th ed. Hafner, Pub. Co., New York. 146 p.

Fitch, H.S. 1948. A study of coyote relationships on cattle range. J. Wildl. Mgmt. 12:73-78.

Fitz, G. 1963. How to measure and score big-game trophies: Boone and Crockett official method; Pope and Young archery method. Outdoor Life, New York. 88 p.

Fitzwater, W.D., Jr. 1943. Color marking of mammals, with special reference to squirrels. J. Wildl. Mgmt. 7:190-192.

Flerov, K.K. 1960. Musk deer and deer. Fauna of USSR: Mammals, vol. 1, no. 2 [Transl. from Russian]. Israel Program for Scientific Translations, Jerusalem. 257 p.

Flook, D.R., J.R. Robertson, O.R. Hermanrude, and H.K. Buechner. 1962. Succinylcholine chloride for immobilization of North American elk. J. Wildl. Mgmt. 26(3):334-336.

Follett, W. 1966. Modern American usage: a guide. Hill and Wang, New York. 436 p.

Foote, L.E., H.S. Peters, A.L. Finkner. 1958. Design tests for mourning dove call-count sampling in seven southeastern states. J. Wildl. Mgmt. 22:402-408.

Forbes, R.D. 1955. Forestry handbook. Ronald Press, New York. v.p.

Forbes, S.A. 1880. The food of birds. Ill. State Laboratory Nat. Hist. Bull. 1:86-161.

Forbes, T.R. 1941. Instructions for collecting reproductive tracts of wild animals for study. U.S. Fish and Wildl. Service Form 3-1486, Washington, D.C. 3 p. (processed).

Forbush, E.H. 1925-29. Birds of Massachusetts and other New England states. Berwick and Smith Co., Norwood, Mass. 3 vol.

Fowler, H.W. 1965. A dictionary of modern English usage, revised by Sir Ernest Gowers. 2nd ed. Oxford Univ. Press, New York. 725 p.

Fowler, J.A. 1965. An information retrieval system for biological researchers. BioScience 15(6):413-417.

Fox, L. 1959. Photos—are yours good enough? Better Farming Methods 31(12):14-16.

Frankel, A.I., and T.S. Baskett. 1961. The effect of pairing on cooing of penned mourning doves. J. Wildl. Mgmt. 25:372-384.

Frankhauser, D. 1964. Plastic adhesive tape for color-marking birds. J. Wildl. Mgmt. 28(3):594.

Fraps, G.S. and V.L. Cory. 1940. Composition and utilization of range vegetation of Sutton and Edwards Counties. Texas Agr. and Mech. Coll. Expt. Sta. Bull. 586. 39 p.

Fraps, G.S. and J.F. Fudge. 1940. The chemical composition of forage grasses of the east Texas timber country. Agr. and Mech. Coll. Texas, Coll. Sta. Bull. No. 582. 35 p.

Fredin, R.A. 1954. Causes of fluctuations in abundance of Connecticut River shad. U.S. Fish and Wildl. Service Fishery Bull. 88, Washington.

French, C.E., L.C. McEwen, N.D. Magruder, R.H. Ingram and R.W. Swift. 1956. Nutrient requirements for growth and antler development in the white-tailed deer. J. Wildl. Mgmt. 20:221-232.

Friend, M., and S.B. Linhart. 1964. Use of the eye lens as an indicator of age in the red fox. N.Y. Fish and Game. 11(1):58-66.

Friley, C.E., Jr. 1949. Age determination by use of the baculum in the river otter Lutra c. canadensis, Schreber. J. Mammal. 30:102-110.

Frings, H. and Mable Frings. 1958. Recorded calls of the eastern crow as attractants and repellents. J. Wildl. Mgmt. 21(1):91.

Fuller, W.A. 1959. The horns and teeth as indicators of age in bison. J. Wildl. Mgmt. 23:342-344.

G

Gabrielson, I.N. 1941. Wildlife conservation. Macmillan, New York. 250 p.

Gabrielson, I.N., and S.G. Jewett. 1940. Birds of Oregon. Oregon State Univ. Monogr., Studies in Zoology no. 2. 650 p.

Gabrielson, I.N. and F.C. Lincoln. 1959. The birds of Alaska. Stackpole Co., Harrisburg, Pa. 922 p.

Galler, S.R. 1965. Perspectives in animal telemetry, p. 237-254. In C.A. Caceres. (Ed.) Biomedical telemetry. Academic Press, N.Y.

Galt, H.D., B. Theurer, J.H. Ehrenreich, W.H. Hale, and S.C. Martin. 1966. Botanical composition of the diet of steers grazing a desert grassland range. West. Sect. Amer. Soc. Animal Sci. Proc. 17:397-401.

Gandal, C.P. 1956. Satisfactory general anaesthesia in birds. J. Am. Vet. Med. Assoc. 128:332-334.

Gans, C. and J.J. Bonin. 1963. Acoustic activity recorder for burrowing animals. Science 140(3565):398.

Gans, C. 1966. An inexpensive arrangement of movie camera and electronic flash as a tool in the study of animal behavior. Animal Behavior 14(1):11-12.

Garfield, E. 1964. "Science Citation Index"—a new dimension in indexing. Science 144(3619):649-654.

Garlough, F.E. 1945. Capturing foxes. U.S. Fish and Wildl. Ser., Circ. 8, Washington, D.C. 11 p.

Garman, E.H. and A.L. Orr-Ewing. 1949. Direct-seeding experiments in the southern coastal region of British Columbia 1923-49. B.C. For. Serv. Tech. Pub. T31, 45 p.

Garst, W. 1962. Technique for capturing young prairie dogs. J. Wildl. Mgmt. 26:108.

Gast, J.A. 1963. Rhodamine-B dye for studying movements of animals. Ecology 44(3):611-612.

Gates, C.E., W.H. Marshall, and D.P. Olson. 1968. Line transect method of estimating grouse population densities. Biometrics 24:(1)135-145.

Gates, J.M. 1966. Validity of spur appearance as an age criterion in the pheasant. J. Wildl. Mgmt. 30(1):81-85.

Gates, W.H. 1932. Use of Nembutal as an anaesthetic for mice. Science 76:349-350.

Geis, A.D. 1955. Trap response of the cottontail rabbit in Southern Michigan. Ph.D. Diss. Mich. State Univ., East Lansing. 208 p.

Geis, A.D. 1959. Annual and shooting mortality estimates for the canvasback. J. Wildl. Mgmt. 23:253-261.

Geis, Mary B. 1956. Productivity of Canada geese in the Flathead Valley, Montana. J. Wildl. Mgmt. 20:409-419.

Gentry, J.W. 1965. Miniature radio-tracking studies on the hosts of vector mites in Malaysia. J. Med. Entomol., 2(2):153-156.

566

George, H.A. 1963. Planting alkali bulrush for waterfowl food. Dept. Fish and Game, Sacramento, Calif. Game Mgt. Leaflet No. 9, 9 p.

George, J.L., and R.T. Mitchell. 1948. Calculations on the extent of spruce budworm control by insectivorous birds. J. Forestry 46:454-455.

Gibb, J., and P.H.T. Hartley. 1957. Bird foods and feeding habits as subjects for amateur research. Brit. Birds 50:278-291.

Gier, H.T. 1957. Coyotes in Kansas. Kan. Agr. Exp. Sta. Bull. 393, Manhattan. 97 p.

Gifford, C.E. and D.R. Griffin. 1960. Notes on homing and migratory behavior of bats. Ecology 41(2):378-381.

Gilbert, D.L. 1964. Public relations in natural resources management. Burgess Pub. Co., Minneapolis, Minn. xiii + 227 p.

Gilbert, F.F. 1966. Aging white-tailed deer by annuli in the cementum of the first incisor. J. Wildl. Mgmt. 30(1):200-202.

Gilbert, P.F., and J.R. Grieb. 1957. Comparison of air and ground deer counts in Colorado. J. Wildl. Mgmt. 21:33-37.

Gill, J.D. and D.C. O'Meara. 1965. Estimating time of death in white-tailed deer. J. Wildl. Mgmt. 29(3):471-486.

Gill, R.B. 1966. A literature review on the sage grouse. Colorado Dept. of Game, Fish, and Parks; Game Research Division and Cooperative Research Unit. Spec. Rept. no. 6. 39 p.

Girard, G.L. 1939. Notes on the life history of the shoveller. Trans. N. Amer. Wildl. Conf. 4:364-371.

Girard, G.L. 1941. The mallard: its management in western Montana. J. Wildl. Mgmt. 5:233-259.

Glading, B. 1938. Studies on the nesting

cycle of the California valley quail in 1937. Calif. Fish and Game 24:318-340.

Glading, B. 1947. Game watering devices for the arid Southwest. Trans. N. Amer. Wildl. Conf. 12:286-292.

Glading, B., H.H. Biswell, and C.F. Smith. 1940. Studies on the food of the California quail in 1937. J. Wildl. Mgmt. 4:128-144.

Glasgow, J.P. 1953. The extermination of animal populations by artificial predation and the estimation of populations. J. Animal Ecol. 22:32-46.

Glass, B.P. 1951. A key to the skulls of North American mammals. Burgess Pub. Co., Minneapolis, Minn. 54 p.

Glossary Committee. Soil Conservation Society of America. 1952. Soil and water conservation glossary. J. Soil and Water Cons. 7:41-52, 93-104, 144-156.

Glover, F.A. 1956. Nesting and production of the blue-winged teal (Anas discors L.) in Northwest Iowa. J. Wildl. Mgmt. 20:28-46.

Godfrey, G.K. 1953. A technique for finding Microtus nests. J. Mammal. 34:503-505.

Godfrey, G.K. 1954. Tracing field voles (Microtus agrestis) with a Geiger-Muller counter. Ecology 35:5-10.

Godfrey, G.K. 1954. Use of radioactive isotopes in small mammal ecology. Nature 174:951-952.

Godfrey, G.K. 1955. A field study of the activity of the mole (Talpa europea). Ecology 36(4):678-685.

Godfrey, W.E. 1966. The birds of Canada. National Museum of Canada Bull. no. 203 (Biol. Ser. no. 73). 428 p.

Godin, A.J. 1960. A compilation of diagnostic characteristics used in aging and sexing game birds and mammals. Unpub. M.S. thesis. Univ. of Mass., Amherst.

Godin, A.J. 1964. A review of the literature on the mountain beaver. U.S. Fish and Wildlife Spec. Sci. Rept. (Wildl.) no. 78, 52 p.

Goforth, W.R., and T.S. Baskett. 1965. Effects of experimental color marking on pairing of captive mourning doves. J. Wildl. Mgmt. 29(3):543-553.

Golley, F.B. 1960. Energy dynamics of a food chain of an old-field community. Ecol. Monogr. 30:187-206.

Golley, F.B. 1961. Energy values of ecological materials. Ecology 42:581-584.

Golley, F.B. 1966. Les methodes de mesure de la productivite secondaire dans les populations de vertebres terrestres. La Terre et la Vie. 4:393-422.

Golley, F.B., G.A. Petrides, E.L. Rauber, and J.H. Jenkins. 1965. Food intake and assimilation by bobcats under laboratory conditions. J. Wildl. Mgmt. 29:442-447.

Gollop, J.B. 1956. The use of retrievers in banding flightless young mallards. Trans. N. Amer. Wildl. Conf. 21:239-248.

Gollop, J.B., and W.H. Marshall. 1954. A guide to aging duck broods in the field. Miss. Flyway Council Tech. Sect. Rep. (Mimeo.).

Goodnight, C.J., and E.J. Koestner. 1942. Comparison of trapping methods in an Illinois prairie. J. Mammal. 23:435-438.

Goodrum, P.D. 1940. A population study of the gray squirrel in eastern Texas. Texas Agric. Exper. Sta. Bull. 591. 34 p.

Goodwin, G.G. 1953. Catalogue of type specimens of recent mammals in the American Museum of Natural History. Bull. Am. Mus. Nat. Hist. vol. 102, art. 3, p. 207-412.

Gower, W.C. 1939. The use of the bursa of Fabricius as an indicator of age in game birds. Trans. N. Amer. Wildl. Conf. 4:426-430.

Graber, R.R. 1965. Night flight with a thrush. Audubon Mag. 67(6):368-374.

Graber, R.R. and W.W. Cochran. 1959. An audio technique for the study of nocturnal migration of birds. Wilson Bull. 71(3):220-236.

Graber, R.R., and S.S. Hassler. 1962. The effectiveness of aircraft-type (APS) radar in detecting birds. Wilson Bull. 74:367-380.

Graber, R.R., and S.L. Wunderle. 1966. Telemetric observations of a robin *(Turdus migratorius)*. Auk 83(4):674-677.

Graetz, K.E. 1967. Plastic plant mounts. J. Soil and Water Cons. 22(3):115-116.

Graham, S.A. 1940. The intersection method of counting animals. J. Wildl. Mgmt. 4:313-314.

Grange, W.B. 1949. The way to game abundance. C. Scribner's Sons, New York. 365 p.

Grasse, J.E., and E.F. Putnam. 1950. Beaver management and ecology in Wyoming. Wyo. Game and Fish Comm. Bull. 6, Cheyenne. 52 p.

Grassland Research Institute. 1961. Research techniques in use at the Grassland Research Institute [Hurley, England] Commonwealth Bureau of Pastures and Field Crops Bull. 45, 166 p.

Gray, P. 1961. The encyclopedia of the biological sciences. Reinhold Publ. Corp., New York. 1119 p.

Gray, P. 1964. Handbook of basic microtechnique. 3rd ed. 302 p. McGraw-Hill, New York.

Gray, P., and Letitia Langord. 1961. Biological societies, p. 117-142. *In* Encyclopedia of the biological sciences. Reinhold Publ. Corp., New York.

Greeley, F. 1953. Sex and age studies in fall-shot woodcock *(Philohela minor)* from southern Wisconsin. J. Wildl. Mgmt. 17:29-32.

Greeley, F., R.F. Labisky, and S.H. Mann. 1962. Distribution and abundance of pheasants in Illinois. Illinois Nat. Hist. Survey, Biol. Notes No. 47, Urbana. 16 p.

Green, G.W. and D.C. Anderson. 1961. A simple and inexpensive apparatus for photographing events at pre-set intervals. Canadian Entomol. 93(9):741-745.

Greenwalt, C.H., and F.M. Jones. 1955. Photographic studies of the feeding of nestling house wrens. Am. Scientist 43:541-549.

Greer, J.K. 1965. A cage for small intractable animals. J. Wildl. Mgmt. 29(4):895-896.

Greer, K.R. 1957. Some osteological characters of known-age ranch minks. J. Mammal. 38:319-330.

Greer, K.R., and W.W. Hawkins, Jr. 1967. Determining pregnancy in elk by rectal palpation. J. Wildl. Mgmt. 31(1):145-149.

Greer, K.R. and R.E. Howe. 1964. Winter weights of northern Yellowstone elk, 1961-1962. Trans. N. Amer. Wildl. Conf. 29:237-248.

Gregory, T. 1927. Random flashlights. J. Mammal. 8(1):45-47.

Grieb, J.R. and M.G. Sheldon. 1956. Radio-controlled firing device for the cannon-net trap. J. Wildl. Mgmt. 20(3):203-205.

Griffen, J. 1964. The hunting dogs of America. Doubleday and Co., N.Y. 311 p.

Griffin, D.R. 1952. Radioactive tagging of animals under natural conditions. Ecology 33:329-335.

Grinnell, J., H.C. Bryant, and T.I. Storer. 1918. The game birds of California. Univ. Calif. Press, Berkeley. 642 p.

Gromme, O.J. 1963. Birds of Wisconsin. Univ. Wisconsin Press, Madison, Wisc. 219 p.

Gross, A.O. 1938. Eider ducks of Kent's Island. Auk 55:387-400.

Gullion, G.W. 1951. A marker for waterfowl. J. Wildl. Mgmt. 15:222-223.

Gullion, G.W. 1952. Sex and age determination in the American coot. J. Wildl. Mgmt. 16:191-197.

Gullion, G.W. 1961. A technique for winter trapping of ruffed grouse. J. Wildl. Mgmt. 25:428-430.

Gullion, G.W. 1965. Improvements in methods for trapping and marking ruffed grouse. J. Wildl. Mgmt. 29(1):109-116.

Gullion, G.W., R.L. Eng, and J.J. Kupa. 1961. A discussion of three methods for individually marking ruffed grouse. Minn. Agr. Exp. Sta., Sci. J. Ser., Paper No. 4767.

Gunderson, H.L., and J.R. Beer. 1953. The mammals of Minnesota. Minnesota Mus. of Nat. History Occas. Paper no. 6, 190 p.

Gunn, W.W.H. 1964. Radar photography study of bird migration. Nat. Res. Council of Canada, Assoc. Committee on Bird Hazards to Aircraft. Field Note No. 19 (mimeo.). 5 p.

Gunn, W.W.H. 1966. Radar views of migration patterns in the Great Lakes region of North America. Proc. 14th Int. Ornithological Congr. Vol. 1 (Abstract).

Gunn, W.W.H. and Solman, V.E.F. 1968. A bird-warning system for aircraft in flight. *In* The problems of birds as pests. London: Institute of Biology Symposium Series. 1967.

Gurr, E. 1962. Staining: practical and theoretical. Williams and Wilkins, Baltimore, Md. 631 p.

568

Gurr, L. 1955. A pneumatic nest-recording device. Ibis 97(3):584-586.

Guyer, M.F., and Elizabeth A. Bean. 1947. Animal micrology. Univ. of Chicago Press. Chicago, Ill.

Gysel, L.W. and E.M. Davis, Jr. 1956. A simple automatic photographic unit for wildlife research. J. Wildl. Mgmt. 20:451-453.

H

Haahn, F. 1965. Designing for physiological data. BioScience 15(2):112-115.

Hafez, E.S.E. 1962. The behavior of domestic animals. Bailliére, Tindall, and Cox, London. 619 p.

Hahn, H.C. 1945. The white-tailed deer in the Edwards Plateau Region of Texas. Texas Game, Fish, and Oyster Comm., Austin. 50 p.

Hahn, H.C., Jr., and W.P. Taylor. 1950. Deer movements in the Edwards Plateau. Tex. Game and Fish 8(12):4-9, 31.

Hale, J.B. 1949. Aging cottontail rabbits by bone growth. J. Wildl. Mgmt. 13:216-225.

Hale, J.B., R.F. Wendt., and G.C. Halazon. 1954. Sex and age criteria for Wisconsin ruffed grouse. Wis. Conserv. Dept. Tech. Wildl. Bull. No. 9, Madison. 24 p.

Hale, L.J. 1965. Biological laboratory data. 2nd ed. John Wiley & Sons, New York. 147 p.

Hall, E.R. 1942. Gestation period in the fisher, with recommendations for the animal's protection in California. Calif. Fish and Game 28:143-147.

Hall, E.R. 1946. Mammals of Nevada. Univ. California Press, Berkeley. 710 p.

Hall, E.R. 1955. Handbook of mammals of Kansas. Univ. Kans. Mus. Nat. Hist. Misc. Pub. no. 7. 303 p.

Hall, E.R. 1962. Collecting and preparing study specimens of vertebrates. Univ. Kans. Mus. Nat. Hist. Misc. Pub. no. 30, 46 p.

Hall, E.R., and K.R. Kelson. 1959. The mammals of North America. 2 vol. Ronald Press, New York, 1079 p.

Hall, J. 1955. Willow and aspen in the ecology of beavers at Sagehen Creek, California. Ph.D. Diss., Zoology, Univ. of Calif., Berkeley.

Hall, T.C., E.B. Taft, W.H. Baker, and J.C. Aub. 1953. Preliminary report on the use of Flaxedil to produce paralysis in the white-tailed deer. J. Wildl. Mgmt. 17:516-520.

Halloran, A.F. 1961. American Bison weights and measurements from the Wichita Mountains Wildlife Refuge. Proc. Okla. Acad. Sci. 41:212-218.

Halloran, A.F. and O.V. Deming. 1956. Water developments for desert bighorn sheep. U.S. Fish & Wildl. Ser. Washington, D.C. Wildl. Mgt. Series Leaflet No. 14. 8 p.

Halloran, Patricia O'C. 1955. A bibliography of references to diseases in wild mammals and birds. Amer. J. Vet. Res. 16(61):xii + 465.

Hammerstrom, F., D.D. Berger, and F.N. Hamerstrom, Jr. 1965. The effect of mammals on prairie chickens on booming grounds. J. Wildl. Mgmt. 29(3):536-542.

Hamerstrom, F.N., Jr. 1936. A study of the nesting habits of the ring-necked pheasant in northwest Iowa. Iowa State Coll. J. Sci. 10:173-203.

Hamerstrom, F.N., Jr., and F.L. Camburn. 1950. Weight relationships in the George Reserve deerherd. J. Mammal. 31(1):5-17.

Hamilton, C.L., and H.G. Jepson. 1940. Stock-water developments: wells, springs, and ponds. USDA, Washington, D.C. Farmer's Bull. No. 1859, 70 p.

Hamilton, R. 1962. An expansible collar for male white-tailed deer. J. Wildl. Mgmt. 26:114-115.

Hamilton, W.J. 1963. Mammals of eastern United States. Hafner, New York. 438 p.

Hamilton, W.J., Jr. 1933. The weasels of New York. Amer. Midland Naturalist 14:289-344.

Hamilton, W.J., III. 1962. Evidence concerning the function of nocturnal call notes of migratory birds. Condor 64(5):390-401.

Hamlett, G.W.D. 1932. Observations on the embryology of the badger. Anat. Record 53:283-303.

Hammond, M.C. and C.J. Henry. 1949. Success of marsh hawk nests in North Dakota. Auk 66:271-274.

Hankla, D.J. and B.J. Verts. 1958. Planning your wildlife on the farm. North Carolina Wildl. Res. Comm., Raleigh. n.p.

Hansen, H.A. and M.R. Huggins. 1966. Waterfowl status report U.S. Fish and Wildl. Ser. Spec. Sci. Report, Wildl. No. 99.

Hanson, H.S. 1954. Criteria of age of incubated mallard, wood duck and bobwhite quail eggs. Auk 71:267-272.

Hanson, H.S. 1962. Dictionary of ecology. Philosophical Library, New York. 382 p.

Hanson, W.R. 1963. Calculation of productivity, survival and abundance of selected vertebrates from sex and age ratios. Wildl. Managr. No. 9.

Hanson, W.R. and D.G. Chapman (unpubl. Ms). A binomial model for estimating population density of animals. 16 p.

Hanson, W.R., and F. Graybill. 1956. Sample size in food-habits analysis. J. Wildl. Mgmt. 20:64-68.

Hanssen, A. 1947. The physiology of reproduction in mink *(Mustela vison* Schreb.) with special reference to delayed implantation. Acta. Zool. Fennica 28:1-136.

Hardy, J.I. and T.M. Plitt. 1940. An improved method for revealing the surface structure of fur fibers. USDI Fish and Wildl. Ser. Bull. No. 7. 10 p.

Harned, B.K., R.W. Cunningham, and E.R. Gill. 1952. An activity analyzer for small animals. Science 116(3014):369-370.

Harper, H.T., C.M. Hart, and D.E. Schaffer. 1951. Effects of hunting pressure and game farm stocking on pheasant populations in the Sacramento Valley, California, 1946-1949. Calif. Fish and Game 37:141-176.

Harper, W.G. 1959. Roosting movements of birds and migration departures from roosts as seen by radar. Ibis 101:201-208.

Harris, S.W., and M.A. Morse. 1958. The use of mist nets for capturing nesting mourning doves. J. Wildl. Mgmt. 22:306-309.

Hartesveldt, R.J. 1951. A simple technique for den-use study. J. Wildl. Mgmt. 15(1):104-105.

Harthoorn, A.M. 1965. Application of pharmacological and physiological principles in the restraint of wild animals. Wildl. Monogr. No. 14, 78 p.

Hartley, P.H.T. 1948. The assessment of the food of birds. Ibis 90:361-381.

Hassler, S.S., R.R. Graber, and F.C. Bellrose. 1963. Fall migration and weather, a radar study. Wilson Bull. 75:56-77.

Haugen, A.O. 1957. Distinguishing juvenile from adult bobwhite quail. J. Wildl. Mgmt. 21:29-32.

Haugen, A.O. 1964. Visual aids with legible slides. J. Wildl. Mgmt. 28(1):177-179.

Haugen, A.O. and F.W. Fitch, Jr. 1955. Seasonal availability of certain bush lespedeza and partridge pea seed as determined from ground samples. J. Wildl. Mgmt. 19:297-301.

Haugen, A.O., and D.W. Speake. 1958. Determining age of young fawn white-tailed deer. J. Wildl. Mgmt. 22:319-321.

Hausman, L.A. 1920. Structural characteristics of the hair of mammals. The Amer. Midland Naturalist 54:496-523.

Hay, K.G. 1958. Beaver census methods in the Rocky Mountain region. J. Wildl. Mgmt. 22:395-402.

Hayden, S.S. 1942. The international protection of wildlife: an examination of treaties and other agreements for the preservation of birds and mammals. Columbia Univ. Press, New York. 246 p.

Hayne, D.W. 1949. An examination of the strip census method for estimating animal populations. J. Wildl. Mgmt. 13:145-157.

Hayne, D.W. 1949. Two methods for estimating populations from trapping records. J. Mammal. 30:399-411.

Hayne, D.W. 1952. A study of bias in the selection of a "representative" sample of small fish. Papers Mich. Acad. Sci., Arts and Letters 37:133-141.

Hayne, D.W., and L. Eberhardt. 1952. Notes on the estimation of survival rates from age distributions of deer. 14th Midwest Wildl. Conf. Unpub. report.

Hayne, D.W., and L. Eberhardt. 1954. Nature of the bias of estimates computed from voluntary reports. 16th Midwest Wildl. Conf. Rep. No. 2325, (mimeo) Game Div., Mich. Dept. Conser., Lansing, Mich.

Hayne, D.W., and D.Q. Thompson. 1965. Methods for estimating microtine abundance. N. Amer. Wildl. and Nat. Res. Conf. 30:393-400.

Heath, R.G. 1961. A theoretical analysis of an auditory index. Mich. Dept. of Cons. Game Div. Report 2273, Lansing, Mich.

Heath, W.B. 1961. A trailing device for small animals designed for field study of the gila monster *(Heloderma suspectum)*. Copeia 1961 (4): 491-492.

Heezen, K.L., and J.R. Tester. 1967. Evaluation of radio-tracking by triangulation with special reference to deer movements. J. Wildl. Mgmt. 31(1):124-141.

Hein, D. 1966. Float counts vs. flight counts as indices to abundance of nesting wood ducks. J. Wildl. Mgmt. 30(1):13-16.

Hein, D. 1967. Sources of literature cited in wildlife research papers. J. Wildl. Mgmt. 31(3):598-599.

Hellmers, H. 1964. A simple and efficient file system for reprints. Bio-Science 14(2):24.

Helm, L.G. 1955. Plastic collars for marking geese. J. Wildl. Mgmt. 19:316-317.

Hendrick, D.J. 1963. The visitometer/a simplified mechanical counter. Passenger Pigeon 25(2):60-68.

Hensley, A.L., and H. Twining. 1946. Some early summer observations on muskrats in a northeastern California marsh. Calif. Fish and Game 32:171-181.

Herzfeld, R.P. 1962. Automation in bird photography. J. Biol. Photogs. Assoc. 30(2):53-62.

Hewitt, O.H. 1967. A road-count index to breeding populations of red-winged blackbirds. J. Wildl. Mgmt. 31:39-47.

Hewitt, O.H. (Ed.) 1967. The wild turkey and its management. The Wildlife Society, Washington, D.C. 589 p.

Hewson, R. 1961. Collars for marking

mountain hares. J. Wildl. Mgmt. 25:329-331.

Hickey, J.J. 1943. A guide to bird watching. Oxford Univ. Press, New York. 264 p.

Hickey, J.J. 1952. Survival studies of banded birds. U.S. Fish and Wildl. Service Spec. Sci. Rep. (Wildl.) No. 15, Washington. 177 p.

Hickey, J.J. 1955. Some American population research on gallinaceous birds, p. 326-396. In A. Wolfson (Ed.). Recent studies in avian biology. Univ. Ill. Press, Urbana. ix+479 p.

Hiehle, J.L. 1961. Improving chamise brushlands for deer and other game. Calif. Dept. Fish and Game, Sacramento, Calif. Leaflet No. 4, 27 p.

Hiehle, J.L. 1964. Measurement of browse growth and utilization. Calif. Fish and Game 50:148-151.

Hiehle, J.L., and J.R. Slosson. 1961. A method of immobilizing bear for ear tagging. Calif. Fish and Game 47:303.

Highton, R. 1965. Amphibians and reptiles. BioScience 15(6):442.

Hildebrand, M. 1955. Skeletal differences between deer, sheep, and goats. Calif. Fish and Game 41:327-346.

Hill, C.E. 1966. Mt. Mitchell deer movement. Wildl. N. Carolina 39(11):20.

Hill, Radah, and Williamina A. Himwich. 1957. Coding a small reprint collection on the central nervous system. Fed. Proc. 16(3):721-725.

Hillway, T. 1964. Introduction to research. 2nd ed. Houghton Mifflin, Boston, Mass. 308 p.

Hitchcock, A.S. 1951. Manual of the grasses of the United States. 2nd ed. USDA Misc. Pub. 200. 1051 p. (revised).

Hjort, J.G., and P. Ottestad. 1933. The optimum catch. Hvalradets Skrifter Oslo 7:92-127.

Hochbaum, H.A. 1942. Sex and age determination of waterfowl by cloacal examination Trans. N. Amer. Wildl. Conf. 7:299-307.

Hoff, W. (Ed.) 1966. American association of zoological parks and aquariums 1966 directory. The Association, Oglebay Park, Wheeling, West Va. 108 p.

Holdenried, R. 1954. A new live-catch rodent trap and comparison with two other traps. J. Mammal. 35:267-268.

Hole, N. 1953. Chloral hydrate as a general anaesthetic for the fowl. J. Comp. Pathol. and Therap. 47:47.

Hollaender, A. 1954. Radiation biology. (3 vols.) McGraw-Hill Book Co., N.Y.

Holmes, Ann C.V., and G.C. Sanderson. 1965. Populations and movements of opossums in east-central Illinois. J. Wildl. Mgmt. 29(2):287-295.

Holmgren, R.C. and J.V. Basile. 1959. Improving southern Idaho deer winter ranges by artificial revegetation. Idaho Dept. Fish and Game, Boise. Wildl. Bull. No. 3, 61 p.

Hood, S.L., R.A. Monroe, and W.J. Visek. 1953. Edge-punched cards for scientific literature references. U.S. Atomic Energy Comm. Tech. Info. Ser. ORO-102, Oak Ridge, Tenn. 19 p.

Hook, Lucyle, and M.V. Gaver. 1952. The research paper: gathering library material; organizing and preparing the manuscript. 2nd ed. Prentice-Hall, Englewood Cliffs, N.J. 85 p.

Hooper, F.F., H.A. Podoliak, and S.F. Snieszko. 1961. Use of radioisotopes in hydrobiology and fish culture. Trans. Amer. Fish. Soc. 90:49-57.

Hopkins, M.N. and E.P. Odum. 1953.

Some aspects of the population ecology of breeding mourning doves in Georgia. J. Wildl. Mgmt. 17:132-143.

Hornaday, W.T. 1929. Taxidermy and zoological collecting. Charles Scribner's Sons, New York, 364 p.

Hornocker, M.G., J.L. Craighead, and E.W. Pfeiffer. 1965. Immobilizing mountain lions with succinylcholine chloride and pentobarbital sodium. J. Wildl. Mgmt. 29(4):880-883.

Hough, A.F. 1949. Deer and rabbit browsing and available winter forage in Allegheny hardwood forests. J. Wildl. Mgmt. 13:135-141.

Houghton, E.W. 1963. Detection, recognition and identification of birds on radar. Memorandum No. 2047. Royal Radar Establishment, Malvern, Worcs., England. 19 p.

Howard, L.O. 1942. The insect book. Doubleday, Doran and Co., N.Y.

Howard, W.E. 1965. Principles of vertebrate animal control. Congrès De La Protection Des Cultures Tropicales. Marseille, France. pp. 627 à 629.

Howard, W.E., and E.M. Brock. 1961. A drift-fence pit trap that preserves captured rodents. J. Mammal. 43:386-391.

Howell, J.C. 1951. Roadside census as a method of measuring bird populations. Auk 68:334-357.

Hubbard, R.L. 1964. A guide to bitterbrush seeding in California. Pacific Southwest Forest and Range Exp. Sta., Berkeley, Calif. 30 p.

Hubbs, C.L. (Ed.) 1958. Zoogeography. American Assoc. For the Advancement of Science Pub. no. 51. 509 p.

Huber, J.J. 1962. Trap response of confined cottontail populations. J. Wildl. Mgmt. 26:177-185.

Hudson, P., and L.G. Browman. 1959. Embryonic and fetal development of the mule deer. J. Wildl. Mgmt. 23: 295-304.

Hughes, Katherine W., R. A. Yoder, and W. I. West. 1953. Forestry theses accepted by colleges and universities in the United States, 1900-1952. Oregon State College Bibliographic Series no. 3. 140 p. [This was supplemented by no. 5, published in 1957, covering the years 1953-1955. Since 1957 this list has been kept up to date by annual compilations in *Forest Science.* The first of these compilations appeared in September 1959 and in the September issue each year thereafter until 1965 when the list began appearing in the June issue.]

Humason, Gretchen L. 1962. Animal tissue techniques. W. H. Freeman, New York. 468 p.

Hungate, R. E. 1962. Ecology of bacteria, p. 95-119. *In* I. C. Gunsalus and R. Y. Stanier (Eds.). The bacteria. Vol. 4. Academic Press, N. Y.

Hungate, R. E. 1966. The rumen and its microbes. Academic Press, N. Y. 533 p.

Hungerford, C. R. 1964. Vitamin A and productivity in Gambel's quail. J. Wildl. Mgmt. 28:141-147.

Hungerford, C. R. 1965. Response of Kaibab mule deer to reseeded forest and meadow. Trans. N. Amer. Wildl. and Natural Res. Conf. 30:310-321.

Hungerford, K. E. 1953. A ruffed grouse drumming count technique for Northern Idaho conditions. Univ. Idaho Forest, Wildl. and Range Expt. Sta. Research Note 10, 3 p. mimeo.

Hungerford, K. E. 1951. Ecology and management of the Idaho ruffed grouse *(Bonasa umbellus phaia).* Unpub. PhD Diss., Univ. Mich., Ann Arbor. 229 p.

Hungerford, K. E. 1957. Evaluating ruffed grouse foods for habitat improvement. Trans. N. Amer. Wildl. Conf. 22:380-395.

Hunt, E. G. and A. E. Naylor. 1955. Nesting studies of ducks and coots

in Honey Lake Valley. Calif. Fish and Game 41:295-314.

Hunt, G. S., and K. J. Dahlka. 1953. Live trapping of diving ducks. J. Wildl. Mgmt. 17:92-95.

Hunter, G. N. 1945. Methods of determining trends in big game numbers and range conditions. Trans. N. Amer. Wildl. Conf. 10:234-241.

Hunter, G. N., and L. E. Yeager. 1956. Management of the mule deer, p. 449-482. *In* W. E. Taylor (Ed.). The deer of North America. The Stackpole Co., Harrisburg, Pa. 668 p.

Huss, D. L. (Chairman). 1964. A glossary of terms used in range management. Am. Soc. of Range Mgmt. Portland, Ore. 32 p.

I

Imler, R. H. 1945. Bullsnakes and their control on a Nebraska wildlife refuge. J. Wildl. Mgmt. 9:265-273.

Ingles, L. G. 1965. Mammals of the pacific states: California, Oregon, and Washington, Stanford Univ. Press, Stanford, Calif. 506 p.

Inglis, J. M., and C. J. Barstow. 1960. A device for measuring the volume of seeds. J. Wildl. Mgmt. 24:221-222.

International Commission on Zoological Nomenclature. 1964. International code of zoological nomenclature, adopted by the 15th International Congress on Zoology. International Trust for Zoological Nomenclature, London. 176 p.

Interstate Antelope Conference. 1962. Recommended specifications for barbed wire fences for benefit of livestock and wildlife. Interstate Antelope Conf. Trans. 13:100-101.

Interstate Deer Herd Committee. 1950. Fourth progress report on the cooperative study of the interstate deer herd and its range. Calif. Fish and Game 36:27-52.

Ireland, Norma O. 1962. Index to scientists of the world from ancient to modern times: biographies and portraits. F. W. Faxon Co., Boston, Mass. 662 p.

Isaacson, I. 1963. Manual for the conservation officer. Legal Publications, Lewiston, Me. 143 p.

Isakov, Y. A. 1961. Organization and methods of censusing terrestrial vertebrate faunal resources; summaries of reports. [transl. from Russian]. Israel Program for Scientific Translations, Jerusalem. 104 p.

J

Jack, H. A. 1945. Biological field stations of the world. Chronica Botanica 9(1):1-73.

Jackson, C. F. 1958. Suggested methods for identifying the meat of the whitetailed deer. N. H. Fish and Game Dept. Tech. Circ. 16, 9 p.

Jackson, C. F. 1962. Use of paper chromatography in identifying meat of game anaimals. N. H. Fish and Game Dept. Tech. Circ. 19, 15 p.

Jackson, C. H. N. 1939. The analysis of an animal population. J. Animal Ecol. 8:238-246.

Jackson, C. H. N. 1944. The analysis of a tsetse-fly population. II. Ann. Eug. 12:176-205.

Jackson, C. H. N. 1948. The analysis of a tsetse-fly population. III. Ann. Eug. 14:91-108.

Jackson, G. L. and T. S. Baskett. 1964. Perch-cooing and other aspects of breeding behavior of mourning doves. J. Wildl. Mgmt. 28:293-307.

Jackson, H. H. T. 1961. Mammals of Wisconsin. Univ. Wisconsin Press, Madison. 504 p.

Jaczewski, Z., and M. Czaja. 1959. The effect of tobucurarine chloride on the red deer, *Cervus elaphus* (L). Trans. N. Amer. Wildl. Conf. 24:408-413.

Jaeger, E.C. 1955. A source-book of biological names and terms. 3rd ed. Charles C. Thomas, Springfield, Ill. 317 p.

Jaeger, E. C. 1960. The biologist's handbook of pronunciations. Charles C. Thomas, Springfield, Ill. 317 p.

Jahoda, G., R.D. Hutchins, and R.R. Galford. 1966. Characteristics and use of personal indexes maintained by scientists and engineers in one university. Am. Doc. 17(2):71-75.

Jenkins, D., A. Watson, and G.R. Miller. 1963. Population studies on red grouse, *Lagopus lagopus scoticus* (Lath.) in North-east Scotland. J. Anim. Ecol. 32(3):317-376.

Jenkins, D.W. 1957. Radioisotopes in entomology. *In* C.L. Comar (Ed.), Atomic Energy and Agriculture. Amer. Assoc. for Adv. of Sci. Publ. 49, Washington, D.C. P. 195-229.

Jensen, G.H., and L.J. Korschgen. 1947. Contents of crops, gizzards, and droppings of bobwhite quail force-fed known kinds and quantities of seeds. J. Wildl. Mgmt. 11:37-43.

Jewell, P.A. 1963. Wild life research in East and Central Africa. Oryx 7: 77-87.

Johansen, D.A. 1940. Plant microtechnique. McGraw-Hill Book Co., N.Y.

Johansen, H. 1952. Ornithology in Russia. Ibis 94(1):1-48.

Johns, J.E. 1963. A new method of capture utilizing the mist net. Bird-Banding 34(4):209-213.

Joint Committee of the American Society of Agronomy, American Dairy Science Association, American Society of Animal Production, American Society of Range Management. 1962. Pasture and range research techniques. Comstock Publishing Associates, Ithaca, New York. 242 p.

Joint Committee of the American Society of Range Management and the Agricultural Board, Subcommittee on Range Research Methods of the Agricultural Board. 1962. Basic problems and techniques in range research. NAS/NRC Pub. no. 890. National Academy of Sciences—National Research Council, Washington, D.C. 341 p.

Jolly, G.M. 1963. Estimates of population parameters from multiple recapture data with both death and dilution—deterministic model. Biometrika 50:113-128.

Jolly, G.M. 1965. Explicit estimates from capture-recapture data with low death and immigration—stochastic model. Biometrika 52:315-337.

Jones, F.L., G. Flittner, and R. Gard. 1954. Report on a survey of bighorn sheep and other game in the Santa Rosa Mountains, Riverside County (California). Calif. Dept. Fish and Game, Sacramento. 26 p. (Mimeo.).

Jonkel, C.J. 1964. Estimating whole weights of black bears from hog-dressed weights. J. Wildl. Mgmt. 28(3):581.

Jordan, P.A. 1958. Marking deer with bells. Calif. Fish and Game 44:183-189.

Judd, S.D. 1903. The economic value of the bobwhite, p. 193-204. *In* 1903 Yearbook of Agriculture. U.S. Gov. Printing office, Washington, D.C. 728 p.

Judd, S.D. 1905. The grouse and wild turkeys of the United States and their economic value. Biol. Survey Bull. No. 24, 55 p.

Judd, S.D. 1905. The bobwhite and other quails of the United States in their economic relations. Biol. Survey Bull. No. 21, 66 p.

Jumber, J.F., H.O. Hartley, E.L. Kozicky, and A.M. Johnson. 1957. A technique for sampling mourning dove production. J. Wildl. Mgmt. 21:226-229.

Justice, K.E. 1961. A new method for measuring home ranges of small mammals. J. Mammal. 42(4):462-470.

K

Kabat, C., N.E. Collias, and R.C. Guettinger. 1953. Some winter habits of white-tailed deer and the development of census methods in the Flag Yard of Northern Wisconsin. Wisc. Cons. Dept. Tech. Wildl. Bull. 7, Madison. 31 p.

Kaiser, Frances E. (Ed.) 1965. Translators and translations: services and sources in science and technology. 2nd ed. Special Libraries Assoc., New York. 214 p.

Kalela, O. 1961. Seasonal change of habitat in the Norwegian lemming, *Lemmus lemmus* (L.) Annales Acadamiae Scientasiarum Fennicae, Biologica Ser. A, 55:1-72.

Kalmbach, E.R. 1934. Field observations in economic ornithology. Wilson Bull. 46:73-90.

Kalmbach, E.R. 1937. Crow-waterfowl relationships. USDA Circ. 433. Washington, D.C.

Kalmbach, E.R. 1954. The continuing need for food habits research. Wilson Bull. 66:276-278.

Kangur, R. 1954. Shrews as tree seed eaters in the Douglas fir region. Oregon State Bd. of Forestry. Research note 17, 23 p.

Karstad, L. (Ed.) 1964. Diseases of Cervidae: a partly annotated bibliography. Wildl. Dis. 43:1-233.

Karstad, L., J. Spalatin, and R.P. Hanson. 1959. Application of the paper disk technique to the collection of whole blood and serum samples in studies on eastern equine encephalomyelitis. J. Inf. Dis. 101:295-299.

Kauffman, E. 1966. The conservation yearbook. Pub. by Conservation Yearbook, Baltimore, Md. v.p.

Kavanau, J.L. 1961. Identification of small animals by proximity sensing. Science 134(3491):1694-1696.

Kavanau, J.L. 1963. Continuous automatic monitoring of the activities of small captive animals. Ecology 44(1):95-110.

Kay, R.H. 1964. Experimental biology: measurement and analysis. Reinhold Pub. Corp., New York, 416 p.

Kearl, W.G. 1965. A survey of big sagebrush control in Wyoming 1952-1964. Agric. Exp. Sta., Laramie, Wyo. Mimeo. Cir. No. 217, 42 p.

Keith, L.B. 1961. A study of waterfowl ecology on small impoundments in southeastern Alberta. Wildl. Monogr. No. 6, 88 p.

Keith, L.B. 1963. Wildlife's ten-year cycle. Univ. Wisc. Press, Madison. 201 p.

Keith, L.B. 1965. A live snare and a tagging snare for rabbits. J. Wildl. Mgmt. 29(4):877-880.

Kelker, G.H. 1940. Estimating deer population by a differential hunting loss in the sexes. Proc. Utah Acad. Sci., Arts and Letters. 17:65-69.

Kelker, G.H. 1944. Sex ratio equations and formulas for determining wildlife populations. Proc. Utah Acad. Sci., Arts and Letters 20:189-198.

Kelker, G.A. 1964. Finding the standard deviation of a sex or age ratio formula by the use of Deming's equations. In Symposium: Estimation of biological populations. Annual Meeting, AAAS, Montreal, Canada.

Kelsh, H.F. 1940. The slotter-templet method for controlling maps made from aerial photographs. USDA Misc. Publ. 404. Washington.

Kendeigh, S.C. 1944. Measurement of bird populations. Ecol. Monogr. 44: 67-106.

Kendeigh, S.C. 1952. Parental care and its evolution in birds. Ill. Biol. Monogr. 22:1-356.

Kendeigh, S.C. 1963. New ways of measuring the incubation period of birds. Auk 80(4):453-461.

Kendeigh, S.C. and S.P. Baldwin. 1930. The mechanical recording of the nesting activities of birds. Auk 47: 471-480.

Kendeigh, S.C. and G.C. West. 1965. Caloric values of plant seeds eaten by birds. Ecology 46:553-555.

Kennedy, A.H. 1952. The sexing of beaver. Ont. Dept. Lands and For., Fish and Wildl. Div. 9 p. (mimeo.).

Kenneth, J.H. 1963. A dictionary of biological terms. 8th ed. D. Van Nostrand, New York. 640 p.

Kenyon, K.W., and C.H. Fiscus. 1963. Age determination in the Hawaiian monk seal. J. Mammal. 44(2):280-282.

Kerr, R. and R. Hoffman. 1964. Buckskin bonanza - exit pinyon and juniper - enter grassland and deer. Colorado Outdoors 13(6):8-11.

Kershaw, K.A. 1964. Quantitative and dynamic ecology. American Elsevier Pub. Co. Inc., New York, 183 p.

Kessler, 1962. Measurement of nest attentiveness in the ring-necked pheasant. Auk 79(4):702-705.

Ketchen, K.S. 1953. The use of catch-effort and tagging data in estimating a flatfish population. J. Fish Res. Bd. Canada. 10:459-485.

Keuffel and Esser Co. n.d. Compensating polar planimeter. Hoboken, N.J.

Keuffel and Esser Co., n.d. Abney levels. Use and applications with appropriate tables. Hoboken, N.J.

Kiel, W.H., Jr. 1955. Nesting studies of the coot in southwestern Manitoba. J. Wildl. Mgmt. 19:189-198.

Kiel, W.H. Jr., and J.T. Harris. 1956. Status of the white-winged dove in Texas. Trans. N. Amer. Wildl. Conf. 21:376-388.

Kimball, J.W. 1944. Age gauge for pheasants. J. Wildl. Mgmt. 8:263-264.

Kimball, J.W. 1949. The crowing count pheasant census. J. Wildl. Mgmt. 13: 101-120.

Kindel, F. 1960. Use of dyes to mark ruminant feces. J. Wildl. Mgmt. 24: 429.

King, T.R., and H.E. McClure. 1944. Chemical composition of some American wild feedstuffs. J. Agr. Res. 69:33-46.

Kinne, R. 1960. How to shoot wildlife with a camera. Popular Photography. 46:32+.

Kinne, R. 1962. The complete book of nature photography. A.S. Barnes, New York. 191 p.

Kirkpatrick, C.M. 1944. The bursa of Fabricius in ring-necked pheasants. J. Wildl. Mgmt. 8:118-129.

Kjellstrom, B. 1955. Be expert with map and compass. The "orienteering" handbook. American Orienteering Service, 220 Fifth Ave., New York.

Kleiber, M. 1961. The fire of life. John Wiley and Sons, Inc., New York. 454 p.

Klement, A.W., Jr. 1965. Natural environmental radioactivity, an annotated bibliography. Wash-1061. Fallout Studies Branch, Div. Biol. and Med. AEC., Washington, D.C. 125 p.

Klement, A.W., Jr., and V. Schultz. 1962, 1963, 1965, 1966. Terrestrial and freshwater radioecology. A selected bibliography - Supplements 1, 2, 3 and 4. TID-3910. USAEC Div. of Biol. and Med. Washington, D.C. 79; 115; 128 p.

Klett, E.V. 1965. A portable observation tower. J. Wildl. Mgmt. 29(1): 206-207.

Klonglan, E. D. 1955. Problems in the use of multiflora rose. Iowa Acad. Sci. 62:626-637.

Klonglan, E. D., I. A. Coleman, and E. L. Kozicky. 1956. A pheasant nest activity recording instrument. J. Wildl. Mgmt. 20(2):173-177.

Kloglan, E. D., and E. L. Kozicky. 1953. Variations in two spring indices of male pheasant populations, Story County, Iowa. Iowa Acad. Sci. 60: 660-664.

Knight, R. R. 1966. Bone characteristics associated with aging in elk. J. Wildl. Mgmt. 30(2):369-374.

Knott, N. O., C. P. Ball, and C. F. Yocum. 1943. Nesting of the Hungarian partridge and ring-necked pheasant in Whitman County, Washington. J. Wildl. Mgmt. 7:283-291.

Knowlton, F. F., E. D. Michael, and W. C. Blazener. 1964. A marking technique for field recognition of individual turkeys and deer. J. Wildl. Mgmt. 28(1):167-170.

Knudsen, J. W. 1966. Biological techniques: collecting, preserving, and illustrating plants and animals. Harper and Row, New York. 525 p.

Koford, C. B. 1962. Catching rhesus monkeys in northern India. Unpub. ms.

Koonz, C. H., and E. J. Strandine. 1945. A rapid and simplified method for revealing the surface pattern of hair. Trans. Am. Microscope Soc. 64:63-64.

Korschgen, L. J. 1948. Late-fall and early-winter food habits of bobwhite quail in Missouri. J. Wildl. Mgmt. 12:46-57.

Korschgen, L. J. 1960. Production of game bird foods in Missouri. J. Wildl. Mgmt. 24(4):395-401.

Korschgen, L. J. 1962. Foods of Missouri deer, with some management implications. J. Wildl. Mgmt. 26: 164-172.

Korschgen, L. J. 1962. Food habits of greater prairie chickens in Missouri. Amer. Midland Naturalist 68: 307-318.

Korschgen, L. J. 1964. Foods and nutrition of Missouri and midwestern pheasants. Trans. N. Amer. Wildl. and Nat. Res. Conf. 29:159-181.

Korschgen, L. J. 1966. Foods and nutrition of ruffed grouse in Missouri. J. Wildl. Mgmt. 30:86-100.

Kortright, F. H. 1943. The ducks, geese, and swans of North America. Amer. Wildl. Inst., Washington, D.C. 476 p.

Koskimies, J. 1957. Flocking behavior in capercaille, *Tetrao urogallus* (L.) and blackgame, *Lyrurus tetrix* (L.) Papers on Game Research (Helsinki) No. 18, 32 p.

Kossack, C. W. 1950. Breeding habits of Canada geese under refuge conditions. Amer. Midland Naturalist 43(3):627-649.

Kothmann, M. M. 1966. Nutrient content of forage ingested in the morning compared to evening. J. Range Mgmt. 19:95-96.

Kozicky, E. L. 1952. Variations in two spring indices of male ring-necked pheasant populations. J. Wildl. Mgmt. 16:429-437.

Kozicky, E. L., T. A. Bancroft, and P. G. Homeyer. 1954. An analysis of woodcock singing ground counts, 1948-1952. J. Wildl. Mgmt. 18:259-266.

Kozicky, E. L., R. J. Jessen, G. O. Hendrickson, and E. B. Speaker. 1956. Estimation of fall quail populations in Iowa. J. Wildl. Mgmt. 20(2):97-104.

Kozicky, E. L. and F. V. Schmidt. 1949. Nesting habits of the clapper rail in New Jersey. Auk 66:355-364.

Kozlik, F. M., A. W. Miller, and W. C. Rienecker. 1959. Color-marking white geese for determining migration routes. Calif. Fish and Game 45:69-82.

Krenz, R. D. 1962. Costs and returns from spraying sagebrush with 2, 4-D. Agric. Exp. Sta., Laramie, Wyoming. Bull. No. 390, 31 p.

Krumholz, L. A. [chairman]. 1957. Glossary of wildlife terms. J. Wildl. Mgmt. 21:373-376.

Kuechle, L. B. 1967. Batteries for biotelemetry and other applications. AIBS Information Module M10. 15 p.

Kuentzel, L. E. (Ed.) 1963. Coden for periodical titles. American Society for Testing and Materials, Philadelphia, Pa. 426 p. [Supplements have been issued to keep this list current].

Kuhring, M. S., and W. W. H. Gunn. 1965. Birds—radar—weather. National Research Council of Canada, Assoc. Committee on Bird Hazards to Aircraft. Field Note No. 29 (mimeo.). 5 p.

L

Labisky, R. F. 1959. Night-lighting: A technique for capturing birds and mammals. Ill. Nat. Hist. Survey Biol. Notes No. 40, Urbana, 11 p.

Labisky, R. F., and R. D. Lord, Jr. 1959. A flexible, plastic eartag for rabbits. J. Wildl. Mgmt. 23:363-365.

Labisky, R. F., and J. F. Opsahl. 1958. A guide to aging pheasant embryos. Ill. Nat. Hist. Survey Biol. Notes No. 39, Urbana. 4 p.

Lacher, J. R., and D. D. Lacher. 1964. A mobile cannon net trap. J. Wildl. Mgmt. 28(3):595-597.

Lack, D. 1947. The significance of clutch size in the partridge *(Perdix perdix)*. J. Animal Ecol. 16:19.

Lack, D. 1954. The natural regulation of animal numbers. Oxford Univ. Press. vii + 343 p.

Lack, D. 1960. The height of bird migration. British Birds 53:5-10.

Lamprey, H. F. 1964. Estimation of the large mammal densities, biomass and energy exchange in the Tarangire Game Reserve and the Masai Steppe in Tanganyika. East African Wildl. J. 2:1-46.

Lanyon, W.E., and F.B. Gill. 1964. Spectrographic analysis of variation in the songs of a population of blue-winged warblers (Vermivora pinus). Amer. Museum Novitates 2176:1-18.

Laramie, H.A., Jr. and D.L. White. 1964. Some observations concerning hunting pressure and harvest on white-tailed deer. Circ. 20, New Hampshire Fish and Game Dept. 55 p.

Larimore, R.W. 1957. A marginal-dot system of indexing reference cards. J. Wildl. Mgmt. 21(1):92-94.

Larrison, E.J., J.L. Tucker, and M.T. Jollie. 1967. Guide to Idaho birds. J. Ida. Acad. Sci. 5:1-220.

Larson, J.S. 1966. Wildlife forage clearings on forest lands—a critical appraisal and research needs. PhD Diss., Va. Poly. Inst., Blacksburg, Va.

Latham, R.M. 1942. Sexing day-old ring-necked pheasant chicks. Pa. Game Comm. Research Circ. No. 2, Harrisburg. 11 p.

Latham, R.M. 1946. The fox as a factor in the control of weasel populations. J. Wildl. Mgmt. 16:516-517.

Latham, R.M. 1951. The ecology and economics of predator management. Pa. Game Comm. Rep. II, Harrisburg. 96 p.

Latham, R.M. 1956. Complete book of the wild turkey. The Stackpole Co., Harrisburg, Pa. 265 p.

Lauritizen, C.W. and A.A. Thayer. 1966. Rain traps for intercepting and storing water for livestock. USDA, Washington, D.C., Agric. Info. Bull. No. 307, 10 p.

Lawrence, G.H.M. 1951. Taxonomy of vascular plants. Macmillan Co., New York. 823 p.

Lawrence, W.H., N.B. Kverno, and H.D. Hartwell. 1961. Guide to wildlife feeding injuries on conifers in the Pacific northwest. Western For. and Cons. Assoc. 44 p.

Lawrence, W.H. and C.A. Sherman. 1963. An electronic traffic counter for recording burrow activity of the mountain beaver. J. Mammal. 44(3): 399-405.

Laws, R.M. 1953. A new method of age determination in mammals with special reference to the elephant seal (Mirouga leonina, Linn.) Falkland Island Depend. Surv. Sci. Reps. 2: 1-12.

Lay, W. 1965. Fruit utilization by deer in southern forests. J. Wildl. Mgmt. 29(2):370-375.

Lechleitner, R.R. 1954. Age criteria in mink, Mustela vison. J. Mammal. 35:496-503.

Lechleitner, R.R. 1957. The black-tailed jackrabbit on Grey Lodge Refuge, California. Unpub. Ph.D. Dissertation (Zoology), Univ. of Calif., Berkeley.

Le Cren, E.D. and M.W. Holdgate (Eds.). 1962. The exploitation of natural animal populations. John Wiley and Sons, Inc., N.Y. 309 p.

Lederberg, J. 1965. Computers and the life sciences. Science 150:1576-1577.

Ledley, R.S. 1964. High-speed automatic analysis of biomedical pictures. Science 146:216-223.

Ledley, R.S. 1965. Use of computers in biology and medicine. McGraw-Hill, New York.

Lee, A.B. 1950. The microtomist's vade mecum. 11th ed. Blakiston Co., Philadelphia. 753 p.

Lee, S.L.B. 1963. Migration in the Outer Hebrides studied by radar. Ibis 105:493-515.

Leedy, D.L. 1948. Aerial photographs, their interpretation and suggested uses in wildlife management. J. Wildl. Mgmt. 12:191-210.

Leftwich, A.W. 1963. A student's dictionary of zoology. Constable, London. 290 p.

Lehman, D. 1966. Woodcock hunting. Mich. Cons. 35(4):24-27.

Lehman, V.W. 1941. Atwater's prairie chicken, its life history and management. USDI, Fish and Wildl. Serv., N. Amer. Fauna. 57.

LeMunyan, C.D., W. White, E. Nyberg, and J.J. Christian. 1959. Design of a minature radio transmitter for use in animal studies. J. Wildl. Mgmt. 23:107-110.

Lenhoff, E.S. 1966. Tools of biology. The Macmillan Co., New York, 120 p.

Lensink, C.J. 1964. Distribution of recoveries from bandings of ducks. Spec. Sci. Rep., Wildl. No. 89. U.S. Fish and Wildl. Ser. 146 p.

Leopold, A. 1933. Game management. Charles Scribner's Sons, New York. 481 p.

Leopold, A.S. 1939. Age determination in quail. J. Wildl. Mgmt. 3:261-265.

Leopold, A.S. 1959. Wildlife of Mexico. Univ. Calif. Press, Berkeley. 568 p.

Leopold, A.S., S.A. Cain, I.N. Gabrielson, C.M. Cottam, and T.L. Kimball. 1964. Predator and rodent control in the United States. A special report available from USDI. 28 p.

Leopold, F. 1951. A study of nesting wood ducks in Iowa. Condor 53:209-220.

Leslie, A.S. and A.E. Shipley. 1912. The grouse in health and disease. Smith, Elder and Co., London.

Leslie, P.H. 1945. On the use of matrices in certain population mathematics. Biometrika 33(3):183-212.

Leslie, P.H. 1948. Some further notes on the use of matrices in population mathematics. Biometrika 35(3,4): 213-245.

Leslie, P.H. 1952. The estimation of population parameters by means of the capture-recapture method. II. The estimation of total numbers. Biometrika 39:363-388.

Leslie, P.H. and D. Chitty. 1951. The estimation of population parameters from data obtained by means of the capture-recapture method. I. The maximum likelihood equations for estimating the death rate. Biometrika 38:269-292.

Leslie, P.H., D. Chitty, and Helen Chitty. 1953. The estimation of population parameters from data obtained by means of the capture-recapture method. III. An example of the practical applications of the method. Biometrika 40:137-169.

Leslie, P.H., and D.H.S. Davis. 1939. An attempt to determine the absolute number of rats on a given area. J. Animal Ecol. 8:94-113.

Levine, N.D. 1955. A punched card system for filing parasitological bibliography cards. J. Parasitology 41(4):343-352.

Levy, S.H., J.J. Levy, and R.A. Bishop. 1966. Use of tape recorded female quail calls during the breeding season. J. Wildl. Mgmt. 30(2):426-428.

Lewin, V. 1960. Reproduction and development of young in a population of California quail. PhD Diss., Univ. Calif., Berkeley.

Lewis, H.F. 1939. Size of sets of eggs of the American eider. J. Wildl. Mgmt. 3:70-73.

Lewis, N. (Ed.) 1964. The new Roget's thesaurus in dictionary form. G.P. Putnam's Sons, New York. 552 p.

Libby, J.L. and J.I. Abrams. 1966. Anticoagulant rodenticide in paper tubes for control of meadow mice. J. Wildl. Mgmt. 30:512-518.

Liers, E.E. 1951. Notes on the river otter (Lutra canadensis). J. Mammal. 32:1-9.

Ligda, M.G.H. 1958. Radar observations of blackbird flights. Texas J. Sci. 10(3):255-265.

Ligon, J.S. 1961. New Mexico birds and where to find them. Univ. New Mexico Press, Albuquerque. 360 p.

Lincoln, F.C., and S.P. Baldwin. 1929. Manual for bird banders. USDA Misc. Publ. No. 58, Washington, D.C. 112 p.

Lindsey, A.A. 1937. The Weddell seal in the Bay of Wales, Antarctica. J. Mammal. 18:127-144.

Linduska, J.P. 1943. A gross study of the bursa of Fabricius and cock spurs as age indicators in the ring-necked pheasant. Auk 60:426-437.

Linduska, J.P. 1945. Age determination in the ring-necked pheasant. J. Wildl. Mgmt. 9(2):152-154.

Lion, K.S. 1959. Instrumentation in scientific research. McGraw-Hill Book Co., New York, 324 p.

Llewellyn, L.M. 1950. Reduction of mortality in live-trapping mice. J. Wildl. Mgmt. 14:84-85.

Longhurst, W.M. 1954. The fecal pellet group deposition rate of domestic sheep. J. Wildl. Mgmt. 18:418-419.

Longhurst, W.M. 1964. Evaluation of the eye lens technique for aging Columbian black-tailed deer. J. Wildl. Mgmt. 28(4):773-784.

Longhurst, W.M., A.S. Leopold, and R.F. Dasmann. 1952. A survey of California deer herds, their ranges and management problems. Calif. Dept. Fish and Game, Game Bull. No. 6, 136 p.

Longhurst, W.M., M.B. Jones, R.R. Parks, L.W. Neubauer, and M.W. Cummings. 1962. Fences for controlling deer damage. Univ. Calif., Davis. Agric. Exp. Sta. Circ. 514. 15 p.

Lord, R.D., Jr. 1957. Estimation of fox populations. Sc.D. Dissertation, School of Public Hygiene and Public Health. John Hopkins University, Baltimore, Md.

Lord, R.D., Jr. 1959. Comparison of early morning and spotlight roadside census for cottontails. J. Wildl. Mgmt. 23:458-460.

Lord, R.D. 1962. Aging deer and determination of their nutritional status by the lens technique. Proc. 1st Nat. White-tailed Deer Symposium. p. 89-93.

Lord, R.D., Jr. 1964. Seasonal changes in the activity of penned cottontail rabbits. Animal Behaviour 12(1): 38-41.

Lord, R.D., Jr., F.C. Bellrose, and W.W. Cochran. 1962. Radio-telemetry of the respiration of a flying duck. Science 137(3523):39-40.

Lotka, A.J. 1939. Théorie analytique des associations biologiques: Deuxième partie: Analyse demographique avec application particuliere a lespèce hamine. p. 1-149, Actualitiés Sceintifiques et Industrielles. Hermann et cie., Paris. 780 p.

Lovaas, A.L., J.L. Egan, and R.R. Knight. 1966. Aerial counting of two Montana elk herds. J. Wildl. Mgmt. 30(2):364-369.

Loveless, C.M., J.D. Coffelt, D.E. Medin, and L.E. Yeager. 1963. A photoelectric-cell device for use in wildlife research. AIBS Bull. 13(4): 55-57.

Loveless, C.M., G.N. Sarconi, H.W. DeGrazio, and C.H. Halvorson. 1966. A simplified data-recording method. J. Wildl. Mgmt. 30(3):519-522.

Low, J.B. 1941. Nesting of the ruddy duck in Iowa. Auk 58:506-517.

Low, J.B. 1945. Ecology and management of the redhead. *Nyroca americana*. Ecol. Monogr. 15:35-69.

Low, J.B. 1957. Banding with mist nets. Bird-Banding 28:115-128.

Low, J.B., and C. Pierce. 1950. Wild ducks and geese—field to kitchen care. Utah Agr. Ext. Service Bull. 206, Logan.

Low, S.H. 1935. Methods of trapping shorebirds. Bird-Banding 6:16-22.

Low, W.A., and I. McT. Cowan. 1963. Age determination of deer by annular structure of dental cementum. J. Wildl. Mgmt. 27(3):466-471.

Lowe, C.E. 1958. Ecology of the swamp rabbit in Georgia. J. Mammal. 39(1): 116-127.

Lowe, C.H. (Ed.) 1964. The vertebrates of Arizona. Univ. Arizona Press, Tucson. 259 p.

Lowe, J.I. 1956. Breeding density and productivity of mourning doves on a county-wide basis in Georgia. J. Wildl. Mgmt. 20:428-433.

Lucas, F.A. 1950. The preparation of rough skeletons. Amer. Mus. of Nat. History, Science Guide no. 59. 20 p.

Luce, R.D. and H. Raiffa. 1957. Games and decisions: introduction and critical survey. John Wiley and Sons, Inc., New York 509 p.

Lydekker, R. 1898. The deer of all lands: a history of the family Cervidae living and extinct. Rowland Ward, London. 329 p.

Lyon, M.W., Jr. 1936. The mammals of Indiana. Amer. Midland Naturalist 17:1-384.

Lysaght, A. (Ed.) 1959. Directory of natural history and other field study societies in Great Britain. British Assoc. for the Adv. of Sci., London. 217 p.

M

MacArthur, R.H. and J.H. Connell. 1966. The biology of populations. John Wiley and Sons, Inc., New York. 200 p.

MacConnell, W.P. 1957. Cover mapping Massachusetts, from aerial photographs. Proc. Soc. Amer. Foresters, p. 159-162, Syracuse, N.Y.

MacGregor, W.G. 1950. The artificial roost - a new management tool for California quail. Calif. Fish and Game 36(3):316-319.

MacGregor, W.G. 1958. A technique for obtaining food habits material from nestling doves. Calif. Fish and Game 44:77-78.

MacKay, A.A. 1962. An easy method of trapping small taiga mammals in winter. J. Mammal. 43(4):556-557.

MacKay, R.S. 1965. Telemetering from within the body of animals and man: Endoradiosondes, p. 147-235. *In:* C.A. Caceres, (Ed.), Biomedical telemetry. Academic Press, New York.

Mackworth-Praed, C.W., and C.H.B. Grant. 1957. Birds of Eastern and North Eastern Africa. 2nd ed. Longmans, Green & Co., London. 2 vol.

MacLennan, J.M. (Comp.). 1958. Russian-English bird glossary. Queen's Printer and Controller of Stationery, Ottawa, Canada. 94 p.

MacLulich, D.A. 1951. A new technique of animal census, with examples. J. Mammal. 32:318-328.

Maguire, H.F., and C.W. Severinghaus. 1954. Wariness as an influence on age composition of deer killed by hunters. N.Y. Fish and Game J. 1(1): 98-109.

Mahoney, R. 1966. Laboratory techniques in zoology. Butterworths, Washington, D.C. 404 p.

Makepeace, Laura I. 1956. Rabbits: A subject bibliography. Denver Public Library, Bibliographical Center for Research, Rocky Mountain Region, Spec. Bibliog. no. 3. 81 p.

Malclés, L.N. 1958. Les sources du travail bibliographique spécialisées: sciences exactes et techniques. Tome III. Librarie E. Droz, Geneva. 575 p.

Maley, G.A., and E.J. Skiko. 1964. Modern digital computers. Prentice-Hall, New Jersey. xvi + 216 p.

Mansfield, A.W. 1958. The biology of the Atlantic walrus *Odobenus rosmarus rosmarus* (Linnaeus) in the eastern Canadian Arctic. Fish Res. Bd. Canada Manuscript Rep. Ser. (Biological). No. 653, 13 + 146.

Manville, R.H. 1962. Specialized mammalian terminology. Turtox News 40:242-247.

Marchinton, R.L. 1964. Activity cycles and mobility of central Florida deer based on telemetric and observational data. M.S. Thesis. Univ. of Fla., Gainesville.

Marks, S.A., and A.W. Erickson. 1966. Age determination in the black bear. J. Wildl. Mgmt. 30(2):389-410.

Marlow, B.J. 1956. Chloral hydrate narcosis for the live capture of mammals. CSIRO Wildl. Res. 1:63-65.

Marples, B.J. and L. Gurr. 1943. A mechanism for recording automatically the nesting habits of birds. Emu 43:67-71.

Marquardt, R.E. 1960. Smokeless powder cannon with lightweight netting for trapping geese. J. Wildl. Mgmt. 24:425-427.

Marquardt, R.E. 1960. Investigations into high intensity projectile equipment for net trapping geese. Proc. Oklahoma Acad. Sci. 41:218-223.

578

Marsh, R.E., R.E. Cole, and W.E. Howard. 1967. Laboratory tests on the effectiveness of Prolin mouse tubes. J. Wildl. Mgmt. 31:342-344.

Marshall, W.H. 1951. An age determination method for the pine marten. J. Wildl. Mgmt. 15:276-283.

Marshall, W.H. 1965. Ruffed grouse behavior. BioScience 15(2):92-94.

Marshall, W.H., G.W. Gullion, and R.G. Schwab. 1962. Early summer activities of porcupines as determined by radio-positioning techniques. J. Wildl. Mgmt. 26(1):75-79.

Marshall, W.H., and J.J. Kupa. 1963. Development of radio-telemetry techniques for ruffed grouse studies. Trans. N. Amer. Wildl. Conf. 28: 443-456.

Martin, A.C. 1946. The comparative internal morphology of seeds. Amer. Midland Naturalist 36:513-660.

Martin, A.C. 1949. Procedures in wildlife food studies. USDI Wildl. Leaf. 325, 10 p.

Martin, A.C. 1960. Food-habits procedures p. 13:1 to 13:9 In H.S. Mosby (Ed.) Manual of Game Investigational Techniques, The Wildlife Society, Washington, D.C.

Martin, A.C., and W.D. Barkley. 1961. Seed identification manual. Univ. of Calif. Press, Berkeley. 221 p.

Martin, A.C., R.H. Gensch, and C.P. Brown. 1946. Alternative methods in upland gamebird food analysis. J. Wildl. Mgmt. 10:8-12.

Martin, A.C., H.S. Zim, and A.L. Nelson. 1951. American wildlife and plants: a guide to wildlife food habits. McGraw-Hill, New York. 500 p.

Martin, F.W. 1964. Woodcock age and sex determination from wings. J. Wildl. Mgmt. 28(2):287-293.

Martin, R.L. 1960. Foreign scientific literature in translation. Amer. Doc. 11(2):135-150.

Martinson, R.K. 1966. Proportion of recovered duck bands that are reported. J. Wildl. Mgmt. 30(2):264-268.

Martinson, R.K. and C.F. Kaczynski. 1967. Factors influencing waterfowl counts on aerial surveys, 1961-66. USDI, Fish and Wildl. Ser. Special Sci. Report, Wildlife No. 105.

Mascher, J.W., B.O. Stolt, and L. Wallin. 1962. Migration in spring recorded by radar and field observations in Sweden. Ibis 104:205-215.

Massey, A.B. 1936. Directions for collecting and mailing plants for identification and making a plant collection. Va. Agr. Ext. Service Circ. E-333, Blacksburg.

Mathiak, H.A. 1938. A rapid method of cross-sectioning mammalian hairs. J. Wildl. Mgmt. 2(3):162-164.

Mathiak, H.A. 1938. A key to hair of the mammals of Southern Michigan. 2(4):251-268.

Mathiak, H.A. 1965. Pothole blasting for wildlife. Wisconsin Cons. Dept., Madison. Publication No. 352, 31 p.

Mathiak, H.A. and A.F. Linde. 1956. Studies on level ditching for marsh management. Wisconsin Cons. Dept., Madison. Tech. Wildl. Bull. No. 12, 48 p.

Matthiessen, P. 1959. Wildlife in America. Viking Press, New York. 304 p.

Mayer, W.V. 1952. The hair of California mammals with keys to the dorsal guard hairs of California mammals. Amer. Midland Naturalist 48:480-512.

Mayer, W.V. 1957. A method for determining the activity of burrowing mammals. J. Mammal. 38:531.

Mayfield, H. 1953. A census of the Kirtland's warbler. Auk 70:17-20.

Mayr, E., and D. Amadon. 1951. A classification of recent birds. Amer. Mus. Novit. no. 1496, 42 p.

Mayr, E., E.G. Linsley, and R.L. Usinger. 1953. Methods and principles of systematic zoology. McGraw-Hill Book Co., New York. 328 p.

McAtee, W.L. 1908. Food habits of the grosbeaks. Biol. Survey Bull. No. 32, 92 p.

McAtee, W.L. 1911. Woodpeckers in relation to trees and wood products. Biol. Survey. Bull. No. 39, 99 p.

McAtee, W.L. 1912. Methods of estimating the contents of bird stomachs. Auk 29:449-464.

McAtee, W.L. 1933. Economic ornithology, p. 111-129. In Fifty years progress of American ornithology. Amer. Ornithologists Union, Lancaster, Pa. 249 p.

McAtee, W.L. (Ed.) 1945. The ringnecked pheasant and its management in North America. Amer. Wildl. Inst., Washington, D.C. 320 p.

McCabe, R.A. and A.S. Hawkins. 1946. The Hungarian partridge in Wisconsin. Amer. Midland Naturalist 36(1): 1-75.

McCall, J.D. 1954. Portable live trap for ducks, with improved gathering box. J. Wildl. Mgmt. 18:405-407.

McClure, H. 1939. Cooing activity and censusing of the Mourning Dove. J. Wildl. Mgmt. 3:323-328.

McClure, H.E. 1944. Censusing pheasants by detonations. J. Wildl. Mgmt. 8:61-65.

McClure, H.E. 1945. Comparison of census methods for pheasants in Nebraska. J. Wildl. Mgmt. 9:38-45.

McClure, H.E. 1956. Methods of bird netting in Japan applicable to wildlife management problems. Bird-Banding 27:67-73.

McCormick, J.A. 1958. Radioisotopes in animal physiology; a selected list of references. TID-3515. USAEC, Tech. Info. Ser., Oak Ridge, Tenn. 118 p.

McCracken, H. and H. Van Cleve. 1947. Trapping: the craft and science of catching fur-bearing animals. Barnes Co., N.Y., 196 p.

McCulloch, J.S.G., and L.M. Talbot. 1965. Comparison of weight estimation methods for wild animals and domestic livestock. J. Appl. Ecol. 2(1):59-69.

McDiarmid, A. 1962. Diseases of free-living wild animals. FAO Agr. Studies No. 57, ix + 119 p.

McDowell, R.D. 1956. Productivity of the wild turkey in Virginia. Va. Comm. Game and Inland Fisheries Tech. Bull. No. 1, Richmond. 44 p.

McEwen, L.C., and R.L. Brown. 1966. Acute toxicity of dieldrin and malathion to wild sharp-tailed grouse. J. Wildl. Mgmt., 30(3):604-611.

McEwan, E.H. and A.J. Wood. 1966. Growth and development of the barren ground caribou. I. Heart girth, hind foot length, and body weight relationships. Canadian J. Zool. 44(3):401-411.

McGill University. 1966. A dictionary catalogue of the Blacker-Wood library of zoology and ornithology. G.K. Hall, Boston, Mass. 9 vol.

McGowan, T.A. 1952. An intensive study of the call count as a census method for mourning doves on the Georgia Piedmont. USDI, Fish and Wildl. Ser., Special Sci. Report No. 17:4-7.

McGowan, T.A. 1953. The call count as a census method for breeding mourning doves in Georgia. J. Wildl. Mgmt. 17:437-445.

McGrady, E., Jr. 1938. The embryology of the opossum. Amer. Anat. Mem. 16:233.

McKinley, D. 1960. A chronology and bibliography of wildlife in Missouri. Univ. Missouri Bull. 61(13):1-128.

McLaughlin, C.L. and D. Grice. 1952. The effectiveness of large scale erection of wood duck boxes as a management procedure. Trans. N. Amer. Wildl. Conf. 17:242-259.

McLean, D.D. 1962. Water developments for upland game birds. Dept. Fish and Game, Sacramento, Calif. Game Mgt. Leaflet no. 5, 10 p.

McMillan, I. 1959. An improved quail roost. Central California Sportsman 19(10):349.

Mech, L.D. 1965. Sodium pentobarbital as an anesthetic for raccoons. J. Mammal. 46(2):343-344.

Mech, L.D. 1967. Telemetry as a technique in the study of predation. J. Wildl. Mgmt., 31(3):492-496.

Mech, L.D., Valerain B. Kuechle, D.W. Warner, and J.R. Tester. 1965. A collar for attaching radio transmitters to rabbits, hares, and raccoons. J. Wildl. Mgmt. 29(4):898-902.

Mech, L.D., J.R. Tester, and D.W. Warner. 1966. Fall daytime resting habits of raccoons as determined by telemetry. J. Mammal. 47(3):450-466.

Meisel, M. 1924-1929. A bibliography of American natural history: the pioneer century, 1769-1865. The Premier Pub. Co., New York. 3 vol.

Melchior, H.R., and F.A. Iwen. 1965. Trapping, restraining, and marking arctic ground squirrels for behavioral observations. J. Wildl. Mgmt. 29(4):671-678.

Mendall, H.L. 1958. The ring-necked duck in the northeast. Univ. Maine Bull. 30(16), 317 p.

Mendall, H.L. and C.M. Aldous. 1943. The ecology and management of the American woodcock. Maine Coop-Wildl. Res. Unit. Orono. 201 p.

Merriam, H. 1962. Immobilization technique for Sitka black-tail deer in southeast Alaska. Alaska Dept. Fish and Game Inform. Leaflet No. 18, 6 p.

Merriam. H.G. 1963. Low frequency telemetric monitoring of woodchuck movements, p. 155-171. In L.E. Slater. (Ed.) Biotelemetry. MacMillan Co., New York.

Merriam, H.G. 1966. Temporal distribution of woodchuck interburrow movements. J. Mammal. 47(1):103-110.

Mess, C.E.K. 1951. Photography. MacMillan Co., New York. 227 p.

Metcalfe, C.R. 1960. Anatomy of the monocotyleclons, I: Gramineae. Oxford, Clarendon Press, Amen House, London.

Michener, M.C., and C. Walcott. 1966. Navigation of single homing pigeons: airplane observations by radio tracking. Science 154(3747):410-413.

Middleton, A.D. 1935. Factors controlling the population of the partridge (Perdix perdix) in Great Britain. Proc. Zool. Soc. London. p. 795-815.

Millais, J.G. 1897. British deer and their horns. Henry Sotheran and Co., London. 224 p.

Miller, A.W., and B.D. Collins. 1953. A nesting study of Canada geese on Tule Lake and Lower Klamath National Refuges, Siskiyou County, California. Calif. Fish and Game 39:385-396.

Miller, A.W. and B.D. Collins. 1954. A nesting study of ducks and coots on Tule Lake and Lower Klamath National Wildlife Refuges. Calif. Fish and Game 40:17-37.

Miller, A.W. and P.H. Arend. 1960. How to grow watergrass for ducks

580

in California. Calif. Dept. Fish and Game, Sacramento, Game Mgmt. Leaflet No. 1, 16 p.

Miller, C. W. 1942. Principles of photographic reproduction. MacMillan Co., New York. 353 p.

Miller, D. R., C. Maguire, and E. Heiman. 1965. An economical, portable intercommunication system for aerial surveys and reconnaissance. J. Wildl. Mgmt. 29(4):896-898.

Miller, G. S., Jr., and R. Kellogg. 1955. List of North American recent mammals. U.S. Natl. Mus. Bull. 205. 954 p.

Miller, H. W. 1957. A modified cannon for use on the projected net trap. Unnumbered pamphlet dist. by Neb. Game, Forestation, and Parks Commission. Bassett. 6 p. (As quoted by Marquardt, 1961).

Miller, W. R. 1962. Automatic activating mechanism for waterfowl nest trap. J. Wildl. Mgmt. 26(4):402-404.

Milne, L. J., and Margery Milne. 1959. Foresight and hindsight on a punchcard bibliography. Amer. Doc. 10(1):78-84.

Mitchell, R. T. and J. T. Linehan. 1967. Protecting corn from blackbirds. USDI Wildl. Leaf. 476, 8 pp.

Moessner, K. E. 1963. Why not use blueprints? Res. Note INT-4, Intermountain Forest and Range Expt. Sta., USFS, Ogden, Utah 2 p.

Moffitt, J. 1942. Apparatus for marking wild animals with colored dyes. J. Wildl. Mgmt. 6:312-318.

Mohr, C. E. 1942. Bat tagging in Pennsylvania turnpike tunnels. J. Mammal. 23:375-379.

Montgomery, G. G. 1961. A modification of the nicotine dart capture method. J. Wildl. Mgmt. 25:101-102.

Montgomery, G. G. 1963. Freezing, decomposition and raccoon lens

weights. J. Wildl. Mgmt. 27(3):481-483.

Montgomery, G. G. 1964. Tooth eruption in the preweaned raccoons. J. Wildl. Mgmt. 28(3):582-584.

Moore, A. W. 1940. Wild animals damage to seed and seedlings on cutover Douglas fir lands of Oregon and Washington. USDA Tech. Bull. 706, 28 p.

Moore, A. W. 1943. The pocket gopher in relation to yellow pine reproduction. J. Mammal. 24:271-272.

Moore, A. M. and E. O. Kluth. 1966. A low frequency radio-location system for monitoring an armadillo population. Proc. Natl. Telemetering Conf. p. 302-304.

Moran, P. A. P. 1951. A mathematical theory of animal trapping. Biometrika 38:307-311.

Morejohn, G. V., and W. E. Howard. 1956. Molt in the pocket gopher, (Thomomys bottae.) J. Mammal. 37:201-212.

Morgan, A. H. 1939. Field book of animals in winter. G. P. Putnam's Sons, New York. 528 p.

Morris, D. 1965. The mammals: a guide to the living species. Hodder and Stoughton, London. 448 p.

Morris, M. J. 1967. An abstract bibliography of statistical methods in grassland research. USDA Misc. Publ. 1030, 222 p.

Morrison, J. A., C. E. Trainer, and P. L. Wright. 1959. Breeding season in elk as determined from known-age embryos. J. Wildl. Mgmt. 23:27-34.

Morse, M. A. 1943. Technique for reducing man-power in deer drive census. J. Wildl. Mgmt. 7(2):217-220.

Morse, M. A. and D. S. Balser. 1961. Fox calling as a hunting technique. J. Wildl. Mgmt. 25:148-154.

Morton, M. L. 1965. An apparatus for continuous recording of food intake in caged birds. Ecology 46(6):888-890.

Mosby, H. S. 1955. Live trapping objectionable animals. Va. Polytechnic Inst. Agr. Ext. Service Circ. 667, Blacksburg, 4 p.

Mosby, H. S. 1963. Using wildlife literature. p. 334-341. In Wildlife investigational techniques. 2nd ed. The Wildlife Society, Washington, D.C.

Mosby, H. S. 1963. Reporting research results p. 342-354. In H. S. Mosby (Ed.) Wildlife investigational techniques. 2nd ed., The Wildlife Society, Washington, D.C.

Mosby, H. S., and D. E. Cantner. 1956. The use of avertin in capturing wild turkeys and as an oral-basal anaesthetic for other wild animals. Southwest Veterinarian 9:132-136.

Mosby, H. S., and C. O. Handley. 1943. The wild turkey in Virginia: Its status, life history, and management. Va. Comm. of Game and Island Fisheries, Richmond. 281 p.

Mosby, H. S., and W. S. Overton. 1950. Fluctuations in the quail population on the Virginia Polytechnic Institute farms. Trans. N. Amer. Wildl. Conf. 15:347-355.

Mossman, A. S. 1960. A color marking technique. J. Wildl. Mgmt. 24:104.

Mossman, A. S., P. A. Johnstone, C. A. R. Savory, and R. F. Dasmann. 1963. Neck snare for live capture of African ungulates. J. Wildl. Mgmt. 27(1):132-135.

Mossman, A. S., and B. G. R. Reynolds. 1962. Some African techniques for capturing mammals. J. Mammal. 43(2):419-420.

Moyer, J. W. 1953. Practical taxidermy: a working guide. Ronald Press Co., New York. 126 p.

Mueggler, W. F. 1966. Herbicide treatment of browse on a big-game winter range in northern Idaho. J. Wildl. Mgmt. 30(1):141-151.

Mundy, K. R. D., and W. A. Fuller. 1964. Age determination in the grizzly bear. J. Wildl. Mgmt. 28(4):863-866.

Murie, A. 1944. The wolves of Mt. McKinley. U.S. Park Service Fauna of the National Parks. Fauna Series no. 5, 238 p.

Murie, A. 1948. Cattle on grizzly bear range. J. Wildl. Mgmt. 12:57-72.

Murie, O. J. 1928. Weighing game animals. J. Mammal. 9(1):74-75.

Murie, O. J. 1946. Evaluating duplications in analysis of coyote scats. J. Wildl. Mgmt. 10:275-276.

Murie, O. J. 1951. The elk of North America. Stackpole Co., Harrisburg, Pa. 376 p.

Murie, O. J. 1954. A field guide to animal tracks. Hoghton Mifflin. Boston, Mass. 374 p.

Murphy, D. A. and J. A. Coates. 1966. The effects of dietrary protein on deer. Trans. N. Amer. Wildl. and Nat. Res. Conf. 31:129-139.

Murra, Kathrine O. 1962. International scientific organizations: a guide to their library, documentation, and information services. Library of Congress, Washington, D.C. 794 p.

Murton, R. K. 1962. Narcotics v. woodpigeons. Agriculture 69(7):336-339.

Murton, R. K., A. J. Isaacson, and N. J. Westwood. 1965. Capturing columbids at the nest with stupefying baits. J. Wildl. Mgmt. 29(3):647-649.

Musil, Albina F. 1963. Identification of crop and weed seeds. Agr. Marketing Service, USDA Handbook No. 219, 171 p. + 43 plates.

Musser, G. G. and E. T. Hooper. 1966. Bibliography: mammalogy. BioScience 16(4):291-292.

Myres, M. T. 1964. Technical details of radar equipment detecting birds and a bibliography of papers reporting the observation of birds with radar. Natl. Res. Council of Can., Assoc. Committee on Bird Hazards to Aircraft. Field Note No. 9 (mimeo.) 21 p.

Myres, M. T. 1966. Western Canadian studies of birds migration by means of radar. Proc. 14th Int. Ornithological Congr. Vol. 1 (Abstract).

N

Nagel, W. O. 1960. Make your technical writing useful. Amer. Fisheries Soc. and Wildl. Soc. Special Publication, Box 483, McLean, Va., 31 p.

Nastuk, W. L. (Ed.) 1964. Physical techniques in biological research: Electrophysiological methods vol. 5(A), Academic Press, New York, 460 p.

National Academy of Sciences. 1959. Joint United States-Canadian tables of feed composition. Nat. Acad. Sci., Nat. Res. Council Publ. 659, Wash., D.C. 80 p.

National Academy of Sciences. 1961. Scientific and technical societies of the United States and Canada. 7th ed. NAS-NRC Pub. 900. v. p.

National Agricultural Library. 1963. Subject heading list: preliminary edition. U.S. Government Printing Office, Washington, D.C. 4 vol.

National Agricultural Library. 1965. Serial publications indexed in Bibliography of Agriculture. USDA Lib. List no. 75, revised. 79 p.

National Agricultural Library. 1966. The dictionary catalog of the National Agricultural Library, 1862-1965. Rowman and Littlefield, New York. 68 vol.

National Agricultural Library. 1967. Agricultural/biological vocabulary. U.S. Government Printing Office. Washington, D.C. 2 vol.

National Federation of Science Abstracting and Indexing Services.

1963. A guide to the world's abstracting and indexing services in science and technology. Report no. 102. The Federation, Washington, D.C. 183 p.

National Library of Medicine. 1966. Medical subject headings. Index Medicus 7 (Pt. 2 of No. 1):1-363.

National Referral Center for Science and Technology. 1965. A directory of information resources in the United States: physical sciences, biological sciences, engineering. Library of Congress, Washington, D.C. 352 p.

National Referral Center for Science and Technology. 1966. A directory of information resources in the United States: water. Library of Congress, Washington. 248 p.

National Referral Center for Science and Technology. 1967. A directory of information resources in the United States: Federal government. Library of Congress, Washington. 411 p.

National Science Foundation. 1961. Specialized science information services in the United States. N.S.F., Office of Science Information Service, Washington, D.C. 528 p.

National Wildlife Federation. 1966. Conservation directory. Natl. Wildl. Fed., Washington, D.C. 123 p.

Naylor, A. E. 1953. Production of the Canada goose on Honey Lake Refuge, Lassen County, California. Calif. Fish and Game 39:83-95.

Naylor, A. E., and E. G. Hunt. 1954. A nesting study and population survey of Canada geese on the Susan River, Lassen County, California. Calif. Fish and Game 40:5-16.

Naylor, A. E. 1962. Wood ducks and nest boxes. Calif. Dept. Fish and Game, Sacramento. Game Mangt. Leaflet No. 6, 8 p.

Neal, B. J. 1959. Technique of trapping and tagging the collared peccary. J. Wildl. Mgmt. 23:11-16.

582

Neave, S.A. 1939-1940. Nomenclator zoologicus. Zoological Society of London, Regent's Park, London. 4 vol. [Two supplements have been published.]

Neave, S.A. 1950. Concerning the zoological record. Science 112(2921): 761-762.

Needy, J.R. 1966. Filing systems. National Recreation and Park Assoc., 8 West 8th St., New York, N.Y. 10011. Management Aids Bul. 57.

Neely, W.W. 1956. How long do duck foods last under water. Trans. N. Amer. Wildl. Conf. 21:191-198.

Neilsen, E.T. and J.S. Haeger. 1955. A simple method of estimating low light intensities. Ecology 36(3):525-526.

Nellis, C.H. 1966. Lens weights of mule deer fetuses. J. Wildl. Mgmt. 30(2): 417-419.

Nelson, B.A. 1948. Pheasant data from a two-year tag study in South Dakota. J. Wildl. Mgmt. 12:20-31.

Nelson, L.K. 1955. A pheasant neck tag. J. Wildl. Mgmt. 19:414-415.

Neronov, V.M. 1962. On the possibility of using observations of predatory birds for determining the nature of rodent distribution over a small range. In Problems of Ecology, Kievsk, Univ. 4:132.

Nesbit, R. 1959. Use of a mechanical goose caller for management purposes. Wis. Cons. Bul. 24(4):23.

New, J.G. 1958. Dyes for studying the movements of small mammals. J. Mammal. 39:416-429.

New, J.G. 1959. Additional uses of dyes for studying the movements of small mammals. J. Wildl. Mgmt. 23:348-351.

Newby, F.E., and V.D. Hawley. 1954. Progress on a marten live trapping study. Trans. N. Amer. Wildl. Conf. 19:452-462.

Newman, D.E. 1959. Factors influencing the winter roadside count of cottontails. J. Wildl. Mgmt. 23:290-294.

Newman, D.W. 1964. Instrumental methods of experimental biology. Macmillan Co., N.Y. xiii + 560 p.

Newton, A. 1893-1896. A dictionary of birds. Adam and Charles Black, London. 1088 p.

Nice, Margaret M. 1938. The biological significance of bird weights. Bird-Banding 9(1):1-11.

Nicholson, A.J. 1954. An outline of the dynamics of animal populations. Aust. J. Zool. 2:9-65.

Nisbet, I.C.T. 1963. Quantitative study of migration with 23-centimetre radar. Ibis 105:435-460.

Nisbet, I.C.T. 1963. Measurements with radar of the height of nocturnal migration over Cape Cod, Mass. Bird-Banding 34:57-67.

Nixon, C.M. 1964. An improved method of mapping forested areas. J. Wildl. Mgmt. 28:870-871.

Nixon, C.M., W.R. Edwards and L. Eberhardt. 1967. Estimating squirrel abundance from livetrapping data. J. Wildl. Mgmt. 31:96-101.

Norton, H.W., T.G. Scott, R. Hanson, and W.D. Klimstra. 1961. Whistling-cock indices and bobwhite populations in autumn. J. Wildl. Mgmt. 25: 398-403.

Novikov, G.A. 1962. Carnivorous mammals of the fauna of the USSR. Keys to the Fauna of the USSR. no. 62. [Transl. from Russian]. Israel Program for Scientific translations, Jerusalem. 293 p.

Novoceh, M., and K. Hudec. 1961. Analysis of the food of the starling by remote control photography. Med. and Biol. Illustration 11(3):172-177.

Numata, M. 1958. Japanese publications

in the field of ecology. Ecology 39(2):566-567.

O

Oberholser, H.C. 1906. The North American eagles and their economic relations. Biol. Surv. Bull. No. 27. 31 p.

Odum, E.P. and E.J. Kuenzler. 1955. Measurement of territory and home range size in birds. Auk 72:128-137.

Office of Water Resources Research, USDI. 1966. Water resources thesaurus. Washington, D.C. 237 p.

Ognev, S.I. 1962-1966. Mammals of the USSR and adjacent countries. [Transl. from Russian]. Israel Program for Scientific Translations, Jerusalem. 7 vol.

Olsen, P.F. 1959. Dental patterns as age indicators in muskrats. J. Wildl. Mgmt. 23:228-231.

Olson, E.C. 1958. Russian literature in the natural sciences. Lib. Quart. 28: 295-307.

Olson, J.S. 1963. Analog computer models for movement of nuclides through eco-systems. In Schultz, V., and A.W. Klement, Jr., Radioecology. Reinhold Publishing Co., N.Y. xx + 746 p.

Omand, D.N. 1951. A study of populations of fish based on catch effort statistics. J. Wildl. Mgmt. 15:88-98.

O'Neal, L.R. 1964. Electronic data processing systems, a self-instructional programmed manual. Prentice-Hall, New Jersey, xiv + 408 p.

Oregon State University. 1967. Herbicide and vegetation management. School of Forestry, Corvallis, Oregon, 356 p.

Orians, G.H. 1958. A capture-recapture analysis of shearwater population. J. Animal Ecol. 27:71-84.

O'Roke, E.C., and F.N. Hamerstrom, Jr. 1948. Productivity and yield of the George Reserve deer herd. J. Wildl. Mgmt. 12:78-86.

Orr, D.J.C., and S.M. Moore-Gilbert. 1964. Field immobilization of young wildebeest with succinylcholine chloride. East African Wildl. J. 2: 60-66.

Orr, R.T. 1949. Mammals of Lake Tahoe. California Academy of Sciences, San Francisco. 127 p.

Osborn, D.J. 1955. Techniques of sexing beaver, *Castor canadensis*. J. Mammal. 36:141-142.

Osborn, Katherine H., R.A. Yoder, and W.I. West. 1959. Forestry theses accepted by colleges and universities in the United States—Supplement January 1956-June 1958, including additions for 1900-1955. For. Sci. 5(3):293-314.

Osgood, W.H. 1947. Biographical memoir of Clinton Hart Merriam, 1855-1942, p. 1-57. *In* Biographical Memoir. Natl. Acad. of Sci., Washington, D.C. Vol. 24.

Oster, G. (Ed.) 1955-1962. Physical techniques in biological research. Academic Press, New York. 6 vol.

Osterberg, D.M. 1962. Activity of small mammals as recorded by a photographic device. J. Mammal. 43(2): 219-229.

Ostrum, C.E. 1937. Deer and rabbit injury to northern hardwood reproduction. Allegheny Forest Exp. Sta. Tech. Notes No. 15, 2 p. mimeo.

Ostrum, C.E. 1942. Forests and rabbits as well as deer destroy seedlings. USFS, Allegheny Forest Exp. Sta. Tech. Notes No. 33, 2 p. mimeo.

Overman, R.T. 1963. Basic concepts of nuclear chemistry. Selected topics in modern chemistry series. Reinhold Pub. Corp., New York. 116 p.

Overman, R.T. and H.M. Clark. 1960. Radioisotope techniques. McGraw-Hill Book Co., New York. 476 p.

Overton, W.S. 1953. Progress reports for investigations project, W-33-R, April 1 and July 1. Fla. Game and Freshwater Fish Comm., Tallahassee.

Overton, W.S. 1954. A preliminary analysis of the strip birddog quail census. Unpub. Ms., Fla. Game and Freshwater Fish Comm., Tallahassee.

Overton, W.S. 1965. A modification of the Schnabel estimator to account for removal of animals from the population. J. Wildl. Mgmt. 29(2): 392-395.

Overton, W.S., Jr. and J.L. Sincock. 1956. Some uses of mark-sensing in collecting game management data in the field. Proc. 10th Ann. Conf. Southeastern Assoc. Game and Fish Comm. 10:131-134.

Overton, W.S., D.L. Eastman and L.R. Bright. 1969. Application of the stratified Lincoln index to two wintering populations of mule deer. In press.

Ozoga, J.J., and L.W. Gysel. 1965. A mechanical recorder for measuring deer activity. J. Wildl. Mgmt. 29(3): 632-634.

Ozoga, J.J., and E.N. Harger. 1966. Winter activities and feeding habits on Northern Michigan coyotes. J. Wildl. Mgmt. 30:809-818.

P

Page, F.J.T. 1959. Field guide to British deer. Mammal Society of the British Isles, Birmingham. 80 p.

Page, I.H. 1965. Why bibliography? Science 149(3679):8.

Palmer, A.M., and A.T. Kruzas. 1965. Research centers directory. Gale Research Co., Detroit, Michigan. 666 p. [Up-dated by a quarterly loose leaf supplement.]

Palmer, E.L. 1957. Palmer's fieldbook of mammals. E.P. Dutton, New York. 321 p.

Palmer, T.S. 1912. Chronology and index of the more important events in American game protection 1776-1911. USDA Biol. Survey Bull. no. 41, 62 p.

Palmer, W.L. 1959. Sexing live-trapped juvenile ruffed grouse. J. Wildl. Mgmt. 23:111-112.

Pan, H.P., J.W. Coslick, D.T. Harke, and D.G. Decher. 1965. A simple animal support for convenient weighing. J. Wildl. Mgmt. 29(4):890-891.

Parke, N.G. 1958. Guide to the literature of mathematics and physics including related works on engineering science. 2nd rev. ed. Dover Publications, New York. p. 35-67.

Parker, R.A. 1955. A method for removing the effect of recruitment on Petersen-type population estimates. J. Fish. Res. Bd. Can. 12:447-450.

Parker, Sheila M. (Comp.). 1959. Scientific translations: a guide to sources and services. U.S. Public Health Service Publication no. 514 (rev.) 19 p.

Parkins, Phyllis V. 1966. BioSciences information service of Biological Abstracts. Science 152(3724):889-894.

Parmalee, P.W. 1955. Some factors affecting nesting success of the bobwhite quail in east-central Texas. Amer. Midland Naturalist 53:45-55.

Patric, E.F., and W.L. Webb. 1960. An evaluation of three age determination criteria in live beavers. J. Wildl. Mgmt. 24:37-44.

Patric, E.F., A. Longacre, and R.F. Doan. 1965. A modified approach to animal position finding. The Wildlife Telemetry Newsletter 4(2):2 mimeo.

Patrick, N.D. 1961. Estimating total weights of black bears from carcass weights. J. Wildl. Mgmt. 25(1):93.

Patterson, R.L. 1952. The sage grouse in Wyoming. Sage Books, Inc., Denver, Colo. 341 p.

Paulik, G. J. 1962. Use of the Chapman-Robson survival estimate for single- and multi-release tagging experiments. Trans. Amer. Fish. Soc. 91(1):95-98.

Paulik, G. J. 1963. Estimates of mortality rates from tag recoveries. Biometrics 19(1):28-57.

Paynter, R. A., Jr. 1951. Clutch-size and egg mortality of Kent Island Eiders. Ecology 32:497-507.

Pearson, A. H. and G. C. Moore. 1940. Feathers may reveal the age of mourning doves. Ala. Cons. Mag. 1(1):9-10.

Pearson, A. K., and O. P. Pearson. 1955. Natural history and breeding behavior of the Tinamou, *Northoprocta ornata*. Auk 72:113-127.

Pearson, H. A. 1965. Rumen organisms in white-tailed deer from south Texas. J. Wildl. Mgmt. 29:493-496.

Pearson, O. P. 1959. A traffic survey of *Microtus reithrodontomys* runways. J. Mammal. 40:169-180.

Pechanec, J. F. and G. Stewart. 1948. Sagebrush burning—good and bad. USDA, Washington, D.C. Farmers' Bull. No. 1948, 32 p.

Pechanec, J. F., G. Stewart, A. P. Plummer, J. H. Robertson, and A. C. Hull, Jr. 1954. Controlling sagebrush on range lands. USDA, Washington, D.C., Farmers' Bull. No. 2072, 36 p.

Pelikan, J., J. Zejda, and V. Holisova. 1964. On the question of investigating small mammal populations by the quadrate method. Acta Theriologica 9(1):24.

Pendleton, R. C. 1952. Some uses of radioisotopes in ecological research. Ph.D. Diss. Univ. Utah, Logan. 162 p.

Pendleton, R. C. 1956. Uses of marking animals in ecological studies: labeling animals with radioisotopes. Ecology 37:686-689.

Pennak, R. W. 1964. Collegiate dictionary of zoology. Ronald Press, New York. 583 p.

Perkins, H. M. 1954. Animal tracks; the standard guide for identification and characteristics. Stackpole, Harrisburg, Pa. 63 p.

Perkins, J. E. 1945. Biology at Little America III. Proc. Amer. Philos. Soc. 89:270-284.

Peterle, T. J., and L. Eberhardt. 1959. Is the Lincoln index reliable for cottontail censusing? Trans. N. Amer. Wildl. Conf. 24:261-271.

Peters, J. L. 1931 to date. Check-list of birds of the world. Harvard Univ. Press, Cambridge.

Petersen, C. G. J. 1896. The yearly immigration of young plaice into the Limfjord from the German Sea. Rep. Danish Biol. Sta. for 1895 6:1-77.

Peterson, R. L. 1955. North American moose. Univ. of Toronto press, Toronto. 280 p.

Peterson, R. L. 1966. The mammals of eastern Canada. Oxford Univ. Press, Toronto. 465 p.

Peterson, R. S. 1965. Drugs for handling fur seals. J. Wildl. Mgmt. 29(4):688-693.

Peterson, R. T. 1961. A field guide to western birds. 2nd ed. Houghton Mifflin, Boston, Mass. 366 p.

Peterson, R. T., I. J. Ferguson-Lees, and D. I. M. Wallace. 1966. A field guide to the birds of Britain and Europe. 2nd ed. Houghton Mifflin, Boston, Mass. 344 p.

Petraborg, W. H., E. G. Wellein, and V. E. Gunvalson. 1953. Roadside drumming counts: a spring census method for ruffed grouse. J. Wildl. Mgmt. 17:292-295.

Petrides, G. A. 1942. Age determination in American gallinaceous game birds. Trans. N. Amer. Wildl. Conf. 7:308-328.

Petrides, G. A. 1946. Snares and deadfalls. J. Wildl. Mgmt. 10:234-238.

Petrides, G. A. 1949. Viewpoints on the analysis of open season sex and age ratios. Trans. N. Amer. Wildl. Conf. 14:391-410.

Petrides, G. A. 1949. Sex and age determination in the opossum. J. Mammal. 30:364-378.

Petrides, G. A. 1950. The determination of sex and age ratios in fur animals. Amer. Midland Naturalist 43:355-382.

Petrides, G. A. 1951. The determination of sex and age ratios in the cottontail rabbit. Amer. Midland Naturalist 46:312-336.

Petrides, G. A. 1951. Notes on age determination in juvenile European quail. J. Wildl. Mgmt. 15:116-117.

Petrides, G. A. 1951. Notes on age determination in squirrels. J. Mammal. 32:111-112.

Petrides, G. A. 1953. Aerial deer counts. J. Wildl. Mgmt. 17:97-98.

Petrides, G. A. 1954. Estimating the percentage kill in ring-necked pheasants and other game species. J. Wildl. Mgmt. 18:294-297.

Petrides, G. A. 1959. Age ratios in raccoons. J. Mammal. 40:249.

Petrides, G. A. and R. Nestler. 1943. Age determination in juvenile bobwhite quail. Amer. Midland Naturalist 30:773-782.

Petrides, G. A. and W. G. Swank. 1966. Estimating the productivity and energy relations of an African elephant population. Proc. IX Internat. Grasslands Cong., Sao Paulo, Brazil. January, 1965:831-842.

Pettingill, O. S., Jr. 1946. A laboratory and field manual of ornithology. Burgess Pub. Co., Minneapolis, Minn. 248 p.

Pettingill, O.S., Jr. 1951. A guide to bird finding. Oxford University Press, New York. 659 p.

Pettingill, O.S., Jr. 1956. A laboratory and field manual of ornithology. 3rd Ed. Burgess Publ. Co., Minneapolis, Minn. 379 p.

Pfeiffer, C.J., and G.H. Gass. 1963. A simple, inexpensive metabolism cage for small animals. Can. J. Comp. Med. and Vet. Sci. 27:69-70.

Phelp, N.R. 1963. Radar recording on film. The Marconi Review 26(148): 35-48.

Phillips, J.C. 1930. American game mammals and birds; a catalogue of books, 1582-1925, sport, natural history, and conservation. Houghton Mifflin, Boston. 638 p. [A catalogue of the books from the Charles Sheldon Library now housed at Yale University.]

Pienkowski, E.C. 1965. Predicting transmitter range and life. BioScience 15(2):115-118.

Pimlott, D.H. 1960. The use of tape-recorded wolf howls to locate timber wolves. 22nd Midwest Wildl. Conf., Toronto, Canada. Dec. 15 p. mimeo.

Pimlott, D.H., and W.J. Carberry. 1958. North American moose transplantations and handling techniques. J. Wildl. Mgmt. 22:51-62.

Pinto, F.C. 1961. Serological identification of ox, buffalo, goat and deer flesh. Brit. Vet. J. 117:540-544.

Pirnie, M.D. 1935. Michigan waterfowl management. Dept. Conservation, Lansing, Mich. 328 p.

Pistey, W.R., and J.F. Wright. 1961. The immobilization of captive wild animals with succinylcholine. Canadian J. Comp. Med. and Vet. Sci. 25:59-60.

Plummer, A.P., A.C. Hull, G. Stewart, and J.H. Robertson. 1955. Seeding rangelands in Utah, Nevada, southern Idaho, and western Wyoming. USDA,

Washington, D.C. Agric. Handbook No. 71, 73 p.

Plummer, A.P., H.D. Stapley, and D.R. Christensen. 1960. Game forage revegetation project. Utah Dept. Fish and Game, Salt Lake City. 51 p.

Plummer, A.P., S.B. Monsen, D.R. Christensen. 1966. Fourwing saltbrush—a shrub for future game ranges. Utah Dept. Fish and Game, Salt Lake City, Publ. No. 66-4, 12 p.

Plummer, P., S. Monsen, D.L. Christensen. 1966. Game forage restoration. Range improvements Notes 11(3):5-6.

Pollack, M.E. 1951. Observations on New England bobcats. J. Mammal. 32:356-385.

Pollack, M.E. 1951. Observations on New England bobcats. J. Mammal. 32:356-385.

Polska Akademia Nauk. Komitet Zoologiczny. 1962. Informator zoologiczny: Directory of Polish zoologists. The Academy, Warsaw. 193 p.

Poole, A.J. and Viola S. Schantz. 1942. Catalog of the type specimens of mammals in the United States National Museum, including the Biological Surveys collection. U.S. Nat. Mus. Bull. 178. 705 p.

Porter, J.R. 1964. The scientific journal—300th anniversary. Bact. Rev. 28(3):211-230.

Pospichal, L.B. and W.H. Marshall. 1954. A field study of sora rail and Virginia rail in Central Minnesota. Flicker 26:2-32.

Post, G. 1959. The use of curare and curare like drugs on elk (wapiti). J. Wildl. Mgmt. 23:365-366.

Post, G. 1967. Methods of sampling and preserving field specimens for laboratory examination or analysis. Pruett Press, Inc., Boulder, Colo. 73 p.

Prenzlow, E.J. 1965. A literature re-

view on pronghorn behavior. Colorado Department of Game, Fish, and Parks; Game Research Division and Cooperative Wildlife Research Unit. Spec. Rept. no. 3, 28 p.

Progulske, D.R. 1957. A collar for identification of big game. J. Wildl. Mgmt. 21:251-252.

Provost, M.W. 1947. Nesting of birds in the marshes of Northwest Iowa. Amer. Midland Naturalist 38:485-503.

Pugh, G.T. 1963. Guide to research writing. 2nd ed. Houghton Mifflin, Boston, Mass. 56 p.

Q

Quast, J.C., and W.E. Howard. 1953. Comparison of catch of two sizes of small mammal live traps. J. Mammal. 34:514-515.

Quattlebaum, Marguerite V. 1966. Subject headings used in the Dictionary Catalogs of the Library of Congress. 7th ed. Library of Congress, Washington, D.C. 1432 p.

Quay, W.B. 1948. A technique for the automatic color marking of shrews. J. Mammal. 29:225-234.

Quenouille, M.H. 1956. Notes on bias in estimation. Biometrika 43:353-360.

Quick, H.F. 1958. Estimating the effects of exploitation by life tables. Trans. N. Amer. Wildl. Conf. 23: 426-442.

Quick, H.F. 1963. Animal population analysis. In H.S. Mosby (Ed.) Wildlife investigational techniques. 2nd ed. The Wildlife Society, Washington, D.C. 419 p.

Quimby, D.C., and J.E. Gaab. 1952. Preliminary report on a study of elk dentition as a means of determining age classes. Proc. Ann. Conf. Western Assn. State Game and Fish Comm. 32:225-227.

Quimby, D.C., and J.E. Gaab. 1957. Mandibular dentition as an age in-

586

dicator in Rocky Mountain elk. J. Wildl. Mgmt. 21:435-451.

R

Radiochemical Centre (The). 1965. Radioactive isotope dilution analysis. RCC review No. 2 UKAEA, Radiochemical Centre, Amersham, England. 12 p.

Raitt, R.J., Jr. 1961. Plumage development and molts of California quail. Condor 63:294-303.

Rampont, R.O. 1926. Black-tailed deer successfully raised. Calif. Fish and Game 12:35-37.

Rand, R.W. 1950. Branding in fieldwork on seals. J. Wildl. Mgmt. 14:128-132.

Randall, P.E. 1941. The life equation of the ring-neck pheasant in Pennsylvania. Trans. N. Amer. Wildl. Conf. 5:300-320.

Ransom, A.B. 1966. Determining age of white-tailed deer from layers in cementum of molars. J. Wildl. Mgmt. 30(1):197-199.

Rassmussen, D.I., and E.R. Doman. 1943. Census methods and their application in the management of mule deer. Trans. N. Amer. Wildl. Conf. 8:369-380.

Rassmussen, D.I. and L.A. Griner. 1938. Life history and management studies of the sage grouse in Utah, with special reference to nesting and feeding habits. Trans. N. Amer. Wildl. Conf. 3:852-864.

Rausch, R. 1947. Suggestions for the handling of certain mammals. J. Wildl. Mgmt. 11:189.

Rausch, R. 1961. Notes on the black bear *Ursus americanus* Pallas, in Alaska, with particular reference to dentition and growth. Sonderdruck aus Zeitschrift fur Saugetier Kunde Bd. 26 (1961), H. 2, S. 65-128.

Rausch, R.A., and R.W. Ritchey. 1961. Narcosis of moose with nicotine. J. Wildl. Mgmt. 25:326-328.

Rawley, E., J.O. Low, and E.O. Greaves. 1950. Venison—its care and cooking. Utah Agr. Ext. Service Bull. 200, Logan.

Rawson, K.S., and P.H. Hartline. 1964. Telemetry of homing behavior by the deermouse, *Peromyscus*. Science 146(3651):1596-1598.

Regier, H.A. and D.S. Robson. 1967. Estimating population number and mortality rates, p. 31-66, *In* S.D. Gerking, The biological basis of freshwater fish production, Blackwell Sci. Publications, Oxford and Edinburgh.

Reichert, R.J. and E. Reichert. 1961. Binoculars and scopes: how to choose, use, and photograph through them. Chilton Co. Book Div., Philadelphia, Pa. 128 p.

Reid, V.H., R.M. Hansen, and A.L. Ward. 1966. Counting mounds and earth plugs to census mountain pocket gophers. J. Wildl. Mgmt. 30(2):327-334.

Reilly, J.R., and W. Curren. 1961. Evaluation of certain techniques for judging the age of red foxes *(Vulpes fulva)*. N.Y. Fish and Game J. 8:122-129.

Reynolds, H.C. 1945. Some aspects of the life history and ecology of the opossum in central Missouri. J. Mammal. 26:361-379.

Richards, S.H. 1961. Rabies. N. Dak. St. Univ. Ext. Serv. Circ. A-358. Processed. 5 p.

Richter, W.C. 1955. A technique for night identification of animals. J. Wildl. Mgmt. 19(1):159-160.

Ricker, W.E. 1958. Handbook of computations for biological statistics of fish populations. Fisheries Res. Board of Canada Bull. No. 119. Ottawa. 300 p.

Rider, G.C. 1961. The starling population of South East England. Baddow Research Laboratories Interim Technical Memorandum No. 916 (Marconi Wireless Telegraph Co.

Ltd., Great Baddow, Essex, England). Unpubl. MS.

Ridgway, R., and H. Friedmann. 1901-. The birds of North and Middle America. U.S. Natl. Mus. Bull. 50. [Eleven parts had been published by 1950.]

Riley, C.V. 1963. Revegetation and management of critical sites for wildlife. Trans. Amer. Wildl. and Nat. Res. Conf. 28:269-283.

Riney, T. 1951. Standard terminology for deer teeth. J. Wildl. Mgmt. 15:99-101.

Ritcey, R.W., and R.Y. Edwards. 1956. Trapping and tagging moose on winter range. J. Wildl. Mgmt. 20(3):324-325.

Robbins, C.S., B. Bruun, and H.S. Zim. 1966. A guide to field identification: birds of North America. Golden Press, New York. 340 p.

Robel, R.J. 1965. Differential winter mortality of bobwhites in Kansas. J. Wildl. Mgmt. 29(2):261-265.

Robel, R.J. and W.R. Harper. 1965. Energy content and retention by ragweed and sunflower seeds during fall and winter. Trans. Kansas Acad. Sci. 68(3):401-405.

Roberts, A. 1940. The birds of South Africa. H.F. & G. Witherby, London. 463 p.

Roberts, A. 1951. The mammals of South Africa. Trustees of "The Mammals of South Africa" Book Fund, Johannesburg, South Africa. 700 p.

Robertson, J.H. 1954. A low-cost portable cage for range and pasture plots. J. Range Mgmt. 20:324-325.

Robinette, W.L. 1947. Deer mortality from gunshot wounds. USDI Fish and Wildl. Ser. Wildl. Leaf. 295, 8 p.

Robinette, W.L., and J.S. Gashwiler. 1950. Breeding season, productivity and fawning period of the mule deer in Utah. J. Wildl. Mgmt. 14:457-469.

Robinette, W.L., R.B. Ferguson, and J.S. Gashwiler. 1958. Problems involved in the use of deer pellet group counts. Trans. N. Amer. Wildl. Conf. 23:411-425.

Robinette, W.L., J.S. Gashwiler, D.A. Jones, and H.S. Crane. 1955. Fertility of mule deer in Utah. J. Wildl. Mgmt. 19(1):115-136.

Robinette, W.L., D.A. Jones, J.S. Gashwiler, and C.M. Aldous. 1954. Methods for censusing winter-lost deer. Trans. N. Amer. Wildl. Conf. 19:511-525.

Robinette, W.L., J.S. Gashwiler, and D.A. Jones. 1957. Differential mortality by sex and age among mule deer. J. Wildl. Mgmt. 21(1):1-16.

Robinette, W.L., D.A. Jones, J.S. Gashwiler, and C.M. Aldous. 1956. Further analysis of methods for censusing winter-lost deer. J. Wildl. Mgmt. 20:75-78.

Robinette, W.L., D.A. Jones, G. Rogers, and J.S. Gashwiler. 1957. Notes on tooth development and wear for Rocky Mountain mule deer. J. Wildl. Mgmt. 21:134-153.

Robinson, W.B. 1943. The "humane coyote-getter" vs. the steel trap in control of predatory animals. J. Wildl. Mgmt. 7:179-189.

Robinson, W.B. 1952. Some observations on coyote predation in Yellowstone National Park. J. Mammal. 33:470-476.

Robinson, W.B. 1953. Population trends of predators and fur animals in 1080 station areas. J. Mammal. 34:221-227.

Robinson, W.B., and E.F. Grand. 1958. Comparative movements of bobcats and coyotes as disclosed by tagging. J. Wildl. Mgmt. 22:117-122.

Robinson, W.B. and M.W. Cummings. 1951. Movements of coyotes from and to Yellowstone National Park. USDI Spec. Sci. Rept. (Wildl.) No. 11. Washington, D.C. 47 p.

Robson, D.S. and D.G. Chapman. 1961. Catch curves and mortality rates. Trans. Amer. Fish. Soc. 90(2):181-189.

Robson, D.S. and H.A. Regier. 1964. Sample size in Petersen mark-recapture experiments. Trans. Amer. Fish. Soc. 93:215-226.

Robson, D.S. and H.A. Regier. 1968. Estimation of population number and mortality rates, In W.E. Ricker (Ed.) Handbook of freshwater fish production. Blackwell Sci. Publications, Oxford and Edinburgh.

Robson, D.S. and J.H. Whitlock. 1964. Estimation of a truncation point. Biometrika 51:33-39.

Roe, F.G. 1951. The North American buffalo: a critical study of the species in its wild state. Univ. Toronto Press, Toronto. 957 p.

Roest, A.I. 1957. Notes on the American sparrow hawk. Auk 74:1-19.

Rogers, D.J. and H.S. Fleming. 1963. Data recording: an inexpensive and efficient method. AIBS Bull. 13(2):42.

Rogers, G., O. Julander, and W.L. Robinette. 1958. Pellet-group counts for deer census and range-use index. J. Wildl. Mgmt. 22:193-199.

Rollman, W.L. 1962. Get it on film. Wisc. Conserv. Bull. 27:23.

Romanox, A.N. 1956. Automatic tagging of wild animals and prospects for its use. Zool. J. Moscow 35:1902.

Roseberry, J.L., and W.D. Klimstra. 1965. A guide to age determination of bob-white quail embryos. Biol. Notes. No. 55. Ill. Nat. Hist. Survey, Urbana.

Rosene, W., Jr. 1957. A summer whistling cock count of bobwhite as an index to wintering population. J. Wildl. Mgmt. 21:153-158.

Ruffner, F.G., Jr. (Ed.) 1964. Encyclopedia of associations. Gale Research Co., Detroit, Mich. 1231 p.

Rupp, R.S. 1966. Generalized equation for the ratio method of estimating population abundance. J. Wildl. Mgmt. 30(3):523-526.

Ryel, L.A. and L.D. Fay. 1960. Deer biological data 1959-1960. Report No. 2307, Game Division, Mich. Dept. of Cons., Lansing (mimeo, 28 p).

Ryel, L.A., L.D. Fay, and R.C. Van Etten. 1961. Validity of age determination in Michigan deer. Papers Mich. Acad. Sci. 47:289-316.

S

Saake, N. 1968. Nevada's Canada geese. Nevada Wildl. 2(2):24-25.

St. Joseph, J.K.S. (Ed.) 1966. The uses of air photography: nature and man in a new perspective. Baker. London. 166 p.

Salt, W.R. 1958. In memoriam: William Rowan. Auk 75(4):387-390.

Salter, S.H. 1966. A note on the recording of egg activity. Animal Behaviour 14(1):41-43.

Salyer, J.C. 1955. Improvements in the cannon net trap. U.S. Fish and Wildl. Ser., Branch of Wildl. Res., Wildl. Mgmt. Ser. No. 12, Washington. 27 p. (multilith).

Sampford, M.R. 1962. An introduction to sampling theory. Oliver and Boyd, London. 292 p.

Sampson, A.W., A. Chase, and D.W. Hedrick. 1951. California grasslands and range forage grasses. Calif. Agric. Exp. Sta., Berkeley. Bull. 724, 131 p.

Sampson, A.W., and B.S. Jesperson. 1963. California range brushlands and browse plants. Calif. Agric. Exper. Sta., Davis, Calif. Manual 33, 162 p.

588

Sanborn, C.C. 1947. Catalogue of type specimens of mammals in Chicago Natural History Museum. Fieldiana: Zoology 32(4):1-293.

Sanderson, G.C. 1950. Methods of measuring productivity in raccoons. J. Wildl. Mgmt. 14:389-402.

Sanderson, G.C. 1961. Estimating opossum population by marking young. J. Wildl. Mgmt. 25:20-27.

Sanderson, G.C. 1961. The lens as an indicator of age in the raccoon. Am. Midland Naturalist 64:481-485.

Sanderson, G.C. 1961. Techniques for determining age of raccoons. Ill. Nat. Hist. Survey Biol. Notes No. 45, Urbana. 16 p.

Sanderson, G.C., and Beverley C. Sanderson. 1964. Radio-tracking rats in Malaya—a preliminary study. J. Wildl. Mgmt. 28(4):752-768.

Sanford, F.B. 1958. Planning your research paper. U.S. Fish and Wildl. Ser. Fishery Leaflet no. 447, 32 p.

Sarton, G. 1960. Notes on the reviewing of learned books. Science 131(3408): 1182-1187.

Sather, J.H. 1954. The dentition method of aging muskrats. Chicago Acad. Sci. Nat. Hist. Misc. Publ., Chicago. 3 p.

Saunders, A.A. 1961. The songs and calls of the wood thrush. Auk 78(4): 595-606.

Saunders, J.K., Jr. 1963. Food habits of the lynx in Newfoundland. J. Wildl. Mgmt. 27:384-390.

Savage, J.C. 1966. Telemetry and automatic data acquisition systems. p. 69-98. *In* K.E.F. Watt (Ed.) Systems analysis in ecology. Academic Press, N.Y.

Scattergood, L.W. 1954. Estimating fish and wildlife populations: a survey of methods, p. 273-285. *In* O. Kempthorne (Ed.), Statistics and

mathematics in biology, Iowa State Coll. Press, Ames.

Schaeffer, G.W. 1966. The study of bird echoes using a tracking radar. Unpub. ms.

Schaeffer, G.W. 1968. Bird recognition by radar. *In* The problems of birds as pests. London: Institute of Biology Symposium series, 1967.

Schaefer, M.B. 1951. Estimation of size of animal populations by marking experiments. U.S. Fish and Wildl. Service Fishery Bull. 69:191-203.

Scheele, M. 1961. Punch-card methods in research and documentation with special reference to biology. [Transl. from German] Interscience Publishers, New York. 274 p.

Scheffer, T.H. and N. Hotchkiss. 1945. Plant-food resources for waterfowl in the Pacific Northwest. Washington Dept. Game, Olympia, Wash. Biol. Bull. No. 7, 39 p.

Scheffer, V.B. 1950. Experiments in the marking of seals and sea lions. U.S. Fish and Wildl. Service Spec. Sci. Rep. (Wildl.) No. 4, Washington, D.C.

Scheffer, V.B. 1950. Growth layers on the teeth of pinnipedia, as an indicator of age. Science 112:309-311.

Schlatterer, E.F. 1960. Productivity and movements of a population of sage grouse in southeastern Idaho. M.S. Thesis, Univ. Idaho, Moscow, 87 p.

Schmeckebier, L.F., and R.B. Eastin. 1961. Government publications and their use. rev. ed. The Brookings Institution, Washington, D.C. 476 p.

Schnabel, Zoe E. 1938. Estimation of the total fish population of a lake. Amer. Math. Monthly 45:348-352.

Schneegas, E.R. and S.N. Zufelt. 1965. Rejuvinating decadent bitterbrush. U.S. Forest Service (Region 5) Inyo National Forest, California. 5 p. mimeo.

Schnell, G.D. 1965. Recording the flight-speed of birds by Doppler radar. The Living Bird 4:79-87.

Schofield, R.D. 1955. Analysis of muskrat age determination methods and their application in Michigan. J. Wildl. Mgmt. 19:463-466.

School of Forestry. 1967. Herbicide and vegetation management. Oregon State Univ., Corvallis. 356 p.

Schorger, A.W. 1966. The wild turkey. Univ. Oklahoma Press, Norman, 625 p.

Schorger, A.W. 1966. In memorium: Paul Lester Errington. Auk 83(1): 52-65.

Schultz, V. 1950. A modified Stoddard quail trap. J. Wildl. Mgmt. 14:243.

Schultz, V. 1958. A selected bibliography on vitamin A in the nutrition of game birds. Maryland Agr. Exp. Sta. Misc. Publ. No. 334, Contrb. No. 2960. 3 p. mimeo.

Schultz, V. 1963. Radionuclides and ionizing radiation in ornithology, a selected bibliography on wild and domestic birds. TID-17762. AEC Div. Tech. Info., Washington, D.C. 27 p.

Schultz, V. and A.W. Klement, Jr. (Eds.) 1962. Radioecology. Reinhold Pub. Co. and Am. Inst. Biol. Sci. New York. 746 p.

Schumacher, F.X., and R.W. Eschmeyer. 1943. The estimate of fish population in lakes or ponds. J. Tenn. Acad. Sci. 18:228-249.

Schuster, J.L. 1965. Estimating browse from twig and stem measurements. J. Range Mgmt. 18:220-222.

Schwabe, C.W., and L.R. Davis. 1954. Marginal punched cards in veterinary research. Amer. J. Vet. Research 15(57):634-638.

Schwartz, C.W., and Elizabeth R. 1959. Wild mammals of Missouri. Univ.

Missouri Press and Missouri Conservation Commission, Columbia, Mo. 341 p.

Schwartz, R.J. 1955. The complete dictionary of abbreviations. Thomas Y. Crowell Co., New York. 211 p.

Scott, J.R., and J.L. Fuller. 1965. Genetics and the social behavior of the dog. Univ. Chicago Press, Chicago, Ill. 468 p.

Scott, T.G. 1941. Methods and computations in fecal analysis with reference to the red fox. Iowa State Coll. J. Sci. 15:279-285.

Scott, T.G. 1942. Ear tags on mice. J. Mammal. 23:339.

Scott, T.G. 1958. Wildlife research. Bull. Ill. Nat. Hist. Surv. 27(2):179-201.

Scott, W.B. 1965. Bibliography of J.R. Dymond. Can. Field Nat. 79(4):224-229.

Searle, S.R. 1966. Matrix algebra for the biological sciences. John Wiley and Sons, New York, 296 p.

Seber, G.A.F. 1962. The multi-sample single recapture census. Biometrika 49:339-350.

Seber, G.A.F. 1965. A note on the multiple recapture census. Biometrika 52:249-259.

Segelquist, C.A. 1966. Sexing whitetailed deer embryos by chromatin. J. Wildl. Mgmt. 30(2):414-417.

Seidenberg, A.J. 1966. Animal ecology. BioScience 16:827-828, 830.

Selby, S.M. (Ed.) 1964. Standard mathematical tables. 14th ed. Chemical Rubber Co., Cleveland, Ohio. 632 p.

Sergeant, D.E., and D.H. Pimlott. 1959. Age determination in moose from sectioned incisor teeth. J. Wildl. Mgmt. 23:315-321.

Seton, E.T. 1920. For a methodic study of life-histories of mammals. J. Mammal. 1(2):67-69.

Seton, E.T. 1937. Lives of game animals. Vol. I. The Literary Guild of America. New York. 640 p.

Seton, E.T. 1954. Ernest Thompson Seton's America. Devin-Adair, New York. 413 p.

Seton, E.T. 1958. Animal tracks and hunter signs. Doubleday, New York. 160 p.

Seubert, J.L. 1948. A technique for nocturnal studies of birds and mammals by the use of infra-red projection and electronic reception. M.S. thesis, Ohio State Univ., Columbus.

Severinghaus, C.W. 1949. Tooth development and wear as criteria of age in white-tailed deer. J. Wildl. Mgmt. 13:195-216.

Severinghaus, C.W. 1950. Anaesthetization of white-tailed deer. Cornell Vet. 40:275-282.

Shafer, E.L., Jr. 1963. The twig-count method for measuring hardwood deer browse. J. Wildl. Mgmt. 27(3):428-437.

Shantz, H.L. 1943. Sexual maturity of deer, p. 288. *In* Hearings Before the Select Comm. of Wildlife Resources, 78th Congress, Washington, D.C.

Sharp, W.M. 1958. Evaluating mast yields in the oaks. Penna. Agr. Exp. Sta. Bull. 635, University Park.

Sharp, W.M. 1958. Aging gray squirrels by use of tail-pelage characteristics. J. Wildl. Mgmt. 22:29-34.

Shaub, B.M. 1951. Photographic records of captured birds. Wilson Bull. 63:327-329.

Sheldon, W.G. 1949. A trapping and tagging technique for wild foxes. J. Wildl. Mgmt. 13:309-311.

Sheldon, W.G., F. Greeley, and J. Kupa. 1958. Aging fall-shot American woodcocks by primary wear. J. Wildl. Mgmt. 22(3):310-312.

Sheppard, C.W. 1962. Basic principles of the tracer method. John Wiley & Sons, New York. 282 p.

Sherborn, C.D. (Comp.). 1940. Where is the ——— collection? Cambridge Univ. Press, Cambridge. 149 p.

Sherwin, C.W. and R.S. Isenson. 1967. Project hindsight—Defense Department study of the utility of research. Science 156 (3782):1571-1577.

Sherwood, G.A. 1965. Recent modifications in banding equipment for Canada geese. J. Wildl. Mgmt. 29(3):640-643.

Shilling, C.W. (Ed.) 1964. Atomic energy encyclopedia in the life sciences. W.B. Saunders Co., Philadelphia, Pa. 474 p.

Shomon, J.J., B.L. Ashbaugh, and C.D. Tolman. 1966. Wildlife habitat improvement. National Audubon Soc., New York, 96 p.

Short, H.L. 1962. The use of rumen fistula in a whitetailed deer. J. Wildl. Mgmt. 26:341-342.

Short, H.L. 1963. Rumen fermentations and energy relationships in whitetailed deer. J. Wildl. Mgmt. 27:184-194.

Short, H.L. 1966. Effects of cellulose levels on the apparent digestibility of feeds eaten by mule deer. J. Wildl. Mgmt. 30:163-167.

Short, H.L. 1966. Methods for evaluating forages for wild ruminants. Trans. N. Amer. Wildl. and Nat. Res. Conf. 31:122-128.

Short, H.L., D.R. Dietz and E.E. Remmenga. 1966. Selected nutrients in mule deer browse plants. Ecology 47:222-229.

Short, H.L. and E.E. Remmenga. 1965. Use of fecal cellulose to estimate

590

plant tissue eaten by deer. J. Range. Mgmt. 18:139-144.

Siegmund, O.H. (Ed.) 1961. The Merck veterinary manual. 2nd ed. Merck and Co., Rahway, N.J. 1630 p.

Siggins, H.W. 1934. Distribution and rate fall of conifer seeds. J. Agr. Res. 47:119-128.

Sigler, W.F. 1956. Wildlife law enforcement. Wm. C. Brown Co., Dubuque, Iowa. 318 p.

Silver, H., N.F. Colovos and H.H. Hayes. 1959. Basal metabolism of white-tailed deer—a pilot study. J. Wildl. Mgmt. 23:434-438.

Simkin, D.W. 1965. Reproduction and productivity of moose in northwestern Ontario. J. Wildl. Mgmt. 29(4):740-750.

Simkin, D.W. 1967. A comparison of three methods used to age moose. Proc. N.E. Sect. Wildl. Soc., Quebec, 16 p. (multilith).

Simmons, N.M., and J.L. Phillips. 1966. Modifications of a dye-spraying device for marking desert bighorn sheep. J. Wildl. Mgmt. 30(1):208-209.

Simpson, G.G. 1945. The principles of classification and a classification of mammals. Bull. Amer. Mus. Nat. History no. 85, 350 p.

Simpson, G.G. 1959. A review of the "Mammals of North America." Science 129(3359):1353-1354.

Simpson, G.G. 1961. Principles of animal taxonomy. Columbia Univ. Press, New York. 247 p.

Sincock, J.L. and J.A. Powell. 1957. An ecological study of waterfowl areas in central Florida. Trans. N. Amer. Wildl. Conf. 22:220-236.

Singleton, J.R. 1965. Waterfowl habitat management in Texas. Texas Parks and Wildl. Dept., Austin. Bull. No. 47, 68 p.

Siniff, D.B., and R.O. Skoog. 1964. Aerial censusing of caribou using stratified random sampling. J. Wildl. Mgmt. 28:391-401.

Siniff, D.B., and J.R. Tester. 1965. Computer analysis of animal-movement data obtained by telemetry. BioScience 15(2):104-108.

Sittler, O.D. 1965. Theoretical basis for estimating deer population from automatically collected data. J. Wildl. Mgmt. 29(2):381-387.

Sivertsen, E. 1941. On the biology of the harp seal, *Phoca groendlandica* Erxl. Investigations carried out in the White Sea, 1925-1937. Hvalrodets Skrifter No. 26. Norske Vidensk.—Akad., Oslo. 166 p.

Skallerup, H.R. 1957. American state academy of science publications. Univ. Illinois Library School, Occasional Papers, no. 50, 20 p.

Skellam, J.G. 1955. The mathematical approach to population dynamics, p. 31-46. *In* J.B. Cragg, and N.W. Pirie (Eds.), The numbers of man and animals. Oliver and Boyd, Edinburgh and London. 152 p.

Slade, N.A., J.J. Cebula, and R.J. Robel. 1965. Accuracy and reliability of biotelemetric instruments used in animal movement studies in prairie grasslands of Kansas. Trans. Kans. Acad. Sci., 68(1):173-179.

Sladen, W.J.L. 1965. Ornithological research in Antarctica. BioScience 15:264-268.

Slagle, A.K. 1965. Designing systems for the field. BioScience 15(2):109-112.

Slater, L.E. (Ed.) 1963. Bio-telemetry: the use of telemetry in animal behavior and physiology in relation to ecological problems. MacMillan Co., New York, 372 p.

Sluiter, J.W. 1961. Abrasion of teeth in connection with age in the bat *Myotis myotis*. Proc. Koninkl. Nederl. Akademic Van Wetenschappen-Amsterdam, Series C 64(3).

Sluiter, J.W., P.F. van Heerdt, and J.J. Bezem. 1956. Population statistics of the bat *Myotis mystacinus*, based on the marking-recapture method. Arch. Neerland. Zool. 12:64-88.

Smart, J., and G. Taylor. 1953. Bibliography of key works for the identification of the British fauna and flora. 2nd ed. The Systematics Assoc., British Mus. Nat. History, London. 126 p.

Smith, A.D. 1964. Defecation rates of mule deer. J. Wildl. Mgmt. 28:435-444.

Smith, A.H. 1963. The mushroom hunter's field guide. rev. ed. Univ. Michigan Press, Ann Arbor. 264 p.

Smith, Anne M. 1962. Canadian theses in forestry and related subject fields, 1913-1962. Forestry Chron. 38(3):376-400.

Smith, B.E. 1946. Wildcat predation on deer. J. Mammal. 26:439-440.

Smith, F.E. 1952. Experimental methods in population dynamics: a critique. Ecology 33(4):441-450.

Smith, N.D., and I.O. Buss. 1963. Age determination and plumage observations of blue grouse. J. Wildl. Mgmt. 27(4):566-578.

Smith, N.S. and H.P. Ledger. 1965. A portable tripod and weighing assembly for large animals. J. Wildl. Mgmt. 29(1):208-210.

Smith, N.S. and H.P. Ledger. 1965. A method of predicting liveweight from dissected leg weight. J. Wildl. Mgmt. 29(3):504-511.

Smith, R.C. 1962. Guide to the literature of the zoological sciences. 6th ed. Burgess Pub. Co., Minneapolis, Minn. 232 p.

Smith, R.C. and R.H. Painter. 1967. Guide to the literature of the zoological sciences. 7th ed. Burgess Pub. Co., Minneapolis. 238 p.

Smith, R.H. 1961. Age classification of the chukar partridge. J. Wildl. Mgmt. 25:84-86.

Smith, R.H., and S. Gallizioli. 1965. Predicting hunter success by means of a spring call count of Gambel quail. J. Wildl. Mgmt. 29:806-813.

Smith, R.L. 1966. Ecology and field biology. Harper and Row, New York. 686 p.

Snead, I.E. 1950. A family type live trap, handling cage, and associated techniques for muskrats. J. Wildl. Mgmt. 14:67-79.

Snyder, L.L. 1935. A study of the sharp-tailed grouse. Univ. of Toronto Studies, Biol. Ser. No. 40, Toronto.

Society of American Foresters, Committee on Terminology. 1958. Forest terminology—a glossary of technical terms used in forestry. S.A.F., Washington, D.C. 97 p.

Soper, J.D. 1962. In memorium: Rudolph Martin Anderson, 1876-1961. Can. Field Nat. 76:127-141.

Southern, H.N. 1964. The handbook of British mammals. Blackwell Scientific Publications, Oxford. 465 p.

Southern, W.E. 1964. Additional observations on winter bald eagle populations: Including remarks on biotelemetry techniques and immature plumages. Wilson Bull. 76(2): 121-137.

Southern, W.E. 1965. Avian navigation. BioScience 15(2):87-88.

Southern, W.E. 1965. Biotelemetry: A new technique for wildlife research. Living Bird 4:45-58.

Southern, H.N. and V.P.W. Lowe. 1968. The pattern and distribution of prey and predation in Tawny owl territories. J. Animal Ecol. 37:75-97.

Southern, H.N., J.S. Watson, and D. Chitty. 1946. Watching nocturnal animals by infra-red radiation. J. Animal Ecol. 15(2):198-202.

Southwood, T.R.E. 1966. Ecological methods with particular reference to the study of insect populations. Methuers & Co., London. 391 p.

Sowles, L.K. 1950. Techniques for waterfowl nesting studies. Trans. N. Amer. Wildl. Conf. 15:478-487.

Sowls, L.K. 1955. Prairie ducks. The Stackpole Co., Harrisburg, Penna. 193 p.

Sowls, L.K. 1961. Hunter-checking stations for collecting data on the collared peccary (Pecari tajacu). Trans. N. Amer. Wildl. Conf. 26: 496-505.

Sowls, L.K. and P.S. Minnamon. 1963. Glass beads for marking home ranges of mammals. J. Wildl. Mgmt. 27(2):299-302.

Sowls, L.K. and R.E. Schweinsburg. 1967. An improved propulsion system for short-range projection of immobilization darts. J. Wildl. Mgmt. 31(2):345-346.

Spear, P.J. 1967. Good practice in vertebrate pest control. Proc. 3rd Vertebrate Pest Conference. San Francisco, Calif. p. 31-35.

Specht, R.C. 1950. Preservation of the color and shape of flowers. Univ. of Florida Eng. and Ind. Exp. Sta. Bull. Series No. 40, Gainesville.

Spence, L.E., Jr. 1963. Study of identifying characteristics of mammal hair. Wyo. Game and Fish. Job Completion Report No. FW-3-R-10.

Spencer, D.A. 1939. Electrical recording of the activities of small mammals. J. Mammal. 20:479-85.

Sperry, C.C. 1941. Food habits of the coyote. USDI, Wildl. Res. Bull. 4. 70 p.

Spillet, J.J., J.B. Low, and D. Sill. 1967. Livestock fences—how they influence pronghorn antelope movements. Utah State Univ., Logan. Agric. Exper. Sta. Bull. 470, 79 p.

Spillett, J.J. and R.S. Zobell. 1967. Innovations in trapping and handling pronghorn antelope. J. Wildl. Mgmt. 31(2):347-351.

Spinner, G.P., and J.S. Bishop. 1950. Chemical analysis of some wildlife foods in Connecticut. J. Wildl. Mgmt. 14:175-180.

Sports Illustrated (Eds.) 1959. Sports Illustrated book of training dogs. Lippincott, Philadelphia 88 p.

Sprungman, O.I. 1951. Photography afield. Stackpole Co., Harrisburg, Pa. 449 p.

Spurr, S.H. 1948. Aerial photographs in forestry. Ronald Press Co., New York. 340 p.

Stacy, R.W., and B.D. Waxman. (Eds.) 1965. Computers in biomedical science. Academic Press. 1:1-562; 2: 1-363.

Stains, H.J. 1958. Key to guard hairs of middle western furbearers. J. Wildl. Mgmt. 22:95-97.

Stains, H.J. 1959. Use of the calcaneum in studies of taxonomy and food habits. J. Mammal. 40:392-401.

Stanka, V. 1958. Institutions of the U.S.S.R. active in arctic research and development. Arctic Inst. of North America, Washington, D.C. 100 p.

Steedman, H.F. 1960. Section cutting in microscopy. Blackwell, Oxford. 172 p.

Steel, P.E., P.D. Dalke, and E.G. Bizeau. 1957. Canada goose production at Gray's Lake, Idaho, 1949-1951. J. Wildl. Mgmt. 21:38-41.

Steinbach, H.B. 1964. The quest for certainty: Science Citation Index. Science 145(3628):142-143.

Stemple, Ruth M. (Comp.) 1963. Author-subject index to articles in Smithsonian annual reports, 1849-1961. Smithsonian Inst., Washington, D.C. 200 p.

592

Stenlund, M.H. 1955. A field study of the timber wolf *(Canis lupus)* on the Superior National Forest, Minnesota. Minn. Dept. of Cons. Tech. Bull. 4, 53 p.

Sterling, I. and J.F. Bendell. 1966. Census of blue grouse with recorded call of a female. J. Wildl. Mgmt. 30(1):184-187.

Stewart, P.A. 1954. Combination substratum and automatic trap for nesting mourning doves. Bird-Banding 25:6-8.

Stewart, R.E. 1951. Clapper rail populations of the Middle Atlantic states. Trans. N. Amer. Wildl. Conf. 16: 421-430.

Stewart, R.E., A.D. Geis, and C.D. Evans. 1958. Distribution of populations and hunting kill of the canvasback. J. Wildl. Mgmt. 22:333-370.

Stickel, L.F. 1946. Experimental analysis of methods for measuring small mammal populations. J. Wildl. Mgmt. 10:150-159.

Stickel, L.F. 1948. The trap line as a measure of small mammal populations. J. Wildl. Mgmt. 12:153-161.

Stickney, P.F. 1966. Browse utilization based on percentage of twig numbers browsed. J. Wildl. Mgmt. 30: 204-206.

Stiles, V.D. 1967. Observations on the behavior of the bobcat *(Lynx rufus rufus)* in the Quabbin Reservation. Unpub. manuscript. Univ. of Mass. 80 p.

Stirling, I., and J.F. Bendell. 1966. Census of blue grouse with recorded calls of a female. J. Wildl. Mgmt. 30(1):184-187.

Stoddard, H.L. 1932. The bobwhite quail; its habits, preservation and increase. Charles Scribner's Sons, New York. 559 p.

Stokes, A.W. 1954. Population studies of the ring-necked pheasants on Pelee Island, Ontario. Ont. Dept.

Lands and Forests. Wildl. Ser. Tech. Bull. 4, 154 p.

Stokes, A.W. 1957. Validity of spur length as an age criterion in pheasants. J. Wildl. Mgmt. 21:248-250.

Stone, W. 1933. American ornithological literature, p. 29-49. *In* Fifty years' progress of American ornithology. American Ornithologists' Union, Lancaster, Pa.

Stoneberg, R., and C. Jonkel. 1966. Age determination of black bears by cementum layers. J. Wildl. Mgmt. 30(2):411-414.

Storey, M. 1957. Stanford University theses and dissertations of interest to researchers in natural history (systematics, morphology, ecology, etc.). Cir. Nat. Hist. Mus. Stanford Univ. 7:1-58.

Storm, G.L. 1965. Movements and activities of foxes as determined by radio-tracking. J. Wildl. Mgmt. 29(1):1-13.

Strandgaard, H. 1967. Reliability of the Petersen method, tested on a roedeer population. J. Wildl. Mgmt. 31: 643-651.

Strelkov, A., and K. Yur'yev (Eds.) 1962. Handbook of Soviet zoologists. Joint Publications Research Service: 13188. [transl. from the Russian] U.S. Department of Commerce, Office of Technical Services, Washington, D.C. 443 p.

Strode, D.H. and D.L. Deedy. 1941. Analysis of pheasant reproduction, cover utilization and mortality, Wood County, Ohio. Ohio Wildl. Res. Sta. Release 167, Columbus. 34 p.

Strong, J.D., and G. Hannauer. 1962. A practical approach to analog computers. Instruments and Control Syst. 35:60-69.

Strong, R.M. 1939-1959. A bibliography of birds. Field Museum of Natural History (Zool. Ser.) vol. 25, pts. 1-4.

Strunk, W., Jr. 1959. The elements of style. MacMillan Co., New York. 71 p.

Stuart, A. 1962. Basic ideas of scientific sampling. Charles Griffin and Co., Ltd. 99 p.

Studer, J.J. 1963. Electronic circuits and instrumentation systems. John Wiley and Sons, Inc. New York.

Stuewer, F.W. 1943. Reproduction of raccoons in Michigan. J. Wildl. Mgmt. 7:60-75.

Sullivan, E.G., and A.O. Haugen. 1956. Age determination of foxes by X-ray of forefeet. J. Wildl. Mgmt. 20:210-212.

Sumner, L. 1953. Birds and mammals of the Sierra Nevada. Univ. California Press, Berkeley. 484 p.

Svardson, G. 1959. Formationsflygande fåglar på stor höjd uppfangade på radarskärm [Birds flying in formation at great altitude registered by radar]. Vå Fågelvarld 18(3): 229-233.

Svihla, A. 1934. Development and growth of deermice *(Peromyscus maniculatus artemisiae)*. J. Mammal. 15:99-104.

Swank, W.G. 1952. Trapping and marking of adult nesting doves. J. Wildl. Mgmt. 16:87-90.

Swank, W.G. 1955. Feather molt as an ageing technique for mourning doves. J. Wildl. Mgmt. 19:412-414.

Swanson, G. 1940. Food habits of the sharp-tailed grouse by analysis of droppings. J. Wildl. Mgmt. 4:432-436.

Swinebroad, J. 1964. Net-shyness and wood thrush populations. Bird-Banding 35(3):196-202.

T

Taber, R.D. 1949. A new marker for game birds. J. Wildl. Mgmt. 13: 228-231.

Taber, R.D. 1953. Studies of black-tailed deer reproduction on three chaparral cover types. Calif. Fish and Game 39:177-186.

Taber, R.D. 1956. Characteristics of the pelvic girdle in relation to sex in black-tailed and white-tailed deer. Calif. Fish and Game 42:5-21.

Taber, R.D. and R.F. Dasmann. 1958. The black-tailed deer of the chaparral. Calif. Dept. Fish and Game, Game Bull. No. 8, 163 p.

Taber, R.D., A. de Vos, and M. Altmann. 1956. Two marking devices for large land mammals. J. Wildl. Mgmt. 20:464-465.

Takos, M.J. 1943. Trapping and banding muskrats. J. Wildl. Mgmt. 7:400-407.

Takos, M.J. 1947. A semi-quantitative study of muskrat food habits. J. Wildl. Mgmt. 11:331-339.

Talbot, L.M. 1965. A survey of past and present wildlife research in East Africa. East African Wildl. J. 3:61-85.

Talbot, L.M. and J.S.G. McCulloch. 1965. Weight estimations for East African mammals from body measurements. J. Wildl. Mgmt. 29(1):84-89.

Talbot, L.M., and D.R.M. Stewart. 1964. First wildlife census of the entire Serengeti-Mara region, East Africa. J. Wildl. Mgmt. 28(4):815-827.

Talbot, L.M. and M.H. Talbot. 1962. A hoisting apparatus for weighing and loading large animals in the field J. Wildl. Mgmt. 26(2):217-218.

Tanaka, R. 1952. Theoretical justification of the mark and release index for small mammals. Bull. Kocki Women's College 1:38-47.

Tanner, J.A. 1962. Reversible blocking of nerve conduction by alternating-current excitation. Nature 195(4842):712-713.

Tanner, J.A. 1965. The effect of microwave radiation on birds: some observations and experiments. Natl. Res. Council of Can., Assoc. Committee on Bird Hazards to Aircraft. Field Note No. 31 (mimeo.). 4 p.

Tanner, W.D., and G.L. Bowers. 1948. A method for trapping male ruffed grouse. J. Wildl. Mgmt. 12:330-331.

Tanner, W.D. and G.O. Hendrickson. 1954. Ecology of the Virginia rail in Clay County, Iowa. Iowa Bird Life 24:65-70.

Taverner, P.A. 1953. Birds of Canada. Natl. Mus. of Canada and the Musson Book Co. 446 p.

Taylor, J.M. and H.J. Taylor. 1964. Rechargeable battery power for a portable photographic recorder. J. Wildl. Mgmt. 28(2):406-408.

Taylor, R.H., and W.B. Magnussen. 1965. Immobilizing live-trapped opossums with succinylcholine chloride. New Zeal. J. Sci. 8(4):531-536.

Taylor, W.P. 1948. Outline for study of mammalian ecology and life histories. U.S. Fish and Wildl. Ser., Wildl. Leaflet No. 304, 26 p.

Taylor, W.P. (Ed.) 1956. The deer of North America. Stackpole Co., Harrisburg, Pa. and the Wildl. Mgmt. Inst., Washington, D.C.

Teer, J.G. 1964. Predation by long-tailed weasels on eggs of blue-winged teal. J. Wildl. Mgmt. 28:404-406.

Telberg, Ina (Comp.) 1964. Who's who in Soviet science and technology. Telberg Book Co., New York. 301 p.

Tener, J.S. 1954. A preliminary study of the musk-oxen of Fosheim Peninsula, Ellesmere Island, N.W.T. Canadian Wildl. Ser., Natl. Pks. Br., Wildl. Mgmt. Bull. Ser. No. 9, 34 p.

Terres, J.K. 1961. Available field check-lists of birds—Canada and the United States. Audubon Mag. 63:44-47, 62, 64, 229, 233, 344.

Tester, J.R. and D.B. Siniff. 1965. Aspects of animal movement and home range data obtained by telemetry. Trans. N. Amer. Wildl. Conf. 30:379-392.

Tester, J.R., D.W. Warner, and W.W. Cochran. 1964. A radio-tracking system for studying movements of deer. J. Wildl. Mgmt. 28(1):42-45.

Thiessen, A.H. (Comp.) 1946. Weather glossary. U.S. Gov. Printing Off., Washington, D.C. 299 p.

Thoma, J.A. 1962. Simple and rapid method for the coding of punched cards. Science 137(3526):278-279.

Thomas, W.D. 1961. Chemical immobilization of wild animals. J. Vet. Med. Assoc. 138:263-265.

Thompson, D.R. 1958. Field techniques for sexing and aging game animals. Wisc. Cons. Dept., Spec. Wildl. Rep. No. 1, Madison. 44 p.

Thompson, H.V., and C.J. Armour. 1954. Methods of marking wild rabbits. J. Wildl. Mgmt. 18:411-414.

Thomson, A.L. (Ed.) 1964. A new dictionary of birds. McGraw-Hill, New York. 928 p.

Thorpe, W.H. 1954. The process of song-learning in the chaffinch as studied by means of the sound spectrograph. Nature 173:465-469.

Tiemeier, O.W., and M.L. Plenert. 1964. A comparison of three methods for determining the age of black-tailed jackrabbits. J. Mammal. 45(3):409-416.

Tilton, E.M. 1964. A union list of publications in opaque microforms. 2nd ed. Scarecrow Press, New York. 744 p.

Toll, J.E., T.S. Baskett, and C.H. Conoway. 1960. Home range, reproduction, and foods of the swamp rabbit in Missouri. Amer. Midland Naturalist 63(2):398-412.

594

Tomlinson, R.E. 1963. A method for drive-trapping dusky grouse. J. Wildl. Mgmt. 27(4):563-566.

Townsend, J.E. 1953. Beaver ecology in Western Montana with special reference to movements. J. Mammal. 34:459-479.

Trapido, H., and P.E. Crowe. 1946. The wing banding method in the study of the travels of bats. J. Mammal. 27:224-226.

Trefethen, J.B. and L. Miracle (Eds.) 1966. New hunter's encyclopedia. 3rd ed. Stackpole Co., Harrisburg, Pa. 1131 p.

Treichler, R., R.W. Stow, and A.L. Nelson. 1946. Nutrient content of some winter foods of ruffed grouse. J. Wildl. Mgmt. 10:12-17.

Trelease, S.F. 1958. How to write scientific and technical papers. Williams and Wilkins, Baltimore, Md. 185 p.

Trippensee, R.E. 1941. A new type of bird and mammal marker. J. Wildl. Mgmt. 5:120-124.

Trippensee, R.E. 1948-1953. Wildlife management. McGraw-Hill, New York. 2 vol.

Troyer, W.A., R.J.Hensel, and K.E. Durley. 1962. Live-trapping and handling of brown bears. J. Wildl. Mgmt. 26(3):330-331.

Trump, R.F., and G.O. Hendrickson. 1943. Methods for trapping and tagging woodchuck. J. Wildl. Mgmt. 7: 420-421.

Turabian, K.L. 1955. A manual for writers of term papers, theses, and dissertations. Univ. Chicago Press, Phoenix Book, Chicago, Ill. vii + 110 p.

Twigg, G.I., and H. Miller. 1963. The use of Ca^{45} as an agent for labeling rat populations. J. Mammal. 43(3):335-337.

Tyson, E.L. 1952. Estimating deer populations from tracks: A preliminary report. Presented at 6th Ann. Conf., S.E. Assn. Game and Fish Comm. Oct. 19-22. Savannah, Ga.

Tyson, E.L. 1959. A deer drive *vs.* track census. Trans. N. Amer. Wildl. Conf. 24:457-464.

U

Uhlig, H.G. 1955. The determination of age of nestling and subadult gray squirrels in West Virginia. J. Wildl. Mgmt. 19:479-483.

Uhlig, H.G. 1956. The gray squirrel in West Virginia. W.Va.Cons.Comm., Div. Game Mgmt., Bull. 3, Charleston. 83 p.

Ullrey, D.E., W.G. Youatt, H.E. Johnson, P.K. Ku and L.D. Fay. 1964. Digestibility of cedar and aspen browse for white-tailed deer. J. Wildl. Mgmt. 28:791-797.

USAEC. 1962. Technical information services of the USAEC. TID-485. Div. Tech. Infor., Oak Ridge, Tenn. 119 p.

USAEC. 1962. Special sources of information on isotopes. TID-4563 (3rd rev). Div. Tech. Infor., Oak Ridge, Tenn. 83 p.

USAEC. 1964. Understanding the atom. Booklets in series: Nuclear terms; a brief glossary; fallout from nuclear tests; atoms in agriculture; neutron activation analysis. Div. Tech. Info., Oak Ridge, Tenn.

U.S. Bureau Land Management. 1964. Water development: range improvements in Nevada for wildlife, livestock, and human use. Reno, Nev. 37 p.

U.S. Bureau of Land Management. 1966. Polyethylene liner for pit reservoir including trough and fencing. Portland Service Center, Portland, Ore. Tech. Notes P 712c, 4 p.

U.S. Bureau of Land Management. 1967. Drawings and specifications for water control and related structures. Washington, D.C. Loose leaf, n.p.

USDA. 1948. Woody-plant seed manual. Forest Service, USDA Misc. Pub. 654, 416 p.

USDA Library. 1958. Botany subject index. G.K. Hall, Boston, Mass. 15 vol.

U.S. Department of Health, Education, and Welfare. 1960. Radiological health handbook. Office Tech. Services, Dept. Commerce, Washington, D.C. 468 p.

USDI. 1960. Controlling deer. U.S. Fish and Wildlife Service. Boston, Mass. Processed. 3 p.

USDI. 1962. Repelling rabbits. U.S. Fish and Wildlife Service. No. 311, Lafayette, Ind. Processed. 1 p.

USDI. 1964. Catalog of the United States Geological Survey library. G.K. Hall, Boston, Mass. 25 vol.

USDI. 1965. Directory of national wildlife refuges. U.S. Fish and Wildlife Service Wildl. Leaf. 466, 16 p.

USDI. 1967. Man and wildlife: a policy for animal damage control. Bureau of Sport Fisheries and Wildlife. Washington, D.C. Processed. 12 p.

USDI. 1966. Focus on the Hudson. U.S. Bureau of Outdoor Rec., U.S.Govmt. Print. Off. 51 p.

U.S. Fish and Wildlife Service. 1941. Directions for collecting materials for food habits studies. Wildl. Leaf. 193, Washington. 8 p. processed.

U.S. Fish and Wildlife Service. 1961. Manual for bird banding. Washington, D.C.

U.S. Forest Service. 1959. Techniques and methods of measuring understory vegetation. Southern Forest Experiment Station and Southeastern Forest Experiment Station, USDA. 174 p.

U.S. Forest Service. 1960. Range improvement standards handbook. Washington, D.C. Loose leaf, n.p.

U.S. Forest Service. 1963. Range research methods. USDA. Misc. Pub. 940, 172 p.

U.S. Forest Service. 1965. Range seeding equipment handbook. Washington, D.C., 150 p.

U.S. Library of Congress. 1913-1940. List of American doctoral dissertation printed in 1912-38. U.S. Government Printing Office, Washington, D.C. 26 vol.

United Nations Educational, Scientific and Cultural Organization. 1953. Directory of institutions engaged in arid zone research. UNESCO, Paris. 110 p.

United Nations Educational, Scientific and Cultural Organization. 1962. Directory of zoological (and entomological) specimen collections of tropical institutions. UNESCO, Paris. 31 p.

United Nations Educational, Scientific and Cultural Organization. 1963. A review of the natural resources of the African continent. UNESCO, Paris. 436 p.

United Nations Educational, Scientific and Cultural Organization. 1965. World guide to science information and documentation services. UNESCO, Paris. 211 p.

Uphof, J.C. Th. 1959. Dictionary of economic plants. Hafner, New York. 400 p.

Usher, G. 1966. A dictionary of botany. D. Van Nostrand Co., Princeton, N.J. 404 p.

V

Van Dyne, G.M. 1962. Micro-methods for nutritive evaluation of range forages. J. Range Mgmt. 15:303-314.

Van Dyne, G.M. 1966. Ecosystems, systems ecology, and systems ecologists. Oak Ridge Nat. Laboratory ORNL-3957, UC-48-Biol. and Med. 40 p.

Van Dyne, G.M. and J.H. Meyer. 1964. A method for measurement of forage intake of grazing livestock using microdigestion techniques. J. Range Mgmt. 17:204-208.

Van Etten, R.C., and C.L. Bennett, Jr. 1965. Some sources of error in using pellet-group counts for censusing deer. J. Wildl. Mgmt. 29:723-729.

Van Gelder, R.G., and S. Anderson. 1967. An information retrieval system for collections of mammals. Curator 1(1):32-42.

Van Nostrand, F.C., and A.B. Stephenson. 1964. Age determination for beavers by tooth development. J. Wildl. Mgmt. 28(3):430-434.

Van Rossem, A.J. 1925. Flight features as age indicators in *Dendragopus*. Ibis (Series 12) 1:417-422.

Van Soest, P.J. 1962. Estimation of forage protein digestibility and determination of the effects of heat-drying upon forages by means of the nitrogen content of acid-detergent fiber. J. Dairy Sci. 45:664.

Van Soest, P.J. 1967. Development of a comprehensive system of feed analyses and its application to forages. J. Animal Sci. 26:119-128.

Van Tyne, J. 1952. Principles and practices in collecting and taxonomic work. Auk 69:27-33.

Vaurie, C. 1964. Russian ornithological literature. Auk 81(2):238-241.

Vaurie, C. 1966. Recent Russian ornithological literature. Auk 83(4):689-691.

Veatch, J.O., and C.R. Humphrys. 1966. Water and water terminology. Thomas Printing and Pub. Co., Kaukauna, Wisc. 375 p.

Verme, L.J. 1963. Effect of nutrition on growth of white-tailed deer fawns. Trans. N. Amer. Wildl. and Nat. Res. Conf. 28:431-443.

Verme, L.J. 1965. Reproduction studies on penned white-tailed deer. J. Wildl. Mgmt. 29:74-79.

Verme, L.J. 1967. Nutritional factors and deer. Trans. N. Amer. Wildl. and Nat. Res. Conf. 32.

Verme, L.J., and K.S. Lowe. 1961. Cusino scientist testing ancient gadgets to bring automation to biologists. The Mining J., Marquette, Mich.

Vernberg, F.J. (Comp.). 1963. Field stations of the United States. Amer. Zool. 3(3):245-386.

Verts, B.J. 1960. A device for administering anesthetics to skunks. J. Wildl. Mgmt. 24(3):335-336.

Verts, B.J. 1961. A convenient method of carrying and dispensing baits. J. Mammal. 42:283.

Verts, B.J. 1963. Equipment and techniques for radio-tracking striped skunks. J. Wildl. Mgmt. 27(3):325-339.

Vogtman, D.B. 1945. Flushing for determining food of game birds. J. Wildl. Mgmt. 9:255-257.

Voigt, M.J. 1961. Scientists' approaches to information. ACRL Monograph 24. Amer. Library Assoc., Chicago, Ill. 81 p.

Voisey, P.W. and W. Kalbfleisch. 1962. A mechanical treadle for the study of small animal traffic in the field or laboratory, J. Mammal. 43(2):281.

Von Marienfrid, S.S. 1939. Jagd und biologie. Verlag v. Julius Springer, Berlin. 136 p.

W

Wadkins, L.A. 1948. Dyeing birds for identification. J. Wildl. Mgmt. 12:388-391.

Wadley, F.M. 1954. Limitations of the "zero method" of population counts. Science 119(3098):689-690.

Wagstaffe, R., and J.H. Fidler. 1955. The preservation of natural history specimens. vol. 1 Invertebrates. H.F. and G. Witherby, London. 205 p.

Wainio, W.W., and E.B. Forbes. 1941. The chemical composition of forest fruits and nuts from Pennsylvania. J. Agr. Res. 62:627-635.

Walker, E.P., *et al.* 1964. Mammals of the world. Johns Hopkins Press, Baltimore, Md. 3 vol.

Walmo, O.C. 1956. Determination of sex and age of scaled quail. J. Wildl. Mgmt. 20:154-158.

Walmo, O.C., A.W. Jackson, T.L. Hailey, and R.L. Carlisle. 1962. Influence of rain on the count of deer pellet groups. J. Wildl. Mgmt. 26:50-55.

Ward, A.L., P.L. Hegdal, V.B. Richens, H.P. Tietjen. 1967. Gophacide, a new pocket gopher control agent. J. Wildl. Mgmt. 31:332-338.

Ward, D.R. 1952. Design of laboratories for safe use of radioisotopes. AECU-2226. Tech. Info. Service, USAEC, Oak Ridge, Tenn. 48 p.

Ward, G.M. and J.G. Nagy. 1966. Bacterial inhibition by the essential oils of sagebrush. Final Report to the Nat. Sci. Foundation., Dep. Animal Sci., Colo. State Univ., Fort Collins. 54 p.

War Department. 1939. Basic field manual. Field service pocketbook: Sketching. FM 21-35. U.S. Gov. Printing Off., Washington, D.C.

War Department. 1944. Advanced map and aerial photography reading. FM 21-26. U.S. Gov. Printing Off., Washington, D.C.

Warren, B.H. 1890. Report on the birds of Pennsylvania. Office of the Ornithologist, State Board Agr., Harrisburg. 434 p.

Warren, D.C., and H.M. Scott. 1953. The time factor in egg formation. Poult. Sci. 14:195.

Warren, E.R. 1942. The mammals of Colorado: their habits and distribution. 2nd ed. Univ. Oklahoma Press, Norman. 330 p.

Watson, D.F. 1953. Avenol-K, its use. N. Amer. Vet., 34:334.

Watt, K.E.F. (Editor). 1966. Systems analysis in ecology. Academic Press, New York, 276 p.

Watt, K.E.F. 1968. Ecology and resource management: a quantitative approach. McGraw-Hill Book Co., New York. 450 p.

Weaver, R.A., F. Vernoy, and B. Craig. 1959. Game water development on the desert. Calif. Fish and Game 45(4):333-342.

Webb, J. 1940. Identification of rodents and rabbits by their fecal pellets. Trans. Kansas Acad. Sci. 43:479-481.

Webb, R. 1957. Range studies in Banff National Park, Alberta, 1953. Canadian Wildl. Service, Mgmt. Bull. 1. 24 p.

Webb, W.L. 1942. Notes on a method for censusing snowshoe hare populations. J. Wildl. Mgmt. 6:67-69.

Webb, W.L. 1943. Trapping and marking white-tailed deer. J. Wildl. Mgmt. 7:346-348.

Weeden, R.B. 1961. Outer primaries as indicators of age among rock ptarmigan. J. Wildl. Mgmt. 25:337-339.

Weil, B.H. (Ed.). 1954. The technical report: its preparation, processing, and use in industry and government. Reinhold Pub. Co., New York. p. 319-332.

Weiland, E.C. 1964. Methods of tripping traps with a solenoid. Inland Bird-Banding News 36(1):3-4, 7, 9.

Weissman, A. 1962. Licking behavior of rats on a schedule of food reinforcement. Science 135:99-101.

Welch, P.S. 1948. Limnological methods. McGraw-Hill Book Co., New York. 381 p.

Weller, M.W. 1956. A simple field candler for waterfowl eggs. J. Wildl. Mgmt. 20:111-113.

Westerskov, K. 1956. Age determination and dating nesting events in the willow ptarmigan. J. Wildl. Mgmt. 20:274-279.

Weston, H.G., Jr. 1953. Ring-necked pheasant nesting activities on Birge and Grass Lakes, Emmet County, Iowa, 1953. Iowa Bird Life 23:26-29.

Wetmore, A. 1960. A classification for the birds of the world. Smith. Misc. Coll. 139(11):1-37.

Wetzel, R., and W. Rieck. 1962. Krankheiten des wildes. Paul Parey, Hamburg. 223 p.

White, K.L. 1960. Notes on use of Clover one-shot deer marker. J. Wildl. Mgmt. 24:102.

Whitehead, G.K. 1964. The deer of Great Britain and Ireland; an account of their history, status and distribution. Routledge and Kegan Paul, London. 597 p.

Whitlock, S.C., and L. Eberhardt. 1956. Large-scale dead deer surveys: methods, results and management implications. Trans. N. Amer. Wildl. Conf. 21:555-566.

Wight, H.M. 1930. Michigan's game dog. Amer. For. 36(10):620-623, 637.

Wight, H.M. 1931. Reproduction in the eastern skunk *(Mephitis mephitis nigra)*. J. Mammal. 12:42-47.

Wight, H.M. 1938. Field and laboratory technic in wildlife management. Univ. Michigan Press, Ann Arbor. 105 p.

Wight, H.M., Jr. 1953. A suggested method of capturing birds with a narcosis-producing drug. Unpub. paper.

Wight, H.M., Jr. 1956. A field technique for bursal inspection of mourning doves. J. Wildl. Mgmt. 20: 94-95.

Wight, H.M., and C.H. Conaway. 1962. A comparison of methods for determining age of cottontails. J. Wildl. Mgmt. 26(2):160-163.

Wight, H.M., R.G. Heath, and A.D. Geis. 1965. A method for estimating fall adult sex ratios from production and survival data. J. Wildl. Mgmt. 29(1):185-192.

Wight, H.M. and E.B. Baysinger. 1963. Mourning dove status report, U.S. Fish and Wildl. Ser. Special Sci. Report No. 73.

Wilbert, D.E. 1963. Some effects of chemical sagebrush control on elk distribution. J. Range Mgmt. 16(2): 74-78.

Wildlife Society. 1963. Statement regarding control of excess wildlife (ungulate) populations within national parks. Wildl. Soc. News. No. 86, p. 3.

Wildlife Society. 1968. Position statement on animal control. Wildl. Soc. News. No. 116, p. 21.

Williams, C.S. 1938. Aids to the identification of mole and shrew hairs with general comments on hair structure and hair determination. J. Wildl. Mgmt. 2:239-250.

Williams, C.S., and W.H. Marshall. 1937. Goose nesting studies on Bear River Migratory Waterfowl Refuge. J. Wildl. Mgmt. 1:77-86.

Williams, H.W. 1961. The influence of physical and biological factors on the rally call of the chukar partridge (*Alectocis graeca*) with regard to the use of the call as a census method. Western Assoc. State Game and Fish Comm. 41:117-129.

Williams, J.G. 1963. A field guide to the birds of East and Central Africa. Houghton Mifflin, Boston, Mass. 288 p.

Williams, L.E. 1966. Capturing wild turkeys with alpha-chloralose. J. Wildl. Mgmt. 30(1):50-56.

Williams, T.C., and Janet M. Williams. 1967. Radio-tracking of homing bats. Science 155(3768):1435-1436.

Williamson, C.S. 1934. A simple method for sectioning mammalian hairs for identification purposes. J. Mammal. 15(3):251-252.

Williamson, C.S. 1938. Aids to the identification of mole and shrew hairs with general comments on hair structure and hair determination. J. Wildl. Mgmt. 2(4):239-250.

Williamson, V.H.H. 1951. Determination of hairs by impressions. J. Mammal. 32:80-84.

Wilson, E.B., Jr. 1952. An introduction to scientific research. McGraw-Hill, New York. 375 p.

Wilson, K.A., and E.A. Vaughn. 1944. The bobwhite quail in eastern Maryland. Md. Game and Inland Fish Comm., Annapolis. 138 p.

Wing, L.W. 1956. The natural history of birds. Ronald Press, New York. 539 p.

Winge, O. 1950. Inheritance in dogs. Comstock Pub. Co., 153 p.

Winston, F.A. 1954. Status, movement and management of the mourning dove in Florida. Fla. Game and Freshwater Fish Comm. Tech. Bull. No. 2, Tallahassee. 86 p.

Wint, G.B. 1951. Improved method for marking game birds for identification in the field. Oklahoma Agr. and Mech. College Bull. 48, Stillwater. 7 p.

Winter, K.B., and R.F. Honess. 1952. The use of transmission spectra

and crystallography of hemoglobin in law enforcement. J. Wildl. Mgmt. 16:111-113.

Witherby, H.F. *et al.* 1943-1944. The handbook of British birds. H.F. and Witherby, London. 5 vols.

Wolf, G. 1964. Isotopes in biology. Academic Press, Inc., New York. 173 p.

Wolfson, A. *et al.* 1954. Unpublished theses in ornithology. Auk 71(2):191-197.

Wood, C.A. 1931. An introduction to the literature of vertebrate zoology. Oxford Univ. Press, London. 643 p.

Wood, D.N. 1966. Chemical literature and the foreign-language problem. Chemistry in Britain 2(8):346-350.

Wood, J.E. 1965. Response of rodent populations to controls. J. Wildl. Mgmt. 29:425-438.

Wood, J.E., D.E. Davis, and E.V. Komarek. 1958. The distribution of fox populations in relation to vegetation in Southern Georgia. Ecology 39:160-162.

Wooten, W.A. 1955. A trapping technique for band-tailed pigeons. J. Wildl. Mgmt. 19:411-412.

Worrall, V. 1964. Wild mammals and the law, p. 168-173. In H.N. Southern, The handbook of British mammals. Blackwell Scientific Pubs., Oxford.

Wright, C.W. 1951. Roadside track counts as a census method for white-tailed deer in southern New Jersey. N.J. Div. Fish and Game. 12 p. mimeo.

Wright, E.G. 1939. Marking birds by imping feathers. J. Wildl. Mgmt. 3:238-239.

Wright, J.G. 1952. Veterinary anaesthesia. (3rd ed.) Williams and Wilkins, Baltimore, Md. 267 p.

598

Wright, P. L. 1947. The sexual cycle of the long-tailed weasel *(Mustela frenata)*. J. Mammal. 28:343-352.

Wright, P. L. 1948. Breeding habits of captive long-tailed weasels. Amer. Midland Naturalist 39:338-344.

Wright, P. L. and M. W. Coulter. 1967. Reproduction and growth in Maine fishers. J. Wildl. Mgmt. 31(1):70-87.

Wright, P. L., and R. W. Hiatt. 1943. Outer primaries as age determiners in gallinaceous birds. Auk 60:265-266.

Wright, P. L., and R. Rausch. 1955. Reproduction in the wolverine *(Gulo gulo)*. J. Mammal. 36:346-355.

Wright, T. Jr. 1941. A study of the fall food supply of the ring-necked pheasant and the bob-white quail in Washington County, Rhode Island. J. Wildl. Mgmt. 5:279-296.

Y

Yale Forestry Library. 1962. Dictionary catalog of the Yale forestry library. G. K. Hall, Boston, Mass. 12 vol.

Yates, F. 1965. Appendix on net shyness. Proc. Roy. Soc. Zool. 144(1):22-23.

Yates, R. F. 1942. Counting the birdhouse visits. Nature Mag. 35:192.

Yeager, L. E. 1940. Subjects for filing wildlife literature. J. Wildl. Mgmt. 4(1):44-54.

Yeager, L. E. 1941. A contribution toward a bibliography on North American fur animals. Ill. Nat. Hist. Survey Biol. Notes no. 16. Urbana. 209 p.

Yeager, L. E., W. W. Sandfort, and L. J. Lyon. 1951. Some problems of pheas-

ant management on irrigated land. Trans. N. Amer. Wildl. Conf. 16:351-367.

Yeatter, R. E. 1948. Bird dogs in sport and conservation. Illinois Nat. Hist. Surv., Circ. No. 42, 64 p.

Yerger, R. W. 1953. Home range, territoriality, and populations of the chipmunk in central New York. J. Mammal. 34:448-458.

Yocum, C. F. 1943. The Hungarian partridge, *Perdix perdix* Linn. in the Palouse Region, Washington. Ecol. Monogr. 13:169-201.

Yocum, C. F., and S. W. Harris. 1965. Plumage descriptions and age data for Canada goose goslings. J. Wildl. Mgmt. 29(4):874-877.

Youatt, W. G., and A. W. Erickson. 1959. Some effects of sodium pentobarbital anesthesia on juvenile black bears. J. Wildl. Mgmt. 23:243-244.

Young, H., J. Neess, and J. T. Emlen, Jr. 1952. Heterogeneity of trap response in a population of house mice. J. Wildl. Mgmt. 16:169-180.

Young, S. 1955. Big game exclosures in wildlife management in Utah. Utah Acad. Sci. Proc. 32:65-69.

Young, S. P. 1955. Hints on coyote and wolf trapping. U.S. Fish and Wildl. Ser. Circ. No. 2 (revised), Washington 8 p.

Young, S. P. 1958. The bobcat of North America. Stackpole Co., Harrisburg, Pa., and The Wildl. Mgmt. Inst., Washington, D.C. 193 p.

Young, S. P., and E. A. Goldman. 1944. The wolves of North America. Amer. Wildl. Inst., Washington, D.C. 636 p.

Young, S. P. and E. A. Goldman. 1946. The puma, mysterious American cat. Amer. Wildl. Inst., Washington, D.C. 358 p.

Young, S. P., and H. H. T. Jackson. 1951. The clever coyote. Stackpole Co., Harrisburg, Pa., and Wildl. Mgmt. Inst., Washington, D.C. 411 p.

Yurgenson, P. B. (Ed.). 1961. Studies of mammals in government preserves. [transl. from Russian]. Israel Program for Scientific Translations, Jerusalem. 224 p.

Z

Ziff-Davis Publishing Co. 1962. 1962 Popular photography directory and buying guide. New York. 176 p.

Zimmerman, O. T., and I. Lavine. 1948. Scientific and technical abbreviations, signs and symbols. 2nd ed. Industrial Research Service, Dover, New Hampshire. 476 p.

Zippin, C. 1956. An evaluation of the removal method of estimating animal populations. Biometrics 12:163-189.

Zippin, C. 1958. The removal method of population estimation. J. Wildl. Mgmt. 22:82-90.

Zucca, J. J. 1954. A study of the California clapper rail. The Wasmann J. Biol. 12:135-153.

Zurowski, W., and M. Sokowicz. 1965. Effects of succinylcholine chloride on wild boars. J. Wildl. Mgmt. 29(3):626-629.

Zweifel, F. W. 1961. A handbook of biological illustration. Univ. Chicago Press, Chicago, Ill. 131 p.

Zwickel, F. C. 1965. Early mortality and the numbers of blue grouse, PhD. Diss. Univ. Brit. Col. 153 p.

Zwickel, F. C., and J. F. Bendell. 1967. A snare for capturing blue grouse. J. Wildl. Mgmt. 31(1):202-204.

INDEX

This index of *Wildlife Management Techniques*, exclusive of Literature Cited, was prepared by Robert H. Giles, Jr. The technique of indexing he employed was to red-line index words on page proofs supplied by the printer. Secretaries and Wildlife Society volunteers copied each word with its page number on one of 11,000 3 x 5-inch cards. These cards were alphabetized, numerated, and copy prepared from them. The total time required was approximately 290 man hours. Computer indexing (e.g. KWIC) was judged uneconomical.

600

618